Ecological and Behavioral Methods for the Study of Bats

Ecological and Behavioral Methods for the Study of Bats

EDITED BY THOMAS H. KUNZ

Smithsonian Institution Press
WASHINGTON, D.C.   LONDON

Library of Congress Cataloging-in-Publication Data

Ecological and behavioral methods for the study
of bats.

  Bibliography: p.
  Includes index.
  Sup. of Doc. no.: SI 1.2:B32
  1. Bats—Ecology. 2. Bats—Behavior.
3. Mammals—Ecology. 4. Mammals—Behavior.
I. Kunz, Thomas H.
QL737.C5E32 1987   599.4'045   86-600400
ISBN 0-87474-596-9
ISBN 0-87474-411-3(pbk.)

Editorial Assistant: Rebecca L. Browning

Typesetter: Compositors, Cedar Rapids, Iowa

∞The paper in this book meets the guidelines for
permanence and durability of the Committee on
Production Guidelines for Book Longevity of the
Council on Library Resources.

Manufactured in the United States of America.

New in paperback 1990

97 96 95 94 93 92 91 90   5 4 3 2 1

To Margaret, Pamela, and David,
who I hope will understand where my
mind was when it was not with them.

Contributors

J. Scott Altenbach
Department of Biology
University of New Mexico
Albuquerque, New Mexico 87131 USA

Edythe L. P. Anthony
Department of Biology
Rhode Island College
Providence, Rhode Island 02908 USA

Robert J. Baker
The Museum
Texas Tech University
Lubbock, Texas 79409 USA

George S. Bakken
Department of Life Sciences
Indiana State University
Terre Haute, Indiana 47809 USA

Robert M. R. Barclay
Department of Zoology
University of Calgary, Calgary
Alberta T2N 1N4 Canada

John E. Bassett
Department of Neurological Surgery
Harborview Medical Center
University of Washington
Seattle, Washington 98195 USA

Gary P. Bell
Department of Biology
Boston University
Boston, Massachusetts 02215 USA

Jack W. Bradbury
Department of Biology
University of California
San Diego, California 92093 USA

James R. Coggins
Department of Zoology
University of Wisconsin—Milwaukee
Milwaukee, Wisconsin 53201 USA

Denny G. Constantine
Department of Health Services
State of California
Berkeley, California 94704 USA

Eric Dinerstein
Smithsonian/
Nepal Terai Ecology Project
Washington, D.C. 20008 USA

M. Brock Fenton
Department of Biology
York University
Downsview, Ontario M3J 1P3 Canada

G. Lawrence Forman
Department of Biology
Rockford College
Rockford, Illinois 61101 USA

Marty S. Fujita
Museum of Comparative Zoology
Harvard University
Cambridge, Massachusetts 02138 USA

Connie L. Gaudet
Department of Biology
University of Ottawa
Ottawa, Ontario K1N 6N5 Canada

Charles O. Handley, Jr.
National Museum of Natural History
Smithsonian Institution
Washington, D.C. 20560 USA

Lawrence H. Herbst
1869 Twain Street
Baldwin, New York 11510 USA

Robert Keen
Department of Biological Sciences
Michigan Technological University
Houghton, Michigan 49931 USA

Thomas H. Kunz
Department of Biology
Boston University
Boston, Massachusetts 02215 USA

Allen Kurta
Department of Biology
Boston University
Boston, Massachusetts 02215 USA

Richard K. LaVal
Apdo 10164
San Jose, Costa Rica

Gary F. McCracken
Department of Zoology
University of Tennessee
Knoxville, Tennessee 37996 USA

Kenneth A. Nagy
Laboratory of Biomedical and Environment
  Sciences
University of California
Los Angeles, California 90024 USA

Carleton J. Phillips
Department of Biology
Hofstra University
Hempstead, New York 11550 USA

Elizabeth D. Pierson
Museum of Vertebrate Zoology
University of California
Berkeley, California 94720 USA

Mazin B. Qumsiyeh
The Museum
Texas Tech University
Lubbock, Texas 79409 USA

Paul A. Racey
Department of Zoology
University of Aberdeen
Aberdeen, AB9 2TN Scotland

David J. Rossi
Etudes et Productions Schlumberger
26 rue de la Cavée
29140 Clamart, France

M. Holly Stack
Muséum National d'Histoire Naturelle
Laboratoire d'Anatomie Comparée
55 rue Buffon
75005 Paris, France

Edward R. Stashko
Brookline Conservation Commission
Town Hall
Brookline, Massachusetts 02146 USA

Eugene H. Studier
Department of Biology
University of Michigan—Flint
Flint, Michigan 48503 USA

Donald W. Thomas
Département de Biologie
Université de Sherbrooke
Sherbrooke, Québec J1K 2R1
Canada

Gerald S. Wilkinson
Department of Zoology
University of Maryland
College Park, Maryland 20742 USA

Don E. Wilson
U.S. Fish and Wildlife Service
National Museum of Natural History
Washington, D.C. 20560 USA

John O. Whitaker, Jr.
Department of Life Sciences
Indiana State University
Terre Haute, Indiana 47809 USA

Preface

During the past two decades there has been a growing interest in the ecological and behavioral study of bats. This interest reflects, in part, an increased appreciation for the extraordinary diversity of bats and their importance in pollination and seed dispersal (by plant-visiting bats in subtropical and tropical regions) and for the voracious insect-eating habits of many other species. Moreover, this interest has come at a time when both natural and man-made habitats of bats are being altered and destroyed at alarming rates. Deforestation (especially in the tropics), narrow-minded forest management practices, channelization of streams and rivers, widespread use of toxic chemicals, surface and subterranean mining operations, and generations of cultural misunderstandings about bats are among the most important factors that have historically threatened or endangered the continued existence of many of the known species. Disturbance by an uninformed public (including some biologists) has also threatened local populations.

Over 850 different species of bats are known worldwide, comprising about one-quarter of the living mammalian fauna. Bats have been reported from each continent (except Antarctica) and from many oceanic islands and archipelagos. They have successfully exploited deserts, grasslands, tropical, subtropical, and temperate forests, and some taxa range from sea level to mountaintops. The diversity of diets, roosting habits, reproduction, social behavior, population structure, physiological responses, sensory adaptations (echolocation), and varied ecological and geographic distributions make them ideal models for the study of evolutionary questions.

The idea for this book began over 20 years ago when, as a beginning graduate student, I was challenged to learn new methods and techniques to study these secretive and often elusive animals. Since that time my ideas and approaches to the study of bats have evolved, as I have learned from my mistakes and from the ideas and methods shared by colleagues. My approach to the study of bats has also been guided by a conservation ethic, which has been to minimize the impact of disturbance to populations. This view is shared by many individuals and has been reinforced recently by the enthusiastic support and commitment of numerous local, national, and international conservation organizations.

There are no books, presently available, that are comparable in scope or contents to the present volume. There are several published reviews of ecological and behavioral methods to study wild, terrestrial mammals, but none of these works include methods used to study bats. The emphasis on bats is especially important because many of the techniques required to study these flying, often highly gregarious, and nocturnal mammals are unique. In spite of the emphasis on bats, many of the methods and techniques reviewed in this book should be equally suitable for ecological and behavioral studies of other terrestrial vertebrates. Although there are several excellent books and monographs that have emphasized specific topics such as radio-telemetry, population censusing, and aging methods, most treatments are either highly specific (for other taxa) or too general to be of practical value to the bat researcher.

Most chapters include reviews of published literature and unpublished works through mid-1985. Chapter topics were selected to represent major areas of interest in modern ecological and behavioral research.

Invariably, all readers will not agree on the breadth of topics or their depth of treatment. The coverage in the various chapters is necessarily varied; some topics include and draw from a wealth of relevant literature. Other chapters treat relatively specific topics on which there is little published literature. In most cases the chapter topics were discrete enough to allow authors freedom to develop their own ideas without the risk of redundancy.

Authors were instructed to prepare comprehensive reviews that summarize traditional as well as state-of-the-art methods and techniques. Each author or group of authors are acknowledged leaders in their respective disciplines. They have either pioneered methods or techniques for studying bats or have developed techniques that have not previously been, but should be, applied to bats. Each author has contributed significantly to his/her discipline through published literature or through works now in preparation.

Mention of commercially available equipment and supplies in the text does not constitute endorsement either by the editor or by the publisher. A selective list of commercially available equipment and supplies either mentioned in the text or otherwise useful to the bat researcher is available upon request from the editor.

I am grateful to the many people who have made this book possible. First and foremost, I want to thank my wife, Margaret, and my children, Pamela and David, for their assistance and companionship in the field, for their support and patience at home, and especially for their tolerance of my physical and (at times) mental absence. I owe special thanks to Duncan Phillips who has always taken the time to design and make special equipment when needed. Kirsten M. Klinghammer faithfully assisted with clerical work, proofreading, and the many other tasks needed to see this book to completion. John Kearney was invariably prompt in accommodating my needs for wordprocessing. Allen Kurta and Arrye Rosser were invaluable as

proofreaders. My sincere thanks are extended to Charles O. Handley, Jr., for introducing me to Edward (Ted) Rivinus, Senior Science Editor, Smithsonian Institution Press, who agreed to publish this book before one word of it had been written. I am especially grateful to Ted who kept his patience and sense of humor throughout the gestation of this project. I am particularly grateful to Mary Frances Bell and Rebecca Browning, editors at the Smithsonian Institution Press, for their dedication and enthusiasm in making the final version of this book readable.

The following colleagues, listed in alphabetical order, unselfishly contributed their time and expertise to anonymously review one or more chapters of this book: C. D. Ankney, E. L. P. Anthony, K. B. Armitage, H. J. Baagøe, G. P. Bell, J. F. Bell, J. J. Belwood, J. W. Bickham, I. L. Brisbin, Jr., E. R. Buchler, M. A. Chappell, J. Chase, S. R. Duncan, H. Edgerton, M. B. Fenton, T. H. Fleming, S. C. Frantz, J. H. Fullard, J. Gaisler, K. N. Geluso, A. M. Greenhall, A. W. Gustafson, E. R. Heithaus, S. R. Humphrey, G. S. Jones, J. K. Jones, Jr., D. Klingener, B. F. Koop, A. Kurta, G. F. McCracken, B. K. McNab, A. G. Marshall, J. S. Millar, L. A. Miller, D. W. Morrison, J. D. Nichols, U. M. Norberg, R. L. Peterson, K. H. Pollock, W. B. Quay, P. A. Racey, R. L. Rausch, J. J. Rasweiler, IV, J. A. Simmons, U. Schmidt, J. R. Speakman, E. W. Stiles, E. H. Studier, R. A. Suthers, R. H. Tamarin, D. W. Thomas, C. V. Trimarchi, M. D. Tuttle, J. E. Ubelaker, P. J. Van Soest, and T. A. Vaughan.

Monetary contributions of several individuals and organizations have helped make the publication of this book possible. These include: R. S. Altenbach (University of New Mexico), E. L. P. Anthony (Rhode Island College), R. M. R. Barclay (University of Calgary), J. E. Bassett (University of Washington), C. O. Handley, Jr. (Smithsonian Institution), R. Keen (Michigan Technological University), T. H. Kunz (Boston University), G. F. McCracken (University of Tennessee), C. J. Phillips (Hofstra University), E. H. Studier (University of Michigan-Flint, J. O. Whitaker, Jr. (Indiana State University), and D. E. Wilson (U.S. Fish and Wildlife Service).

Because this book represents a cooperative effort of many dedicated authors and reviewers, I want to thank each of them for helping to set new standards for future studies on the ecology and behavior of bats. It is my hope in bringing this book to completion that it will stimulate increased research and understanding of this fascinating group of mammals.

Thomas H. Kunz
Boston, Massachusetts

Contents

Chapter 1
**Capture Methods and
Holding Devices**

Thomas H. Kunz and Allen Kurta

1. Introduction   1
2. General Considerations   2
   2.1. Light Sources   2
   2.2. Handling Bats   3
3. Capture Methods   3
   3.1. Hand Capture   3
   3.2. Hand (Hoop) Nets   4
   3.3. Bucket Traps   5
   3.4. Bag (Hopper) and Funnel
        Traps   5
   3.5. Mist Nets   6
   3.6. Harp Traps   17
   3.7. Miscellaneous Methods   21
4. Holding Devices   21
5. Summary   24
6. Acknowledgments   25
7. References   25
   Appendices   28

Chapter 2
Reproductive Assessment in Bats

Paul A. Racey

1. Introduction   31
2. Sex Identification and Secondary Sex
   Characteristics   31
   2.1. Size   32
   2.2. Pelage   32
   2.3. Integumentary Glands   33
   2.4. Vocalization   35
   2.5. Behavior   36
3. Reproductive Status of Males   36
   3.1. Testicular Descent   36
   3.2. Puberty and Seasonal
        Spermatogenesis   37

4. Reproductive Status of Females   39
   4.1. Estrus   39
   4.2. Copulation   40
   4.3. Pregnancy   40
   4.4. Parturition and Lactation   41
5. Summary   42
6. Acknowledgments   42
7. References   43

Chapter 3
Age Determination in Bats

Edythe L. P. Anthony

1. Introduction   47
2. Characteristics of Teeth   48
   2.1. Tooth Wear   48
   2.2. Incremental Lines   51
   2.3. Size of Pulp Cavity   52
3. Characteristics of Bones   52
   3.1. Lengths of Long Bones   52
   3.2. Epiphyseal-Diaphyseal
        Fusion   53
4. Miscellaneous Criteria   55
   4.1. Body Mass   55
   4.2. Pelage Coloration   55
5. Summary and Conclusions   56
6. Acknowledgments   56
7. References   57

Chapter 4
Marking and Observational Techniques

Robert M. R. Barclay and Gary P. Bell

1. Introduction   59
2. Marking Techniques   59
   2.1. Wing Bands   60
   2.2. Necklaces   62
   2.3. Light Tags   62
   2.4. Radiotransmitters   64

2.5. Miscellaneous Techniques 65
3. Observational Techniques 66
   3.1. Visual Monitoring 66
   3.2. Acoustic Monitoring 68
   3.3. Other Remote Monitoring Techniques 69
4. Data Collection and Recording 69
5. Summary 70
6. Acknowledgments 71
7. References 71
   Appendix 75

Chapter 5
Survey and Census Methods

Donald W. Thomas and Richard K. LaVal

1. Introduction 77
2. Surveys and Censuses at Roosts 77
3. Methods Used at Enclosed Roosts 78
   3.1. Monitoring from the Outside 78
   3.2. Monitoring from the Inside 81
4. Estimating Numbers of Foliage Roosting Bats 83
5. Estimating Bat Abundance in Habitats or Other Geographic Areas 83
   5.1. Summing Roost Counts 83
   5.2. Visual Counts of Foraging Bats 84
   5.3. Ultrasonic Detectors 84
   5.4. Vampire Bites 84
   5.5. Mist Netting and Trapping 85
6. Estimates from Capture-Mark-Recapture 85
7. Summary and Conclusions 86
8. Acknowledgments 87
9. References 87

Chapter 6
Detecting, Recording, and Analyzing Vocalizations of Bats

M. Brock Fenton

1. Introduction 91
2. Detection 92

2.1. Narrow Band Microphone 92
2.2. Tunable Broadband Electret Microphone 94
2.3. Tunable Broadband Condenser Microphone 95
2.4. Divide-by-Ten (Countdown) Detector 95
2.5. Envelope Detection 95
2.6. Uppsala Detector 95
2.7. Period Meter 96
2.8. Remote Monitoring 96
3. Broadband Condenser Microphones 96
4. Recording 97
5. Playback Experiments 98
6. Analysis 99
   6.1. Amplitude 100
   6.2. Duration 100
   6.3. Power Spectra 100
   6.4. Frequency-Time Analysis: Period Meter 101
   6.5. Frequency-Time Analysis: Sonograph 101
7. Some Pitfalls 101
   7.1. Background Noise 101
   7.2. Batteries 102
   7.3. Connectors 102
8. Summary 102
9. Acknowledgments 102
10. References 103
   Appendix 104

Chapter 7
Radiotelemetry: Techniques and Analysis

Gerald S. Wilkinson and Jack W. Bradbury

1. Introduction 105
2. Transmitter Construction and Attachment 106
   2.1. Basic Cochran Transmitter 106
   2.2. Triggered Circuits 108
   2.3. Pulsed Telemetry Units 109
   2.4. Power Sources 110
   2.5. Potting 111
   2.6. Attachment 111

3. Equipment Selection   111
   3.1. Receivers   111
   3.2. Antennas   112
4. Data Collection   112
   4.1. Recording Data   112
   4.2. Error Estimation   112
5. Home Range Estimation   113
   5.1. Definitions   113
   5.2. Parametric Methods   113
   5.3. Nonparametric Methods   114
   5.4. Sample Considerations   116
6. Association among Individuals   118
   6.1. Spatial Association   118
   6.2. Temporal Association   118
7. Summary   118
8. Acknowledgments   119
9. References   119
   Appendices   120

Chapter 8
Techniques for Photographing Bats

J. Scott Altenbach

1. Introduction   125
2. Still Photography   126
   2.1. Motionless Subject: Adequate
        Illumination   126
   2.2. Moving Subject: Inadequate
        Illumination   126
   2.3. Supplemental
        Illumination   126
   2.4. Portrait Photography   129
   2.5. Multiflash Still
        Photography   130
   2.6. Simultaneous Photographs with
        Multiple Angles   130
   2.7. Automatic Triggering of
        Photographs   131
3. Time-Lapse Photography   133
4. Cinematography   134
   4.1. Real Time   134
   4.2. High Frame Rates   136
   4.3. Timing of Camera and Flash
        Operation   137
5. Summary   137
6. References   137
   Appendix   138

Chapter 9
**Allozyme Techniques and Kinship
Assessment in Bats**

Gary F. McCracken and Gerald S.
Wilkinson

1. Introduction   141
2. Sample Collection and
   Preparation   142
   2.1. Blood   142
   2.2. Other Tissues   142
3. Electrophoresis   143
4. Intepreting Gels   145
   4.1. Scoring   145
   4.2. Mendelian Inheritance and
        Linkage   148
5. Kinship Assessment   148
   5.1. Paternity   148
   5.2. Maternity   149
   5.3. Kinship Among Group
        Members   150
6. Practical Considerations   151
7. Summary   152
8. Acknowledgments   152
9. References   152
   Appendices   154

Chapter 10
Mark-Recapture Estimates of Bat Survival

Robert Keen

1. Introduction   157
   1.1. Survival Estimates from Marked
        Vertebrates   157
   1.2. Studies of Bat Survival   158
   1.3. Difficulties of Analysis   158
2. Analysis of Mark-Recapture
   Data   159
   2.1. Cormack's Method of Survival
        Analysis   159
   2.2. Assumptions of Analysis   160
3. Other Analytical Approaches   163
   3.1. Regression Techniques   164
   3.2. Life-Table Analyses   166

4. Interpreting and Using Survival
    Rates   167
    4.1. Average Survival Rates   167
    4.2. Average Life Expectancy   167
    4.3. Comparing Survival
          Rates   168
5. Summer Banding Studies   168
6. Conclusion   169
7. Acknowledgments   169
8. References   169

Chapter 11
Food Habits Analysis of Insectivorous Bats

John O. Whitaker, Jr.

1. Introduction   171
2. Material Available for Food Habits
    Analysis   172
    2.1. Stomach Content and
          Feces   172
    2.2. Culled Parts   173
    2.3. Observations of Feeding
          Bats   173
    2.4. What Method(s) Should Be
          Used?   173
3. Methods of Food Habits
    Analysis   174
    3.1. Collection of Bats   174
    3.2. Sample Preparation   174
    3.3. Identification   174
    3.4. Percent Volume and Percent
          Frequency Estimates   175
    3.5. Number and Size of Prey   175
    3.6. Interpretation of Moth
          Scales   175
4. Sources of Variation   176
    4.1. Collection of Bats   176
    4.2. Sample Size   176
    4.3. Statistical Analysis   176
    4.4. Insect Prey Selection versus Insect
          Availability   176
5. Topics for Further Study   177
6. Summary   177
7. Acknowledgments   178
8. References   178
    Appendix   179

Chapter 12
Methods of Assessing the Availability of
Prey to Insectivorous Bats

Thomas H. Kunz

1. Introduction   191
2. Factors Affecting Insect
    Activity   191
3. Sample Units   192
    3.1. Subdivision of Habitat   192
    3.2. Insect Sampling   192
4. Trapping Devices   192
    4.1. Non-Attractant Traps   193
    4.2. Attractant Traps   200
5. Radar Observations and Remote
    Sensing   201
6. Treatment of Field Data   202
    6.1. Enumeration and
          Transformations   202
    6.2. Prey Selection Analyses   202
    6.3. Insect Biomass and Energy
          Content   203
7. Summary and Conclusions   203
8. Acknowledgments   204
9. References   205
    Appendices   209

Chapter 13
Analysis of Diets of Plant-Visiting Bats

Donald W. Thomas

1. Introduction   211
2. Diet Analysis for Frugivorous
    Bats   212
    2.1. Feces from Netted Bats   212
    2.2. Feces Below Day Roosts   214
    2.3. Rejected Pellets and Fruit Parts
          Below Feeding Roosts   215
    2.4. Sampling Biases   215
    2.5. Non-Random Fruit
          Selection   217
3. Diet Analysis for Nectarivorous
    Bats   217
4. Summary and Conclusions   219
5. Acknowledgments   219
6. References   219

Chapter 14
Methods of Estimating Fruit Availability to Frugivorous Bats

Edward R. Stashko and Eric Dinerstein

1. Introduction   221
2. Brief Synopsis of Fruit Sampling Studies   221
3. Conceptual and Procedural Problems   223
   3.1. What is a "Bat Fruit"?   223
   3.2. Fruiting Phenology and Fruit Production   225
   3.3. Seed Traps   225
   3.4. Mapping Studies   226
   3.5. Fruit Production Transects   227
   3.6. Spatial and Temporal Variation in Fruit Production   227
   3.7. Statistical Problems   228
4. Summary and Conclusions   229
5. Acknowledgments   230
6. References   230

Chapter 15
Methods of Nutritional Ecology of Plant-Visiting Bats

Lawrence H. Herbst

1. Introduction   233
2. Digestibility   234
3. Preservation and Preparation of Samples for Analysis   236
4. Nutritional Analysis of Food Components   237
   4.1. Ash and Mineral Content   237
   4.2. Dietary Fiber   237
   4.3. Total Available Carbohydrates   238
   4.4. Lipids   239
   4.5. Nitrogen and Protein Content   240
   4.6. Energy Content   241
5. Analytical Schemes   242
6. Acknowledgments   243
7. References   243

Chapter 16
Maintaining Bats for Captive Studies

Don E. Wilson

1. Introduction   247
2. Diet   248
   2.1. Insectivorous Species   248
   2.2. Carnivorous Species   252
   2.3. Fish-Eating Bats   252
   2.4. Vampires   252
   2.5. Frugivorous and Nectarivorous Species   253
3. Nutrition   254
   3.1. Nutritional Requirements   254
   3.2. Feeding Requirements   255
4. Housing   256
   4.1. Cages   256
   4.2. Lighting   257
   4.3. Climate Control   257
   4.4. Sanitation   257
5. Management   258
   5.1. Transportation   258
   5.2. Special Handling Techniques   258
   5.3. Behavior and Reproduction   259
   5.4. Other Laboratory Techniques   259
6. Health Precautions   260
   6.1. Parasites   260
   6.2. Diarrhea   260
   6.3. Hair Loss   260
   6.4. Sores   261
7. Summary   261
8. Acknowledgments   261
9. References   261
   Appendix   263

Chapter 17
Training Bats for Behavioral Studies

Connie L. Gaudet

1. Introduction   265
2. Training Prerequisites   265
   2.1. Conditioning   266

2.2. Unconditioned
      Responses   266
2.3. Behavioral
      Methodologies   266
3. The Training Process   267
    3.1. The Preconditioning
          Period   267
    3.2. Behavior-Shaping in
          Practice   267
    3.3. Trial-and-Error Learning   268
    3.4. Unconditioned
          Responses   269
4. Other Considerations   269
    4.1. Reinforcement   270
    4.2. Controls   270
    4.3. Motivation   270
    4.4. Accommodating Species
          Differences   271
    4.5. Handling   272
    4.6. The Training Chamber   272
5. Is Training Really Necessary?   273
6. Summary   273
7. Acknowledgments   273
8. References   273

Chapter 18
Methods of Energy Budget Analysis

Thomas H. Kunz and Kenneth A. Nagy

1. Introduction   277
2. Doubly Labeled Water Method   278
    2.1. Rationale   278
    2.2. Field Metabolic Rate   278
    2.3. Assumptions and Potential
          Errors   278
    2.4. Practical Considerations   280
    2.5. Validation Experiments   286
    2.6. Isotopes and Isotope
          Analysis   286
3. Food Consumption   287
    3.1. Gravimetric Methods   287
    3.2. Isotope Dilution   289
    3.3. Milk Yield and Energy Intake by
          Sucklings   290

4. Time-Budget Method   292
    4.1. Rationale and General
          Procedures   292
    4.2. Roosting Activity   292
    4.3. Foraging Activity   293
5. Rates and Efficiencies of Energy
    Transfer   294
    5.1. Integration of Complete and
          Partial Energy Budgets   294
    5.2. Feeding Rates and Foraging
          Efficiencies   294
    5.3. Parental Investment   294
    5.4. Energetics of Fat and Protein
          Deposition   296
6. Comparison of Methods   296
7. Summary   297
8. Acknowledgments   297
9. References   297

Chapter 19
Microclimate Methods

George S. Bakken and Thomas H. Kunz

1. Introduction   303
2. Biophysics of
    Thermoregulation   304
    2.1. Heat Transfer Analysis   304
    2.2. Operative (T_e) and Standard
          Operative (T_{es})
          Temperatures   307
3. Measurement of the Thermal
    Environment   307
    3.1. Direct Integrated Measurement of
          T_e and T_{es} with Test
          Bodies   307
    3.2. Individual Measurements of
          Microclimate and Animal
          Parameters   308
    3.3. Temperature
          Measurement   309
    3.4. Radiation Measurement   310
    3.5. Wind Measurement   313
    3.6. Conduction to Roosting
          Surface   315

4. Humidity and Mass Transport   316
    4.1. Evaporative Water Loss   316
    4.2. Measurement of Vapor
          Density   317
5. National Meteorological Service
    Data   318
6. Summary   319
7. Acknowledgments   319
8. References   319
    Appendices   326

Chapter 20
**Design and Interpretation of Laboratory
Thermoregulation Studies**

Allen Kurta and Marty S. Fujita

1. Introduction   333
2. Temperature Sensors   334
    2.1. Thermocouples   334
    2.2. Thermistors   335
    2.3. Radiotransmitters   335
    2.4. Mercury Thermometers   336
3. Methodological Considerations   336
    3.1. Site of Measurement   336
    3.2. Continuous Measurements and
          Restraints   338
    3.3. Noncontinuous
          Measurements   339
    3.4. Nutritional State   339
    3.5. Body Water and Environmental
          Moisture   340
    3.6. Transport from Field to
          Laboratory   341
    3.7. Simulated Roosts as Experimental
          Chambers   341
4. Physiological Considerations   341
    4.1. Acclimation and the "Captivity
          Effect"   341
    4.2. Daily and Seasonal
          Rhythms   342
    4.3. Reproductive Condition   343
    4.4. Sexual Differences   343
5. Behavioral Considerations   343
    5.1. Clustering   343
    5.2. Social Facilitation   344

5.3. Social Stress   344
6. Summary   345
7. Acknowledgments   345
8. References   345

Chapter 21
**Methods of Measuring Metabolic Rate:
Respirometry**

M. Holly Stack and David J. Rossi

1. Introduction   353
2. Direct vs. Indirect Calorimetry   354
3. Metabolic Terminology   354
4. Closed System   356
5. Open System   356
    5.1. Single-Channel Open-Flow
          System   357
    5.2. Multiple-Channel Open-Flow
          System   364
    5.3. Computerized Data-Gathering
          and Analysis   366
6. Summary   366
7. Acknowledgments   367
8. References   367
    Appendix   370

Chapter 22
**Methods for Determining Water Balance
in Bats**

John E. Bassett and Eugene H. Studier

1. Introduction   373
2. Continuous Parameters   374
    2.1. Metabolic Water
          Production   374
    2.2. Pulmocutaneous Water
          Loss   375
3. Discontinuous Parameters   378
    3.1. Drinking   379
    3.2. Preformed Water in Food   379
    3.3. Fecal Water Loss   380
    3.4. Milk Production   380
    3.5. Urinary Water Loss   380

4. Summary   383
5. Acknowledgments   383
6. References   383

Chapter 23
Methods of Body Composition Analysis

Elizabeth D. Pierson and M. Holly Stack

1. Introduction   387
2. Data Collection and Analysis   388
   2.1. Conditions of Capture   388
   2.2. Data Recording and
        Analysis   388
   2.3. Computing Energy Values   389
3. Water Content   389
   3.1. *In Vitro* Methods   390
   3.2. *In Vivo* Methods   392
4. Fat Content   392
   4.1. *In Vitro* Methods   392
   4.2. *In Vivo* Methods   393
5. Ash-Free Lean Dry Mass (Proteins and
   Carbohydrates)   393
   5.1. *In Vitro* Methods   393
   5.2. *In Vivo* Methods   394
6. Ash Content   394
   6.1. *In Vitro* Methods   395
   6.2. *In Vivo* Methods   396
7. Energy Content   397
8. Summary   398
9. Acknowledgments   398
10. References   398

Chapter 24
**Preparation and Fixation of Tissues for
Histological, Histochemical,
Immunohistochemical, and Electron
Microscopical Studies**

G. Lawrence Forman and Carleton J.
Phillips

1. Introduction   405
2. Preparation and Handling of Tissues for
   Fixation   406
3. Immersion, Perfusion, and Vapor
   Fixation   407
4. Selection and Use of Fixatives   410

5. Fixatives for Light Microscopy   411
   5.1. "Primary" Fixatives and Their
        Actions   411
   5.2. Aldehydes   412
   5.3. General Fixatives   412
   5.4. Histochemistry   412
6. Immunohistochemistry   415
7. Fixation for Transmission Electron
   Microscopy   417
8. Preservation by Freezing   419
9. Special Applications   419
   9.1. Tissue Smears and
        Spreads   419
   9.2. Fixation of Embryonic
        Tissues   420
   9.3. Decalcification   420
10. Summary   421
11. Acknowledgments   422
12. References   422
    Appendix   423

Chapter 25
**Methods in Chiropteran Mitotic
Chromosomal Studies**

Robert J. Baker and Mazin B. Qumsiyeh

1. Introduction   425
2. Bone Marrow Preparations   425
   2.1. Standard Karyotypes   427
   2.2. Preparations of Air-dried Slides
        for Banding   427
   2.3. Problems   427
3. G-Banding Procedure   428
4. C-Banding Procedure   429
5. Cell Culture and Harvesting
   Techniques   430
   5.1. Procedures for Taking Tissue for
        Culture   430
   5.2. Procedure for Initiating Primary
        Cultures   431
   5.3. Initiating and Maintaining
        Primary Cell Lines   432
   5.4. Karyotyping from Cultured
        Cells   432
6. Summary   433
7. Acknowledgments   433
8. References   433
   Appendices   434

Chapter 26
Specimen Preparation

Charles O. Handley, Jr.

1. Introduction   437
2. Supplies and Equipment   438
   2.1.   Tools   438
   2.2.   Supplies   438
3. Sacrificing and Storage Before
   Preservation   438
4. Data   440
   4.1.   Labeling   440
   4.2.   Reproductive Data   440
   4.3.   Other Data   440
   4.4.   External Measurements   441
5. Preparing Specimens   443
   5.1.   Wet Preservation   443
   5.2.   Dry Preservation   445
6. Protecting Specimens from Insects and
   Fungus   454
7. Packing and Shipping   455
8. Summary   456
9. Acknowledgments   456
10. References   456

Chapter 27
**Collecting and Preserving Ectoparasites for
Ecological Study**

John O. Whitaker, Jr.

1. Introduction   459
2. Parasites and Parasitism   459
3. Biology of Ectoparasites   460
   3.1.   Behavior and Life History   460
   3.2.   Host Specificity   460
   3.3.   Effects on the Host   461
4. Collecting and Preserving
   Ectoparasites   461
5. Recording and Analyzing Data   462
6. Identification of Bat
   Ectoparasites   463
7. Suggestions for Future Study   464
   7.1.   Host Taxonomy   464
   7.2.   Parasite Life History   464
8. Summary   464
9. Acknowledgments   465
10. References   465
    Appendices   469

Chapter 28
**Methods for the Ecological Study of Bat
Endoparasites**

James R. Coggins

1. Introduction   475
2. Methods of Capturing Bats and Host
   Examinations   476
   2.1.   Methods of Host
          Preservation   476
   2.2.   Methods of Host
          Examination   477
   2.3.   General Fixation
          Techniques   478
   2.4.   Fixation of Nematodes   479
   2.5.   Fixation of Protozoa   479
3. Slide Preparation   479
   3.1.   Staining Permanent Slides   480
   3.2.   Restoration Procedures   480
   3.3.   Deposition of Voucher
          Specimens   480
4. Ecological Factors   481
   4.1.   Terminology   481
   4.2.   Statistical Considerations   481
   4.3.   Seasonal Ecology   481
   4.4.   Effects of Migration   482
   4.5.   Effects of Host
          Hibernation   483
   4.6.   Life Cycles   484
   4.7.   Host Feeding and Foraging
          Strategy   484
5. Summary   485
6. References   485

Chapter 29
Health Precautions for Bat Researchers

Denny G. Constantine

1. Introduction   491
2. Hazardous Atmospheric Gases in Caves
   and Mine Tunnels   492
   2.1.   Detecting and Measuring
          Atmospheric Gases   492
   2.2.   Protection, First Aid, and
          Rescue   495
   2.3.   Ammonia   496
   2.4.   Carbon Dioxide   497
   2.5.   Methane   498

2.6.   Carbon Monoxide   499
2.7.   Hydrogen Sulfide   499
2.8.   Sulfur Dioxide   500
2.9.   Oxygen Deficit   501
2.10. Other Problematic Atmospheric
       Factors in Mines and
       Caves   502
2.11. Deliberate Contamination of Bats
       and Bat Roosts with
       Anticoagulants and Poisonous
       Gases   502
3. Ectoparasites and Urine   503
4. Rabies   504
   4.1.   Transmission Cycle   504
   4.2.   Viral Strain
          Compartmentalization   504
   4.3.   Prevalence and Sampling
          Techniques   505
   4.4.   Disease Development   508
   4.5.   Rabies Exposures   510

4.6.   Rabies Prevention   514
5. Rabies-Related Viruses and Other Viral
   Infections in Bats   514
6. Histoplasmosis   515
   6.1.   Host Species and Geographic
          Distribution   515
   6.2.   The Disease in Man   518
   6.3.   The Disease in Bats   519
   6.4.   Prevention   519
7. Bat Health and Human Health
   Problems Caused by Bat
   Biologists   520
8. Summary   521
9. Acknowledgments   521
10. References   522
    Appendix   526

Subject Index   529

Chapter 1

Capture Methods
and Holding Devices

Thomas H. Kunz

and

Allen Kurta

Department of Biology
Boston University
Boston, Massachusetts 02215 USA

1. INTRODUCTION

There are few, if any, topics in ecology and behavior that are more fundamental than methods used to capture animals. Bats can be captured during flight and in their roosts. Methods used and the success of capturing flying bats will depend mostly upon their flight speed and maneuverability, and the habitats being sampled. Methods used and the success of capturing bats in roosts will depend upon the type of roost, the number of bats present, the dispersion of bats within the roost, their physiological state (active vs. torpid), their age and reproductive condition (pregnant or lactating), their alertness to visual, auditory, or olfactory stimuli, and the location and accessbility of bats to the investigator.

Methods used to capture bats were reviewed by Greenhall and Paradiso (1968) and Tuttle (1976a). Recent reports have described new or improved methods of capturing bats (Tuttle, 1974b; Tidemann and Woodside, 1978; Rautenbach, 1985), or have included brief descriptions of novel capture methods (e.g., Bradbury and Emmons, 1974; Gaisler et al., 1979; McCracken and Bradbury, 1981; Kunz et al., 1983). Much of what is known about capture methods and related techniques is often transmitted informally among colleagues, leaving descriptions in research reports to brief statements such as "bats were captured by hand" or "mist nets were used to capture bats." Success in capturing bats requires a knowledge of roosting habits, nightly emergence and dispersal behavior, and foraging habits. Although space does not permit a review of these topics, the reader is encouraged to consult original sources and review papers for details (e.g., Dalquest and

Walton, 1970; Erkert, 1982; Fenton, 1982; Fleming, 1982; Heithaus, 1982; Kunz, 1982).

The purpose of this chapter is to review methods used to capture bats that are applicable to ecological and behavioral research. Where there have been no previously published reports, or where the methods are not readily available in the published literature, we include additional details. We briefly discuss methods for holding bats in the field and for transporting them to the laboratory. Illustrations are often used in place of lengthy discussions to highlight various devices, techniques, and strategies. A brief treatment of laws and regulations governing collecting, import, and export of scientific specimens is given in Appendix 1. In addition to being a practical guide, we hope that this chapter will stimulate others to develop new methods and to improve existing ones.

2. GENERAL CONSIDERATIONS

Knowledge of where and when bats roost and forage is essential to the success of any study that requires captured animals. There is no "best" time to capture bats; the most appropriate time will depend upon the objectives of the study, the season, as well as the behavior, age, and life history stage of the bats. Barbour and Davis (1969) suggested that roosting bats are best captured in the late morning, when individuals are least active. We generally concur with this; however, flightless young are best captured in maternity roosts, following the nightly departure of adults (also see Chapter 18). Certainly the times and season of capture should be chosen carefully to minimize disturbance to the colony. Some census methods may require periodic capture (see Chapter 5). In practice, compromises between frequent and infrequent trapping are needed; frequent trapping may lead to abandonment, and infrequent trapping may mean that important life history events will be missed. Other factors to consider include the nutritional status of the animals at the time of cap-

ture and whether special care is required for transport. If bats are to be transported to the laboratory, it is advisable to capture them as soon as possible after they have fed and taken water. By contrast, if one wishes to compare daily or seasonal changes in body mass for a particular population, individuals that are captured and weighed at the time of nightly emergence will provide the most reliable data, since bats are postabsorptive at this time.

2.1. Light Sources

Reliable light sources are essential for most types of capture, since most bats are typically active at night and roost in dark or dimly illuminated places. Many different types of light sources are available commercially (see Appendix 2). Electric sources are preferable to those which use combustible fuels (kerosene, refined gasoline, calcium carbide, etc.). Electric light sources are safer, cleaner, and produce a minimum amount of heat (an important consideration when capturing bats during winter in caves and mines). Carbide lamps are reliable light sources used by many cavers, but they are not recommended for work with bats. Such lamps generate a measurable amount of heat, which can adversely modify the microclimate of roosting bats. Moreover, it is unsafe to use combustible fuels in buildings and where the risks of starting grass or forest fires is high.

It is preferable to use light sources that can be mounted on the head, freeing the hands to manipulate nets, traps, poles, and other devices for capturing bats. Lights that can be adjusted for intensity are ideal (Tuttle, 1979). When choosing a particular type of light, one should consider such factors as cost, performance, durability, reliability, and battery requirements. Koehler Wheat lamps and MineSpot miner's lamps come equipped with rechargeable batteries and are among the most durable and reliable light sources. These lamps are designed to accommodate lead-acid batteries or sealed, maintenance-free gel batteries. If lead-acid batteries are used, a small supply of distilled water and an injection syringe are needed. A line power-source or generator is needed to recharge batteries, and the lamps may be used continuously for up to 12 h between charges with little loss of intensity. Although the initial cost of these lamps (including the charger) is high (about U.S. $220 each), they more than pay for themselves when weighed against the cost of having to replace conventional batteries.

Other less expensive head lamps (e.g., Burgess and Justrite) are reliable and relatively inexpensive. They are designed to operate on four, 1.5 v, D-cell batteries or one, 6 v, lantern battery. Rechargeable gel or nickel-cadmium (ni-cad) batteries are preferable to alkaline batteries for reliability and service. Whichever light source is used, one should always be equipped with spare bulbs, extra batteries, and alternate light sources.

In many situations, a small pocket-sized pen-light can be invaluable. Pen-lights with clips can be attached to a hat or shirt collar when handling bats or recording notes. Pen-lights fitted with flexible necks are extremely useful for examining small crevices and cavities for roosting bats. A pen-light may be all that is needed to make an unobtrusive approach to capture bats roosting in a dark or dimly lit building or cave. They also provide a temporary light source if the primary one fails. When working alone in dimly lit and dark places, one should establish a "rule" to carry two alternate light sources. A Cyalume (chemical light) stick makes a good emergency light source. It can be tied to a cord around the neck and activated by bending, to break, the inner capsule when needed. Light emitted from a single Cyalume stick is often adequate to remove bats from mist nets or traps and to dismantle equipment in emergency situations. The use of Cyalume for marking bats is described in Chapter 4.

2.2. Handling Bats

Leather gloves are usually recommended for handling bats; other precautions to be taken are discussed in Chapter 29. Generally, gloves are not needed when handling suckling bats and adults of most small (<10 g) species. Lightweight leather gloves are adequate for handling most bats weighing between 10 and 30 g. Batter's gloves used in baseball are ideal for this purpose. Gloves made of thicker leather may be needed for handling larger species and small aggressive ones. Usually only one glove is needed to remove bats from mist nets (Section 3.5.5). We highly recommend that gloves be worn on both hands when handling vampire bats (e.g., *Desmodus, Diphylla*) and large carnivorous species (e.g., *Macroderma, Vampyrum*). Gloves should be as pliable as possible to enhance the sensitivity of the wearer to the form and movements of the bat. Generally, we prefer loose-fitting gloves to tight-fitting ones, since loose-fitting ones can be removed quickly when needed. Moreover, parts of loose-fitting gloves can provide places for bats to chew, especially when removing bats from mist nets.

3. CAPTURE METHODS

3.1. Hand Capture

Many roosting bats can be successfully captured without the aid of special devices. For example, bats that are specialized for roosting on the smooth inner surfaces of unfurled leaves of *Heliconia, Musa,* and *Strelitza* (see Kunz, 1982) may be captured by grasping the open end of a bat-occupied leaf and quickly bending it downward toward eye level (e.g., Brosset, 1976; LaVal and LaVal, 1977; D. E. Wilson, pers. comm.). By squeezing and prodding bats that occupy such leaves, individuals will eventually move to the open end where they can be removed by hand. Hibernating bats can often be taken from their roosting places using hands alone. At times, however, it may be necessary to use long tissue forceps to remove bats from crevices and cavities (e.g., Griffin, 1940; Barbour and Davis, 1969). In other situations, a blunt and flexible wire-probe may be helpful to prod or pull bats from crevices. When extracting bats from crevices and cavities using such devices, extreme care should be taken to avoid injury to delicate wing bones and membranes.

When bats are to be captured in small, enclosed roosts (e.g., small caves, buildings, buttress cavities, etc.), we suggest that the exit routes be covered with netting material (Section 3.7) to prevent bats from escaping. This may not be necessary in large caves where bats have alternate roosts within the same cave. However, in roosts that have small internal spaces, it is particularly important that netting be left up long enough after the colony has been disturbed so that bats have time to settle and reestablish social contacts before the nightly departure.

3.2. Hand (Hoop) Nets

Hand nets with adjustable-length handles are particularly valuable for capturing bats in caves, mines, buildings, tree and buttress cavities, and in foliage. Commercially available insect nets may be used, but the bag should be deep enough to prevent bats from escaping. Often simple hoop nets can be made from heavy-duty wire, mosquito netting, and almost any type of pole. Extension handles for hoop nets can be made in the field by securely taping the net handle to a bamboo or other pole. Handles should be as lightweight as possible so as not to impede rapid motion and maneuvering of the net. The Tropics Net (available from BioQuip Products) is excellent for capturing bats. It has a deep bag (85 cm) made from mosquito netting, a 45 cm diameter hoop, and it comes with four, lightweight aluminum extension handles (each 61 cm long) that can be quickly screwed together. Handles from these nets are interchangeable and can be connected to increase the length beyond four sections. Individual sections are short enough to be carried in a standard-size suitcase.

Hand nets in which the angle of the hoop can be adjusted relative to the handle can be invalulable in certain situations. Agaconi (1938a, 1938b) described such a net that

included a joint of the type used on beach umbrellas. The angle of the net can be set by tightening a wing-nut. Hoop nets that have a "gimbal-like" frame may provide greater flexibility for capturing bats that roost on irregular ceilings (Hamilton-Smith, 1964). Net bags may be fabricated to include sleeves with drawstrings to facilitate the transfer of bats from a hoop net to holding bags.

Hoop nets have been used successfully in many roost situations, including hollow trees (Turner, 1975; Wilkinson, 1985), buttress cavities (Bradbury and Emmons, 1974; Bradbury and Vehrencamp, 1976), caves and mines (e.g., Bels, 1952; Barbour and Davis, 1969; Kunz, 1973; Tuttle, 1975, 1976a), buildings (Gaisler, 1963; T. H. Kunz, unpubl.), and foliage (e.g., Constantine, 1966; T. H. Kunz and G. F. McCracken, unpubl.). Constantine (1966) used a hoop net attached to a long extension pole to capture foliage-roosting *Lasiurus borealis* and *L. cinereus*. A flap of smooth plastic was attached to the hoop and extended inside the net bag to prevent bats from escaping. Bradbury and Emmons (1974) and Bradbury and Vehrencamp (1976) used a hoop net to capture bats inside buttress cavities that had been closed off with black nylon netting (see Section 3.7). When using hand nets to capture bats in hollow trees and foliage, one should remain alert to the presence of bees and wasps (see Brosset, 1966) and other potential dangers (e.g., snakes, ants, etc.).

Quickness and accuracy are extremely important in using hand nets. Approaches to foliage roosts, and other open-roost situations, should be made with considerable planning to minimize noise and disturbance of adjacent vegetation. For example, tent-making bats (T. H. Kunz, 1982) can easily evade capture unless one moves quickly with an upward sweeping motion when making the final approach to the roost (T. H. Kunz, pers. obs.). Use of the lightest, most maneuverable handle is essential in these situations.

If hoop nets are used repeatedly to capture roosting bats, one should be aware that some individuals (those that have been captured previously) may avoid capture. Tuttle (pers. comm.) has observed that previously captured *Myotis grisescens* may avoid subsequent captures in hoop nets. Harem males of *Artibeus jamaicensis, Phyllostomus hastatus,* and *Hipposideros caffer* remain in roost cavities after females have dropped into hoop nets and bucket traps thrust beneath roosting groups (T. H. Kunz and G. P. Bell, pers. obs.).

Hibernating bats that roost high on the ceilings of caves, mines, and buildings can sometimes be dislodged with long sections of bamboo poles or extension poles to which small hoop nets are attached (Barbour and Davis, 1969). Disturbance to bats during energy- or water-critical periods (e.g., hibernation, lactation) should be minimized to avoid depletion of critical fat reserves and body water (Tuttle, 1976b, 1979, and Chapter 4).

Although hand nets are most commonly used to capture roosting bats, they can also be used successfully to capture bats in flight as they depart from small openings in buildings and caves (e.g., Brown et al., 1983; Kunz, unpubl.) and at predictable feeding sites (Fenton and Bell, 1979). When hoop nets are used to capture flying bats, special care should be taken not to swing nets too vigorously, as this may break or damage wings or in other ways cause injury.

3.3. Bucket Traps

In some situations it may be more practical and convenient to use bucket traps to capture bats. McCracken and Bradbury (1981) modified a large cylindrical plastic trash bucket by removing the bottom half and replacing it with a hardware cloth basket (6-mm mesh). Harem groups of *Phyllostomus hastatus* were captured by quickly placing a bucket trap over the openings of solution cavities (potholes) formed in the ceilings of small caves. Roosting bats were dislodged by inserting a small wire "spatula" between the top edge of the bucket and the ceiling of the cave. This method works best when one person holds the bucket and the other person manipulates the spatula and watches for bats that may attempt to escape. Care should be taken with such a system to ensure that all individuals are dislodged from their roost before removing the bucket (see Section 3.2).

A similar device was used by Kunz et al. (1983) to capture groups of *Artibeus jamaicensis* that roosted high (>3 m) on cave ceilings. A cylindrical trash bucket, like that described in McCracken and Bradbury (1981), was attached to a long extension pole with durable tape. Instead of using a spatula that is not easily manipulated from such a great height, a small hole was cut into the bottom of the wire cage, and a long pole was inserted through the hole for use as a probe to maneuver and dislodge bats from their roost cavity. Care should be taken to ensure that bats do not escape from this hole when the pole is withdrawn after bats have entered the bucket.

3.4. Bag (Hopper) and Funnel Traps

Bag and funnel traps have been used successfully to capture bats as they depart from small holes and crevices in buildings and trees. Bag and funnel traps, originally described by Griffin (1940), were made from fabric supported by wire hoops. Polyethylene, however, works more effectively, since bats slide better on smooth surfaces than on fabric. Small bag-traps made from polyethylene, wire screen, and waterproof (duct) tape can be made inexpensively and positioned over roost exits to capture bats (Fig. 1 A). When bags are made from plastic, bats are unable to climb back into the roost and exit via alternative routes. Depending upon the height of the exit hole above the ground, a funnel (or "laundry chute") may be added to direct the departure of bats into a holding bag near the ground (Griffin, 1940). Morrison and Handley (*in press*) captured harem groups of *Artibeus jamaicensis* with laundry-chute traps as individuals departed from tree holes located up to 6 m above the ground.

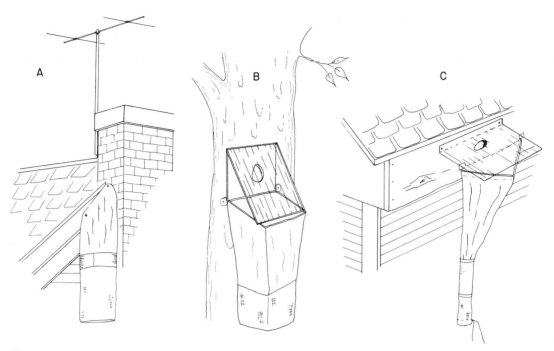

Figure 1. Bag (hopper) traps. Upper parts are made of polyethylene and bottom parts of wire screen. (A) Modified after Griffin (1940). (B) After Gaisler et al. (1979). (C) Davis' hopper trap, modified after Greenhall and Paradiso (1968).

Bels (1952) described a folding, wire trap that he placed over openings of hollow trees to capture members of a *Nyctalus noctula* colony as they departed at dusk. A disadvantage of this trap was that it required constant attention to prevent bats from crawling back into the cavity. Gaisler et al. (1979) described a bag (hopper) trap that was made from polyethylene and a wire-cloth bag, supported by a wire frame (Fig. 1 B). A trap guide, strung with monofilament fishing line, deflected departing bats into the bag below. Deployment of several such traps allowed bats to be captured at different roost cavities simultaneously without the requirement of constant attendance. A similar trap was used by Davis et al. (1962; see Greenhall and Paradiso, 1968) to capture *Tadarida brasiliensis* as individuals emerged from exit holes in buildings (Fig. 1 C). A transparent plastic "guide" covered and deflected the bats into the bag as they departed and prevented them from escaping.

3.5. Mist Nets

Mist nets are the most commonly used devices for capturing flying bats. Important practical guides have been written emphasizing their use with bats (e.g., Handley, 1968; Tuttle, 1976a). Some of the advantages of using mist nets to capture bats are that they are inexpensive, lightweight, compact, and easily transported and erected in the field. As recently as 20 years ago, Handley (1967) commented that "the great potential of mist nets as a tool for ecological study has been little tested or explored." Since that time, the use of mist nets for studies other than collecting has increased markedly (e.g., Jones, 1965; O'Farrell et al., 1967; O'Farrell and Bradley, 1970; Fleming et al., 1972; Gaisler, 1973; Kunz, 1973; Turner, 1975; LaVal and Fitch, 1977; Kurta, 1982).

3.5.1. Types of Nets

Generally, two types of mist nets [braided nylon and terylene (monofilament) nylon] are available commercially (see Appendix 2). Terylene nets are softer, stronger, and more durable than braided nylon, and are highly effective for capturing bats. Because of their softness and extremely fine fiber, however, some workers have found it difficult to remove bats from these nets. Both types of nets are available in the same mesh sizes and lengths. Black is the most common "color" and likely the most suitable for capturing bats. In addition to standard black, nets are available in dark forest-green, sand, and white. To our knowledge there have been no published reports comparing the success of bats taken in nets of different color.

Mist nets that are most preferred for capturing bats have a mesh size of 36 mm (ca. 1½ in), are of 50 or 70 denier/2 ply nylon, and have four shelves (Handley, 1968; Bleitz, no date). Mesh size is determined as the distance between two diagonal corners in the mesh of a stretched net. "Denier" is the number of grams in 9,000 m of fiber. For example, the specifications of a 50d/2 ply nylon net indicate that it is made of nylon fiber (9,000 m of which weighs 50 g) and that two strands are braided together to form the thread. Heavier denier nets are more durable than those of lighter construction, but they also are easier for bats to detect both visually and acoustically.

Four-shelf mist nets are typically about 2 m high and range in length from approximately 6 to 36 m. Short nets (<12 m) are the most versatile and are the easiest for one person to handle. Longer nets are often difficult for one person to erect alone and may require additional net poles in the middle for support. Several short nets may be stacked or butted end-to-end to increase the aerial coverage. Tethered and untethered nets are available but the former are slightly more expensive than the latter. Tethered nets are tied at regular intervals to horizontal shelf cords to keep the net from bunching at one end under windy conditions. Some nets come with extra-full netting that has the affect of increasing the depth of the bag.

3.5.2. Preparation of New Nets for Field Use

New nets are usually shipped in small transparent plastic bags. The small nylon cord that often secures the folded net should be removed and saved to repair damaged shelf-cords. A net should be carefully unfolded to expose the end loops. Many nets are supplied with color-coded top loops and different colors at opposite ends to facilitate handling. Even if the top loop is not color-coded, it still can be identified by its attachment to a double shelf-cord.

To prepare nets for field use, the loops at one end of the net should be arranged and tied in the appropriate order. To accomplish this, loops at one end of the net can be placed sequentially over the fingers of the left hand. This is done after first locating the top loop. Then, by lifting the right hand to extend the cord to the next loop, it in turn is placed over the fingers of the left hand. This procedure is continued until all five loops have been gathered and placed in order. Loops may be tied together by threading the top loop through the others, and by tying an overhand knot to secure them. Another method is to tie a small cloth string to the top loop (Fig. 2 A). When the loops are gathered, this string is used to tie them together (Handley, 1968). Wire and plastic "twist-ties" (Fig. 2 B), commonly used to close plastic trash bags or bread wrappers, work fairly well, but these can be easily misplaced in the field. Tying net loops together in the proper order before field use helps to keep the loops from becoming tangled when the net is deployed. Additional techniques on preparing mist nets for field use are given in Bleitz (no date).

3.5.3. Net Poles

In tropical regions one rarely experiences difficulty in obtaining poles for setting mist nets. Poles may be cut from bamboo culms or from small trees. Cut poles should be as straight as possible, rigid, and not more than 4-5 cm in diameter (Tuttle, 1976a). A cutlass or ma-

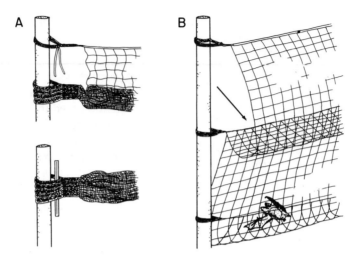

Figure 2. (A) One end of a mist net gathered on poles to illustrate two methods (cloth tie strings and wire "twist-ties") for securing net loops. (B) Properly adjusted vertical spacing of net loops and shelf-cords to form net pockets. A bat should be removed from the side of the net on which it entered, as determined from the position of the pocket relative to the shelf cord.

chete is invaluable for cutting poles, removing branches, and for sharpening the ends. One should obtain permission and use good judgment in cutting trees for net poles at local study sites.

Relatively inexpensive poles can be made from sections of electrical conduit. Simple poles can also be made from a single 10-ft (~3 m) piece of aluminum tubing. However, two, 5-ft. (~1.5 m) lengths often are more convenient to handle, assemble, and transport in the field. When short sections are used, the ends can be compressed or expanded, or joined with conduit couplers, so that two or more poles can be connected. Specially machined, aluminum net poles are available commercially in several different precut lengths.

3.5.4. Net Deployment

Mist nets may be deployed successfully at almost any site where bats are expected to fly. Strategies of net placement have a major influence on capture success. The most successful sites are near roosts, at water holes, and across trails that are used as flyways (Figs.

3 and 4 A–F). The most productive netting sites can often be identified from visual observations of flying bats, by listening to audible or ultrasonic sounds of echolocating bats (Chapter 6), and from the sounds made by falling fruit when plant-visiting bats are feeding. The use of ultrasonic detectors (Chapter 6) can be particularly valuable in distinguishing potentially productive from unproductive netting sites.

Bats can be netted at openings to caves, mines, and buildings, where bats regularly exit and enter. However, when mist nets are used in attics (Fig. 3 A) and in passages or openings of caves and mines (Fig. 3 B), bat populations should be relatively small and the nets should be monitored constantly to avoid the capture of large numbers of bats at one time. Appropriate spacing and horizontal tension on shelf cords can be maintained on high nets by tying net loops to net poles before the net is raised (Fig. 3 B).

When mist nets are set over streams and ponds (Fig. 3 C–E), the lower shelf-cord should be set near enough to the water surface to prevent bats from flying under the net, but high enough so that the lowest net-pocket

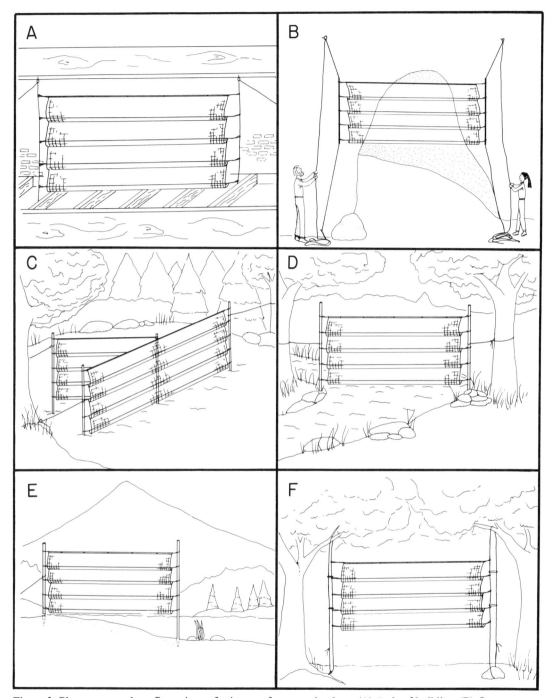

Figure 3. Placements and configurations of mist nets for capturing bats. (A) Attic of building. (B) Cave entrance. (C) Over a pond. (D) Over a stream. (E) Edge of lake. (F) Forest trail.

does not hang into the water. Also, it is best to select sites where the water is calm (Fig. 3 C and D) and, if possible, where there are overhanging branches to direct the flight of bats into the net (e.g., Barbour and Davis, 1969; Kunz, 1973; Kunz and Brock, 1975). Nets stretched across large bodies of water can be attended using 2-man rubber rafts (Easterla, 1973). Nets set across forest trails also are most effective if they are positioned beneath overhanging branches (Fig. 3 F).

Several alternative methods of setting net poles (for single and multiple nets) are illustrated in Figs. 3 and 4. Methods of setting poles and rigging for canopy nets are discussed in Section 3.5.6. Sites where poles can be used effectively depend on the type of substrate (e.g., sand, rock, soil, water, etc.) and the presence of, and type of, vegetation. Net poles can be stabilized by placing large stones at the base of each pole, by bracing them against rock ledges (Fig. 4 A), or by inserting one end of the pole deep into a soft, sandy or muddy substrate. Guy ropes tied to the middle of a pole can be anchored to other objects (e.g., large stones, small bushes, etc.) for stability. When poles are not available or desirable, ropes suspended from tree branches may be used as substitutes (Fig. 4 B). Even if no lateral branches are available, as on palm trees, nets can be secured to a rope that has been strung from the trunk of a tree (Fig. 4 B). Net poles also may be anchored to bat traps set in shallow water where one or more mist nets can be extended out from the trap (Fig. 9 C).

It is often profitable to use mist nets in V-configurations (Fig. 4 C) or a combination of high and low nets in a T-configuration (Fig. 4 D). As bats attempt to avoid one net they frequently become captured in another. Often bats can be captured if the perimeters of roosts are either partially or completely surrounded by one or more nets (Fig. 4 E and F). Depending upon the length of the net and the space available for setup, angled configurations can be made using one net by looping the horizontal shelf-cords over a pivotal net pole (Fig. 5 A). Two nets can be attached to a single net pole (Fig. 5 B) to achieve the same configuration.

In most studies, mist nets should be set up well in advance of darkness to capture early flying bats, but not so early as to capture late flying birds. In attempts to capture bats that rely mostly upon vision for orientation (e.g., pteropodids), it may be more profitable to set nets well after dark (see Walton and Trowbridge, 1982). Often bats are easiest to capture in areas such as roost openings and flyways, where they often rely mostly on spatial memory for orientation (see Neuweiler and Möhres, 1967; Mueller and Mueller, 1979). Bats are more difficult to capture in nets at feeding sites, where their sensory perception is the keenest.

3.5.5. Removal of Bats from Mist Nets

When a bat flies into a net, it usually drops into a pocket formed by the netting and shelf cords (Fig. 2 B). To remove a bat, one should first determine from which side of the net the bat entered. There are no universally accepted methods of removing bats from mist nets. We usually start with one wing, pulling it gently to keep the net taut, and use the net tension to free the head, feet, and finally the other wing. At times it may be easier to start with the feet instead of a wing. A good "rule" to follow is to start with the part of the bat that last entered the net. In either case, special care should be taken in removing the wings from the net; the long, narrow wing bones can easily be broken by rough handling. It sometimes helps to allow a captured bat (especially a large species) to clasp its teeth onto a cloth bag or loose part of a glove, as this may prevent it from chewing the net (or the hand). With a little practice, bats can be removed from a net within seconds of being captured. The longer a bat remains in a net, the more difficult and time-consuming it may be to remove it without causing injury to the bat or damage to the net. Constant attendance at a net is important, since some bats are able to chew themselves out within minutes, often leaving gaping holes. If a bat should become badly entan-

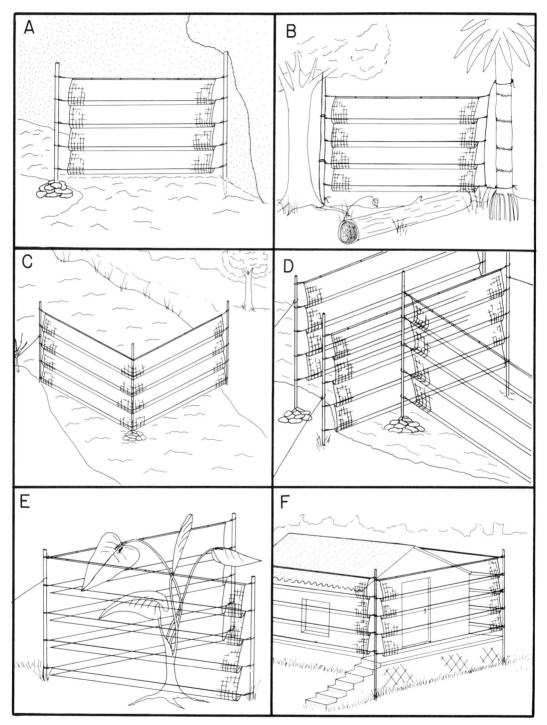

Figure 4. Multiple net configurations and alternative pole uses for setting mist nets to capture bats. (A) Use of large rocks and crevices in rock ledges to anchor net poles. (B) Use of ropes as "poles." (C) V-net configuration; poles anchored in soft substrate or with large rocks. (D) T-net configuration with a high and low net. (E) Foliage roost partially surrounded by a net. (F) Building partially surrounded by nets.

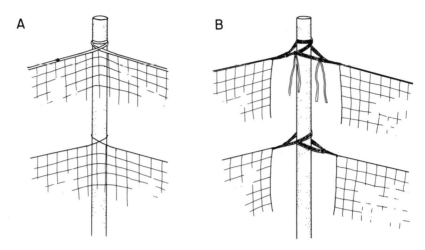

Figure 5. Alternative methods used to attach one or two mist nets to a pivotal net pole to form an angle in net. (A) Attachment of single net. (B) Attachment of two nets.

gled in a net, it may be necessary to cut some strands to free it, although this should only be done as a last resort. A small pair of scissors or a fingernail clipper comes in handy for this.

3.5.6.   Canopy Nets

Several descriptions of canopy net-systems have been published (e.g., Greenlaw and Swinebroad, 1967; Humphrey et al., 1968; Rautenbach, 1985) or have been used by various investigators (e.g., Handley, 1967; Cope et al., 1974; Humphrey et al., 1977; Bonaccorso, 1979; Kurta, 1980, 1982; R. K. LaVal, pers. comm.). The canopy net-system used by Handley (1967) and described by Humphrey et al. (1968) employed a horizontal rope stretched between two forest trees. It included separate rope attachments to the ground and a series of metal (noncorrosive) rings used as pulleys. Three or four, 12-m mist nets were attached to a continuous nylon cord so that the entire system could be raised or lowered by one person. Nets were attached by tying the top loop of the first net to the vertical cord. The spacing and attachment of the other net loops was accomplished by tying vertical spacing lines to shower curtain rings that were then attached to each net loop. The shower

curtain rings were clipped around the vertical cords to provide horizontal tension to the shelf-cords. This system allowed nets to be raised as high as 30 m above the forest floor and yielded striking differences in species when compared to captures in "ground-level" nets (Handley, 1967; also see Bonaccorso, 1979).

Where it is impractical to use a rope-system suspended from trees, use of poles allows nets to be raised to considerable heights (Fig. 6 A). Poles have the advantage of allowing net placement wherever desired, although the additional bulk makes them impractical in some field situations. Relatively inexpensive poles (at least 2.5 cm in diameter) can be made from 3 to 3.5 m lengths of electrical conduit or aluminum tubing. Two sections can be joined together by using tubes or solid rods of a smaller diameter, with larger tubes added to the outside of joints to increase the rigidity of the pole. Alternatively, the ends of each pole also can be machined so that they will fit together firmly. When three long poles (each ~ 3 m in length) are fitted together, the combined length is great enough to raise four standard-size mist nets or one extra large net (6 m high x 30 m wide) to a height about 9 m. Poles made from tubing

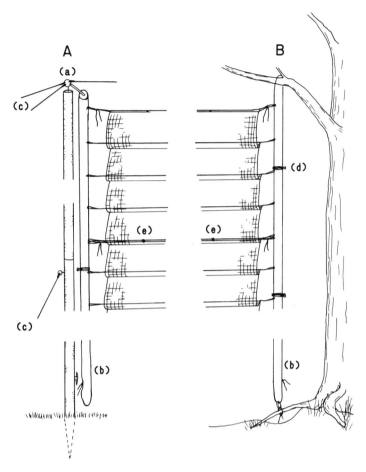

Figure 6. Two types of simple rigging used to erect canopy nets. Only one net and part of a second are shown. (A) Pole rigging. (B) Rope rigging. Guy lines are secured to eye-bolts on net poles with quick-release swivel snaps (a). The ends of the vertical net-ropes (b) guy lines (c) are secured with a quick-release knot (see Fig. 8). Nets are tied together with nylon string (e) and shower curtain rings (d) are used to help maintain horizontal tension on nets.

with a wall thickness of at least 1.6 mm are preferred; a pole with a lesser wall thickness may buckle under its own weight when raised, or it may bend as a net-rope is tightened. Poles greater than 10 m in height are generally impractical owing to the difficulty encountered in erecting and transporting them.

Large poles need at least two, and sometimes four, guy ropes to keep them upright. If two poles or one pole and one tree branch are used, a horizontal rope should be run from the tops to connect the two poles, or it should be run from one pole to the tree branch to stabi-

lize the system. Guy lines can be secured to eyebolts at the top and middle of the pole (Fig. 7 A). Guy ropes are best attached to net poles with quick-release swivel snaps (R. K. LaVal, pers. comm.) to avoid the inconvenience of having to tie and untie knots. We recommend O-rings in place of mechanical pulleys when suspending net ropes from poles (Fig. 7 B). If a pulley sticks, or a rope slips off, the entire system may have to be dismantled to correct the problem.

When suspending nets from tree branches, accurate placement of the rope over

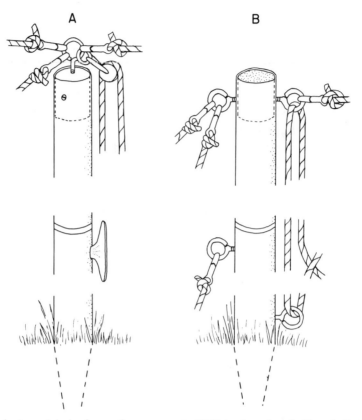

Figure 7. Two types of poles and rigging for erecting canopy nets. (A) Net pole equipped with eyebolts, O-rings, and vertical net-cord. (B) Net pole equipped with eyebolts, pulley, and net-cord. Guy lines are connected to poles with quick-release swivel snaps (see Fig. 6)

a branch 10 m or more above the ground may be difficult. Climbing the tree, especially with the aid of tree-climbing spikes, is a possibility, but this should only be done by experienced climbers. Rope-climbing techniques used by cavers (e.g., Daunt-Mergens, 1981) can be adapted for gaining access to areas within and above the forest canopy (e.g., Perry, 1978; Perry and Williams, 1981; Whitacre, 1981). Another method of getting a rope over a high branch is to use a bow and arrow or a slingshot. Virgil Brack (in litt.) used a compound bow and a blunt, one-meter steel rod as an arrow. An arrow can be shot over a desired branch pulling a lightweight nylon line along with it. A heavier rope used to support the nets is then tied to the line and pulled up and over a branch. Kurta (1980, 1982) used a

baseball attached to a nylon string that was wound on a fishing reel. This method was satisfactory for reaching branches up to a height of 14 m. Use of sticks and stones make accurate placement difficult on branches over 4-5 m in height, and is not generally recommended. Once the rope is over the branch, a continuous loop is formed by passing the rope under a log, exposed root, or large stone. Another option is to tie a small length of rope around a log or root and through an O-ring, carabiner, or pulley (Fig. 7 B), allowing the main rope to move freely and reducing friction. Alternatively, the rope may be threaded through an eye-bolt screwed into the base of a tree or log.

Once the rope is placed over a branch or threaded through an O-ring (or eye-bolt) at the top of a pole, one end is passed through each loop of the mist nets (Fig. 6). The ends of the rope are securely tied to form a continuous net line. A quick-release knot (Fig. 8) is useful for joining the two ends of a net rope or for securing a guy line. The upper loop of the top net should be tied to the vertical net line (Fig. 6 B). The net rope is then raised, and each successive loop is placed at the desired spacing. Net loops seldom have to be tied to the vertical rope, as they seldom slip. If they do, it may be necessary to tie separate spacing-cords between each loop (see Humphrey et al., 1968). Individual nets may be joined together at 1.5 to 2 m intervals along their length with small pieces of string or monofilament fishing line.

The mass of the nets may cause the rope to bow out near the middle, causing the nets to sag. This can be overcome by placing a few shower curtain rings around both parts of the continuous net rope (Fig. 6 B). These rings are

inexpensive, lightweight, and are easily attached and detached. They will slide up and down the rope, and they usually do not pull the net loops out of position. Small pieces of string tied around the rope will also work but they tend to abrade easily. When lowering the net, one simply pulls the vertical rope through the hand, and all the net loops will collect on top of the fist. The entire group of nets can be taken off the rope, folded and stored as one.

Rautenbach (1985) described an elaborate pole-system to support a large, 12-shelf mist net (6 m high x 30 m wide), using 6.2 m lengths of aluminum-alloy sailboat masts and a series of ropes and stainless steel pulleys. Each end of the net is attached to the mast by a series of curtain-rail runners, designed to slide freely up and down within the sail track of the mast. Each pole is secured in an upright position with four guy lines anchored with large tent pegs. Rautenbach (1985) noted that capture success was 300% better with one

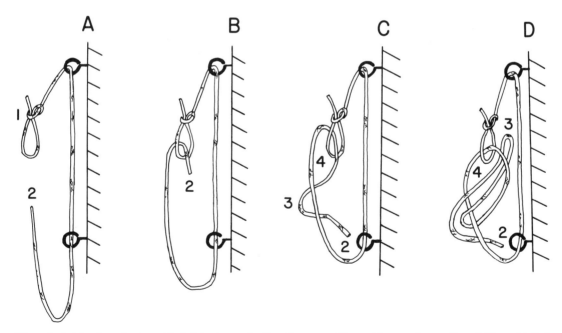

Figure 8. Quick-release knot used for joining two ends of continuous net-line and for securing guy lines. (A) Loop 1 is tied at the free end of rope. (B) End 2 is threaded through loop 1 and pulled downward to create desired tension. (C) Fold 3 is made near loose end of 2 and is passed behind the rope. (D) Fold 3 is then threaded through loop 4. By pulling on 3, the knot is tightened. By pulling on 2, the knot is released so that 2 can be quickly drawn back through 1, allowing a mist net to be added or removed from the rope, or to allow the release of a guy line.

large net than when serially-strung conventional nets of comparable surface area were used.

3.5.7. Disadvantages and Potential Biases

The principal disadvantage of using mist nets is that they require constant attention. If nets are left unattended, captured bats may become badly entangled and difficult to remove before they cause damage to the net. Moreover, bats may drown, strangle, become injured, or die of stress if they are not removed promptly. Unattended nets set across trails and streams also pose a risk of entangling unsuspecting people, cattle, and other animals that may blunder into them. Predation on bats captured in mist nets is also sufficiently common (e.g., Fleming et al., 1972; Morrison, 1978; August, 1979) to warrant constant vigilance.

Potential biases of using mist nets have been discussed by several authors, including Dalquest (1954), Cranbrook and Barrett (1965), Kunz and Brock (1975), and Tidemann and Woodside (1978). Some bats are unusually proficient at avoiding nets especially on their second encounter (e.g., LaVal, 1970; Kunz, 1973; LaVal and Fitch, 1977). Reduced capture success on successive nights has often been attributed to "net shyness," although Cranbrook and Barrett (1965) found no statistical evidence of such bias for *Nyctalus noctula*. Several workers (e.g., Dalquest, 1954; Kunz and Brock, 1975; Turner, 1975) have noted that capture success can be improved markedly when net configurations and positions are changed on successive netting nights.

Other capture biases may reflect differences in food habits, energy and water requirements of the bats, habitat type, environmental conditions (e.g., moonlight, rain, wind, etc.), visual and acoustic resolution by the bats, and their flight behavior (altitude, speed, and maneuverability). Activity of bats netted over water may yield more information about drinking behavior than about flight and feeding behavior (see Fenton and Morris, 1976; Bell, 1980). Different species may commute and forage at different elevations in the forest. Handley (1967) reported that when mist nets were set in the forest canopy of Brazil, more fruit-eating bats were captured than insectivorous or carnivorous species. LaVal and Fitch (1977) captured a disproportionate number of plant-visiting bats along trails in secondary growth where there was an abundance of fruiting and flowering trees (also see Palmerim and Etheridge, 1985).

Several workers have commented on the effects of environmental conditions on the capture success of bats using mist nets. Wind causes pockets of mist nets to billow and often makes the netting accumulate at one end (see Section 3.5.1). Lower capture success was reported by Nyholm (1965) on windy nights, although O'Farrell and Bradley (1970) noted that capture success was not affected until wind speed reached 9 mph. Apparently, visually-oriented bats are quite adept at avoiding mist nets, but acoustically-oriented bats can vary considerably in their ability to detect mist nets. When mist nets get wet from rain they apparently are easier to detect, allowing bats to avoid capture.

3.5.8. Net Maintenance and Dismantling Procedures

If nets capture large insects, or if sticks and leaves accumulate during a netting session, these should be removed before the net is dismantled. Sticks may be removed by first breaking them into small pieces (Tuttle, 1976a). Large insects may need to be dismembered before they can be removed. If bats chew holes in nets, the holes can be repaired using nylon thread or monofilament fishing line. If a shelf cord is broken, it can be restrung with a section left over from a previously damaged net.

At the end of a netting session, when all bats and debris have been removed, the loops at each end of the net should be gathered and secured in the appropriate order (Section 3.5.2). Before removing the net from its poles, the netting may be twirled slightly to tighten it into a bundle. Then, by holding one set of loops in one hand, the other hand can be moved along the net away from the loops, gathering the net to form a single bundle about 1 m from the loops. The gathered net may be grasped at this point with the right hand, continuing to fold it into 1-m lengths until the opposite end is reached. The bundle of loops at this end can be wrapped around the folded net to ensure that the end loops do not become entangled and that the net can be easily unraveled at the next deployment. After folding the net into smaller lengths, the entire bundle can be placed into a plastic bag for storage and transport. Additional details for handling and dismantling mist nets are found in Handley (1968) and Bleitz (no date).

3.6. Harp Traps

Constantine (1958) first described an automatic trap for capturing Mexican free-tailed bats (*Tadarida brasiliensis*) as they departed from large cave openings. Constantine's trap essentially was one large frame with a single bank of fine wires, each individually attached to coil springs, spaced approximately 2.5 cm apart. The trap worked on the principle that the wires could not be easily detected by the echolocation cries of bats, and that the bank of wires was sufficient to stop the flight momentum of bats. A large bag attached beneath the trap served as a hopper to collect the falling bats. Although this single-frame trap proved successful in capturing flying *Tadarida,* it was less efficient at capturing other bats such as *Myotis* and it lacked portability (Constantine, 1958). Subsequent designs were smaller (Constantine, 1958, 1969; Constantine and Villa-R, 1962), have incorporated two frames instead of one (Tuttle, 1974a; Tidemann and Woodside, 1978), and can be folded for increased portability (Tidemann and Woodside, 1978).

3.6.1. Double-Frame Trap Design

The Tuttle trap consists of two rectangular frames of aluminum tubing, approximately 2 m high and 1.8 m wide (Fig. 10). The frame is typically supported by four tubular extension legs but the traps may be used without legs when suspended from above. A canvas bag, partially lined with polyethylene is supported beneath the trap frame to catch bats as they fall after having been intercepted by the trap. Plastic flaps or heavy wires also can be suspended inside the bag to prevent hovering bats and other highly maneuverable species from escaping (Tuttle, 1974b). In Tuttle's (1974a) original description, coil springs were attached to vertically-strung, steel wires to maintain tension. Many workers have found 6- or 8-pound monofilament fishing line preferable to the steel wire. Monofilament nylon line may be attached directly to horizontal tension bars using small, fishing swivels, or alternatively, they may be tied directly through the holes drilled in the tension bar. As with the Constantine trap, the recommended spacing for the vertical wires is 2.5 cm. The distance between the frames should be adjusted to not less than 7 or more than 10 cm (see Section 3.6.3). Net bags should include drain holes in the bottom to prevent the accumulation of water when it rains.

The Tuttle trap works on the same principle as the Constantine trap except, that with the addition of a second frame and associated bank of vertically-strung "wires," bats that are able to fly through a single bank of wires are usually stopped by a second. Such bats become temporarily "trapped" between the two banks of wires and drop or flutter into the bag which is suspended below.

Tidemann and Woodside (1978) described a folding, double-frame harp trap that is highly portable. This trap has the same basic features of the Tuttle trap, but it can be dismantled or set up in about 30 min. It also can be collapsed, for transport, into a bundle that is less than 1 m long, approximately 15

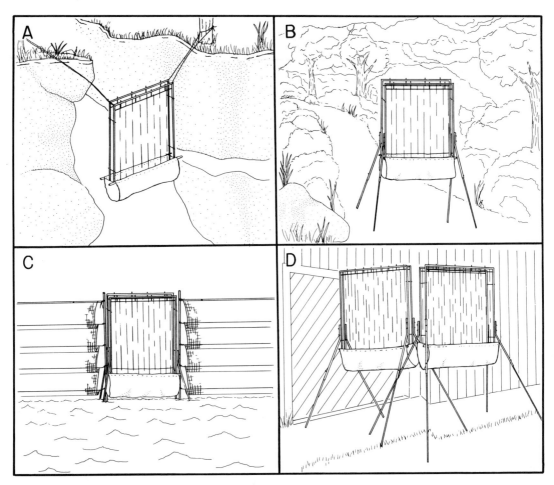

Figure 9. Alternative placements of double-frame harp traps. (A) Suspended in a canyon. (B) Set on forest trail. (C) Set in shallow pond for support of mist nets. (D) Two traps set in L-configuration in front of closed door (opposite crevice). (E) Suspended beneath ridge-pole inside barn. (F) Set in front of open barn door. (G) Set at cave opening. (H) Suspended outside building near roof-line.

cm in diameter, and weighs about 7 kg.

Harp traps have several advantages over other methods used to capture flying bats. Since only minimum attendance is required, several traps can be set and run simultaneously. Moreover, once bats are captured in the trap, they are reasonably well protected from inclement weather. However, one should be alert to the possibility that certain predators can take advantage of bats that enter a trap bag. One of us (THK) has observed snakes feeding on bats confined in harp-trap bags. Other potential problems that can occur when bats are in trap bags include biting and predation of one species on another, rabies transfer from one bat to another, and the suffocation of some bats if large numbers are caught in a short time.

3.6.2. Trap Placement

As with mist nets, harp traps are best set at sites where bats use natural flyways, such as trails, along slowly flowing streams, between trees and rock faces, over water holes, and at roost openings (Fig. 9 A-H). Harp traps are

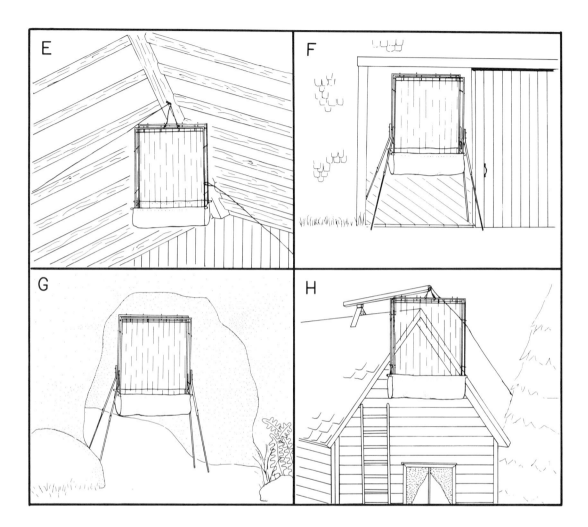

most effective when they are partially hidden by the natural terrain and adjacent to objects that form natural flyways, such as canyon walls (Fig. 9 A) and forest trails with overhanging tree branches (Fig. 9 B). A harp trap may also be used successfully if placed in the middle of a shallow pond or stream and abutted with mist nets that function much like a funnel (Fig. 9 C). In capturing bats that depart and return through small crevices in buildings, we have successfully used two harp traps set at right angles to each other, with one placed perpendicular to a closed barn door (Fig. 9 D). This configuration is analogous, in principle, to T or V sets using mist nets (see Section 3.5.4) and it takes advantage of the circling behavior of bats to capture them as they return to their roost. We have also used harp traps suspended in the attics of barns (Fig. 9 E), in front of open barn doors (Fig. 9 F), and caves (Fig. 9 G) to capture bats as they depart or return from feeding. Suspension of traps near the ridge pole of large barns is the only effective method to capture some bats as they return from feeding. If there is no access to the ridge pole of a barn or to the attic of a house, it may be necessary to suspend a harp trap outside of the building, in front of crevices used by bats for exit and entry (Fig. 9 H).

If harp traps are used to study emergence activity, only a small fraction of the opening should be blocked by the trap when bats are present in large numbers (Tuttle, 1976a). Otherwise, the normal flow pattern of departing bats can be disrupted, causing a distortion of activity. At sites where only a few bats may be present, one may want to block areas around the trap with branches, nylon netting, or some other material to funnel as many bats as possible into the path of the trap. When a harp trap begins to capture more bats than can be conveniently handled, the bag can be removed from the trap, or the trap can be turned sideways. The trap should not be laid down on the ground as the lines may become entangled in vegetation.

3.6.3. Trap Effectiveness and Potential Biases

Adjustments in wire tension and frame spacing appear to be two important factors that influence the capture success of harp traps (Tuttle, 1974b). Tension on the monofilament "wires" is adjusted using wingnuts on the threaded rods that support the tension bar at the top of the trap. Tuttle (1974b) suggested that tension on the wires should be proportional to the speed of the bat. If bats escape by bouncing off the wire, the tension should be reduced. If bats pass through the wires the tension should be increased. These adjustments usually are made empirically and some compromise in tension is usually needed when traps are used at places where several different species are present. When the spacing between frames is greater than 10 cm the number of bats that escape tends to increase. Species that are particularly adept at avoiding mist nets are often caught in double-frame harp traps. They are especially effective in capturing small bats that weigh less than 30 g. Bats weighing more than 30 g are seldom captured. However, certain species, such as gleaning and hovering bats, appear to be better at avoiding harp traps (and mist nets) than larger, heavy-bodied frugivorous bats.

Variations in size, shape, and position of openings used by departing bats pose unique challenges in trap placement. When traps are placed in doorways of buildings or at cave or mine entrances, the location of the trap with respect to the door frame or opening of the cave is an important factor governing trap success. To maximize capture success at cave openings and in open doorways, harp traps can be hidden from "view" by positioning them immediately outside the openings when bats are exiting and inside the openings when bats are returning. Kunz and Anthony (1977) compared capture results of Tuttle traps set in front of doors, crevices above doors, and in front of open windows of barns used by departing *Myotis lucifugus*. Capture efficiency (captures/encounters) varied with trap placement, ranging from 80% as they departed from a crevice into the pathway of the trap, to about 30% when bats flew directly through an open door or window. These differences were attributed to variation in flight speed and momentum as bats encountered the trap, angle of encounter, and the opportunities available for avoidance. Bats departing from crevices seldom had sufficient momentum to pass through the two banks of wires, whereas bats that were flying at full speed often did.

Prior experience, age, sex, and reproductive condition may also bias capture success. Adults are generally more adept at avoiding harp traps than are naive juveniles, and lactating bats are more adept at avoiding capture than are near-term pregnant bats (e.g., Kunz, 1973; Kunz and Anthony, 1977; LaVal and LaVal, 1980). In trapping *Myotis grisescens*, LaVal and LaVal (1980) found that a larger percentage of females avoided Tuttle traps than did males. Kunz and Anthony (1977) noted that banded bats were seldom recaptured on the same night and that capture success decreased over the period that a trap was used successively at a single site. LaVal and Fitch (1977) noted that the Tuttle trap was superior to mist nets in light rain. Tidemann and Woodside (1978) found that double-frame harp traps were 10 times more efficient than mist nets, when both number and diversity of species were considered.

3.7. Miscellaneous Methods

Other methods have been used to capture bats when more conventional methods have not been effective. Although Bradbury and Emmons (1974) and Bradbury and Vehrencamp (1976) successfully captured harem groups of emballonurid bats with hoop nets, they only did so after enclosing buttress cavities with black nylon seine-netting. After bats had departed from their roosts to feed, one end of the net was nailed to the tree above the buttress cavity, and the other end was rolled onto a pole. After the bats returned, the net was allowed to roll down on the outside of the buttress cavity, trapping the bats inside (G.F. McCracken, pers. comm.). Roosting groups of emballonurids that occupied the sides of tree boles and cliffs were captured by approaching them with mist nets stretched between two hand-carried poles, or by using a 1.5-m diameter hoop net, strung with mesh from a mist net (Bradbury and Emmons, 1974). To contain previously marked *Mactotus californicus* for ease of capture, and to avoid disturbing an entire colony, mosquito netting and 6-mm mesh seine-netting was used to block off sections of caves and mine tunnels (G.P. Bell, pers. comm.). Turner (1975) attached a frame of poles to a hollow tree used by *Desmodus rotundus* and draped the frame with mist nets. Bats were captured in the nets as they attempted to emerge at dusk.

Night-roosting groups of *Myotis lucifugus* that often occupy mortices in barns (see Anthony et al., 1981) have been captured with a nylon-mesh (mosquito netting) bag sewn to a small (10 x 30 cm) frame. The frame and mesh bag are placed over an occupied mortice, and with one hand holding the frame over the mortice, the bag is inverted into the cavity with the other hand to dislodge the bats. Once the bats are in the bag, a drawstring is tightened to prevent bats from escaping.

Bats may be captured by attracting or luring them with insects, sounds or odors of other bats, and odors from ripe fruits and flowers. Bats are commonly attracted to insects active near lights (e.g., Constantine, 1958; O'Farrell and Miller, 1972; Fenton and Morris, 1976; Bell, 1980, 1985; Buchler and Childs, 1981). Youngson and McKenzie (1977) used such a response to attract bats to areas where they could be conveniently shot. Some bats appear to respond to the sounds produced by calling insects (e.g., Buchler and Childs, 1981; Bell, 1985), or the sounds of other bats feeding on insects (Fenton and Morris, 1976; Barclay, 1982). Nyholm (1965) used this type of response to capture bats by placing insects in a mesh bag and suspending it inside an open trap from the tip of a pole. When a bat landed on the bag, a cord was pulled capturing it inside the trap. Similarly, it should be possible to lure plant-visiting bats using lures made from ripe fruits and flowers set near harp traps or mist nets. Many bats respond to distress calls of conspecifics and to those of other species (Tuttle, 1976a; also see August, 1979). Tying holding bags containing bats onto mist net poles or traps may also increase capture success. Whether bats are attracted to distress calls or to odors of these captive bats is unknown.

4. HOLDING DEVICES

Holding devices are used to temporarily house captured bats as they await processing in the field or for use in transporting bats to the laboratory. The type of holding device that is used will depend upon the length of time that bats are to be held, the numbers and kinds of species, and the prevailing environmental conditions. Bats should not be housed in overly crowded conditions, left in potentially stressful environments, or held longer than absolutely necessary (Tuttle, 1979). When bats are to be transported by automobile or other forms of transport, they should be protected from extreme temperatures and forced convection.

Nylon mesh or muslin (cotton) bags make good, temporary holding devices for some species. They can be made by sewing the fabric into bags of a desired size (Fig. 10 A). We prefer bags that are 30 cm wide and 45 cm deep, with draw-strings or velcro tabs for securing the open end. The mesh of net bags should be small enough to prevent bats from escaping, to prevent their wings from getting caught, and to keep them from chewing escape holes. Ace and Delta style netting (3-mm mesh) is ideal for making holding bags. Net laundry-bags, often available as military surplus, commercially available "bird holding bags," and bags used for washing lingerie also make good holding bags. When using small, net bags it is advisable to house each species separately. One of the advantages of net or muslin holding bags, made from an absorbant fabric, is that they may be kept moist with water in hot, dry environments to help reduce overheating and water loss. Muslin bags may be preferred to open-mesh bags if bats are to be held separately to collect feces for food habits analysis (see Chapters 11 and 13) or for the examination of ectoparasites (Chapter 27). Some bats (e.g., *Lasiurus, Macrotus*) do not adjust well to small cloth holding bags (G. P. Bell, pers. comm.).

Several types of larger holding devices were described in Greenhall and Paradiso (1968) and Barbour and Davis (1969). The Myers bag (Fig. 10 B) is a versatile, collapsible bag made from 3-mm mesh seine-netting. The top is made from a piece of rubber from a tire innertube, secured between two pieces of plywood with staples and small bolts. A slit, cut into the rubber top, allows entry and removal of a bat with one hand without the risk of other bats escaping. A convenient size for a Myers bag is about 38 cm in diameter and 60 cm deep. Such a bag will hold up to 200 small (<12 g), active bats without causing injury or suffocation.

A nylon-net bag attached to a metal or plastic cylinder at one end also makes a good holding device. A large rubber band (cut as a cross section from a tire innertube) can be used to secure a net bag to a cylinder (e.g., stove pipe, PVC pipe, plastic paint cans, etc.).

A nylon cord may be attached to the cylinder as a handle. The open end of the cylinder should be large enough to allow entry with a handful of bats but small enough to prevent bats from flying out. Bats can be prevented from escaping if the diameter of the cylinder is no greater than the wing span. Griffin (1940) described a cylindrical holding device in which the bottom part of the cage was made from ¼ inch (6-mm mesh) hardware cloth (Fig. 10 C). A wood disk was fitted into the end of the wire-mesh cylinder so that it would be self-supporting.

Metal or plastic minnow buckets also make good cages for holding and transporting bats (Easterla, 1973). The bottom half of the inner bucket is made of wire or plastic mesh and provides suitable roosting places. A small amount of water may be kept in the bottom of the outer bucket to help maintain humidity. Minnow buckets are especially valuable for holding and transporting hibernating bats (A. W. Gustafson, pers. comm.).

Plastic trash (waste) containers have been modified for use as holding containers. Cockrum (1969) used 20-gallon, plastic garbage cans, in which ventilation holes were cut into the sides. These containers were partly lined with hardware cloth inserts, and a hole was cut into the lid which left a 10-cm wide rim to prevent bats from crawling out. We have successfully used rectangular trash containers (Fig. 10 E) to hold bats that were removed from small mortices and crevices in barns. A nylon cord is attached to the top rim so that the bucket can be carried around the neck, freeing the hands to capture bats. Wire-mesh screen may be inserted into the container to line the inner perimeter. McCracken and Bradbury (1981) used a large, round plastic trash bucket and modified it by removing the bottom and attaching a hardware cloth basket (Fig. 10 E). Although this bucket was used primarily as a device to capture harem groups of *Phyllostomus hastatus* (Section 3.1); it secondarily served as a holding device while bats were being processed (G. F. McCracken, pers. comm.).

One of the most serious problems en-

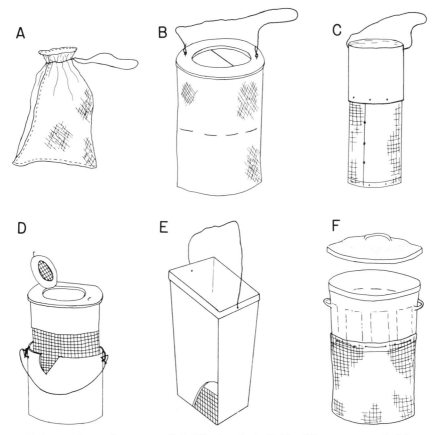

Figure 10. Portable bags and cages for temporarily holding bats in the field and for transport to the laboratory. (A) Net holding bag. (B) Myers bag. (C) Griffin cage. (D) Minnow bucket. (E) Rectangular, plastic trash container. (F) Cylindrical, plastic and wire-mesh "bucket."

countered when bats are held in environments that differ from their natural roosts is that they may become hyperactive, dehydrated, overheated, or hypothermic. An aluminum-frame insect rearing cage, lined with 6-mm mesh seine-netting and fitted into a plywood box that was painted white, was used to house and transport *Macrotus californicus* in desert regions. This device provided a stable thermal environment and allowed the bats to move freely as they were being transported (G. P. Bell, pers. comm.).

Holding cages that simulate roost environments offer many advantages for studies on field energetics, feeding ecology, and postnatal growth. We have regularly used a six-

chamber, wooden holding cage that provides roosting conditions that approximate the natural roost environment of *Myotis lucifugus* and *Eptesicus fuscus* (Fig. 11). Each chamber (5 x 5 x 12 cm) is designed to hold up to 12 adult bats weighing 7-10 g or 6 adult bats weighing 12-20 g. The bottom of each chamber is covered with hardware cloth and the top is covered with a removable wooden lid. When these gregarious species are permitted to cluster, individuals stay warm and active, and theoretically have reduced metabolic requirements (see Kunz, 1980; Kurta, 1985). The metabolic heat that is produced by active bats becomes trapped in occupied cage-chambers comparable to that observed in

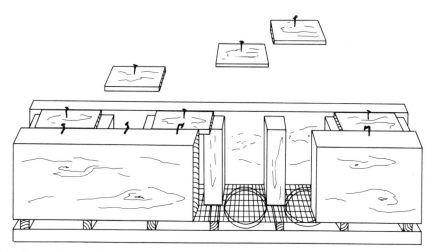

Figure 11. Wooden holding cage that simulates the roost environment of house-dwelling bats. A complete unit contains six separate chambers. The bottom of each chamber is covered with 3-mm mesh hardware cloth, and the top of each chamber has a removable wooden lid. Space beneath each chamber accommodates a Petri dish for collecting feces and urine, if needed.

their natural roost environments. At times it may be valuable to hold bats separately in these chambers (see Chapter 18).

Excellent holding cages can be made from styrofoam coolers by cutting small ventilation holds (covered with screen wire) and inserting a hardware cloth liner to provide roosting places. Adequate ventilation, however, is needed to prevent bats from overheating or suffocating in such devices. Bags of ice or gel coolants may be added to styrofoam coolers to hold and/or transport hibernating bats.

When live bats are to be shipped over long distances, special holding devices are required to reduce stress, minimize energy expenditure and water loss, and to prevent individuals from biting one another. Additional comments on cage design and requirements for shipping live bats can be found in Chapter 22.

5. SUMMARY

Methods used to capture bats will depend on the objectives of the study, the species in ques-

tion, and whether bats are to be captured in the roost or during flight. Whichever method is used, efforts should be made to minimize disturbance to the bats.

Reliable light sources are essential for capturing flying bats at night or as they roost in dimly-lit or dark places. When selecting a light source, factors such as reliability, durability, and cost are important considerations. When working alone in the dark, at least two spare light sources should be carried. Leather gloves are recommended for handling most bats; they should be heavy enough to provide protection against bites, but pliable enough to allow sensitivity to the form and movement of bats which are being held.

Many bats can be captured by hand without the aid of special devices. Long forceps, hand (hoop) nets, and bucket traps are important aids to capturing bats in roost situations. Some bats can be captured as they depart from roost sites using hoop nets or with specially designed bag (hopper) traps positioned over or near exit holes. Mist nets and harp traps are the most successful devices used for capturing flying bats. Monofilament nets are preferred by many workers, but bats may be more difficult to remove from monofilament nets than from standard (2 ply) nylon nets. Canopy nets may be erected using a system of ropes and/or long poles, steel rings (or pulleys), quick release snaps, and guy lines. A major disadvantage when using mist nets is that they require constant attention. Double-frame harp traps can be used most successfully to capture bats as they emerge from or return to roost sites, and as they commute to and from foraging areas. Although harp traps cover a smaller area than mist nets, they frequently capture species that cannot be taken using mist nets. Harp traps offer the advantages of not requiring constant attention and that large numbers of bats can be captured and processed quickly.

There are several types of devices that can be used to hold bats in the field while they are being processed or transported. Small net or cloth bags are relatively inexpensive to make or purchase, and they are highly versatile. Other types of holding devices, such as trash (waste) containers, minnow buckets, styrofoam coolers, and large collapsible net bags may prove valuable for certain applications. Holding devices that provide protection from extreme environments and that simulate natural roost conditions are preferred so that energy expenditure, water loss, and physiological and psychological stress can be minimized.

6. ACKNOWLEDGMENTS

We are grateful to V. Brack, R. K. LaVal, and A. R. Richter who generously shared their experience in setting canopy nets. We thank C. O. Handley, Jr., D. W. Morrison, and I. L. Rautenbach for allowing us to examine their unpublished manuscripts, and Louane E. Hann who skillfully prepared the illustrations. G. P. Bell kindly reviewed the manuscript and K. M. Klinghammer verified references. The research of THK has been generously supported by the National Science Foundation, National Geographic Society, American Philosophical Society, Organization of American States, and the Boston University Graduate School. The research of AK has been supported by the U.S. Fish and Wildlife Service (Cooperative Agreement with Michigan Department of Natural Resources and Michigan State University), Nongame Wildlife Program of the Michigan Department of Natural Resources, Sigma Xi, the American Society of Mammalogists, and the Theodore Roosevelt Memorial Fund.

7. REFERENCES

Agaconi, E. M. 1938a. Un nouvel appareil pour la capture de chiroptères. Mammalia, 2:89-94.

Agaconi, E. M. 1938b. Note complémentaire sur un nouvel appareil pour la capture de chiroptères. Mammalia, 2:137-139.

Anthony, E. L. P., M. H. Stack, and T. H. Kunz. 1981. Night roosts and the nocturnal time budget of the little brown bat, *Myotis lucifugus*: Effects of reproductive status, prey density, and environmental conditions. Oecologia, 51:151-156.

August, P. V. 1979. Distress calls in *Artibeus jamaicensis:* Ecology and evolutionary implications. Pp. 151-159, *in* Vertebrate ecology in the northern Neotropics. (J. F. Eisenberg, ed.). Smithsonian Institution Press, Washington, D.C.

Barbour, R. W., and W. H. Davis. 1969. Bats of America. Univ. Press of Kentucky, Lexington, 286 pp.

Barclay, R. M. R. 1982. Interindividual use of echolocation calls: Eavesdropping by bats. Behav. Ecol. Sociobiol., 10:271-275.

Bell, G. P. 1980. Habitat use and response to patches of prey by desert insectivorous bats. Can. J. Zool., 58:1876-1883.

Bell, G. P. 1985. The sensory basis of prey location by the California leaf-nosed bat *Macrotus californicus* (Chiroptera: Phyllostomidae). Behav. Ecol. Sociobiol., 16:343-347.

Bels, L. 1952. Fifteen years of bat banding in the Netherlands. Publ. Natuurhist. Gen. Limburg, 5:1-99.

Bleitz D. no date. Mist nets and their use. Bleitz Wildl. Publ., Mimeographed, 18 pp.

Bonaccorso, F. J. 1979. Foraging and reproductive ecology in a Panamanian bat community. Bull. Florida State Mus., Biol. Ser., 24:359-408.

Bradbury, J. W., and L. H. Emmons. 1974. Social

organization of some Trinidad bats. I. Emballonuridae. Z. Tierpsychol., 36:137-183.

Bradbury, J. W., and S. L. Vehrencamp. 1976. Social organization and foraging in emballonurid bats. I. Field studies. Behav. Ecol. Sociobiol., 1:337-381.

Brosset, A. 1966. La biologie des chiroptères. Masson, Paris, 237 pp.

Brosset, A. 1976. Social organization in the African bat, *Myotis boccagei,* Z. Tierpsychol., 42:50-56.

Brown, P. E., T. W. Brown, and A. D. Grinnell. 1983. Echolocation, development, and vocal communication in the lesser bulldog bat, *Noctilio albiventris.* Behav. Ecol. Sociobiol., 13:287-298.

Buchler, E. R., and S. B. Childs. 1981. Orientation to distant sounds by foraging big brown bats (*Eptesicus fuscus*). Anim. Behav., 29:428-432.

Cope, J. B., A. R. Richter, and R. S. Mills. 1964. A summer concentration of the Indiana bat, *Myotis sodalis,* in Wayne County, Indiana. Proc. Indiana Acad. Sci., 83:482-484.

Constantine, D. G. 1958. An automatic bat-collecting device. J. Wildl. Manage., 22:17-22.

Constantine, D. G. 1966. Ecological observations on lasiurine bats in Iowa. J. Mammal., 47:34-41.

Constantine, D. G. 1969. Trampa portátil para vampiros usada en programas de campana antirábica. Bol. Ofic. Sanit. Panamer., 67:39-42.

Constantine, D. G., and B. Villa-R. 1962. Métodos de lucha contra los vampiros transmisores de la rabia. Bol. Ofic. Sanit. Panamer., 53:7-12.

Cockrum, E. L. 1969. Migration of the guano bat. Pp. 303-336, *in* Contributions in mammalogy. (J. K. Jones, Jr., ed.). Misc. Publ. 51, Mus. Nat. Hist., Univ. Kansas, Lawrence.

Cranbrook, The Earl of, and H. G. Barrett. 1965. Observations on noctule bats (*Nyctalus noctula*) captured while feeding. Proc. Zool. Soc. Lond., 144:1-24 (with and Appendix on net shyness by F. Yates).

Dalquest, W. W., 1954. Netting bats in tropical Mexico. Trans. Kansas Acad. Sci., 57:1-10.

Dalquest, W. W., and D. W. Walton 1970. Diurnal retreats of bats. Pp. 162-187, *in* About bats: A chiropteran symposium. (B. H. Slaughter and D. W. Walton, eds.). Southern Methodist Univ. Press, Dallas, 339 pp.

Daunt-Mergens, D. O. (ed.). 1981. Cave Research Foundation Personnel Manual. Cave Research Foundation, Mammoth Cave, Kentucky, 155 pp.

Davis, R. B., C. F. Herreid II, and H. L. Short. 1962. Mexican free-tailed bats in Texas. Ecol. Monogr., 32:311-346.

Easterla, D. A. 1973. Ecology of the 18 species of Chiroptera at Big Bend National Park, Texas. Part I. Northwest Missouri State Studies, 34:1-43.

Erkert, H. 1982. Ecological aspects of bat activity rhythms. Pp. 201-242, *in* Ecology of bats. (T. H. Kunz, ed.). Plenum Press, New York, 425 pp.

Fenton, M. B. 1982. Echolocation, insect hearing, and feeding ecology of insectivorous bats. Pp. 261-285, *in* Ecology of bats. (T. H. Kunz, ed.). Plenum Press, New York, 425 pp.

Fenton, M. B., and G. P. Bell. 1979. Echolocation and feeding behaviour of four species of *Myotis* (Chiroptera). Can. J. Zool., 57:1271-1277.

Fenton, M. B., and G. K. Morris. 1976. Opportunistic feeding by desert bats (*Myotis* spp.). Can. J. Zool., 54:526-530.

Fleming, T. H. 1982. Foraging strategies of plant-visiting bats. Pp. 287-325, *in* Ecology of bats. (T. H. Kunz, ed.). Plenum Press, New York, 425 pp.

Fleming, T. H., E. T. Hooper, and D. E. Wilson. 1972. Three Central American bat communities: Structure, reproductive cycles, and movement. Ecology, 53:555-569.

Gaisler, J. 1963. The ecology of lesser horseshoe bat (*Rhinolophus hipposideros hipposideros* Bechstein, 1800) in Czechoslovakia. Part I. Acta Soc. Zool. Bohemoslov., 27:211-233.

Gaisler, J. 1973. Netting as a possible approach to study bat activity. Period. Biol., 75: 129-134.

Gaisler, J., V. Hanak, and J. Dungel. 1979. A contribution to the population ecology of Nyctalus noctula (Mammalia: Chiroptera). Acta Sc. Nat. Brno, 13:1-38.

Greenhall, A. M., and J. L. Paradiso. 1968. Bats and bat banding. Bureau Sports Fisheries Wildl., Resource Publ. 72, Washington, D.C., 47 pp.

Greenlaw, J. S., and J. Swinebroad. 1967. A method for constructing and erecting aerial-nets in a forest. Bird-Banding, 38:114-119.

Griffin, D. R. 1940. Migration of New England bats. Bull. Mus. Comp. Zool., 86:217-246.

Hamilton-Smith, E. 1964. Field equipment for collecting bats. Bull. Aust. Mamm. Soc., 7:7-10.

Handley, C. O., Jr. 1967. Bats of the canopy of an Amazonian forest. Atas do Simposio sobre Biota Amazonica (Zoologia), 5:211-215.

Handley, C. O., Jr. 1968. Capturing bats with mist nets. Pp. 15-19, *in* Bats and bat banding. (A. M. Greenhall and J. L. Paradiso). Bureau Sports Fisheries Wildl., Res. Publ. 72, Washington, D.C., 47 pp.

Heithaus, E. R. 1982. Coevolution between bats and plants. Pp. 327-368, *in* Ecology of bats. (T. H. Kunz, ed.). Plenum Press, New York, 425 pp.

Humphrey, P. S., D. Bridge, and T. E. Lovejoy. 1968. A technique for mist-netting in the forest canopy. Bird-Banding, 39:43-50.

Humphrey, S. R., A. R. Richter, and J. B. Cope. 1977. Summer habitat and ecology of the endangered Indiana bat, *Myotis sodalis.* J. Mammal., 58:334-346.

Jones, C. 1965. Ecological distribution and activity periods of bats of the Mogollon Mountains area of New Mexico and adjacent Arizona. Tulane Stud. Zool., 12:93-100.

Kunz, T. H. 1973. Resource utilization: Temporal and spatial components of bat activity in central Iowa. J. Mammal, 54:14-32.

Kunz, T. H. 1980. Daily energy budgets of free-living bats. Pp. 369-392, *in* 5th Internat. Bat Res. Conf. (D. E. Wilson and A. L. Gardner, eds.). Texas Tech Press, Lubbock, 434 pp.

Kunz, T. H. 1982. Roosting ecology of bats. Pp. 1-55, *in* Ecology of bats. (T. H. Kunz, ed.). Plenum Press, New York, 425 pp.

Kunz, T. H., and C. E. Brock. 1975. A comparison of mist nets and ultrasonic detectors for monitoring flight activity of bats. J. Mammal., 56:907-911.

Kunz, T. H., and E. L. P. Anthony. 1977. On the efficiency of the Tuttle bat trap. J. Mammal., 58:309-315.

Kunz, T. H., P. V. August, and C. D. Burnett. 1983. Harem social organization in cave roosting *Artibeus jamaicensis* (Chiroptera: Phyllostomidae). Biotropica, 15:133-138.

Kurta, A. 1980. The bats of southern Lower Michigan. Unpubl. M. S. Thesis, Michigan State Univ., East Lansing, Michigan, 147 pp.

Kurta, A. 1982. Flight patterns of *Eptesicus fuscus* and *Myotis lucifugus* over a stream. J. Mammal., 63:335-337.

Kurta, A. 1985. External insulation available to a non-nesting mammal, the little brown bat, *Myotis lucifugus.* Comp. Biochem. Physiol., 82A:413-420.

LaVal, R. K. 1970. Banding returns and activity periods of some Costa Rican bats. Southwest. Nat., 15:1-10.

LaVal, R. K., and H. S. Fitch. 1977. Structure, movements and reproduction in three Costa Rican bat communities. Occas. Pap., Mus. Nat. Hist., Univ. Kansas, 69:1-28.

LaVal, R. K., and M. L. LaVal. 1977. Reproduction and behavior of the African banana bat *Pipistrellus nanus.* J. Mammal., 58:403-410.

LaVal, R. K., and M. L. LaVal. 1980. Ecological studies and management of Missouri bats, with emphasis on cave-dwelling species. Terrest. Ser. No. 8, Missouri Dept. Conserv., Jefferson City, Missouri, 56 pp.

McCracken, G. F., and J. W. Bradbury. 1981. Social organization and kinship in the polygynous bat *Phyllostomus hastatus.* Behav. Ecol. Sociobiol., 8:11-34.

Morrison, D. W. 1978. Lunar phobia in a neotropical fruit bat, *Artibeus jamaicensis* (Chiroptera: Phyllostomatidae). Anim. Behav., 26:852-856.

Morrison, D. W., and C. O. Handley, Jr. *in press.* Roosting behavior *in* Demography and natural history of the common fruit bat, *Artibeus jamaicensis,* on Barro Colorado Island, Panama. (C. O. Handley, Jr., ed.). Smithsonian Institution Press, Washington, D.C.

Mueller, H. C., and N. S. Mueller. 1979. Sensory basis for spatial memory in bats. J. Mammal., 60:198-201.

Neuweiler, G., and F. P. Möhres. 1967. Die Rolle des Ortsgedächtnisses bei der Orientierung der Grossblatt-Fledermaus *Megaderma lyra.* Z. Vergl. Physiol., 57:147-171.

Nyholm, E. R. 1965. Zur Ökologie von *Myotis mystacinus* (Leisl.) und *M. daubentoni* (Leisl.) (Chiroptera). Ann. Zool. Fenn., 2:77-123.

O'Farrell, M. J., and W. G. Bradley. 1970. Activity patterns of bats over a desert spring. J. Mammal., 51:18-26.

O'Farrell, M. J., and B. W. Miller. 1972. Pipistrelle bats attracted to vocalizing females and to a blacklight insect trap. Amer. Midl. Nat., 87:462-463.

O'Farrell, M. J., W. G. Bradley, and G. W. Jones. 1967. Fall and winter bat activity at a desert spring in southern Nevada. Southwest. Nat., 12:163-171.

Palmeirim, J., and K. Etheridge. 1985. The influence of man-made trails on foraging by tropical frugivorus bats. Biotropica, 17:82-83.

Perry, D. R. 1978. A method of access into the crowns of emergent and canopy trees. Biotropica, 10:155-157.

Perry, D. R., and J. Williams. 1981. The tropical rain forest canopy: A method providing total access. Biotropica, 13:283-285.

Rautenbach, I. L. 1985. A new technique for the efficient use of macro-mistnets. Koedoe, 28:81-86.

Tidemann, C. R., and D. P. Woodside. 1978. A collapsible bat-trap and a comparison of results obtained with the trap and with mist-nets. Aust. Wildl. Res., 5:355-362.

Turner, D. C. 1975. The vampire bat. Johns Hopkins Univ. Press, Baltimore, 145 pp.

Tuttle, M. D. 1974a. An improved trap for bats. J. Mammal., 55:475-477.

Tuttle, M. D. 1974b. Bat trapping: Results and suggestions. Bat Research News, 15:4-7.

Tuttle, M. D. 1975. Population ecology of the gray bat (*Myotis grisescens*): Factors influencing early growth and development. Occas. Pap., Mus. Nat. Hist., Univ. Kansas, 36:1-24.

Tuttle, M. D. 1976a. Collecting techniques. Pp. 71-88, *in* Biology of the bats of the New World family Phyllostomatidae. Part I. (R. J. Baker, D. C. Carter, and J. K. Jones, Jr., eds.). Spec. Publ., Mus., Texas Tech Univ., Lubbock, Texas, 218 pp.

Tuttle, M. D., 1976b. Population ecology of the gray bat (*Myotis grisescens*): Philopatry, timing and patterns of movement, weight loss during migration, and seasonal adaptive strategies. Occas. Pap., Mus. Nat. Hist., Univ. Kansas, 54:1-38.

Tuttle, M. D. 1979. Status, causes of decline, and management of endangered gray bats. J. Wildl. Manage., 43:1-17.

Walton, R., and B. J. Trowbridge. 1982. The use of radio-telemetry in studying the foraging behaviour of the Indian flying fox (*Pteropus giganteus*). J. Zool., 47:575-595.

Whitacre, D. F. 1981. Additional techniques and safety hints for climbing tall trees, and some equipment and information sources. Biotropica, 13:286-291.

Wilkinson, G. S. 1985. The social organization of the common vampire bat. I. Pattern and cause of association. Behav. Ecol. Sociobiol., 7:111-121.

Youngson, W. K., and N. L. McKenzie. 1977. An improved bat-collecting technique. Bull. Aust. Mammal. Soc., 3:20-21.

Appendix 1.   Collecting, Import, and Export Laws and Regulations

Many countries have passed laws and regulations for collecting bats (and other animals) for research.

These laws and regulations are often complicated and sometimes ambiguous; they usually require written permits. Researchers have an obligation to learn and comply with the laws and regulations of their own as well as that of the host country where research is to be conducted. Many bats are protected under local, state and federal legislation and international agreements for the capture, transport, and holding of endangered species. Bats that are protected under endangered species legislation should not be disturbed or collected except under special permit.

Many countries require import and export permits in addition to collecting permits. These should be obtained *before* departing for work in a host country. Addresses of permit issuing agencies in various countries are available from the Permit Branch, Federal Wildlife Permit Office, U.S. Fish and Wildlife Service, Washington, D.C. 10140. Applications for such permits should request authorization to possess, transport, and import scientific specimens. Copies of USFWS form 3-177 "Declaration for importation or exportation of fish and wildlife" also should be filed in the United States.

Export permits may be required before species can be removed from the country of origin. Usually the agency that issues scientific collecting permits also issues export permits. In the United States, fisheries and wildlife or customs inspectors at designated ports of entry are instructed to examine specimens and retain copies of customs papers for specimens carried by hand or in luggage. The same papers must accompany specimens shipped from other countries to the United States, and the package must be marked "Contains no protected species." Detailed information on federal and state guidelines is thoroughly treated in a three volume set entitled "Controlled wildlife."[1]

---

[1]Estes, C., and K. W. Sessions. 1983. Controlled wildlife. Vol. 2. Federally controlled species. Association for Systematic Collections, Allen Press, Lawrence, Kansas, 327 pp.

Estes, C., and K. W. Sessions. 1984. Controlled wildlife. Vol. 1. Federal permit procedures. Association for Systematic Collections, Allen Press, Lawrence, Kansas, 304 pp.

King, S. T., and J. R. Schrock. 1985. Controlled wildlife. Vol. 3. State wildlife regulations. Association for Systematic Collections. Allen Press, Lawrence, Kansas, 315 pp.

Appendix 2. Selected Commercially Available Equipment and Supplies Mentioned in Text for the Capture and Holding of Bats.

LIGHT SOURCES

Justrite Electric Headlamp

Petzl Zoom Head Lamp (Model E04)

Koehler Wheat Electric Cap Lamp*
(Model 5200) Lead-acid or Gel
Battery and Charger

Seal Beam Spot Light
Rechargeable Nite Lite battery

Bob and Bob, Speleo General Store
P.O. Box 441
Lewisburg, West Virginia 24901 USA

Burgess Miners Lamp

Burgess Battery Division
Clevite Corporation
1916 Tubeway
Los Angeles, California 90028 USA

MineSpot Cap Lamp * (Model ML-1
and ML-2) Lead-acid or
"maintenance-free" gel battery
(Model ML-200) and charger

Mine Safety Appliances Company
600 Penn Center Boulevard
Pittsburgh, Pennsylvania 15208 USA

FORCEPS

Tissue Forceps (Model 46125)

Edward Weck and Company, Inc.
4 Idyl Wilde Circle
Marshfield, Massachusetts 02050 USA

**Approved by the U.S. Mine Safety and Health Administration and the Canadian Bureau of Energy, Mines, and Resources.

HOOP NETS

Tropics Net, with 61-cm length segments

BioQuip Products
P.O. Box 61
Santa Monica, California 20245 USA

NYLON NET SUPPLIES

Nylon Netting
(mosquito and seine netting,
"Ace" and "Delta" styles)

Nichols Net and Twine, Inc.
Rural Route 3, Bend Road
East St. Louis, Missouri 62201 USA

Memphis Net and Twine Company
2481 Matthews Avenue
Memphis, Tennessee 38108 USA

MIST NETS

British Trust for Ornithology
Beech Grove
Tring, Hertfordshire HPZ3 5NR
England

Eastern Bird Banding Association
EBBA Net Committee
Biology Department
Indiana University of Pennsylvania
Indiana, Pennsylvania 15701 USA

Northeastern Bird Banding Association
Manomet Bird Observatory
Box 936
Manomet, Massachusetts 02345 USA

Nippon Kenmo Company, Ltd.
Gintomi Building
No. 4, 2-Chome, Ginza
Chuoku, Tokyo, Japan

CLIMBING EQUIPMENT

Rope, harnesses, ascenders,
descenders, carabiners,
pulleys, D-rings, etc.

Bob and Bob, Speleo General Store
P.O. Box 441
Lewisburg, West Virginia 24901 USA

Chapter 2

Reproductive Assessment in Bats

Paul A. Racey

Department of Zoology
University of Aberdeen
Aberdeen AB9 2TN Scotland

1. INTRODUCTION

Reliable assessment of the reproductive status of bats is fundamental to most field and laboratory studies. However, some reproductive categories can only be separated with difficulty and few studies have attempted to verify assumptions about reproductive state made from external examination (Racey, 1974; Sluiter, 1954, 1961; Sluiter and Bouman, 1951).

2. SEX IDENTIFICATION AND SECONDARY SEX CHARACTERISTICS

The presence of a conspicuous penis in male bats facilitates sex identification. The penes of rhinolophid bats are directed cranially whereas those of vespertilionids vary from cranial to pendulous (Wood Jones, 1916; Harrison Matthews, 1937). The penis of Megachiroptera is also pendulous (Wood Jones, 1916). Directionality of the penis may depend to some extent on the presence or length of the baculum (or penis). Both vary within genera, from absent to short and small to long and large, especially among the Vespertilionidae.

Most female bats have a single anterior pair of mammary glands and nipples in a subaxillary or anterolateral position, although some genera of vespertilionids (*Lasiurus, Dasypterus,* and *Otonycteris*) have two, and occasionally three, such pairs (Quay, 1970; Medkow, 1976). Pubic nipples, which are not associated with mammary glands but appear to function for the attachment of young, have been reported among the Craseonycteridae, Hipposideridae, Mega-

A

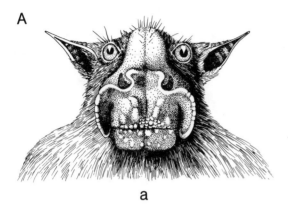

a

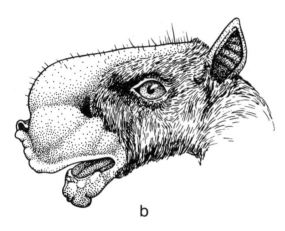

b

B

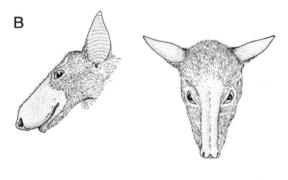

Figure 1. *Hypsignathus monstrosus:* (A) Adult male (redrawn from Allen, Lang & Chapin, 1917). Seen (a) frontally and (b) laterally. (B) Adult female (redrawn from an original pencil sketch by C. H. Fry).

dermatidae, Nycteridae, Nyctophilinae, Rhinolophidae, Rhinopomatidae, and possibly also the Phyllostomidae (Hill, 1974; Harrison Matthews, 1937, 1942; Quay, 1970; Rosevear, 1965).

2.1. Size

Sexual dimorphism in size, where females are larger than males, may occur in adult bats and is well documented among vespertilionids (Myers, 1978; Williams and Findley, 1979), some emballonurids (Bradbury and Emmons, 1974; Nicoll and Suttie, 1982) and in the phyllostomid *Ametrida centurio* (Peterson, 1965). This dimorphism is seldom marked enough to be of use as a field characteristic. However, among mammals in general, sexual dimorphism is well marked in polygynous species, and extreme dimorphism is associated with lek mating systems, as in the hammer-headed bat *Hypsignathus monstrosus.* Males weigh almost twice as much as females and have a grotesquely ornamented muzzle (Bradbury, 1977a) (Fig. 1). In other pteropodids, such as *Pteropus* and *Epomops,* males are also larger than females, although this situation is reversed in *Megaloglossus* (Hill and Smith, 1984) and *Nycteris* (Brosset, 1966).

2.2. Pelage

Visually striking secondary sexual characteristics which allow sexes to be distinguished at a distance are uncommon in Nearctic or Palearctic bats but are more common in tropical species, particularly in the Megachiroptera. They include the shoulder tufts or epaulettes of the adult male *Epomops, Epomophorus, Megaloglossus, Micropteropus,* and *Nanonycteris.* Such epaulettes consist of a brush of long, white or yellowish hairs on each shoulder which, when not displayed as a dense rounded tuft, are hidden in a deep pocket (Rosevear, 1965) (Fig. 2). They are usually associated with skin glands and together they function in territorial and sexual behavior. Another male characteristic is a

Figure 2. *Epomops franqueti:* Adult male displaying shoulder tufts (redrawn from Rosevear, 1965).

collar or ruff around the neck and chest composed of stout, stiff, light-colored hairs as in some *Rousettus* species, *Lissonycteris, Nanonycteris,* and *Megaloglossus* or of soft texture but bright orange in color as in *Eidolon* (Rosevear, 1965). In male *E. helvum,* the collar is also associated with skin glands that produce a musky secretion during the breeding season (Hill and Smith, 1984).

Secondary sex characteristics are less well marked in the Microchiroptera. The most conspicuous is a tuft of long, dense hairs, the interaural crest, which develops during the breeding season in males of some African molossids. This crest is located behind the membrane that connects the ears across the top of the head (Fig. 3), as illustrated recently by Fenton (1983) for *Tadarida chapini.* In two African rhinolophids, *Rhinolophus landeri* and *R. alcyone,* adult males have axillary tufts of long hairs associated with skin glands (Rosevear, 1965). Among the Phyllostomidae, *Sturnira* has epaulettes.

Sexual dimorphism is sometimes manifest in the color of the pelage. The males of some *Lasiurus* and *Taphozous* species are more strongly colored than females. The head region of male *Cynopterus sphinx* is a bright reddish-brown, whereas females are a dull olive-brown (Brosset, 1966). Sexual dimorphism of pelage color occurs to some extent in *Hipposideros gigas* (Brosset, 1966). Such dimorphism extends to nose leaves in *Hip-*

posideros larvatus (Brosset, 1966), and to saggital crests which are larger in males, as for example on the skull of *H. gigas* (McWilliam, 1982). The canine teeth of male *Tadarida brasiliensis* are larger than those of females, and such measurements were suggested by Herreid (1959) to be of value in estimating sex ratios of bats found dead in caves.

2.3. Integumentary Glands

The occurrence of a wide variety of integumentary glands in Chiroptera has been extensively reviewed by Quay (1970), although the functional role of these glands has received little critical attention. There is marked sexual dimorphism in the development of the median frontal sac gland in many hipposiderids. Situated above the noseleaf, this gland is a raised dermal invagination with an apical longitudinal slit which prompted Temminck to name one hipposiderid *cyclops.* The sac of male *Hipposideros gigas* and *H. commersoni* is twice as large as that of females (McWilliam, 1982; Mainoya and Howell, 1977). It also contains prominent white hairs that form a

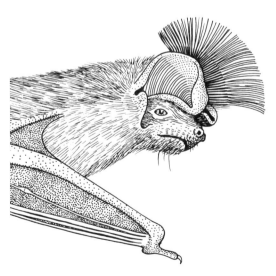

Figure 3. *Tadarida chapini:* Adult male showing interaural crest (redrawn from Allen, in Allen, Lang, and Chapin, 1917).

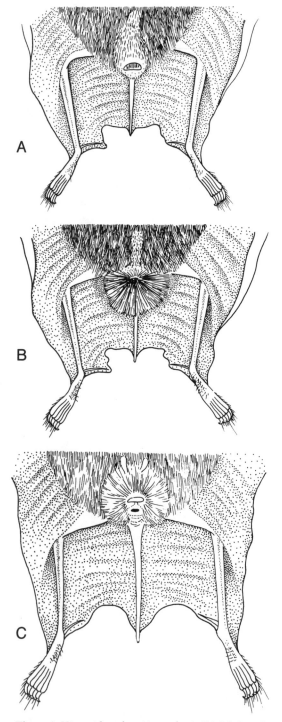

Figure 4. *Hipposideros langi* (= *cyclops*). (A) Adult male showing anal sac invaginated. (B) Adult male showing anal sac everted. (C) Pubic region of adult female showing pubic nipples (redrawn from Allen, in Allen, Lang, and Chapin, 1917).

fan when the sac is everted. In contrast, females possess only a small tuft of shorter brown hairs in their sacs, which are never evaginated. Eversion of the sac gland of males occurs directly over the noseleaf of females during courtship (McWilliam, 1982). *Hipposideros lylei, H. pratti,* and *H. armiger* have a large, fleshy, lobate prominence on each side of the frontal sac resembling a supplementary posterior noseleaf behind the true posterior noseleaf. This achieves its greatest development in old males and is less developed in young males and females (Lekagul and McNeely, 1977).

A median glandular pouch was described by Allen et al. (1917) just anterior to the anus in male *Hipposideros langi* (= *cyclops*). It is lined with long rust-brown bristly hairs which form a conspicuous medial tuft when the pouch is everted (Fig. 4). Kingdon (1974) also refers to anal sacs in *Tadarida cistura* (= *bemmelini*).

Male bulldog bats (*Noctilio*) have a gland equipped with many fringe-like papillae, located on the outer surface of the scrotum. This is everted when the testis distends the scrotum, and its musky secretion can be detected over several meters (Hill and Smith, 1984).

A large glandular swelling between and in front of the eyes was described in males of the family Natalidae by Dalquest (1950), although it is not clear whether it is conspicuous enough to enable sexes to be distinguished at a distance. Chin and throat glands are also present in some emballonurids, phyllostomids, vespertilionids, and molossids (Fig. 5) (Quay, 1970; Brosset, 1966), although the extent of sexual dimorphism in these glands is not always clear. *Craseonycteris thonglongyai* has a rounded glandular swelling at the base of the throat which is well-developed and prominent in males but much less so or absent in females (Hill, 1974). Such a swelling may be unique among bats.

Male *Taphozous melanopogon* have a prominent beard, and during the rut, small glands under the chin produce a thick secretion which mats the hairs of the beard

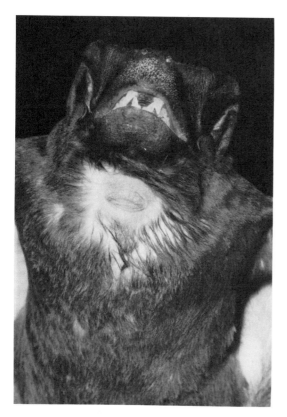

Figure 5. *Molossus molossus* showing throat gland of male (photo by T. H. Kunz).

diameter together with a deep circular gland in the upper part of the thorax, both of which are more distinct in spring. In the female, the gular sac is less obvious and there is no thoracic gland. The gular sac is also larger in male *T. longimanus* than in females and produces a disagreeable red secretion (Brosset, 1962). Kitchener (1976) also described a pouch at the posterior part of the gular glandular region in *T. georgianus,* the depth of which is closely correlated with the degree of enlargement of the seminiferous tubules and accessory glands of reproduction.

Bradbury and Emmons (1974) and Starck (1958) described pronounced sexual dimorphism of the wing gland of *Saccopteryx bilineata* which forms a dorsally-opening pocket in the antebrachial membrane. In adult males, it is lined with pink ridges and folds which produce a mild, sweet-smelling secretion. The gland has a muscular orifice and can apparently be opened at will, as during salting behavior when the male shakes his wings at a female. In contrast, the gland in the female is a simple shallow pocket without ridges, secretion or a muscular orifice.

Sexual dimorphism in the throat gland of *Molossus rufus* (= *ater*) was studied by Horst (1966), who showed that castration led to its involution in males, but that administration of hormones failed to stimulate the gland in females. Davis and Herreid (1960) recorded that sexually active male *Tadarida brasiliensis mexicana* had a sweet odor which distinguished them from females or sexually inactive males.

2.4. Vocalization

As more information becomes available on social vocalizations in Chiroptera, it has become clear that the sexes have different repertoires. Males of such species as *Saccopteryx bilineata* have distinctive courtship songs (Bradbury and Emmons, 1974). Males of *Hypsignathus* make a characteristic honk and staccato buzz at the lek (Bradbury, 1977a), male *Epomophorus* make distinctive calls (Wickler and Seibt, 1976), and several male

together, resulting in an unmistakeable field characteristic (Brosset, 1962). McWilliam (1982) also observed that mature male *T. hildegardeae* are readily distinguishable in the field by the presence of a prominent beard associated with a glandular area of skin. This throat gland secretes a strong smelling substance, the production and odor of which are more pronounced during periods of sexual activity. The mainly white venter of male *T. hildegardeae* has a marked yellow-brown wash to the pelage, especially on the chest. No beard is present in adult females, which have a pure white front. The throat gland is used frequently by males to annoint their own forearms and wings, to mark females in their harem, and more rarely to mark the roost substrate. Adult male *T. kachhensis* possess a large and deep gular sac about a centimeter in vespertilionids make calls which may function in social communication (Ahlen, 1981; M. I. Avery, pers. comm.; R. Wolton, pers. comm.). A distinctive call, audible to the human ear, is emitted by copulating *Myotis lucifugus* (Barclay and Thomas, 1979) and can be used to locate copulating bats in caves.

2.5. Behavior

It is sometimes possible to identify male bats by their spacing behavior with respect to other bats in a social group, particularly in the case of female-defense polygyny (Bradbury, 1977b). Thus, male *Saccopteryx bilineata* actively defend a territory in buttress cavities in trees and perform elaborate vocal, visual, and olfactory displays to attract and retain their harem of up to eight females (Bradbury and Emmons, 1974).

The disturbance caused by the presence of human observers in caves is frequently sufficient to cause harem males of *Phyllostomus hastatus* to identify themselves by coming to the edge of the cluster to investigate (McCracken and Bradbury, 1981). Male *Coleura afra* surrounded by harem females can also be identified in caves. Other behaviors characteristic of males include wing flapping displays by territorial male *Hipposideros commersoni* and *H. gigas,* wingflick and forearm attacks directed towards other males by male *Taphozous hildegardeae,* and a "zipped up" posture when males draw the tips of the forearms underneath the chin with each partially unfurled wing meeting in the midline to create an umbrella of wing membrane around the front of the bat (McWilliam, 1982).

3. REPRODUCTIVE STATUS OF MALES

3.1. Testicular Descent

The position of the testes varies among the families of bats. In many Microchiroptera (Vespertilionidae, Emballonuridae, Hippo-

sideridae, and Nycteridae) the testes are descended at birth and lie on the ventral surface of the thigh either lateral or slightly cranial to the base of the penis (Harrison Matthews, 1942). Although these testes form an enlargement beneath the skin which is referred to as a scrotal pouch or scrotum by Harrison Matthews (1942), pocketing of the skin is not always apparent. In pteropodids, however, the testes descend into a distinct scrotum which forms a heavily pigmented pouch with a well-marked median raphe, around the base of the penis (Fig. 6).

Several authors have referred to seasonal testicular descent corresponding with seasonal spermatogenesis (Carter, 1970; Harrison Matthews, 1942), although neither Baker and Baker (1936) nor Sanborn and

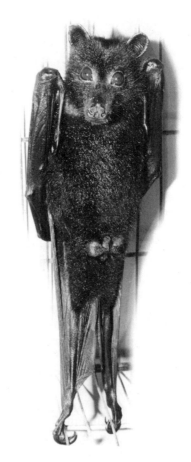

Figure 6. *Pteropus giganteus.* Adult male showing external genitalia and well-developed scrotum.

Nicholson (1950) could confirm this for *Pteropus*. Other authors distinguish between intra- or extra-abdominal testes, as for example in *Artibeus jamaicensis* (Kunz et al., 1983a). Seasonal testicular descent is certainly not the case in the hibernating vespertilionid species with which I am familiar, nor have I ever observed bats in this family withdrawing their testes into the inguinal canal, albeit slightly. However, Kitchener (1976) noted that the testes of male *Taphozous georgianus* descend into scrotal sacs in summer and ascend inguinally or abdominally during the remainder of the year. Nelson (1965a) observed that the testes of *Pteropus poliocephalus* and *P. gouldii* (= *alecto*) are withdrawn from the scrotum into the wide inguinal canal when the bats are disturbed, but descend in response to elevated environmental temperatures.

3.2. Puberty and Seasonal Spermatogenesis

Puberty, defined as the ability to produce fertile gametes and to copulate, is achieved in most male bats in the first full season of food abundance following their birth. However, in some vespertilionids, a proportion of females achieve puberty (defined as receptivity to the male) in their first autumn, and in some rhinolophids the prepubertal period is extended for several years (see Racey, 1982; Tuttle and Stevenson, 1982). The occurrence of pregnancy in epomophorine bats with unfused skull sutures suggests that puberty may occur before adult size has been achieved (Bergmans, pers. comm.) and shows the importance of considering both somatic and sexual development in determining the age at which puberty takes place (Gustafson and Damassa, 1984). In vespertilionids and rhinolophids, both testes and epididymides are covered with a pigmented sheath of peritoneum—the tunica vaginalis. In sexually immature male vespertilionids the tunica around the cauda epididymidis can typically be seen through the skin as a densely pigmented sheath (Fig. 7A, B). Increase in size of the testes associated with growth of the

seminiferous tubules and spermatogenesis is apparent through the perianal skin. After their release from the testes, spermatozoa pass through the epididymides to the caudae, which become distended between the layers of skin forming the interfemoral membrane. The rapid shrinkage of the testes at the end of spermatogenesis and the correspondingly rapid swelling of the caudae is very striking in vespertilionid bats kept in captivity. As a result of this swelling, the tunica vaginalis over the epididymis becomes stretched and the melanocytes separate so that the distended epididymal tubules appear white through the skin (Fig. 7C, D). After this initial separation has occurred, the melanocytes seldom return to their former density, even though the distension of the cauda may be markedly reduced by loss of spermatozoa (Racey, 1974). The apparent reduction in pigmentation of the tunica, accompanied by varying degrees of distension of the epididymis, is a criterion of sexual maturity in male bats which has been used throughout hibernation in a number of studies of vespertilionids (Pearson et al., 1952; Sluiter, 1961; Davis, 1969; and Racey, 1974). Where testicular swelling is apparent, but the cauda is still heavily pigmented, the individual is probably undergoing its first spermatogenesis and is therefore described as pubertal.

Not only do immature bats have pigmented tunicae, but their testes are also smaller than those of individuals which have experienced spermatogenesis. This may be seen when the testes are examined through the skin, a procedure which may be aided by a stereo-microscope (Racey, 1974). In larger bats the testes may be measured through the skin using calipers (for example, Kunz et al., 1983a).

The distinction between those males which have lost most of their epididymal spermatozoa and immature individuals is complicated when adipose tissue is deposited within the tunica vaginalis around the convoluted tubule of the epididymis. This deposition causes the tunica to appear stretched.

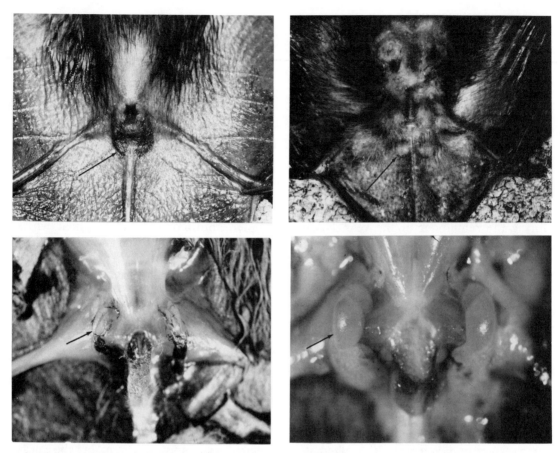

Figure 7. The ventral surface of an immature male pipistrelle *Pipistrellus pipistrellus*. Top left: The deeply pigmented tunica vaginalis (arrowed) can be seen through the skin of the perianal region. Lower left: The same area after the skin has been removed. A testis is arrowed. The ventral surface of an adult male pipistrelle: Top right: The distended cauda epididymidis (arrowed) can be seen through the interfemoral membrane. Lower right: The same area after the skin has been removed. A testis is arrowed.

This may result in an immature individual being described as mature. In cases of heavy perianal and subcutaneous deposition of adipose tissue in hibernating bats, both testes and epididymides may be completely obscured from view. These complications resulted in a 22% error being recorded by Racey (1974) in assigning males taken from hibernation to categories of sexually mature or immature on the basis of epididymal distension. Distinction between adult and immature hibernating vespertilionids is further complicated by an autumnal molt when the dark pelage of immature individuals is replaced by the lighter one characteristic of adult animals. During the annual molt, adults of some species such as *Miniopterus minor* (McWilliam, 1982) and *M. schreibersii* (Dwyer, 1963) regain a darker pelage which is also seen in immature individuals. In *M. minor* in Kenya, regrowth of pelage occurred in April and May at the same time as the reproductive organs were increasing in weight, and pelage color was a useful additional character in the determination of reproductive class (McWilliam, 1982).

In circumstances where it is important to ascertain reproductive status, such as in the allocation of individuals to different experimental groups, Racey (1974) resorted to surgical examination by making a tiny slit in the skin through which the testis was withdrawn to facilitate examination of its size and degree of distension. This also allowed examination of the pigmentation of the tunica vaginalis. The testes of juvenile animals were small, white, and turgid, whereas those of adults were larger, flaccid, and had a light brown tunica albuginea. These latter characteristics were more strikingly developed in individuals with worn teeth.

The diagnosis of maturity based on the criteria described above can be verified in individuals which die or which are killed for experimental purposes. In these cases, the ultimate criterion of sexual maturity is the size of the complex of accessory glands of reproduction at the base of the bladder. These are diminutive in sexually immature animals and generally well developed in adults. The increase in thickness and pigmentation of the tunica albuginea in adults can also be verified histologically, although it remains to be established whether the relationship between increased tunica thickness and the number of times the testis has undergone spermatogenesis is progressive.

The criteria described above apply to those vespertilionids of temperate latitudes which have a pigmented tunica vaginalis and epididymides extending between the two layers of the interfemoral membrane where they can be examined. They also apply to some tropical vespertilionids such as *Eptesicus capensis* (A. N. McWilliam, pers. comm.). The extent to which they apply more widely has yet to be established. In *Miniopterus,* for example, although the arrangement of the genitalia is broadly similar to *Pipistrellus,* the tunica vaginalis is not pigmented in immature individuals (A. N. McWilliam, pers. comm.). In addition, the epididymides are seldom visible in species with scrotal pockets.

4. REPRODUCTIVE STATUS OF FEMALES

4.1. Estrus

Estrus is the time when females will allow males to mate with them, and in general the best criteria of its occurrence are behavioral, particularly if females solicit copulation. This generalization applies to bats but is complicated by some pteropodid species such as *Pteropus poliocephalus* and *P. alecto* in which copulation occurs throughout pregnancy (A. N. McWilliam, pers. comm.).

Kleiman and Racey (1969) used vaginal smears in an attempt to identify which female noctule bats (*Nyctalus noctula*) in a laboratory breeding colony were in estrus. Nucleated epithelial cells predominated most smears throughout the year. Cornified epithelial cells increased in abundance in August and were present until May, when smears were discontinued because bats were pregnant. Polymorphonuclear leucocytes appeared mainly in March and April, although they were observed in the smears of some individuals from as early as November to as late as May. By analogy with vaginal cytology in rodents, a proestrus phase could be identified in noctules during August, as the leucocytes disappeared and only epithelial cells were present. Estrus in rodents is associated with smears which contain large numbers of fully cornified enucleate cells and no leucocytes. Mating occurs during this stage, rarely during proestrus. The presence in the noctule bat of nucleated and cornified epithelial cells during autumn and the first half of winter indicated that bats were in extended estrus at this time (referred to as submaximal estrus by Guthrie and Jeffers, 1938).

Smears from *N. noctula* during the second half of winter resembled more closely the metestrous smear of a rodent; the vagina was filled with sheets of enucleate epithelial cells in varying stages of keratinization. At the time of suspected ovulation in noctules, leucocytes appeared, disappeared, and then reappeared in the same individual. Orr (1954) also found that there was no continuous invasion of the vagina of *Antrozous pallidus* with leucocytes at ovulation. The metestrus type of smear in the noctule appeared to last several months. It was first apparent in some animals in December and was almost universally present at the end of April.

Although it is clear that vaginal smears will be of little value in determining the time of ovulation in hibernating bats, this technique can be readily applied to bats and may prove of value in establishing the time of estrus in those species with more conventional reproductive cycles.

4.2. Copulation

Copulation occurs ventro-dorsally in most species, and is generally accompanied by distinctive vocalizations and body positions (Roer and Egsbaek, 1969; Khajuria, 1972; Nelson, 1965b; Thomas et al., 1979). Some vespertilionids such as the little brown bat (*Myotis lucifugus*) and the serotine bat (*Eptesicus serotinus*) may remain *in copula* for one to several hours respectively, and may give the impression of one bat roosting on top of another (Racey and Kleiman, 1970). However, copulatory ties are formed in vespertilionids as a result of massive distension of the penis after intromission (Wimsatt and Kallen, 1952). Active males frequently copulate with torpid females (Gilbert and Stebbings, 1958; Roer and Egsbaek, 1969; Thomas et al., 1979). Males frequently bite the fur of the nape during copulation and such disturbed pelage in torpid females is often an indication that sexual activity has taken place, as is the presence of dried semen around the vulva. Vaginal smears or lavages may be examined for the presence of spermatozoa with a McArthur microscope in the field, or with a phase contrast microscope in the laboratory, to provide a rapid and convenient indication of the occurrence of ejaculation.

4.3. Pregnancy

Early pregnancy is difficult to diagnose in bats and immunological tests routinely used to detect pregnancy in humans have not been developed for other orders of mammals (because they depend on the production and purification of antisera to species-specific proteins produced during pregnancy). However, elevation of plasma progesterone levels as the corpus luteum becomes established (Racey and Swift, 1981) may provide an indication that the animal is pregnant.

Pearson et al. (1952) found that the nipples of nulliparous female *Plecotus townsendii* remain tiny until near the time of first implantation, and this may be used as a criterion of nulliparity until the young females are about nine months old. Racey (1969) compared nipple morphology, body masses, palpation, and x-rays as indicators of pregnancy in *Pipistrellus pipistrellus*. Few female pipistrelles fail to become pregnant each year. Parous animals with large flaccid nipples which had previously suckled young were assumed to be pregnant, whereas nulliparous animals with turgid developing nipples were assumed to be primigravid. Of 28 females classed as pregnant, based on nipple development, only two were later diagnosed as not pregnant by palpation and x-ray. Conversely, only one of four bats classified as non-pregnant from the state of the nipples was later found to be pregnant. There was, however, an absolute correlation between a positive diagnosis of pregnancy from palpation and a diagnosis from x-rays as definitely or probably pregnant (Fig. 8). Conversely a negative diagnosis from palpation correlated with a diagnosis from x-rays as possibly pregnant or not pregnant. All bats diagnosed as pregnant subsequently gave birth or aborted, whereas none of those diagnosed as not pregnant did so. At the stage of pregnancy when the bats were examined (between half and two thirds progressed), palpation gave the most convenient and accurate diagnosis of pregnancy. Distension of the lower abdomen caused by the developing fetus may be determined in bats which have

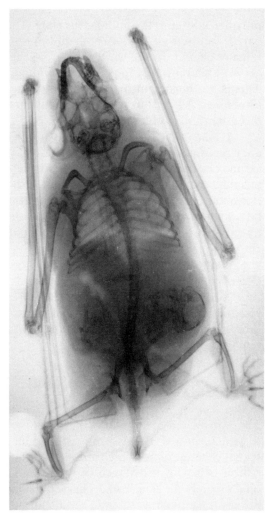

Figure 8. A radiograph of a pregnant female noctule showing the fetus distending the abdomen.

not recently fed by apposition of thumb and index finger. A fetus as such cannot be recognized until late pregnancy, only by the degree of distension and resistance to digital pressure.

Toward the end of pregnancy, the nipples enlarge as the mammary system develops, and it becomes progressively more difficult to distinguish between parous and nulliparous pregnant females.

4.4. Parturition and Lactation

The pubic ligament expands before parturition to allow the fetus to leave the birth canal

(Crelin, 1969). For a day or two following parturition, the vulva may appear blood-stained and contused, and the pubic symphysis is still separated. The young attach to their mother's nipples immediately after birth and can be removed only with considerable difficulty. A blunt instrument may be inserted between the lips of the young and twisted slightly to open the jaws. Attempts to pull the young off the nipple will cause the mother pain as the deciduous teeth are recurved (Friant, 1951; Harrison Matthews, 1950). The white mammary glands of lactating females can be seen under the skin extending into the axillary region. During lactation the nipples become enlarged, and milk can be extruded from them by gently massaging the mammary glands and squeezing the nipples (e.g., Kunz et al., 1983b).

After lactation, the nipples retain their enlarged keratinized appearance, and in most species of bats, as in other mammals, such nipples are the criterion of parity. Although multiparity can quickly be established by identification of large nipples, the distinction between primiparous and nulliparous females outside the breeding season may require careful examination with the aid of a lens or binocular microscope. The nipples of nulliparous females are rudimentary and often give rise to body hair (Fig. 9A). The nipples of parous animals show the expected characteristics of previous suckling—a dark keratinized protuberance of the skin with either no emergent hair or short, wavy emergent hair (Fig. 9B). These distinctions have been followed in pipistrelles born and giving birth in captivity (Racey, 1974). Nipple morphology is a widely used characteristic which has been successfully used to assess reproductive class in both temperate and tropical bats. Pearson et al. (1952) estimated that at least 90% of female *Plecotus townsendii* captured from summer to early spring can be correctly sorted into parous and nulliparous categories on the basis of nipple morphology, and this criterion has also been used to distinguish between parous and nulliparous *Myotis myotis* and *M. emarginatus* by Sluiter and Bouman (1951) and Sluiter (1954). Baagøe

Figure 9. (A) The nipples (arrowed) of a nulliparous pipistrelle (*Pipistrellus pipistrellus*). (B) The nipple of a parous pipistrelle.

(1977) categorized nipples of *M. daubentoni* into large, medium, small, and not found, but considered that only the first category indicated parity. Bats in the remaining categories had not suckled young. When used in the field, criteria of parity based on nipple morphology have sometimes produced results which are difficult to explain. Thus 172 parous and 179 nulliparous female *Pipistrellus pipistrellus* were caught from many hibernacula by Racey (1974) over four winters. Most (52/60) nulliparous female pipistrelles were found to be inseminated when taken from their hibernacula (Racey, 1974) and probably would have become pregnant the following summer, so they passed

only one winter in the nulliparous state. The equal numbers of parous and nulliparous females caught during winter therefore suggests a high mortality in parous individuals. This is not borne out by population studies (Stebbings, 1976), but it could be explained by emigration of older females.

At dissection, the uteri of parous animals are larger than those of nulliparous individuals and one horn is frequently more conspicuous than the other (Sluiter, 1954; Sluiter and Bouman, 1951; Wimsatt, 1979). The uterine artery winding along the cranial border of the uterus is tortuous and surrounded by a white sheath in parous animals, but is relatively straight and thin-walled in nulliparous ones (Pearson et al., 1952). Histological examination frequently reveals the presence of a Graafian follicle in the ovaries of parous hibernating individuals (Wimsatt and Parks, 1966).

5. SUMMARY

The conspicuous penis allows the sex of bats to be determined with assurance. Secondary sexual characteristics which aid the determination of sex at a distance include dimorphisms of body size, facial characteristics, pelage, integumentary glands, vocalizations, and behavior. In species where spermatozoa are stored by the male for some time after the cessation of spermatogenesis and involution of the testes, the distension of the epididymis is a criterion of sexual maturity. This can be seen directly through the skin or inferred from the separation of melanocytes in the investing tunica vaginalis. The state of the nipples allows nulliparous and parous females to be distinguished and palpation provides a convenient diagnosis of well-established pregnancies.

6. ACKNOWLEDGMENTS

I am grateful to M. B. Fenton, J. E. Hill, T. H. Kunz, A. N. McWilliam, and two anonymous reviewers for helpful comments on earlier drafts of this chapter and for providing additional information; to R. Duthie for the drawings, and to M. Milliken for typing the manuscript. C. H. Fry kindly provided his own drawing of female *Hypsignathus* and T. H. Kunz provided the photograph of *Molossus molossus*.

7. REFERENCES

Ahlen, I. 1981. Identification of Scandinavian bats by their sounds. Swedish Univ. Agric. Sci., Depart. Wildl. Ecol. Report No. 6. Uppsala, 56 pp.

Allen, J. A., H. Lang, and J. P. Chapin. 1917. The American Museum Congo expedition collection of bats. Bull. Amer. Nat. Hist., 37:405-563.

Baagøe, H. J. 1977. Age determination in bats (Chiroptera). Vidensk. Meddr. Dansk. Naturh. Foren., 140:53-92.

Baker, J. R., and Z. Baker. 1936. The seasons in a tropical rain forest (New Hebrides). 3. Fruit bats (Pteropidae). J. Linn. Soc. (Zool.) 40:123-141.

Barclay, R. M. R., and D. W. Thomas. 1979. Copulation call of *Myotis lucifugus*: A discrete situation—specific communication signal. J. Mammal., 60:632-634.

Bradbury, J. W. 1977a. Lek mating behaviour in the hammer-headed bats. Z. Tierpsychol., 45:225-255.

Bradbury, J. W. 1977b. Social organization and communication. Pp. 1-72, *in* Biology of Bats. Vol. III. (W. A. Wimsatt, ed.). Academic Press, London, 655 pp.

Bradbury, J. W., and L. H. Emmons. 1974. Social organization of some Trinidad bats. 1. Emballonuridae. 2. Tierpsychol., 36:137-183.

Brosset, A. 1962. The bats of Central and Western India. J. Bombay Nat. Hist. Soc., 59:1-57 (part I); 583-624 (part II).

Brosset, A. 1966. La biologie des chiroptères. Masson, Paris, 240 pp.

Carter, D. C. 1970. Chiropteran reproduction. Pp. 233-246, *in* About Bats. (B. H. Slaughter and D. W. Walton, eds.). Southern Methodist Univ. Press, Dallas, Texas, 339 pp.

Crelin, E. S. 1969. Interpubic ligament: Elasticity in pregnant free-tailed bat. Science, 164:81-82.

Dalquest, W. W. 1950. The genera of the Chi-

ropteran family Natalidae. J. Mammal., 31:436-443.

Davis, R. 1969. Growth and development of young pallid bats, *Antrozous pallidus*. J. Mammal., 50:729-736.

Davis, D. E., and C. F. Herreid II. 1960. Comments on the odors of bats. J. Mammal., 41:396.

Dwyer, P. D. 1963. Seasonal changes in pelage of *Miniopterus schreibersii blepotis* (Temminck) (Chiroptera) in north-eastern New South Wales. Aust. J. Zool., 11:219-240.

Fenton, M. B. 1983. Just bats. Univ. Toronto Press, Toronto. 165 pp.

Friant, M. 1951. La dentition temporaire dite lactéale de la Rouzette Chiroptère frugivore. C. R. Hebd. Séanc. Acad. Sci. Paris. 233:890-892.

Gustafson, A. W., and D. A. Damassa. 1984. Perinatal and postnatal patterns of plasma sex steroid-binding protein (SBP) and testosterone in relation to puberty in the male little brown bat. Endocrinology, 115:2347-2354.

Guthrie, M. J., and K. R. Jeffers. 1938. Growth of follicles in the ovaries of the bat *Myotis lucifugus lucifugus*. Anat. Rec., 71:477-496.

Harrison Matthews, L. H. 1937. The form of the penis in the British rhinolophid bats, compared with that in some of the vespertilionid bats. Trans. Zool. Soc. Lond., 23:213-223.

Harrison Matthews, L. 1942. Notes on the genitalia and reproduction of some African bats. Proc. Zool. Soc. Lond. B. (1941), 111:289-346.

Harrison Matthews, L. 1950. La dentition de lait chez *Nycteris leisleri*. Mammalia, 40:11-13.

Herreid, C. F., II. 1959. Sexual dimorphism in teeth of the free-tailed bat. J. Mammal., 40:538-541.

Hill, J. E. 1974. A new family, genus and species of bat (Mammalia: Chiroptera) from Thailand. Bull. Brit. Mus. Nat. Hist. Zool., 27:301-336.

Hill, J. E., and J. D. Smith. 1984. Bats. A natural history. Univ. Texas Press, Austin, Texas, 243 pp.

Horst, G. R. 1966. Observations on the gular gland of *Molossus rufus nigricans*. Anat. Rec., 154:465.

Khajuria, H. 1972. Courtship and mating in *Rhinopoma l. hardwickei* Gray (Chiroptera: Rhinopomatidae). Mammalia, 36:307-309.

Kingdon, J. 1974. East African Mammals—An atlas of evolution in Africa, Vol. II. Part A. Insectivores and bats. Academic Press, London, 341 pp.

Kitchener, D. J. 1976. Further observations on reproduction in the common sheath-tailed bat, *Taphozous georgianus*. Thomas, 1915 in Western Australia, with notes on the gular pouch. Rec. West. Aust. Mus., 4:335-347.

Kleiman, D. G., and P. A. Racey. 1969. Observations on noctule bats (*Nyctalus noctula*) breeding in captivity. Lynx, 10:65-75.

Kunz, T. H., P. V. August, and C. D. Burnett. 1983a. Harem social organization in cave roosting *Artibeus jamaicensis* (Chiroptera: Phyllostomidae). Biotropica, 15:133-138.

Kunz, T. H., M. H. Stack, and R. Jenness. 1983b. A comparison of milk composition in *Myotis lucifugus* and *Eptesicus fuscus* (Chiroptera: Vespertilionidae). Biol. Reprod., 28:229-234.

Lekagul, B., and J. A. McNeely. 1977. Mammals of Thailand. Association for the Conservation of Wildlife, Bangkok, 758 pp.

McCracken, G. F., and J. W. Bradbury. 1981. Social organization and kinship in the polygynous bat *Phyllostomus hastatus*. Behav. Ecol. Sociobiol., 8:11-34.

McWilliam, A. N. 1982. Adaptive responses to seasonality in four species of Microchiroptera in coastal Kenya. Unpubl. Ph.D. dissertation, Univ. Aberdeen, Aberdeen, Scotland. 290 pp.

Madkour, G. 1976. External genitalia and mammary glands of Egyptian female bats. Zool. Anz., 197:62-66.

Mainoya, J. R., and K. M. Howell. 1977. Histology of the frontal sac in three species of leaf-nosed bats (Hipposideridae). E. Afr. Wildl. J., 15:147-155.

Myers, P. 1978. Sexual dimorphism in size of vespertilionid bats. Amer. Nat., 112:701-711.

Nelson, J. E. 1965a. Movements of Australian flying foxes (Pteropodidae: Megachiroptera). Aust. J. Zool., 13:55-73.

Nelson, J. E. 1965b. Behaviour of Australian Pteropodidae (Megachiroptera). Anim. Behav., 13:544-557.

Nicoll, M. E., and J. M. Suttie. 1982. The sheath-tailed bat *Coloura seychellensis* (Chiroptera: Emballonuridae) in the Seychelles Islands. J. Zool., 197:421-426.

Orr, R. T. 1954. Natural history of the pallid bat, *Antrozous pallidus* (Le Conte). Proc. Calif. Acad. Sci., 28:165-246.

Pearson, O. P., M. R. Koford, and A. K. Pearson. 1952. Reproduction in the lump nosed bat *Corynorhinus rafinesquei* in California. J. Mammal., 33:273-320.

Peterson, R. L. 1965. A review of the bats of the

genus *Ametrida*, family Phyllostomidae. Life Sci. Contr. R. Ont. Mus., 64:1-32.

Quay, W. B. 1970. Integument and derivatives. Pp. 1-56, *in* Biology of bats. Vol. II. (W. A. Wimsatt, ed.). Academic Press, London. 477 pp.

Racey, P. A. 1969. Diagnosis of pregnancy and experimental extension of gestation in the pipistrelle bat *Pipistrellus pipistrellus*. J. Reprod. Fertil., 19:465-474.

Racey, P. A. 1974. Ageing and assessment of reproductive status of Pipistrelle bats, *Pipistrellus pipistrellus*. J. Zool., 173:264-271.

Racey, P. A. 1982. Ecology of bat reproduction. Pp. 57-104, *in* Ecology of bats. (T. H. Kunz, ed.). Plenum Press, New York. 425 pp.

Racey, P. A. and D. G. Kleiman. 1970. Maintenance and breeding in captivity of some vespertilionid bats, with special reference to the noctule *Nyctalus noctula*. Int. Zoo. Yearbook, 10:65-70.

Racey, P. A., and S. M. Swift. 1981. Variations in gestation length in a colony of pipistrelle bats *(Pipistrellus pipistrellus)* from year to year. J. Reprod. Fertil., 61:123-129.

Roer, H., and W. Egsbaek. 1969. Uber die Balz der Wasserfledermaus *(Myotis daubentoni)* (Chiroptera) in Winterquartier. Lynx, 10:85-91.

Rosevear, D. R. 1965. The bats of West Africa. British Museum (Natural History), London. 418 pp.

Sanborn, C. C., and A. J. Nicholson. 1950. Bats from New Caledonia, the Solomon Islands, and New Hebrides. Fieldiana (Zool.), 31:313-338.

Sluiter, J. W. 1954. Sexual maturity in bats of the genus *Myotis*. II. Females of *M. mystacinus* and supplementary data on female *M. myotis* and *M. emarginatus*. Proc. Kon. Ned. Akad. Wet. Ser. C., 57:696-700.

Sluiter, J. W. 1961. Sexual maturity in males of the bat *Myotis myotis*. Proc. Kon. Ned. Akad. Wet. Ser. C., 64:243-249.

Sluiter, J. W., and M. Bouman. 1951. Sexual maturity in bats of the genus *Myotis*. I. Size and histology of the reproductive organs during hibernation in connection with age and wear of the teeth in female *Myotis myotis* and *Myotis emarginatus*. Proc. Kon. Ned. Akad. Wet. Ser. C., 54:594-601.

Starck, D. 1958. Beitrag zur Kenntnis der Armtaschen und anderer Hautdrusenorgane von *Saccopteryx bilineata* Temminck 1838 (Chiroptera, Emballonuridae). Gegenbauer. Morph. Jahrbuch, 99:3-25.

Stebbings, R. E. 1976. Studies on the population ecology of bats. Ph.D. Thesis, University of East Anglia, Norwich, England.

Thomas, D. W., M. B. Fenton, and R. M. R. Barclay. 1979. Social behaviour of the little brown bat, *Myotis lucifugus*. 1. Mating behaviour. Behav. Ecol. Sociobiol., 6:129-136.

Tuttle, M. D., and D. Stevenson. 1982. Growth and survival of bats. Pp. 105-150, *in* Ecology of Bats. (T. H. Kunz, ed.), Plenum Press, New York. 425 pp.

Wickler, W., and U. Seibt. 1976. Field studies on the African fruit bat *Epomophorus walhlbergi* (Sunderall) with special reference to male calling. Z. Tierpsychol. 40:345-376.

Williams, D. F., and J. S. Findley. 1979. Sexual size dimorphism in vespertilionid bats. Amer. Midl. Nat., 102:113-126.

Wimsatt, W. A. 1979. Reproductive asymmetry and unilateral pregnancy in Chiroptera. J. Reprod. Fertil., 56:345-357.

Wimsatt, W. A., and F. C. Kallen. 1952. Anatomy and histophysiology of the penis of a vespertilionid bat, *Myotis lucifugus lucifugus* with particular reference to its vascular organization. J. Morph., 90:415-466.

Wimsatt, W. A., and H. F. Parks. 1966. Ultrastructure of the surviving follicle of hibernation and of the ovum-follicle cell relationship in the vespertilionid bat *Myotis lucifugus*. Symp. Zool. Soc. Lond., 15:419-454.

Wood Jones, F. 1916. The genitalia of the Chiroptera. J. Anat., L1(51), pp. 36-60 (3rd Series, Vol. XII).

Chapter 3

Age Determination in Bats

Edythe L. P. Anthony[1]

Department of Anatomy and
    Cellular Biology
Tufts University Schools of
    Medicine
Boston, Massachusetts 02111 USA

1. INTRODUCTION

The age of any animal can be established precisely by marking it at birth—at all subsequent observations, the exact age will be known and can be directly correlated with any anatomical, behavioral, or physiological characteristics of interest. When working with natural populations of bats, however, banding or otherwise marking animals at birth is not always possible, and is often unwise. Therefore, a need exists for techniques with which one can estimate the age of bats at any time during their life span using directly observable morphological criteria. In surveying field and laboratory studies of bat biology, one is impressed by the variety of techniques that have been applied to estimating age. This multiplicity of approaches attests, perhaps, to the difficulties encountered in assigning accurate ages to wild-caught individuals in the face of such ecological realities as individual variation, geographical variation, and environmental influences on growth and development.

In choosing the most appropriate method(s) of age determination for use in a particular study, investigators should address the following questions:

1) What age groups must be discriminated, and what degree of accuracy is required?

For some behavioral and ecological studies, placing bats into broad relative age groups (e.g., juveniles vs. adults) may be a sufficient degree of categorization. However, for other purposes, it is often desirable to pinpoint the ages of developing animals (e.g., 3 days, 1 week, 1 month, etc.) or to break down the adult group into more specific age categories (e.g., 2-4 years, 4-6 years, etc.).

[1]Present Address: Department of Biology, Rhode Island College, Providence, Rhode Island 02908 USA

2) What constraints apply with regard to inspection of specimens?

In many field studies, it is necessary to correlate the age of living wild-caught bats with behavioral observations that are made on the same individuals. In this situation, one must utilize only those age determination methods that do not harm the bats, and that minimize interference with their normal behavior or activity patterns. At the other extreme, in population or taxonomic studies in which the age at death of museum specimens is the issue, one has available a wider selection of criteria. However, even in this case, choice of tissues for examination should be made judiciously with concern for maintaining the value of the specimen collection for additional research, especially if parts of the skeleton or dentition are removed for histological sectioning or other invasive analyses (see Chapter 24).

3) How much time, equipment, and technology are available for making age estimates?

Often, in field situations, the choice of methods is limited by the necessity of making rapid age estimations in remote locations, relying on a minimum of equipment and personnel. A greater variety of methods is available, however, if circumstances allow access to laboratory equipment and trained technicians, and the use of more time-consuming procedures.

4) What is the existing data base regarding age criteria for a particular species?

When initiating any study which requires age estimates, it is important to consult the literature to determine whether reliable reference standards exist for the species of interest, or whether one needs to generate such a data base. Optimally, one requires measurements or observations of a particular morphological characteristic made on a known-age series of bats. Generating these kinds of data can be a laborious task which can require many years to complete. Thus, one can profit from working with species and choosing age estimation techniques for which these baseline studies are already available.

With regard to preexisting reference data, one must keep in mind potential sources of error that may be introduced into age estimates by geographic variation and by environmental influences on growth rates. Growth curves obtained for a given species in one locality may not necessarily be valid in other parts of the species' range. Furthermore, growth patterns observed in captive bats may differ considerably from those that occur in the wild.

Reproductive criteria can be used to discriminate sexually immature from sexually mature individuals. Criteria that can be used to establish these age-related categories for bats are discussed in Chapter 2. For the purposes of many studies, distinguishing these two behaviorally and ecologically important groups is sufficient. However, reproductive assessments are of limited usefulness in the broader sense of age determination in bats, as they are irrelevant to determining ages of juveniles during the important post-natal growth period; furthermore, they cannot be used to predict ages of animals once they are sexually mature. For long-lived animals such as bats, this means that one must use alternative age criteria over most of their lifetime.

Hard tissues, such as those comprising teeth and bones, provide criteria that are potentially useful for age determination throughout the life span of bats. Changes in teeth and bones occur rapidly during the postnatal growth period. Because teeth and bones continue to be modified throughout life, they provide potential sources of age information that are applicable to adults as well as juveniles.

2. CHARACTERISTICS OF TEETH

2.1. Tooth Wear

The dentition of bats is diphyodont. Juveniles of most species are born with a complete or nearly complete set of deciduous teeth; these are generally replaced by permanent teeth by the time young bats can fly and feed independently. Patterns of loss and replacement of teeth in juveniles have been related to age and/or body size in several species (Orr, 1954; Stegeman, 1956; Short, 1961; Jones, 1967; Kleiman, 1969; Fenton, 1970; Kunz, 1973). The permanent teeth, once erupted and fully formed, cease to increase in size as viewed from the external aspect. Thus, over the course of a lifetime, abrasion of tooth surfaces resulting from repeated mastication is reflected in progressive erosion of enamel. With age, therefore, the cheek teeth become shorter due to reduction in height of cusps, and sharply pointed teeth (especially the canines) become not only shorter, but also dulled, as reflected quantitatively in increased width of the tip.

This process of tooth wear begins when an animal is weaned and continues until the animal's death. Therefore, degree of tooth wear presents a potential age measure which could minimally serve to place adult animals into broad relative age groups. Furthermore, as tooth wear can be assessed qualitatively or quantitatively, this technique is potentially valuable both for live animals as well as for cleaned skulls of museum specimens. In theory, quantitative measurements could be made using anesthetized living bats (Baagøe, 1977), but to the author's knowledge, this innovation has not as yet been attempted.

When using tooth wear as an index of age in bats, most investigators have established several subjective "age" categories, which represent progressive stages of wear observed on canines and/or molars. Focusing on the degree of wear on maxillary canines, Twente (1955) set up six such categories for live *Myotis velifer,* ranging from 1=tip "unworn and pointed" to 6=tooth "worn completely to the gums." Supporting the assertion that these morphologically defined groupings represent successive age classes, he found that in winter populations the number of bats assigned to each category progressively decreased from group 1 to group 6. Furthermore, a cohort of *M. velifer* (of unknown age) banded five years previous to the study fell primarily into intermediate groups (#2 to #4);

none fell into the youngest category. Thus, he concluded that tooth wear may be a broad indicator of age in bats; however, he warned that the validity of assigning absolute ages on this basis appeared "doubtful".

A lack of adequate known-age series of specimens with which to calibrate tooth wear patterns has probably contributed to the "doubtful" status of this technique. A great deal of variability in tooth wear has been pictorially illustrated in skull samples of *Rhinolophus rouxi* (Andersen, 1917) and *Eptesicus fuscus* (Christian, 1956). The extent of this variability suggests that the technique may have substantial potential, at least for separating broad adult age classes. Unfortunately, without specimens of known age, both of these investigators were limited to assigning arbitrary age groups and assuming that each group was one year older than the preceding. Stegeman (1956) was similarly limited after establishing molar wear categories in *Myotis lucifugus.* These assumptions undermine the potential value of the method and generally have led to longevity predictions which fall far short of the maximum lifespan of species revealed by banding studies.

Davis et al. (1962) used statistical methods to estimate maximum age ranges for tooth wear classes established for a population of Mexican free-tailed bats (1-3 years, 4-7 years, etc.). The validity of these ranges was tested in a limited manner by Perry and Herreid (1969) using known-age bats. They found that 42 out of 48 (87.5%) known-age bats were placed into the correct age category using the tooth wear criteria of Davis et al. (1962); however, most of these bats were less than three years old and were members of their youngest age class. Therefore, accuracy of the technique for older free-tailed bats has not yet been adequately tested. The teeth of relatively old *M. lucifugus* (N=4) and *M. keenii* (N=1) recovered 18-19 years after banding were described by Hall et al. (1957) as having "little wear." The molars of these bats showed slightly more attrition than Stegeman's (1956) oldest group of *M.*

lucifugus, but these bats fell into Twente's (1955) next to youngest group on the basis of canine wear for *M. velifer.* Given this discrepancy, and because they viewed the teeth of these old bats as being "in very good condition," Hall et al. (1957) suggested that tooth wear may be a "highly unreliable criterion" of age in these bats. Alternatively, lack of agreement in this case may reflect nonparallelism between subjective age categories set up by different authors, and/or the dangers of applying age criteria developed for one species even to a closely related bat species.

In an attempt to standardize the process of age estimation in bats and to include wear patterns of more than one tooth into the estimation process, quantitative indices of tooth wear have been developed by at least three independent investigators. Christian (1956) found a combination of three measurements (made from photographs) to be most useful in segregating tooth wear classes in *E. fuscus:* width of upper canine occlusal tip, lateral anterior canine length, and length of median upper incisor. Sluiter (1961) developed an "abrasion index" for *M. myotis* which included measurements of 30 different cusps, but he found considerable overlap in this index between animals judged to be in their first and second years on the basis of reproductive criteria. Thus, he concluded that these measurements were not useful for determining age of this bat species. Baagøe (1977) made similar (though not as extensive) measurements on skulls of *Eptesicus serotinus, Nyctalus noctula, Pipistrellus pipistrellus,* and *M. daubentonii.* He found a "gross correlation" between tooth wear index and age of bats indicated by X-ray of forelimbs (see below), but lacking known-age adults, he was limited to showing differences in degree of tooth wear between bats classified by other means as either immature or adult.

In general, it appears that tooth wear as a criterion of age in bats merits further investigation. Use of tooth wear classes in recent field studies has contributed to understanding social organization in tropical bats. Kunz et al. (1983) found that in *Artibeus jamai-*

censis, harem males have shorter canines (more tooth wear) than males in bachelor groups. Furthermore, among harem males, increased harem size is correlated with increased tooth wear, suggesting a relationship between age and harem acquisition and maintenance. McCracken and Bradbury (1981) used an otoscope to examine tooth wear in *Phyllostomus hastatus* and also found that harem males appeared older than bachelor males. In addition, they used tooth wear categories to compare age distributions of females comprising different harems as an indicator of stability of the female groups. In these studies, McCracken and Bradbury used a set of known-age (banded) bats as a guide in establishing relative age categories.

With more extensive use of known-age adult bats for calibrating tooth wear estimates, this criterion could provide a reliable means of establishing broad adult age categories in many species. The potential for pinpointing absolute age must, however, be questioned. Twente (1955) pointed out that individual bats recaptured after an interval of a year were usually assigned to the same age category, indicating that changes in live bats are noticeable only over relatively long time periods, and identifiable age categories must be proportionately broad. Quantitation of dental attrition might narrow the identifiable age categories, but as already mentioned, measurements may be difficult to obtain and standardize in live animals.

If tooth wear is used in the field as a qualitative indicator of age, it is important to note that informed estimates based solely on appearance of the dentition can be made only by investigators who have considerable experience making this observation, and who are thus familiar with the range of variation in tooth wear seen in a particular species. When cleaned skull material is used for quantitative analysis of tooth wear, on the other hand, it is important to avoid damage to the delicate teeth of small bat species by handling or by dermestid larvae (see Stegeman, 1956). Finally, it should be kept in mind that variations in diet and latitudinal differences in annual activity periods can introduce error into age estimation based on dental abrasion, and that tooth wear changes may be more reliable age criteria for bats that feed on hard prey items (e.g., insectivores and carnivores) than for bats with soft diets (e.g., nectarivores, frugivores, and sanguivores).

2.2. Incremental Lines

Dentin, cementum, and bone tissue grow by apposition; that is, newly forming tissue is laid down on a pre-existing surface. This growth pattern predisposes these tissues to form in layers, which under some circumstances can be visualized in histological sections of teeth and bones. When layers of variable, but regularly repeating appearance can be identified at the light microscopic level, the layers have been referred to as "incremental lines" or "annuli." The exact physiological basis of formation of these units is uncertain, although cyclic changes in formation and/or composition of the tissues are clearly suggested (Klevezal' and Sukhovskaya, 1983).

The primary proponents of use of these incremental lines for age determination in bats are Klevezal' and Kleinenberg (1967). In their extensive survey of mammals, they found the number of incremental lines counted in sectioned teeth and bones to be reliable predictors of age—each line representing one year of life. According to this view, cyclic changes in tissue formation are seasonal, formation being slower in winter than in summer, especially in hibernators. In eleven known-age *N. noctula* (ranging in age from 1 to 7 years), they reported exact agreement between age in years and the number of incremental lines in dentin of canines. Furthermore, for a given individual, numbers of dentinal lines in canines and cheek teeth were equal. Incremental lines were observed in cementum of this species, but they were considered too fine to count. Cementum lines were, however, more robust in *M. myotis,* and within a single tooth the number of lines in cementum and dentin were equal. Incremental lines in mandibular bones of both species

were considered inappropriate for age estimation.

Subsequent to these findings, incremental growth lines have been used as indicators of age in vampire bats (Linhart, 1973; Lord et al., 1976) and in various vespertilionid species (Baagøe, 1977; Schowalter et al., 1978; Funakoshi and Uchida, 1982). However, Phillips et al. (1982) conducted the most rigorous test of the validity of the method. In eleven female *M. lucifugus* of known age (2 to 7 years) and six female *M. velifer* (8 years), these investigators found only a "loose correlation" between the number of incremental lines and age. Within a single tooth, the number of dentinal lines was generally not equal to absolute age, and was not correlated with the number of lines observed in the cementum. Furthermore, considerable variation was observed in the number of dentinal and cementum lines counted at different cross-sectional levels of a single tooth, as well as among different teeth of a single bat. A lack of correlation between numbers of lines in dentin and cementum was also noted by Baagøe (1977) in *P. pipistrellus* and in *N. noctula,* the latter species being one of those originally investigated by Klevezal' and Kleinenberg (1967). Because of the extreme variability that has been recently demonstrated in these dental parameters, incremental lines in teeth may not be as reliable indicators of absolute ages as has sometimes been assumed. At minimum, use of this criterion should be approached with caution.

In addition to its questionable accuracy, this technique has several additional inherent limitations. As extraction of teeth and histological preparation of sections are required, the method is applicable only to dead specimens (dried or preserved in fluid), is highly labor-intensive, and requires considerable amounts of time and laboratory facilities. Furthermore, dental incremental lines can be difficult to enumerate in small bat species (Baagøe, 1977; Schowalter et al., 1978). Finally, as Phillips et al. (1982) suggest, the assumption that incremental lines invariably represent annual cycles of tissue deposition ignores many important aspects of tooth dynamics. Deposition of cementum in response to mechanical stress and dental drift, age-related loss of cellular elements responsible for dentin formation, and other normal and pathologic processes can affect temporal patterns of hard tissue formation in teeth, and thus represent potential sources of error in estimating age by dental annuli.

2.3. Size of Pulp Cavity

In mammalian teeth, layers of secondary dentin are deposited during the post-eruptive life of a tooth in such a way that the most recently formed layer abuts the pulp cavity. Addition of successive layers, therefore, results in a progressive decrease in the size of the pulp cavity with time. The potential for use of pulp cavity size as a measure of age in bats was investigated by Baagøe (1977). He attempted to use X-rays to determine the size of the canine pulp cavity; however, he found that a simpler and more successful method was to extract the canines and suspend them in glycerine. Under a dissecting microscope, the teeth appeared translucent enough to measure the width of the pulp cavity using an eyepiece reticle. Among his sample of bats, representing four vespertilionid species, the width of the pulp cavity exhibited considerable variation (30-90% of the width of the tooth), and this measure was generally correlated with estimates of age based on tooth wear and condition of the metacarpal and phalangeal epiphyses (see Section 3.2). However, the potential reliability of this technique for assigning absolute ages cannot be properly assessed until it is applied to known-age bats.

Because this technique, as described above, requires extraction of teeth, it can be used only with dead specimens. Baagøe (1977) suggested, however, that in some small bats, the pulp cavities of canine teeth could be visualized in live animals. A limited amount of equipment is required for visualization and measurement of the pulp cavity (microscope, reticle, light source, glycerine). Baagøe

(1977) points out that size of the pulp cavity decreases rapidly among young bats due to rapid deposition of dentin, but seems to decrease more slowly among adults. This may potentially limit the utility of the criterion, especially for older age groups. Because tooth wear changes may be more pronounced in older bats than in younger ones, Baagøe (1977) suggested that an index combining pulp cavity and tooth wear measurements may provide a more sensitive indicator of age over the lifetime of bats than either criterion alone.

3.   CHARACTERISTICS OF BONES

3.1.   Lengths of Long Bones

Post-natal growth analyses conducted with both free-living (e.g., Dymond, 1936; Pearson et al., 1952; Short, 1961; Davis, 1969b; O'Farrell and Studier, 1973; Kunz, 1973, 1974; Pagels and Jones, 1974) and captive (e.g., Jones, 1967; Kleiman, 1969; Gould, 1971; Bogan, 1972; Maeda, 1972; Bradbury, 1977; Kleiman and Davis, 1979) bats have consistently shown that lengths of the forearm and bones of the fingers (as well as other long bones) increase rapidly during the first few weeks of life. Thus, forearm and finger lengths can be used not only as reliable means of distinguishing juvenile from adult bats, but measurements of these structures are extremely well suited for accurately estimating the absolute age of juveniles during the initial linear phase of growth. Measurements of long bones are quickly and easily made in the field or on museum specimens using only a ruler or dial calipers, and these measurements are generally highly repeatable (both within and between observers). Because taking these measurements causes no harm to living bats, and the process can be repeated many times on individual bats during the growth period, this simple criterion of age is a potentially powerful tool for many types of studies.

Age estimates can be generated from these measurements by entering forearm length into species-specific linear regression equations that are generated from data obtained in known-age bats. The reliability of estimates made by this technique has been investigated extensively in developing *M. lucifugus, E. fuscus,* and *P. subflavus* (Kunz and Anthony, 1982; Burnett and Kunz, 1982; Hoying, 1983). During the linear phase of growth in each of these species, forearm measurement provides age estimates with 95% prediction intervals of only ± 1-2 days. This interval refers to the error involved in predicting the age of a single bat on the basis of its forearm length alone. Although length of the forearm has thus proved to be a reliable age criterion in young bats, the major limitation of this technique is the short length of time spanned by the linear growth spurt (1-11 days in *M. lucifugus,* 1-15 days in *E. fuscus,* and 1-14 days in *P. subflavus*). When growth of the forearm slows (and its length begins to overlap that of adults), forearm length ceases to be a useful determinant of age, and other criteria must be sought.

3.2. Epiphyseal-Diaphyseal Fusion

Following the initial growth phase of long bones, patterns of closure of the cartilaginous epiphyseal growth plates in long bones can be used to extend the period of reliable age estimation in young bats. It is well known that young bats can be distinguished qualitatively from adults by the presence of cartilaginous epiphyseal plates in finger bones (Andersen 1917; Davis, 1963; Cranbrook and Barrett, 1965; Stebbings, 1968; Barbour and Davis, 1969). These plates are readily visible to the unaided eye when a bat's wing is transilluminated; the cartilaginous zones appear lighter than ossified parts of the bones, as lesser mineralization allows more light to pass through (Fig. 1). When these cartilaginous plates are no longer grossly visible, the shapes of the finger joints of young bats remain less knobby and more evenly tapered than those of adults, allowing some young bats to be provisionally identified by this characteristic until they are almost a year old.

This feature has been used to identify young of the year during the winter in some hibernating species (Davis and Hitchcock, 1965).

The qualitative criteria described above are applicable to both field and laboratory situations, as the required observations are quick and easy and require no sophisticated equipment. Baagøe (1977) has shown, however, that X-ray techniques can improve the sensitivity of age-determination in bats using characteristics of epiphyseal-diaphyseal fusion, as traces of this fusion process can be detected in older juveniles with X-rays than with transmitted light.

Developmental changes in cartilaginous growth plates can also be used to generate quantitative estimates of age in bats. Changes in epiphyseal cartilages of the fourth metacarpal-phalangeal joint have been studied in detail in known-age juvenile *M. lucifugus, E. fuscus,* and *P. subflavus* (Kunz and Anthony, 1982; Burnett and Kunz, 1982; Hoying, 1983). Length of the total cartilaginous gap between the bony diaphyses of the metacarpal and the proximal phalanx (Fig. 1) was determined in the field in live bats using a binocular microscope equipped with an eyepiece reticle and a substage light source. In all three species, the length of this "total gap" increased linearly with age during the early post-natal period. The size of this gap reached a maximum between 9 and 15 days, depending on the species. Subsequently, the length of this gap decreased linearly with age.

When used in a linear regression equation during this decreasing phase, measurements of the total cartilaginous gap generate age estimates with prediction intervals ranging from ± 3-5 days in these species. Individual variability in size of the growth zone causes the accuracy of prediction to be less than that for younger bats based on forearm measurements. However, this technique extends the period of quantitative age estimation from the time that the forearm approaches adult size until the rate of closure of the epiphyseal plate slows, and the cartilaginous regions become so small that measurement is difficult (approximately 4 weeks in

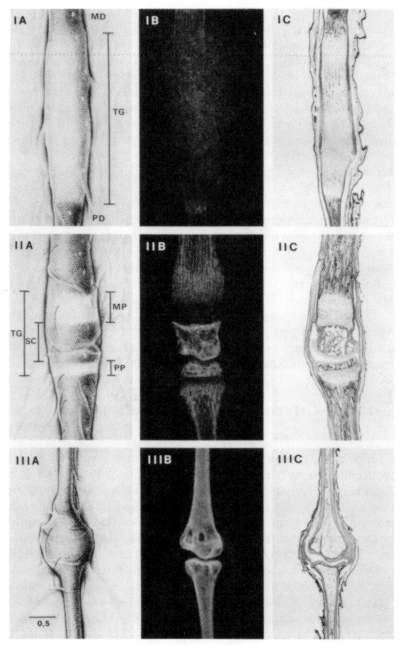

Figure 1. Growth progression in the fourth metacarpal-phalangeal joint of *Myotis lucifugus* from the neonatal (I) to adult (III) stage, based on changes perceived in transilluminated wings (A), X-rays (B), and histological sections (C). Measurements made in the field on transilluminated joints of young bats are indicated in IA and IIA. In neonates (IA), the total gap (TG) measurement represents the length of the cartilaginous regions between the bony diaphysis of the metacarpal (MD) and the diaphysis of the proximal phalanx (PD). In older juveniles, in which secondary centers of ossification (SC) have developed in the epiphyses of both bones, the total gap measurement (TG) can still be made as in neonates. However, measurements can also be made of the lengths of the two individual epiphyseal plates of the metacarpal (MP) and phalanx (PP). These latter measurements provide additional potential age criteria for bats. Reference bar = 0.5 mm. From: Kunz and Anthony (1982).

M. lucifugus, 6 weeks in *E. fuscus,* and 7 weeks in *P. subflavus*).

Measurements of epiphyseal cartilages are also appropriate for determining the age of alcohol-preserved specimens. However, as tissues are likely to shrink due to dehydration in alcohol, the exact relationship between length of the gap and age may be different than in live individuals, and separate regression equations should be developed for each (see Kunz and Anthony, 1982).

Rybář (1969a; 1971) combined measurements of epiphyseal cartilages of the metacarpal and proximal phalanx of the third finger with measurements of lengths of these long bones to develop an "ossification index." He found that this index can be used to predict age of either live or preserved *M. myotis* from the age of 3 weeks until approximately 3 months, when the epiphyseal cartilages in the third finger disappear. Error associated with this method of age determination was estimated at 10% or a maximum of five days (Rybář, 1969a), a level of uncertainty comparable to that observed in studies discussed above in which the length of the fourth metacarpal-phalangeal epiphyseal gap was used alone as an age predictor in North American vespertilionids. A similar index was developed for live *Rhinolophus hipposideros* (Rybář, 1971); this index is valid from 3 weeks to 2 months of age. Patterns of ossification of tail vertebrae, pelvic girdle, and sternum have been found to be unsuitable for age determination in bats (Rybář, 1969b).

4. MISCELLANEOUS CRITERIA

4.1. Body Mass

Growth studies in bats have shown that the body mass of juveniles increases quickly in a linear fashion during the early post-natal growth period (see Tuttle and Stevenson, 1982, for review), suggesting that mass could provide an alternative criterion of age at that time. The potential for use of mass as a pre-

dictor of age has been carefully examined in juvenile *M. lucifugus, E. fuscus,* and *P. subflavus* (Kunz and Anthony, 1982; Burnett and Kunz, 1982; Hoying, 1983). In all three species, the linear phase of mass increase is short, ending at approximately 2-3 weeks of age. Furthermore, due to individual variation in mass increment, regression equations predicting age on the basis of mass alone have relatively wide prediction intervals. Thus, for these species, it has been suggested that forearm length (which increases linearly over the same time period, but with less individual variation) is a preferable age indicator for growing juveniles.

Individual variations in mass, which render this physical characteristic relatively unreliable for age determination, probably arise from differences in juveniles' energy budgets. Even within a single maternity roost, individual pups undoubtedly differ in energy intake (as a consequence of the amount of milk provided by their mothers) and in energy expended in maintenance and thermoregulation (as a consequence of variations in microenvironment; see Tuttle, 1975). Additional fluctuations in body mass that are unrelated to age would be expected during the process of weaning and are known to occur annually in hibernators (e.g., Davis, 1969a, 1969b; Beasley et al., 1984). Thus, body mass must be considered an inadequate criterion of age at any developmental stage in bats (see Morris, 1972).

4.2. Pelage Coloration

In many species of bats, the pelage color of juveniles differs from that of adults (Pearson et al., 1952; Orr, 1954; Davis, 1963; Gaisler and Titlbach, 1964; Davis and Hitchcock, 1965; Davis, 1969b; Racey, 1974; Hoying, 1983). In many cases, however, these differences in color are subtle, and because there are normal ranges of color variation among adults and among juveniles, differentiating adults from young on the basis of pelage color alone can be difficult. In a detailed study of hair development and molt in *M. myotis,* Mazák (1965) observed that juvenile pelage is dull gray-brown, whereas the subadult and adult pelage is a more lustrous gray-brown to dull brown with a "slight yellowish shade." The problem of discrimination, especially in the field under limited light conditions, is obvious. Stebbings (1968) attempted to avoid subjective elements in color perception by comparing the pelage colors of juvenile and adult *P. pipistrellus* with those in a standard color atlas in "good north daylight." However, this analysis revealed a considerable amount of between-group overlap in color and did not seem to improve his ability to discriminate between various age classes of this species.

Pelage color itself, therefore, cannot be considered a sufficient or reliable criterion of age in bats if used alone. However, subtle age-related differences in pelage color or quality which are perceived in many bat species by experienced observers may sometimes be profitably used to supplement other criteria, especially when other available criteria provide ambiguous age information.

5.   SUMMARY AND CONCLUSIONS

During the period of post-natal somatic growth, the age of bats can be accurately estimated using a combination of skeletal characteristics. Measurements of the lengths of long bones provide the best predictors of age during the brief linear growth phase. When these bones approach adult size, measurements of epiphyseal cartilages can then be used to calculate age as long as the cartilage remains visible. After this developmental period, sexually immature bats can still be distinguished from sexually mature adults on the basis of reproductive criteria. However, after attainment of sexual maturity, estimating age in adult bats becomes much more difficult. One criterion that could potentially be used to assign ages or age ranges to adults—tooth wear—requires

more thorough validation in bats. A second technique—counting incremental growth lines in teeth—has been shown to have serious drawbacks. Thus, determining age in adult bats in the absence of banding data holds somewhat of a challenge for future investigators.

When quantitative age estimates are made in young bats for use in ontogenic studies, it is important to consider the degree of accuracy of those estimates. Criteria of age for a particular species are reliable only if they are based on reference standards obtained in known-age bats—that is, individuals marked at birth and followed through the developmental period. Furthermore, only baseline data obtained in natural populations are applicable to wild-caught animals; growth rates of captive bats may be sharply different. Statistical estimates of error should also be taken into account when generating and using reference data (see Dapson, 1980). In natural bat populations, error in age estimation can be severe in cases of individuals born prematurely or very late in the parturition period (Hoying, 1983). Furthermore, variations in environmental conditions that may influence prenatal and/or postnatal growth (Racey and Swift, 1981; Hoying, 1983) may complicate the age determination process. These unavoidable circumstances should not deter researchers from attempting accurate age estimation in bats; instead they point to the need for collection of adequate reference data in known-age cohorts and for use of common sense in application of these data.

6.   ACKNOWLEDGMENTS

The author would like to thank Drs. Alvar W. Gustafson and David A. Damassa for sharing their observations on growth and reproductive development in bats and for offering helpful comments on an earlier draft of this manuscript.

7. REFERENCES

Andersen, K. 1917. On the determination of age in bats. J. Bombay Nat. Hist. Soc., 25:249-259.

Baagøe, H. J. 1977. Age determination in bats (Chiroptera). Vidensk. Meddr dansk naturh. Foren., 140:53-92.

Barbour, R. W., and W. H. Davis. 1969. Bats of America. University Press of Kentucky, Lexington, 286 pp.

Beasley, L. J., K. M. Pelz, and I. Zucker. 1984. Circannual rhythms of body weight in pallid bats. Am. J. Physiol., 246:R955-R958.

Bogan, M. A. 1972. Observations on parturition and development in the hoary bat, *Lasiurus cinereus.* J. Mammal., 53:611-614.

Bradbury, J. W. 1977. Lek mating behavior in the hammer-headed bat. Z. Tierpsychol., 45:225-255.

Burnett, C. D., and T. H. Kunz. 1982. Growth rates and age estimation in *Eptesicus fuscus* and comparison with *Myotis lucifugus.* J. Mammal., 63:33-41.

Christian, J. J. 1956. The natural history of a summer aggregation of the big brown bat, *Eptesicus fuscus fuscus.* Amer. Mid. Nat., 55:66-95.

Cranbrook, The Earl of, and H. G. Barrett. 1965. Observations on noctule bats (*Nyctalus noctula*) captured while feeding. Proc. Zool. Soc. Lond., 144:1-24.

Dapson, R. W. 1980. Guidelines for statistical usage in age-estimation technics. J. Wildl. Manage., 44:541-548.

Davis, R. 1969a. Wing loading in pallid bats. J. Mammal., 50:140-144.

Davis, R. 1969b. Growth and development of young pallid bats, *Antrozous pallidus.* J. Mammal., 50:729-736.

Davis, R. B., C. F. Herreid II, and H. L. Short. 1962. Mexican free-tailed bats in Texas. Ecol. Monogr., 32:311-346.

Davis, W. H. 1963. Aging bats in winter. Trans. Kentucky Acad. Sci., 24:28-30.

Davis, W. H., and H. B. Hitchcock. 1965. Biology and migration of the bat, *Myotis lucifugus,* in New England. J. Mammal., 46:296-313.

Dymond, J. R. 1936. Life history notes and growth studies on the little brown bat, *Myotis lucifugus lucifugus.* Can. Field-Nat., 50:114-116.

Fenton, M. B. 1970. The deciduous dentition and its replacement in *Myotis lucifugus* (Chiroptera: Vespertilionidae). Can. J. Zool., 48:817-820.

Funakoshi, K., and T. A. Uchida. 1982. Age composition of summer colonies in the Japanese house-dwelling bat, *Pipistrellus abramus.* J. Fac. Agr., Kyushu Univ., 27:55-64.

Gaisler, J., and M. Titlbach. 1964. The male sexual cycle in the lesser horseshoe bat (*Rhinolophus hipposideros hipposideros* Bechstein, 1800). Věst. Česk. Spol. Zool., 28:268-277.

Gould, E. 1971. Studies of maternal-infant communication and development of vocalizations in the bats *Myotis* and *Eptesicus.* Comm. Behav. Biol. (A), 5:263-313.

Hall, J. S., R. J. Cloutier, and D. R. Griffin. 1957. Longevity records and notes on tooth wear of bats. J. Mammal., 38:407-409.

Hoying, K. M. 1983. Growth and development of the eastern pipistrelle bat, *Pipistrellus subflavus.* Unpublished M.A. thesis, Boston Univ., Boston, Massachusetts, 148 pp.

Jones, C. 1967. Growth, development, and wing loading in the evening bat, *Nycticeius humeralis* (Rafinesque). J. Mammal., 48:1-19.

Kleiman, D. G. 1969. Maternal care, growth rate, and development in the noctule (*Nyctalus noctula*), pipistrelle (*Pipistrellus pipistrellus*), and serotine (*Eptesicus serotinus*) bats. J. Zool., 157:187-211.

Kleiman, D. G., and T. M. Davis. 1979. Ontogeny and maternal care. Pp. 387-402 *in* Biology of bats of the New World family Phyllostomatidae. Part III. (R. J. Baker, J. K. Jones, Jr., and D. C. Carter, eds.). Spec. Publ. Mus., Texas Tech Univ., Lubbock, 16:1-441.

Klevezal', G. A., and S. E. Kleinenberg. 1967. Age determination of mammals from annual layers in teeth and bones. Israel Program for Scientific Translations, Jerusalem, TT 69-55033 (1969), 128 pp. (Translated from Russian.)

Klevezal', G. A., and L. I. Sukhovskaya. 1983. On causes of differences in the optical density of dentine layers in mammalian teeth. Zool. Zh., 62:1407-1416. (In Russian, English summary.)

Kunz, T. H. 1973. Population studies of the cave bat (*Myotis velifer*): Reproduction, growth, and development. Occas. Pap. Mus. Nat. Hist. Univ. Kansas, 15:1-43.

Kunz, T. H. 1974. Reproduction, growth, and mortality of the vespertilionid bat, *Eptesicus fuscus,* in Kansas. J. Mammal., 55:1-13.

Kunz, T. H., and E. L. P. Anthony. 1982. Age estimation and post-natal growth in the bat

Myofis lucifugus. J. Mammal., 63:23-32.

Kunz, T. H., P. V. August, and C. D. Burnett. 1983. Harem social organization in cave roosting *Artibeus jamaicensis* (Chiroptera: Phyllostomidae). Biotropica, 15:133-138.

Linhart, S. B. 1973. Age determination and occurrence of incremental growth lines in the dental cementum of the common vampire bat (*Desmodus rotundus*). J. Mammal., 54:493-496.

Lord, R. D., F. Muradall, and L. Lazaro. 1976. Age composition of vampire bats (*Desmodus rotundus*) in northern Argentina and southern Brazil. J. Mammal., 57:573-575.

Maeda, K. 1972. Growth and development of large noctule, *Nyctalus lasiopterus* Schreber. Mammalia, 36:269-278.

Mazák, V. 1965. Changes in pelage of *Myotis myotis myotis* Borkhausen, 1797 (Mammalia, Chiroptera). Věst. Česk. Spol. Zool., 29:368-376.

McCracken, G. F., and J. W. Bradbury. 1981. Social organization and kinship in the polygynous bat *Phyllostomus hastatus*. Behav. Ecol. Sociobiol., 8:11-34.

Morris, P. 1972. A review of mammalian age determination methods. Mammal Review, 2:69-104.

O'Farrell, M. J., and E. H. Studier. 1973. Reproduction, growth, and development in *Myotis thysanodes* and *M. lucifugus* (Chiroptera: Vespertilionidae). Ecology, 54:18-30.

Orr, R. T. 1954. Natural history of the pallid bat, *Antrozous pallidus* (LeConte). Proc. California Acad. Sci., 28:165-246.

Pagels, J. F., and C. Jones. 1974. Growth and development of the free-tailed bat, *Tadarida brasiliensis cynocephala* (Le Conte). Southwestern Nat., 19:267-276.

Pearson, O. P., M. R. Koford, and A. K. Pearson. 1952. Reproduction of the lump-nosed bat (*Corynorhinus rafinesquei*) in California. J. Mammal., 33:273-320.

Perry, A. E., and C. F. Herreid II. 1969. Comparison of the tooth-wear and lens-weight methods of age determination in the guano bat, *Tadarida brasiliensis mexicana*. J. Mammal., 50:357-360.

Phillips, C. J., B. Steinberg, and T. H. Kunz. 1982. Dentin, cementum, and age determination in bats: A critical evaluation. J. Mammal., 63:197-207.

Racey, P. A. 1974. Ageing and assessment of reproductive status of Pipistrelle bats, *Pipistrellus pipistrellus*. J. Zool., 173:264-271.

Racey, P. A., and S. M. Swift. 1981. Variations in gestation length in a colony of pipistrelle bats (*Pipistrellus pipistrellus*) from year to year. J. Reprod. Fert., 61:123-129.

Rybář, P. 1969a. Ossification of bones as age criterion in bats (Chiroptera). Práce a studie-Přír., Pardubice, 1:115-136. (In Czech, English summary)

Rybář, P. 1969b. A contribution to the study on ossification of bones in the bat *Myotis myotis* Borkhausen, 1797 in regard to the age determination. Acta Musei Reginaehradecensis S. A.: Scientiae Naturales, X:89-101. (In Czech, English summary.)

Rybář, P. 1971. On the problems of practical use of the ossification of bones as age criterion in the bats (Microchiroptera). Práce a studie-Přír., Pardubice, 3:97-121. (In Czech, English summary)

Schowalter, D. B., L. D. Harder, and B. H. Treichel. 1978. Age composition of some vespertilionid bats as determined by dental annuli. Can. J. Zool., 56:355-358.

Short, H. L. 1961. Growth and development of Mexican free-tailed bats. Southwestern Nat., 6:156-163.

Sluiter, J. W. 1961. Abrasion of teeth in connection with age in the bat *Myotis myotis*. Proc. Kon. Ned. Akad. Wet. Ser. C, 64:424-434.

Stebbings, R. E. 1968. Measurements, composition and behaviour of a large colony of the bat *Pipistrellus pipistrellus*. J. Zool., 156:15-33.

Stegeman, L. C. 1956. Tooth development and wear in *Myotis*. J. Mammal., 37:58-63.

Tuttle, M. D. 1975. Population ecology of the gray bat (*Myotis grisescens*): Factors influencing early growth and development. Occas. Pap. Mus. Nat. Hist. Univ. Kansas, 36:1-24.

Tuttle, M. D., and D. Stevenson. 1982. Growth and survival of bats. Pp. 105-150, *in* Ecology of bats. (T. H. Kunz, ed.). Plenum Press, New York, 425 pp.

Twente, J. W., Jr. 1955. Aspects of a population study of cavern-dwelling bats. J. Mammal., 36:379-390.

Chapter 4

Marking and Observational Techniques

Robert M. R. Barclay

Department of Biology
University of Calgary
Calgary, Alberta T2N 1N4 Canada

and

Gary P. Bell

Department of Biology
Boston University
Boston, Massachusetts 02215 USA

1. INTRODUCTION

Bats are often difficult to observe in their natural habitats. They are volant, essentially nocturnal, and acoustically oriented, and these very features which make them such vital subjects for study have severely limited our ability to obtain even the most basic data on their ecology and behavior. Relative to what we know about other groups of mammals, research on bats is years behind. Some of the methods used to capture, mark and observe bats have been borrowed from studies of birds and other small mammals, but the unique characteristics of bats have called for more specialized means of study. Technological advances of the past decade have led to the development of new methods for detecting and observing bats in the dark, as well as more generalized methods of data collection. Few of these techniques are specifically designed for, or limited to, the study of bats, and few are universally applicable to all bats. Each species presents its own challenges, and frequently trial and error are required to determine the most appropriate methods. In our experience there are only two hard-and-fast rules for the study of bats in the field; 1) know your study animal and what you can expect of it, and 2) be inventive. The following is a summary of methods that have been employed in various studies and have proved effective for observing bats.

2. MARKING TECHNIQUES

Bats can be marked for individual or group identification. The marking technique employed will depend upon the species and the objectives of the study. Before selecting a particular technique the following questions should be considered.

1) For what period of time must the markings last?
2) Will individual identity be required?
3) How near will the observer need to be to identify the marked animals?
4) Will the mark be visible from the observer's vantage point?
5) How many individually distinct marks will be required?
6) How rapidly will animals have to be marked?
7) How much time will be available for identifying a marked animal?
8) Will the mark affect the survival or behavior of the animal?

2.1. Wing Bands

Attachment of bands (rings) to the forearms of bats has been the most widely used method for marking (see Eisentraut, 1960; Greenhall and Paradiso, 1968; Stebbings, 1978). Several different band types are available including serially numbered metallic bands, color-anodized aluminum bands, and numbered and unnumbered colored plastic bands. The type of band used will depend upon the application, and there are advantages and disadvantages associated with each type.

2.1.1. Metallic Bands

Metallic bands have been used for individually marking large series of bats with a unique number combination (Trapido and Crowe, 1946). Initially bird leg-bands were used (Hitchcock, 1957); later flanged bands were developed specifically for bats (see W. H. Davis, 1966). Large scale banding of bats with numbered metallic bands (see Appendix 1) began in the 1930s in both North America (Hitchcock, 1965) and Europe (Bels, 1952; Abel, 1960; Balliot, 1964), and later in Australia (Dwyer, 1963), and has yielded valuable information on survival (e.g., Hitchcock, 1964; Tuttle and Stevenson, 1982; Chapter

10), homing (e.g., R. Davis, 1966), roost movements (e.g., Twente, 1955), and migration (e.g., Griffin, 1970; Baker, 1978). Identification of individuals using this technique requires recapture and handling of banded individuals which seriously limits the kind of information it can provide.

There are other disadvantages associated with banding. The disturbance associated with banding animals during an energetically critical period may be stressful enough to reduce survival. For example, winter banding of temperate hibernating bats has been implicated as one of the major causes of population declines (e.g., Jones, 1976; Tuttle, 1979; Keen and Hitchcock, 1980). Several countries, including the United States (Jones, 1976) and Great Britain, have restricted or prohibited banding of bats in an effort to stop these apparent declines. Bell et al. (1986) have indicated that, when first applied, bands may cause distress sufficient to interfere with daily time and energy budgets. It must be appreciated that any disturbance, including handling, may reduce survival.

Bands may cause injuries to bats (e.g., Davis, 1960, 1961; Herreid et al., 1960; Beaucournu, 1962; Dwyer, 1965; Cockrum, 1969). This varies with the type of band, species of bat, age of individual, season of banding, and care taken in band application (Eisentraut, 1960). In species with a small propatagium, bands should be applied loosely enough to allow them to slide freely along the forearm (Stebbings, 1978), but care must be taken to ensure that the band is not so loose that it can slide over the wrist or elbow joint, which can result in immobility, extreme injury, or simply band loss. It is also imperative that bands be closed evenly. If bands are pinched at one end and open at the other injury to a joint may result.

Species with a wide propatagium (e.g., pteropodids, rhinolophoids, mormoopids, and phyllostomids) cannot be banded in the same way; constriction of the propatagium by a band can seriously affect manoeuverability and often results in injury and infection. Bradbury (1977) reported serious wrist and forearm injuries when *Hypsignathus monstrosus* was banded as described above. Some small pteropodids, emballonurids, mormoopids, and phyllostomids have been banded successfully by making a small incision in the propatagium just in front of the forearm and slipping the band through it and around the forearm (Bateman and Vaughan, 1974; Bonaccorso et al., 1976; D. W. Thomas, pers. comm.). In work with the small phyllostomid, *Macrotus californicus,* in the laboratory and the field (G. P. Bell, unpubl.), injury, infection, and distress (i.e., time spent chewing the bands) have all been minimized by making small incisions in the propatagium and the chiropatagium such that the band completely encircles the forearm. For pteropodids larger than about 50 g, D. W. Thomas (pers. comm.) recommends inserting the band through a single incision made through the chiropatagium and closing it forward over the forearm. Flightless young bats may be prone to developmental damage from bands (Perry and Beckett, 1966), although T. H. Kunz (pers. comm.) regularly bands day-old bats with adult-size bands without injury. If very young bats are to be banded, the bands should be large enough to allow for continued growth, and it is important that the bands do not interfere with wrist or elbow joints.

Some bats may chew bands, making all or some of the numbers unreadable. This behavior varies with species, sex, age and individual behavior of the bat, but is generally a greater problem with frugivores (Bonaccorso and Smythe, 1972). Anodizing aluminum bands may alleviate this problem somewhat (Davis, 1963; Haarr, 1963; Cockrum, 1969), but metallic bands may not be suitable for some species, in which case plastic bands or necklacing should be considered.

2.1.2. Plastic Bands

Plastic split-rings, developed for individual marking of caged birds, are now commonly used for marking birds and bats in the field (e.g., Gaisler and Nevrly, 1961; Nyholm,

1965; Bradbury and Emmons, 1974; Thomson et al., 1985). These bands come in a variety of single colors and striped color combinations with or without embossed numbers (Appendix 1). Various sizes are available. The use of more than one color band per bat allows individuals or group members to be uniquely marked (e.g., Bradbury and Vehrencamp, 1976; McCracken and Bradbury, 1978, 1981; Thomson et al., 1985; Wilkinson, 1985), which provides the distinct advantage of being able to identify individual animals without handling. The convention of banding males on the right forearm and females on the left allows sexes to be distinguished as well. Colored bands are especially useful in studies of social organization, mother-infant interactions, mating behaviors, and movements of bats within roosts.

Plastic bands are less subject to damage by chewing, and appear to hold up well even on some frugivorous species (Morrison, 1978). Unlike metallic bands, plastic split-rings are easily removed from the bat's forearm at the end of a study or if physical problems develop without risk of further injury. The greater range of available sizes and the small mass of plastic split-rings reduces the overall influence of the band on the bat's behavior and flight performance; however, when used in conjunction with radio-tagging (Chapter 7), the added mass and particularly the interference of wing bands should be considered when estimating increased wing-loading and reduced power of tagged bats.

2.1.3. Reflective Bands

Reflective colored tape (Scotch Lite, 3M Co.) can be applied to metallic or plastic split-ring bands to aid in the identification of individual bats, sexes, or species during flight or while in the roost (e.g., Williams et al., 1966; Voûte, 1972; Bradbury and Vehrencamp, 1976; Humphrey et al., 1977; Racey and Swift, 1985; Bell et al., 1986). Reflective tape greatly enhances the visibility of tags in artificial light, with TV cameras, or with image intensifiers (i.e., night vision scopes and goggles). Reflective tape is available in a wide range of colors; however, in practice many colors are easily confused beyond a few meters. Red, white, and yellow have the highest reflective properties and are generally easiest to distinguish with a headlamp or battery-powered spotlight and binoculars at ranges of up to 100 m. Illuminating a bat for a prolonged period to determine identity may have a marked disturbing effect on its behavior.

2.2. Necklaces

In some situations where wing bands have been inappropriate because of risk of injury, infection, or excessive band chewing, some workers have marked their animals using a bead-clasp "keychain" neck collar (e.g., Wilkinson, 1985; C. O. Handley, pers. comm.). Extreme care must be taken to ensure a proper fit of the collar to an individual bat. Collars made of rachet-style plastic ties (available at electronics stores) have been successfully used to necklace some bats (G. S. Wilkinson, pers. comm.) and appear to cause less abrasion and allow finer size adjustment than the key-chain type. Collars that are either too tight or too loose can cause open wounds and infection. Necklacing should not be used on growing juveniles and should probably be avoided on species with sternal, gular, or shoulder scent glands. Necklacing appears to work well, although rehandling of the bats is necessary for identification. Excessive handling should be avoided, especially with some small tropical species, as it may result in shock and death (Bradbury and Emmons, 1974; M. D. Tuttle, pers. comm.).

2.3. Light Tags

Affixing small lights to bats permits observation of roosting or foraging behavior from a distance. At present, several types of light-emitting tags are available.

2.3.1. Battery Powered Lights

Earliest attempts at light-tagging bats involved attaching small, battery powered incandescent bulbs (pin-lights) to the backs of the animals (Barbour and Davis, 1969). The high current drain of such bulbs limits the usefulness of such a technique. Recently, a number of studies on other nocturnal animals have relied on light-emitting diodes (LEDs) as a light source (e.g., Brooks and Dodge, 1978; Batchelor and McMillan, 1980), and this should prove a useful technique in future long-term studies of bats. The low current drain of LEDs reduces the required battery mass, compared with pin-lights, and increases the life of the light. LEDs come in a variety of colors, sizes, and light intensities and can be powered by small 'watch' batteries. Flashing can be produced using a single, small integrated circuit oscillator, which increases the life of the battery to as much as 5 days. The total mass of an LED tag can be kept under 2 g (Brooks and Dodge, 1978). Such lights may be visible with binoculars at distances of up to 150 m. Color combinations for individual identification and long duration are distinct advantages of LED light tags; however, such tags are fairly expensive compared with simpler methods.

2.3.2. Chemical Light Tags

Inexpensive chemiluminescent tags can be prepared using Cyalume (Buchler, 1976). Cyalume consists of a greenish-yellow phosphor compound and a peroxide-based reactant which are mixed to produce a bright, cold light. The chemicals come in sealed, flexible plastic tubes, the peroxide isolated in a thin glass capsule such that bending the tube breaks the capsule and initiates the chemiluminescent reaction. The catalyzed liquid can be drawn off in a syringe and placed in small blown glass spheres or gelatin pill capsules to create light-tags weighing less than 0.5 g which can be attached to the bats with minimal discomfort or interference with flight. Although Buchler (1976) suggested storing the two component liquids in opaque stock bottles and mixing 1:1 proportions from them, for most purposes the contents of a single intact stick can be used as is. Freezing the sticks will prolong their shelf life. The chemical light begins to fade as reactants are used up, therefore the tags should be prepared immediately before use.

Although gelatin pill capsules are much less expensive, easier to handle, and can be obtained in a range of sizes and colors, there is some evidence that bats can bite through the gelatin and can die from ingesting the liquid (LaVal et al., 1977), although Racey and Swift (1985) found no evidence of such toxicity. Small glass spheres may therefore be preferred, especially where threatened or endangered species are under study, but care must be taken to seal the aperture of the sphere to prevent leakage. Buchler (1976) suggested using plasticine as a plug, but gases produced in the chemiluminescent reaction tend to push such plugs out. An alternative approach is to heat seal the Cyalume into short lengths of flexible tygon tubing. T. H. Kunz (pers. comm.) has had success using transparent heat-shrink tubing (available at electronics supply stores) for this purpose.

The complete tag may be glued to the dorsal or ventral surface of the bat's body, depending on the vantage point of the observer and the elevation at which the bat is expected to fly. While the bats may be able to groom adhesive out of their fur over time, it is preferable to clip the fur at the site of attachment and glue the tag directly to the skin. A number of different types of adhesive have been used to attach light tags to bats including branding cement (Buchler, 1976; Brown et al., 1983) and Crazy Glue (cyanoacrylate ester), both of which are irritants and may be toxic. Surgical appliance adhesive (pure latex in n-hexane) is the best adhesive to use as it is non-toxic and can be easily groomed from the skin and fur by the bat within a few days. It is best to make a thin film of adhesive on the tag and on the skin, blow gently to dry the surfaces, then press the tag into place. Using

large amounts of adhesive increases the drying time and reduces the firmness of attachment. One should be sure that the adhesive is dry before releasing the bat, and that its wing and tail membranes are free of the adhesive; adhesive solvent can be obtained in volume for this purpose. When releasing a tagged bat it should be held aloft and allowed to leave of its own volition. Bats should never be tossed into the air, since this adds to the animals' stress and disorientation.

Depending upon its size and chemical composition, a Cyalume light tag may be clearly visible to the naked eye up to 200 m, and at greater distances in open areas using binoculars (Buchler, 1976; Buchler and Childs, 1981). Artificial lights in urban areas and moonlight reduce the visibility of light-tagged bats. Bioluminescent insects, and even bright stars, can also cause confusion in tracking light-tagged bats. An effective way of following light-tagged bats is to station several observers equipped with citizens' band radios, or "walkie-talkies" over a large area (Brown et al., 1983; Harrison, 1983; Racey and Swift, 1985). Two-way "head-set" radios are especially suitable for such studies. Other individuals can track the initial movements of the bats by following them from the release point; however, it is well to bear in mind that chasing bats in the dark may be treacherous. Bats can be released and observed individually or en masse, although the latter method obscures individual patterns of behavior. A useful approach, when dealing with different sexes, age groups, or species is to work with a single group on any one night to avoid confusion. A portable tape recorder is valuable for recording observations and can be easily interfaced with a walkie-talkie to directly collect relayed information from observers.

Light tags have been used to delineate foraging habitats and ranges, hunting patterns, and dispersal routes of bats (e.g., LaVal et al., 1977; LaVal and LaVal, 1980; Buchler, 1980; Buchler and Childs, 1981; Racey and Swift, 1985). Individual bats have been followed using this technique for up to 13 km (Harrison, 1983). With some species traditional flight paths may become apparent over time, allowing better placement of observers. Light tagging has also proved useful in echolocation studies for making recordings of known, free-flying individuals (e.g., Bell, 1980; Fenton and Bell, 1981).

2.3.3. Betalights

Another type of light tag which has considerable potential is the Betalight, a phosphor-coated glass capsule containing a small quantity of tritium gas. Low level beta radiation from the tritium strikes and excites the phosphor producing visible light of a color characteristic of the type of phosphor used. The glass is impervious to tritium and completely absorbs any beta radiation not absorbed by the phosphor. The unit is thus a completely sealed source and does not present a radiation hazard. Nevertheless, Betalights are considered controlled products by most countries, and applicable federal and state radioisotope permits are usually required for their use.

Betalights have been used on a variety of small- to medium-sized terrestrial mammals, (e.g., pocket mice, kangaroo mice, rabbits), but no studies with bats have been published. Preliminary studies using the smallest size of Betalights available (0.05 cm) on small (ca. 10 g) vespertilionids were not successful, as the lights were not bright enough to follow the bats at long distances (P. A. Racey, pers. comm.). Observations at 300 m have been made using larger (1 cm diameter) tags on rabbits (Davy et al., 1980), and presumably such tags could be used on larger species of bats. The major advantage of these lights is their extremely long service life (10-15 years). A special collar for attachment would obviously be required for such long periods.

2.4. Radiotransmitters

Radiotelemetry is a specialized and relatively expensive method of tracking animals and is addressed in detail by Wilkinson and Bradbury (see Chapter 7). The technique employs small battery-powered radiotransmitters which emit a pulsed signal detectable on portable receivers with directional antennae. Information on movements between roosts, size of home ranges, foraging behaviors, and time budgets of bats can be obtained. As with other forms of attachment markers, it is important to keep the transmitter as small as possible to avoid interfering with the animal's ability to fly and forage. A commonly used "rule" in working with flying animals has been to keep the mass of the transmitter below 5% of the body mass (Brander and Cochran, 1969; Cochran, 1980). While 5%, or even 10%, of body mass may be a safe margin for small flying animals, larger animals are operating closer to the energetic limits of powered flight. Caccamise and Heddin (1985) recommend that maximum transmitter mass should be calculated as the mass which would result in a 5% increase in power required to maintain normal flight speed. Aldridge and Brigham (unpubl.), however, have shown that, for small bats, Caccamise and Heddin's approach is inappropriate. While a 10 g bat may be physically able to carry a 4 g transmitter with only a 5% increase in power, such a mass would increase flight speed and reduce manoeuverability, which could have a serious effect upon foraging success. The safest approach, then, is probably to use the 5% of body mass rule for bats under 100 g, and use Caccamise and Heddin's 5% power increase formula for species over 100 g (H. Aldridge and R. M. Brigham, unpubl.). The smallest transmitters currently available weigh 0.75 to 0.85 g (Holohil Systems, Ltd.), making tracking of bats as small as 15 g feasible. It is important to emphasize that these rules suggest 'maximum' allowable transmitter masses, and in reality the smallest possible transmitter should be used to minimize physical and behavioral interference. In calculating maximum allowable transmitter mass it is also important to consider the cumulative mass of other appliances such as wing bands, light tags, and adhesive.

2.5. Miscellaneous Techniques

Several other marking techniques have been used on bats with varying degrees of success. Temporary marking (i.e., less than one year) has been attempted by gluing colored plastic disks to the animal (e.g., Downing and Marshall, 1959; Daan, 1969), however, at least some individuals remove their markers within a few days or weeks. Applying fluorescent powders to the fur (e.g., Dorgelo and Punt, 1969; G. F. McCracken and D. W. Thomas, pers. comm.) may be suitable for short periods, but the powder is soon groomed from the fur and may be carcinogenic (H. G. Merriam, pers. comm.) or may interfere with spermatogenesis because of high zinc content (P. A. Racey, pers. comm.). Non-toxic fluorescent paints (e.g., Pactra Acrylic Colors) can be used for short periods (a few days) to individually mark newborn bats with little or no fur (e.g., McCracken, 1984), and have also been used to color-code aluminum numbered bands in roost studies (Stebbings, 1966). Fluorescent paints and powders fluoresce under ultraviolet (UV) light which can be supplied from a battery-powered source. The brightest colors are pink, orange, and yellow, although pink and orange are difficult to distinguish (G. F. McCracken, pers. comm.).

Techniques such as toe-clipping (e.g., Gould, 1975), ear-notching or ear-tagging (e.g., Heerdt and Sluiter, 1958), fur-bleaching (e.g., Porter, 1978), and punch-marking (e.g., Findley and Wilson, 1974) are routinely used with other types of mammals (see Schemnitz, 1980) and have been used in some bat studies. Fur-bleaching (see Fitzwater, 1943) has some potential for short-term studies (less than one year), but Bradbury (1977) found that bleached marks in the fur of *Hypsignathus monstrosus* were lost within one year through molt. Toe-clipping and ear-notching are not advised since, for most bats, the toes are essential for roosting and grooming, and the ear is critical for orientation and prey location in most Microchiroptera. Tattoo punch-marking has been employed in short-term studies (less than one year), but the technique is slow and rehandling the bats is necessary for individual identification (Bonaccorso and Smythe, 1972; Bonaccorso et al., 1976). Kleiman and Davis (1974) reported using punch-marking for individual identification in a laboratory colony, but note that such marks must be renewed at regular intervals. An additional method which, to our knowledge, has not been employed for marking bats is freeze-branding. This technique creates a permanent colorless (white) mark on skin or fur.

Tags of thin radioactive wire (e.g., Tantalum-182, Cobalt-60) have been attached to bands or directly to the uropatagium, or implanted beneath the skin of the forearm to permit location and identification of individuals within hibernacula and diurnal roosts, and to monitor their arrival and exit (e.g., Punt and Nieuwenhoven, 1957; Gifford and Griffin, 1960; Cope, et al., 1961; Harvey, 1965; Davis et al., 1968; Hardin and Hassell, 1970). No adverse effects on survival or behavior were observed in these studies. Radioactive tags have a short range of detection, but they have proven useful in studies of roost occupancy, within roost movement, and the ontogeny of flight (Buchler, 1980).

One final caution must be made concerning all marking techniques. Bats may, temporarily or permanently, abandon sites where they have been captured and handled (Chapter 1). Therefore, whenever possible, it is advisable to capture bats for marking away from roosts or other areas where future observations are planned. This is especially important where roost sites are limited, or during stressful times of the year, where forced movements may have an adverse effect on survival. Neonates and other non-volant young have been successfully marked at roost sites at night while their mothers are foraging (e.g., Davis et al., 1968; Kunz, 1973; Kunz and Anthony, 1982; Thomson et al., 1985), and they quickly grow accustomed to their tags (T. H. Kunz, pers. comm.).

3. OBSERVATIONAL TECHNIQUES

Many studies require techniques for observing behavior of bats that will minimize disturbance. Specialized techniques are usually required in such studies because bats fly, are mostly nocturnal, and often occupy dimly lit roosts during the day. Suitable techniques are available for observing bats in confined areas such as maternity roosts, night roosts, and hibernacula, and for observing and monitoring bats in flight. Both visual and acoustic means of observation are available.

3.1. Visual Monitoring

3.1.1. Ambient Light

Visual observations making use of ambient light should not be ruled out when studying bats. Several researchers have gathered data by moonlight or twilight (e.g., Sazima and Sazima, 1977; Swift, 1980). Many species of bats begin their nocturnal activities well before dark and are easily observed and counted at that time (e.g., Erkert, 1978). Observations can be made, at least at short range (i.e., less than 20 m) under all but the darkest conditions by backlighting bats against the sky. With practice different species can be identified in flight by their size, shape, and flight pattern (Ahlen, 1981). At high latitudes, extended, or even continuous, summer twilight provides excellent opportunities for observing natural foraging behavior of bats (e.g., Nyholm, 1965). The major advantage in making such observations is that the behavior of the animals is not influenced by artificial lighting or tags.

Nocturnal observations in roosts almost always require supplemental light, but diurnal observations can be made at many roost sites using nothing more than wide-field binoculars. An observation blind (hide) may be advisable to reduce the influence of the observer on the behavior of roosting bats (Burnett and August, 1981). Mirrors may be used under some circumstances to illuminate roosts in crevices (e.g., O'Shea and Vaughan,

1977) and in foliage and leaf-tents (A. Brooke, pers. comm.). Since many diurnal roosts are used predictably by bats and many social interactions take place in them, considerable information can be gathered by making observations in these roosts. For example, observations of individually marked bats in diurnal roosts can indicate the social structure of groups, and this information has been used in conjunction with observations at feeding areas to determine the relationship between social behavior and foraging strategies (e.g., Bradbury and Emmons, 1974; Bradbury and Vehrencamp, 1976).

3.1.2. Artificial Light

Bats possess essentially all-rod retinae, and thus appear to lack color vision (Chase, 1972). It has often been assumed that bats are therefore insensitive to long-wavelength light and, thus, a number of studies of bat behavior have relied upon dim red lights with wavelengths greater than 580 nanometers (e.g., Sazima and Sazima, 1978; Thomas et al., 1979; see also Finley, 1959). Dieterich and Dodt (1972) and Hope and Bhatnagar (1979), however, have demonstrated that at least some species have secondary visual pigments with peak sensitivities between 580 and 600 nanometers. Thus, caution should be used in interpreting results obtained under red light illumination. Red light sources include darkroom safety lights (e.g., General Electric Red Ruby, wavelength 580-740 nm) or photographic filters (e.g., Kodak Wratten No. 29 far-red filter, wavelength >600 nm). In such circumstances the use of the light should be kept to a minimum to limit disturbance.

3.1.3. Night Vision Devices

Night vision devices, or image intensifiers, electronically intensify ambient light to produce an image on a phosphor screen (see Slusher, 1978) and have proved invaluable for making behavioral observations of nocturnal animals (Southern et al., 1946). Several different types and models are commercially available (see Appendix 1). Many of these are extremely light-weight, give high resolution, are battery operated, and can be fitted with standard camera lenses to allow zoom or tele-photo viewing. For long-term observations bi-ocular viewers are available for night view-ing scopes which reduce eye fatigue. Night vision scopes can also be adapted for use with film or television cameras to provide perma-nent records (Boogher and Slusher, 1978). For stationary situations, these devices per-mit detailed observations without undue dis-turbance and have been used to observe bats in roosts and in flight (e.g., Anthony et al., 1981; Burnett and August, 1981; Thompson and Fenton, 1982). Night viewing goggles should prove useful for observing bats since they allow an observer to move about while wearing them. Individual animals can thus be followed and kept in sight for longer periods than with a stationary scope. Although moon-light or starlight may be sufficient to produce an image with a night vision scope, higher res-olution images are obtained by using an infra-red radiation source. In such cases a Kodak Wratten No. 87 infrared filter is recom-mended (Slusher, 1978). An excellent illumi-nator can be constructed for short-range work using a series of small infrared LEDs (e.g., Bell, 1985; Bell and Fenton, 1986).

3.1.4. Television Cameras

Several manufacturers produce television cameras capable of low-light or infrared oper-ation (e.g., Mitsubishi, RCA). These are useful for observing bats at roosts or at pre-dictable foraging sites (e.g., Barclay, 1982). Most models require mainline power supplies but may be operated using gasoline-powered generators. Although TV cameras are rela-tively costly, they have the advantage of allow-ing remote monitoring. Remotely operated zoom, tilt, and pan mechanisms can be added to increase the field of view.

A problem inherent to both night vision devices and low-light television cameras is that they operate in monochrome, rendering color-marking of individuals useless. This problem can be overcome, to some extent, by using combinations of dark, intermediate and light-colored bands which show up as black, grey and white respectively (C. E. Thompson, pers. comm.). Still photography using electronic flash (Chapter 8) can also be used to supplement such observations—individuals can later be identified from color photographs. This method has been used for monitoring bats in roosts (Barclay, 1982), although some species may abandon roosts in response to a flash (G. S. Wilkinson, pers. comm.). A still camera can also be mounted on a night vision device to photograph flying bats (Boogher and Slusher, 1978).

3.1.5. Photography

A number of workers have developed sophis-ticated techniques and methodologies for making high quality photographs of bats (Chapter 8), but these methods have not been widely used in field research. Field photogra-phy can provide detailed information on hunting mechanics (e.g., Griffin et al., 1960), ear and facial orientation during echoloca-tion (J. A. Simmons, pers. comm.), and can be used to remotely record visitation and identi-fication of species at roosts (e.g., Daan, 1970, 1973) and feeding sites (D. W. Thomas, pers. comm.). Edgerton et al. (1966) used photo-graphs of free-tailed bats in flight to estimate their flight speed from the trailing-edge blur of the wings.

Multiple-image strobe photography (Chapter 8) has been used to estimate flight speeds of various bats by measuring distances between successive images. Single-image photographs are best obtained with multiple, high intensity, short duration Thyristor flash units. Use of a power-winder or motor-drive on the camera allows one to use remote, elec-tronic triggering of the shutter. Triggering may be done manually, or remotely. In the lat-ter case "split-beam triggers," similar to those used in burglar alarm systems, may be con-structed using infrared emitter/detector pairs. These inexpensive units vary widely in performance, but, through trial and error selection, pairs can be found which operate at beam-lengths as long as 2 m. A bat (or other object) passing through the beam blocks the light to the detector, which closes a relay to the camera shutter and flash array. More precise positioning of the bat can be ensured by using two light beams intersecting at the desired point—in such an arrangement, both beams must be broken to trigger the camera (also see Chapter 8).

3.2. Acoustic Monitoring

In situations where visual observation is not possible, valuable information on behavior and ecology of bats may be obtained by monitoring their vocalizations. Fenton (Chapter 6) describes equipment for detecting echolocation and other vocalizations made by bats. Bats produce a variety of vocalizations, including echolocation and discrete social calls (Gould, 1975) which, properly interpreted, can reveal details of foraging behavior and social interactions between individuals.

3.2.1. Audible Vocalizations

Many bats produce social calls that are audible to the unaided human ear (e.g., Nelson, 1964; Brown, 1976; Barclay et al., 1979) and these can indicate what individuals are doing once such calls have been associated with individual behavior patterns. This technique has been used in a number of studies (e.g., Bradbury, 1977; O'Shea and Vaughan, 1977; Thomas et al., 1979). Agonistic vocalizations, for example, are often audible and can be used to indicate the presence of bats; however, vocalizations must first be associated with particular behaviors by visual observations. Audible echolocation calls are also produced by a number of species of bats (Griffin, 1971; Fenton and Bell, 1981) and have proven useful in determining the foraging ranges and behaviors of these animals (e.g., Woodsworth et al., 1981; Leonard and Fenton, 1983).

3.2.2. Ultrasonic Vocalizations

For strictly observational purposes, both inexpensive detectors (e.g., QMC Mini) and more expensive signal analysers (e.g., period meter) are useful for detecting echolocation calls of bats (also see Simmons et al., 1979). These have been used to detect the presence of bats, determine their habitat preferences, and identify species (e.g., Bell, 1980; Ahlen, 1981; Fenton and Bell, 1981; Miller and Degn, 1981; Fenton, 1982). Transects or individual stations can be monitored and the number of bat passes and/or feeding buzzes (Griffin, 1958) can be counted. Unfortunately the number of bats involved cannot be determined. Automated ultrasonic systems using chart recorders (Fenton et al., 1973) or tape recorders can be used with bat detectors, thereby allowing several sites to be monitored simultaneously. Species identification is not possible with strip or chart recorders (see Chapter 6).

Sound monitoring equipment can be expensive and the drawbacks of its use should be considered. For species recognition, echolocation calls must first be associated with their respective species by observing known individuals. Light tags or reflective bands are useful for this purpose (Section 2.3.). Most detection systems are limited in their range (usually under 20 m; Downes, 1982) and are directional so that only a relatively small area can be sampled. Not all species are equally detectable, depending upon frequencies and intensities of their echolocation calls. Some high frequency, low intensity species are only detectable at 1 m or less, and are thus under-represented relative to species producing high intensity, low frequency calls. Furthermore, in areas with diverse bat faunas, correct identification of species may not be possible. The limited range of ultrasonic detectors can also be a problem with species that fly at high altitude. For example, some molossids are known to fly at altitudes up to 1000 m (Williams et al., 1973; Griffin and Thompson, 1982; D. Thompson, pers. comm.). In such circumstances these bats may be monitored using helium-filled kite-balloons (see Griffin and Thompson, 1982).

3.3. Other Remote Monitoring Techniques

Other remote monitoring methods are available for specialized studies. Light emitter/detector pair series (such as those mentioned in photography above) may be arranged to monitor entry and exit from a roost site (Böhme and Natuschke, 1967). Breaking any light beam in the series will trigger a relay which may record the event on a strip recorder, tape-recorder, or other such device. By arranging two sets of emitter/detector arrays at the entrance to a roost a few cm apart, direction of the flight of bats breaking the beams can be determined with a simple timing circuit or other arrangement (e.g., Laufens, 1969; Daan, 1970). Emitter/detector pairs can also be arranged in confined spaces using fibre optics. Hamilton (1979) described such a system for monitoring flower visitation by hummingbirds by placing the fibre optic gap in the carolla of a flower.

Proximity detectors sense a change in capacitance in their surroundings as an animal approaches, producing a corresponding voltage output. Such detectors were developed for applications such as burglar alarms and anti-personnel mines. Hamilton (1979) developed the idea of proximity detectors for monitoring flower-visitation by hummingbirds which could be adapted for studies of flower-visiting bats. Such a system can be built around an inexpensive IC capacitance switch. The receiver of the detector is wound around the base of the monitoring flower. Approach by a bat could be recorded as an event or as an analog voltage which can be recorded on a tape recorder or field computer. If temperature-compensated and properly calibrated, such a system can measure the distance of the animal to the flower, allowing determination of the distance at which a decision to feed is made. Moreover, wingbeat fre-

quency can also be measured, which might be used to identify species in a large community. The resolution of the system could allow feeding rates to be determined for individual animals by the recorded rate of tongue flicks into the nectary of the flower. As an added feature of such a system, the voltage event can be used to trigger a camera to identify species or even color-banded bats.

Laufens (1969) used magnetic detectors for monitoring roosting activity, and this technique was adapted by Hamilton (1979) for electronically monitoring flower-visitation. The approach used by Hamilton was to wind a wire coil, supplied with a current source, around the carolla of a flower to create an inexpensive magnetic detector. Individual animals dusted with small amounts of ferrous powder were easily detected by the system. Laufens (1969) used ferrous wire inserted under the skin of the animal, or ferrous bands or tags, which alleviated the problem of the animals grooming off the powder.

Radar has been used extensively for studies of bird migration, but has not been widely applied to corresponding studies of bats. Williams et al. (1973) used various types of radar to observe high altitude flight of foraging columns of *Tadarida brasiliensis* in Texas and verified the method with visual observations from a helicopter. Such studies are, of course, extremely expensive, and generally require the assistance and cooperation of military radar installations; however, the technique may prove useful for special applications.

4. DATA COLLECTION AND RECORDING

Once the marking and observational techniques have been selected for a particular study, the type of sampling method and the means of recording the data must also be determined. Sampling methodology and data recording are broad topics which are discussed in detail in a number of excellent reviews (e.g., Altmann, 1974; Lehner, 1979).

Rarely can all events or behaviors be observed or recorded; thus, a sample must be taken. The sampling technique best suited to a particular study depends upon the type of information that is required and the practical limitations imposed by particular situations. Ideally a totally random sample should be obtained, although in practice this is seldom possible. For example, in making observations at a bat roost, a random sample of individual behavior could be made if all individuals were marked and if each individual in the roost was equally observable. Techniques such as focal animal, scan sampling, and instantaneous sampling can be used to overcome this obvious problem (Altmann, 1974; Lehner, 1979; Jacobson and Wiggins, 1982).

Focal animal sampling involves the recording of the behavior(s) of one individual over a predetermined sampling period, and Altmann (1974) suggests that this may be the best method available. It can be used, for example, to investigate individual differences in behavior related to sex, age, or reproductive condition.

Instantaneous and scan sampling involve recording the behavior(s) of an individual or individuals at predetermined time points, and are particularly valuable for determining time budgets (see Chapter 18).

Since many observations of bat behavior and ecology are made under low light conditions, and events often occur rapidly, data recording can be difficult. There are many useful recording techniques that can be employed (see Lehner, 1979, for more in-depth discussion). For many sampling techniques a digital stopwatch with an illuminated readout or an electronic metronome (e.g., Reynierse and Toevs, 1973) may be used as time indicators. Written notes can be made using an illuminated pen, a clip-on penlight, or a headlamp if this does not disturb the animals or, just as importantly, reduce the dark-adaptation of the observer. The problems of hand-written notes can be obviated by recording voice notes on a tape recorder for later transcription. Inexpensive (under US$

100), battery-operated, pocket-sized recorders are available. Voice activated (VOX) systems allow discontinuous notes to be made without wasting batteries or tape. The main disadvantage of recording voice notes is the time required for later transcription, and the added step of transcription which can result in additional data errors. These problems are usually outweighed by making more complete observations and minimizing disturbance to the animals.

Coded information can be recorded on a strip or chart recorder. Electrical signals activate marking pens, and discrete categories are marked on moving chart paper, eliminating the need for a stopwatch (see Lehner, 1979). A more sophisticated approach is to use a digital data recorder such as a lap computer (e.g., Datamyte 1000 series; Data-Mac Model 16; Omnidata Polycorder; MSI Model 80; TRS100 Computer). Detailed notes or discrete categories can be recorded against an accurate internal clock. Digitized data can later be analyzed on the lap computer, or dumped to a larger computer for further analysis. This approach has the obvious advantage of by-passing intermediate steps of data recording if computer analysis is to be used. This advantage may be offset to some degree by the possibility of error in keying in data in the dark. Data-gathering software has been developed for a number of portable and non-portable computers (e.g., TRS100, Apple II, Acorn BBC) by various users. The Acorn computer has a built-in, 4-channel, A/D (analog to digital) converter, and can be used for collecting data from a variety of monitoring instruments with analog voltage, resistance, or pulsed outputs (e.g., thermocouples, weather instruments, light emitter/detector arrays, bat detectors, etc.). Software for data-gathering and analysis is available for this device (see Chapter 6).

5. SUMMARY

Methods are described for marking and observing bats. Marking methods include metal and plastic bands, reflective bands, radiotransmitters, fluorescent powders, and radioisotope tags. Observational apparatus discussed includes night vision devices, low-light television, photography, acoustic monitors, and various remote monitoring techniques including proximity detectors and light beam triggers. None of these techniques or devices will be universally applicable to all species of bats. Some species are more prone to disturbance than others and thus require more remote observation; others may be "unobservable." The mass of the bat will dictate the size of marking device that can be successfully applied, and the mode of flight and prey capture may restrict the type of collars or tags that can be used. Inevitably, some trial and error is required before a workable, efficient system can be devised for a particular study, and considerable patience is usually needed. In all cases, there is no substitute for having background knowledge of the species under study before attempting any detailed marking or observational technique.

6. ACKNOWLEDGMENTS

We wish to thank the many people who provided details of unpublished studies and new techniques. We are especially grateful to M. B. Fenton, D. W. Thomas, P. Herbert, J. Wilkinson, and T. H. Kunz who read earlier drafts of this chapter and offered valuable comments and suggestions, and to K. Klinghammer who proofed the final draft. Our own research has been supported by grants from Sigma Xi and Sigma Xi Canada, the American Society of Mammalogists, Carleton University, the University of Manitoba (RMRB), and the Natural Sciences and Engineering Research Council of Canada.

7. REFERENCES

Abel, G. 1960. 24 Jahre Beringung von Fledermäusen im Lande Salzburg. Bonner Zool. Beitr., Sonderheft, 11:25-32.

Ahlen, I. 1981. Identification of Scandinavian bats by their sounds. Swed. Univ. Agr. Sci., Dept. Wildl. Ecol. Report 6, 56 pp.

Altmann, J. 1974. Observational study of behaviour: Sampling methods. Behaviour, 49:227-265.

Aldridge, H., and R. M. Brigham. (unpubl.). A test of the 5% rule of radio-telemetry: Load-carrying and manoeuvrability in an insectivorous bat.

Anthony, E. L. P., M. H. Stack, and T. H. Kunz. 1981. Night roosting and the nocturnal time budget of the little brown bat, *Myotis lucifugus:* Effects of reproductive status, prey density, and environmental conditions. Oecologia, 51:151-156.

Baker, R. R. 1978. The evolutionary ecology of migration. Holmes and Meier, New York, 1012 pp.

Balliot, M. 1964. Bilan de 25 années de baguage des chauves-souris en France. Pp. 9-53, *in* CRMMO Mus. Nation. Hist. Nat. Paris. Suppl. à la Rev. Mammalia, Paris.

Barbour, R. W., and W. H. Davis. 1969. Bats of America. Univ. Press of Kentucky, Lexington, 286 pp.

Barclay, R. M. R. 1982. Night roosting behavior of the little brown bat, *Myotis lucifugus.* J. Mammal., 63:464-474.

Barclay, R. M. R., M. B. Fenton, and D. W. Thomas. 1979. Social behavior of the little brown bat, *Myotis lucifugus.* II. Vocal communication. Behav. Ecol. Sociobiol., 5:137-146.

Batchelor, R. A., and J. R. MacMillan. 1980. A visual marking system for nocturnal animals. J. Wildl. Manage., 44:497-499.

Bateman, G. C., and T. A. Vaughan. 1974. Nightly activities of mormoopid bats. J. Mammal., 55:45-65.

Beaucournu, J. C. 1962. Observations sur le baguage des Chiroptères. Résultant et dangers. Mammalia, 26:539-565.

Bell, G. P. 1980. Habitat use and response to patches of prey by desert insectivorous bats. Can. J. Zool., 58:1876-1883.

Bell, G. P. 1985. The sensory basis of prey location by the California leaf-nosed bat, *Macrotus californicus* (Chiroptera: Phyllostomidae). Behav. Ecol. Sociobiol., 16:343-347.

Bell, G. P., and M. B. Fenton. 1986. Visual acuity, sensitivity, and binocularity in a gleaning, insectivorous bat, *Macrotus californicus* (Chiroptera: Phyllostomidae). Anim. Behav., 734:409-414.

Bell, G. P., G. A. Bartholomew, and K. A. Nagy.

1986. The roles of energetics, water economy, foraging behavior, and geothermal refugia in the distribution of the bat, *Macrotus californicus.* J. Comp. Physiol. B, 156: 441-450.

Bels, L. 1952. Fifteen years of bat banding in the Netherlands. Publ. Nat. Genoot. Limburg, 5:1-99.

Böhme, W., and G. Natuschke. 1967. Untersuchung der Jagdflugaktivität freilebender Fledermäuse in Wochenstuben mit Hilfe einer doppelseitigen Lichtschranke und einige Eregebnisse an *Myotis myotis* (Borkhausen, 1797) und *Myotis nattereri* (Kuhl, 1818). Säugtierk. Mitt., 15:129-138.

Bonaccorso, F. J., and N. Smythe. 1972. Punchmarking bats: An alternative to banding. J. Mammal., 53:389-390.

Bonaccorso, F. J., N. Smythe, and S. R. Humphrey. 1976. Improved techniques for marking bats. J. Mammal., 57:181-182.

Boogher, B., and Slusher, J. A. 1978. Successful photographic techniques through night vision devices. Bull., Ent. Soc. Amer., 24:203-206.

Bradbury, J. W. 1977. Lek mating behavior in the hammer-headed bat. Z. Tierpsychol., 45:225-255.

Bradbury, J. W., and L. H. Emmons. 1974. Social organization of some Trinidad bats. I. Emballonuridae. Z. Tierpsychol., 36:137-183.

Bradbury, J. W., and S. L. Vehrencamp. 1976. Social organization and foraging in emballonurid bats. I. Field studies. Behav. Ecol. Sociobiol., 1:337-381.

Brander, R. B., and Cochran, W. W. 1969. Radiolocation telemetry. Pp. 95-103, *in* Wildlife Management Techniques. (Giles, R. H., ed.) Wildlife Society, Washington, D.C., 633 pp.

Brooks, R. P., and W. E. Dodge. 1978. A night identification collar for beavers. J. Wildl. Manage., 42:448-452.

Brown, P. E. 1976. Vocal communication in the pallid bat, *Antrozous pallidus.* Z. Tierpsychol., 41:34-54.

Brown, P. E., T. W. Brown, and A. D. Grinnell. 1983. Echolocation, development, and vocal communication in the lesser bulldog bat, *Noctilio albiventris.* Behav. Ecol. Sociobiol., 13:287-298.

Buchler, E. R. 1976. A chemiluminescent tag for tracking bats and other small nocturnal animals. J. Mammal., 57:173-176.

Buchler, E. R. 1980. The development of flight, foraging, and echolocation in the little brown bat (*Myotis lucifugus*). Behav. Ecol. Sociobiol., 6:211-218.

Buchler, E. R., and S. B. Childs. 1981. Orientation to distant sounds by foraging big brown bats (*Eptesicus fuscus*). Anim. Behav., 29:428-432.

Burnett, C. D., and P. V. August. 1981. Time and energy budgets for dayroosting in a maternity colony of *Myotis lucifugus.* J. Mammal., 62:758-766.

Caccamise, D. F., and R. S. Heddin. 1985. An aerodynamic basis for selecting transmitter loads in birds. Wilson Bull., 97:306-318.

Chase, J. 1972. The role of vision in echolocating bats. Ph.D. Thesis, Indiana University, Bloomington, 191 pp.

Cochran, W. W. 1980. Wildlife telemetry. Pp. 507-520, *in* Wildlife Management Techniques Manual, 4th Edn., (Schemnitz, S.D., ed.). Wildlife Society, Washington, D.C.

Cockrum, E. L. 1969. Migration in the guano bat, *Tadarida brasiliensis.* Misc. Publ. 51, Univ. Kansas. Mus. Nat. Hist. Pp. 303-336.

Cope, J. B., E. Churchwell, and K. Koontz. 1961. A method of tagging bats with radioactive gold-198 in homing experiments. Proc. Indiana Acad. Sci., 70:267-269.

Daan, S. 1969. Frequency of displacements as a measure of activity of hibernating bats. Lynx, 10:13-18.

Daan, S. 1973. Activity during natural hibernation in three species of vespertilionid bats. Netherlands J. Zool., 23:1-71.

Davey, C. C., P. J. Fullager, and C. Kogon. 1980. Marking rabbits for individual identification and a use for betalights. J. Wildl. Manage., 44:494-497.

Davis, R. 1966. Homing performance and homing ability in bats. Ecol. Monogr., 36:201-237.

Davis, W. H. 1960. Band injuries. Bat Banding News, 1:1-2.

Davis, W. H. 1961. Band injuries. Bat Banding News, 2:30.

Davis, W. H. 1963. Anodizing bat bands. Bat Banding News, 4:12-13.

Davis, W. H. 1966. The new bat bands. Bat Banding News, 7:39.

Davis, W. H., R. W. Barbour, and M. D. Hassell. 1968. Colonial behavior of *Eptesicus fuscus.* J. Mammal., 49:44-50.

Dieterich, C. E., and E. Dodt. 1972. Structural and some physiological findings on the retina of the bat, *Myotis myotis.* Pp. 120-132, *in* Proc. VIII Symp. Internat. Soc. Clinical Electroretinography. (Wirth, A., ed.). Pacini, Pisa, Italy.

Dorgelo, J., and A. Punt. 1969. Abundance and "internal migration" of hibernating bats in an artificial limestone cave ("Sibbergroeve"). Lynx, 10:101-125.

Downes, C. M. 1982. A comparison of the sensitivities of three bat detectors. J. Mammal., 63:343-345.

Downing, R., and C. Marshall. 1959. A new plastic tape marker for birds and mammals. J. Wildl. Manage., 23:223-224.

Dwyer, P. D. 1963. Bat banding. Aust. Nat. Hist., 14:198-200.

Dwyer, P. D. 1965. Injuries due to bat banding. Pp. 19-23, *in* 3rd & 4th Ann. Report on Bat Banding in Australia. (Simpson, K. G., and E. Hamilton-Smith, eds.). Div. Wildl. Res. Tech. Paper No. 9., CSIRO, Melbourne, 24 pp.

Edgerton, H. E., P. F. Spangle, and J. K. Baker. 1966. Mexican freetail bats: Photography. Science, 153:201-203.

Eisentraut, M. 1960. Die Fledermausberingung, ihre Entwicklung, ihre Methode und ihre Bedeutung für die wissenschaftliche Forschung. (Mit Anhang: "Richtlinien für die Beringung von Fledermäusen" und "Bestimmungsschlüssel der heimischen Fledermausarten"). Kosmos, Stuttgart, 11:112-123.

Erkert, H. G. 1978. Sunset-related timing of flight activity in neotropical bats. Oecologia, 37:59-67.

Fenton, M. B. 1982. Echolocation calls and patterns of hunting and habitat use of bats (Microchiroptera) from Chillagoe, Queensland. Aust. J. Zool., 30:417-425.

Fenton, M. B., and G. P. Bell. 1981. Recognition of species of insectivorous bats by their echolocation calls. J. Mammal., 62:233-243.

Fenton, M. B., S. L. Jacobson, and R. N. Stone. 1973. An automatic ultrasonic sensing system for monitoring the activity of some bats. Can. J. Zool., 51:291-299.

Findley, J. S., and D. E. Wilson. 1974. Observations on the neotropical disk-winged bat, *Thyroptera tricolor* Spix. J. Mammal., 55:562-571.

Finley, R. B., Jr. 1959. Observation of nocturnal animals by red light. J. Mammal., 40:591-594.

Fitzwater, W. D., Jr. 1943. Color marking of mammals with special reference to squirrels. J. Wildl. Manage., 7:190-192.

Gaisler, J., and M. Nevrly. 1961. The use of colored bands in investigating bats. Acta Soc. Zool. Bohemoslov., 25:135-141.

Gifford, C., and D. R. Griffin. 1960. Notes on homing and migratory behavior of bats. Ecology, 41:378-381.

Gould, E. 1975. Neonatal vocalizations in bats of eight genera. J. Mammal., 56:15-29.

Greenhall, A. M., and J. L. Paradiso. 1968. Bats and bat banding. Publ. No. 72, Bur. Sport Fish. Wildl. Resour., Washington, D.C. 47 pp.

Griffin, D. R. 1958. Listening in the dark. Yale Univ. Press, New Haven, Connecticut, 413 pp.

Griffin, D. R. 1970. Migrations and homing of bats. Pp. 233-264, *in* Biology of Bats. Vol. 1. (W. A. Wimsatt, ed.), Academic Press, New York, 406 pp.

Griffin, D. R. 1971. The importance of atmospheric attenuation for the echolocation of bats (Chiroptera). Anim. Behav., 19:55-61.

Griffin, D. R., and D. Thompson. 1982. High altitude echolocation of insects by bats. Behav. Ecol. Sociobiol., 10:303-306.

Griffin, D. R., F. A. Webster, and C. R. Michael. 1960. The echolocation of flying insects by bats. Anim. Behav., 8:141-154.

Haarr, A. 1963. Anodizing bat bands. Bat Banding News, 4:26-27.

Hamilton, M. P. 1979. The application of electronic monitoring to the study of pollination ecology. M.S. Thesis, California State Polytechnic University, Pomona, 82 pp.

Hardin, J. W., and M. W. Hassell. 1970. Observations on waking periods and movements of *Myotis sodalis* during hibernation. J. Mammal., 51:829-831.

Harrison, T. M. 1983. Patterns of feeding and habitat use by little brown bats, *Myotis lucifugus* (Chiroptera: Vespertilionidae) over and around Lake Opinicon, Ontario, Canada. M.Sc. Thesis, Carleton Univ., Ottawa, Ontario.

Harvey, M. J. 1965. Detecting animals tagged with Co^{60} through air, soil, water, wood and stone. Trans. Kentucky Acad. Sci., 26:63-66.

Heerdt, P. F. van, and J. W. Sluiter. 1958. The Polish ear tags for the Dutch bats. De Levende Natur, Arnhem, 61:216.

Herreid, C. F., R. B. Davis, and H. L. Short. 1960. Injuries due to bat banding. J. Mammal., 41:398-400.

Hitchcock, H. B. 1957. The use of bird bands on bats. J. Mammal., 38:402.

Hitchcock, H. B. 1964. Survival of bats banded during hibernation. Bat Res. News, 5:29.

Hitchcock, H. B. 1965. Twenty-three years of bat-banding in Ontario and Quebec. Ontario Field Nat., 79:4-14.

Hope, G. M., and K. P. Bhatnagar. 1979. Electrical response of bat retinas to spectral stimulation: Comparison of four microchiropteran species. Experientia, 35:1189-1191.

Humphrey, S. R., A. R. Richter, and J. B. Cope. 1977. Summer habitat and ecology of the endangered Indiana bat, *Myotis sodalis.* J. Mammal., 58:334-346.

Jacobsen, N. K., and A. D. Wiggins. 1982. Temporal and procedural influences on activity estimated by time sampling. J. Wildl. Manage. 46:313-324.

Jones, C. 1976. Economics and conservation. Pp. 133-145., *in* Biology of Bats of the New World Family Phyllostomatidae. Part 1. (Baker, R. J., J. Knox Jones, and D. C. Carter, eds.). Texas Tech Univ. Press, Lubbock, 218 pp.

Keen, R., and H. B. Hitchcock. 1980. Survival and longevity of the little brown bat (*Myotis lucifugus*) in southeastern Ontario. J. Mammal., 61:1-7.

Kleiman, D. G., and T. M. Davis. 1974. Punchmark renewal in bats of the genus *Carollia.* Bat Res. News, 15:29-30.

Kunz, T. H. 1973. Resource utilization: Temporal and spatial components of bat activity in central Iowa. J. Mammal., 54:14-32.

Kunz, T. H., and E. L. P. Anthony. 1982. Age estimation and post-natal growth in the bat *Myotis lucifugus.* J. Mammal., 63:23-32.

Laufens, G. 1969. Untersuchungen zur Aktivitätsperiodik von *Myotis nattereri* Kuhl, 1818. Lynx, 10:45-51.

LaVal, R. K., and M. L. LaVal. 1980. Ecological studies and management of Missouri bats, with emphasis on cave-dwelling species. Terrestrial Ser. No. 8, Missouri Dept. Conserv., Jefferson City, 53 pp.

LaVal, R. K., R. L. Clawson, M. L. LaVal, and W. Caire. 1977. Foraging behavior and nocturnal activity patterns of Missouri bats, with emphasis on the endangered species *Myotis grisescens* and *Myotis sodalis.* J. Mammal., 58:592-599.

Lehner, P. N. 1979. Handbook of ethological methods. Garland STPM Press, New York, 403 pp.

Leonard, M. L., and M. B. Fenton. 1983. Habitat use by spotted bats (*Euderma maculatum,* Chiroptera: Vespertilionidae): Roosting and foraging behaviour. Can. J. Zool., 61:1487-1491.

McCracken, G. F. 1984. Communal nursing in Mexican free-tailed bat maternity colonies. Science, 223:1090-1091.

McCracken, G. F., and J. W. Bradbury. 1977. Paternity and genetic heterogeneity in the polygynous bat, *Phyllostomus hastatus.* Science, 198:303-306.

McCracken, G. F., and J. W. Bradbury. 1981.

Social organization and kinship in the polygynous bat, *Phyllostomus hastatus.* Behav. Ecol. Sociobiol., 8:11-34.

Miller, L. A., and H. J. Degn. 1981. The acoustic behavior of four species of vespertilionid bats studied in the field. J. Comp. Physiol., A, 142:67-74.

Morrison, D. W. 1978. Foraging ecology and energetics of the frugivorous bat *Artibeus jamaicensis.* Ecology, 59:716-723.

Nelson, J. E. 1964. Vocal communication in Australian flying foxes (Pteropodidae: Megachiroptera). Z. Tierpsychol., 21:857-870.

Nyholm, E. S. 1965. Zur Ökologie von *Myotis mystacinus* (Leisl.) und *M. daubentoni* (Leisl.) (Chiroptera). Ann. Zool. Fenn., 2:77-123.

O'Shea, T. J., and T. A. Vaughan. 1977. Nocturnal and seasonal activities of the pallid bat, *Antrozous pallidus.* J. Mammal., 58:269-284.

Perry, A. E., and G. Beckett. 1966. Skeletal damage as a result of band injury in bats. J. Mammal., 47:131-132.

Porter, F. L. 1978. Roosting patterns and social behavior in captive *Carollia perspicillata.* J. Mammal., 59:627-630.

Punt, A., and P. J. van Nieuwenhoven. 1957. The use of radioactive bands in tracing hibernating bats. Experientia, 13:51-54.

Racey, P. A., and S. M. Swift. 1985. Feeding ecology of *Pipistrellus pipistrellus* (Chiroptera: Vespertilionidae) during pregnancy and lactation. I. Foraging behaviour. J. Anim. Ecol., 54:205-215.

Reynierse, J. H., and J. W. Toevs. 1973. An ideal signal generator for time sampling observation procedures. Behav. Res. Meth. Inst., 5:57-58.

Sazima, I., and M. Sazima. 1977. Solitary and group foraging: two flower-visiting patterns of the lesser spear-nosed bat *Phyllostomus discolor.* Biotropica, 9:213-215.

Sazima, M., and I. Sazima. 1978. Bat pollination of the passion flower, *Passiflora mucronata,* in southern Brazil. Biotropica, 10:100-109.

Schemnitz, S. D. (ed.) 1980. Wildlife Management Techniques Manual. 4th edn. The Wildlife Society, Washington, D. C., 686 pp.

Simmons, J. A., M. B. Fenton, W. R. Ferguson, M. Jutting, and J. Palin. 1979. Apparatus for research on animal ultrasonic signals. Life Sci. Misc. Publ., R. Ont. Mus., 31 pp.

Slusher, J. A. 1978. Night vision equipment developments: Where we've been, where we are today, and where we're going. Bull. Ent. Soc. Amer., 24:197-200.

Southern, H. N., J. S. Watson, and D. Chitty. 1946. Watching nocturnal animals by infra-red radiation. J. Anim. Ecol., 15:198-202.

Stebbings, R. E. 1966. A population study of bats of the genus *Plecotus*. J. Zool., 150:53-75.

Stebbings, R. E. 1978. Marking bats. Pp. 81-94, *in* Animal Marking. (R. Stonehouse, ed.), University Park Press, Baltimore, Maryland.

Swift, S. M. 1980. Activity patterns of pipistrelle bats (*Pipistrellus pipistrellus*) in north-east Scotland. J. Zool., 190:258-295.

Thomas, D. W., M. B. Fenton, and R. M. R. Barclay. 1979. Social behavior of the little brown bat, *Myotis lucifugus*. I. Mating behavior. Behav. Ecol. Sociobiol., 6:129-136.

Thomson, C. E., M. B. Fenton, and R. M. R. Barclay. 1985. The role of infant isolation calls in mother-infant reunions in the little brown bat, *Myotis lucifugus* (Chiroptera: Vespertilionidae). Can. J. Zool. 63:1982-1988.

Thompson, D., and M. B. Fenton. 1982. Echolocation and feeding behaviour of *Myotis adversus* (Chiroptera: Vespertilionidae). Aust. J. Zool., 30:543-546.

Trapido, H., and P. E. Crowe, 1946. A wing-banding method in the study of the travels of bats. J. Mammal., 27:224-226.

Tuttle, M. D. 1979. Status, causes of decline, and management of endangered gray bats. J. Wildl. Manage., 43:1-17.

Tuttle, M. D., and D. Stevenson. 1982. Growth and survival of bats. Pp. 105-150, *in* Ecology of bats. (Kunz, T. H., ed.). Plenum Press, New York, 425 pp.

Twente, J. W., Jr. 1955. Aspects of a population study of cavern-dwelling bats. J. Mammal., 36:379-390.

Voûte, A. M. 1972. Contributions to the ecology of the pond bat, *Myotis dasycneme* (Boie, 1825). Unpubl. Doctoral dissertation, Universiteit Utrecht, Utrecht, 159 pp.

Wilkinson, G. S. 1985. The social organization of the common vampire bat. I. Pattern and cause of association. Behav. Ecol. Sociobiol., 17:111-121.

Williams, T. C., J. M. Williams, and D. R. Griffin. 1966. The homing ability of the neotropical bat *Phyllostomus hastatus*, with evidence for visual orientation. Anim. Behav., 14:468-473.

Williams, T. C., L. C. Ireland, and J. M. Williams. 1973. High altitude flights of the free-tailed bat, *Tadarida brasiliensis*, observed with radar. J. Mammal., 54:807-821.

Woodsworth, G. C., G. P. Bell, and M. B. Fenton. 1981. Observations of the echolocation, feeding behaviour, and habitat use of *Euderma maculatum* (Chiroptera: Vespertilionidae) in southcentral British Columbia. Can. J. Zool., 59:1099-1102.

Appendix 1. **Selected Commercially Available Equipment and Supplies for Marking and Observing Bats**

MARKING SUPPLIES

Aluminum Bands (rings)

> Gey Band and Tag Company
> P.O. Box 363
> Norristown, Pennsylvania
> 19404 USA

> Lambournes, Ltd.
> 170 Hampton Row
> Birmingham, England

> National Band & Tag Co.
> 721 York Street
> Newport, Kentucky
> 41071 USA

> L & M Bird Leg Bands
> P.O. Box 2943
> San Bernardino
> California 92406 USA

Plastic Split-rings

> A. C. Hughes
> 1 High Street
> Hampton Hill
> Middlesex TW12 1NA
> England

> L & M Bird Leg Bands
> P.O. Box 2943
> San Bernardino
> California 92406 USA

Reflective Tape

> 3M Company
> 3M Center
> St. Paul, Minnesota
> 55101 USA

Betalights

> Saunders-Roe Developments
> North Hyde Road
> Hayes, Middlesex
> UB3 4N3 England

Self-Powered Lighting Ltd
8 Westchester Plaza
Elmsford, New York
10523 USA

Cyalume

American Cyanamid Corp.
Organic Chemicals Division
Bound Brook
New Jersey 08805 USA

Fluorescent Powders

Radiant Color
2800 Radiant Road
Richmond, California
94804 USA

Punch Marker (Tattoo Outfit)
and Freeze Branding Equipment

Weston Manufacturing and
 Supply Company
1942 Speer Boulevard
Denver, Colorado 80204
USA

Nasco Corporation
Fort Atkinson
Wisconsin 53538 USA

Night Vision Devices
Scopes and Goggles

Baird Corporation
125 Middlesex Turnpike
Bedford, Massachusetts
01730 USA

Communication Systems of
 Virginia
2010 Clark Street
Richmond, Virginia
23228 USA

ITT, Electro-optical
 Products Division
7635 Plantation Road
Box 7065, Roanoke
Virginia 24019 USA

Lenzar Optics Corporation
1006 West 15th Street
Riviera Beach, Florida
33404 USA

Litton Systems, Inc.
Electron Devices Division

1215 South 52nd Street
Tempe, Arizona
85281-6987 USA

Varo, Inc.
Systems Division,
2201 West Walnut Street
P.O. Box 469051
Garland, Texas
75046-9015 USA

Wild Heerbrugg Ltd.
CH-9435 Heerbrugg
Switzerland

Low-light Television Cameras

Mitsubishi Electronic Corporation
2-3 Marunuchi, 2-Chome
Chiyoda-ku
Tokyo 100, Japan

RCA
New Holland Avenue
Lancaster, Pennsylvania
17604 USA

Field Data Recorders

DataMyte Corporation
14960 Industrial Road
Minnetonka
Minnesota 55345 USA

Epic Data
P.O. Box 314
Powder Springs
Georgia 30073 USA

Forestry Suppliers
P.O. Box 8397
Jackson
Mississippi 39204 USA

MSI Data Corporation
350 Fischer Avenue
Costa Mesa
California 92626 USA

Omnidata International
P.O. Box 3489
Logan, Utah 84321 USA

Universal Data, Inc.
3960 M-15
Clarkston
Michigan 48016 USA

Chapter 5

Survey and Census Methods

Donald W. Thomas

Département de Biologie
Université de Sherbrooke
Sherbrooke, Québec JIK 2R1
Canada

and

Richard K. LaVal

Apdo 10164
San Jose, Costa Rica

1. INTRODUCTION

Behavioral and ecological studies of bats frequently require some index of numbers within a designated area, whether it is a colony, cave, habitat, or some broader geographic region. Depending on the objectives of the study, this index may be relative and qualitative or absolute and quantitative. In this chapter we provide an overview of the survey and census methods that may be employed in bat studies. Because of the increasing number of research reports on bats, we cannot cover the entire literature in detail. Instead we cite selected examples to give direction to future researchers. Clearly the approaches taken toward surveying or censusing bats depend on the field logistics, the inventiveness and experience of the investigator, and the available information base for a particular species. For this reason we do not intend this chapter to be a recipe for surveying or censusing, nor do we endorse particular methods. Methods suitable in one situation may be entirely inappropriate in another. Obviously the researcher must convince him/herself and others of the effectiveness of a given method in a particular situation.

2. SURVEYS AND CENSUSES AT ROOSTS

The majority of published studies employing survey or census methods to estimate bat numbers have focused on roosting aggregations. Roosting groups may consist of one or more species of active bats roosting either in enclosed areas such as caves, hollow trees, or man-made structures or in the foliage of vegetation (see Kunz, 1982). They may also involve inactive bats hibernating in enclosed areas such as caves and mines. Roosts lend themselves to survey or census studies because 1) they are relatively easily located, 2) they frequently harbour moderate to large numbers of individuals, 3) they can be relatively permanent, and 4) in the case of enclosed roosts, they may be logistically simple to study. Estimates of bat numbers may be restricted to specific roosts or may be extended to infer population sizes within some specified region (e.g., Humphrey and Kunz, 1976). To extend this to a regional scale, considerably more information is required than can be collected simply by counting bats at roosts. Specifically, the researcher should 1) establish the precise geographic limits to the study region, 2) determine the number and size of roosts present in the study region, 3) be assured that all roosts have been located, 4) determine how far individuals in these roosts disperse on a daily or seasonal basis and how this compares with the defined limits of the region, and 5) determine whether individuals from other areas disperse into the study region. Without this knowledge biologically meaningful population size and density estimates are likely to remain elusive and illusory.

3. METHODS USED AT ENCLOSED ROOSTS

Survey and census methods aimed at estimating the numbers of bats within single enclosed roosts fall into two broad categories: 1) those which monitor bats from outside the roost and generally attempt to avoid or minimize disturbance and 2) those which monitor bats from inside the roost and usually entail minor to major levels of disturbance. Clearly the former approach is most desirable, but this is not always practical.

3.1. Monitoring from the Outside

3.1.1. Visual Emergence Counts

Enclosed roosts usually have a limited number of routes that bats use when exiting or entering. These provide convenient locations for making visual counts, usually undertaken at dusk when bats emerge over a relatively short period (e.g., Easterla and Watkins, 1970; Humphrey and Cope, 1976; Jacobsen and duPlessis, 1976; Humphrey et al., 1977; Norton and Van der Merwe, 1978; Barclay et al., 1980; Swift, 1980). One or more observers placed in positions where they can backlight flying bats against the sky can tally individuals exiting and entering the roost with hand counters. It is important to keep track of bats re-entering the roost both during the early "light sampling" period when the first bats frequently loop and re-enter and later when individuals returning from foraging may overlap with others exiting for the first time. Without keeping tally of re-entering bats, some individuals would be counted twice, resulting in overestimates of colony size. In cases where the horizon or sky is obstructed and backlighting is impossible, night vision devices (see Chapter 4) with or without a supplementary light source may be profitably employed.

At roosts housing only one species, counting individuals is not difficult and relatively large numbers of bats can be accurately recorded. The upper size of a "manageable" colony depends on the number of exits and the rate at which bats emerge. Even low numbers of bats can overwhelm an observer if individuals emerge in rapid succession. In practice, counts of several thousands can be accomplished from single exits (e.g., Dwyer, 1966; Kunz, 1974). Jacobsen and duPlessis (1976) reported counts as high as 9000 *Rousettus aegyptiacus*. At roosts numbering in the hundreds, counts can be extremely accurate. At *Pipistrellus pipistrellus* roosts, Swift (1980) had counts that varied by as little as 0.5% over successive weeks. It is likely that the accuracy of counts decreases when colony sizes exceed 500, and it may be important to have two independent observers at large colonies to verify accuracy.

In situations where the numbers overwhelm the observer, bats can be counted at intervals (e.g., one minute every five min), but this approach assumes that bats emerge as a continuous stream rather than in bursts. When these counts are plotted against time, the area under the curve represents an estimate (without confidence limits) of the total population (Norton and Van der Merwe, 1978).

Where colonies consist of more than one species, it may still be possible to obtain accurate counts for each species. Co-habiting species often differ sufficiently in size, flight style, or emergence times to permit visual separation (e.g., Gaisler, 1979; Swift and Racey, 1983).

A major drawback to visual emergence counts is that they are labor intensive. Because the emergence period is synchronized among colonies, each observer is limited to watching but one exit route per night. Some roosts may have several exit routes and require more than one observer. This places severe limitations on the number of roosts that can be adequately studied in a given period.

3.1.2. Electronic Counting Devices

Where visual emergence counts are not possible, where there are insufficient observers to cover all roosts, or where longitudinal records of colony size are required, electronic counting devices may prove valuable. Difficulties with design and reliability aside, one of the most promising electronic devices is the photo-electric "beam splitter" (Nyholm, 1965; Böhme and Natuschke, 1967; Englander and Laufens, 1968; Watkins, 1971; Daan, 1970, 1973; Voûte et al., 1974). This consists of either a single or a double bank of light beams which cause a counter to be activated when interrupted by a flying bat (or any other opaque object). The light emitters and photoreceptors are usually built into a short square or rectangular tunnel which can be mounted to cover an exit. By ensuring that all exits are either blocked or covered by counters, all the bats in a roost can be forced to fly through, interrupt the light beams, and so be counted. Single bank systems, having only one vertical column of light emitter/detector pairs, cannot separate bats leaving a roost

from those re-entering and so will consistently overestimate colony size. On these devices, counters would have to be stopped and read immediately following the emergence of the last bat to gather meaningful colony size information. Double-bank systems can detect the direction of flight by the sequence in which the banks are interrupted and thus can add to and subtract from the count. If continuous or interval records of the count are kept the total colony size (= the highest count) and the number of individuals inside or outside the roost at any time can be determined. Double-bank systems can perform a function analogous to what Swift (1980) achieved in her labor-intensive study and thus can free up a researcher to accomplish other tasks.

Beam splitters suffer some drawbacks compared with visual emergence counts. They are incapable of distinguishing between species and therefore cannot provide accurate counts at mixed species roosts. Just as observers can be overwhelmed by bursts of emerging bats, so can beam splitters. Several bats interrupting one or more beams simultaneously may be recorded as a single individual. As with any remote sensing system, the lack of an on-site observer precludes any evaluation of potential problems.

Although beam splitters can provide accurate counts of the numbers of bats using a particular roost (i.e., perform a census), other systems may be used to obtain information on the relative size of colonies (i.e., perform a survey). Ultrasonic bat detectors (see Simmons et al., 1979 and Chapter 6) using narrow or broad-band microphones and coupled with a chart recorder or other counting device (Fenton, 1970; Fenton et al., 1973; Fullard and Barclay, 1980) can potentially provide a record of the number of "bat passes" at an exit if the roosts are used by echolocating bats. If roosts are used by more than one bat species which differ in their echolocation frequencies, tuneable broad band detectors such as the QMC Mini Bat Detector may be used with each detector tuned to "listen" to and count individuals of each species (but see Thomas and West, 1985).

Ultrasonic detectors positioned at or near roost exits cannot provide an absolute count of the number of individuals present in a roost. They can only provide a relative index of activity. Bat passes do not directly correspond with the number of individuals present since bats exiting in close succession may not be counted as separate events, and bats that circle above the detector tend to inflate bat-pass counts.

Two other devices may be useful for counting bats. Doppler shift radar (Watson, 1970) might be used to scan exits from a distance and detect bats by the Doppler shift caused by their wing beats. Similarly, Polaroid ultrasonic distance detectors as are used in auto-focus cameras might be modified to detect and count bats (Anonymous, 1984).

3.1.3. Photographic Methods

Some roosts house such large populations that neither visual emergence counts nor any electronic devices can be used to estimate numbers. For example, some bats (e.g., *Tadarida brasiliensis*) roosting in caves can number from hundreds of thousands to millions. A column of bats emerging from such roosts can be so dense that the only means of estimating numbers is by photographing sections of the column at intervals and counting bats in these samples. Photographic techniques have been used to estimate the numbers of *T. brasiliensis* and *Pteronotus fuliginosus* (Humphrey, 1971; Altenbach et al., 1979; Rodriguez-Duran and Lewis, 1985). Humphrey (1971) photographed a column of emerging *T. brasiliensis* at 1 min intervals throughout the emergence period as the bats departed along a narrow canyon, using a knotted rope to provide scale in the pictures. By interrupting the column periodically and timing the passage of this break along a 79m distance he was able to estimate the bats' average flight speed. Counts of bat numbers in each frame coupled with the column dimensions and the flight speed provided the information necessary to estimate the total popu-

lation. A similar procedure was used by Rodriguez-Duran and Lewis (1985) to estimate the numbers of *P. fuliginosus.* They calculated a standard error of the estimate based on the number of bats per photograph. Altenbach et al. (1979) used a modified version of the photographic technique because the bats could not be conveniently photographed outside the cave. They combined results of still pictures taken at 30 sec intervals at a constriction inside the cave entrance with 5 sec runs of high speed motion pictures at the same site. From the motion pictures they were able to measure the bats' flight speed and the proportion of bats "committed" to exiting. The still photographs provided a total count at each interval. From the flight speed, the proportion of bats exiting, and the total bats per unit volume they estimated the total population.

Photographic techniques such as these are appropriate only in situations where large numbers of bats form a cohesive column of small diameter and relatively homogeneous density. Photographic techniques are less likely to be useful at multi-species roosts or at roosts where the bats disperse widely at the exit. For additional discussion of photographic methods, see Chapter 8.

3.1.4. Captures

Mist nets, Tuttle traps (Tuttle, 1974), or other specialized traps (Gaisler et al., 1979) set to cover roost exits may capture some proportion or all of the individuals leaving the roost and so provide an estimate of roost population size. In most situations, however, some individuals avoid being caught (see Chapter 1), so capture techniques will frequently underestimate colony sizes. Possibly more important is the level of disturbance caused by such disruption. Individuals may abandon roosts following trapping, therefore such methods should not be used for repeated roost sampling. By forcing bats to move, captures at one roost may also affect the numbers of others in the region, thus it is imperative to mark all captured bats in some fashion.

3.2. Monitoring from the Inside

3.2.1. Direct Counts and Surface Area Estimates

When in their roosts, bats may hang in conspicuous positions alone, in small clusters, in large densely packed clusters, or they may roost in inaccessible crevices. Except by forcing bats out with a long wire or forceps there is no method for accessing and counting bats in crevices. For those bats which hang in visible and conspicuous locations within roosts and are not easily disturbed, direct counts can be used. A deep red filter (e.g., Kodak Wratten filter No. 29) placed over a headlamp will minimize disturbance when making observations (Thomas et al., 1979).

Many species commonly hibernate in large, densely-packed, single species clusters which are too large and tightly packed to permit extensive head counts. In these cases surface area estimates coupled with a measure of the mean packing density for the given species can be used to estimate numbers. In theory this is a simple and straightforward approach that should give reliable results if surface areas can be accurately measured. However, in practice, irregular cluster shapes and uneven surfaces conspire to make surface area estimates difficult. Moreover, packing densities are variable between species, within species for different age classes, and apparently within species for the same age class (Table 1). For example, packing densities of juvenile *Miniopterus schreibersii* are approximately twice as high as those for adults (Dwyer, 1966). Within adult size classes, packing densities reported by different authors vary by 50% and 59% for *Myotis sodalis* and *Miniopterus schreibersii* respectively (Table 1). Reasons for these differences are unclear, but they probably represent true differences in packing density due to environmental effects as well as observer error. For whatever reason, this variation is large and would have a serious effect on the accuracy of population estimates. Clearly each researcher should calculate packing density for the species under study and verify that it is constant for all locations within and between study sites.

3.2.2. Stains and Other Signs

Regular use of roosts by bats can leave signs from which population size can be inferred regardless of whether the bats are present or not. Tuttle (1976) reported that clusters of *Myotis grisescens* left stains on cave ceilings if they used the same sites consistently over long time periods (years). Using a packing density and the surface areas of the stains, he estimated historic population sizes for *M. grisescens* in some caves. Since these stains could only result from long term use of the sites, they represent a good average population size rather than transient fluctuations. It is important to note that some cave ceilings stain faster than others, thus some caves and mines may not show evidence of use as clearly as others.

When bats are actively foraging on a daily basis, they leave signs in roosts from

Table 1. Reported packing densities for clusters of hibernating bats.

Species	Bats/m^2	References
Myotis austroriparius	1613	Rice, 1957
Myotis grisescens	1828	Tuttle, 1976
Myotis sodalis	3226	LaVal and LaVal, 1980
Myotis sodalis	2151	A. Hicks, pers. comm.
Miniopterus schreibersii adults	1763	Dwyer, 1966
Miniopterus schreibersii juveniles	3957	Dwyer, 1966
Miniopterus schreibersii adults	2800	Norton and Van der Merwe, 1978

deposits of feces. Analogous to measuring cluster or stain areas to estimate populations, feces can be used to provide an outline of the roost area used by bats. Since feces fall directly downward and do not roll any great distance, the area covered by feces represents a vertical projection of the cluster area onto the floor. If the cluster substrate is flat and parallel to the floor the feces area will equal the cluster area. However, any irregularities or angling of the ceiling relative to the floor will cause the feces area to underestimate the true cluster area.

At night roosts many insectivorous bats form tight clusters in crevices, such as mortices in barn beams (e.g., Anthony et al., 1981; Barclay, 1982; Kunz, 1982). Having fed prior to roosting, these bats provide evidence of their presence from deposits of feces. Anthony et al. (1981) estimated the use of night roosts (bat hours of use) from the mass of feces collected beneath the roosts. To make these calculations, they assumed that all roosting individuals arrived with full stomachs and that the gut load and fecal production rates of all individuals of a particular sex or age group were represented by the means collected from trapped bats. While this is probably true on good foraging nights, on cool nights when feeding rates are depressed this method may underestimate the use of night roosts by bats.

3.2.3. Captures

Bats which hang freely from the roost substrates but are too active to permit head counts may be captured with hand nets and held in bags or cylinder cages until all individuals have been accounted for. Bats which roost in crevices cannot be accurately counted by this means, despite the fact that most may appear to be in flight and available for capture at any one time. Gaisler (1975) captured and marked all free flying *Myotis daubentonii* in several roosts, yet on subsequent visits found that the majority of bats were unmarked. Although immigration cannot be ruled out, it is likely that the majority of

bats had avoided capture on the first occasion despite his best efforts.

3.2.4. Capture-Mark-Recapture

If the bats are too active to be counted and all individuals cannot be captured in their roost, mark-recapture may be an appropriate means of estimating their numbers. Dwyer (1966) estimated the population sizes of *Miniopterus schreibersii* in caves by releasing marked individuals into the cave, disturbing the bats in order to mix the marked and unmarked bats, then collecting a sample of the flying population. The total number of bats was estimated from a simple Lincoln Index. Mark-recapture techniques, however, are subject to a number of assumptions (section 6), the most important of which is that all marked and unmarked bats are equally "catchable". If "experienced" marked bats are more difficult to catch than others, the resulting population estimates will be inflated.

3.2.5. Photographic Methods

Daan (1970, 1973) described a photo-electric beam splitter that could trigger a camera and flash for recording bat movements inside caves or mines in winter. With this apparatus it was possible to identify the direction of flight and the species, so he was able to monitor additions to and deletions from populations of hibernating bats. Where bat traffic is low and periodic counts inside hibernacula are unacceptable, this apparatus might be useful in monitoring changes in population size at single hibernacula during the winter period.

Where direct observations and counts result in major disturbances to roosting bats, cameras equipped with remote shutter releases may be useful for monitoring numbers (see Chapter 8). In West Africa, *Hypsignathus monstrosus* roost in groups of 3-15 individuals where overhanging vegetation forms a semi-enclosure. Roosts will be permanently abandoned if disturbed, making counting difficult (D. W. Thomas, pers. obs.). A camera installed during the night might successfully record group size during the day without causing any disturbance.

4. ESTIMATING NUMBERS OF FOLIAGE ROOSTING BATS

Bats which roost singly or in small groups in foliage are extremely difficult to locate and surveys or censuses of these species are problematical. Noteable exceptions are those of McClure (1942) and Constantine (1966), who both observed *Lasiurus borealis* roosting in trees. By making regular searches of all available roost trees, the numbers of roosting bats could be estimated. However, it is important to note that two factors influenced the reliability of these estimates. Not all bats were located on each census, so the counts were adjusted by some arbitrary factor to arrive at the final population estimates. In these studies the only trees available for roosts were in a small town, thus population and density estimates could not be considered as an average for the region. It is likely that some bats dispersed considerable distances from their day roosts, so the actual density of foraging bats would be much lower than the roosting density.

Some foliage roosting pteropodids, most notably *Eidolon helvum* and *Pteropus* spp., congregate in large colonies numbering from thousands to millions (e.g., Nelson, 1965; Huggel-Wolf and Huggel-Wolf, 1965). The large numbers of bats and their excitability make counting difficult. Mutere (1980) used two different techniques to estimate the size of an *E. helvum* colony in Kampala, Uganda. In one approach he counted the number of bats roosting in "average" trees and arrived at a total by counting the number of occupied trees. In another approach he counted the number of bats roosting in average "patches" and multiplied this by the number of patches in the roost. Although the results of the two methods differed by as much as 33%, they were generally in good agreement. Neither

technique consistently over- or underestimated colony size.

5. ESTIMATING BAT ABUNDANCE IN HABITATS OR OTHER GEOGRAPHIC AREAS

5.1. Summing Roost Counts

In situations where roosts can be easily located and the number of bats counted, it may be possible to estimate the population density of a given species within a specified region by summing the roost counts. This approach requires making several assumptions that may or may not hold. Roosts must be approximately evenly distributed throughout a broad region. Daily or short term emigration from the defined area resulting from commuting and foraging movements must be balanced by immigration from adjacent areas. Gaisler et al. (1979) used this approach to estimate the population density of the hole roosting species, *Nyctalus noctula,* in Czechoslovakia. Using intensive searches for roost holes and trapping and banding individuals at these sites throughout the summer, they attempted to locate and account for all individuals within two 2.25km^2 study areas. The resulting population structure predicted from this approach, however, was unrealistic. The number of juvenile males had to be adjusted to equal juvenile females, and the number of adult females had to be adjusted to account for a sliding proportion of 1.8 to 1.6 juveniles per adult female between July and September. The resulting discrepancy between the actual captures and the theoretical population size (differing by over a factor of two in some months) underlines the difficulties and the logistical problems with this approach.

Perez (1973) attempted to estimate population densities of *Pteropus marianus* on Guam using a similar approach. He made monthly strip surveys to locate roosts in three undelineated areas and transformed roost counts to the number of bats/100 acres. It is difficult to interpret these results, however, since not all roosts were located, the search areas were selected because they had relatively high bat abundances, and because the areas used by these roosting bats was unknown.

Where bats roost in readily identified and accessible vegetation structures (such as the rolled young leaves of banana and *Heliconia*) some populations may be censused by hand. For example, *Myotis bocagei, Pipistrellus nanus,* and *Thyroptera tricolor* all can be easily captured in their roosts (Findley and Wilson, 1974; Brosset, 1976; LaVal and LaVal, 1977). If the distribution of these roosts is homogeneous, the number of bats can be translated to population densities directly. If the distribution of roosts is patchy, then information on the foraging ranges is required before meaningful density estimates can be made.

5.2. Visual Counts of Foraging Bats

Bats frequently begin foraging when it is sufficiently bright to permit sightings and species recognition. In this situation, strip counts or variable circular plot techniques analogous to those used in bird surveys might be employed. Gaisler (1979) trained 16-30 observers to recognize three size classes of bats corresponding with *P. pipistrellus* (small), *Plecotus austriacus* (medium), and *Eptesicus serotinus* (large), and had the observers record all the bats seen along transects of variable length during a period of 30 minutes after dusk. These counts provided the data base for subsequent population density estimates but could not be used directly. *Eptesicus serotinus* was more easily detected than the other species. To compensate, their numbers were adjusted downward (by some unspecified means) before density estimates were made. Densities on the census routes were used to calculate overall habitat densities. The reliability of such estimates is unclear. The areas actually sampled by observers when searching for bats depends on the light levels and other environmental variables. Coupled with

inter-observer variability this can result in important biases. Ralph and Scott (1981) provide a comprehensive review of factors affecting bird censuses by these same techniques.

5.3. Ultrasonic Detectors

Ultrasonic detectors are receiving increasing attention as a tool for assessing general bat activity in various habitats (e.g., Fenton, 1970, 1982; Voûte, 1972; Kunz and Brock, 1975; Bell, 1980; Fenton and Thomas, 1980; Fenton and Bell, 1981; Ahlen, 1980, 1981). Simple narrow band detectors tuned to a single frequency cannot discriminate between species, but they can provide an index of habitat use and relative bat abundance (Fenton, 1970; Fenton et al., 1973). More sophisticated broad band detectors can, in many cases, permit the recognition of individual species and so refine these activity data (see Simmons et al., 1979 and Chapter 6). Bat detectors provide no more than a relative index of activity (a survey) because there is no one-to-one correlation between bat passes and the number of individuals present. Moreover, they cannot be used to compare activity levels between species. More intense echolocators and those using lower frequencies are detected at greater distances than less intense or higher frequency echolocating species (Griffin, 1971, Fenton and Fullard, 1981). In fact, low intensity echolocators may not be detected at all. Despite these limitations, ultrasonic detectors are rapidly proving to be one of the most valuable tools available for surveying free-ranging echolocating bats.

5.4. Vampire Bites

Foraging vampire bats leave evidence of their presence through bite wounds on livestock or other animals. Because the number of bite wounds can be correlated with the number of foraging individuals (Turner, 1975), this provides an indirect means of estimating populations. Schmidt et al. (1970) showed that 80% of the vampire bats (*Desmodus rotundus*) at their study sites in Mexico fed on cattle. By removing known numbers of bats from the population and monitoring the reduction in fresh wounds, they were able to calculate the mean number of bats feeding per wound. With this number a simple regression of the number of bats removed from the population against the decrease in wound incidence could permit the original population to be calculated (although they did not do so). This removal/response method is conceptually similar to the removal curve technique applied to small mammal trap grids (Otis et al. 1978); however, in the case of vampire bats, it would be difficult to judge the area being sampled.

Turner (1975) inferred the size of the resident vampire bat population on one ranch in Costa Rica from four sets of data. From measures of the number of cattle bitten per night, the number of vampire bats feeding from the same wound through the night, the number of days between feedings for each bat, and the number of feeding bouts per night for each individual he arrived at a population estimate (88-176 individuals) that agreed well with his estimates from roost searches. Capture and banding results, however, indicated that on a given night the total number of individuals present in the area far exceeded the number estimated from either bites or roost surveys. Turner (1975) used this discrepancy to indicate that there was a large transient population that was excluded from feeding on livestock by the resident population. Such an explanation requires further testing.

5.5. Mist Netting and Trapping

A phenomenon known to anyone netting or trapping the same site over successive days is the regular decline in catch rate with time (e.g., Kunz and Brock, 1975; Humphrey et al., 1977). This is likely due to the avoidance of nets by or emigration of previously captured individuals. MacArthur and MacArthur (1974) relied on this pattern to estimate bird populations. Regressing the number of new unmarked individuals caught/unit time

against the total catch previous to that sample on a logarithmic scale shows a steep negative slope. The Y-intercept of this line estimates the total original population. Manly (1977) refined this model to permit the calculation of resident and drifting populations of birds at a site as well as the variances of these estimates. To our knowledge this approach has never been applied to bats, but it may prove valuable. A major limitation, however, is the problem of identifying the area being sampled by an array of nets.

6. ESTIMATES FROM CAPTURE-MARK-RECAPTURE

Mark-recapture techniques potentially provide a method of estimating population sizes over large areas and over long time periods. A detailed review of these techniques is beyond the scope of this chapter and we refer readers to Brownie et al. (1978), Otis et al. (1978), Pollock (1981), and White et al. (1982) for excellent reviews.

All mark-recapture models, whether the simple Petersen or Lincoln Indexes or the more sophisticated multiple mark-recapture models, are based upon five assumptions which must hold true if the estimates are to be reliable: 1) animals carrying marks must not suffer higher mortality than those not carrying marks, 2) once released, marked animals must mix at random within the study population, 3) marked animals must be no more or less easily captured than unmarked "naive" animals, 4) marks must not be lost or overlooked in samples, and 5) some models permit no additions or deletions to the population through birth, immigration, death, and/or emigration during the study period. The development of computer-based multiple mark-recapture methods (see Otis et al., 1978) has relaxed the latter assumption, providing a more realistic modeling of populations. Many models permit the population to be subdivided into sex and age classes that may differ in "catchability" (assumption 3); however, no models can account for varying catchability between marked and unmarked animals within the same class unless this is measured directly and entered as a known variable. No models can account for non-random distributions of marks in the population. These latter two assumptions (2 and 3) are the ones most likely to affect the reliability of estimates in bat studies and should be subjected to close examination. Non-random segregation by sex and age is common within roosts and hibernacula as well as over geographic areas (Bezem et al., 1960; Tinkle and Milstead, 1960; Humphrey and Cope, 1976; Stevenson and Tuttle, 1981), thus mark-recapture studies should subdivide the population on the basis of sex and age. Few data are available to permit the evaluation of varying catchability, but Stevenson and Tuttle (1981) showed that for *M. grisescens* the marking experience affected capture rates and distributions for at least 10 years. The problem of addressing the assumption of equal catchability is additionally complicated by the lack of statistical tests sufficiently sensitive to detect departures (Roff, 1973). Roff (1973: p. 47) took a pessimistic view of the value of mark-recapture methods: "The general insensitivity of the present statistical methods for testing the assumption of equal catchability makes the method of mark-recapture of limited use."

Mark-recapture methods have not often been used in bat studies, and those efforts that have been made preceded the development of rigorous and sophisticated models (see also Chapter 10). Dwyer (1966) used the simple Lincoln Index to estimate roost populations. Tinkle and Milstead (1960) also used a simple Lincoln Index to estimate populations of hibernating *M. velifer.* In this case their own data show that emigration and segregation by sex occurred during the study and these violations cast doubt on the validity of their population estimates. Herzig-Straschil and Robinson (1978) also used the Lincoln Index to estimate an *R. aegyptiacus* roost population and, although their recapture rate was low, they achieved comparable results (3%

difference) on two recapture occasions. The largest mark-recapture effort undertaken to date was by Sluiter et al. (1956) and Bezem et al. (1960) involving *Myotis dasycneme, M. daubentonii, M. emarginatus, M. mystacinus, M. myotis,* and *Rhinolophus hipposideros* based on more than a decade of marking. Not all hibernacula present in the region (South Limburg, Netherlands) were visited, and they presented little data on the movements of marked individuals among hibernacula, thus it is difficult to assess whether their population estimates pertain to a region or only to individual hibernacula.

The paucity of mark-recapture studies conducted since the 1950-1960 period may be attributed to a heightened awareness of the assumptions inherent in these models and the difficulties in satisfying them in bat studies. There has also been an increased awareness of the detrimental effects of banding on some species (e.g., Humphrey and Kunz, 1976; Chapter 10). Certainly any future studies should at least make special efforts to include confidence limits on population estimates.

7.   SUMMARY AND CONCLUSIONS

In this chapter we have provided an overview of direct and indirect methods for surveying and censusing roosting or free-ranging bats. These methods may involve simple observations or captures or may require somewhat sophisticated electronic equipment. All of the outlined methods involve inherent biases and assumptions and it is imperative that investigators explicitly state what these are and where their data violate them. Without consideration of biases, assumptions, and natural variability in the data, many of the survey and census results will remain difficult to interpret. In reviewing the literature on bat population studies involving any surveys or censuses, three points are striking. Relative to students of other areas of ecology, "bat biologists" have often been lax in making efforts to specify and test the assumptions, biases, and limitations inherent in the methods they employ. Variances and confidence limits on the resulting population estimates are generally non-existent. Furthermore, the exact surface area or geographic region relating to the population estimates is rarely clearly defined. It would seem imperative that future studies make special efforts to increase the rigor of quantitative population measurement.

It is all too frequently tempting to ignore biases and assumptions that are violated when undertaking studies in order to achieve the goal—having a number representing population size or density. It is often felt that inaccurate estimates are better than no estimates at all. On this point we disagree. Well intentioned but inaccurate estimates have a way of becoming entrenched in the literature, used, and accepted as "truth". Given that census and density information form the basis for evaluating the health of populations and directing future conservation efforts, we believe that extreme caution should be exercised before spurious values are entered into the literature. Work on the endangered gray bat, *Myotis grisescens,* might be taken as a good example of the cautious application of surveys and censuses to conservation-oriented research (Tuttle, 1976; Tuttle, 1979; Stevenson and Tuttle, 1981).

8. ACKNOWLEDGMENTS

We thank T. H. Kunz, J. Gaisler, and M. B. Fenton for valuable comments on manuscript drafts.

9. REFERENCES

Ahlen, I. 1980-81. Field identification of bats and survey methods based on sounds. Myotis, 18-19:128-136.

Ahlen, I. 1981. Identification of Scandinavian bats by their sounds. Swedish Univ. Agric. Sci., Dept. Wildl. Ecol., Rep. 6, Uppsala, 56 pp.

Altenbach, J. S., K. N. Geluso, and D. E. Wilson. 1979. Population size of *Tadarida brasiliensis* at Carlsbad Caverns in 1973. Pp. 341-348. *in* Biological investigations in the Guadalupe Mountains National Park, Texas. (H. H. Genoways and R. J. Baker, eds.). Proc. Trans. Series No. 4., Nat. Parks Service, 442 pp.

Anonymous. 1984. Polaroid ultrasonic ranging system handbook: Application notes/technical papers. Polaroid Corp., Cambridge, Massachusetts, 40 pp.

Anthony, E. L. P., M. H. Stack, and T. H. Kunz. 1981. Night roosting and the nocturnal time budget of the little brown bat, *Myotis lucifugus:* Effects of reproductive status, prey density, and environmental conditions. Oecologia, 51:151-156.

Barclay, R. M. R. 1982. Night roosting behavior of the little brown bat, *Myotis lucifugus.* J. Mammal., 63:464-474.

Barclay, R. M. R., D. W. Thomas, and M. B. Fenton. 1980. Comparison of methods used for controlling bats in buildings. J. Wildl. Manage., 44:502-506.

Bell, G. P. 1980. Habitat use and response to patches of prey by desert insectivorous bats. Can. J. Zool., 58:1876-1883.

Bezem, J. J., J. W. Sluiter, and P. F. Van Heerdt. 1960. Population statistics of five species of the bat genus *Myotis* and one of the genus *Rhinolophus* hibernating in the caves of S. Limburg. Arch. Neerl. Zool., 13:511-539.

Böhme, W., and G. Natuschke. 1967. Untersuchung der Jagdflugaktivitat freilebender Fledermause in Wochenstuben mit Hilfe einer doppelseitigen Lichtschranke und einige Ergebnisse an *Myotis myotis* (Borkhausen, 1797) und *Myotis natteri* (Kuhl, 1818). Saugetierk. Mitt., 15:129-138.

Brosset, A. 1976. Social organization in the African bat, *Myotis bocagei.* Z. Tierpsychol., 42:50-56.

Brownie, C., D. R. Anderson, K. P. Burnham, and D. S. Robson. 1978. Statistical inference from band recovery data: A handbook. U.S. Fish Wildl. Serv. Res. Publ., 212 pp.

Constantine, D. G. 1966. Ecological observations on lasiurine bats in Iowa. J. Mammal., 47:34-41.

Daan, S. 1970. Photographic recording of natural activity in hibernating bats. Bijd. Dierk., 40:13-16.

Daan, S. 1973. Activity during natural hibernation in three species of vespertilionid bats. Netherlands J. Zool., 23:1-71.

Dwyer, P. D. 1966. The population pattern of *Miniopterus schreibersii* (Chiroptera) in North-eastern New South Wales. Aust. J. Zool., 14:1073-1137.

Easterla, D. A., and L. Watkins. 1970. Nursery colonies of evening bats (*Nycticeius humeralis*) in northwestern Missouri and southwestern Iowa. Trans. Missouri Acad. Sci., 4:110-117.

Engländer, H., and G. Laufens. 1968. Aktivitätsuntersuchungen bei Fransenfledermäusen (*Myotis nattereri* Kuhl, 1818). Experientia, 24:618-619.

Fenton, M. B. 1970. A technique for monitoring bat activity with results obtained from different environments in southern Ontario. Can. J. Zool., 48:847-851.

Fenton, M. B. 1982. Echolocation calls and patterns of hunting and habitat use of bats (Microchiroptera) from Chillagoe, North Queensland. Aust. J. Zool., 30:417-425.

Fenton, M. B., and G. P. Bell. 1981. Recognition of species of insectivorous bats by their echolocation calls. J. Mammal., 62:128-136.

Fenton, M. B., and J. H. Fullard. 1981. Moth hearing and the feeding strategies of bats. Amer. Sci., 69:266-274.

Fenton, M. B., S. L. Jacobson, and R. N. Stone. 1973. An automatic ultrasonic sensing system for monitoring the activity of some bats. Can. J. Zool., 51:291-299.

Fenton, M. B., and D. W. Thomas. 1980. Dry season overlap in activity patterns, habitat use, and prey selection by sympatric African insectivorous bats. Biotropica, 12:81-90.

Findley, J. S., and D. E. Wilson. 1974. Observations on the neotropical disk-winged bat, *Thyroptera tricolor* Spix. J. Mammal., 55:562-571.

Fullard, J. H., and R. M. R. Barclay. 1980. Audition in spring species of arctiid moths as a possible response to different levels of insectivorous bat predation. Can. J. Zool., 58:1745-1750.

Gaisler, J. 1975. A quantitative study of some populations of bats in Czechoslovakia (Mammalia: Chiroptera). Acta Sci. Nat., Brno, 9:1-44.

Gaisler, J. 1979. Results of bat census in a town (Mammalia: Chiroptera). Vestnik. Cesk. Spol. Zool., 43:7-21.

Gaisler, J., V. Hanák, and J. Dungel. 1979. A contribution to the population ecology of *Nyctalus noctula* (Mammalia: Chiroptera). Acta Sci. Nat., Brno, 13:1-38.

Griffin, D. R. 1971. The importance of atmospheric attenuation for the echolocation of bats (Chiroptera). Anim. Behav., 19:55-61.

Herzig-Straschil, B., and G. A. Robinson. 1978. On the ecology of the fruit bat, *Rousettus aegyptiacus leachi* (A. Smith, 1828) in the Tsitsikama Coastal National Park. Koedoe, 21:101-110.

Huggel-Wolf, H. J., and M. Huggel-Wolf. 1965. La biologie d'*Eidolon helvum* (Kerr) (Megachiroptera). Acta Tropica, 22:1-10.

Humphrey, S. R. 1971. Photographic estimation of population size of the Mexican free-tailed bat, *Tadarida brasiliensis*. Amer. Midl. Nat., 86:220-223.

Humphrey, S. R., and J. B. Cope. 1976. Population ecology of the little brown bat, *Myotis lucifugus*, in Indiana and North-central Kentucky. Spec. Publ., Amer. Soc. Mammal., 4: 79 pp.

Humphrey, S. R., and T. H. Kunz. 1976. Ecology of a Pleistocene relict, the western big-eared bat (*Plecotus townsendii*), in the southern Great Plains. J. Mammal., 56:470-494.

Humphrey, S. R., A. R. Richter, and J. B. Cope. 1977. Summer habitat and ecology of the endangered Indiana bat, *Myotis sodalis*. J. Mammal., 58:334-346.

Jacobsen, N. H. G., and E. DuPlessis. 1976. Observations on the ecology and biology of the cape fruit bat, *Rousettus aegyptiacus leachi* in the eastern Transvaal. S. Afr. J. Sci., 72:270-273.

Kunz, T. H. 1974. Feeding ecology of a temperate insectivorous bat (*Myotis velifer*). Ecology, 55:693-711.

Kunz, T. H. 1982. Roosting ecology of bats. Pp. 1-55. *in* Ecology of bats. (T. H. Kunz, ed.). Plenum Press, New York. 425 pp.

Kunz, T. H., and C. E. Brock. 1975. A comparison of mist nets and ultrasonic detectors for monitoring flight activity of bats. J. Mammal., 56:907-911.

LaVal, R. K., and M. L. LaVal. 1977. Reproduction and behavior of the African banana bat, *Pipistrellus nanus*. J Mammal., 58:403-410.

LaVal, R. K., and M. L. LaVal. 1980. Ecological studies and management of Missouri bats, with emphasis on cave dwelling species. Terrest. Ser. Missouri Dept. Conserv., 8:1-56.

MacArthur, R. H., and A. T. MacArthur. 1974. On the use of mist nets for population studies of birds. Proc. Nat. Acad. Sci., 71:3230-3233.

Manly, B. F. J. 1977. The analysis of trapping records for birds trapped in mist nets. Biometrica, 33:404-410.

McClure, H. E. 1942. Summer activities of bats (genus *Lasiurus*) in Iowa. J. Mammal., 23:430-434.

Mutere, F. A. 1980. *Eidolon helvum* revisited. Pp. 145-150. *in* Proc. 5th Int. Bat Res. Conf. (D. E.

Wilson and A. L. Gardner, eds.). Texas Tech Univ. Press, Lubbock. 434 pp.

Nelson, J. E. 1965. Movements of Australian Pteropodidae (Megachiroptera). Anim. Behav., 13:544-557.

Norton, P. H., and M. Van der Merwe. 1978. Winter activity of bats in a Transvaal highveld cave. S. Afr. J. Sci., 74:216-220.

Nyholm, E. S. 1965. Zur Ökologie von *Myotis mystacinus* (Leisl.) und *M. daubentonii* (Leisl.). Ann. Zool. Fenn., 2:77-123.

Otis, D. L., K. P. Burnham, G. C. White, and D. R. Anderson. 1978. Statistical inference from capture data on closed animal populations. Wildl. Monogr., 62:1-135.

Perez, G. S. A. 1973. Notes on the ecology and life history of the Pteropodidae on Guam. Period. Biol., 75:163-168.

Pollock, K. H. 1981. Capture-recapture models: a review of current methods, assumptions and experimental design. Pp. 426-435. *in* Estimating the numbers of terrestrial birds. (C. J. Ralph and J. M. Scott, eds). Studies in avian biology. No. 6., Allen Press Inc., Lawrence, Kansas, 630 pp.

Ralph, C. J., and J. M. Scott, (eds.). 1981. Estimating numbers of terrestrial birds. Studies in avian biology. No. 6., Allen Press Inc., Lawrence, Kansas, 630 pp.

Rice, D. W. 1957. Life history and ecology of *Myotis austroriparius* in Florida. J. Mammal., 38:15-32.

Rodriguez-Duran, A., and A. R. Lewis. 1985. Seasonal predation by merlins on sooty mustached bats in western Puerto Rico. Biotropica, 17:71-74.

Roff, D. A. 1973. An examination of some statistical tests used in the analysis of mark-recapture data. Oecologia, 12:35-54.

Schmidt, U., A. M. Greenhall, and W. Lopez-Forment. 1970. Vampire bat control in Mexico. Bijd. Dierk., 40:74-76.

Simmons, J. A., M. B. Fenton, W. R. Ferguson, M. Jutting, and J. Palin. 1979. Apparatus for research on animal ultrasonic signals. Life Sci. Misc. Publ. R. Ont. Mus., 31 pp.

Sluiter, J. W., P. F. Van Heerdt, and J. J. Bezem. 1956. Population statistics of the bat, *Myotis mystacinus,* based on the marking-recapture method. Arch. Neerl. Zool., 12:63-88.

Stevenson, D. E., and M. D. Tuttle. 1981. Survivorship in the endangered gray bat (*Myotis grisescens*). J. Mammal., 62:244-257.

Swift, S. M. 1980. Activity patterns of pipistrelle bats (*Pipistrellus pipistrellus*) in north-east Scotland. J. Zool., 190:285-295.

Swift, S. M., and P. A. Racey. 1983. Resource partitioning in two species of vespertilionid bats (Chiroptera) occupying the same roost. J. Zool., 200:249-259.

Thomas, D. W., M. B. Fenton, and R. M. R. Barclay. 1979. Social behavior of the little brown bat, *Myotis lucifugus.* I. Mating behavior. Behav. Ecol. Sociobiol., 6:129-136.

Thomas, D. W., and S. D. West. 1985. On the use of ultrasonic detectors for bat species identification and the calibration of the QMC Mini Bat Detector. Can. J. Zool., 62:2677-2679.

Tinkle, D. W., and W. W. Milstead. 1960. Sex ratios and population density in hibernating *Myotis.* Amer. Midl. Nat., 63:327-334.

Turner, D. C. 1975. The vampire bat. Johns Hopkins Press, Baltimore, Maryland, 145 pp.

Tuttle, M. D. 1974. An improved trap for bats. J. Mammal., 55:475-477.

Tuttle, M. D. 1976. Population ecology of the gray bat (*Myotis grisescens*): philopatry, timing and patterns of movement, weight loss during migration, and seasonal adaptive strategies. Occas. Paper Mus. Nat. Hist., Univ. Kansas, 54:1-38.

Tuttle, M. D. 1979. Status, causes of decline, and management of endangered gray bats. J. Wildl. Manage., 43:1-17.

Voûte, A. M. 1972. Contributions to the ecology of the pond bat, *Myotis dasycneme* (Boie, 1825). Unpublished doctoral dissertation, Universiteit Utrecht., 159 pp.

Voûte, A. M., J. W. Sluiter, and M. P. Grimm. 1974. The influence of the natural light-dark cycle on the activity rhythm of pond bats (*Myotis dasycneme* Boie, 1825) during summer. Oecologia, 17:221-243.

Watkins, L. C. 1971. A technique for monitoring the nocturnal activity of bats with comments on the activity patterns of the evening bat, *Nycticeius humeralis.* Trans. Kansas Acad. Sci., 74:261-268.

Watson, A. 1970. Electronic aids to the identification of bats in flight and to their study under natural conditions. Bijd. Dierk., 40:99-102.

White, G. C., D. R. Andersen, K. P. Burnham, and D. L. Otis. 1982. Capture-recapture and removal methods for sampling closed populations. Los Alamos Natl. Lab., Los Alamos, New Mexico, 235 pp.

Chapter 6

Detecting, Recording, and Analyzing Vocalizations of Bats

M. Brock Fenton[1]

Department of Biology
Carleton University
Ottawa, Ontario
K1S 5B6 Canada

1. INTRODUCTION

Bats are among the most vocal of animals, in some instances producing over 200 calls per second. Most species use the echoes of sounds they produce to detect prey items and other objects in their paths (e.g., Griffin, 1958; Novick, 1977; Simmons and Stein, 1980). The sounds of bats, particularly those involved with echolocation, are often labeled as being "ultrasonic," implying that they are beyond the range of human hearing (arbitrarily, 20 kHz). This generalization is incorrect, since some species of Microchiroptera produce echolocation calls that are readily audible to humans (Fenton and Bell, 1981). Moreover, the tendency to treat echolocation sounds as being audible to humans, and distinctly different from echolocation calls, also is incorrect. Most bats also rely on vocalizations to some extent in communication (reviewed in Fenton, 1985), including the use of echolocation calls (Barclay, 1982; Leonard and Fenton, 1984).

Vocalizations of bats can provide a window on their behavior and allow relatively easy access to information about their ecology. Of special note in terms of echolocation are "feeding buzzes," the high pulse-repetition rates associated with attempted captures of prey (Griffin, 1958). The importance of feeding buzzes to bat researchers is that they permit unambiguous identification of foraging bats.

The purpose of this chapter is to examine different ways to detect, record, reproduce, and analyze the vocalizations of bats. The amount and nature of information needed about the animals and/or their vocalizations will dictate the selection of apparatus. Readers are referred to a general treatment of ultra-

[1]Present Address: Department of Biology, York University, Downsview, Ontario M3J 1P3 Canada

sonic sounds (Sales and Pye, 1974), a review of bat detectors (Griffin, 1975), and descriptions of some of the equipment that is available to study the ultrasonic sounds of animals (Simmons et al., 1979a; Pye, 1983a, 1983b). Several papers discuss the use of bat detectors and the identification of bats by their echolocation calls (e.g., Andersen and Miller, 1977; Simmons et al., 1979b; Ahlen, 1980, 1981; Fenton and Bell, 1981; Downes, 1982; Fenton, 1982; Fenton et al., 1983; Miller and Andersen, 1983; Ahlen et al., 1983-1984). An excellent overview of echolocation can be found in Busnel and Fish (1980). A discussion of echolocation in bats from an ecological perspective is given in Fenton (1984).

General treatments of sound are available in handbooks produced by companies that manufacture instruments for the study of sound (e.g., General Radio—Peterson and Gross, 1974; Bruel and Kjaer—Hassal and Zabseri, 1978) and in basic textbooks of physics and acoustics. Instruments and apparatus for the study of bat vocalizations, including a

component-by-component consideration of the elements, are outlined in Fig. 1. Distinctions are made between detection of sounds, recordings, playbacks, and analyses. A list of selected instruments for recording vocalizations of bats is given in Appendix 1.

2. DETECTION

The apparatus reviewed in this section can be used to detect the presence of ultrasonic sounds and, in some cases, to identify the frequencies involved (see Table 1).

2.1. Narrow Band Microphone

The simplest and least expensive detector of ultrasonic sound ("bat detector") uses the output of a narrowly tuned crystal as a transducer (Fig. 2). The transducer (microphone) with associated circuitry (Simmons et al., 1979a) provides an audio representation of sounds at the frequency to which such crys-

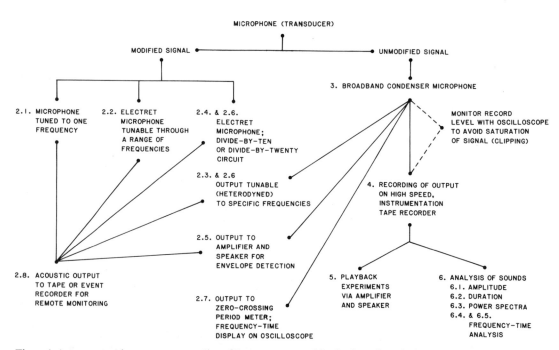

Figure 1. A component-by-component outline of the apparatus used for the detection, playback, recording, and analysis of vocalizations. Numbered headings correspond to sections in the text. Also see Table 1.

Table 1. Apparatus for detecting the vocalizations of bats. The instruments mentioned here are all battery operable, and all produce an output that permits the observer to distinguish between passing and feeding bats. Prices refer to approximate U.S. dollars. Versatility of output refers only to the context of signal detection. Species identification (ID) refers to the utility of the instrument in identification of echolocating bats by their calls. Also see Fig. 1 and text (heading adjacent to type of transducer corresponds to sections in text). Westek refers to detectors having a divide-by-ten circuit. The Uppsala (D-940) detector operates in a divide-by-ten or divide-by-twenty mode. The QMC S200 detector is referred to as having a "countdown" mode that reduces the incoming signal by 4, 8, 16, or 32.

Sections	Type of Transducer	Means of Detection	Means of Display	Relative Cost	Species ID[1]	Other Equipment Required	Versatility of Output	Available Instruments
2.1	tuned crystal	narrowly tuned	audio	≤200	+	headphones	poor	leak detectors
2.2	electret	tunable	audio	≤200	+++	none	good	QMC mini
2.4	electret	÷ by 10	audio	<1000	++++	none	good	Westek
2.3 & 2.6	broadband condenser	tunable	audio	>1000	+++	none	very good	QMC S100, S200, D-940
2.4 & 2.6	broadband condenser	÷ by 10, or 20	audio	>1000	++++	none	very good	QMC S100, S200, D-940
2.5	broadband condenser	envelope	audio	>1000	?	none	poor	QMC S100, S200
2.7	broadband condenser	period meter	visual	>2000	+++++	period meter oscilloscope	excellent	use broadband condenser mic

[1] Increasing levels of effectiveness at identification of species from + to ++++.

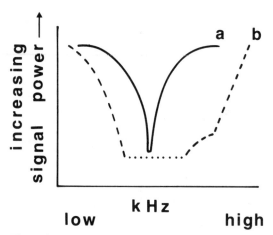

Figure 2. A comparison of narrowly tuned "a" and broadband "b" microphones, illustrating changes in the threshold to signals of different frequencies. The broadband microphone "b" shows a flat response to some frequencies (. . . .) and a variable response across others (- - - -).

make them inoperable. The extra cost to waterproof them is justified.

2.2.   Tunable Broadband Electret Microphone

A more versatile bat detector is one that relies on an electret microphone that is sensitive over a broad range of frequencies and can be tuned to specific frequencies (Fig. 2). One such model is available commercially as the QMC Mini Bat Detector (QMC Instruments Ltd.). This instrument allows the operator to scan through a range of frequencies (10 to 180 kHz), although only one frequency can be monitored with maximum sensitivity at any given time. The acoustic output, representing the animals' ultrasonic sounds, indicates the amount of energy at different frequencies. Differences in output, from a sharp "tick" through a "putt" to a more tonal "chirp" (Fig. 3) are distinctive, often permitting one species to be distinguished from another. These instruments are useful for identifying potential netting and trapping sites (Chapter 1) and

tals are tuned. These simple instruments, available commercially as "leak detectors," are designed to detect hissing sounds of leaks in high pressure gas lines. They are relatively directional but useful in situations where the vocalizations of bats include significant energy in the frequency to which the transducer is tuned (usually 40 kHz). This kind of instrument can be valuable in studies where the echolocating bats include the range of frequencies (frequency sweep) covered in their calls. Researchers that have been interested in the activity patterns of bats, whose echolocation calls include energy at 40 kHz, have used these detectors to good advantage (e.g., Fenton et al., 1973; Kunz and Brock, 1975). They can also be a valuable asset in public education programs; simple design, ease of construction, and low cost also make them suitable for classroom (laboratory) projects.

Important limitations of these detectors include the relatively narrow tuning of the transducer (some species are not detectable). An important practical limitation is the susceptibility of some transducers to water; droplets of rain or high humidity can rapidly

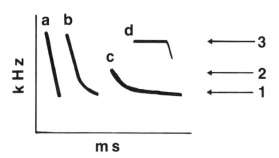

Figure 3. Frequency-time displays (sonograms) of four hypothetical echolocation calls showing how frequency changes over time. A bat detector tuned to frequency 1 would register call "a" as a sharp "tick," call "b" as a "putt" sound, and call "c" as a tonal "chirp"; at frequency 1, call "d" would not be detected. The audio output of the tuned detector, from "tick" through "putt" to "chirp," reflects the amount of energy at the frequency to which the instrument is tuned. When tuned to a frequency of 2, calls "a", "b", and "c" would be registered as sharp "ticks." At frequency 3, calls "a" and "b" would produce sharp "ticks," whereas call "d" would result in a long tonal output; call "c" would not be registered.

for making field surveys of echolocating bats (see Chapter 4 and Fenton et al., 1983). Their insensitivity to more than one frequency at any given time is a major limitation.

2.3. Tunable Broadband Condenser Microphone

A similar arrangement of a broadband, condenser microphone (Fig. 2) and circuitry, permitting tuning to a particular frequency (heterodyning), uses a condenser microphone (Section 3). One of the earliest commercially available bat detectors (Holgate Ultrasonic Detector) works on this heterodyne principle. Currently, another commercially available bat detector (QMC S100) uses such a system. Compared to the tunable electret microphones, detectors having condenser microphones are bulkier and more expensive. However, condenser microphones are more versatile, since they can provide unmodified output of the original ultrasonic signal (Fig. 1).

2.4. Divide-by-Ten (Countdown) Detector

The electret microphone or broadband condenser microphone, with its broader frequency ranges, can be operated with different circuitry to provide an audible sound representing the entire vocalization. Such a detector, described by Andersen and Miller (1977) and Miller and Andersen (1983) is based on a "divide-by-ten" (countdown) circuit. The output of this detector may enable an observer to distinguish between one species of bat and another by their echolocation calls. Moreover, it has the considerable advantage of permitting the entire range of frequencies commonly used by bats to be scanned simultaneously. Such a system also facilitates preliminary analysis of sounds (Section 6), although details of sound pressure-levels and harmonics are lost (Andersen and Miller, 1977; Miller and Andersen, 1983). The Westek Bat Monitor (Westek Services, Inc.) includes a divide-by-ten circuit and an electret microphone. The QMC S200 Detector incorporates a countdown (divide-by-ten) circuit and a broadband condenser microphone.

2.5. Envelope Detection

The output of a broadband microphone can be fed into an amplifier and audio speaker to produce an audible signal representing the envelope of an ultrasonic pulse. Such detectors are often more sensitive than tuned models, but the output provides no information about the frequencies of the vocalizations. This means that envelope detectors are less versatile than the tunable instruments described above. The QMC S100 and S200 both can be used as envelope detectors.

2.6. Uppsala Detector

An ultrasonic detector (D-940) described by Ahlen et al., (1983-1984) and I. Ahlen and L. Pettersson (pers. comm.) incorporates two ultrasonic conversion systems: an amplitude linear frequency-division system and a highly sensitive heterodyne system. The advantage of having two systems is that they can be monitored simultaneously with stereo headphones and recorded on a cassette tape-recorder for later analysis. In the frequency division mode, two scales can be selected, 1/10 (divide-by-ten) or 1/20 (divide-by-twenty). This means that the original frequency range of 0-200 kHz is compressed to the range of 0-20 or 0-10 kHz, respectively. This detector is equipped with a high-pass filter in the frequency division mode to filter extraneous noises. It also has the facility to record spoken comments (the heterodyne signal is temporarily replaced by a direct microphone signal). This detector includes a digital, frequency read-out that displays the frequency at the maximum amplitude of the last emitted burst of sound.

An advantage of the D-940 detector, over the QMC S200 detector (countdown mode) or a divide-by-ten detector, is that it gives the best agreement with the original signal in both frequency and amplitude. In other systems, the amplitude information is either lost or the waveform does not conform to the original signal (see Figs. 1 and 4-6 in Ahlen et al., 1983).

A recent improvement in the D-940 detector is a time-expansion unit, which can be used to store electronic signals (within limited time segments) into a digital memory (I. Ahlen and L. Pettersson, pers. comm.). This signal can be read out at slower speeds (e.g., 1/10) and recorded on an ordinary tape recorder. The result of incorporating a time-expansion circuit is equivalent to recording on an instrument tape recorder and then playing it back at reduced speed. This improved unit may eliminate the need for heavy and expensive instrumentation tape recorders. Moreover, this time-expanded signal can facilitate immediate identification of different species and improve documentation for rapid analysis.

2.7. Period Meter

The output of a broadband condenser microphone (Section 3) can also be analyzed by a zero-crossing period meter (Simmons et al., 1979a) to provide a frequency-time (oscilloscope) display of an acoustical signal (Fig. 3). This provides the observer with a sound "picture" or sonogram of a vocalization showing how frequency changes with time. This display can often permit the calls of species to be distinguished from one another (Fenton and Bell, 1981; Fenton, 1982; Fenton et al., 1983). The apparatus can also be used for frequency-time analysis (Section 6.4).

The principal disadvantage of the period meter, in detection of bat calls, is that an observer watching an oscilloscope display cannot simultaneously watch for bats. Furthermore, strong harmonics may produce misleading signals. The advantage of using a period meter is the ability to scan a broad bandwidth (adjustable in most designs of period meters) to allow the study of vocalizations of several species (Fenton and Bell, 1981). Detection with a period-meter system has been the basis for ecological studies of habitat use by sympatric species (e.g., Bell,

1980). Period meters are not available commercially, but they can be assembled by competent electronics technicians.

2.8. Remote Monitoring

The output of the detection systems can be monitored remotely as outlined above. The simplest means is to tape record (on a cassette recorder) the acoustic output of the detector. Alternatively, the output can be recorded on an event recorder using an appropriate amplifier (e.g., Fenton et al., 1973). The advantage of an event recorder is in the speed of analysis; disadvantages include loss of detailed information and the inability to distinguish ultrasonic emissions from other sources (e.g., insects).

3. BROADBAND CONDENSER MICROPHONES

These include electrostatic or condenser microphones in which a thin layer of plastic (mylar) separates two metal surfaces that form the plates of a condenser (Kuhl et al., 1954). Vibration of the mylar head causes changes in the capacitance and encodes vibrational information into changes in voltage. With appropriate amplification (Fig. 8 in Simmons et al., 1979a), the signal can be registered over a broad bandwidth (< 4 to > 200 kHz) without modification. This original signal can then be processed in a variety of ways involving recording, playback, analysis, or heterodyning, to produce an acoustic output at specific frequencies.

Broadband condenser microphones are sensitive to changes in humidity and the mylar on the microphone head is particularly fragile. The broadband, unmodified output of these microphones, however, makes them highly versatile, allowing use of several detection modes (Section 2). Microphone designs are available commercially from QMC Instruments Ltd., with (QMC S100) or without (QMC SM1) heterodyne circuitry, and with a countdown (divide-by-ten) circuit

(QMC S200). Bruel and Kjaer (B & K) produces a quarter inch (3 mm) microphone that is sensitive to frequencies over 100 kHz; however, it is an expensive, high-precision instrument that is relatively insensitive at distances more than a few meters (Griffin, 1975). It is best suited for laboratory situations where the distances between the animal and microphones are short.

An important characteristic of a microphone is the flatness of its response across the frequency range. Not all microphones are equally sensitive to sounds at different frequencies (Fig. 2). Some microphones, like some auditory systems, are sharply tuned to specific frequencies or they are tunable to several frequencies (Section 2). Other microphones are sensitive to sounds over a broad range of frequencies (Fig. 2). B & K microphones that are operable with measuring amplifiers and used to measure the intensity of sounds are flat over the specified frequency range. Because the flatness of a microphone's responses influences the sounds it detects, and the apparent energy at different frequencies in these sounds, the response curve of the microphone is an important characteristic. Thus, the threshold of a microphone to signals at different frequencies has important implications in the analysis of different sound components.

4. RECORDING

The choice of a tape recorder will depend upon the frequencies in the signals to be recorded. Instrumentation tape-recorders with direct record boards are ideal for recording sounds of bats. The frequency response of the tape recorder is, in part, a function of the tape speed at which it is operated (e.g., at 76 cm/sec the bandwidth extends to 150 kHz, at 152 cm/sec it reaches 300 kHz). Recorders operable at tape speeds of 38 cm/sec are usually sensitive to frequencies up to 30 kHz.

A disadvantage of instrumentation tape recorders, is that they are approximately 10

times more expensive than high-quality audio-frequency recorders. An excellent instrument tape-recorder, manufactured by Racal Thermionic Ltd., is operable through a wide range of tape speeds (up to 152 cm/sec), using AC (110 or 220 volts) or DC (12 to 34 volts) power supplies.

A potentially serious problem associated with the recording of animal vocalizations involves the signal-to-noise ratio (Section 7.1). One facet of this problem is the minimum intensity of sound needed to generate an electric voltage greater than the internal electrical noise of the microphone (its threshold). Amplification of output from the microphone, resulting from the signal in question, will not change this sensitivity since the internal noise is also amplified. Lowering the threshold of the microphone necessitates reduction of this internal electrical noise relative to the signal (Fig. 4). The internal noise level of some microphones makes them virtually unusable outside of a laboratory setting (Griffin, 1975).

Another problem is that artifacts may be added to a recorded signal. The saturation of the input results in clipping of sound waves when the circuit is overloaded. The effects of clipping can be demonstrated by considering

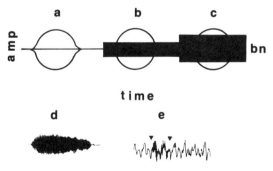

Figure 4. Five time-amplitude displays showing how increasing background noise ("a" through "c") obscures the signal, with a deteriorating signal-to-noise ratio. Displays "a," "b," and "c" are hypothetical; "d" and "e" are displays of recorded bat echolocation calls showing one ("d") with a good signal-to-noise ratio, and another ("e", call is between arrows) where the signal is barely detectable against the background noise.

the spectral differences between sounds composed of sine versus square waves (Fig. 5). Clipping associated with signal saturation produces a square wave, adding overtones or harmonics to the signal; this is undesirable when the signal is to be analyzed or played back in behavioral experiments.

By monitoring the incoming signal one can minimize the changes in saturation. The most effective means to accomplish this is through the time-amplitude display of the input on an oscilloscope. By adjusting the sweep rate (horizontal or time scale) an observer can see the sound waves of the incoming signal (even at high frequencies) and adjust the amount of gain or attenuation (the recording level) accordingly. If a Racal (Store 4 D) tape recorder is used, I suggest that the recorded signal be monitored instead of the incoming signal, since this permits one to see what is actually being recorded onto the tape. Such monitoring should be done through the output jack on the instrument. If a Racal recorder is used to record bat calls one should either cover (with tape) the recording-level window or ignore the display, since the response times of the needles in the display

are greater than the duration of many bat signals. One cannot rely upon this sound meter to detect saturated signals.

When dealing with signals which are audible to the human ear, it is reasonable to rely on one's perception of the incoming signal to identify and correct distortion. Incoming ultrasonic signals should always be monitored with an oscilloscope display. One should not purchase a high-speed instrumentation tape recorder with the capacity to record ultrasonic sound unless an oscilloscope is available.

A major problem encountered in field detection of bat vocalizations concerns the changes in the position of bats relative to the microphone. A flying bat may in the space of a few seconds be anywhere from 1 cm to 10 m from the microphone, and be in front of or behind it. These changes in position can produce a series of recorded signals ranging from totally saturated to barely above the threshold of the microphone. This situation has important implications for descriptions of how the sounds of bats change under different circumstances.

In spite of these caveats, recording bat vocalizations in the field can significantly improve our understanding of bat behavior, especially when coupled with direct behavioral observations.

5. PLAYBACK EXPERIMENTS

Recorded vocalizations of bats can be amplified (Fig. 16, in Simmons et al., 1979a) and played back through speakers. Although some audio tweeters [e.g., Kef T27, Technics Ribbon Tweeter (8 ohm) ESA 10th 400B] may cover part of the ultrasonic range, many workers rely on electrostatic speakers; I recommend the design of Macmerth et al. (1975). Conventional amplifiers may be used to drive conventional speakers, but electrostatic speakers must be supplied with a polarizing voltage source (ca. 200 volts, DC) between the amplifier and the speaker, located as closely as possible to the speaker.

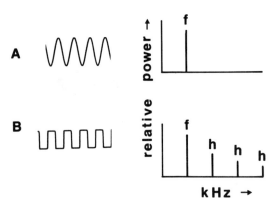

Figure 5. Different waveforms produce different power spectra. The sine wave "A" has all of its energy concentrated in the fundamental frequency (f), whereas a square wave "B" of the same frequency shows energy in the fundamental (f) and in harmonics (h) or overtones. Saturation of recorded signals causes clipping of the sound waves, producing square waveforms and distorting the signal by adding harmonics or overtones.

Amplified speaker circuits (Fig. 16 in Simmons et al., 1979a) and the Macmerth et al. (1975) are operable from a 45 volt battery supply and are suitable for field work.

One should regularly calibrate (measure the response curves of) individual speakers and microphones. This can be accomplished by monitoring the output of the speaker with a calibrated measuring amplifier. The B & K microphone with an appropriate amplifier is useful for such calibrations. The calibrated speaker can then be used to present signals of known strength to the microphone for calibration. A signal generator is required to produce signals of known frequency.

The presentation of ultrasonic signals from a speaker entails several important problems. First, a sound emanating from the speaker becomes more directional at increasing frequencies. This makes interpretation of results difficult since one cannot be certain that an animal, particularly a distant one, was exposed to the stimulus presented from the speaker. Second, one should monitor the output of the speaker with an appropriate microphone to ensure that the stimulus is actually being presented. Cautions about clipping and similar distortions of the presented signal apply equally to recordings and to playbacks of the signals.

Control stimuli can be a problem in experiments involving playback presentations. Control stimuli are ideally presented by reversing the recorded sounds. The Racal tape recorder can be operated in a forward or backward mode, permitting presentation of natural sounds in a modified context (Barclay, 1982). Artificial signals may be used as controls, and a signal generator may be appropriate in this role. However, presentation of a pulsed signal from a signal generator should be made via a pulse shaper to eliminate transient clicks associated with onset of the stimulus (Fig. 6). Since these transient clicks are broadband, they can confound frequencies to which the animals are responding. Several appropriate pulse shapers are available commercially.

Behavioral responses of animals to play-

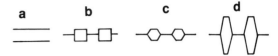

Figure 6. Stages in the production of an artificial signal from a continuous sound (a), to a pulsed sound (b), shaped to delete transient clicks (c), and amplified (d) for presentation to a study subject. In each case, a time-amplitude display is shown.

back presentations should be recorded. For night-time observations this can be accomplished with night vision devices or low-light level video cameras (see Chapter 4).

6. ANALYSIS

Several variables of sound can be measured and used to describe vocalizations. Different instrumentation may be required to measure some of these variables, although recent technological developments and (most notably minicomputers) have expanded the capacity of some instruments for sound analysis. Some variables of sound are discussed below.

Intensity is the power of the signal; the acoustic energy flowing through a unit area perpendicular to the direction of the wave form propagation. *Amplitude* refers to the sound pressure of the signal; it is what one measures with a sound-level meter or an oscilloscope. Amplitude is usually expressed as decibels (dB) relative to 20 microPascals (µPa). By definition, the threshold of human hearing is 0 dB (20 µPa). Intensity is not to be confused with loudness, which is a psychological dimension that reflects perception of a signal. Because of the way auditory systems of animals, including humans, are tuned, some signals that are perceived as "loud" may not be as intense as others, and some may only be heard faintly or not at all.

Duration is the length of time that a signal lasts, measured in seconds or milliseconds. Many vocalizations of bats, particularly some echolocation calls, are transient and last only a few milliseconds or less.

Power Spectrum is the distribution of acoustic energy over the frequency spectrum (bandwidth) of the signal. This is usually presented as dB (vertical axis) and kHz (horizontal axis); this display also contains information on the presence of harmonics.

Frequency-time Display (Sonogram) shows how frequency changes over the duration of the signal. Frequency is on the vertical (y) axis, duration is on the horizontal (x) axis, and intensity (or relative power) is shown as the third (z) axis (usually displayed as darkness of the trace). A frequency-time display provides information about the duration of the signal.

Describing these parameters for the vocalizations of bats allows accurate characterization of the signals. In spite of current media concepts about voice prints (sonograms) and even with the advanced state of some sound analysis equipment, the human brain is usually more effective for analysing sounds (see McDermot, 1983). Reducing the tape speed (to bring ultrasonic frequencies into an audible range) allows the observer to actually hear the vocalizations under study.

6.1. Amplitude

To measure the amplitude of transient signals is complicated because the duration of the signal is usually less than the response time of the measuring instrument. Therefore, reading the scale on a measuring amplifier (sound-level meter) provides an underestimate of amplitude of the signal. The amplitude of the signal can be measured as the peak-to-peak voltage from the time-amplitude display on an oscilloscope screen (Section 6.2). With this information, and knowledge of the frequency(ies) in the signal, a signal generator, appropriate amplifier, pulse shaper, and speaker (Section 5), can be used to produce an artificial signal of longer duration of comparable amplitude and frequency. The amplitude of the longer signal can be measured with a sound-level meter, and from this an approximation of the original signal can be deduced.

Measurements of amplitude are expressed as dB at a designated distance from the sound source. This introduces an additional problem for measuring the amplitude of the calls of flying bats, whose distance and angle relative to the microphone may change considerably within a short time. Problems associated with measuring the amplitude of bat calls are reflected in publications dealing with vocalizations of bats, where the topic is either avoided (e.g., Gustafson and Schnitzler, 1979) or addressed in relative terms (e.g., Fenton and Bell, 1981). Griffin (1958) and Fullard and Thomas (1981) discuss at some length the problem of measuring amplitude.

Sound-level meters are available commercially from several suppliers. Good meters with frequency responses into the ultrasonic range (with flat responses over this range) are expensive. Griffin (1975) has reviewed some limitations of these instruments.

6.2. Duration

The simplest and most accurate way to measure the duration of an acoustic signal is from the amplitude display of an oscilloscope. By adjusting the trigger level of the instrument, specific signals can be displayed and time can be measured on the horizontal axis according to its scale (the sweep rate). This measurement is best performed on a storage oscilloscope. Alternatively, the display of a non-storage instrument can be photographed. An excellent discussion of oscilloscopes and their uses can be found in Oakely and Schafer (1978). Oscilloscopes are available commercially in a range of capabilities (and prices). Non-Linear Systems Division (Kaypro Corporation) manufactures several relatively inexpensive, portable oscilloscopes (e.g., Miniscope).

6.3. Power Spectra

The power spectra indicate the distribution of acoustic energy over different frequencies in the signal. From a power spectrum it is easy to identify harmonics, but the display provides no indication on how the frequencies in the signal change over time. Spectrum analyzers that are currently available work rapidly and efficiently, usually by Fast Fourier Transform analysis of the input. With most of these instruments it is possible to monitor the input (time-amplitude mode) and avoid saturation of the signal.

Frequency spectrum analyzers (whether spectrum or frequency-time display) have advanced dramatically in the past few years, not only in their capacity for rapid (real-time) analysis and in the sophistication of their displays, but also in their cost. Anyone planning to purchase such an instrument should carefully investigate state-of-the-art equipment. Significant savings can be achieved by purchasing used or "obsolete" models, provided that their capacity meets the specifications of a particular study. It should be borne in mind that if the tape speed is decreased, the bandwidth of the signals can be brought within the bandwidth of the spectrum analyzer.

6.4. Frequency-Time Analysis: Period Meter

An oscilloscope display from the output of a zero-crossing period meter (Simmons et al., 1979a) provides a real-time "picture" of changes in the fundamental frequency (Section 2.6). Although a period meter does not provide sufficient resolution for detailed analysis of signals with harmonics, it is convenient for quickly searching through lengthy recordings to locate appropriate signals for detailed analysis.

6.5. Frequency-Time Analysis: Sonograph

The frequency-time display (sonogram) of the signal is typically obtained from a sonograph, but it is possible to modify the output of other frequency analyzers to this mode (e.g., Hopkins et al., 1974). The bandwidth of many of the commercially available instruments (e.g., Kay Sona-Graph)

does not extend into the ultrasonic range. This limitation, however, is easily overcome for recorded signals by slowing the tape speed so that the vocalization frequencies are in the range of the instrument.

Frequency-time displays may indicate the presence of harmonics in the signal but the potential for saturating (clipping) the input signals is sufficient for one to proceed with caution (see Fig. 5). Use of an analyzer that provides a power spectrum (Section 6.3) may be the preferable method for verifying the presence of harmonics.

7. SOME PITFALLS

There is no substitute for experience and practice with sound instruments. One should thoroughly read instruction manuals that accompany newly acquired instruments to ensure their most effective use. When possible, it is advisable to gain experience in a laboratory setting where sound instruments are regularly used. Moreover, a good electronics technician can be an invaluable resource when assembling components, trouble shooting, and making repairs.

7.1. Background Noise

Recordings of animal vocalizations are often "contaminated" with background noise. Such noise is particularly evident when a generator is used to provide power to the instruments. Other sources of background noise may come from stridulating insects, automobile traffic, and voices of co-workers. Some background noise can be eliminated if signals are filtered. Use of variable bandpass filters can convert mediocre recordings into useful data if the noise is not in the same frequency-band as the signal of interest. One annoying source of background noise (a "whine") comes from operating a Racal tape recorder off of a 12-volt DC power supply. This problem can be avoided, however, by using an 18- or 24-volt DC power supply for playback experiments and by filtering the signals. It is best to filter signals in playback experiments.

7.2. Batteries

Most instruments for detection, recording, and playback of ultrasonic sound are operable from batteries. Inexpensive, dry-cell batteries are prone to leakage and use of them may cause considerable damage to expensive equipment. Low charges on dry-cell or rechargeable batteries can seriously affect the responses of instruments and result in misleading results. Rechargeable batteries are ideal if they are well-charged. Considerable frustration can be avoided if batteries are routinely charged after use. Batteries should always be removed from instruments when not in use to avoid battery leakage and instrument damage. It is preferable to operate instruments on main-line power when possible.

7.3. Connectors

There is a bewildering variety of commercially available connectors, and one can be forgiven for thinking that each manufacturer invents and markets a new type of connector to maximize compatibility between different kinds of instruments. To reduce the aggravation associated with the incompatibility of connectors, I strongly recommend that connectors be standardized on instruments being used by each investigator, even if this means spending money to have special cables prepared for interfacing with unconventional instruments. The BNC connector seems to be the most practical, but this view is not shared by all manufacturers.

8. SUMMARY

The range of instruments currently available to detect, record, and analyze vocalizations of bats opens a window on many aspects of their behavior and ecology. The choice of instruments will be determined by the objective of the study, and by the vocal repertoire and behavior of the animal. It is unnecessary to spend large sums of money to record high frequency sounds of bats when all that may be needed is a knowledge of whether or not the animals are producing sounds. Certainly, detection and recording equipment should be responsive to the sounds that the study animals are producing.

Electronic apparatus need not be intimidating to the field biologist. Instruction manuals, common sense, and the plethora of references makes this approach to animal biology accessible to almost anyone. Overcoming the mental barriers and finding funds are the two principal obstacles to success. Throughout this chapter, I have alluded to instruments that are relatively expensive. In 1986 U.S. dollars, an instrument tape recorder (Racal) costs about $14,000; a QMC S200 bat detector is about $1,200; a Westek Bat Monitor is about $1,000; a Non-Linear Systems Miniscope, $500; a period meter (from Carleton University Science Technology Centre), $1,000; a QMC Mini Bat Detector, $200; B & K (3 mm) microphone, over $500; and an appropriate amplifier, over $2,000. Signal generators are produced by many manufacturers and are available, starting at about $500. The cost of instruments for sound analysis usually exceeds $10,000. When ordering equipment, one should verify expected delivery dates, recognizing that some companies are more dependable than others.

9. ACKNOWLEDGMENTS

I am grateful to the following individuals for reading and commenting on earlier drafts of this manuscript: R. M. R. Barclay, G. P. Bell, E. R. Buchler, J. H. Fullard, T. H. Kunz, L. A. Miller, and D. W. Thomas. My research on bats has been supported by the Natural Sciences and Engineering Research Council of Canada.

10. REFERENCES

Ahlen I. 1980. Problems of bat identification on sounds. Biophon, 7:112-14.

Ahlen, I. 1981. Identification of Scandinavian bats by their sounds. Swedish Univ. Agric. Sci., Dept. Wildl. Ecol., Rep. 6, Uppsala, 56 pp.

Ahlen, I., L. Pettersson, and A. Svardstrom. 1983-1984. An instrument for detecting bat and insect sounds. Myotis, 21-22:82-88.

Andersen, B. B., and L. A. Miller. 1977. A portable ultrasonic detecting system for recording bat cries in the field. J. Mammal., 58:226-229.

Barclay, R. M. R. 1982. Interindividual use of echolocation calls: Eavesdropping by bats. Behav. Ecol. Sociobiol., 10:271-275.

Bell, G. P. 1980. Habitat use and response to patches of prey by desert insectivorous bats. Can. J. Zool., 58:1876-1883.

Busnel, R. -G., and J. F. Fish (eds.). 1980. Animal sonar systems. NATO Advanced Study Institute. Vol. A28. Plenum Press, New York, 1135 pp.

Downes, C. M. 1982. A comparison of the sensitivities of three bat detectors. J. Mammal., 63:343-345.

Fenton, M. B. 1982. Echolocation, insect hearing, and feeding ecology of insectivorous bats. Pp. 261-285, *in* Ecology of bats. (T. H. Kunz, ed.). Plenum Press, New York, 425 pp.

Fenton, M. B. 1984. Echolocation: Implications for the ecology and evolution of bats. Q. Rev. Biol., 59:33-53.

Fenton, M. B. 1985. Communication in the Chiroptera. Indiana Univ. Press, Bloomington, 161 pp.

Fenton, M. B., and G. P. Bell. 1981. Recognition of species of insectivorous bats by their echolocation calls. J. Mammal., 62:233-243.

Fenton, M. B., S. L. Jacobson, and R. N. Stone. 1973. An automatic ultrasonic sensing system for monitoring the activity of some bats. Can. J. Zool., 51:291-299.

Fenton, M. B., H. G. Merriam, and G. L. Holroyd. 1983. Bats of Kootenay, Glacier, and Mount Revelstoke National Parks in Canada: Identification by echolocation calls, distribution and biology. Can. J. Zool., 61:2503-2508.

Fullard, J. H., and D. W. Thomas. 1981. Detection of certain African insectivorous bats by sympatric, tympanate moths. J. Comp. Physiol., 143:363-368.

Griffin, D. R. 1958. Listening in the dark. Yale Univ. Press, New Haven, 413 pp.

Griffin, D. R. 1975. Portable apparatus for observing high frequency sounds under natural conditions. Bat Res. News, 16:31-36.

Gustafson, V., and H. -U. Schnitzler. 1979. Echolocation and obstacle avoidance in the hipposiderid bat, *Asellia tridens.* J. Comp. Physiol., 131:161-168.

Hassal, J. F., and K. Zaveri. 1978. Application of Bruel and Kjaer equipment to acoustic noise measurements. Bruel and Kjaer, Denmark, 280 pp.

Hopkins, C. D., M. Rosestto, and A. Lutzjen. 1974. A continuous sound spectrum analyzer for animal sounds. Z. Tierpsychol., 34:313-320.

Kuhl, W., G. R. Schodder, and F. K. Shroder. 1954. Condenser transmitters and microphones with dielectrics for airborne ultrasonics. Acustica, 4:519-532.

Kunz, T. H., and C. E. Brock. 1975. A comparison of mist nets and ultrasonic detectors for monitoring flight activity of bats. J. Mammal., 56:907-911.

Leonard, M. L., and M. B. Fenton. 1984. Echolocation calls of *Euderma maculatum* (Chiroptera: Vespertilionidae): Use in orientation and communication. J. Mammal., 65:122-126.

Macmerth, von H., D. Theiss, and H. -U. Schnitzler. 1975. Konstructktion eines Luftultraschallgebers mit konstantem Frequenzgang im Bereich von 15 kHz bis 130 kHz. Acustica, 34:81-85.

McDermitt, J. 1983. The solid-state parrot. Science 83, June: 59-65.

Miller, L. A., and B. B. Andersen, 1984. Studying bat echolocation signals using ultrasonic detectors. Z. Saugetierk., 49:6-13.

Novick, A. 1977. Acoustic orientation. Pp. 73-289, *in* Biology of bats. Vol. 3. (W. A. Wimsatt, ed.). Academic Press, New York, 651 pp.

Oakley, B., and R. Schafer. 1978. Experimental neurobiology, a laboratory manual. Univ. Michigan Press, Ann Arbor, 367 pp.

Peterson, A. P. G., and E. E. Gross, Jr. 1974. Handbook of noise measurement. 7th ed. General Radio, Concord, Massachusetts.

Pye, J. D., 1983a. Techniques for studying ultrasound. Pp. 39-65, *in* Bioacoustics. (B. Lewis, ed.). Academic Press, New York, 322 pp.

Pye, J. D. 1983b. Echolocation and countermeasures. Pp. 407-429, *in* Bioacoustics. (B. Lewis, ed.). Academic Press, New York, 322 pp.

Sales, G. D., and J. D. Pye. 1974. Ultrasonic communication by animals. Chapman and Hall, London, 281 pp.

Simmons, J. A., and R. A. Stein. 1980. Acoustic imaging in bat sonar: Echolocation and the evolution of echolocation. J. Comp. Physiol., 135:61-84.

Simmons, J. A., M. B. Fenton, W. R. Ferguson, M. Jutting, and J. Palin. 1979a. Apparatus for research on animal ultrasonic signals. Life Sci. Misc. Publ., R. Ont. Mus., 31 pp.

Simmons, J. A., M. B. Fenton, and M. J. O'Farrell. 1979b. Echolocation and pursuit of prey by bats. Science, 203:16-21.

Appendix 1. Selected Instruments for Recording Vocalizations of Bats.

BAT DETECTORS

Bat Monitor

Westec Services, Inc.
3211 Fifth Avenue
San Diego, California
92103 USA

QMC Bat Detector
(Model S200)

QMC Instruments, Ltd.
229 Mile End Road
London, England
E1 4AA UK

QMC Mini Detector

QMC Instruments, Ltd.

Uppsala Ultrasonic Detector
(Model D-940)

L. Petterson Elektronik
Sjudatarp, Lagga
S-741 00 Kniusta
Sweden

MICROPHONES

B & K Condensor Microphone

Bruel and Kjaer Instruments
185 Forest Street

Marlborough, Massachusetts
01752 USA

TAPE RECORDERS

Racal Tape Recorder

Racal Thermionic Ltd.
Hythe, Southampton
England, UK

PORTABLE OSCILLOSCOPES

Miniscope
(Model MS-15)

Non Linear Systems
Box N
Delmar, California
92014 USA

Nicolet Oscilloscope
(Model 2090C)

Nicolet Instrument
5225 Verona Road
Madison, Wisconsin
53711 USA

SOUND SPECTRUM ANALYZERS

Kay Sona-Graph

Kay Elemetrics Corporation
12 Maple Avenue
Pine Brook, New Jersey
07050 USA

Nicolet Spectrum Analyzer
(Model 446 A)

Nicolet Scientific Corporation
245 Livingston Street
Northvale, New Jersey
07647 USA

B & K Spectrum Analyzer

Bruel & Kjaer Instruments
185 Forest Street
Marlborough, Massachusetts
01752 USA

Chapter 7

Radiotelemetry:
Techniques and Analysis

Gerald S. Wilkinson[1]

and

Jack W. Bradbury

University of California at San Diego
Department of Biology, C-016
La Jolla, California 92093 USA

1. INTRODUCTION

Determining the movement patterns of individuals, especially with respect to a resource such as food, shelter, or another animal, is vital for understanding the ecology and behavior of any species. Obtaining this information for bats is particularly challenging because of their nocturnal and aerial habits. Although light-tagging and sonar detection can be used occasionally to study the movements of particular species and individuals (Chapter 4), radiotelemetry has become the method of choice for studying movement patterns and activity of many nocturnal mammals, including bats. The benefits include: 1) the location of individuals can be monitored over considerable distances, often for periods of weeks; 2) more than one individual can be tagged using transmitters with unique transmission frequencies; 3) direct observations of individuals during the day and night frequently become possible because the animal's location can be determined; and 4) aspects of an individual's behavior, physiology, or environment can be deduced by noting changes in the signal pulse caused either by the animal through characteristic movements or by the investigator through temperature-sensitive or other signal-altering components.

The most serious limitation of radiotelemetry for many researchers may be the initial investment required. To triangulate an animal's position, at least two receivers with antennas are needed. Depending on the quality of the equipment and its capabilities, a receiver and antenna can cost (in U.S. dollars) between $650 and $2500 or more. In comparison, each transmitter is relatively inexpensive ($70–$150, commercial, or $25, home-

[1]Present Address: Department of Zoology, University of Maryland, College Park, Maryland 20742 USA

made). A step-by-step guide for assembling a very simply designed transmitter can be found in Appendix 1. Although the construction details have changed, our earlier summary (Bradbury et al., 1979) should be consulted for general principles of tracking bats. Selected commercially-available equipment and supplies are listed in Appendix 3.

Our intent in this chapter is to provide enough information for a biologist with a minimal background in telemetry to be able to construct inexpensive transmitters and to collect and analyze radio-tracking data efficiently. Readers with absolutely no prior exposure to this technique should consult Mech (1983) or our earlier paper cited above. We first describe the types of transmitters available and how to construct them, and then discuss the utility of several receivers and antennas that are currently on the market. Next, we describe a method for collecting data in the field which permits rapid recording of accurate bearings from flying animals and subsequently discuss several statistical procedures which have been developed to estimate home range size and associations between individuals in time or space. The motivation behind a discussion of data collection and analysis is to alert the novice and perhaps experienced radio-tracker to the

problems associated with making these kinds of statistical measurements, particularly on bats. Because our interest is in methodology, we do not review radio-tracking studies on bats in detail; however, to aid those interested in the primary literature, in Table 1 we list references to several studies that used radio-telemetry to follow bats. For compilations of recent radio-tracking studies on other vertebrates and methodological reviews, consult Long (1979), Amlaner and MacDonald (1980), the 1982 symposium of the Zoological Society of London, and Mech (1983).

2. TRANSMITTER CONSTRUCTION AND ATTACHMENT

2.1. Basic Cochran Transmitter

The simple Cochran transmitter design is a reliable starting radio for most tracking studies on bats. This transmitter is produced by several wildlife telemetry companies; the AVM instrument company sells them under the code SM-1. With practice, one can build one of these transmitters in 30-40 minutes. Our earlier publication (Bradbury et al. 1979) recommended construction using a printed circuit base. The printed circuit has since

Table 1. Species, mass, and references for some bats that have been radio-tracked to estimate home range (HR), homing ability (H), foraging location (F), or associations (A).

Species	Mass (g)	Purpose	Reference
Carollia perspicillata	15-20	F	Fleming et al. (1977)
		HR,F	Heithaus and Fleming (1978)
Euderma maculatum	18-20	F	Leonard and Fenton (1983)
Antrozous pallidus	20-30	F,A	Brown and Berry (1982)
Eptesicus fuscus	20-30	F,A	Brigham (1983)
Desmodus rotundus	30-40	HR,F,A	Wilkinson (1985)
Noctilio albiventris	30-40	F	Brown et al. (1983)
Artibeus jamaicensis	40-50	F	Morrison (1978a, 1978b, 1979, 1980)
		F	Morrison and Morrison (1980)
Phyllostomus hastatus	60-110	H	Williams and Williams (1967, 1970)
		HR,F	McCracken and Bradbury (1981)
Rousettus aegyptiacus	100-120	HR,F	Thomas and Fenton (1978)
Epomophorus gambianus	100-130	HR,F	Thomas and Fenton (1978)
Vampyrum spectrum	170-190	F	Vehrencamp et al. (1977)
Hypsignathus monstrosus	240-425	HR,F	Bradbury (1977)

been deleted as unnecessary because of extra weight and expense. The majority of designs now combine components using the crystal case as a substrate. Most bat researchers have used radios operating in the 2 m band (around 150 Mhz). This frequency range seems a reasonable compromise to the trade-off of increasing antenna efficiency (by using shorter wave-lengths) and reducing scatter and transmission loss (by using longer wave-lengths). All transmitters used to find and follow animals produce pulses of radio energy. This increases battery life over that when signals are produced continuously, and the sharp onsets of each pulse facilitate better judgements about signal strength when using acoustical monitors. For moving bats, pulse rates in the range of 1-2 pulses/s seem ideal. Where transmitters are being used to telemeter physiological parameters, continuous signal output has been the rule. However, it is possible to track some slowly-varying physiological parameters, such as body temperature, with a pulsed signal by modulating the pulse rate with the parameter of interest (see Section 2.3.).

The basic Cochran design (Fig. 1) can be divided into two core parts: 1) the timing circuit, and 2) the oscillator. The simplest design uses a resistor and capacitor in series as a timing circuit. The resistor limits the rate at which the battery can charge the capacitor. When the capacitor is sufficiently charged, it switches the oscillating circuit on. The latter oscillates at some fixed frequency for as long as it takes the capacitor to discharge below the switching threshold; then the oscillator switches off. Both the pulse rate and the duration of each pulse are set by the values of the timing circuit capacitor and resistor. To change pulse rates, it is usually more convenient to vary the timing resistor; lower resistances increase the pulse rate, whereas higher values (up to a maximum at which the radio will not switch on at all) decrease the rate. In the design described in Appendix 1, a timing capacitor of 4.75 MFD and a timing resistor of 220 kohms will produce a pulse rate of about 1/s.

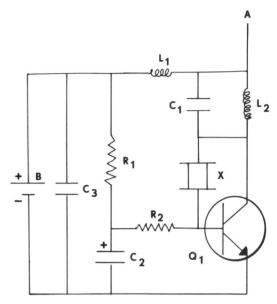

Figure 1. Schematic for simple Cochran radio transmitter. Key: B: 1.2-1.5 V battery; C3: bypass capacitor; R1: timing resistor; C2: electrolytic timing capacitor; R2: bias resistor; Q1: transistor; X: crystal; C1: tank circuit capacitor; L2: tank circuit coil; L1: choke coil; A: antenna. See text for component values and Appendix 1 for construction procedures.

The oscillating circuit in the Cochran radio consists of a tank circuit (a coil and a capacitor in parallel), a transistor, and a crystal. The characteristics of the tank circuit and the transistor set the basic range of oscillating frequencies that the radio will support. The crystal then imposes a specific frequency on the system. By combining the same tank circuit and transistor with different crystals, one can produce a series of radios with separable and stable frequencies. For a transmitted frequency of 148.2+/−0.1 MHz, the radio in Appendix 1 uses a 2N3904 transistor, a 33 PFD capacitor, and a 21 turn coil in the tank circuit. For slightly different frequencies in the 2 m band, the same transistor is sufficient, but slightly different tank circuit capacitors with greater (or fewer) turns on the coil are needed. This circuit will not work unmodified for frequencies above 159 MHZ because it relies on 3rd overtone crystals; above 159

MHZ a 5th overtone crystal must be used. One can also modify both the pulse emission characteristics and reduce current drain (and concomitantly power output and range) by using another transistor. A number of miniature Siemen's transistors (e.g., BFS 17 and BF 599) occupy less space than 2N3904's and draw less current. As with shifting the crystal frequency, a substitution of another transistor will require some adjustments to the tank circuit to produce pulsing and oscillation.

When first building this radio at a new frequency or with a different transistor, it is best to assemble all but the tank circuit and then to try several combinations of tank circuit capacitors and coils. Not all combinations will allow the radio to oscillate at all, and among those that do, some combinations produce louder and sharper pulses than others. Alternatively, one can add an additional variable capacitor in parallel in the tank circuit and adjust this for preferred output characteristics.

The final four components of the basic design are a choke coil, which helps match the impedance of the antenna to the air; a bypass capacitor, which helps isolate the battery from the oscillating circuit; a bias resistor, which couples the transistor to the timing circuit; and an antenna. In the radio of Appendix 1, the choke coil is a 4-turn coil and the bypass capacitor is 0.001 MFD. Earlier circuit diagrams called for an electrolytic bypass capacitor. This is unnecessary and in fact, a ceramic non-electrolytic capacitor is preferred. The bias resistance depends on what transistor is being used. The 2N3904 used in the Appendix 1 radio (as well as the BF 599) works well with a 1.8 kohm bias resistor.

The most practical antenna for most bat tracking is a whip antenna. This is a single wire 38-45 cm long attached at the point indicated in Figs. 1-3. The wire must be durable and relatively stiff to maintain proper transmission efficiency. Guitar strings are commonly used because they are inexpensive and easy to obtain, but they can be kinked and sometimes break. Steel fishing leader does not kink but it lacks stiffness. It must be silver-soldered to a regular wire with a torch and the latter attached to the radio with regular solder. Various grades of orthodontist's wire have also been used as antenna materials. Antenna wires may be threaded into hollow spaghetti insulation to reduce kinking and oxidation. Some radio manufacturers also pass the insulated wire through a small spring which is imbedded in the potting material. This restores the preferred direction of the antenna and resists efforts of the animal to break the antenna wire at the solder joint. Breakage at the solder joint can also be reduced by adding a kink to the antenna distal to the solder joint and potting the kink with the transmitter. Any flexing or pulling thus is directed at the kink in the potting and not on the solder joint. Note that it is possible to cut shorter antennas for bats that roost in crevices. The tradeoff, however, is reduced antenna efficiency which results in a smaller range.

2.2. Triggered Circuits

Several modifications of this design are now in use. The Carleton University bat research group has used a "triggered" circuit for some years. This circuit was designed by Donald W. Thomas, modified by Sandra Vincent, and is now available commercially from Holohil Systems Ltd. (Appendix 3). In this circuit (see Fig. 2) the resistor and capacitor of the Cochran timing circuit (see Fig. 1) are replaced with a multi-vibrator trigger consisting of three transistors and associated resistors and capacitors. The advantage of this design is that the pulse rate and pulse duration can be varied independently; this is not possible with the simple timing circuit. By keeping the pulse rate high, but by shortening pulse duration (see Fig. 2 for details), the total drain on the battery can be reduced. In principle, this change should have no effect on actual peak power radiated. In practice, there is an upper limit on how short pulses should be. This is a consequence of the fact that both the ear (if using acoustic monitors) and the needle (if using a meter on the receiver) have

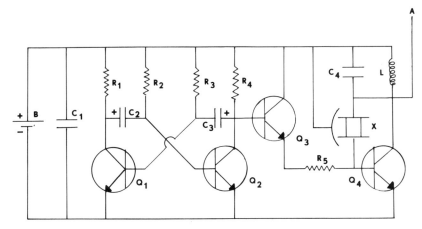

Figure 2. Schematic for Holohil Systems Ltd. trigger circuit. Oscillator components: Q4: transistor; R5: bias resistor; X: crystal; C4: tank circuit capacitor; L: tank circuit coil. Trigger components: R1 and R3: pulse rate control resistors; R2: pulse duration resistor; C3: pulse rate capacitor; C2: pulse duration capacitor; Q1, Q2, Q3: trigger transistors. Other components: R4: trigger resistor; C1: bypass capacitor; B: 1.2-1.5 V battery. Sandra Vincent uses: C1 = 0.01 MFD; C2 = C3 = 0.047 MFD; C4 = 3-5 turns of #34 coil wire around the crystal case; R1 = R2 = 1 Mohm; R3 = 22 Mohm; R4 = 47 kohm; R5 = 10 kohm; Q1 = Q2 = Q3 = Siemens BCW 65 or BCW 66 or BCW 71 or BCW 31; Q4 = Siemens BFS 20. We have used the same trigger circuit to replace our timing resistor and capacitor to fire the oscillating circuit in Fig. 1. We used the same trigger components recommended by Vincent except we substituted 2N3904 transistors for all transistors in the radio, used R5 = 1.8 kohm, and replaced C1 with 0.001 MFD. By varying R2 and R3, various pulse rates and pulse durations can be obtained.

damping constants that require a minimum "on-time" to achieve accurate measures of signal intensity. Disadvantages of the triggered circuit are greater size and mass; however, Holohil Systems Ltd. produces completely potted transmitters weighing less than 1 g by using very tiny resistors, winding coils on these resistors, and using micro-transistors. The change in transistors has also required some minor changes in the original tank circuit components.

2.3. Pulsed Telemetry Units

By replacing the timing circuit with an appropriate resistive transducer, the Cochran radio can be modified to telemeter other information. A temperature sensitive radio can be constructed by replacing the 220 kohm timing resistor with a 180 kohm resistor and 100 kohm thermistor (e.g., Yellow Springs Instruments, Model No. 44011) in series. (WARNING: Do not overheat thermistor when soldering it into the circuit!) Once calibrated using warm water baths, this radio can be used to measure temperature of the radio (and of an animal, once implanted in the animal's body cavity) by varying pulse rates (also see Chapter 20).

A simple position detector can be made by replacing the single timing resistor with two parallel resistors, one of which is connected to the circuit via a mercury switch. When the radio is in a particular position, the mercury switch is closed and the radio pulses at a high rate; when the radio, say due to animal movement, is in a perpendicular position, the switch is open and the radio will pulse at a slower rate. Pierre Charles-Dominique (1977) devised a similar modification to monitor urine marking in galagos. Each animal was outfitted with a small waist harness so that two exposed wires were posed near the urethral opening. These wires were connected to a second timing resistor. When the galago urine-marked, the conductive

urine bridged the two wires, the second resistor was added into the timing circuit, and the
radio pulse rate was increased. When the
urine dried, the pulse rate returned to normal.
Finally, by combining a small amplifier and
integrated circuit with surgically implanted
electrodes, the Cochran radio can monitor
heart rate.

2.4. Power Sources

Most bat researchers power their transmitters
with small mercury batteries such as those
used in hearing aids and watches. These may
be purchased from AVM with metal tabs spot-
welded on. If they are bought without tabs
(usually much cheaper), tabs can be glued to
the battery case with a cyanoacrylate glue and
then conductivity established with a drop of
copper circuit board repair paint. Tabs make
connection easier and reduce damage to the
battery from over-heating during soldering. A
typical Cochran radio (without battery)
weighs about 0.8 g. Batteries range in mass
and life from 0.3 g and 5-10 days expected life
to 40 g and years of life. The upper limit on life
for bat transmitters is usually set by the

requirement that potted radio and attachment material not exceed about 10% of the
bat's body mass. The life also depends on the
current drain and duty cycle (fraction of time
on) of the transmitter. Transmitters using the
mini-transistors sold by Siemens tend to have
longer life since they draw less current per
pulse. However, they also tend to have less
range since this results in lower peak power
radiated per pulse. Selected battery suppliers
in the United States are listed in Appendix 3.

Although not useful for most micro-
chiropterans, megabats which roost in well-lit
sites may be amenable to solar-powered transmitters. These utilize a bank of photo voltaic
solar cells connected in parallel with a nicad
battery and the transmitter. The circuit must
have a voltage sensitive switch that turns the
radio off when the battery voltage drops
below about 1 V (see Fig. 3). Nicad batteries
which are allowed to run down completely are
often difficult to recharge. The switching circuit turns the radio off before this can happen. The circuit also uses a diode to prevent
the battery from discharging through the
photo cells when the radio is in the dark. One
difficulty with solar transmitters is that the

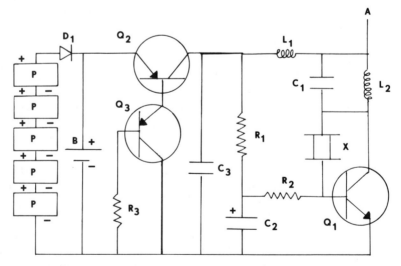

Figure 3. Schematic for solar-powered radios. Key: Q2 = Q3 = 2N4403; R3 = 100-400 kohm; D1 = 1N914 diode; P =
VACTEC VTS3013 photo-cells (or larger size); other components as in Fig. 1.

size of each photo cell (not the number of cells) must be large enough to both recharge the battery and run the radio during daytime hours. To keep total mass down and still have enough solar cell surface, the drain of the radios may have to be reduced by lowering pulse rates or using the smaller drain transistor systems. WARNING: Nicad batteries seem particularly vulnerable to invasion by potting solvents. Pot these batteries in a thin coating of wax before potting entire radio in casting resins.

2.5. Potting

Radios may be potted in a variety of materials. Potting should waterproof the units and be resistant to chewing. Potting materials include mixtures of beeswax and paraffin overlaid with dental acrylic or other casting resins. The latter are usually too thin to dab on finished radios without the addition of thickening powders. Most plastics stores stock both resins and thickening powders appropriate for electronic components.

2.6. Attachment

Harnesses have not been used successfully on bats to our knowledge. Although collars have been used on some of the larger species (e.g., *Pteropus* and *Epomophorus*), most workers have preferred to glue the radios to the fur or skin in the middle of the back between the shoulder blades. Attachment materials have included cyanoacrylate glue, epoxy glue, rubber silastic, and surgical cement. Radios attached in this manner may remain on the bat for days to months depending on the care used in attachment and the grooming abilities of the bat (or its roost mates). Careful layering of glue, a circle of hair, more glue, more hair and finally the radio appears to be the best method. In our experience, repeated attachments to the same animal with silastic may cause permanent reductions in pelage

thickness. The same may be true of other glues.

3. EQUIPMENT SELECTION

3.1. Receivers

The LA-12 model receiver sold by the AVM instrument company has remained the standard in the industry for over 10 years. Several other companies (including Custom Electronics and Wildlife Materials) produce identical receivers and also offer models that are about half the size and mass of the LA-12. These smaller receivers retain the same circuitry as the LA-12 but use miniaturized components. For an additional charge, several options to the basic receiver can be requested, including a recharge capability, more channels (up to 48), a pulse interval timer, and a sweep feature which automatically scans a few Khz around the receiving frequency. AVM and Wildlife Materials also offer receivers which can be programmed to search for designated frequencies, can measure pulse width and interval, and can interface with either strip recorders or microcomputers. To reliably record the properties of the signal pulse, a strong, nonmodulating signal is essential. Consequently, remote recording of pulse components using this kind of equipment has limited utility for field work on bats. The programmable receivers, however, can be used to monitor the presence or absence of many radio-tagged individuals which share a roosting site and, therefore, could be useful for time budget studies. If information is required for only a single animal, an inexpensive ($30) amplifier can be constructed (see Appendix 2 for circuit diagram) and then connected between the high-voltage headphone output jack of the LA-12 type receiver and a Rustrak chart recorder. The 1985 price of the basic 12-channel receiver is either $600 (Custom Electronics) or $750 (AVM and Wildlife Materials). A pulse interval timer is an additional $300 and a receiver/interface system costs about $2500 from either AVM or Wildlife Materials.

3.2. Antennas

We prefer Yagi style receiving antennas made from aluminum tubing (available from Cushcraft) because of their directionality and low mass. For mobile ground reception a 3 or 4-element antenna is most easily carried through vegetation. Seven and 11 element antennas increase directionality and gain but are too cumbersome (especially in the 2 m band) to use except at a fixed station. To obtain rapid reliable bearings on a flying animal, we recommend a null-peak antenna system, two 4- or 7-element Yagis mounted in parallel with specially matched cabling and hardware to add or subtract the signal from each antenna (sets can be obtained from AVM and Wildlife Materials). Superior directionality can be obtained from this system because the "null window," where there is no signal, is usually only a few degrees wide. To easily determine direction we mount our antennas on 2-4 m aluminum poles which pass through a portable wooden table. On top of the table we inscribe a large 360° compass and attach a pointer, such as a 25 cm shelf bracket, and a handle to the mast with hose clamps. The system can be calibrated with a transmitter located in a known direction by adjusting the direction of the pointer. With experienced trackers we have recorded the positions of up to 10 bats every ten minutes using this system. The method has the constraint that if the bat flies low or out of range frequently, the rig may be difficult to move. We have mounted such systems in the back of a pickup truck with success.

4. DATA COLLECTION

4.1. Recording Data

To facilitate the plotting of triangulations we arbitrarily impose a Cartesian coordinate system over our study area. A convenient orientation puts 0° to magnetic north. If a third person can communicate with two tracking parties by walkie-talkie or other means, then triangulations can be plotted immediately onto gridded maps of the study area in the field with the aid of a handheld programmable calculator or a laptop computer. We recommend this procedure for two reasons. First, instantaneous feedback often uncovers error or bias in observers or equipment. Second, if the third party is mobile and equipped with receiver and antenna, it is often possible to triangulate a bat's position and then walk or drive to the location to verify the sighting. Direct observation of foraging behavior of radio-tagged individuals can then be made, especially if night vision equipment (Chapter 4) is available (e.g., Wilkinson, 1985).

If the coordinates of the two tracking stations are X_1, Y_1 and X_2, Y_2, then the coordinates of the bat's location (X, Y) can be found as follows:

$$X = X_2 + \frac{[(X_1 - X_2) + (Y_2 - Y_1)\tan(\theta_1)]\tan\theta_2}{\tan(\theta_2) - \tan(\theta_1)} \quad (1)$$

$$Y = Y_2 + \frac{(X_1 - X_2) + (Y_2 - Y_1)\tan(\theta_1)}{\tan(\theta_2) - \tan(\theta_1)} \quad (2)$$

θ_i represents the bearing taken clockwise on the bat from station i. Station 1 always has the smallest x coordinate. Equations 1 and 2 can be programmed easily on a calculator or microcomputer. Error routines should be included to identify nonconverging or parallel angles.

4.2. Error Estimation

Two types of errors often complicate a triangulation. The first is a function of the directionality of the equipment and the precision of the observer. This sampling error frequently has no bias, that is, it has no systematic deviation from the true coordinates of the animal. The magnitude of the sampling error may be important if exact locations are desired. The best method for estimating this error is to make direct observations of radio-tagged bats in the field. If that is difficult or impossible, then the sampling error can be approximated by having a third person walk through the study area while holding a transmitter and recording his or her position as two people in base stations take successive bearings on the radio. This method will also uncover the second type of error which depends primarily on the topography of the area. Sometimes signals from transmitters behind or near obstructions relative to a base station may be deflected or hidden. Identifying these "problem" directions for each base station can aid in interpreting a tracking session.

Incorporating sampling error into subsequent analyses may or may not be possible depending on the statistical technique employed. Springer (1979) makes several suggestions for estimating and adjusting for sampling error. Bias, once discovered, can often be corrected if the magnitude can be estimated.

5. HOME RANGE ESTIMATION

5.1. Definitions

Radio-tracking data can be used to estimate the size of the area an animal uses, commonly referred to as its home range, better than capture/recapture methods because it enables the researcher to specify an animal's position independently of its behavior and movements (assuming it does not move out of range). To obtain a quantitative estimate of home range, an exact definition is needed. Some workers (e.g., Odum and Kuenzler, 1955) suggest that the home range is that area enclosed by a polygon which is constructed by connecting the animal's outermost x,y coordinates. Although this area is easy to visualize graphically, the computational algorithm is complex. Furthermore, the area within this minimum convex polygon (or MCP) is very sensitive to extreme points. Consequently, several probabilistic home range models have been proposed which are not as sensitive to outliers. Critical reviews of several of these models can be found in Amalaner and MacDonald (1980), Schoener (1981), and Anderson (1982). The basic notion underlying these models is that an animal's pattern of

movement through space can be represented as a bivariate probability distribution where the z axis represents the probability of encountering the animal at that x,y coordinate. The home range is then defined by the area encompassed by the probability level (e.g., 0.5 or 0.95) which specifies the proportion of time the animal should be found inside that area [denoted by MAP(0.5) and MAP(0.95), respectively, for minimum area probability]. These utilization distributions (or UDs) can be fitted to defined distributions (a parametric estimate) or to the animal's actual pattern of movement (a nonparametric estimate). Here we want to emphasize the differences between these methods and suggest that the nonparametric method developed by Anderson (1982) may be most appropriate for depicting and analyzing foraging ranges of bats.

5.2. Parametric Methods

These techniques rely on the assumption that the frequency distribution of an animal's x and y coordinates can be specified. The most common distribution assumed is the normal. If the variance is equal in both x and y directions, and there is no correlation between x and y values, then the data may fit a circular normal distribution. The center of this distribution is the geometric center of all sightings, also known as the center of activity (Hayne, 1949). Its coordinates are defined as

$$\bar{x} = \Sigma \frac{x_i}{n} \ , \bar{y} = \Sigma \frac{y_i}{n} \qquad (3)$$

where x_i and y_i are the coordinates of the animal at sample i in a total of n observations. The radius of the circle which includes 95% of all sightings is defined as

$$r = \left[\sum_{i=1}^{n} \frac{r_i^2}{(n-1)} \right]^{1/2} \qquad (4)$$

where

$$r_i = \left[(x_i - \bar{x})^2 + (y_i - \bar{y})^2 \right]^{1/2} \qquad (5)$$

The area bounded by a given percentage of the UD can be easily calculated from r (Harrison, 1958). The area encompassing 95% of the UD is $2\pi r^2$, and for 99% of the UD it is $(9\pi r^2)/2$. To fit this distribution, a bat would have to fly in all directions around a central roost, with time spent at any one location inversely proportional to the distance from the roost.

If a bat does not move in certain directions, but otherwise shows central tendencies, then an elliptical home range (e.g., Jennrich and Turner, 1969; Koeppl et al., 1977; Dunn and Gipson, 1977) may be appropriate. This method assumes that the data are normally distributed in both directions, but the variance in X can be different from the variance in Y. Instead of calculating r^2, the appropriate statistic for this distribution is

$$|S|^{1/2} = \left[s_{xx}s_{yy} - s_{xy}^2\right]^{1/2} \qquad (6)$$

where

$$s_{xx} = \frac{\Sigma(x_i - \bar{x})^2}{(n-2)}, \qquad (7)$$

$$s_{yy} = \frac{\Sigma(y_i - \bar{y})^2}{(n-2)}, \qquad (8)$$

and

$$s_{xy} = \frac{\Sigma(x_i - \bar{x})(y_i - \bar{y})}{(n-2)} \qquad (9)$$

The 95% home range estimate is $6\pi|S|^{1/2}$ and the 99% estimate is $9\pi|S|^{1/2}$. Note that if there are more samples in the tails of the X and Y distributions than are expected, the home range estimate given by these equations will be too large. If this technique is desired and the data are not bivariate normal [Schoener (1981) discusses tests for bivariate normality], transformations can sometimes be used to attain bivariate normality (e.g., Dunn and Brisbin, 1983).

5.3. Nonparametric Methods

If an animal has two or more activity centers, then all parametric home range estimation techniques will poorly describe the true home range and the UD. In this situation, which we suspect is typical of many bats, it is preferable to use the distribution of the actual coordinates to define the UD. Two methods have been proposed for this purpose. Ford and Krumme (1979) divide the x,y plane into small quadrants, count the number of sightings in each quadrant, and then calculate the percentage of total to estimate z. The problem with their technique is that the result may be sensitive to quadrant size and there is no *a priori* rule for deciding what the proper grid size should be. A copy of their Fortran program can be obtained from Ford; however, a prospective user should be aware that the method requires a substantial amount of computer time and memory.

Another nonparametric method has been proposed recently by Anderson (1982). This method uses a Fourier transformation of the raw data to break the oscillating topographic surface into a sum of sine waves. Low frequency sine waves correspond to the general shape of the UD and high frequencies generate small peaks and valleys. Because there is a standard algorithm for eliminating frequencies of a certain value or higher, the surface formed by recombining the sine waves after excluding high frequencies is smoothed. In essence, this algorithm circumvents the problem of specifying grid size which plagues the Ford and Krumme method. In addition, Anderson's method is less susceptible to small sample bias than that of Ford and Krumme (1979). A listing of his Pascal program, as well as a document which explains its details, are available from Anderson or as ESA Supplementary Document No. 101 from the Managing Editor of the Ecological Society of America. The program is very economical in computer time and requires a sufficiently small amount of memory, 56Kb, to be implemented on many microcomputers.

To illustrate Anderson's method we have plotted UDs for eight consecutive nights of radio-tracking of a female *Desmodus rotundus* in Fig. 4 with the three-dimensional plotting routine, Surface II.

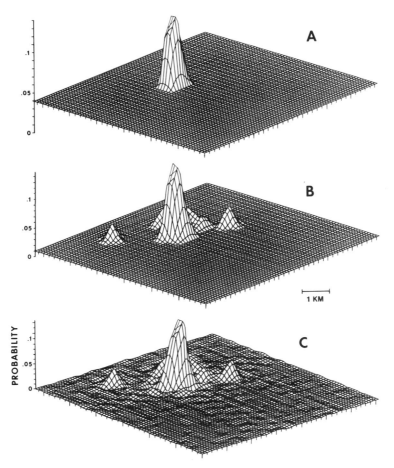

Figure 4. Utilization distributions calculated using the nonparametric technique of Anderson (1982) for a female *Desmodus rotundus* which was tracked for 8 consecutive nights between 15-23 September 1981. See text for further explanation.

Bearings were taken every ten minutes while the animal was outside its roost tree. Detailed description of the methods can be found in Wilkinson (1985). Panel C shows the entire UD; the volume beneath the surface has been normalized to one (Anderson's program sets this sum equal to the number of samples). The shallow irregularities represent residual effects of the Fourier smoothing algorithm and have no biological basis. The surface in panel B corresponds to a 0.95 UD. It was constructed by setting to zero those z-coordinates which, after being ranked, had a cumulative sum less than 0.05. This UD represents the true home range most accurately because the

artificial irregularities present in C have been removed, but the relative topography remains. This panel shows how multiple activity centers can appear. In panel A z-values which had a cumulative sum less than 0.5 were set to zero. This UD corresponds to what many workers have termed the "core use area." In fact, a bivariate normal distribution would probably produce a reasonable fit to this UD. The area circumscribed by the base of the UDs in panels A and B estimates the MAP(0.5) and MAP(0.95), respectively.

A non-UD based method for estimating activity centers and home ranges uses the harmonic mean of an areal distribution (Dixon and Chapman, 1980). The harmonic center is that location at which the inverse of the sum of reciprocal distances between it and all sample coordinates is minimized. One nice feature of this measure is that it always lies within a region of active use. Dixon and Chapman (1980) discuss how this technique can be used to compute isopleths which contain any percentage of all sample coordinates and are, therefore, analogous to MAP ( ) measurements. The harmonic mean method is relatively independent of grid size but can produce biased home range estimates if the grid size is large or the areal distribution is highly non-normal (Spencer and Barrett, 1984). This method, along with a minimum convex polygon algorithm, an elliptical home range program, and Anderson's UD program, has been implemented in Turbo Pascal under the acronym McPaal for IBM PC compatible computers. McPaal can be obtained from its authors, Michael Stuwe and Charles Blohowiak at the Conservation and Research Center, National Zoological Park, Front Royal, Virginia 22630.

Deciding on the appropriate percentage to use to delimit a home range estimate from a UD or harmonic mean distance can either be made arbitrarily or with some statistical justification. Samuel et al. (1985) suggest that core areas be delineated by enscribing those areas within the home range where use exceeds that expected from a uniform distribution, i.e., that distribution expected if an animal spends equal time in all parts of its home range. Clearly, other distributions, such as the Poisson, could be used as well.

5.4. Sample Considerations

The rate at which data are recorded depends on the speed of the animal and the purpose of the study. If activity patterns are the primary interest, then fairly short intervals (5-10 minutes) will ensure that infrequent, brief flying bouts are not missed; however, if home range estimation is an objective, then short intervals may be inappropriate because consecutive samples will show a high level of spatial correlation. This inter-sample dependency

biases almost all methods of home range estimation. Two solutions to this problem are available. Either the data can be checked for serial dependency and nonindependent points discarded or the serial correlation can be statistically removed when estimating the home range. Schoener (1981) suggests that a test of the independence assumption can be made by checking to see if the ratio of the mean squared distance from the geometric center, the r^2 defined above, to the mean squared distance between successive observations, t^2, equals 2, where

$$t^2 = \sum_{i=1}^{N-1} \left[\frac{(x_i-x_{i+1})^2 + (y_i-y_{i+1})^2}{(n-1)} \right] \quad (10)$$

Although Schoener only considered data which either follow a bivariate normal or uniform distribution, Swihart and Slade (1985) have shown that the relationship is also true for other distributions and provides standard errors for testing the significance of the ratio. If a bat spent long periods of time at one place, such as a fruiting tree, then some data may have to be discarded to meet this condition.

Alternatively, any serial correlation which exists in the data can be removed by using the multivariate Ornstein-Uhlenbeck diffusion process to estimate home range size as proposed by Dunn and Gipson (1977). This technique assumes a bivariate normal data distribution and approximates the movement of a movable ball tethered with an elastic band to a central location. Dunn and Brisbin (1983) discuss estimation techniques when data are spaced unequally in time.

The problem of sample dependency may not be as severe for radio-tracking studies on bats as it is for studies on terrestrial mammals. Because of their potential for rapid movement, some bats may change position sufficiently often such that little serial correlation exists between sample coordinates. For example, our unpublished radio tracking studies on the nectarivorous bat *Phyllostomus discolor* show that individuals often spend less than ten minutes at a flowering tree and move a kilometer or more between trees.

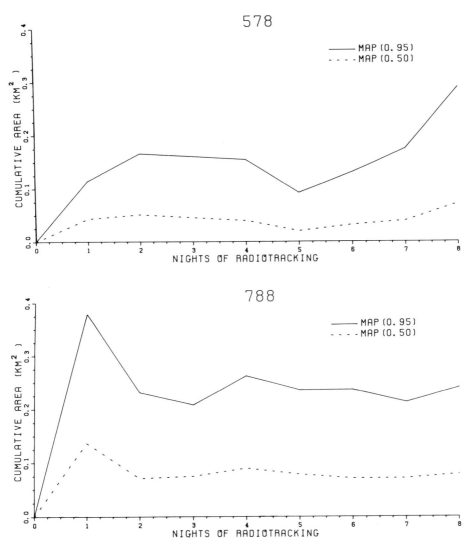

Figure 5. Cumulative home range estimates for two adult female *Desmodus rotundus* calculated by using the MAP(0.95) and MAP(0.5) from the Anderson nonparametric UD. Female 578 was radiotracked from 15-23 September 1981, while female 788 was followed from 18-22 December 1981 and, 3-6 January 1983.

Bats which "trap-line" like this may show little, if any, serial correlation between samples. Species which have more localized feeding "beats," on the other hand, may show significant amounts of serial correlation.

The number of samples required from a given individual to accurately estimate its home range or some other statistical property of its movements depends on the pattern of spatial variation exhibited by the animal over time. Estimates of the home range of many

mammals usually reach a plateau after 20-40 independent samples have been taken (e.g., Hawes, 1977). Not enough radio-tracking data from bats have been analyzed in this way to know if this generalization can be extended to bats. However, our studies on the vampire bat, *Desmodus rotundus,* show that home range can be estimated for females of this species in just a few nights. In Fig. 5 we have plotted the home range estimates obtained from the Anderson nonparametric technique over

8 nights of data collection. We believe these are representative because the data from one individual came from two sets of four consecutive nights of tracking separated by over 12 months. For this bat, #788, the MAP(0.95) home range estimate stabilized after two nights of tracking. The MAP(0.5) estimates of both bats also remained stable after only two nights. Studies of the greater spear-nosed bat, *Phylostomus hastatus,* show similar persistence in use of foraging ranges over time (cf. McCracken and Bradbury, 1981) by adult females. Some species, of course, may show seasonal movements, such as *Carollia perspicillata* (Heithaus and Fleming, 1978), and much longer tracking periods may be necessary to characterize their home range use.

6. ASSOCIATION AMONG INDIVIDUALS

6.1. Spatial Association

A distinct advantage of the UD methods proposed by Ford and Krumme (1979) and Anderson (1982) is that the intersection of the UDs of two animals can be used to estimate the proportion of time the two animals should be found in overlapping regions of their home ranges. This provides a more meaningful measure of their spatial association than just their overlap in space, which can be estimated by any of the home range techniques. Furthermore, the intersection of two UDs is not biased by any serial correlation which exists between samples, if the samples are equally spaced in time. Alternatively, a different measure of association can be made if several individuals frequent discrete resources, such as fruiting trees. In this case transition probabilities for each individual can be calculated between each site, and associations between individuals can then be detected with first-order Markov models as described in chapter 7 of Bishop et al. (1975).

6.2. Temporal Association

The multivariate Ornstein-Uhlenbeck diffusion process can be used to not only measure serial correlation within an individual's movements but also temporal correlations between individuals. Dunn (1979) discusses the computations involved in this measurement and describes how the SAS general multiple linear regression program can be used to make the appropriate tests. Dunn and Brisbin (1983) discuss the sensitivity of this test and provide examples for several terrestrial mammals. Because bats can move so rapidly, temporal associations can only be estimated between individuals from whom fixes have been obtained almost simultaneously. For this reason we recommend that any estimates of this type should be verified, if possible, with direct observations of radio-tagged individuals.

The sensitivity of any association measurement to the sampling error involved in measuring should always be reported. This can be done by adding and subtracting the sampling error from all measurements and then recalculating the association statistics. These values could then be used to show the error associated with the measurement. Alternatively, if data from several tracking sessions are available, confidence limits for these statistics can be calculated using jackknife techniques (Sokal and Rohlf, 1981).

7. SUMMARY

Radiotelemetry is the most effective method for determining the movement patterns and activity of wide-ranging nocturnal mammals such as bats. In this chapter we discuss methods of collecting and analyzing tracking data based on many joint years of experience. The section on collecting data begins with a simple, yet detailed, explanation for constructing small inexpensive pulsing transmitters and includes modifications to the basic circuit for monitoring physiological parameters, such as body temperature or position, as well as for running on solar power. Currently available commercial equipment for receiving and recording radio data are evaluated and an efficient method for taking bearings in the field is described.

We then describe several statistical methods for analyzing sequential spatial data to obtain estimates both of home range area and utilization and of associations among individuals in space and time. After reviewing both parametric and nonparametric techniques of calculating home range area, we suggest that the nonparametric technique for estimating home range area and utilization developed by Anderson (1982) is preferable for describing the home range of most animals including bats. This method is illustrated with data obtained from a long-term study on *Desmodus rotundus.* Because all methods of estimating home range area require independent data points, we also discuss ways to avoid and detect sample dependency. We recommend using the Anderson method for estimating spatial associations between individuals and caution against using the multivariate Ornstein-Uhlenbeck method developed by Dunn (1979) to calculate temporal associations both because the underlying assumptions are often implausible and because obtaining simultaneous bearings on more than one bat is inherently difficult.

8. ACKNOWLEDGMENTS

This work was supported by a grant (DEB-8001165) from the National Science Foundation. We thank Sandra Vincent for the triggered transmitter circuit and Forrest Gompf both for designing the circuit presented in Appendix 2 and modifying the Cochran circuit for solar power.

9. REFERENCES

Amlaner, C. J., and D. W. MacDonald (eds.). 1980. Proc. Int. Conf. Telemetry and Radio Tracking in Biology and Medicine. Oxford, England, 826 pp.

Anderson, D. J. 1982. The home range: A new nonparametric estimation technique. Ecology, 63:103-112.

Bishop, Y. M., S. E. Feinberg, and P. W. Holland. 1975. Discrete multivariate analysis. MIT, Cambridge, Massachusetts, 557 pp.

Bradbury, J. W. 1977. Lek mating behavior in the Hammer-headed bat. Z. Tierpsychol., 45:225-255.

Bradbury, J. W., D. Morrison, E. Stashko, and R. Heithaus. 1979. Radio-tracking methods for bats. Bat Res. News, 20:9-17.

Brigham, R. M. 1983. Roost selection and foraging by radio-tracked big brown bats (*Eptesicus fuscus*). Bat Res. News, 24:50-51.

Brown, P. E., and R. Berry. 1982. Activity patterns and foraging in *Antrozous pallidus* as determined by radiotelemetry. Bat Res. News, 23:62.

Brown, P. E., T. W. Brown, and A. D. Grinnell. 1983. Echolocation, development, and vocal communication in the lesser bulldog bat, *Noctilio albiventris.* Behav. Ecol. Sociobiol., 13:287-298.

Charles-Dominique, P. 1977. Urine marking and territoriality in *Galago alleni* (Waterhouse, 1837)—Lorisoidea, Primates—A field study by radio-telemetry. Z. Tierpsychol., 43:113-138.

Dixon, K. R., and J. A. Chapman. 1980. Harmonic mean measure of animal activity areas. Ecology, 61:1040-1044.

Dunn, J. E. 1979. A complete test for dynamical territorial interaction. Pp. 159-169, *in* Proc. 2nd Int. Conf. Wildlife Biotelemetry. (F. M. Long, ed.). Int. Conf. Wildlife Biotelemetry, Laramie, Wyoming.

Dunn, J. E., and I. L. Brisbin, Jr. 1983. Characterizations of the multivariate Ornstein-Uhlenbeck diffusion process in the context of home range analysis. Univ. Arkansas Stat. Lab. Tech. Report No. 16, 135 pp.

Dunn, J. E., and P. S. Gipson. 1977. Analysis of radio telemetry data in studies of home range. Biometrics, 33:85-101.

Fleming, T. H., E. R. Heithaus, and W. B. Sawyer. 1977. An experimental analysis of the food location behavior of frugivorous bats. Ecology, 58:619-627.

Ford, R. G., and D. W. Krumme. 1979. The analysis of space use patterns. J. Theor. Biol., 76:125-155.

Harrison, J. L. 1958. Range of movement of some Malayan rats. J. Mammal., 39:190-206.

Hawes, M. L. 1977. Home range, territoriality, and ecological separation in sympatric shrews, *Sorex vagrans* and *Sorex obscurus*. J. Mammal., 58:354-367.

Hayne, D. W. 1949. Calculation of size of home range. J. Mammal., 30:1-18.

Heithaus, E. R., and T. H. Fleming. 1978. Foraging movements of a frugivorous bat, *Carollia perspicillata* (Phyllostomatidae). Ecol. Monogr. 48:127-143.

Jennrich, R. I., and F. B. Turner. 1969. Measurement of non-circular home range. J. Theor. Biol., 22:227-237.

Koeppl, J. W., N. A. Slade, K. S. Harris, and R. S. Hoffman. 1977. A three dimensional home range model. J. Mammal., 58:213-220.

Leonard, M. L. and M. B. Fenton. 1983. Habitat use by spotted bats (*Euderma maculatum*, Chiroptera: Vespertilionidae): Roosting and foraging behaviour. Can. J. Zool., 61:1487-1491.

Long, F. M. (ed.). 1979. Wildlife Biotelemetry. Proc. 2nd Int. Conf. Wildlife Biotelemetry, Laramie, Wyoming.

McCracken, G. F., and J. W. Bradbury. 1981. Social organization and kinship in the polygynous bat, *Pyhllostomus hastatus*. Behav. Ecol. Sociobiol., 8:11-34.

Mech, L. D. 1983. Handbook of animal radiotracking. Univ. Minnesota Press, Duluth, Minnesota, 128 pp.

Morrison, D. W. 1978a. Foraging ecology and energetics of the frugivorous bat, *Artibeus jamaicensis*. Ecology, 59:716-723.

Morrison, D. W. 1978b. Lunar phobia in a neotropical bat, *Artibeus jamaicensis* (Chiroptera: Phyllostomatidae). Anim. Behav., 26:852-856.

Morrison, D. W. 1979. Apparent male defense of tree hollows in the fruit bat *Artibeus jamaicensis*. J. Mammal., 60:11-15.

Morrison, D. W. 1980. Foraging and day-roosting dynamics of canopy fruit bats in Panama. J. Mammal., 61:20-29.

Morrison, D. W. and S. H. Morrison. 1981. Economics of harem maintenance by a neotropical bat. Ecology, 62:864-866.

Odum, E. P., and E. J. Kuenzler. 1955. Measurement of territory and home range size in birds. Auk, 72:128-137.

Samuel, M. D., D. J. Pierce, and E. O. Garton. 1985. Identifying areas of concentrated use within the home range. J. Anim. Ecol., 54:711-719.

Schoener, T. W. 1981. An empirically based estimate of home range. Theor. Pop. Biol., 20:281-325.

Sokal, R. R., and F. J. Rohlf. 1981. Biometry. 2nd ed., W. H. Freeman, San Francisco, California, 859 pp.

Spencer, W. D., and R. H. Barrett. 1984. An evaluation of the harmonic mean measure for defining carnivore activity areas. Acta Zool. Fenn., 171:255-259.

Springer, J. T. 1979. Some sources of bias and sampling error in radio triangulation. J. Wildl. Manage., 43:926-935.

Swihart, R. K., and N. A. Slade. 1985. Testing for independence of observations in animal movements. Ecology, 66:1176-1184.

Thomas, D. W., and M. B. Fenton. 1978. Notes on the dry season roosting and foraging behavior of *Epomophorus gambianus* and *Rousettus aegyptiacus* (Chiroptera: Pteropidae). J. Zool., 186:403-406.

Vehrencamp, S. L., F. G. Stiles, and J. W. Bradbury. 1977. Observations on the foraging behavior and avian prey of the neotropical carnivorous bat, *Vampyrum spectrum*. J. Mammal., 58:469-478.

Wilkinson, G. S. 1985. Social organization of the common vampire bat. I. Pattern and cause of association. Behav. Ecol. Sociobiol., 17:123-134.

Williams, T. C., and J. M. Williams. 1967. Radio tracking of homing bats. Science, 155:1435-1436.

Williams, T. C., and J. M. Williams. 1970. Radio tracking of homing and feeding flights of a neotropical bat. *Phyllostomus hastatus*. Anim. Behav., 18:302-309.

Appendix 1.   Construction of Cochran Radio

Materials

Construction will require a small pencil-tipped soldering iron, a roll each of #32 and #36 insulated coil wire, fine solder, cyanoacrylate glue, GC Strip-X, GC Q-Dope, GC circuit board repair paint, and Duco cement. A pair of hemostats in a flytying vise and fine jeweler's forceps are helpful

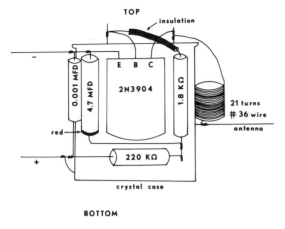

TOP

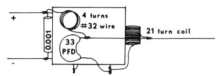

BOTTOM

Figure 6. Construction view of simple Cochran radio transmitter. See text for details.

for holding and manipulating the radio during construction. Fine spaghetti insulation (e.g., medic tubing) is recommended to prevent shorting between exposed leads. The following parts are required per transmitter:

1—Third overtone crystal, SC-45 case with 35 ohms maximum resistance,
series +1.156 KC, 2.4 PFD maximum capacitance pin-to-pin in desired frequency range
1—2N3904 transistor
1—33 PFD non-electrolytic capacitor
1—0.001 MFD non-electrolytic capacitor
1—4.75 MFD electrolytic capacitor
1—1.8 kohm resistor (⅛ watt or smaller)
1—220 kohm resistor (⅛ watt or smaller)
1—4 turn coil of #32 wire
1—21 turn coil of #36 wire

Methods

A. See Fig. 6 for orientation. Using a ⅛ inch (3.2 mm) diameter glass or metal rod as a form, wind the appropriate size wire the designated number of turns around the form and twist the wire ends together. Hang hemostat or other

weight on wire ends and use tweezers to gently press coils into close contact. Dab a tiny amount of Duco cement on two sides of the coil, being careful not to glue coil to form. Remove mass and gently slide coil off of form. Dip into Q-Dope. When dry, untwist wire ends and strip with Strip-X. Do not despair; coils just take practice to make.

B. If desired, file transistor case down to reduce weight. Hump and opposite side constitute the greatest excess. Transistors are cheap; experiment on one until you go too far. Arrange transistor and crystal so that leads of both are at same ends and glue side opposite hump on transistor to crystal case with cyanoacrylate glue. Attach so edge of transistor is touching edge of crystal case.

C. Holding crystal so transistor and crystal leads point up and transistor faces you, bend left transistor lead (emitter) to left. Solder central transistor lead (base) to left crystal lead and final transistor lead (collector) to other crystal lead. Do not trim either crystal lead yet.

D. Solder 4.75 MFD capacitor and 0.001 MFD capacitors in parallel to bent left hand lead of transistor. Be sure negative (non-red) end of 4.75 MFD capacitor is attached to this wire. Trim 2 of the wires and leave the third long for negative battery lead.

E. Place small piece of insulation over one lead of the 1.8 kohm resistor, place parallel to right side of transistor, and bending insulated part across collector wire of transistor, solder to left hand crystal lead. Trim all wires to this contact point.

F. Bend positive end of 4.75 MFD capacitor across bottom end of transistor and solder to free end of 1.8 kohm resistor. Trim excess of capacitor wire but not resistor lead.

G. Solder 220 kohm resistor to same end of 1.8 kohm resistor and orient parallel to bottom of transistor. Trim all remaining wires at this contact point.

H. Solder free end of 0.001 MFD capacitor to free end of 220 kohm resistor. Cut one of these wires at joint and use the other for positive battery lead.

I. File 33 PFD capacitor slightly on one side to make surface flat. Flip crystal over, and use cyanoacrylate to glue capacitor to crystal case as shown in Fig. 6. Attach outside wire to remaining (untrimmed) crystal lead. Bend other capacitor lead up and out from crystal case for antenna lead.

J. Glue 4-turn coil to crystal case and attach one stripped end to positive battery lead and other end to antenna lead. OPTION: You may want to attach positive battery lead to crystal case. This adds extra capacitance into the system which may affect timing and power output. Experiment.

K. Carefully attach 21-turn coil with one stripped end soldered to untrimmed crystal lead and the other soldered to the antenna lead. Now trim final crystal lead contact point. NOTE: The most likely sites of bad contacts are the coil wire attachments. A little solder paste often ensures a better contact. Glue 21-turn coil to crystal case to protect it. In principle, axis of 21-turn coil should be oriented perpendicular to antenna axis. Anticipate what you will do with antenna before gluing this coil to case.

L. Test radio with 1.5 V battery and current meter. Current meter should show pulses of current, the peaks of which are an indication of maximum current drain. If there is a steady DC current but no pulses, then either coils are not properly attached, or you have the wrong number of turns in the tank circuit coil or the wrong capacitance in the tank circuit capacitor. If no current is drawn, you have a bad contact in some other part of the circuit. If the radio draws over 500 microamps and is steady, there is a short in the circuit.

Appendix 2. Amplifier Circuit for Strip Recorder

The circuit diagram in Fig. 7 illustrates the components that are needed to construct a small amplifier which can be used to boost the signal from a LA-12 type receiver to activate the needle of a Rustrak (1 ohm, 1 milliamp) strip recorder. It is convenient to house these components in a watertight BNC junction box which can be connected easily to the strip recorder and the receiver. The power supply that drives the strip recorder can be used to power the amplifier.

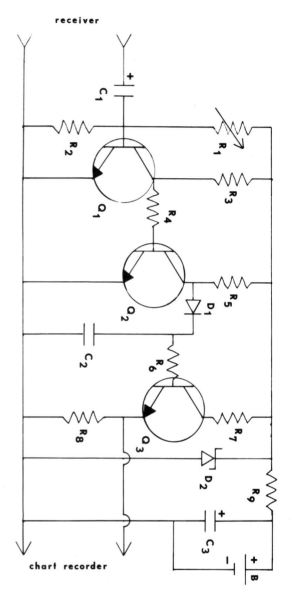

Figure 7. Schematic for amplifier to connect a strip recorder to a LA-12 type receiver. Resistors: R1 = 0-200 kohm variable; R2 = R7 = 10 kohm; R3 = 100 kohm; R4 = R8 = 1 kohm; R5 = 5 kohm; R6 = 1 Mohm; R9 = 100 ohm. Capacitors: C1 = 5 MFD electrolytic; C2 = 3.3 MFD; C3 = 10 MFD. Diodes: D1 = 1N914; D2 = 1N4733. Transistors: Q1 = 2N3904; Q2 = Q3 = 2N4401. Battery = 6-12 V.

Appendix 3. Selected List of Equipment and Sources

PRODUCT

Receivers

AVM Instrument Company
2368 Research Drive
Livermore, California
94550 USA

Custom Electronics, Inc.
2009 Silver Court West
Urbana, Illinois
61801 USA

Telonics
932 East Impala Avenue
Mesa, Arizona 85204 USA

Wildlife Materials, Inc.
R.R. #1, Giant City Road
Carbondale, Illinois
62901 USA

Antennas

AVM Instrument Company
2368 Research Drive
Livermore, California
94550 USA

Cushcraft Corporation
621 Hayward Street
Manchester, New Hampshire
03108 USA

Wildlife Materials, Inc.
R.R. #1, Giant City Road
Carbondale, Illinois
62901 USA

Radio-transmitters

AVM Instrument Company
2368 Research Drive
Livermore, California
94550 USA

Biotrack
Manor Farmhouse
Church Causeway
Sawtry, Huntingdon
Cambridgeshire, England

Custom Electronics, Inc.
9009 Silver Court West
Urbana, Illinois
61801 USA

Holohil Systems Ltd.
R.R. #2 Woodlawn
Ontario K0A 3M0
Canada

Telonics
932 East Impala Avenue
Mesa, Arizona 85204 USA

Wildlife Materials, Inc.
R.R. #1, Giant City Road
Carbondale, Illinois
62901 USA

Transmitter Components

Micro Miniature carbon film resistors

BREL
P.O. Drawer C
Sarasota, Florida
33578 USA

Crystals

Sentry Manufacturing Company
Crystal Park
Chickasha, Oklahoma
73018 USA

Miniature transistors
(2N3904, BF599)

Siemens Corporation
186 Wood Avenue South
Iselin, New Jersey
08830 USA

Tank capacitors (non-electrolytic)
(33 PFD #CN 15A-330K)

Wyle Distribution Group
9525 Chesapeake Drive
San Diego, California
92123 USA

Tantalum minicapacitors
(4.75 MFD MZP-002-475-A-40)
(0.001 MFD MZY-020-102-A-40)

Copper enamel coil wire
(32-gauge Beldon 8056)
(36-gauge Beldon 8058)

Corning Components
Biddleford, Maine
04005 USA

Batteries

Button-type nicad batteries

Tauber Electronics
4901 Morena Boulevard
San Diego, California
92117 USA

Mercury batteries

Newark Electronics
500 North Pulaski Road
Chicago, Illinois
60624 USA

Soldering Tools

Unger 9100

Mitchell-Hughes Company
7534 Atoll Avenue
North Hollywood, California
60624 USA

Chapter 8

Techniques for Photographing Bats

J. Scott Altenbach

Department of Biology
University of New Mexico
Albuquerque, New Mexico 87131 USA

1. INTRODUCTION

Photography of bats presents unique problems to the would-be photographer. Because of the tremendous variability in their activity, ranging from a state of motionless torpor to sudden movement, reaching airspeeds approaching 18 m/sec, and completing a wingbeat cycle at frequencies up to 20 Hz, a variety of techniques and instrumentation is needed to record these images on film. The secretive nature of most bats and their preference for illumination far below that suited to most photography provide enumerable challenges. Obviously, some photographic data can be obtained only with complicated equipment and techniques. However, photographs useful to a researcher can be taken of still and moving subjects with a minimum of equipment and techniques.

In writing this, I have remembered the difficulties I encountered in trying to photographically record bat locomotion as well as other aspects of their biology. The information presented here should serve as a *starting point* for anyone interested in bat photography as a tool for data gathering or for those considering an unfamiliar technique or use of an unfamiliar type of equipment. The equipment discussed here will hopefully narrow the search for a suitable photographic mechanism and minimize costly trial and error methods. Schematics of some of the electronic equipment I have used might provide solutions or at least ideas for those on a modest budget in a world of high-priced technology. I have not attempted to make the discussion of available equipment complete. To do so would only invite criticism because of omission.

2. STILL PHOTOGRAPHY

Still photographs of bats can be taken in virtually infinite situations. Almost any aspect of bat biology can be recorded in a still photograph, although some require specialized equipment and techniques. The categories that follow are photographic situations and possible equipment and techniques applicable to each.

2.1. Motionless Subject: Adequate Illumination

Adequate illumination is a function of shutter speed, light gathering capability of optics, and film speed. Unless a dead bat is to be photographed, movement of the subject or camera during the exposure is a possibility and a shutter speed of 1/100 sec or faster would be desirable. Fast lenses, with maximum apertures of 1.2, are available for most cameras which accommodate interchangeable lenses. Very fast black and white film stock is available in 35mm format as well as in larger roll film and cut sizes. Many of these film stocks can be exposed at far higher ASA values than rated by using forced processing. However, a substantial increase in grain size will result. Fast color film (ASA 1000) is available and could readily be used in this application.

The tradeoffs for utilizing fast lenses, long exposure duration, and fast films are respectively shallow depth of field, blur because of even slight subject or camera movement, and increase in grain in the negative or transparency. The photography of bats under these conditions should be a last resort when other approaches are not feasible.

Even if incident illumination is adequate for an exposure, use of electronic flash as additional light or fill light is recommended. Electronic flash units are discussed in detail in the following sections.

2.2. Moving Subject: Inadequate Illumination

Illumination may be inadequate because it cannot expose even a fast emulsion film at a long shutter duration with the lens aperture at maximal opening. Any of the above approaches may produce intolerably shallow depth of field, blur, or grain. Another problem is that continuous higher illumination necessary for proper exposure may not be tolerated by the subject. Possible alternatives for providing supplemental light (incandescent, flashbulbs, or electronic flash) are discussed below.

2.3. Supplemental Illumination

2.3.1. Arrangement of Lights

The mistakes seen most frequently in bat photographs are those resulting from improper placement of light sources. Anyone considering taking a bat photograph should consult an introductory reference on photographic lighting. These are available at most stores selling photographic supplies. Others are available in the photography section of most libraries. Some examples are Mortensen (1947), Jacobs (1962, 1980), Cooper and Abbott (1979), and Life library of photography (1970).

Illumination with a single light source at the camera produces a shadowless, flat image, whereas a single light source to one side of the camera produces dark shadows in which detail is lost. Even if only one light source is available, this problem can be minimized by using reflective material to bounce light onto the subject from a different angle. A main or key light placed to one side of the camera will provide the majority of the illumination while a reflector placed nearer to the camera's line of view will provide a softer fill light to add detail and soften the shadows. The results are vastly superior to those using a single light source. Obviously a second, less intense light (or one placed at a greater distance from the subject) could be used as a fill to give a similar result. As a discussion of lighting will illustrate, the possibilities are limitless and can involve many lights. I have used four lights to provide a main source and three fill sources around the camera (the photographs in Fig. 3 and in Altenbach (1979), Vaughan (1972), are examples), but I prefer one main and two fill lights around the camera and a backlight to produce highlights on hair and wing edges Geluso et al. (1987). Tuttle (1982, 1983) and Dalton (1976) used a system similar to this while Greenawalt (1960) produced beautiful hummingbird photographs with an array of three lights arranged close to the camera.

2.3.2. Continuous Incandescent Illumination

Illumination can be supplied by virtually any kind or combination of incandescent lamps for black and white photography. For color photography, lamps should be color balanced for the film being used. The color-film manufacturer supplies information on necessary color temperature in degrees Kelvin (K°) of photo lamps. An alternative is color correction of incandescent illumination with over-the-lamp or over-the-lens filters. If lens filters are used, a compensation must be made for reduced light in cameras without through-the-lens metering.

The only limits to the levels of incandescent illumination that can be directed on a photographic subject are: 1) the power available from an alternating current source or battery, 2) the heat the photographic "set" will tolerate (e.g., backdrop, baffles, etc.), and 3) the level of light and heat the subject will tolerate and still cooperate with the photographer. In bat photography, the last limitation is probably the most serious. Under high continuous incandescent illumination, an already light-shy subject is not likely to remain motionless in an "ideal pose." A flying subject is somewhat easier to photograph under high illumination if its flight path can be briefly directed past the light and camera. A series of baffles with openings for lights and camera works well. This creates a limited flight path and bats can readily be acclimated to fly through it and past the camera and light array. Rapid shutter duration (up to 1/4000 sec) is available in some current focal plane shutter cameras and electro-mechanical shutter assemblies can interface with single lens reflex cameras to provide even shorter dura-

tions. An example is the UniBlitz shutter manufactured by A. W. Vincent Associates. With these short shutter durations, reasonable photographs of flying bats can be taken under high incandescent illumination. Motion stopping is discussed in the section on still photography with electronic flash.

2.3.3. Flashbulb Illumination

Flashbulbs are still applicable in situations where a brilliant burst of light is needed to illuminate a large area over a relatively long distance. Such an application might be an exposure of a group of bats roosting in the top of a large attic or in a large chamber in a cave. Although high-output electronic flash units are available or can readily be constructed, their expense would not warrant use in making a few such exposures. In applications where a large area or an object at a great distance must be illuminated, multiple flashbulbs may be fired in synchrony by wiring them in parallel and discharging a capacitor into the parallel circuit.

2.3.4. Electronic Flash Illumination

There are many commercially available electronic flash units and the variety of units that can be constructed for specific applications is practically infinite. Examples of commercially available units and some of their characteristics are discussed below and listed in Appendix 1.

An *ideal* electronic flash unit for bat photography would have a short duration flash, high light output, color temperature suitable for color films, and rapid recycle time. It would be portable and inexpensive. These features can be achieved but with great difficulty in a single unit since some are achieved at the expense of others. Some of the features most critical to bat photography are considered below.

Flash duration of an electronic flash unit is typically measured as the duration between $1/3$ peak light levels. A consideration of how long the flash duration should be for still photography of moving bats is essentially one of how much stop motion is necessary. As the following example illustrates, this is a question of how much blur is acceptable in the photograph. Assume a flying bat completes 10 wingbeats per sec and that the wing tip travels 40 cm on each wingbeat cycle. Thus the wing tip is moving at a velocity of 4 m per sec and a flash that lasted 1/1000 (.001) sec would illuminate the wing tip as it traveled 4 mm. The photograph would be blurred and useless for interpretation of wing detail. Airspeed of the bat, wingbeat frequency, and position of the camera relative to motion of the bat must be taken into consideration in deciding how much blur will be present in a photograph of a given duration. For example, an exposure at 1/1000 sec of a slow-flying or hovering bat would produce a sharp image of body and head, but would produce badly blurred wings. A comparable exposure of a fast-flying molossid bat would be virtually useless. An exposure that would be inadequate for a side view of a flying bat might be adequate for a head-on shot. An exposure inadequate to "freeze" wing motion in a head-on or side shot might be adequate for a photograph taken from above or below during mid-stroke.

In practice, a flash duration of 1/10,000 (.0001) sec is the maximal duration that will produce a reasonably sharp image of a flying bat photographed from the most difficult angle for motion stopping. However, short duration is achieved at a cost of other desirable features.

The majority of commercially available electronic flash units use electrolytic capacitors and thus produce a *full energy* flash of rather long duration (1/1000 sec or longer) for use in any rapid-motion bat photography.

Many commercially available "automatic" units are advertised as having very short flash durations, often shorter than 1/20,000 sec. Some examples are the Sunpak Auto 231, Vivitar Auto 215, Nikon SB-9, Honeywell Auto Strobolite 57, and Nissin 24 ASO. Automatic units have a photosensor which monitors reflected light from the subject. When sufficient light has been detected

to make an adequate exposure, the flashtube is shut down. They can be made to flash at the lowest light output and therefore shortest duration by deceiving the light sensor. A piece of reflective material can be placed a few cm in front of the sensor or a piece of lucite can be bent with heat to act as a "light pipe" to channel light from the flash to the sensor (Cooper and Abbott, 1979). Other units have a manual setting which can reduce light and duration in addition to the photosensor. The Vivitar 285, Nissin 360 TW Auto Thyristor and 3200 GT Auto Thyristor, Minolta 360 PX and 280 PX, Sunpak Auto 611, Auto 422 D, and Auto 522, and Nikon SB-5 are examples.

When the duration of the flash is reduced, so is the light output. The short duration photographs produced by these units are achieved with short lamp-to-subject distance and/or high film speed and wide open lens aperture settings. Thus, depth of field, grain size, and awkward positioning of a flash unit close to a subject are the costs of short duration flashes achieved by this means.

Thus, *sufficient light producing capability* must be added to the short flash duration criterion for an ideal electronic flash unit. This would mean production of sufficient light for a convenient lamp-to-subject distance and small lens aperture setting to provide necessary depth of field. The automatic or adjustable units described above can satisfy the light output requirements *if* multiples of them are used in a "slave" mode. The slave feature is built into some units and is simply a light sensor which triggers the unit when another unit is flashed. Small accessory slave triggers that clip onto or plug into the trigger contacts of other units convert them into slave units. Examples are the Micro Slave (Wein Products Incorporated) and the Super Slave (Preferred Photo Products). Groups of these slave units, each operating at low light output and flash duration, can produce the "sufficient" light levels discussed above. Clusters of three or four such units can be used as described in the section on Arrangement of lights for Supplemental Illumination. This is a technique used by Tuttle (1982,

1983) (M. D. Tuttle, pers. comm.).

In my opinion the other desirable features in an electronic flash unit for photography of flying bats are less important than short duration and adequate light output. The Presto 180/25 High Speed Flash Unit manufactured by Press-Tige Pictures Ltd. seems ideal for bat photography. It features a 1/40,000 sec duration and has an output which is variable between 72 and 180 watt-seconds. Units used to provide supplemental illumination for various kinds of motionless or slow-moving subjects can be selected for minimal mass, bulk, and cost.

Anyone interested in constructing an electronic flash unit for bat photography would be well advised to read *Electronic Flash, Strobe,* by Harold Edgerton (1979). All aspects of electronic flash are discussed, a variety of solutions to design problems are presented, and schematics for various flash producing systems are also given. Electronic flash units that feature short duration flashes and high light output have been constructed by or for several nature photographers (Greenawalt, 1960; Dalton, 1976; Altenbach, 1979). Edgerton (1979, 1982) and Mott (1974) provide additional information useful in electronic flash design and construction. Although it is now out of print, the General Electric Flashtube Data Manual provides valuable information on design and flashtube theory, as does the current EG&G Flash Lamp Applications Manual.

2.3.5. Electronic Flash Exposure Testing

Electronic flash manufacturers rate light output of their units in watt-seconds (a measure of power delivered to the flashtube, equation 6), beam-candle-power-seconds (BCPS) (a measurement of light output at the center of the beam of light), or guide number at an EI (exposure index or ASA rating) rating of 25 or 100. The guide number (GN) is the product of f-stop and distance (in ft or m) from lamp to subject. The formula

$$GN \text{ (ft)} = \sqrt{0.05 \times BCPS \times \text{daylight EI of film}} \quad (1)$$

is useful for determining a GN if the manufacturer lists light output in BCPS. If a film is used with a different EI than the one prescribed in the manufacturer's rating, the following formula is useful.

$$GN_x = GN_y \sqrt{\frac{EI_x}{EI_y}} \quad (2)$$

where: GN_x = guide number for film x
GN_y = guide number for film y
EI_x = exposure index for film x
EI_y = exposure index for film y

Whether an electronic flash unit has been purchased or constructed, a test to determine its *actual* light output is *essential.* Guide numbers or BCPS ratings provided by manufacturers are often *higher* than the units are capable of delivering. The most useful test is to take a "bracketed" series of exposures with the lamp, lamp power setting, subject, and backdrop arrangement you plan to use. A study skin of the type of bat to be photographed, the best test subject, is positioned at the center of the field and lamp-to-subject-distances are carefully measured. A trial f-stop, based on the stated or calculated GN, is set and an exposure is taken. Allowing *twice* the charging (or recycle) time between flashes, this is repeated in half-stop increments for at least two stops each side of the starting point. The f-stop of the best exposure should be the one used for that bat and that light and backdrop arrangement. Once the proper settings have been determined, the output of individual units can be verified with a flash meter like the Minolta III or the Smith Victor XE88.

2.4. Portrait Photography

Closeup photographs of bats require brilliant illumination to permit a small aperture and adequate depth of field. Fast films are of minimal value since their grain in a detailed portrait is often noticeable and objectionable. Electronic flash is preferable since the bat is not subjected to sustained bright light and heat, and movement during exposure causes no blur. If continuous lighting must be used, a reflected light reading must be taken close to the bat. A reading from a bat *plus* a black or nonilluminated background will produce an exposed photograph. Many temperate-zone bats can be induced into torpor using refrigeration to facilitate positioning and focusing.

Portraits taken against a black, non-reflective backdrop like black velveteen are attractive, although any uniform background with higher or lower reflectance than the bat will work if placed far enough behind the bat to eliminate shadows. Multiple lamps (electronic flash or incandescent) can provide attractive key, fill, and backlighting. A wooden or metal bracket to hold lamps in the desired position saves time if many portraits are to be taken. The bracket can also hold two or more lights on a camera for photography in the field.

2.5. Multiflash Still Photography

Multiple electronic flash-illuminated exposures of moving bats on a single film frame is a technique used by Griffin et al. (1960), Webster and Griffin (1962), and Altenbach (1979). The technique is simple in that the flash does not need to fire in synchrony with a cine camera. A darkened room and a black backdrop allow an open lens during multiple exposures. A single-flash exposure test dis-

cussed above is essential and flash and camera operation can be actuated manually or automatically as discussed below.

A suitable flash unit might be the Nikon Repeating Flash Unit SB-6 which can be used in the "MULTI" mode up to 5 flashes per sec at 1/4 power and up to 40 flashes per sec at 1/32 power. The Chadwick Helmuth 236 power supply and lamp, the EG&G 501 High-Speed Stroboscope, and the repetitive flash described by Brandon (1977) could all be used in this application if triggered by an external contactor or pulse generator. Repetitive units available from Edmund Scientific can also be used. The Dale "intervalometer/sequencer/camera tripper" (Pollock, 1983) should be useful in triggering camera or flash.

2.6. Simultaneous Photographs with Multiple Angles

In studies of bat locomotion, simultaneous photographs from different viewpoints are necessary to resolve position of limbs and limb rotation. This can be done by using multiple cameras with open shutters (T or B) and having an electronic flash unit triggered by a photocell-servo circuit (Norberg, 1976). An alternative approach is to use mirrors positioned to show additional views of the bat to a single camera. Mirrors mounted in black, wooden frames supported by an adjustable

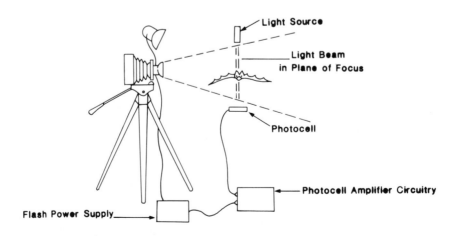

Figure 1. Diagram of light beam-photocell technique for automatic trip of electronic flash and/or camera.

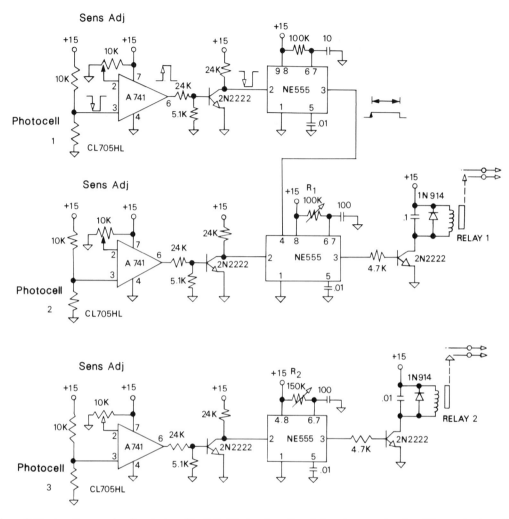

Figure 2. Photocell-servo circuitry designed by Fritz Husher for still and cine photography of rapidly moving bats. The system is powered by a filtered DC supply that can deliver 15 VDC at 200 ma.

frame of iron pipe have worked well in my studies.

2.7. Automatic Triggering of Photographs

A problem that must be solved for photographing flying or rapidly moving bats is insuring that the bat is in the center of the field of view and in the plane of focus at the instant the photograph is taken.

A solution to this problem is the use of a light beam-photocell combination with appropriate servo circuitry to actuate a camera-flash system. A beam of light from a microscope illuminator or flashlight is directed through the center of the field and through the plane of focus onto a photocell. The photocell detects the bat's shadow as it intersects the light beam and associated servo circuitry completes a camera trip or flash trigger circuit. Fig. 1 shows a diagrammatic setup of this apparatus.

If the ambient light in the area is low, it is convenient to use the camera on B or T setting, i.e., open shutter, and the interruption of the beam of light triggers the flash. This is the method I have used most successfully. A schematic (Fig. 2) of a photocell-servo circuit

Figure 3. Stages in the approach and capture sequence used in foraging by *Noctilio leporinus.*

which was designed in 1975 by Mr. Fritz Husher is included. Note that this circuit has three photocells and amplifier units. The first two can be used in a decision-making setup where a bat first has to shadow photocell number 1, then number 2 to trigger the flash with closure of the relay. A bat flying the wrong direction and shadowing number 2 first does not close the relay. Photocell number 3 and its amplifier can be used independently in a non-decision-making mode. The use of this system to operate a cine camera and repetitive electronic flash unit is discussed below (Section 3.4). If ambient light does not permit an open shutter method, the photocell circuitry can activate a camera shutter which in turn can trigger a flash.

Pollock (1983) reported on a commercially available flash and/or camera trigger called the Dale Beam. This unit is actuated by light beam interruption or by a sound pickup and is battery powered. Merlin D. Tuttle (pers. comm.) has used this unit in a bat photography application and reports it to be highly effective. Edgerton (1979) presents two such circuits and Cooper and Abbott (1979) illustrate another.

In the setup shown in Fig. 1, an obvious problem is that the position of the bat along the axis of the light beam can vary and cause a photograph with the subject above or below the center of the field. This can be minimized by positioning the light source and photocell close to the edges of the field or by providing baffles to direct the flight path toward the center of the field. Another solution would be the use of a dual light beam-dual photocell system whose perpendicular beams of light intersect at the center of field and plane of focus. Only simultaneous interruption of both beams of light would trigger the camera or flash and would produce a centered and focused image.

Successive stages in some repeatable events may be photographed by positioning the light beam and photocell in such a way that the beam is intersected earlier or later in the event during successive repetitions by the same animal or by different ones. Good examples are the stages in the jump of the common vampire bat (Altenbach, 1979) or the stages in the approach, capture, and transfer of a prey item to the mouth by a greater bulldog bat (Fig. 3). The photocell assembly was moved about 3.0 cm along the bottom of the pool between groups of 2 to 4 photos. The result was a photo series that included all of the stages in the sequence.

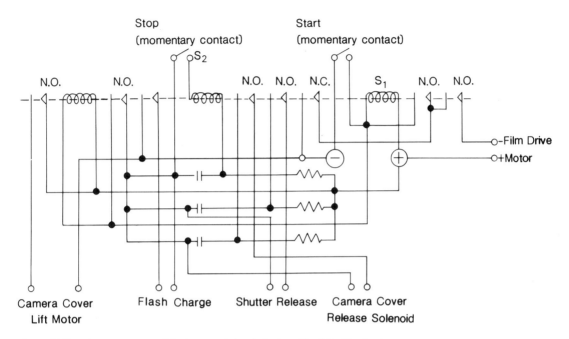

Figure 4. Time-lapse camera and flash control circuit designed by J. S. Altenbach.

3. TIME-LAPSE PHOTOGRAPHY

The term time-lapse (or pulse) photography refers to frame rates below 10 frames per second (Hyzer, 1962) and finds several applications in bat research. Minute by minute, hourly, daily, weekly, or monthly recording of position and number of bats in a roost and cluster configuration would be two examples. Daily or hourly photos of guano accumulation, roost floor biota activity or infant mortality, and entry triggered surveillance of night roosts or pool utilization would be additional applications.

This technique could be accomplished simply by the photographer directly or remotely releasing the camera at a predetermined time or at a time of some event occurrence. Virtually any size format camera and any illumination from low light augmented by a night vision scope connected to a flashbulb or electronic flash could be used. This approach was used in a population estimation technique described by Altenbach et al. (1979).

A more automated approach would be to use a motor-drive still camera with an auxiliary bulk film magazine. A mechanical or electronic timer could easily trigger the camera and the advance mechanism by discharging a capacitor into a solenoid. The most reasonable illumination in this application would be an electronic flash. The difficulty here, however, is that the electronic flash will consume some power if left on between flashes. This is particularly serious if the interflash interval is long. A better approach would be a system which, when activated by the timer, would first turn on the electronic flash charge circuit, advance the camera, trip the camera and flash, and then turn off the electronic flash. A schematic for a control circuit for this application is shown in Fig. 4.

Several cine cameras are ideal for time lapse photography and are designed to be operated in this mode. The Bolex 16 mm H-16 SBM and 16 mm H-16 REX-5 spring-wound cameras feature single frame control which can be actuated by a Bolex Variometer. This device features a single-frame motor which attaches to the camera, a variable exposure control (1/10 sec—10 sec per frame), and a timing unit that permits automatic single-frame filming at intervals from 0.3 sec to 6 h. Another feature of this camera is synchronization with electronic flash in the single-frame mode. Comparable features are available in several other commercially available 16 mm cine cameras.

4. CINEMATOGRAPHY

One of the variables in cinematography is frame rate, i.e. number of frames per sec (fps). If the film is to be exposed at the same frame rate at which it is projected, the recorded event would be viewed in the same time scale as the eye would see it. This is called *real time.* Since the typical frame rate of most projectors is about 24 fps, pictures filmed at this rate would be in real time. Motion pictures filmed at frame rates higher than 30 fps, and projected at rates below filming rate can be referred to as *slow motion.* That is, when viewed at 24 fps these will produce time magnification.

The frame rate of most cine cameras commonly used is adjustable between about 10 and 72 fps. With more specialized cameras, frame rates up to many thousands of fps are available.

The film drive mechanism in commonly used 16 mm cine cameras such as the Bolex or Arriflex is intermittent or pin-registered and 50-75 fps is usually the upper limit. After the film is advanced, single or paired pins engage sprocket perforations and hold the film stationary during the exposure. The image quality is determined only by the quality of lens optics, grain characteristics of the film stock, amount of image movement during exposure, and accuracy of focus. There are several pin-registered or intermittent cameras capable of frame rates up to 400, 500, and 1000 fps. The Red Lake Labs Locam, Teledyne Camera Systems (Miliken) DBM series, and Photo-Sonics 1PD are examples in 16 mm format. Some, like the Teledyne DBM 45 and 55 are

continuously variable from 1 to 500 fps, while others like the Photo-Sonics 1PD are variable in increments (16, 24, 50, 100, 200, 300, and 400 fps).

Cine cameras capable of higher frame rates are typically non-intermittent, optical-compensating. Since the optical compensation involves a prism assembly which moves an image in synchrony with continuously moving film, these cameras are often referred to as "rotating prism" cameras. Cameras like Red Lake Labs Hycam series are continuously variable from 1 to 11,000 fps, while those such as the Photo-Sonics 1 BAC are variable in increments (200 to 1000 fps in increments of 200 fps).

Another variable in cinematography is the duration of the exposure. In a cine camera, the shutter duration can be expressed as follows:

$$D = \frac{P}{F} \qquad (4)$$

Where: D = shutter duration in seconds
P = shutter duration—period ratio
F = picture frequency in fps

The duration-period ratio is the time fraction of one exposure cycle that the shutter is open.

In some cine cameras the duration-period ratio is fixed (often at 0.5 in older cameras), while in others it is adjustable. Adjustability can be facilitated by a disc shutter which has an adjustable angular opening or by replaceable disc shutters with varying angles. Typical variation in angular opening is from about 7° to 180° (0.019-0.5 duration-period ratio).

4.1. Real Time

4.1.1. Daylight or Incandescent Illumination

Cine photos can be taken in real time with cameras designed for that range as well as with those designed for "high speed." If research objectives are fulfilled by cine photography in the range of frame rates available in commonly used cine cameras such as a Bolex or Arriflex, these cameras are recommended. They feature easy through-the-lens focus and some have through-the-lens light metering and viewing while running. Some have rewind capability and automatic threading and are generally easier to operate than are "high-speed" cameras.

Virtually the only necessity is to select a film stock that is fast enough to permit a minimal f-stop under existing illumination. (A minimal f-stop means one which will give adequate depth of field to cover the limits of movement excursion of the subject.) In cameras that do not have a variable shutter, the shutter duration-period ratio cannot be changed and will vary as frame rate is changed, if this is adjustable. If through-the-lens metering is available, proper exposure is directly determined by varying the f-stop until the proper setting is found. If this feature is not available, a reflected light reading is taken with an appropriate meter. As discussed in the section on portraiture (Section 2.4), the light reading must be taken from the bat only, not bat and background. A study skin of the type of bat to be photographed makes an ideal subject on which to take a trial reading.

Films, in color and black and white, are available with sufficiently high ASA ratings that cine photographs in real time can be taken with minimal illumination. A wide variety of flood lamps or lamp-reflector combinations can provide supplemental illumination. The only difficulties encountered in supplying incandescent illumination are those discussed above.

4.1.2. Electronic Flash Illumination

There are situations in cinematography in real time where a reduced blur is desired. If rapid motion is photographed in real time and a short exposure is desired, electronic flash provides a solution that is more tolerable to bats than is a low shutter duration-period ratio and necessary bright continuous illumination. Gans (1966) described a system such as this utilizing a Bolex 16mm camera and two synchronized repetitive electronic flash units triggered by the camera shutter mechanism. An electronic flash system manufactured by Chadwick Helmuth Co. has a power supply (No. 236) capable of driving a helical flash lamp at frequencies over 200 flashes per sec at a power input of 200 watts. In repetitive flash applications power is computed by:

$$P = WS(F) \tag{5}$$

Where: P = power in watts
F = flashes per sec
WS = watt seconds per flash
$(WS = 0.5CV^2)$ (6)

Where: C = capacitance of flash capacitor in microfarads
V = voltage of flash capacitor in kilovolts

At lower flash frequency, e.g. real time, the energy per flash could be much higher. The flash duration varies inversely with the energy input per flash. The manufacturer supplies data on light output at various settings that can readily be used to compute the guide number. The Nikon Repeating Flash Unit SB-6 also is suitable in this application as are the units discussed in the section on equipment for high-frame-rate illumination.

Although some of the electronic flash equipment described above is reasonably priced, it is possible for the serious researcher to construct a repetitive flash unit adequate for the requirements of real time cinematography as well as one with considerably higher frame rates. *However, no one unfamiliar with high-voltage, high-current energy discharge circuitry should attempt their construction unless under the supervision of a competent and qualified person!* Persons interested should consult Edgerton (1979) and Brandon (1977).

4.2.   High Frame Rates

High frame rates are those above the range available in commonly used 16mm cine cameras. A variety of data are available from high-frame-rate cine film. Obviously, time magnification would allow viewing of events not visible to the eye in real time (e.g., the wingbeat cycle, an alighting maneuver, a capture of a prey item, a drink while flying over water, the movement of the tongue or mouth while feeding, or ear movements during echolocation). Anyone interested in high-frame-rate cinematography should consult Hyzer (1962).

It seems reasonable that short exposures which maximally reduce blur would be as desirable in high-frame-rate cinematography as they are in still photography. However, if the film is to be projected at standard rates, very sharp images make the film difficult to watch. For this application, some blur (e.g., at wingtips) is an advantage as long as it does not obscure details that are critical in the image. Since frame rate cannot be adjusted during filming, it must be set at the minimal rate to adequately sample the most rapid portion of a movement continuum. For high-frame-rate analysis of bat movement, this rate must be determined by trial and error. For example, one cycle of a 15 cycle per sec wingbeat should last 1/15 (0.066) sec. Twenty photos taken during the 0.066 sec cycle (300 fps) provide 10 sample points on both downstroke and upstroke. This is adequate for analysis of wing positions and relative rates of limb movement, but it does not consistently resolve short-duration events like the turnover point in upstroke to downstroke transition. Consistent resolution of this event requires a frame rate of about 450 fps.

4.2.1.   Continuous Illumination

Continuous daylight or incandescent illumination is commonly used for high-frame-rate cinematography, especially if the film is destined for projection and viewing. Incandescent illumination is relatively easy to provide, and lamps that are color balanced for particular color films can be used to insure "natural color." The only reasonable upper limits to the amount of light that can be directed on a photographic subject are those discussed in the section on still photography. A reflectance reading is taken *from the subject* with a remote light meter set to the proper exposure duration and ASA rating of the film.

4.2.2.   Electronic Flash Illumination

Electronic flash illumination for high-frame-rate filming has advantages of: 1) being much cooler on the subject than incandescent illumination to achieve comparable exposure, 2) providing flashes shorter than shutter duration at a given frame rate (especially important for lower frame rates and for cameras with non-variable duration-period ratio), 3) no warmup time, i.e., lights do not have to be on for warmup before the first exposure can be made, and 4) illumination of only a chosen portion of a roll of film, i.e., not exposing film with camera running after action has ceased or moved out of field of view.

Disadvantages of electronic flash illumination in this application are: 1) relative cost of commercially available repetitive units, 2) spectral output from some units not suitable for color cinematography, and 3) noise during operation disturbing the subject.

Many cine cameras produced in recent years feature some kind of flash synchronizing device. In considering the purchase of a camera and/or a repetitive electronic flash unit, one should establish how readily the camera and flash system will interface.

4.2.3.   Electronic Flash Equipment for High Frame-rate Illumination

The Strobex 236 system, manufactured by Chadwick-Helmuth, discussed in the section on cinematography in real time, features a variety of basic modules and a wide variety of accessories, including different lamp heads. Flash rates up to 400 fps are available, as are photocell and magnetic pickups for synchronization. This system is capable of operation in synchrony at about the highest frame rates available in intermittent high-frame-rate cameras.

The 501 High-Speed Stroboscope, manufactured by EG&G Corporation, will operate at flash rates up to 6000 fps. Different lampheads are available for illuminating a variety of subjects. EG&G also manufactures other repetitive electronic flash equipment and a wide variety of flashtubes and associated components. Brandon (1977) designed a repetitive electronic flash system around a compact-arc flashtube manufactured by United States Scientific Instruments (USSI). The system has two lamp heads, operates at over 1000 fps, and is driven by the correlation pulse generator of a high-speed cine camera. USSI is now owned by EG&G Corporation, and inquiries about equipment described in Brandon's system should be addressed to EG&G (see Appendix 1).

4.3. Timing of Camera and Flash Operation

The photocell-amplifier-servo circuitry described in the section on still photography with electronic flash (Fig. 2) is readily used in cinematography in triggering both camera and flash operation. In this application, shadowing of photocell number 1 *then* number 2 closes relay 1 for a time period (0.2–2.0 sec) determined by R_1. This actuates the camera for the predetermined period. If the bat then flies into the camera field in the plane of focus, it shadows photocell number 3 and relay 2 closes for a time period (0.1–1.0 sec) determined by R_2. This connects the electronic flash driving circuitry to the camera synchronization pulse and operates the flash.

5. SUMMARY

This chapter reviews methods suitable for still photography, real time, and high-frame-rate cinematography of bats, including use of ambient light, supplemental incandescent, flashbulb, and electronic flash illumination. A discussion of electronic flashes includes a general description of electronic flash operation, requirements of flash duration for motion stopping, and techniques for calculating and experimentally determining guide numbers for flash units. A system for the automatic triggering of photographs is described for portrait, multiflash, and simultaneous multiangle photography. Techniques and applications of time-lapse photography are reviewed. Useful electronic circuit schematics are provided for equipment that is unavailable commercially. An incomplete list of manufacturers of equipment for use in bat photography is included in an Appendix.

6. REFERENCES

Altenbach, J. S. 1979. The locomotor morphology of the vampire bat, *Desmodus rotundus.* Spec. Publ., Amer. Soc. Mamm., 6. 137 pp.

Altenbach, J. S., K. N. Geluso, and D. E. Wilson. 1979. Population size of *Tadarida brasiliensis* at Carlsbad Caverns in 1973. Pp. 341-348. *in* Biological investigation in the Guadalupe Mountains National Park, Texas. (H. H. Genoways and R. J. Baker, eds.) Natl. Park Serv. Proc. Trans. Ser. No. 4.

Brandon, C. 1977. High-speed cinematography of animals: A strobe design. J. Biol. Photo. Assn., 45:143-145.

Cooper, J. D., and J. D. Abbott. 1979. Exposure control and lighting, Nikon Handbook Ser. Amer. Photo. Book Publ. Co., New York, 160 pp.

Dalton, S. 1976. Bourne of the wind. 2nd ed. Reader's Digest Press, New York. 158 pp.

Edgerton, H. E. 1979. Electronic flash, strobe. 2nd ed. MIT Press, Cambridge, Massachusetts, 133 pp.

Edgerton, H. E. 1982. Exposure time: It can be important. *in* Proc. SPIE (L. L. Endelman, ed.), 348:67-74.

Gans, K. 1966. An inexpensive arrangement of movie camera and electronic flash as a tool in the study of animal behavior. Anim. Behav. 14:11-12.

Geluso, K. N., J. S. Altenbach, and R. C. Kerbo. 1987. Bats of Carlsbad Caverns National

Park. Carlsbad Caverns Natural History Assn., Carlsbad, New Mexico, 34 pp.

Greenawalt, C. H. 1960. Hummingbirds. Doubleday and Co., New York. 250 pp.

Griffin, D. R., F. A. Webster, and C. Michael. 1960. The echolocation of flying insects by bats. Anim. Behav., 8:141-154.

Hyzer, W. G. 1962. Engineering and scientific high-speed photography. MacMillan Co., New York. 526 pp.

Jacobs, L. 1962. Electronic flash. Amer. Photo. Book Pub. Co., New York, 128 pp.

Jacobs, L. 1980. Basic guide to photography, 2nd ed. Petersen Publ. Co., Los Angeles. 144 pp.

Life Library of Photography. 1970. Light and film. Time-Life Books, New York, 227 pp.

Mortensen, W. 1947. Pictorial lighting. 2nd ed. Camera Craft Publ. Co. San Francisco, 222 pp.

Mott, V. 1974. Electronic flash equipment. Howard W. Sams and Co., Indianapolis, Indiana, 112 pp.

Norberg, U. 1976. Aerodynamics, kinematics, and energetics of horizontal, flapping flight in the long-eared bat, *Plecotus auritus*. J. Exp. Biol., 65:179-212.

Pollock, S. 1983. Greg Dale and his magic black box. Pop. Photo. 90: 50-54, 114.

Tuttle, M. D. 1982. The amazing frog-eating bat. Natl. Geogr., 161:78-91.

Tuttle, M. D. 1983. In celebration of bats. Int. Wildlife, 13:4-13.

Vaughan, T. A. 1972. Mammalogy. W. B. Saunders, Philadelphia, 463 pp.

Webster, F. A., and D. R. Griffin. 1962. The role of flight membranes in insect capture by bats. Anim. Behav., 10:332-340.

Appendix 1. Selected Equipment (and Sources) for Use in Bat Photography (Still Cameras Not Included)

PRODUCT

Cine Cameras (normal and high speed, 16 mm) Standard Frame-rate

Arriflex Corporation
1 Westchester Plaza
Elmsford, New York
10523 USA

Eastman Kodak Company
343 State Street
Rochester, New York
14650 USA

Eclair Corporation
Eram Company (distributor)
1430 North Cahuenga Blvd.
Hollywood, California
90028 USA

Pallard, Inc.
1900 Lower Road
Linden, New Jersey
07036 USA

Richter Cine Equipment, Inc.
Essex, New York 12936 USA

Rotating Prism Cine

Photo-Sonics, Inc.
Instrumentation Marketing
    Corporation
820 South Mariposa Street
Burbank, California
91505 USA

Red Lake Labs
15005 Concord Circle
Morgan Hill, California
95037 USA

Pin-registered Cine

Photo-Sonics, Inc.
Instrumentation Marketing
    Corporation
820 South Mariposa Street
Burbank, California
91505 USA

Red Lake Labs
15005 Concord Circle
Morgan Hill, California
95037 USA

Electronic Flash and Flashtubes

Amglo Division of CMR
5265 Michigan Avenue
Rosemont, Illinois
60018 USA

Agfa-Gavaert, Inc.
275 North Street
Teterboro, New Jersey
07608 USA

Ehrenreich Photo-Optical
  Industries
Brown Electronic Flash
  Division
623 Stewart Avenue
Garden City, New York
11530 USA

Chadwick Helmuth Co., Inc.
4601 North Arden Drive
El Monte, California
91731 USA

EG & G, Inc.
Electro Optics Division
35 Congress Street
Salem, Massachusetts
01970 USA

General Electric Company
Nela Park
Cleveland, Ohio
44101 USA

Honeywell Photo Products
P.O. Box 5227
Denver, Colorado
80204 USA

Kemlite Laboratories
1819 West Grand Avenue
Chicago, Illinois
60622 USA

Knot Elektronix-Muncher
8021 Hohenschafllarn bie
  Munchen
Postfach 57
West Germany

Minolta Camera Company, Ltd.
30.2-chome
Azuchi-Machi
Higashi-ku, Osaka 541
Japan

Nikon, Inc.
623 Stewart Avenue
Garden City, New York
11530 USA

Nissin America Corporation
2539 237th Street
Suite B
Torrance, California
90505 USA

Norman Enterprises
2601 Empire Avenue
Burbank, California
91504 USA

Photogenic Machine Company
P.O. Box 3365
Youngstown, Ohio
44512 USA

Press-Tige Pictures, Ltd.
3 Newmarket Road
Cringleford, Norwich
NR4 6VE
England

Tim Simon, Inc.
20 Sunnyvale Avenue
Mill Valley, California
94941 USA

Sunpak Division
Berkey Marketing Companies
25-20 Brooklyn-Queens Expwy
West Woodside, New York
11377 USA

Vivitar Corporation
P.O. Box 2100
Santa Monica, California
90406 USA

Slave Trigger Units

Dot Line Corporation
North Hollywood, California
91605 USA

Preferred Photo Products
8420 Sylvia Avenue
Northridge, California
91324 USA

Wein Products, Inc.
P.O. Box 34647
Palms, California
90034 USA

Incandescent Photo Lamps

Smith-Victor Sales Corp.
301 North Colfax Street
Griffith, Iowa
46319 USA

Sylvania Lighting Center
Danvers, Massachusetts
01923 USA

Photo Triggering Devices

Dale Engineering
P.O. Box 5222
Arlington, Virginia
22205 USA

Press-Tige Pictures, Ltd.
3 Newmarket Road

Cringleford, Norwich
NR4 6VE
England

Short-duration Shutters

A. W. Vincent Associates
1225 University Avenue
Rochester, New York 14607 USA

Chapter 9

Allozyme Techniques and Kinship Assessment in Bats

Gary F. McCracken

Department of Zoology
University of Tennessee
Knoxville, Tennessee 37996 USA

and

Gerald S. Wilkinson[1]

Department of Biology
University of California at San Diego
La Jolla, California 92093 USA

1. INTRODUCTION

Most outcrossing animals and plants carry an enormous amount of cryptic genetic variation (see Ayala, 1982, for a recent review). Although no available technique short of DNA sequencing can detect all variation that is present at a locus, gel electrophoresis can be used to detect genetically determined differences in protein structures and to reveal a portion of the variation present at "structural" gene loci. Because these "allozyme" techniques are relatively simple and cost efficient, and because a large number of loci can be examined in almost any macroscopic individual (recipes for 76 different protein stains are given in Harris and Hopkinson 1978), they are at present the most widely used biochemical techniques for examining the genotypes of individuals and genetic variation within and among populations.

Patterns of protein variation as observed on gels often agree with the expectations of multiple codominant alleles at single loci (Selander et al., 1971; Fig. 1a and b). And breeding studies show that these variants often are inherited as such (Selander et al., 1971; McCracken and Brussard, 1980). Therefore, it frequently is possible to score genotypes directly from gels, to estimate genotype and allele frequencies within populations, and to compare the overall genetic constitutions of different populations and taxa. Such information is of major importance in many areas of evolutionary biology and a vast literature concerns applications of these techniques to the study of population structure, systematics, and animal behavior. Collections of papers representative of this literature, or reviewing portions of it can be found in volumes edited by Ayala (1976), Brussard

[1]Present Address: Department of Zoology, University of Maryland, College Park, Maryland 20742 USA

(1978), Smith and Joule (1981), and Milk-man (1982).

This paper will be restricted to the application of these techniques to kinship assessment, with special reference to research on bats. We will specifically address the use of allozymes for establishing parentage and for assessing kin relationships among individuals in bat social groups. Readers who desire a more general description of the biochemical genetic basis of allozyme variation, or an overview of the techniques and their application to other questions in evolutionary biology are referred to the edited volumes listed above or any of several recent texts (e.g., Lewontin, 1974; Dobzhansky et al., 1977; Hartl, 1980). Those intending to use these techniques in their research also are referred to the excellent and more rigorous description of allozymes in Harris and Hopkinson (1978).

2. SAMPLE COLLECTION AND PREPARATION

Proteins are extracted from blood, muscle, or other tissues. Because the presence and concentration of the protein products from different loci vary among tissues, it is advisable to get samples of more than one tissue type. Although it may be necessary to kill animals to obtain extracts of sufficient volume for a survey to establish which electrophoretic buffers and protein stains give the best results, we find that once these systems are established, routine examination of a great many loci is possible using samples that can be collected from even the smallest bats without killing them. Because bats typically have long life spans and low fecundities, considerations of demography and conservation make non-lethal sampling preferable for studies involving large sample sizes. Of course, longitudinal behavioral studies require non-lethal sampling. All samples should be placed on ice immediately after collection and frozen within several hours. Samples can be stored for several months on dry ice, in liquid nitro-gen, or in an ultracold freezer ($<-65°$C) with no apparent degradation of enzymatic activity. Samples should not be stored in a conventional freezer ($\sim-20°$) for longer than several weeks. Unnecessary thawing and refreezing of samples should be avoided as it may result in a decrease in enzyme activity.

2.1. Blood

Blood samples of 50 to 100 µl have been collected from bats as small as *Saccopteryx leptura* (4-5 g body mass) by piercing an antebrachial blood vessel with a hypodermic needle and collecting blood in a heparinized capillary tube (McCracken, 1984b). Herd (1983) collected similar sized blood samples from the interfemoral vein of *Myotis lucifugus* (7-9 g) and *M. yumanensis* (6-7 g). Plasma and red blood cells should be separated by centrifugation before freezing and stored separately.

Blood cells are prepared for electrophoresis by diluting (1:1) and thoroughly mixing them with cold deionized water. Plasma is used without dilution. A sample of 50 µl of whole blood is sufficient for 1-2 gels using plasma and 3-4 gels using red blood cells.

2.2. Other Tissues

If animals are killed, muscle, heart, and liver, in addition to blood, are the most commonly used tissues. These can be prepared by mincing the sample in 1:1 mass: volume of cold grinding buffer (Selander et al., 1971), allowing the minced tissue to stand for at least 15 min in the cold buffer, centrifuging, and removing the supernatant for use in electrophoresis.

The excision of small ($\leq.1$g) chest muscle biopsies can provide sufficient tissue for examination of many enzymes without killing bats. The following procedure is used to obtain a biopsy: 1) trim fur from a small area covering pectoralis muscle; 2) clean the area with antiseptic wash; 3) make a short (3-5 mm) slit in the skin; 4) excise the muscle using extremely fine forceps and dissecting scissors; 5) dress the wound with a topical antiseptic. We find that use of ether occasionally kills bats. Without use of a general anesthetic the mortality rate with this procedure has been zero. Biopsies were used successfully in studies on *Saccopteryx leptura* and its larger congener *S. bilineata* (7-9 g body mass; McCracken, 1984b), and also on *Tadarida brasiliensis* (12-15 g; McCracken, 1984a). Other non-destructive samples such as small pieces of wing membrane and the tips of tails proved to have usable enzymatic activity. Generally, a greater variety of enzymes are available at higher concentrations in muscle. Single toes amputated from several relatively large species (*Phyllostomus hastatus,* 70-100 g, McCracken and Bradbury, 1981; *Carollia perspicillata,* 15-23 g, Porter and McCracken, 1983; *Desmodus rotundus,* 15-40 g, Wilkinson, 1985) provided sufficient tissue to examine a variety of loci. However, toes taken from species smaller than these (e.g., *S. leptura, S. bilineata,* and *T. brasiliensis*) had little usable enzymatic activity. All of these tissues are minced finely in chilled porcelain spot plates in approximately 1:1 mass: volume of cold grinding buffer. The tissue and buffer are mixed well, allowed to stand for at least 15 min, taken into 100 μl capillary tubes, and centrifuged. The supernatant is used for electrophoresis. Samples should be kept on ice as much as possible during sample preparation. Again, unnecessary thawing and refreezing are to be avoided.

3. ELECTROPHORESIS

Gels can be prepared from any of several media (starch, acrylamide, agar, cellulose acetate), and a variety of apparatus for electrophoresis (vertical slab, horizontal slab, disc) are available commercially or can be built in the laboratory (Brewer, 1970; Harris and Hopkinson, 1978). We rely exclusively on horizontal slab, starch gel electrophoresis, which has become more or less the standard for studies of natural populations. Advantages of this system are that 1) starch is inexpensive and non-toxic, 2) extracts from 20 or

so individuals can be placed side by side on a gel so that allelomorphs can be compared directly and easily cross-referenced, and 3) gels can be cut horizontally into at least four slices that can each be placed in a different protein stain. Appendix 1 provides schematics of the homemade apparatus that is used routinely by one of us (GFM). Other more efficient designs are available, but our design functions adequately. The Heath Company retails an inexpensive power supply that is ideal for this work (Appendix 2). Our gels consist of 11.75% electrostarch (47 g starch/400 ml buffer).

Step by step descriptions of procedures for gel preparation, sample application, and running and staining gels are provided by Shaw and Koen (1968), Brewer (1970), Selander et al. (1971), Harris and Hopkinson (1978), O'Malley et al. (1980), and Conkle et al. (1982). We most closely follow the procedures of Selander et al. (1971) and Harris and Hopkinson (1978). Exceptions to the instructions in Harris and Hopkinson (1978) are that we run gels at room temperature and cool them with a pan of ice on a thin glass plate placed on top of the gel, and prior to staining we slice gels into four approximately 2 mm thick slices using a fine, tightly stretched, metal (G) guitar string.

Compilations of buffer and stain recipes are available in the publications listed above and in Shaw and Prasad (1970). Selander et al. (1971), in particular, provide a useful list of gel and electrode buffer and stain recipes. Harris and Hopkinson (1978) provide the most extensive list of protein stain recipes available. It will be apparent from these references that a variety of different buffers have been developed, and the reader is advised that determination of what buffers best reveal variation at a given locus, and provide the best resolution of it, is largely empirical. In this regard we make two recommendations. First, before beginning allozyme studies on a species, it is advisable to examine the methods of studies on the same or other taxa classified at least to the same family, because a given protein from a given tissue often shows

Table 1. Family, species, and the number of presumptive loci examined in previous allozyme studies of bats. The references given provide details on the electrophoretic conditions used.

Taxon	No. of Presumptive Loci Examined	Reference to Techniques
Emballonuridae		
Saccopteryx leptura	33	McCracken, G. F., 1984b
S. bilineata	33	McCracken, G. F., 1984b
Noctilionidae		
Noctilio leporinus	18	Arnold, M. L., et al., 1982
Mormoopidae		
Pteronotus parnellii	18	Arnold, M. L., et al., 1982
P. davyii	18	Arnold, M. L., et al., 1982
P. personatus	18	Arnold, M. L., et al., 1982
Mormoops megalophylla	18	Arnold, M. L., et al., 1982
Phyllostomidae		
Macrotus waterhousii	21	Greenbaum, I. F., and R. J. Baker, 1976
M. californicus	21	Greenbaum, I. F., and R. J. Baker, 1976
M. californicus	17	Straney, D. O., et al., 1976a
Phyllostomus discolor	17	Straney, D. O., et al., 1979
P. hastatus	17	Straney, D. O., et al., 1979
P. hastatus	5	McCracken, G. F., and J. W. Bradbury, 1981
Glossophaga soricina	17	Straney, D. O., et al., 1979.
G. soricina	17	Honeycutt, R. L., et al., 1981
G. soricina	17	Baker, R. J., et al., 1981
Monophyllus redmani	17	Baker, R. J., et al., 1981
M. plethodon	17	Baker, R. J., et al., 1981
Anoura geoffroyi	17	Straney, D. O., et al., 1979
Carollia perspicillata	17	Straney, D. I., et al., 1979
C. perspicillata	17	Porter, F. L., and G. F. McCracken, 1983
Sturnira lilium	17	Honeycutt, R. L., et al., 1981
Sturnira sp.	17	Straney, D. O., et al., 1979
Uroderma bilobatum	17	Straney, D. O., et al., 1979
U. bilobatum	22	Greenbaum, I. F., 1981
U. bilobatum	22	Koop, B. F., and R. J. Baker, 1983
Vampyrops helleri	17	Straney, D. O., et al., 1979
V. brachycephalus	22	Koop, B. F., and R. J. Baker, 1983
Chiroderma villosum	22	Koop, B. F., and R. J. Baker, 1983
C. villosum	17	Straney, D. O., et al., 1979
Artibeus cinereus	17	Straney, D. O., et al., 1979
A. cinereus	22	Koop, B. F., and R. J. Baker, 1983
A. watsoni	22	Koop, B. F., and R. J. Baker, 1983
A. phaeotis	22	Koop, B. F., and R. J. Baker, 1983
A. toltecus	22	Koop, B. F., and R. J. Baker, 1983
A. concolor	22	Koop, B. F., and R. J. Baker, 1983
A. jamaicensis	22	Koop, B. F., and R. J. Baker, 1983
A. lituratus	17	Straney, D. O., et al., 1979
Ametrida centuria	17	Straney, D. O., et al., 1979
Erophylla sezekorni	17	Baker, R. J., et al., 1981
Brachyphylla cavernarum	17	Baker, R. J., et al., 1981
Phyllonycteris aphylla	17	Baker, R. J., et al., 1981
Desmodus rotundus	17	Straney, D. O., et al., 1979
D. rotundus	17	Baker, R. J., et al., 1981
D. rotundus	22	Honeycutt, R. L., et al., 1981
D. rotundus	7	Wilkinson, G. S., 1985
Diaemus youngii	22	Honeycutt, R. L., et al., 1981
Diphylla ecaudata	22	Honeycutt, R. L., et al., 1981

Table 1. Continued

Taxon	No. of Presumptive Loci Examined	Reference to Techniques
Natalidae		
Natalus sp.	17	Straney, D. O., et al., 1979
Vespertilionidae		
Myotis velifer	17	Straney, D. O., et al., 1976a
M. yumanensis	20	Reduker, D. W., et al., 1983
M. auriculus	20	Reduker, D. W., et al., 1983
M. evotis	20	Reduker, D. W., et al., 1983
M. milleri	20	Reduker, D. W., et al., 1983
M. thysanodes	20	Reduker, D. W., et al., 1983
M. californicus	21	Straney, D. O., et al., 1976b
Pipistrellus hesperus	20	Straney D. O., et al., 1976b
Molossidae		
Molossus molossus	17	Straney, D. O., et al., 1979
Tadarida brasiliensis	27	McCracken, G. F., in prep.

good resolution on the same buffers in similar taxa. Second, kinship assessment requires comparison of genotypes at polymorphic loci and the information needed for these studies increases as additional polymorphic loci and alleles are resolved. Therefore, it is advisable to examine as many different proteins using as many gel and electrode buffer systems as possible within the limits of time and money available for a given project. Table 1 lists forty-seven bat species that have been studied using allozyme techniques. For each species, we list the number of presumptive loci examined, and we reference the methods used to resolve those loci. Individuals beginning allozyme studies on almost any bat species will undoubtedly benefit from referring to this literature; however, readers are advised that most of the studies listed (and most published work on allozymes in bats) involve investigation of systematic relationships, not kinship assessment. Many of these systematic studies do not involve examination of large samples from single populations and, since identification of within population polymorphism is not a primary concern, many probably do not reflect the results of rigorous searching for the buffer systems that best reveal these polymorphisms. Therefore, the methods referenced in Table 1 will only provide, in most cases, an indication of where to begin a survey of buffers and enzyme stains.

4. INTERPRETING GELS

4.1. Scoring

Allozyme studies require scoring allelic products of single gene loci. In some cases (e.g., Fig. 1a), this is straightforward. However, two or more loci often code for the same protein and these multilocus products often appear on the same gel. Such multiple loci are usually attributed to gene duplications (Harris and Hopkinson, 1978), but distinguishing among their products is essential. In some cases (e.g., Fig. 1b), distinguishing among multiple loci is also very straight forward. But in other cases (e.g., Fig. 1c), the allelic products of multiple loci may overlay one another on a gel and scoring single loci may be difficult or impossible. Staining for multiple loci is a particular problem with relatively non-specific stains such as esterases and some peptidases. It is sometimes possible to selectively stain for some loci and not others by use of different esterase or peptidase substrates, or to selectively inhibit the activity of some loci (as with eserine sulfate; Selander et al., 1971) so as to make scoring of others possible. Occasionally a change in the pH of the gel buffer will separate multiple loci. In difficult cases a pH gradient can be created across the gel to separate loci. This technique causes enzyme variants to migrate until they reach their isoelectric

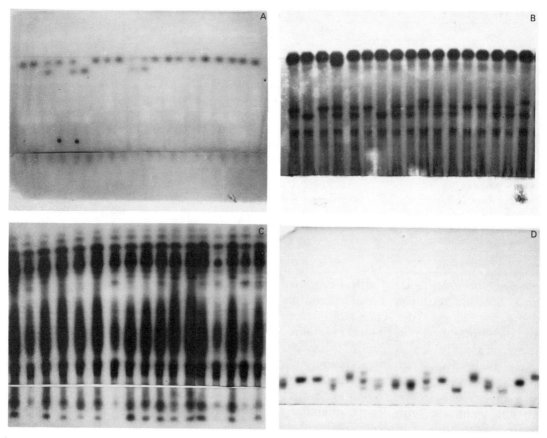

Figure 1. Photographs of 4 gels stained for different enzymes and showing banding patterns typical of allozyme studies. The proteins produced by one or more presumptive structural gene locus are visualized as the stained regions on each gel. The anode is at the top and cathode at the bottom of each gel. (A) A gel stained for the enzyme mannose phosphate isomerase. The allozyme "phenotypes" of 20 individuals are seen for a single darkly staining locus. Two alleles are present and, because the protein is a monomer, heterozygotes have 2 bands and homozygotes a single band. Designating the more rapidly (anodally) migrating allele as "A" and the more slowly migrating allele as "B," and reading the gel from left to right, the genotypes of the first six individuals are: AA; AA; AB; AA; AB; BB. (B) A gel stained with a non-specific "general protein" stain. Three darkly staining loci and 2 other more lightly staining loci are visible. Two darkly staining loci show polymorphism. The most anodal locus (uppermost on gel) has a single heterozygote (4th individual from the left). All other individuals appear homozygous at this locus for the more anodal allele. The locus in the center of this gel is highly polymorphic with 3 alleles visible. Reading left to right the genotypes of the first five individuals are: BB; CC; BB; BC; BC. The tenth individual from the left has genotype AB, the last individual on the gel, genotype AC. (C) A gel stained for esterase with many loci staining for each individual. The large number of loci makes identification of genotypes at single loci difficult or impossible. (D) A gel stained for α-glycerophosphate dehydrogenase showing a 3 allele polymorphism for a dimeric protein. Reading left to right, the genotypes of the first six individuals are: BC; BB; BB; BC; AB; AC.

point (see Harris and Hopkinson, 1978 for details).

The genotypes seen in Figs. 1a and 1b result from polymorphic loci for which protein products are monomeric (i.e., the protein coded by an allele is composed of a single polypeptide). Many proteins are multimeric (i.e., composed of two or more polypeptide chains), and, if so, heterozygotes show "hybrid" bands with intermediate mobility. Figure 1d shows genotypes of a polymorphic, dimeric (2 subunits) protein for which heterozygotes have a single hybrid band. Proteins may also be composed of three, four, or

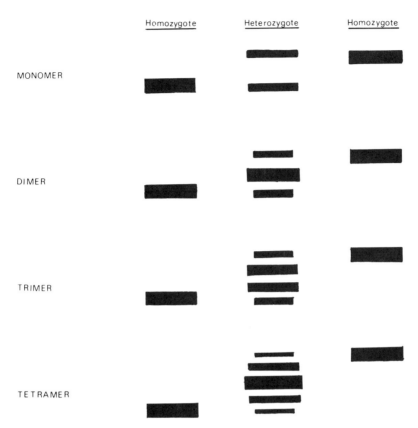

Figure 2. Schematic showing expected banding patterns for 2 allele polymorphisms at loci that code for proteins consisting of 1, 2, 3, or 4 polypeptide subunits. When proteins are composed of two or more subunits, these recombine in heterozygotes and form hybrid (heteromeric) allozyme patterns. For example, if a protein is dimeric consisting of 2 subunits X^1 and X^2, this protein in homozygotes will be either X^1X^1 or X^2X^2, whereas in heterozygotes the proteins X^1X^1, X^1X^2, X^2X^1 and X^2X^2 will all be present. In these heterozygotes the X^1X^2, X^2X^1 combinations stain as a single hybrid band with twice the intensity of either the X^1X^1 or X^2X^2 proteins. Trimeric and tetrameric proteins will form 2 and 3 hybrid bands, respectively. In this drawing, the enzymatic activities of each allele are equivalent. See Harris and Hopkinson (1978) for additional explanation (drawing after Harris and Hopkinson, Fig. 1).

more subunits, for which heterozygotes show two, three, or more hybrid bands, respectively. Figure 2 illustrates diagrammatically the patterns expected for monomers, dimers, trimers, and tetramers. In this figure (and in Figs. 1a,b,d) the electrophoretic patterns are symmetrical in that the alternative allelic products of a locus have approximately equal activity and stain on the gel with approximately equal intensity. However, in some cases alternative alleles do not have equal activity and staining intensity will not be symmetrical between the alleles in heterozygotes. An extreme situation occurs with

so-called "null" alleles where a segregating allele has no apparent enzymatic activity. Because a heterozygote with a null allele appears identical to the homozygote for the "active" allele, the presence of a null allele in a population makes confident scoring of all genotypes impossible. The presence of a null allele will be detected when homozygote null genotypes are observed. Its presence may be suspected when an apparent deficiency of heterozygotes is recorded from population samples.

A final caveat on scoring gels pertains to "secondary isozyme" bands resulting from post-translational changes in proteins. These changes may occur *in vivo,* or *in vitro* during extraction, storage, or electrophoresis of the proteins. Harris and Hopkinson (1978) address the causes (deamidations, acetylations, oxidation of sulphydryls, etc.) of these secondary banding patterns, and make recommendations on how to limit *in vitro* effects. If secondary modifications affect the appearance of all individuals with a given genotype equivalently, they may pose no great difficulty to scoring. However, in other situations they can pose serious problems.

To conclude this section, proficient scoring of gels will come only with practice. However, if in doubt because banding patterns are unclear, rerun the samples in question or do not score them at all. Independent scoring of each gel by two or more individuals should be a rule.

4.2. Mendelian Inheritance and Linkage

Ideally, the allelic basis of an allozyme polymorphism should be established through breeding experiments (e.g., McCracken and Brussard, 1980). Researchers are strongly encouraged to obtain breeding data, but where this is impractical or impossible (as is usually the case) two lines of indirect evidence are generally accepted as sufficient evidence for Mendelian inheritance of an allozyme polymorphism. These are that 1) the patterns as seen on gels agree with the known biochemistry of the protein and a model of multiple codominant alleles at a single locus and 2) the observed "genotype" proportions in a population sample agree with those expected under the Hardy-Weinberg model (Selander et al., 1971).

Given that a polymorphism results from multiple alleles at a locus, it also is important to establish whether alleles at different loci assort independently of one another. In the absence of selection and pleiotropy (a single gene having many effects), evidence for gametic disequilibria (non-random assortment) may indicate either linkage due to physical proximity of the loci on a chromo-

some or some form of non-random mating such as inbreeding or polygyny. Because many statistical analyses used in allozyme studies require independence between all pairs of loci, detecting any such association between alleles is essential. If random mating is assumed, tests for non-random association of alleles from different loci are possible using population samples alone (Hill, 1974; Selander and Foltz, 1981). However, this assumption may not be warranted, and examination for non-random mating may, in fact, be an objective of the research being performed (see below). In such cases examination for gametic disequilibrium requires knowledge of the genotypes of offspring and at least one parent (Smouse and Neel, 1977; Cockerham and Weir, 1977; Weir and Cockerham, 1978; also see Spiess, 1977). By using only mother-offspring data, Wilkinson (1985) discounted physical linkage between pairs of loci in *Desmodus rotundus* and was able to attribute any remaining association between alleles to non-random mating. Testing for gametic disequilibrium in this fashion is a much more sensitive way of detecting non-random mating than testing for Hardy Weinberg equilibrium. This test is more sensitive because one generation of random mating does not return a population to gametic equilibrium, but will restore Hardy-Weinberg equilibrium. Because both inbreeding and a highly skewed mating system can have significant consequences on the level of kinship within social groups, this analysis is an appropriate starting point for evaluating kinship. In the following section we discuss complementary techniques for more refined assessment of kinship.

5. KINSHIP ASSESSMENT

5.1. Paternity

In many animals paternity cannot be determined by direct observation. Reasons for this may include multiple mating by females, a less than perfect correlation between mating and fertilization, and/or difficulty of observing mating. In such cases, indirect methods may be necessary to determine paternity. The gene markers revealed by allozyme techniques are ideal for this. At this writing, we are aware of paternity tests using allozymes for three species of bats (*Phyllostomus hastatus,* McCracken and Bradbury, 1977, 1981; *Carollia perspicillata,* Porter and McCracken, 1983; *Desmodus rotundus,* Wilkinson, 1985). Similar studies have been conducted on a variety of other animals (e.g., rodents: Foltz, 1981; Foltz and Hoogland, 1981; Hanken and Sherman, 1981; Patten and Feder, 1981; lagomorphs: Daly, 1981; primates: Smith, 1980; insects: Pamilo, 1982; Ward, 1983; McCauley and O'Donnell, 1984; isopods: Sassaman, 1978).

Paternity tests require that a female and her offspring are identified and that their genotypes are known so that the allelic contribution of an offspring's father can be inferred. In the simplest case (and in human courts of law) these data may be used only for paternity exclusion. That is, males not possessing the necessary alleles can be excluded as possible fathers. This information coupled with behavioral observations may prove useful in many situations (e.g., Patton and Feder, 1981; Daly, 1981; Porter and McCracken, 1983). If the genotypes of other males that are possible fathers of an offspring also are known, then additional analyses are possible. By examining genotypes in populations of adult males, nursing females, and their offspring, McCracken and Bradbury (1977, 1981) and Wilkinson (1985) examined whether paternal allelic contributions to offspring differed from the allele frequencies in the adult male population, thereby testing for demonstrable skewness in male reproductive success. McCracken and Bradbury (1977, 1981) also used data from several polymorphic loci to calculate the probability of detecting a "nonpaternity" (i.e., whether a given baby was *not* fathered by the male in question). In doing so, they were able to calculate, with 95% confidence, the minimum reproductive success of harem-holding *P. hastatus* males.

In many animals, females produce groups of offspring in litters or clutches. In studies on rodents, Foltz (1981) and Foltz and Hoogland (1981) employed an analysis that utilized the genotypes of two or more putative fathers, a female, and her offspring to estimate the relative "likelihood of paternity" for each male. These authors and others (Hanken and Sherman, 1981; Patton and Feder 1981; Pamilo, 1983; Ward, 1983) also used allozymes to examine for evidence of multiple paternity in litters or clutches. Even if the genotypes of none of the presumptive fathers are known, evidence of multiple paternity can be provided by the presence of three or more paternally-contributed alleles in a group of offspring from a single female, or by offspring genotypic distributions that could not result from the allelic contributions of a single father. Given that most bats produce only one or two offspring at a time, multiple paternity tests will not apply to most bat research. But, it should be apparent that paternity testing using allozymes has many applications. Additional methods of data analysis can be developed and tailored to particular research projects.

5.2. Maternity

In bats, maternity can often be determined through observation of birth or nursing. However, in some situations, as with suspected communal nursing, maternity tests may be needed. Because knowledge of paternity is unlikely, maternity tests must rely solely on comparison of the genotypes of adult females and the young in question. McCracken (1984a) examined the genotypes of females and nursing pups in maternity colonies of *Tadarida brasiliensis mexicana* to establish the occurrence and extent of possible communal nursing. Such tests rely on two types of statistical analysis. One involves examining females and the pups they nurse for "non-parental" genotype combinations (i.e., for females nursing a pup that could not be their offspring because they do not carry common alleles at one or more loci). Another analysis involves comparing the observed frequencies at which alleles are shared between females and nursing pups, with the frequencies at which shared alleles are expected if females nurse only their own pups. In this latter analysis it is necessary to assume the frequency at which paternal alleles are contributed (for example, at the same frequency as they occur in the adult male population). Maternity tests using allozymes also are possible if polymorphism occurs in proteins produced by maternally inherited mitochondrial DNA (e.g., Pamilo, 1983). However, to our knowledge these proteins have not been exploited for maternity tests.

5.3. Kinship Among Group Members

A number of studies have attempted to use allozyme polymorphisms to assess kinship within social groups. Although numerous statistical tests have been employed in these studies, two basic approaches can be distinguished. These can be categorized as either attempts to 1) detect genetic heterogeneity among social groups or to 2) estimate relatedness among individuals within these groups.

The first approach involves examining the distributions of genotypes and alleles among groups. These analyses can involve examining each polymorphic locus individually or can employ multivariate tests which permit comparison of several loci simultaneously. The study by McCracken and Bradbury (1977, 1981) on *Phyllostomus hastatus* is an example of a single locus approach. McCracken and Bradbury questioned whether adult females resident in *P. hastatus* harem groups were kin. They reasoned that if this were so a non-random distribution of alleles should result, with relative genetic homogeneity within harems and greater than random genetic heterogeneity among harems. Using the G-test for heterogeneity (Sokal and Rohlf, 1981), they examined several polymorphic loci and found no evidence for non-random distribution of alleles among harems. They concluded that individuals within harems are only randomly related and

documented this conclusion with data on juvenile dispersal patterns. The work by Selander (1970) on house mice is an early, very similar example of this approach as are the studies by Schwartz and Armitage (1980) on marmots, Patton and Feder (1981) on gophers, and Daly (1981) on rabbits. Schwartz and Armitage's work differs from the others in their use of F-statistics, which allow partitioning of genetic variance into within group, among group, and among population components, in addition to use of heterogeneity tests.

In contrast to these single locus analyses, Wilkinson (1985) used discriminant function analysis described by Smouse et al. (1982) to compare the genotypic distributions of adult female *Desmodus rotundus* found in sympatric stable female groups. Because female groups in this species form primarily from female offspring that do not disperse, non-random assemblages of genotypes should be produced. As expected, most (81%) of the adult females could be assigned to their correct group using the discriminant scores. This method of assessing genetic heterogeneity is much better at detecting differences among small groups than single locus tests as demonstrated by the failure of single locus G-tests to reveal any heterogeneity among the *Desmodus* female groups ranging in size from six to eleven bats.

The second approach considers that the level of relatedness among two or more individuals is proportional to the probability that they share homologous alleles. At least two published analyses examine allozyme "genotypes" of individuals within groups to obtain quantitative estimates of degree of kinship. The most widely used of these analyses was developed in research on social hymenoptera and employs regression analysis to obtain an average coefficient of relatedness among individuals in groups of any size (down to two individuals). This technique is described by Pamilo and Crozier (1982), and Pamilo (1984), and applications are in Pamilo (1982) and Ward (1983). The technique presented in Pamilo and Crozier (1982) utilizes only two alleles at a locus but has been extended to incorporate multiple alleles (Pamilo, 1984; McCauley and O'Donnell, 1984). With use of computer simulations, Pamilo and Crozier (1982) and Pamilo (1984) established that the standard error of this estimate is sensitive to the relative frequencies of alleles, the number of individuals within a group, and the number of groups used in regression. Our own simulation studies (Wilkinson and McCracken, 1985) show that this technique can return reliable estimates of kinship within groups, and that these estimates can be obtained with sampling regimes that are feasible for research on bat and other vertebrate populations. However, our simulations also show that the most precise estimate of relatedness obtained with this technique is the average of estimates calculated individually from several independent loci. Therefore, workers wishing to use this method should attempt to resolve as many polymorphic loci as possible.

Schwartz and Armitage (1983) developed another method for estimating relatedness among individuals within single groups of animals. Basically, a genetic similarity measure is calculated between all pairs of individuals in a group and these are compared to genetic similarities that have been calculated between individuals of known relatedness. This method, therefore, requires knowledge of the pedigrees of several animals for which genotypic data are available. Although Schwartz and Armitage found a positive relationship between their index of genetic similarity and level of relatedness, they found that the predictability of relatedness from this index was very poor. They concluded that estimates of levels of kinship could not be obtained with their data. We have also examined the utility of this technique using computer simulations (Wilkinson and McCracken, 1985) and found that, within the range of conditions we simulated, large standard errors in the genetic similarity index precluded its utility as an estimator of relatedness. Our results suggest that this technique will provide reliable estimates of

kinship, but only if a large number (in the vicinity of 10) of robustly polymorphic loci are available for study.

One should bear in mind that the estimates of relatedness based on allozyme markers depend on genetic similarity resulting from alleles shared through common descent as well as those shared because of assortative dispersal. If the object of the study is to determine the cause of any genetic similarity as well as describe it, then information additional to allelic and genotypic frequencies will be needed. We know of no substitute for actual observation of dispersal patterns of marked animals to both add this information and confirm any deductions derived from allozyme analyses. In situations where dispersal information is difficult to obtain, computer simulations can be used to determine the likelihood of sharing alleles under different immigration regimes (cf. Wilkinson, 1985).

6. PRACTICAL CONSIDERATIONS

Establishing a functional allozyme lab will require at least $500 in specialized equipment per set up (i.e., one power supply, a pair of buffer boxes, electrodes, gel trays). A minimal stock of biochemical reagents to prepare standard buffers and a small suite of protein stains will easily involve an additional $1000. Ready access to distilled water and some basic laboratory equipment (balance that weighs to at least 10 mg, pH meter, centrifuge, refrigerator and freezer, glassware) also is essential. In addition to the financial commitment involved, becoming proficient in the techniques will require a few weeks of practice. Proficiency in scoring gels and interpreting data will take longer. Although these commitments may not be overwhelming, beginning or part-time allozyme geneticists should gauge their expected involvement in such studies and consider the options of collaborating with someone who is already set up, or doing their allozyme research at one of the established "centers" and paying costs to the center. The Section of Ecology and

Systematics at Cornell University and the Museum of Comparative Zoology at the University of California at Berkeley currently have centers that specialize in this work.

Also, when large numbers of animals are sampled, many of the statistical analyses referenced above become prohibitively tedious unless conducted on a computer. Several software packages have been developed recently for use on the Apple microcomputer, including BIOSYS which performs most single-locus genetic analyses, and ELF (available from the Winchendon Group, 3907 Lakoto Rd., P.O. Box 10114, Alexandria, Virginia 22310) which can be used to perform discriminant analyses and multiple regressions.

Finally, it should be apparent that anyone collecting allozyme data needs a foundation in population genetics.

7. SUMMARY

This chapter describes and provides reference to the techniques necessary to examine variation in structural gene loci (allozymes) in natural populations of bats. Our emphasis is on the use of these gene markers to assess kinship; however, these techniques can be applied to a wide variety of other questions in population and evolutionary biology. Since our application is to behavioral studies, we describe non-lethal sampling techniques. The major concerns of resolving polymorphism and interpreting the patterns of variation seen on gels are addressed. We also consider the criteria and methods for establishing Mendelian inheritance and for assessing possible linkage associations among loci. We discuss and illustrate with representative literature the use of gene markers to establish paternity, maternity, and relatedness among individuals within social groups in natural populations.

8. ACKNOWLEDGMENTS

We have both benefited greatly from our studies with J. W. Bradbury. Many other people also have participated in establishing the techniques described here and we are grateful to them. We thank Kitty Gustin for assembling the appendices, and T. H. Kunz, Kitty Gustin, and two reviewers for their comments on the manuscript. Portions of this work were funded by NSF grants to J. W. Bradbury and to GFM, by the National Geographic Society, and the University of Tennessee.

9. REFERENCES

Arnold, M. L., R. L. Honeycutt, R. J. Baker, V. M. Sarich, and J. K. Jones, Jr. 1982. Resolving a phylogeny with multiple data sets: A systematic study of phyllostomatid bats. Occas. Papers Mus., Texas Tech Univ., 77:1-15.

Ayala, F. J. (ed.) 1976. Molecular evolution. Sinauer Associates, Sunderland, Massachusetts, 277 pp.

Ayala, F. J. 1982. The genetic structure of species. Pp. 60-82, in Perspectives on evolution, (R. Milkman, ed.), Sinauer Associates, Sunderland, Massachusetts, 241 pp.

Baker, R. J., R. L. Honeycutt, M. L. Arnold, V. M. Sarich, and H. H. Genoways. 1981. Electrophoretic and immunological studies on the relationship of the Brachyphyllinae and the Glossophaginae. J. Mammal., 62:665-672.

Brewer, G. J. 1970. An introduction to isozyme techniques. Academic Press, New York, 186 pp.

Brussard, P. F. (ed.). 1978. Ecological genetics: The interface. Springer-Verlag, New York, 247 pp.

Cockerham, C. C., and B. S. Weir. 1977. Digenic descent measures for finite populations. Genet. Res., 30:121-147.

Conkle, M. T., P. D. Hodgkiss, L. B. Nunnally, S. C. Hunter. 1982. Starch gel electrophoresis of conifer seeds: a laboratory manual. USDA General Technical Report PSW-64, Pacific Southwest Forest and Range Experiment Station, Berkeley, California, 18 pp.

Daly, J. C. 1981. Effects of social organization and environmental diversity on determining the genetic structure of a population of the wild rabbit, Oryctolagus cuniculus. Evolution, 35:687-706.

Dobzhansky, Th., F. J. Ayala, G. L. Stebbins, J. W. Valentine. 1977. Evolution. W. H. Freeman, San Francisco, California, 572 pp.

Foltz, D. W. 1981. Genetic evidence for long-term monogamy in a small rodent, Peromyscus polionotus. Amer. Nat., 117:665-675.

Foltz, D. W., and J. L. Hoogland. 1981. Analysis of the mating system in the black-tailed prairie dog (*Cynomys ludovicianus*) by likelihood of paternity. J. Mammal., 62:706-712.

Greenbaum, I. F. 1981. Genetic interactions between hybridizing cytotypes of the tent making bat (*Uroderma bilobatum*). Evolution, 35:306-321.

Greenbaum, I. F., and R. J. Baker. 1976. Evolutionary relationships in *Macrotus* (Mammalia: Chiroptera): Biochemical variation and karyology. Syst. Zool., 25:15-25.

Hanken, J., and P. W. Sherman. 1981. Multiple paternity in Belding's ground squirrel litters. Science, 212:351-353.

Harris, H., and D. A. Hopkinson. 1978. Handbook of enzyme electrophoresis in human genetics. American Elsevier, New York.

Hartl, D. L. 1980. Principles of population genetics. Sinauer, Sunderland, Massachusetts, 488 pp.

Herd, R. M. 1983. A simple antibody test for field identification of morphologically similar mammals. J. Mammal., 64:700-701.

Hill, W. G. 1974. Estimation of linkage disequilibrium in randomly mating populations. Heredity, 33:229-239.

Honeycutt, R. L., I. F. Greenbaum, R. J. Baker, and V. M. Sarich. 1981. Molecular evolution of vampire bats. J. Mammal., 62:805-811.

Koop, B. F., and R. J. Baker. 1983. Electrophoretic studies of relationships of six species of *Artibeus* (Chiroptera: Phyllostomatidae). Occas. Pap. Mus., Texas Tech Univ., 83:1-12.

Lewontin, R. C. 1974. The genetic basis of evolutionary change. Columbia Univ. Press, New York, 346 pp.

McCauley, D. E., and R. O'Donnell. 1984. The effect of multiple mating on genetic relatedness in larval aggregations of the imported willow leaf beetle. Behav. Ecol. Sociobiol., 15:287-292.

McCracken, G. F. 1984a. Communal nursing in Mexican free-tailed bat maternity colonies. Science, 223:1090-1091.

McCracken, G. F. 1984b. Social dispersion and genetic variation in two species of emballonurid bats. Z. Tierpsychol., 66:55-69.

McCracken, G. F., and J. W. Bradbury. 1977. Paternity and genetic heterogeneity in the polygynous bat, *Phyllostomus hastatus*. Science, 198:303-306.

McCracken, G. F., and J. W. Bradbury. 1981. Social organization and kinship in the polygynous bat *Phyllostomus hastatus*. Behav. Ecol. Sociobiol., 8:11-34.

McCracken, G. F., and P. F. Brussard. 1980. The population biology of the white-lipped land snail, *Triodopsis albolabris:* Genetic variability. Evolution, 34:92-104.

Milkman, R. (ed.). 1982. Perspectives on evolution. Sinauer Associates, Sunderland, Massachusetts, 241 pp.

O'Malley, D., N. C. Wheeler, and R. P. Guries. 1980. A manual for starch gel electrophoresis. Staff Paper Series 11, Dept. of Forestry, Univ. of Wisconsin, Madison, 16 pp.

Pamilo, P. 1982. Multiple mating in *Formica* ants. Hereditas, 97:37-45.

Pamilo, P. 1983. Genetic differentiation within subdivided populations of *Formica* ants. Evolution, 37:1010-1022.

Pamilo, P. 1984. Genotypic correlation and regression in social groups: Multiple alleles, multiple loci and subdivided populations. Genetics, 107:307-320.

Pamilo, P., and R. H. Crozier. 1982. Measuring genetic relatedness in natural populations: Methodology. Theor. Pop. Biol., 21:171-193.

Patton, J. L., and J. H. Feder. 1981. Microspatial genetic heterogeneity in pocket gophers: Nonrandom breeding and drift. Evolution, 35:912-920.

Porter, F. L., and G. F. McCracken. 1983. Social behavior and allozyme variation in a captive colony of *Carollia perspicillata*. J. Mammal., 64:295-298.

Reduker, D. W., T. L. Yates, and I. F. Greenbaum. 1983. Evolutionary affinities among southwestern long-eared *Myotis* (Chiroptera: Vespertilionidae). J. Mammal., 64:666-677.

Sassaman, C. 1978. Mating systems in porcellionid isopods: Multiple paternity and sperm mixing in *Porcellio scaber* latr. Heredity, 41:385-397.

Schwartz, O. A., and K. B. Armitage. 1980. Genetic variation in social mammals: The marmot model. Science, 207:665-667.

Schwartz, O. A., and K. B. Armitage 1983. Problems in the use of genetic similarity to show relatedness. Evolution, 37:417-420.

Selander, R. K. 1970. Behavior and genetic variation in natural populations. Amer. Zool., 10:53-66.

Selander, R. K., M. H. Smith, S. V. Yang, W. E. Johnson, and J. B. Gentry. 1971. Biochemical polymorphism and systematics in the genus *Peromyscus*. I. Variation in the old field mouse. Pp. 49-90, *in* Stud. Genet. VI., Univ. of Texas. Publ., No. 7103, Austin, Texas.

Selander, R. K., and D. W. Foltz. 1981. Gametic disequilibrium between esterase loci in populations of *Cepaea nemoralis* in Western New York. Evolution, 35:190-192.

Shaw, C. R., and A. L. Koen. 1968. Zone electrophoresis of enzymes. Pp. 325-364, *in* Chromatographic and electrophoretic techniques. (I. Smith, ed.). Vol. II. Pitman Press, Bath, England.

Shaw, C. R., and R. Prasad. 1970. Starch gel electrophoresis of enzymes—a compilation of recipes. Biochem. Genet., 4:297-320.

Smith, D. G. 1980. Paternity exclusion in six captive groups of rhesus monkeys *Macaca mulatta*). Amer. J. Phys. Anthropol., 53:243-249.

Smith, M. H., and J. Joule (eds.) 1981. Mammalian population genetics. The University of Georgia Press, Athens, Georgia, 380 pp.

Smouse, P. E., and J. V. Neel. 1977. Multivariate analysis of gametic disequilibrium in the Yanomama. Genetics, 85:733-752.

Smouse, P. E., R. S. Spielman, and M. H. Park. 1982. Multiple-locus allocation of groups as a function of the genetic variation within and differences among human populations. Amer. Nat., 119:445-463.

Sokal, R. R., and F. J. Rohlf. 1981. Biometry. W. H. Freeman, San Francisco, California, 859 pp.

Spiess, E. B. 1977. Genes in populations. John Wiley and Sons, New York, 780 pp.

Straney, D. O., M. H. Smith, R. J. Baker, and I. F. Greenbaum. 1976a. Biochemical variation and genic similarity of *Myotis velifer* and *Macrotus californicus*. Comp. Biochem. Physiol., 54B:243-248.

Straney, D. O., M. J. O'Farrell, and M. H. Smith. 1976b. Biochemical genetics of *Myotis californicus* and *Pipistrellus hesperus* from southern Nevada. Mammalia, 40:344-347.

Straney, D. O., M. H. Smith, I. F. Greenbaum, and R. J. Baker. 1979. Biochemical genetics. Pp. 157-176, *in* Biology of bats of the new world family Phyllostomatidae. Part III. (R. J. Baker, J. K. Jones, Jr., and D. C. Carter, eds.), Texas Tech Univ., Lubbock, Texas, 16:1-441.

Ward, P. S. 1983. Genetic relatedness and colony organization in a species complex of Ponerine ants. Behav. Ecol. Sociobiol., 12:285-299.

Weir, B. S., and C. C. Cockerham. 1978. Testing hypotheses about linkage disequilibrium with multiple alleles. Genetics, 88:633-642.

Wilkinson, G. S. 1985. Genetic subdivision and relatedness in the common vampire bat. Behav. Ecol. Sociobiol., 17:123-134.

Wilkinson, G. S., and G. F. McCracken. 1985. On estimating relatedness using genetic markers. Evolution, 39:1169-1174.

Appendix 1. Specifications for Construction of Apparatus for Starch-Gel Electrophoresis

Unless specified otherwise, 3 mm (⅛″) plexiglass is used for construction of this apparatus. The electrode consists of 26 ga platinum wire.

Dimensions for buffer boxes with lids and gel trays are shown in Figure 3. The lid should fit squarely on the buffer box. There is a 1.5 cm wide slit centered along the long axis of the lid for insertion of a wick (we use sponge cloths that are available in most grocery stores). There is also a 6 mm × 6 mm strip of plexiglass cemented along the border of the slit on the side opposite the electrode. This facilitates centering the gel tray between the buffer boxes. Gel trays should be constructed using high quality extruded plexiglass. Otherwise, the hot starch used to form gels may cause the tray to warp. The gel tray pictured is 9 mm deep with inside dimensions of 17.8 cm × 19.8 cm.

The short leg of the "L" shaped slicing guide (Fig. 4) fits against the outside margin of the shorter side of the gel tray, and the long (6.1 cm) leg provides a guide for cutting the gel for insertion of samples. A stainless steel micro-spatula is used to make this cut. The shallow, open-ended slicing tray is designed for use with a Buchler tubular gel slicer.

Figure 5 shows the placement of a gel tray between a pair of buffer boxes.

Appendix 2. Commercially Available Special Equipment and Supplies

ITEM

Power Supply for Electrophoresis
Model SP-2717 (assembled)
Model IP-2717 (kit)

Heath Company
Benton Harbor, Michigan 49022 USA

Electrostarch
(we are using Lot #392)

Otto Hiller Co.
P.O. Box 1294
Madison, Wisconsin 53701 USA

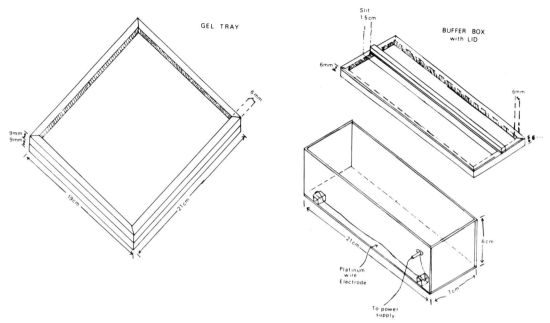

Figure 3. Gel tray and buffer box for starch-gel electrophoresis.

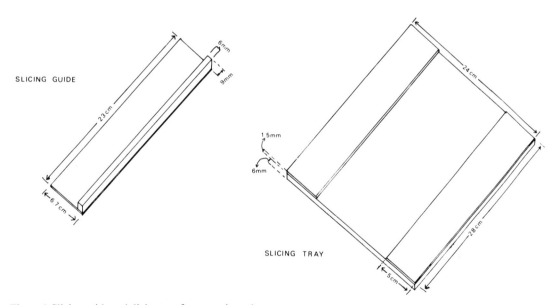

Figure 4. Slicing guide and slicing tray for preparing gels.

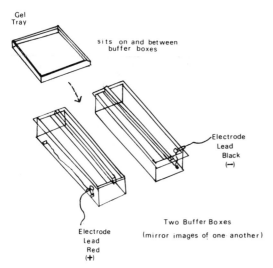

Figure 5. Placement of a gel tray between two buffer boxes.

Purified Enzymes,
Catalysts, Other Stain
Reagents

    Sigma Chemical Co.
    P.O. Box 14508
    St. Louis, Missouri 63178 USA

Dissecting equipment for biopsies:
#12 scalpel blade Cat. # RS9800

Microdissecting scissors Cat. # RS500
Microdissecting forceps Cat. # RS5135

    Roboz Surgical Instrument Co.
    1000 Connecticut Ave., N.W.
    P.O. Box 19148
    Washington, D.C. 20036 USA

Single Compartment Plastic Boxes
for Incubating Gels in Stain.
Cat. # A401

    Flambeau Vlchek
    P.O. Box 97
    Middlefield, Ohio 44062 USA

Sponge Cloths (used as wicks between
buffer boxes and gels during electro-
phoresis)

    O-Cel-O
    General Mills, Inc.
    305 Sawyer Ave.
    Tonawanda, New York 14150 USA

Whatman 3 Filter Paper
(used to blot samples and for application
of samples to gels). Most other
standard laboratory supplies and
equipment

    Fisher Scientific
    2775 Pacific Dr.
    P.O. Box 829
    Norcross, Georgia 30091 USA

Chapter 10

Mark-Recapture Estimates of Bat Survival

Robert Keen

Department of Biological Sciences
Michigan Technological University
Houghton, Michigan 49931 USA

1. INTRODUCTION

Military planners, insurance actuaries, and animal ecologists all study survival rates. The ecologists have more fun than demographers, but often have more problems collecting and analyzing data. This is partly because the really interesting survival estimates usually come from natural populations. Field studies of survival are particularly difficult with mobile animals, for which mark-recapture techniques are commonly used. While bats have been studied with mark-recapture methods since Allen (1921), most studies have been of movement rather than of survival. Using mark-recapture methods to study bat survival has always been problematical. In a brief review of the subject, Tuttle and Stevenson (1982) commented that "the pitfalls and difficulties awaiting the student of chiropteran survival are numerous." The objective here is to explore some paths past the pitfalls.

The discussion will principally concern winter-banded bats. This focus is appropriate because most survival studies have used data obtained from bats concentrated in winter hibernacula where banding is relatively easy. Fortunately, winter studies reveal much about bat survival. Greater effort will be required to address the questions about bat survival that winter banding cannot answer. Some summer-banding problems will also be considered.

1.1. Survival Estimates from Marked Vertebrates

In mark-recapture studies, individuals are marked, tagged, or banded to provide a subset of the population which can be sampled later.

Observations or recaptures of banded individuals make up samples of the banded subset and, from these samples and population properties, including movement, survival, fecundity, growth rate, exploitation may be estimated.

Early mark-recapture analyses used *ad hoc* methods aimed at estimating age-specific mortality with actuarial approaches. In the past 25 years, methods with significant advantages over these life-table analyses have been developed, particularly the Jolly-Seber models for estimating both mortality and population size (Seber, 1973) and the models of Brownie et al. (1978), for estimating survival of gamebirds from recovery of bands by hunters. More recently, techniques for estimating age-specific variation in survival rates have been incorporated into modern approaches (Stokes, 1984; Pollock, 1981b).

1.2. Studies of Bat Survival

Most studies of bat survival have involved bats banded in winter hibernacula and recaptured there in subsequent years. The experimental procedure is straightforward. In winter hibernacula researchers band a number of bats, usually with a small wing band which is coded so each tagged bat is uniquely identifiable (see Chapter 4). Individuals to be banded are usually selected without conscious bias, with sex and species of banded bats noted at banding. Age of bats in winter hibernacula cannot be determined, although relative tooth wear or other correlates of age may be noted (see Chapter 3). In subsequent winters, researchers return and intensively inspect hibernating bats for previously banded individuals, noting band numbers, sex, and species. Additional bats may be banded each winter.

Bats belonging to a single species and sex in a given hibernaculum are usually considered to be a single population. By conventional definition, survival must be studied in "open" populations, where individuals may be lost from the population through death or permanent emigration, and also added with

immigration and births. Individual bats are quite faithful to a particular hibernaculum and winter recaptures of banded bats at other than original hibernacula are rare (see Section 1.3). Studies of winter-banded bats produce observations like the hypothetical data in Table 1. Proper methods for survival analysis of these data are not immediately apparent.

1.3. Difficulties of Analysis

The modern, generalized Jolly-Seber approach to survival estimation does not apply readily to the survival analysis of winter banding data, because the procedures for bats do not provide information on population size. Specifically, there is no attempt to meet the critical criterion that marked and unmarked individuals have equal probabilities of capture at each sampling episode (Seber, 1973; Pollock, 1981a). Even Jolly's (1965) outline of a separate sampling and marking process does not cover the bat mark-recapture procedure. Stated a bit differently, the number of bats that a researcher marks at any time is a known constant and not an informative random variable. The number of bats banded is determined by the time available for work in the hibernaculum, independently of the number of bats. Practicalities of working in hibernacula make it difficult to collect large random samples of bats to be inspected for tags before being released.

The models of Brownie et al. (1978) for analysis of band returns from hunted birds can in some cases be applied to data from recaptures of living, marked animals. However, these models are not very efficient with typical data from bat populations, where some individuals are repeatedly recaptured and where survival rates are usually high.

Earlier analytical methods also are not applicable to winter bats because it seems impossible to determine ages of bats when they are banded. Some anatomical differences may be detected visually on site to distinguish older bats of some species from young animals overwintering for the first

Table 1. Illustrative set of hypothetical data for mark and recapture over 7 years for a single species and sex of bats in a winter hibernaculum. For a particular bat, "O" indicates marking, "X" indicates finding, and "-" indicates non-finding. Usually more bats are banded, and fewer banded individuals are recovered in real situations. The ages of the bats at time of banding are unknown.

Bat	Year						
Number	1971	'72	'73	'74	'75	'76	'77
1	O	X	X	X	-	X	X
2	O	-	X	-	-	-	-
3	O	-	X	X	X	X	-
4	O	X	X	-	-	-	-
5	O	X	-	-	-	-	-
6		O	-	-	X	X	X
7		O	X	X	-	-	-
8		O	-	X	-	-	-
9		O	X	-	-	-	-
10			O	X	-	X	X
11			O	-	-	-	-
12			O	X	X	-	-
13			O	-	-	-	-
14			O	X	X	-	X
15				O	X	X	-
16				O	-	-	-
17				O	X	X	-
18				O	-	X	X
19				O	X	-	X
20				O	X	X	X
21					O	X	-
22					O	X	-
23					O	-	X
24						O	X
25						O	-
26						O	X
27						O	-
28						O	X

2. ANALYSIS OF MARK-RECAPTURE DATA

Mark-recapture data from unaged bats in a hibernating population may be analyzed when a series of more or less reasonable assumptions about the populations and the data are met. Accuracy of survival estimates will depend directly and completely upon the validity of these associated assumptions. Some assumptions may be verified using the mark-recapture records, but other assumptions are not subject to rigorous verification. Unfortunately, some unverifiable assumptions can make an entire analysis questionable.

2.1. Cormack's Method of Survival Analysis

At present, the best general method for analysis of winter-banding data appears to be Cormack's (1964). The method is a subset of the Jolly-Seber method for analyzing mark-recapture data (Seber, 1973), although Cormack's work preceded development of the generalized method. (Cormack's approach is in fact more general than Jolly-Seber methods.) In particular, Cormack's method is suited for analysis when marking and recapture of individuals is performed on a non-random sample of the whole population (Cormack, 1972). The method was developed for the analysis of survival of island birds (Dunnet et al., 1963; Dunnet and Ollason, 1978; Cormack, 1973; Buckland, 1982), and has been applied to bats by Keen and Hitchcock (1980) and Hitchcock et al. (1984).

The summary data needed for analysis are: 1) numbers of bats newly banded each year of study, 2) numbers of previously-banded bats found each year, and 3) numbers of both previously- and newly-banded bats found each year that were never found again. Data may be analyzed following Cormack (1964) or a reformulation (Seber, 1973:215-217). The procedure is demon-

time. These differences appear to be not completely reliable (see Chapter 3), and require considerable experience (Davis and Hitchcock, 1965).

It is of course possible to obtain minimal records of maximum life span of bats in winter banding studies. A recent comprehensive listing of such records is in Tuttle and Stevenson (1982). Longevity records are important and interesting, but clearly are not good estimates for average longevity and survival.

strated in Table 2, using the hypothetical data of Table 1.

Table 2 illustrates a problem that Cormack's method has in common with the Jolly-Seber method with calculated survival rates greater than 1.0 over some sampling intervals. In the example, these biologically impossible values are produced by small sample sizes. Out-of-range values may be avoided by applying Buckland's (1980, 1982) modification, which produces estimates always less than unity using a lengthy iterative technique requiring a computer. However, the statistical properties of these constrained estimates are poorly known. Other variations on the basic method of Cormack will be discussed below.

2.2. Assumptions of Analysis

Several assumptions are always involved in finding survival rates from mark-recapture procedures. Some assumptions are common to all analytical methods, and others pertain only to winter-banding procedures. Five assumptions are really significant for analyzing bat-banding data.

1) Survival rate of the banded groups is representative of the whole, unbanded population.
2) Permanent disappearance of individuals is due to death, not permanent emigration.
3) Banded individuals have equal probabilities of being recaptured.
4) Bands are not lost over the course of the study.
5) Probability of survival between searches is equal for all banded bats.

Other assumptions may also be important; for example, it must be assumed that data are tabulated correctly, and that sex and species of banded bats are properly identified.

When assumptions can be checked, verification usually involves accepting a null hypothesis of no difference; for example, that the probabilities of recapture of individual bats are all equal. It is an unfortunate statistical truism that acceptance of a null hypothesis does not demonstrate its truth, but merely indicates lack of evidence for rejection. Researchers wishing to verify assumptions of mark-recapture analysis are in an awkward position of not being able to demonstrate positively the validity of the assumptions. Despite this, assumptions should be verified where possible.

2.2.1. Assumption of Representativeness

The assumption that survival of the tagged bats represents that of the population at large is important in interpreting results of the analysis. This assumption is common to mark-recapture methods generally, but for

Table 2. Analysis with Cormack's method of illustrative data from Table 1. Notation follows Cormack (1964) and Keen and Hitchcock (1980). Mean survival rate = 0.884 ± 0.052 (SD of mean).

Year	Year Number i	Number Banded b_i	Number of Recaptures a_i	Number Seen for Last Time c_i	Annual Survival Rate $\hat{\phi}$	Var $\hat{\phi}$
1971	1	5	0	0	1.0667	0.00652
1972	2	4	3	1	1.0357	0.04919
1973	3	5	6	5	0.5659	0.02481
1974	4	6	7	3	0.7902	0.01500
1975	5	3	8	1	1.0909	0.02852
1976	6	5	10	7	—	—
1977	7	0	11	11	—	—

winter-banded bats a particular problem occurs where band-recapture processes alter survival rates directly. If banding itself alters survival rates, this may be detected within limits using techniques discussed for the equal-survival assumption (Section 2.2.5). However, if wearing a band should cause a uniform decrease in survival rate of 10%, for example, then survival estimates from the banded group will not be accurate for the population at large, and this will be undetectable. Gentle handling and banding in winter hibernacula is therefore important to assure that survival of banded bats is similar to unbanded ones.

2.2.2. Assumption of Death vs. Emigration

Assuming that death rather than permanent emigration causes permanent disappearance of banded bats is also important in interpretation. Analysis actually estimates loss from the banded group. The usual source of loss is death, but if emigration rates are significant, then calculated survival rates for a sex and species will be underestimates for the whole population in a geographic region. However, a calculated loss rate may be accurate for an individual population in one hibernaculum. Knowing how bats behave in the hibernating population at large is the only real verification of this assumption. Bels (1952), Stevenson and Tuttle (1981), and Humphrey and Cope (1976) illustrate the information needed to verify this assumption with their data on movements of bats among different winter hibernacula. The switching of winter hibernacula appears uncommon.

2.2.3. Assumption of Equal Probability of Recapture

Mark-recapture analysis assumes all banded bats to be equally catchable for any given year. This differs from the general Jolly-Seber assumption of equal probability of catching any living individual, marked or unmarked, during a given sampling episode, and it also differs from an assumption of constant, year-to-year recapture probability.

In the case of winter-banded bats, equal catchability assumptions should be met easily. However, knowledge of different possible behaviors of individual bats in the population is valuable in justifying the assumption. Eberhardt (1969) lists three general reasons for unequal catchability, two of which are important for winter-banded bats: 1) some bats may become recapture-shy or -prone as a result of banding, and 2) some banded individuals may place themselves consistently in areas within the hibernaculum that are inaccessible to the investigator or are searched either very regularly or rarely. The first of these will be produced by individual differences in responses of bats to banding and the second by differences in methods of searching for banded bats. Searches for banded bats should produce random discoveries of any particular banded individual, even where individuals may be returning to specific areas of the hibernaculum each year, or of "hiding" to avoid successive recaptures. Stevenson and Tuttle (1981) have documented hiding of individual banded bats in winter hibernacula.

If the hiding response of bats to banding and successive recaptures is permanent, then all banded bats are either more or less prone to being recaptured. In this case, estimates of survival rate will be unbiased, although precision of the estimate will depend directly upon recapture probabilities. When the hiding response is temporary, it may be difficult to distinguish unequal catchability from band-induced mortality (Section 2.2.5). Unequal catchability may severely bias some parameters associated with mark-recapture techniques (Pollock, 1981a), but estimates of survival made with Jolly-Seber methods (and Cormack's method by implication) may be biased only slightly (Nichols and Pollock, 1983; Carothers, 1979).

Except for Keen and Hitchcock (1980), studies of bat survival have not tested this assumption. Cormack (1979) reviews the difficult problem of testing for homogeneity of catchability among banded individuals. For populations of winter-banded bats, procedures of Leslie (1958), extended by Carothers (1971, 1973) are apparently best. The critical assessment of these tests by Roff (1973) and by Caughley (1977) may not be entirely correct (Cormack, 1979).

2.2.4. Assumption of No Loss of Bands

Avoiding band loss is important in preventing underestimates of survival rates. Like emigration assumptions above, methods for calculating survival do not distinguish among ways that banded individuals may disappear. Loss of a band from a living individual will be interpreted as mortality.

Bands attached to bats seem at least as permanent as any marking system employed for any vertebrate (Chapter 4). The double-banding procedure of Farner (1949) might be used to produce an independent test of this assumption. The analysis of data from double-banding procedures should follow Seber (1973).

2.2.5. Assumption of Equality of Survival

The equal survival assumption requires all banded bats (and by inference all untagged bats) to have equal chances of survival between annual sampling episodes. More than any other assumption, this has produced difficulties and confusion in analysis of winter-banding data. The assumption is not one of constant survival rate from year to year, but that for a given year all banded individuals have the same probability of survival until the next annual search.

Two possibly interacting problems account for most of the difficulties with the assumption: 1) bats of differing but unknown ages may have differing age-dependent survival rates, and 2), the banding process may produce heterogenous survival.

The most vexing problem arises where individuals of differing ages may have different probabilities of survival to the next year. A group of bats banded in any winter will be

composed of bats of several ages, as Humphrey and Cope (1977) point out clearly. The critical point is whether differences in age-specific survival rate are large enough to bias the survival estimates produced by analysis of banding data.

One source of bias arises from a single estimate not being applicable to any age group. If, for example, 7-year-old bats have a much higher or lower survival rate than other age classes, then clearly the single estimate will be biased with respect to 7-year-olds. This is inherent in the analysis and might be considered inconsequential when bats cannot be aged. A second potential source of bias is that estimates of survival produced by methods assuming equal survival will differ from an estimate of average survival when both age structure and age-specific survival rates are known. A third source of bias, related to the second, is that the age composition of the banded group will not be representative of the population at large, depending upon differences in age-specific survival rate.

Caughley (1966) concluded that age-specific mortality rate of mammals typically follows a U-shaped trend with age. There are few data available for long-term analysis of age-specific mortality rates of bats, and these may not be general. Stevenson and Tuttle (1981) and Humphrey and Cope (1976) gathered data for survival over several years for *Myotis* spp. marked as neonates. Neither of these data sets seemed amenable to rigorous analysis for age-specific mortality.

Circumstantial evidence about the age-independence assumption seems divided. In some species, individuals that have lived for a relatively long time show no senescent changes (Stevenson and Tuttle, 1981; Keen and Hitchcock, 1980). For these species, the bottom of the U-shaped curve of age-specific mortality may be very wide and flat, so that survival is effectively constant after maturation. A 4-year-old bat of these species could therefore have the same chance as a 30-year-old of surviving for one more year. (In this case, the observed curve of age-specific mortality rate will eventually rise sharply to 1.0 because even-aged cohorts are finite and the last individual in a cohort must die sometime. The age at which this rise occurs will be indeterminate, varying among different cohorts. It may be preceded by a number of years with a zero rate of mortality, if the last bat does not die.)

Among some other species, senescence may be observed (e.g., tooth wear). An older bat with physiological or behavioral effects of aging may not have the same chance of survival as a younger bat, and the assumption of equal survival may not hold for these species. However, if mortality rates are relatively higher and constant in the middle of the U-shaped curve of age-specific mortality rate, then most bats will not survive to an age where senescence influences survival probability. If this is so, then the equal survival assumption may hold sufficiently to allow estimation with minimal bias.

Jolly-Seber and related estimates of survival are little influenced by heterogeneity of survival among individuals (Cormack, 1972). Pollock and Raveling (1982) showed this to be true only if probability of survival is independent of capture probability. If banded bats learn slowly over a period of years to avoid recaptures, then survival estimates will be underestimated.

The two problems of differing age-specific survival rate and banding-induced change of survival rate are combined in the case of young bats born during the summer and banded during their first winter. Although young individuals in their first winter are usually not distinguishable from older bats, they may have lesser probabilities of survival. Davis and Hitchcock (1965) discuss factors that may contribute to lower yearling survival. Lower survival of yearlings in particular could invalidate the equality assumption, because these bats will usually represent more of the population than any other year-age group.

Some survival analyses of winter-banded bats indicate that rates of mortality may be higher the first year after banding than

subsequently (e.g., Humphrey and Cope, 1977). Lower survival in the first year after banding may be produced either by 1) including young bats which have lower survival rates than older age groups, or by 2) mortality cause by banding. An independent verification of handling/banding mortality may be possible by attaching a second band to some previously-banded bats, and testing whether mortality rate is higher in the doubly-banded individuals (Seber, 1973). Where a short-term (one-year) effect of initial banding and/or increased yearling mortality is suspected of biasing survival estimates, it is possible to circumvent the problem with the method of Brownie and Robson (1983). Their analysis permits estimating survival rates where first-year effects can be demonstrated with goodness of fit tests.

2.2.6. Cormack's Assumption of Sampling Intensity

In addition to the assumptions above, Cormack's method assumes that intensity of sampling in any given year is fixed by the investigator independently of the number of tagged bats recovered. While recovery will depend upon sampling effort, there should be no dependence of effort upon number recovered. The assumption is validated in the sampling process by fixing, before entering the hibernaculum, either the areas of the hibernaculum to be inspected or the time alotted to inspection. The assumption will be invalidated for example, by deciding during the recapture process either to keep searching for tagged bats if few are found, or to terminate the search early if many are found initially.

3. OTHER ANALYTICAL APPROACHES

Most studies of survival in winter-banded bats have used some type of actuarial or life-table analysis. Usually regression techniques have been used to estimate survival rates, with life tables developed as follow-up inter-

Table 3. Tabulation of illustrative data from Table 1, for analysis with the common regression method for survival rate estimation.

Years after Banding	Number Banded that Could Be Alive	Number Known to Be Alive	Percent Alive	Log Percent Alive
0	28	28	100.00	2.000
1	28	23	82.14	1.915
2	23	16	69.57	1.842
3	20	8	40.00	1.602
4	14	5	35.71	1.553
5	9	3	33.33	1.523
6	5	1	20.00	1.301

pretive tools. Numerous proponents of modern methods recommend that older regression and life-table methods be abandoned (e.g., Brownie et al., 1978). The older methods discussed below are prominent in bat-banding work, but have obvious difficulties.

3.1. Regression Techniques

An intuitive method for survival estimates has been used by Humphrey and Cope (1976, 1977), Elder and Gunnier (1981), Stevenson and Tuttle (1981), and others. This approach assumes that survival rate is constant from year to year, so that the number of known survivors will decline exponentially with time after banding. A regression of logarithm of known survivors vs. time after banding will then be linear, and the antilog of the slope of the least-squares-fit regression will estimate survival rate (Table 3 and Fig. 1). Using proportions of known survivors avoids difficulties that accompany work with artificial groups of size 1000 or 10,000, as discussed by Humphrey and Cope (1977). (Fig. 1 in their paper illustrates the difficulties: the ordinate should be labeled 1.0 at the origin, not 0).

A variation of the intuitive approach is Bezem's method (Bezem et al., 1960; Sluiter et al., 1956, 1971a, 1971b; Stebbings, 1966). This method uses not only known survival over a period after the initial banding, but also survival over similar periods following any observation of a banded bat. All observa-

tions of any bat one year apart are counted as "survival one year after marking." Thus, each banded bat may appear several times in the estimate of each regression point.

Variability of survival rate cannot be estimated with either the intuitive or Bezem's methods. The data used in the regression are not independent statistically. The same banded bats are used to determine the different regression points, which violates the important assumption of independence (Snedecor and Cochran, 1967:141). Confidence intervals and tests of difference between different rates will be biased because the data are not independent (Stevenson and Tuttle, 1981).

Bezem's method and the intuitive approach both are based on all five assumptions listed above (Section 2.2). Both have additional assumptions that are difficult to meet and cannot be checked using the recapture data. Two added assumptions are especially critical. The first, that rate of survival remains constant from year to year, is superimposed on the assumption of age-independence. In practice, this constancy assumption is most unrealistic because environmental influences on survival will almost certainly vary from year to year. This variability will bias regression estimates continually for subsequent years because number surviving to any given year after banding depends directly upon survival in preceding years.

The second critical assumption is that

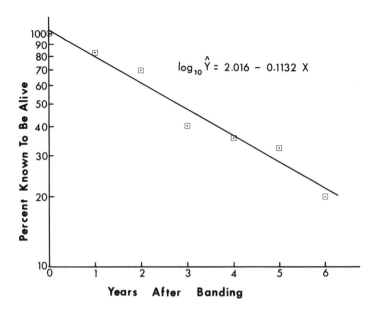

Figure 1. Plot of hypothetical data from Table 1 using the common regression method. Data points are from Table 2. Calculated annual survival rate = antilog slope = 0.77.

rates of recapture are constant each year. Not only must each banded bat have an equal probability of being recaptured during the search of any given year (Section 2.2.3), but this probability must also be constant between years. This effectively requires knowing in advance of sampling how many banded bats are in the hibernaculum, to allow recapture of a constant fraction of living, tagged bats. A constant recapture effort, measured in either numbers of bats recaptured, amount of time spent searching, or area of hibernaculum searched does not satisfy the assumption.

If the annual rates of survival or recapture are assumed to be constant during the study, then the models of Jolly (1982) apply. Given the same assumptions as the intuitive approach and Bezem's method, survival rates may be estimated with known precision.

Sluiter et al. (1956) discuss some assumptions which do not apply to survival estimates. For example, it is not necessary to assume a stationary population size. If rates of survival and recapture are constant and independent of year, age, and recapture his-

tory, the estimates of survival rate are unbiased, even though population size may be changing. Obviously, any change in population size must be caused by corresponding changes in rate of birth or survival of young before they first hibernate, or the rate constancy assumptions are violated.

To determine whether survival rates are constant and age- and year-independent, Sluiter et al. (1956) suggest inspecting the distribution of points around the regression line. They argue that "no appreciable systematic deviation from the straight regression line" indicates constancy. This argument seems weak: first, the combined failure of two or more assumptions may interact to produce both biased estimates and lack of systematic deviation; second, with Bezem's method, the grouping of all sightings one year apart as "recaptures-one-year-after-banding" prevents detecting higher yearling mortality; and third, any method for detecting "systematic deviation" of points, e.g., a Runs test (Zar, 1984:416), has a problem with lack of independence of data points.

Davis (1966) stated wrongly that Bezem's

Table 4. A "life table" developed as an arthimetic exercise with a constant, age-independent rate of survival = 0.400.

Years x	Proportion Surviving l_x	Survival Rate p_x	Age-specific Mortality Rate q_x	Proportion Dying d_x
0	1.0000	0.400	0.600	0.6000
1	0.4000	0.400	0.600	0.2400
2	0.1600	0.400	0.600	0.0960
3	0.0640	0.400	0.600	0.0384
4	0.0256	0.400	0.600	0.0154
5	0.0102	0.400	0.600	0.0061
6	0.0041	0.400	0.600	0.0025
7	0.0016	0.400	0.600	0.0010
8	0.0007	0.400	0.600	0.0004
9	0.0003	0.400	0.600	0.0002
10	0.0001	0.400	0.600	0.0001

method assumes a constant sex ratio and equality of survival of the two sexes. In fact, males and females may be analyzed independently. Although Sluiter et al. (1956) found survival of the sexes to be equal, this was not a necessary assumption.

3.2. Life-Table Analyses

Since Deevey's (1947) classic paper, life tables have been recognized as useful tools in population ecology (Caughley, 1977). Unfortunately, efforts to use life tables for analysis of winter-banding data have been unsuccessful. Most of the problems are the result of confusing the time after banding of unaged bats with the time after birth of known-aged cohorts. It is possible, given the assumption of a constant, age-independent survival rate, to make a "life table" as an exercise in arithmetic (Table 4). Table 4 is truncated arbitrarily at 10 years; it may be extended indefinitely. Sluiter et al. (1956) produced a similar table as an illustration of exponential die off. They noted correctly that the age class x could indicate either years after banding, or age of a group of bats measured from first hibernation, but not from birth. The age option is available only when rate of survival is assumed constant. The table of Sluiter et al. (1956) is not a true life table because it was calculated from an assumed constant rate (Caughley, 1966).

Beer's (1955) early work with winter-banded bats has the common defect of confusing years after banding with age, when the banded bats were all of unknown age. His method of analysis also appears inappropriate, since he used Hickey's (1952) method which was developed for analyzing data from hunter recovery of birds banded as nestlings.

Davis (1966) derived life tables for winter-tagged *Pipistrellus subflavus*. However, rather than determining an average survival rate with regression, he calculated survival rates for each year after banding, and found an unusually high rate of survival between 2-3 years after tagging for all tagged groups. These high rates were apparently not artifacts of the mark-recapture process, and could not be an age-specific phenomenon, because banded bats were selected with the usual "random" procedure. The origin of the anomalous rates is obscure.

Davis (1966) misinterpreted survival rates, giving age-specific meaning to them in setting up life tables and age distributions. Assuming his banding-time-specific rates were accurate, Davis correctly supposed that bats banded as yearlings would follow the rate schedule. However, a group of newly-tagged 10-year-old bats would also follow the same schedule. Hence, the theoretical age distributions were improperly formulated.

Brenner's (1974) life tables for *Myotis lucifugus* were derived much like Davis'

(1966), again with a confusion of age-specific and banding-time-specific rates. Brenner discussed life expectancy correctly, clearly referring only to tagged individuals. If his banded groups were unbiased selections from the population, then the high first-year mortality rates (>90 percent) must have been associated with the tagging process. Thus, calculated survival rates and remaining life expectancies probably do not represent the population at large.

Humphrey and Cope (1976) give life tables of winter-banded *Myotis lucifugus,* with survival rates estimated from intuitive regression methods. First-year survival rates are estimated separately, appearing higher and attributable to banding mortality. The decline in the estimates of remaining life after the first year is an artifact of using Deevey's (1947) method for estimating life expectancy. Remaining life should be estimated following the easily-derived formulas in Brownie et al. (1978:207). For example, the winter-banded females have first-year survival rates of 0.313, and 0.857 subsequently (Humphrey and Cope, 1976:44). The remaining life for a newly banded female should be 2.62 years, and 6.48 years subsequently. Summary life table analysis for *M. grisescens* (Stevenson and Tuttle, 1981) needs similar correction.

4. INTERPRETING AND USING SURVIVAL RATES

For estimating survival rates, stochastic methods like Cormack's are preferable to older methods for reasons of fewer and more plausible assumptions, and because estimates of variance are possible. Other reasons are detailed in Brownie et al. (1978:170). Some general aspects of interpreting survival estimates are presented here, although exact uses will depend upon objectives of a given study.

4.1. Average Survival Rates

Cormack's and related methods produce estimates of survival for each year over the study period. The motivation of a particular study will indicate whether an "average rate" is required. When annual estimates are presumed to be a random sample of some overall survival rate, with variation produced by randomly varying environmental factors, averaging of rates may be justified. Cormack (1964) gives formulas for estimating geometric mean survival rate and standard deviation. Brownie et al. (1978:16) recommend arithmetic mean rates and give appropriate formulas, including 95 percent confidence intervals where samples are large. [The necessary covariance estimates may come from Cormack (1964).] Usefulness and validity of an average rate will be limited by variability and time trends of yearly estimates. Mean rate will not be a useful descriptor where variability is high, or where survival rates continually decline or increase during the study.

4.2. Average Life Expectancy

The basic idea of life expectancy is clear, but application to winter-banding studies has been confused. Some confusion arises from estimating expectancies with life tables as noted above, but other problems stem from vague terminology. To be clear, "life expectancy" usually needs a modifying term. Strictly, life expectancy is the average age at death of a group (cohort) of individuals born simultaneously. However, a life expectancy may be calculated for individuals of any given age, indicating mean lifetime remaining to individuals of that age (Deevey, 1947). Life expectancy values cannot be calculated with life-table based analysis until all individuals in a cohort have died (Gehan, 1969).

In those studies where an average survival rate may be valid, a life expectancy value for bats in a hibernaculum may be estimated with

$$\frac{-1}{\ln \hat{S}}$$

where $\hat{S}$ is the estimated mean rate of survival (Cormack, 1964; DeSapio, 1976). Cormack

(1964) gives methods for estimating standard error of life expectancy. Brownie et al. (1978) show how to find confidence intervals where recaptures are numerous. If Brownie and Robson's (1983) techniques show that survival differs between the first and subsequent years after banding, then the formula of Brownie et al. (1978:207) may be used where the first-year difference is attributable to effects of including young bats. If lower first-year rates are attributable to banding mortality, then mean survival rate excluding newly-banded bats should be used to estimate life expectancy of the population at large.

4.3. Comparing Survival Rates

A frequent objective of survival study is to compare rates from different populations. Interesting comparisons may be made between sexes within a hibernaculum, between different populations of the same sex, or between different years for the same population. When samples from bat populations are large, statistical tests for differences in survival rate can follow the approximate Z-testing procedures outlined in Brownie et al. (1978:180). The covariance estimates indicated in these tests can be neglected, except when comparing survival for different years of the same population; here, covariances may come from Cormack (1964).

5.   SUMMER BANDING STUDIES

In temperate regions, most bat species produce young in the summer. Summer banding studies conducted carefully on accessible, definable populations can address directly some important questions about survival of young bats that winter studies cannot.

Survival between birth and first hibernation is an obvious problem that only summer studies may explore. Survival of newborn and young animals usually is significantly lower than for adults. Although little is known of bat survival during the critical first summer, it is

likely that survival will be strongly age-dependent. Even recently developed recapture models for age-dependence (e.g., Stokes, 1984) are not adequate for descriptions of summer survival. Where a summer maternity colony can be censused repeatedly and intensely, conventional life-table analysis of newborn survival may be possible (Caughley, 1977; Foster et al., 1978).

Because bats may be banded as identifiable young in the summer, several important questions can be addressed. Summer tags on young will serve as age indicators when recaptures are made in later years. This resembles approximately the banding of nestling birds, and has similar analytical problems. Characteristics of individual species will be important in planning studies of summer-banded bats. If recaptures are made in successive summers, site will be important. For example, females, but not males, will be readily recaptured in maternity colonies. Recapture of males may require procedures such as intensive mist netting. Planning for recapture in winter hibernacula will require either detailed knowledge of summer-winter movements, or banding of massive numbers of young, to insure adequate numbers of recaptures.

With bats banded as young, the different survival rates of young vs. adult bats may be investigated. In effect, this will verify one assumption of winter-banding analysis. When sufficient numbers of young can be tagged and recaptured, the mark-recapture models of Pollock and Mann (1983) may be used to estimate survival for each age group. It will be necessary to tag numbers of adults in the summer also, to obtain independent estimates of sampling intensity (Brownie et al., 1978:112). A related, important question concerns changes of survival and mortality rates as bats age. Numerous young bats will have to be banded over several years to ensure statistically adequate samples of older bats for testing hypotheses of different survival rates. Extensions of the models of Stokes (1984) or Pollock (1981b) will be useful in analyzing such data.

6. CONCLUSION

Mark-recapture studies of bats are time-consuming, long-term, and therefore expensive. Before field work begins, a study should be planned carefully and thoroughly, including assessing the assumptions. This may require consultation with biometricians familiar with mark-recapture analysis. Regardless of the statistical model chosen as the basis for analysis, mark-recapture studies of any animal rarely meet all the assumptions. Value of resulting estimates will therefore be open to question. For interpreting results, it will be important to have quantified judgements about how robust the analysis is to failure of assumptions.

7. ACKNOWLEDGMENTS

H. B. Hitchcock stimulated my examination of bat banding, S. R. Humphrey has been generous with his time and criticisms, and J. D. Nichols and K. H. Pollock critiqued a previous draft. R. C. Stones, B. K. Whitten, T. H. Kunz, and Karen Keen have been patient and sometimes understanding.

8. REFERENCES

Allen, A. A. 1921. Banding bats. J. Mammal., 2:53-57.

Beer, J. R. 1955. Survival and movements of banded cave bats. J. Mammal., 36:242-248.

Bels, L. 1952. Fifteen years of bat banding in the Netherlands. Pub. Natuurhist. Genootsch. Limburg, 5:1-99.

Bezem, J. J., J. W. Sluiter, and P. F. van Heerdt. 1960. Population statistics of five species of the bat genus *Myotis* and one of the genus *Rhinolophus,* hibernating in the caves of S. Limburg. Arch. Neerl. Zool., 13:511-539.

Brenner, F. J. 1974. A five-year study of a hibernating colony of *Myotis lucifugus.* Ohio J. Sci., 74:239-244.

Brownie, C., D. R. Anderson, K. P. Burnham, and D. S. Robson. 1978. Statistical inference from band recovery data: A handbook. U.S. Fish and Wildl. Serv., Res. Publ. No. 131., 212 pp.

Brownie, C., and D. S. Robson. 1983. Estimation of time-specific survival rates from tag-resighting samples: A generalization of the Jolly-Seber model. Biometrics, 39:437-453.

Buckland, S. T. 1980. A modified analysis of the Jolly-Seber capture-recapture method. Biometrics, 36:419-435.

Buckland, S. T. 1982. A mark-recapture survival analysis. J. Anim. Ecol., 51:833-847.

Carothers, A. D. 1971. An examination and extension of Leslie's test of equal catchability. Biometrics, 27:615-630.

Carothers, A D. 1973. The effects of unequal catchability on Jolly-Seber estimates. Biometrics, 29:79-100.

Carothers, A. D. 1979. Quantifying unequal catchability and its effect on survival estimates in an actual population. J. Anim. Ecol., 48:863-869.

Caughley, G. 1966. Mortality patterns in mammals. Ecology, 47:906-918.

Caughley, G. 1977. Analysis of vertebrate populations. Wiley-Interscience, New York, 234 pp.

Cormack, R. M. 1964. Estimates of survival from the sightings of marked animals. Biometrika, 54:429-438.

Cormack, R. M. 1972. The logic of capture-recapture estimates. Biometrics, 28:337-343.

Cormack, R. M. 1973. Common sense estimates from capture-recapture studies. Pp. 225-234, *in* The mathematical theory of the dynamics of biological populations. (M. S. Bartlett and R. W. Hiorns, eds.). Academic Press, New York, 347 pp.

Cormack, R. M. 1979. Models for capture-recapture. Pp. 217-255, *in* Sampling biological populations. Statistical ecology. Vol. 5. (R. M. Cormack, G. P. Patil, and D. S. Robson, eds.). Int. Co-op. Publ. House, Fairland, Maryland, 329 pp.

Davis, W. H. 1966. Population dynamics of the bat *Pipistrellus subflavus.* J. Mammal., 47:383-396.

Davis, W. H., and H. B. Hitchcock. 1965. Biology and migration of the bat, *Myotis lucifugus,* in New England. J. Mammal., 46:296-313.

Deevey, E. S. 1947. Life tables for natural populations of animals. Quart. Rev. Biol., 22:283-314.

DeSapio, R. 1976. Calculus for the life sciences. W. H. Freeman, San Francisco, 740 pp.

Dunnet, G. M., A. Anderson, and R. M. Cormack. 1963. A study of survival of adult fulmars with observations on the pre-laying exodus. Brit. Birds, 56:2-18.

Dunnett, G. M., and J. C. Ollason. 1978. The estimation of survival rate in the fulmar, *Fulmarus glacialis.* J. Anim. Ecol., 47:507-520.

Eberhardt, L. L. 1969. Population estimates from recapture frequencies. J. Wildl. Manage., 33:28-39.

Elder, W. H., and W. J. Gunnier. 1981. Dynamics of a grey bat population (*Myotis grisescens*) in Missouri. Amer. Midl. Nat., 105:193-195.

Farner, D. S. 1949. Age groups and longevity in the American robin: Comments, further discussion, and certain revisions. Wilson Bull., 61:68-81.

Foster, G. W., S. R. Humphrey, and P. P. Humphrey. 1978. Survival rate of young southeastern brown bats, *Myotis austroriparius,* in Florida. J. Mammal., 59:299-304.

Gehan, E. A. 1969. Estimating survival functions from the life table. J. Chron. Dis., 21:629-644.

Hickey, J. J. 1952. Survival studies of banded birds. U. S. Fish Wildl. Serv., Spec. Sci. Rept., 15:1-177.

Hitchcock, H. B., R. Keen, and A. Kurta. 1984. Survival rates of *Myotis leibii* and *Eptesicus fuscus* in southeastern Ontario. J. Mammal., 65:126-130.

Humphrey, S R., and J. B. Cope. 1976. Population ecology of the little brown bat (*Myotis lucifugus*) in Indiana and north-central Kentucky. Spec. Publ., Amer. Soc. Mammal., 4:1-81.

Humphrey, S. R., and J. B. Cope. 1977. Survival rates of the endangered Indiana bat, *Myotis sodalis.* J. Mammal., 58:32-36.

Jolly, G. M. 1965. Explicit estimates from capture-recapture data with both death and immigration-stocastic model. Biometrika, 52:225-247.

Jolly, G. M. 1982. Mark-recapture models with parameters constant in time. Biometrics, 38:301-321.

Keen, R., and H. B. Hitchcock. 1980. Survival and longevity of the little brown bat (*Myotis lucifugus*) in southeastern Ontario. J. Mammal., 61:1-7.

Leslie, P. H. 1958. Statistical appendix. J. Anim. Ecol., 27:84-86.

Nichols, J. D., and K. H. Pollock. 1983. Estimation methodology in contemporary small mammal capture-recapture studies. J. Mammal., 64:253-260.

Pollock, K. H. 1981a. Capture-recapture models:

A review of current methods, assumptions and experimental design. Pp. 426-435, *in* Estimating the numbers of terrestrial birds. Studies in avian biology, 6. (D. J. Ralph and J. M. Scott, eds.). Cooper Ornith. Soc., Allen Press, Lawrence, Kansas.

Pollock, K. H. 1981b. Capture-recapture models allowing for age-dependent survival and capture rates. Biometrics, 37:521-529.

Pollock, K. H., and R. H. K. Mann. 1983. Use of an age-dependent mark-recapture model in fisheries research. Canadian J. Fish Aquat. Sci., 40:1449-1455.

Pollock, K. H., and D. G. Raveling. 1982. Assumptions of modern band recovery models with emphasis on heterogenous survival rates. J. Wildl. Manage. 46:752-757.

Roff, D. A. 1973. An examination of some statistical tests used in the analysis of mark-recapture data. Oecologia, 12:35-54.

Seber, G. A. F. 1973. The estimation of animal abundance and related parameters. Griffin, London, 506 pp.

Sluiter, J. W., P. F. van Heerdt, and J. J. Bezem. 1956. Population statistics of the bat *Myotis mystacinus,* based on the marking-recapture method. Arch. Neerl. Zool., 12:63-88.

Sluiter, J. W., P. F. van Heerdt, and M. Gruet. 1971a. Paramètres de population chez le Grande Rhinolephe fer-a-chevel (*Rhinolophus ferrum-equinum* Schreber), estemes par la méthode de reprises après baguages. Mammalia, 35:254-272.

Sluiter, J. W., P. F. van Heerdt, and A. M. Voûte. 1971b. Contribution to the population biology of the pond bat, *Myotis dasycneme,* (Boie, 1825). Deuchiana (Bonn), 18:1-44.

Snedecor, G. W., and W. G. Cochran. 1967. Statistical methods. 6th ed. Iowa State Univ. Press, Ames, 593 pp.

Stebbings, R. E. 1966. A population study of bats of the genus *Plecotus.* J. Zool., 150:53-75.

Stevenson, D. E., and M. D. Tuttle. 1981. Survivorship in the endangered grey bat (*Myotis grisescens*). J. Mammal., 62:244-257.

Stokes, S. L. 1984. The Jolly-Seber method applied to age-stratified populations. J. Wildl. Manage., 48:1053-1059.

Tuttle, M. D., and D. Stevenson. 1982. Growth and survival of bats. Pp. 105-150, *in* Ecology of bats. (T. H. Kunz, ed.). Plenum Press, New York, 425 pp.

Zar, J. H. 1984. Biostatistical analysis. 2nd ed. Prentice-Hall, Englewood Cliffs, New Jersey, 718 pp.

Chapter 11

Food Habits Analysis of Insectivorous Bats

John O. Whitaker, Jr.

Department of Life Sciences
Indiana State University
Terre Haute, Indiana 47809 USA

1. INTRODUCTION

An important question often asked about members of a species is: What do they eat? The purpose of this chapter is to examine and compare methods of analyzing the prey consumed by insectivorous bats. Most Nearctic bats, and many species of the world, are almost exclusively insectivorous. This chapter is concerned mostly with aerial feeding bats, but some information is given for other species such as foliage gleaning insectivores. Food habits analysis of plant-visiting bats is treated in Chapter 13.

It has been stated that "only a very small fraction of stomach contents escape reduction to an unidentifiable soup" (e.g., Gould, 1955). While it is true that most bats thoroughly chew their food, it is usually possible to identify most of the prey remains to a reasonable level, at least to order and often to family. In the case where a single item forms a major part of the diet, it is often possible to identify it to species if one has adequate comparative material and can spend the time to do the analysis (e.g., Whitaker and Tomich, 1983). Fortunately, some considerations ease the task. First, except for some foliage gleaners, mainly tropical, many of the prey species are flying insects. Therefore, immature insects can be essentially eliminated from consideration. Second, most bats do not eat many different kinds of insects at any one time, thus a single stomach (or fecal pellet) often contains only one to four kinds of insects. Furthermore, when large numbers of insects are present, they are often of one species, reflecting successful feeding in a swarm of insects.

2. MATERIAL AVAILABLE FOR FOOD HABITS ANALYSIS

Gardner (1977) stated, "If we could observe and record the variety and quantity of foods as they are gathered and consumed by bats, the determination of diets would be a relatively simple matter. Because this usually is not possible, the examination of feces or digestive tract contents would appear to be the next best method. However, the comminuted remains of insects and small vertebrates are usually difficult to identify; a problem intensified by the habit of many bats to discard the harder, and often the only diagnostic, parts of their prey."

Gardner's statement alludes directly or indirectly to several ways by which information on food habits of bats can be obtained: stomach or fecal analysis, culled items, and direct observation. These approaches will be discussed below.

2.1. Stomach Content and Feces

Much of the published data on prey taken by insectivorous bats is from stomach contents or fecal analysis. Stomach analysis allows examination of the bats' last meal in undigested form, whereas digestion tends to destroy soft insect parts, resulting in a bias toward less digestible items in fecal analysis.

For analysis of stomach contents, bats should be killed immediately upon capture to minimize digestion. This raises ethical and legal questions with respect to sampling large numbers of bats, especially where endangered or threatened species are involved. In the future, however, it should be possible to develop techniques for sampling stomach contents without killing bats, as have been developed for other vertebrates (e.g., Jernejcic, 1969; Wrazen and Svendsen, 1978).

Analysis of fecal contents, of course, permits non-destructive sampling. Furthermore, the problems associated with differential digestion may not be as serious in insectivorous bats as they are in other mammals, because most food passes through the gut of

bats rapidly and because most insects have hardened exoskeletons composed of protein and chitin. Although chitin was long thought to be undigestible by vertebrate enzymes (Snodgrass, 1935), some bat species apparently synthesize chitinase in the gastric mucosa (e.g., Jeuniaux, 1961). Nonetheless, large pieces of the exoskeleton pass undigested through the digestive tract, and digestion of chitin does not seem to greatly limit analysis of feces for determining bat diets. Feces can be collected from individually captured bats which can subsequently be released unharmed. Feces can also be collected beneath roosts, assuming that the identity of the bats is known. The disadvantages of fecal analysis include lack of data about differential digestion, and the uncertainty of the time period over which the food was eaten in the case of feces collected sporadically from beneath a roost. However, this source of variation can be controlled by making regular collections of fresh pellets at short time intervals. For the food analyst examining stomach or fecal material, the lack of culled parts (Section 2.2) can increase the difficulty of identification, since these items often include diagnostic characters (Gardner, 1977).

Whitaker et al. (1981) found relatively good agreement between results from stomach and scat analysis of bats from eastern Oregon. Also, Kunz and Whitaker (1983) showed that analysis of feces provided a relatively accurate picture of insect food consumed by *Myotis lucifugus* as compared to stomach analysis. However, Belwood and Fenton (1976) found that mayflies fed to little brown bats could not be identified in feces; and Rabinowitz and Tuttle (1982) demonstrated that 1) mayflies (and thus presumably other soft-bodied forms) can be underrepresented in fecal analysis, and 2) the assumption of Coutts et al. (1973), that each fecal pellet contains the remains of one large or several small insects, is not necessarily true.

For analysis of feces or stomach contents, higher magnification (e.g., SEM) may provide more characters for identification of prey. Coutts et al. (1973) found that, for SEM analysis, fecal pellets were easier to examine because the layer of "scum" present on stomach material was absent. This approach might be useful at times in identifying specific foods but, because of cost and time, it is not very helpful in gross food analysis.

2.2. Culled Parts

Culled parts can be exceedingly useful in food habits analysis. For this method to give reliable results, it is necessary that most or all foods be regularly culled, that the culled parts can be recovered, and that they can be linked to the proper bat species. LaVal and LaVal (1980a) pointed out some of the biases inherent in this method, including the fact that insects eaten whole will not appear as cullings, and insect larvae will most likely be underrepresented. Coutts et al. (1973) found that culling by the North American aerial feeders, *Myotis lucifugus* and *Eptesicus fuscus,* was not uniform or predictable, varying by the amount eaten and the bats' state of hunger.

The prerequisites for food habits analysis based on culled parts are fulfilled in many of the tropical gleaners (many of the Phyllostomidae, Nycteridae, and Megadermatidae) which take food from a surface—the ground or leaves. Bell (1982) estimated that nearly 30% of the mirochiropterans are gleaners. Many of the gleaners eat relatively large items which almost always need to be culled (Vaughan, 1976, 1977; Fenton et al., 1983). Gleaners often depend on sounds made by the prey along with or instead of echolocation. Roosts are often used night after night by the same individual bats (Vaughan, 1977; Wilson, 1971; LaVal and LaVal, 1980b; Belwood and Fullard, 1984), although one should be aware that sometimes more than one species of bat will use the same roost.

An important advantage of analyzing culled parts is greater ease and accuracy in identification of prey, since individual items are often large and diagnostic (e.g., wings, head parts, etc.). However, this approach does not allow estimates of the relative volumes of the various foods, or of the percentage of bats eating the food. Moreover, foods that are entirely eaten will not be represented, thus inflating values for foods which are culled.

In spite of these limitations, much useful data on food habits of bats has been gained by study of culled parts (e.g., Poulton, 1929; Nyholm, 1965; Ross, 1967; LaVal and LaVal, 1980a,b; Vaughan, 1976, 1977; Fenton et al., 1981, Belwood and Fullard, 1984).

2.3. Observations of Feeding Bats

Vaughan (1976) used a night viewing device equipped with a 135 mm f-1.8 lens to study foraging behavior of *Cardioderma cor* (Megadermatidae). During the dry season this bat fed primarily by flying rapidly to the ground from a low roost to pick up prey (mainly large beetles and centipedes). During the rainy season beetles were still important, but a greater variety of items was eaten, including moths, locusts and katydids, and other mostly large insects. Racey and Swift (1985) used reflective tape and chemiluminescent tags to study foraging behavior of *Pipistrellus pipistrellus.*

2.4. What Method(s) Should Be Used?

This decision depends on the species of bat being considered and the availability of material for food habits analysis. Often a combination of methods will aid in the determination of food habits (and foraging behavior). If bats are already dead, stomach contents should be examined and compared with fecal pellets in the posterior portion of the gut. If the bats are alive and are to be released, they should first be allowed to defecate (they should not be kept too long in captivity; this should be done immediately upon capture). If culled parts are available, they too should be examined. Even if only sporadically available, they can provide valuable information on some of the foods eaten and can aid in the identification process.

The use of more than one method can

help supplement or support results. For example, Fenton et al. (1981) found that remains of prey items below a roost of *Nycteris grandis* compared favorably with those from fecal analysis. Vaughan (1976) used a combination of observations with a night viewing device and an analysis of culled parts to study the foraging behavior and food habits of *Cardioderma cor.*

3. METHODS OF FOOD HABITS ANALYSIS

3.1. Collection of Bats

If one captures live bats for food analysis, it is essential to collect fecal samples or to sacrifice the bats immediately upon collecting them, otherwise food in the tract will be digested and the remnants voided (i.e., the tract will be empty). Bats kept alive in captivity even for short periods are of little or no use for food habits analysis.

Bats should be collected for food habits analysis during or soon after they return from a foraging bout, not simply plucked at any time from a roost. This is particularly important because food can pass through the gut quite rapidly (35-170 minutes for *Myotis lucifugus* [Buchler, 1975]; 90-130 minutes for *Eptesicus fuscus* [Lukens et al., 1971]). Bats are voracious feeders and can consume a sizable portion of their body mass per night in insects (e.g., Gould, 1955; Kunz, 1974; Anthony and Kunz, 1977). If bats have recently fed, they are easily recognizable by their fully distended stomachs. However, one can not always assume that the tract has been completely voided even after many hours. Kunz and Whitaker (1983) found a few items had not been voided even after 20 h.

3.2. Sample Preparation

The first step in analysis of feces or stomach contents is to soften them so that they can be teased apart. I recommend a petri dish with enough water in it to cover the items. If particulate matter clouds the water, pour some of the water off one or more times until the items in the dish can be clearly seen. One should do this with the aid of a dissecting microscope so as not to lose any major parts. Other wetting agents (Photo-flow or alcohol) have been used in place of water (Belwood and Fenton, 1976; Anthony and Kunz, 1977). When stomach contents cannot be examined immediately after bats are killed, the entire stomach or its contents alone can be preserved in 70% alcohol. Feces can be stored dry or in alcohol. In the tropics, feces should be oven-dried if not analyzed immediately, and a preservative (PDB) should be added to inhibit mold and insects. Hansson (1970) gives additional information on sample preparation.

3.3. Identification

To identify the food items present, the material should be sorted into piles containing larger parts and/or diagnostic characteristics. Wings, tarsi, and antennae are particularly useful, but details of color, texture, epidermal patterns, and sculpturing aid in sorting parts into piles representing one taxon. Small wings can be mounted on slides for permanent preservation.

Identification takes considerable practice, and it is most efficiently done by comparing unknown material with whole insects or a systematic collection of insect parts (e.g., wings, legs, head capsules), preferably collected at the same time and place as the bats (see Chapter 12). Insects can be collected at lights, using various methods such as blacklights (Black, 1974), sticky panels (Weseloh, 1981), suction traps (Anthony and Kunz, 1977; Buchler, 1976), and malaise traps (Belwood and Fenton, 1976). Whole insects can be identified and verified, if necessary, by specialists. It is inconsiderate and often non-productive to send pieces of insects to insect taxonomists.

An illustrated key to items commonly appearing in digestive tracts of insectivorous bats appears in Appendix 1 and should aid in identification. Abundant items are, of course, worth a greater expenditure of time and effort than foods that are relatively uncommon.

3.4. Percent Volume and Percent Frequency Estimates

After items are identified, the percent volume of each food item for each stomach can be estimated. When only a few large parts are present for each food type, percent volume could be measured by displacement in water. However, this would seldom be feasible for bat stomachs as the food is too finely chewed and mixed. Visual estimates can be made of the volume of each food category for each sample. A small grid can be helpful for this work. Volumetric data can be recorded as follows:

Sample No.	Scarabaeidae	Formicidae	Lepidoptera	Cicadellidae	
1	100				
2	50	40	10		
3	40		60		
4	8	90		2	
5			100		
	198	130	170	2	= 500

Horizontal rows represent stomachs; each should total 100, and the total for a sample should be 100× the number of stomachs.

Two values can be calculated from these data:

1) Percent Frequency—the percentage of bats eating each food type
2) Average Percent Volume—the average percentage by volume of each food type in the total sample

Data for the five stomachs in the example above would be summarized as follows:

	Average Percent Volume	Percent Frequency
Scarabaeidae	39.6	80
Lepidoptera	34.0	60
Formicidae	26.0	40
Cicadellidae	0.4	20
Total	100.0	

Thus, scarabaeids made up 198/500 = 39.6% of the volume of food in the stomachs examined and were found in 4/5 or 80% of the individuals examined. The total average percent volumes should add to approximately 100% (usually between 99.6 and 100.4).

3.5. Number and Size of Prey

An estimate of the minimum number of prey items from each sample (e.g., Pine, 1969; Buchler, 1976; Anthony and Kunz, 1977) can sometimes be obtained. This gives information useful in assessing the number and kinds of insects eaten relative to their availability (See Chapter 12). Such estimates can be made by counting the number of individual parts such as heads, posterior parts of abdomens, legs, wings, antennae, etc.

It is relatively easy to determine the size of insects by comparison when distinctive parts are present (e.g., legs, wings, antennae, parts of abdomen). This approach was used extensively by Ross (1967). Moths are among the easiest of items to identify in bat stomachs because of the great number of scales, but Ross (1967), Whitaker (1972), and Black (1972) found it difficult to assess their size. Ross (1967), Black (1974), Buchler (1976), Anthony and Kunz (1977), and Swift et al. (1985) made size estimates by placing insect prey into a series of body length categories (e.g., 0-2.0, 2.1-4.0, 4.1-6.0 mm, etc.).

3.6. Interpretation of Moth Scales

Adult moths are a major food item of many species of insectivorous bats. When a bat has eaten a moth the stomach or fecal pellet contains numerous scales along with other parts. Scales can be easily identified, and the volume of moths eaten can be satisfactorily estimated. Black (1972, 1974) recommended using moth scales as an indication of the relative consumption of moths by bats. However, this method neither gives an indication of the actual volume of Lepidoptera nor any comparison between Lepidoptera and other foods. Furthermore, a few scales could remain in the tract and be detectable for several days, and because each moth has so many scales, I suspect that a moth or two per week may well provide a continuous although minimal number of scales in a bat digestive tract. Therefore, Black's technique can not be used except as a relative index to moth consumption. This is valuable, however, since moths are such an important bat food.

4. SOURCES OF VARIATION

4.1. Collection of Bats

An important aspect of bat food habits is that the foods eaten often vary greatly in different times and places (e.g., nightly, seasonally, or in different habitats). For instance, one food item may be particularly abundant and form the bulk of all food being eaten on one day, but a few days later it may form a minor portion of the food eaten. One needs to be aware that this occurs, and one should not make broad generalizations based on small samples. Overall, one wishes to adequately sample bats in different habitats and at different times to draw meaningful conclusions. It is desirable to establish a sampling schedule that best accomplishes this objective within the constraints of time available.

4.2. Sample Size

Sample sizes adequate for study of bat food habits, as in other cases, depend upon the amount of variation involved in the material being sampled, with more heterogeneous samples requiring a larger number of samples. Sample size is often determined intuitively based on variation involved; at other times it is simply determined by using all of the data available.

In my judgement, at least 15 stomachs, or feces sets, are the minimum for estimating bat food habits at any one time or place when relative variability is low. I feel much more confident, however, when I can include at least 30-50 samples per site and time in an analysis.

In practice, one must often settle for smaller samples because of the difficulty of obtaining sufficient numbers of bats or feces, both because of the necessity to minimize disturbance of populations, and because of the ethical and legal questions involved in collecting large numbers of bats.

4.3. Statistical Analysis

Statistical analysis of food habits data is difficult because of the diversity of items often found in samples. Various comparisons can be made, especially with major foods, and analyzed using statistics such as Analysis of Variance (ANOVA) and Discriminant Analysis coupled with Duncan's or other multiple range tests for significance. These tests can be performed on either original or transformed values (arcsin of the percentage estimate). Emlen's diversity index for comparison of dietary diversity between various groupings of bats also may be useful (Anthony and Kunz, 1977). For additional information on statistical treatment see Humphrey et al. (1983) and Chapter 12.

4.4. Insect Prey Selection versus Insect Availability

Do bats select prey or simply eat whatever is available? To determine this, it is necessary to compare the foods eaten against those available. Differences in these two data sets should represent selectivity. This question is addressed in Chapter 12, but a few comments are relevant here. First, it is difficult to estimate the kinds and numbers of insects available to bats. Various insect traps using suction or lights have been used at different heights above the ground, particularly at levels where bats are active, in order to assess insect communities. The problem is the selection of an appropriate collecting method that will sample insects in the same size ranges and in the same proportion that they are available to the bats. See Swift et al. (1985) for a recent example of an assessment of fecal analysis as compared to insect availability using a suction trap. The bats fed mainly on Diptera (Nematocera) and Trichoptera, and their diets "reflected the availability of these insects over a wide range of abundance." However, the authors add that "Ephemeroptera and Neuroptera were significantly overrepresented in the diet and Nematocera, Coleoptera and Lepidoptera were significantly underrepresented."

5. TOPICS FOR FURTHER STUDY

1) For most species of insectivorous bats, little or no food habits information is available.
2) Much more work is needed on availability of foods as related to foods actually eaten (Chapter 12).
3) There is almost no information on food preferences of bats (as opposed to foods actually eaten) (e.g., Buchler, 1976; Anthony and Kunz, 1977; Swift et al., 1985).
4) There is need for long term study of bat foods, relating various factors such as time of year and night, age, sex, and reproductive conditions of bats, and foraging habitat, to foods eaten (e.g., Anthony and Kunz, 1977; Racey and Swift, 1985).
5) There is little or no information on energy budgets of most species of bats (e.g., Kunz, 1980; Chapters 15 and 18).
6) Much more information is needed on food partitioning in bats (e.g., Humphrey et al., 1983).
7) It would be of interest to learn more about the relationship of bat food habits to time and place of foraging and to behavior patterns of both bats and insects (e.g., Nyholm, 1965; Anthony et al., 1981; Racey and Swift, 1985).
8) What are the morphological adaptations of bats in relation to food and feeding (e.g., Freeman, 1979, 1981; Norberg, 1982; and Humphrey et al., 1983)?
9) To what extent do bats feed on non-flying arthropods, or on flying arthropods at rest (e.g., ground feeders and foliage gleaning insectivores—Vaughan, 1976, 1977; Bell, 1982; Fenton et al., 1983)?
10) What nutritional value is derived from various food items eaten by bats? Is there any nutritive value derived from the digestion of insect exoskeleton?
11) How much information can bats obtain about potential prey through echolocation, and within what limits do they select for and against certain kinds of prey using echolocation (e.g., Habersetzer, 1981; Goldman and Henson, 1977; Fenton, 1982, 1984)? How much do they use other cues in the selection of prey, for example sounds produced by insects (e.g., Bell, 1982; Bell and Fenton, 1984)?
12) Do bats fly regular routes in search of food (e.g., Buchler and Childs, 1981)? If so, on what basis do they establish these routes, how often do they fly them, and how extensive are the routes?
13) Bats are often heavily parasitized with trematodes (Chapter 28). How do bats become infected? Are various species of trematodes associated with certain species of insect prey?

6. SUMMARY

Food habits analysis of bats can be done by stomach analysis, fecal analysis, under special circumstances by examination of culled prey remains beneath roosts, and sometimes one can watch bats catching prey through use of a night viewing device. Stomach analysis means the sacrifice of some bats. Fecal analysis is very useful since bats need not be killed, but one must be aware of bias against softer food items through differential digestion. Culled items are generally much easier to identify than are items in stomachs or feces, but culled items may not be available. Even if they are, it may be difficult to determine which bat species has deposited them, or bats may not cull parts from all prey species. Identification of food items are best made by comparing fragments with whole organisms collected in the field, as whole organisms are much easier to identify than are fragments. Data are generally presented as average percent volume, percent frequency, and/or percent of prey items eaten. Some combination of techniques may be used in any particular case, and night viewing devices or bat detectors may allow one to get valuable data on food habits or hunting behavior of bats (see Rabinowitz and Tuttle, 1982).

7. ACKNOWLEDGMENTS

I thank J. J. Belwood and T. H. Kunz for their many helpful comments on this manuscript.

8. REFERENCES

Anthony, E. L. P., and T. H. Kunz. 1977. Feeding strategies of the little brown bat, *Myotis lucifugus,* in southern New Hampshire. Ecology, 58:775-786.

Anthony, E. L. P., M. H. Stack, and T. H. Kunz. 1981. Night roosting and the nocturnal time budget of the little brown bat, *Myotis lucifugus:* Effects of reproductive status, prey density, and environmental conditions. Oecologia, 51:151-156.

Bell, G. P. 1982. Behavioral and ecological aspects of gleaning in a desert insectivorous bat, *Antrozous pallidus (Chiroptera: Vespertilionidae).* Behav. Ecol. Sociobiol., 10:217-223.

Bell, G. P., and M. B. Fenton. 1984. The use of Doppler-shifted echoes as a flutter detection and clutter rejection system: The echolocation and feeding behavior of *Hipposideros ruber* (Chiroptera: Hipposideridae). Behav. Ecol. Sociobiol., 15:109-114.

Belwood, J. J., and M. B. Fenton. 1976. Variation in the diet of *Myotis lucifugus* (Chiroptera: Vespertilionidae). Can. J. Zool., 54:1674-1678.

Belwood, J. J., and J. H. Fullard. 1984. Echolocation and foraging behavior in the Hawaiian hoary bat, *Lasiurus cinereus.* Can. J. Zool., 62:2113-2120.

Black, H. L. 1972. Differential exploitation of moths by the bats *Eptesicus fuscus* and *Lasiurus cinereus.* J. Mammal., 53:598-601.

Black, H. L. 1974. A north temperate bat community: Structure and prey populations. J. Mammal., 55:138-157.

Borror, D. J., D. M. DeLong, and C. A. Triplehorn. 1981. An introduction to the study of insects. 5th ed. Saunders College Publ., Philadelphia, 827 pp.

Buchler, E. R. 1975. Food transit time in *Myotis lucifugus* (Chiroptera: Vespertilionidae). J. Mammal., 56:252-255.

Buchler, E. R. 1976. Prey selection by *Myotis lucifugus* (Chiroptera: Vespertilionidae). Amer. Nat., 110:619-628.

Buchler, E. R., and S. B. Childs. 1981. Orientation to distant sounds by foraging big brown bats (*Eptesicus fuscus*). Anim. Behav., 29:428-432.

Comstock, J. H. 1950. An introduction to entomology. Comstock, Ithaca, New York, 1064 pp.

Coutts, R. A., M. B. Fenton, and E. Glen. 1973. Food intake by captive *Myotis lucifugus* and *Eptesicus fuscus* (Chiroptera: Vespertilionidae). J. Mammal., 54:985-990.

Fenton, M. B. 1982. Echolocation calls and patterns of hunting and habitat use of bats (Microchiroptera) from Chillagoe, North Queensland, Australia. Aust. J. Zool., 30:417-425.

Fenton, M. B. 1984. Echolocation: Implications for ecology and evolution of bats. Quart. Rev. Biol., 59:33-53.

Fenton, M. B., C. L. Gaudet, and M. L. Leonard. 1983. Feeding behavior of the bats, *Nycteris grandis* and *Nycteris thebaica* (Nycteridae) in captivity. J. Zool., 200:347-354.

Fenton, M. B., D. W. Thomas, and R. Sasseen. 1981. *Nycteris grandis* (Nycteridae): an African carnivorous bat. J. Zool., 194:461-465.

Freeman, P. W. 1979. Specialized insectivory: Beetle-eating and moth-eating molossid bats. J. Mammal., 60:467-497.

Freeman, P. W. 1981. Correspondence of food habits and morphology in insectivorous bats. J. Mammal. 62:166-173.

Gardner, A. L. 1977. Feeding habits. Pp. 293-350, *in* Biology of bats of the New World family Phyllostomatidae. Part II. (R. J. Baker, J. K. Jones, Jr., and D. C. Carter, eds.). Spec. Publ. Mus., Texas Tech Univ., 13:1-364.

Goldman, L. J., and O. W. Henson, Jr. 1977. Prey recognition and selection by the constant frequency bat, *Pteronotus p. parnelli.* Behav. Ecol. Sociobiol., 2:411-419.

Gould, E. 1955. The feeding efficiency of insectivorous bats. J. Mammal., 36:399-407.

Habersetzer, J. 1981. Adaptive echolocation sounds in the bat *Rhinopoma hardwickei:* A field study. J. Comp. Physiol. 144:559-566.

Hansson, L. 1970. Methods of morphological diet micro-analysis in rodents. Oikos, 21:255-266.

Humphrey, S. R., F. J. Bonaccorso, and T. L. Zinn. 1983. Guild structure of surface-gleaning bats in Panama. Ecology, 64:284-294.

Jeuniaux, C. 1961. Chitinase: An addition to the list of hydrolases in the digestive tract of vertebrates. Nature, 192:135-136.

Jernejcic, F. 1969. Use of emetics to collect stomach contents of walleye and largemouth bass. Trans. Amer. Fish. Soc., 98:698-702.

Kunz, T. H. 1974. Feeding ecology of a temperate insectivorous bat (*Myotis velifer*). Ecology, 55:693-711.

Kunz, T. H. 1980. Daily energy budgets of free-living bats. Proc. 5th Int. Bat Res. Conf. (D. E. Wilson and A. L. Gardner, eds.) Texas Tech Press, Lubbock, 434 pp.

Kunz, T. H., and J. O. Whitaker, Jr. 1983. An evaluation of fecal analysis for determining food habits of insectivorous bats. Can. J. Zool., 61:1317-1321.

LaVal, R. K., and M. L. LaVal. 1980a. Prey selection by a neotropical foliage-gleaning bat, *Micronycteris megalotis*. J. Mammal., 61:327-330.

LaVal, R. K., and M. L. LaVal. 1980b. Prey selection by the slit-faced bat *Nycteris thebaica* (Chiroptera: Nycteridae) in Natal, South Africa. Biotropica, 12:241-246.

Lukens, M. M., J. Van Eps, and W. H. Davis. 1971. Transit time through the digestive tract of the bat, *Eptesicus fuscus*. Exp. Med. Surg., 29:25-28.

Norberg, U. M. 1982. Allometry of bat wings and legs and comparison with bird wings. Phil. Trans. R. Soc. London, 292:359-398.

Nyholm, E. S. 1965. Zur Ökologie von *Myotis mystacinus* (Leisl.) und *Myotis daubentoni* (Leisl.) (Chiroptera). Ann. Zool. Fenn., 2:77-123.

Pine, R. H. 1969. Stomach contents of a free-tailed bat, *Molossus ater*. J. Mammal., 50:162.

Poulton, E. B. 1929. British insectivorous bats and their prey. Proc. Zool. Soc. Lond., 1:277-303.

Rabinowitz, A. R., and M. D. Tuttle. 1982. A test of the validity of two currently used methods of determining bat prey preferences. Acta Theriol., 27:283-293.

Racey, P. A., and S. M. Swift. 1985. Feeding ecology of *Pipistrellus pipistrellus* (Chiroptera:

Vespertilionidae) during pregnancy and lactation. I. Foraging behaviour. J. Anim. Ecol., 54:205-215.

Ross, A. 1967. Ecological aspects of the food habits of insectivorous bats. Proc. West. Found. Vert. Zool., 1:205-263.

Snodgrass, R. E. 1935. Principles of insect morphology. McGraw-Hill Book Co., New York, 667 pp.

Swift, S. M., P. A. Racey, and M. I. Avery. 1985. Feeding ecology of *Pipistrellus pipistrellus* (Chiroptera: Vespertilionidae) during pregnancy and lactation. II. Diet. J. Anim. Ecol., 54:217-225.

Vaughan, T. A. 1976. Nocturnal behavior of the African false vampire bat (*Cardioderma cor*). J. Mammal., 57:227-248.

Vaughan, T. A. 1977. Foraging behavior of the giant leaf-nosed bat (*Hipposideros commersoni*). E. Afr. Wildl. J., 15:237-248.

Weseloh, R. M. 1981. Relationship between colored sticky panel catches and reproductive behavior of forest tachinid parasitoids. Environ. Entomol., 10:131-135.

Whitaker, J. O., Jr. 1972. Food habits of bats from Indiana. Can. J. Zool., 50:877-883.

Whitaker, J. O., Jr., C. Maser, and S. P. Cross. 1981. Food habits of eastern Oregon bats, based on stomach and scat analysis. Northwest Science, 55:281-292.

Whitaker, J. O., Jr., and P. Q. Tomich. 1983. Food habits of the hoary bat, *Lasiurus cinereus*, from Hawaii. J. Mammal., 64:151-152.

Wilson, D. E. 1971. Food habits of *Micronycteris hirsuta* (Chiroptera: Phyllostomidae). Mammalia, 35:107-110.

Wrazen, J. A., and G. E. Svendsen. 1978. Feeding ecology of a population of eastern chipmunks (*Tamias striatus*) in southeastern Ohio. Amer. Midl. Nat., 100:190-201.

Appendix 1.   Key to Some Arthropods Commonly Eaten by Insectivorous Bats (Figures by Elizabeth Lyons)

The following key is intended as an aid to study food habits of insectivorous bats. It includes only a few of the most common items eaten, and is intended to assist in the identification of a few major foods, not to identify all possible foods. In many cases it will be necessary to use keys to insects representing local faunas. Other valuable keys for identifying insects eaten by bats can be found in Borror et al. (1981) and Comstock (1950).

This key is constructed using insect parts that are commonly found among food items of insectivorous bats, e.g., scales, wings, legs, etc. Figures are given for each (but no sizing scale is given, as most items vary greatly in size). The figures are of complete parts, whereas in stomachs or feces only fragments are generally present.

The key is based on those parts most useful in identification. As one becomes more familiar with the material, it is possible to recognize a food item from other less characteristic parts. Ultimately, one should be able to match other characteristics such as similarity of coloration, pattern, consistency, etc.

A collection of materials in alcohol and/or on slides (wings, especially) that are commonly eaten should be developed, maintained, and continually used in comparison with material from stomach contents and feces.

Non-food items are occasionally found among foods, including vegetation, mistnet fiber, fur from grooming, and parasites. These can be ignored.

1. Numerous characteristic scales over body (Fig. 1); stomach or fecal contents often consisting of a mass of scales mixed with other parts
......................................Moths (Lepidoptera)
Scales as figured above absent
....2

2. Wings present
....3
Wings absent or not found
....24

3. Insects with hard bodies (Beetles, True Bugs); hind wings membranous, folding under front wings and with complicated venation (difficult to determine names of individual veins, as they branch in various directions) (Figs. 2-5)
....4
Body softer; wings membranous and not folding, at least as above, although venation may be complicated by having numerous crossveins
....9

4. Legs usually with 4 or 5 tarsal segments; mouthparts chewing
..................Beetles (Coleoptera)...................5
Legs with 2-3 tarsal segments; mouthparts

piercing-sucking, originating in anterior part of head
...............True Bugs (Hemiptera)...............8

5. Tarsal segments 5 (Figs. 2, 3)
....6
Tarsal segments apparently 4; third segment "Y" shaped (Fig. 6)
....7

6. Claws originating at a wide angle to one another; antennae long and many segmented (Fig. 2)
.......................Ground Beetles (Carabidae)
Tarsal claws originating parallel to one another, antennae knobbed with segments of knob capable of close apposition (Fig. 3)
...........................May Beetles (Scarabaeidae)

7. With normal chewing mouthparts
.......................Leaf Beetles (Chrysomelidae)
Mouth protracted into an elongate curved snout (Fig. 7)
.......................Snout Beetles (Curculionidae)

8. Hard pieces of body and front wings present and with punctations, hind wings as in Fig. 4. color brown
...............................Chinch Bugs (Lygaeidae)
Hind wings as in Fig. 5; color may vary, but often bright green
...............................Stinkbugs (Pentatomidae)

9. Wings parchmentlike as in Fig. 8 or wing delicate with series of closely spaced veins which meet the first series diagonally as in Fig. 9
...............(Orthoptera, Isoptera)...............10
Not as above
....11

10. Size large, usually brown, long many segmented cerci or antennae may be present; tarsi with 5 simple segments. Wings parchmentlike and as in Fig. 8
......................................Crickets (Gryllidae)
Size smaller, usually light colored. Wing delicate and with outer veins diagonal. Tarsi with 4 segments with first 3 segments short, last one long (Fig. 9)
......................................Termites (Isoptera)

11. Wings with large numbers of crossveins
....12
Wings relatively simple, with usually not more than 2-3 crossveins
....14

12. Wings with very large numbers of crossveins throughout wings, bodies with long, multi-

segmented cerci (Fig. 10)

.............................Mayflies (Ephemeroptera)

Wings with smaller numbers of crossveins, and with larger, elongate cells in center portions of wing (Figs. 11, 12)

..............Lacewings (Neuroptera) 13

13. Color brown and with some of costal veins of forewing forked (Fig. 11)

.................Brown Lacewings (Hemerobiidae)

Color green in life, but usually faded in stomach or fecal material, costal veins of front wing not forked (Fig. 12)

....................Green Lacewings (Chrysopidae)

14. Venation usually relatively simple and relatively clear with R veins, M veins mostly running to margin (Fig. 15)

....15

Venation with veins more often anastomosing, making it more difficult to identify specific veins (Figs. 17-19)

....Bees, Ants, & Wasps (Hymenoptera) 22

15. Two pairs of wings (can tell by shape and differing venation); venation relatively complete and veins with hair (Fig. 20) (although hair may have come off wings) or tiny insects with spots along wing veins (Fig. 26)

....16

One pair of wings; second pair represented by balancing organ (haltere) which can sometimes be seen among food items (Fig. 13)

.................True Flies (Diptera) 17

16. Mouthparts vestigial, venation relatively complete and veins with hairs (Fig. 20)

..............................Caddisflies (Trichoptera)

Mouthparts piercing sucking; tiny insects with membranous wings, spots present along veins and with flattened spur at apex of hind tibiae (Fig. 26)

.........Delphacid Planthoppers (Delphacidae)

17. Many segmented antennae

....18

Antennae with few segments (less than 5)

....21

18. Venation of similar thickness throughout wings

....19

Anterior veins heavy, posterior ones much weaker

....20

19. Venation as in Fig. 14, no scales or hairs on veins

...................................Crane Flies (Tipulidae)

Venation as in Fig. 15, scales or hairs on veins and wing margins (though often lost)

...................................Mosquitoes (Culicidae)

20. Venation as in Fig. 21, eyes broadly emarginate

...................................Midges (Chironomidae)

Venation as in Fig. 22, eyes not broadly emarginate, but meeting over eyes

...................................Blackflies (Simuliidae)

21. Venation as in Fig. 23

...................................Sciarid Flies (Sciaridae)

Venation as in Fig. 16

........Muscoid Flies (superfamily Muscoidea)

22. Antennae with numerous segments, venation as in Figs. 17, 18

....23

Antennae with about 10-11 segments, elbowed, venation as in Fig. 19, characteristic node in "waist" between "thoracic" and "abdominal" areas

....Ants (Formicidae)

23. Vein present separating vein M1 from first M2 (Fig. 17)

...............Ichneumon Wasp (Ichneumonidae)

This vein lacking (Fig. 18)

.........................Braconid Wasp (Braconidae)

24. Triangular head capsule with piercing sucking mouthparts placed rather far back on ventral side of head (Fig. 24)

.........................Homoptera.......................25

Not as above; legs are generally the best characteristic available

....27

25. Hind tibia with row or rows of small spines (Fig. 25). End of tibia usually lacking cluster of spines

............................Leafhoppers (Cicadellidae)

Hind tibia with 1 or 2 strong spines (Figs. 26, 27), end of tibia with cluster of spines

....26

26. Tiny form with membranous wings with veins often marked with spotting (Fig. 26). Hind tibia with flattened spur at apex

.........Delphacid Planthoppers (Delphacidae)

Larger forms; wings, if present, not as above (Fig. 27)

............................Froghoppers (Cercopidae)

27. Legs with 3 claws, usually in or protruding from hairs (Fig. 28)

....Spiders (Aranaea)

Legs not with 3 claws

....28

28. Tarsi 2-3 segmented
....29
Tarsi 4-5 segmented
....30
29. Animals hard bodied
....go back to couplet 8
Animals soft bodied
....go back to couplet 25
30. Animals hard bodied, look for pieces of hard exoskeleton

...........Coleoptera...........go back to couplet 5
Animals soft bodied
....31
31. Tarsi 4 segmented, first 3 segments short, last one much longer (Fig. 9)
....Termites (Isoptera)
Soft bodied animal; tarsi with 5 segments
....go back to couplet 9
(these are very difficult without additional characteristics)

Figure 1. Lepidopteran scales.

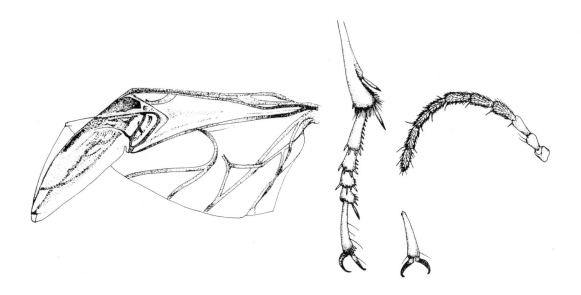

Figure 2. Hind wing, tarsi, and antenna of carabid beetle.

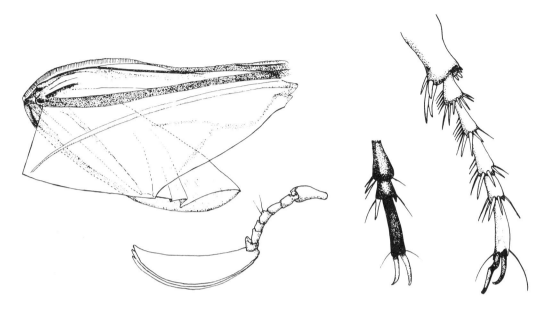

Figure 3. Hind wing, tarsus, and antenna of scarabaeid beetle.

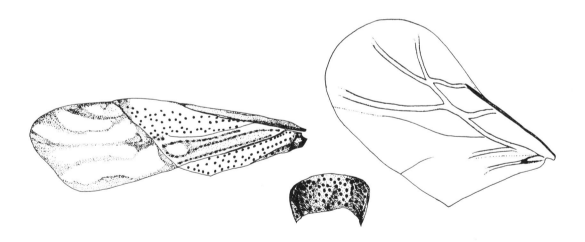

Figure 4. Front wing, portion of body wall, and hind wing of lygaeid bug.

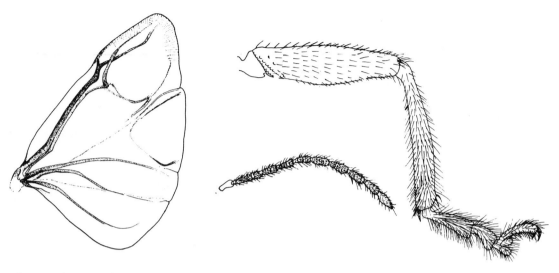

Figure 5. Hind wing of pentatomid bug.   Figure 6. Leg and antennae of Chrysomelidae.

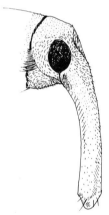

Figure 7. Mouth parts of snout beetle, Curculionidae.

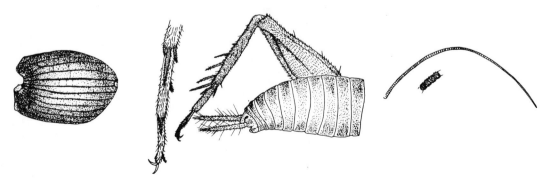

Figure 8. Front wing, tarsus, and abdomen, including cerci, and antenna of cricket, Gryllidae.

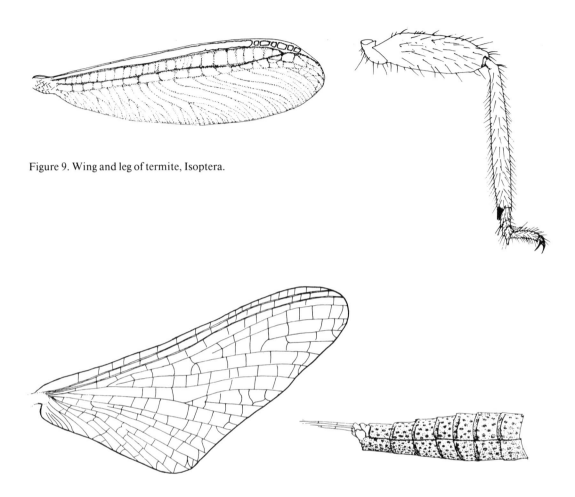

Figure 9. Wing and leg of termite, Isoptera.

Figure 10. Wing and abdomen, including cerci, of mayfly, Ephemeroptera.

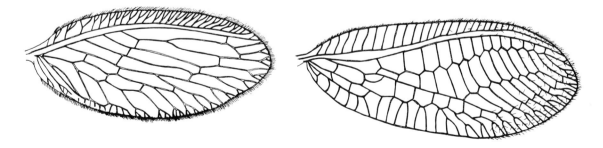

Figure 11. Wing of brown lacewing, Hemerobiidae.   Figure 12. Wing of green lacewing, Chrysopidae.

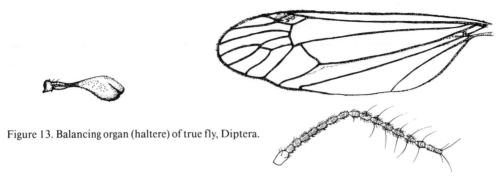

Figure 13. Balancing organ (haltere) of true fly, Diptera.

Figure 14. Wing and antenna of crane fly, Tipulidae.

Figure 15. Wing of mosquito, Culicidae.

Figure 16. Wing of Muscoidea (group that includes houseflies).

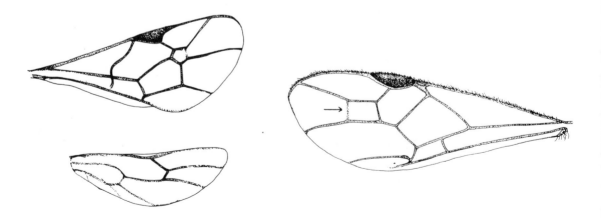

Figure 17. Wings of ichneumon wasp, Ichneumonidae.

Figure 18. Wing of Braconidae.

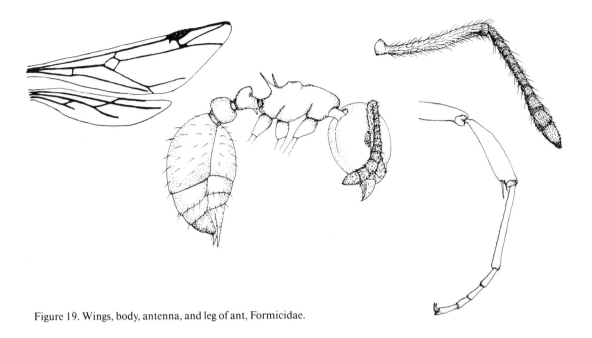

Figure 19. Wings, body, antenna, and leg of ant, Formicidae.

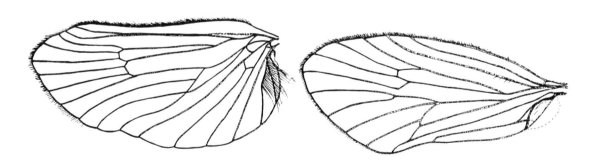

Figure 20. Wings of caddisfly, Trichoptera.

Figure 21. Wing of midge, Chironomidae.   Figure 22. Wing of blackfly, Simuliidae.

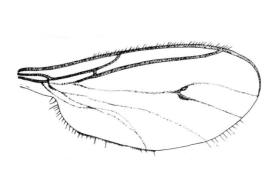

Figure 23. Wing of dark-winged fungus gnat, Sciaridae.   Figure 24. Head capsule of Homoptera.

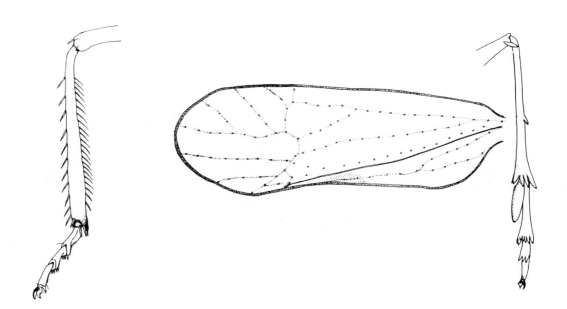

Figure 25. Hind leg of leafhopper, Cicadellidae.   Figure 26. Wing and hind leg of delphacid planthopper, Delphacidae.

Figure 27. Hind leg of leafhopper, Cercopidae.

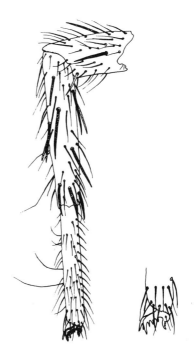

Figure 28. Leg of spider.

Chapter 12

Methods of Assessing the Availability of Prey to Insectivorous Bats

Thomas H. Kunz

Department of Biology
Boston University
Boston, Massachusetts 02215 USA

1. INTRODUCTION

Accurate assessment of the food available to predators is one of the more perplexing problems facing animal ecologists. Even if it were possible to accurately assess insect abundance in a given habitat, such estimates may not actually represent the prey available to insectivorous bats. In part, this problem arises because not all insects that can be captured by conventional methods are equally detectable by bats. For example, small insects may "appear" less available to bats as prey than the abundance from an insect trap sample might indicate. By contrast, large insects may "appear" more abundant than they actually are, especially if they reflect more intense echoes than small insects. Moreover, the success of a bat in capturing an insect is partly determined by its speed and maneuverability relative to the insect. Some insects actually avoid being captured by bats when insects take evasive action in response to the high frequency sounds of bats. Also, many bat species feed in several different and often unknown habitats in the course of a night consequently they may encounter prey different from where insect traps are deployed.

2. FACTORS AFFECTING INSECT ACTIVITY

Knowledge of factors affecting temporal and spatial activity of insects is vital for developing effective methods for assessing their availability to insectivorous bats. Flight activity and apparent numbers of insects are influenced by several factors, including time of day (or night), climate, local weather conditions, habitat variables, and, of course, the kind of capture or detection device (e.g., Wellington, 1945; Southwood, 1978). The diel periodicity and trappability of many insect species are strongly influenced by the natural light cycle (including moon phase and moon brightness), air temperature, and precipitation. Flight activity of insects may be high when the ambient temperature is warm and low when it is cool. The flight activity of insects may also be influenced by wind and rain. For example, heavy rain can have a depressant effect on the flight activity of some species and light rain may increase the activity of others. Some insects cease flight during windy conditions, and others, especially the small ones, may be blown passively and accumulate on the lee sides of tree shelters and other such barriers (e.g., Lewis, 1965, 1970).

3. SAMPLE UNITS

3.1. Subdivision of Habitat

When designing a sampling protocol to assess the availability of insect prey, it is best to evaluate the habitat from the perspective of the predator. The diversity of foraging strategies that characterize insectivorous bats in general, and the foraging flexibility of some species in particular, highlight the complexity of choosing appropriate habitat(s) for sampling. Some aerial feeding bats detect and capture prey only in open areas; a few take prey from within or near foliage (e.g., Black, 1974; Fenton et al., 1977; Fenton and Thomas, 1980; Fenton, 1982; Neuweiler, 1984); still others detect and glean insects from various surfaces (e.g., ground, foliage, and walls of buildings (e.g., Kolb, 1976; Bauerova, 1978; Fenton and Bell, 1979; Bell, 1982; Bell and Fenton, 1984). A few species may actually employ a combination of aerial and gleaning strategies (e.g., Vaughan, 1976, 1977; Bell and Fenton, 1984). Finally, some bats specialize by capturing prey from upon or near the water surface (e.g., Dwyer, 1970; Novick and Dale, 1971; Voûte, 1972; Fenton and Bell,

1979). Thus, knowledge of a bat's foraging behavior and diet (Chapter 11) is essential for choosing appropriate sampling sites and capture methods. Selected commercially available insect traps and supplies are given in Appendix 2.

3.2. Insect Sampling

If there is little or no previous knowledge of distribution and variation of insect prey for a particular habitat, it is best to obtain preliminary data using a stratified sampling procedure (e.g., samples taken in habitats at the time and place where the predator was observed feeding). Information gained from using this approach should help to establish the spatial (vertical and horizontal) distribution, sample sites, and the amount of variation to be expected between samples. Knowledge of sample variation can be used to determine how large a sample is needed to detect significant differences between habitats. When a study is being planned, statistical references (e.g., Zar, 1984) should be consulted for discussions of sample design and analysis. Morris (1960) and Southwood (1978) specifically discuss these topics as they relate to insect populations.

4. TRAPPING DEVICES

Insect trapping devices may be classified according to whether insects are captured randomly (non-attractant traps) or whether traps employ sensory stimuli (attractant traps). Each trap or device has its own inherent biases (Service, 1976; Southwood, 1978). Reliable assessment of prey availability may require the use of several different kinds of traps or devices, depending upon the foraging behavior of the bat and the biases associated with particular kinds of traps. Non-attractant traps are often considered to be free of biases, although the mere physical presence of such a trap may elicit visual responses, causing insects to be either attracted or repelled. Even the hum of a fan in a "non-attractant" suction

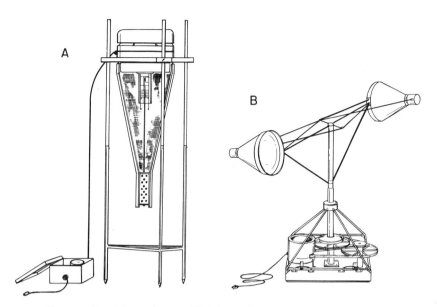

Figure 1. Insect traps for capturing airborne insects. (A) Johnson-Taylor suction trap designed to segregate captured insects at fixed intervals (after Johnson and Taylor, 1955b). (B) A stationary, mechanized rotary trap (after Nicholls, 1960).

trap (Section 4.1.1) may influence the number of insects captured. Non-attractant traps generally yield smaller but more representative samples than attractant traps (Service, 1976).

Trapping methods can yield data appropriate for making estimates of absolute or relative density. Absolute estimates of aerial insect density are commonly expressed as numbers (or the log $_{10}$ of numbers) per unit of quantifiable habitat (air volume). Relative estimates are typically expressed as the number of captured insects per hour, night, season, or habitat. Trapping methods that yield relative estimates commonly employ relatively simple traps. These methods have an advantage in yielding more data than those used for making absolute estimates, based on the amount of time and effort invested. The actual distinction between these two approaches, however, is not always clear (Southwood, 1978). Devices used to estimate absolute density can also be used to estimate relative density, but seldom is the opposite situation true. Moreover, air is the only habi-

tat used by insectivorous bats that can be sampled efficiently enough to give a reasonable estimate of absolute insect density.

Of the methods commonly used for trapping airborne insects (e.g., Taylor and Palmer, 1972; Service, 1976; Southwood, 1978), only a few are suitable for assessing absolute density. The usual procedure is to count the number of insects in a measurable volume of air. Suction traps (Section 4.1.1) probably yield the most reliable estimates for both absolute and relative density. Other trapping methods can yield data needed for making relative estimates of insect abundance in the air, on the ground, and near the water surface.

4.1. Non-Attractant Traps

4.1.1. Suction Traps

The Johnson-Taylor suction trap (Johnson, 1950a; Taylor, 1951; Johnson and Taylor, 1955b) is one of the most widely used and reliable traps for assessing aerial insect densities at elevations near the ground (Fig. 1A). This trap has a fan that pushes air through a metallic gauze cone that filters out the captured insects. A receptacle at the bottom of the cone is fitted with a segregating device that is activated by a clock-operated solenoid that separates the catch at designated intervals. This trap is available commercially and has long been a standard for sampling aerial insects (e.g., Taylor, 1960; Johnson, 1969). A modification of this trap uses collecting vials suitable for liquid preservation (Goodenough et al., 1983). Deployment of these traps is limited to areas where electrical power is available (either from a line or generator source).

The absolute efficiency of the Johnson-Taylor trap varies with wind speed, size (length x width) of insects, and performance of the fan (Taylor, 1962a). Use of correction coefficients allows a catch to be converted to $\log_{10}$ density per unit volume of air (conversion to antilogs yields actual density). In recent years, the manufacturer (Burkard Manufacturing Ltd.) has increased the airflow from earlier models by using different fans. Correction tables given in Taylor (1962a) and Southwood (1978) based on earlier models are no longer valid for the more recent 23 cm and 30 cm "vent-axia" models (Service, 1976). Correction tables given in Service (1976) are for these fans operated at normal speed. If the trap fan is operated at "boost" speed, the difference between $\log_{10}$ of the volume of air sampled each hour should be subtracted from the appropriate conversion factors. Conversely, when a fan is used at low speed, the differences between $\log_{10}$ of the volumes should be added to the conversion factor (Service, 1976). Although the volume of air sampled by a Johnson-Taylor suction trap is given by the manufacturer, it is advisable to verify the air displacement of each fan, especially if absolute density is to be estimated. For estimates of relative density, it is unnecessary to know the volume of air sampled as long as each trap displaces the same, but unknown, quantity of air.

Johnson-Taylor suction traps have been used to assess the prey available to aerial feeding bats (e.g., Anthony et al., 1981; Swift et al., 1985; Racey and Swift, 1985) and birds (e.g., Holmes et al., 1978). Larger and more powerful suction traps (Johnson and Taylor, 1955b) have been used for sampling airborne insects where wind is more likely to affect trap efficiency and where insect density is low. Others (e.g., Bryant, 1973, 1975; Bryant and Westerterp, 1980, 1983; Turner, 1982) have used this trap to assess prey available to aerial feeding birds. Turner (1982) noted that this trap was ineffective for estimating the abundance of prey found in the diet of aerial feeding swallows.

Portable suction traps of simpler designs (e.g., Buchler, 1976; Bradbury and Vehrencamp, 1976; Service, 1976; Warnhouse, 1980) offer alternatives to the more expensive, commercially available traps. These simple traps, however, may suffer a disadvantage in lacking established conversion factors to estimate absolute density (but see Warnhouse, 1980).

4.1.2. Rotary Traps

Mechanized rotary traps also can be used to estimate numbers and density of airborne insects. Instead of using a fan to draw insects into the trap, rotary traps are designed to move one or more nets through a fixed air space at a constant speed. Nicholls (1960) described such a trap with two conical nets that rotate in a horizontal plane around a central axis (Fig. 1B). This motor-driven trap completes an arc that has a maximum diameter of 3 m. An inexpensive rotary trap described by Taylor (1962a) employs a single net, designed so that the effects of air turbulence at the opening of the net are minimal. Both traps are easy to construct and relatively portable, but as with suction traps they do require electricity, and thus deployment in remote areas is limited. In general, the efficiency of rotary traps tends to be more or less independent of wind speed until the speed of the wind exceeds that of the trap. The latter situation, however, is seldom a problem at night.

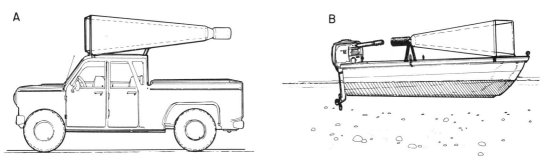

Figure 2. Tow nets mounted on (A) a truck and (B) a power boat (see Steelman et al., 1968).

4.1.3. Tow Nets

Samples of airborne insects taken in nets attached to vehicles (Fig. 2A) can also be used to estimate absolute or relative densities. By traversing a fixed course and adjusting the speed of the vehicle, it is possible to control the volume of air sampled and thus permit estimates of absolute density. Tow nets can be attached to bicycles, motorcycles, automobiles, airplanes, or boats. Nets attached to land-based vehicles (e.g., McClure, 1938; Loy et al., 1968; Hill, 1971; Barnard, 1979; Karg, 1980; Holbrook and Wuertheie, 1984) make it possible to quantify airborne insect abundance along roadsides, trails, and over open fields where bats often forage. Traps mounted on bicycles (Hill, 1971) and motorcycles (Karg, 1980) may permit insect sampling along narrow trails that are often inaccessible using other vehicles. With some vehicle-mounted nets, it is possible to sample insects at periodic intervals without the driver having to stop the vehicle repeatedly to remove samples (Sommerman and Simmet, 1965).

The success of tow nets, when attached to vehicles, is limited by the height above the ground that a net can be attached and by the type of terrain that can be successfully traversed by the vehicle. Ideally, tow nets should be attached in such a way so as to avoid the effects of air turbulence caused by the motion of the vehicle. A potential bias is that lights on "tow-net" vehicles may attract insects, although this is unavoidable with night-time sampling (J. J. Belwood, pers. comm.).

Adult stages of aquatic, emergent insects may be captured by attaching tow nets to motor boats (e.g., Steelman et al., 1968) and traversing rivers, lakes, and reservoirs where bats forage (Fig. 2B). As with vehicle-mounted nets, boat-mounted nets should be attached to minimize the effects of air turbulence on the potential catch.

Tow nets attached to aircraft also have been used to sample airborne insects (e.g., Glick, 1939; Gressitt et al., 1961; Rainey, 1976; Reling and Taylor, 1984). Limitations include high cost, restrictions imposed by low altitude flight of aircraft at night, and the often severe damage to and dehydration of the captured insects (Reling and Taylor, 1984).

Large tow nets suspended from kites or gas-filled balloons have been used to capture airborne arthropods at high elevations (Hardy and Milne, 1938; Johnson, 1950b; Johnson and Taylor, 1955a; Farrow and Dowse, 1984). A variety of ready-to-assemble kites are available commercially (Jenkins, 1981). Tow nets can be raised and lowered independently of the kite, so that when wind conditions are calm in the lower atmosphere (often at night), the kite can remain aloft. These nets may be suitable for assessing insects available to bats that fly (and forage) at high altitude (e.g., Williams et al., 1973).

4.1.4. Malaise Traps

The Malaise trap (Malaise, 1937) is one of the most versatile traps used for catching airborne insects. Several variations of the origi-

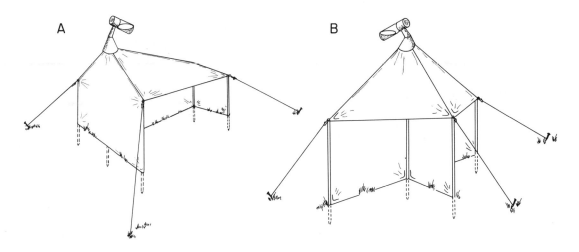

Figure 3. (A) Two-sided Malaise trap (after Townes, 1972). (B) Four-sided Malaise trap (after Gressitt and Gressitt, 1963).

nal design have been described (e.g., Townes, 1962, 1972; Gressitt and Gressitt, 1962; Butler, 1965; Marston, 1965; Roberts, 1972). The basic design is of a "tent" made from netting into which insects either crawl or fly (Fig. 3A). Once inside, most insects crawl up the netting and enter vials at the peak of the tent, where insects are either collected alive or are killed and preserved. Most Malaise traps require guyed poles or frames to support the netting (e.g., Townes, 1962, 1972). The trap described by Marston (1965) incorporates a free-standing overhead frame made of aluminum tubing of the type used to suspend camping tents. Many of the most successful Malaise trap designs are available commercially.

Advantages of using a Malaise trap include its simple design and versatility, which allows it to be used in a variety of habitats. Malaise traps are typically set at ground level, but small versions can be suspended in trees or over streams. A disadvantage, when the trap is positioned at ground level, is a bias toward catching insects that may not be available to aerial feeding bats. Other disadvantages of Malaise traps include potential biases against capturing Coleoptera and Hemiptera (Juillet, 1963), relatively small catches, and their unsuitability for temporal (e.g., hourly)

sampling. A modification that may improve the capture of Coleoptera is to place pans of water (with detergent) beneath the baffles when a trap is positioned near the ground. Insects that would otherwise drop to the ground upon impact (and likely escape) can thus be recovered (J. J. Belwood, pers. comm.).

Factors that affect the efficiency of Malaise traps include trap size, number, shape, and size of openings, number and size of baffles, color and contrast with the background, and trap placement (e.g., Townes, 1972; Mathews and Mathews, 1983). Traps with two openings appear to catch more insects than those with four, and traps constructed with dark-colored (black) netting are more efficient than those with light-colored netting (Townes, 1972). Dacron or Terylene fabric is preferred to cotton or nylon netting because of its durability (Townes, 1972).

4.1.5. Impaction Traps

Impaction or flight traps work on the principle that when a flying insect hits a surface, it becomes stunned and drops upon impact. Impaction traps are easy to assemble and work most effectively when they are posi-

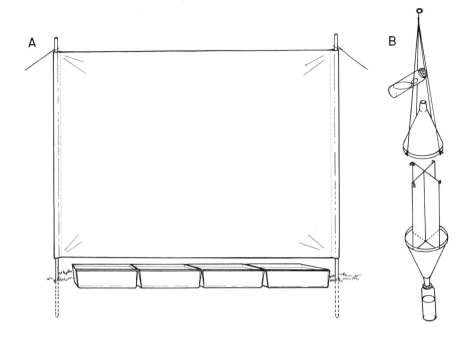

Figure 4. (A) Portable bi-directional impaction trap (after J. J. Belwood, pers. comm.). (B) Portable omnidirectional flight (impaction) trap (after Wilkening et al., 1981).

tioned along flyways used by insects. Several designs of impaction traps have been described, and most are constructed from glass or plexiglass plates (Service, 1976; Southwood, 1978). Mosquito netting stretched tightly between two poles may substitute for glass or plexiglass (Fig. 4A). Wood or aluminum poles can be inserted through the hemmed netting and guyed with nylon cord to keep the netting as taut as possible. Collecting pans (filled with water and a wetting agent) may be positioned below impaction traps to capture stunned insects as they fall. A plastic sheet, angled like a roof, may be placed above a trap to shield it from rain. Although most impaction traps are highly portable and easy to assemble in the field, the principal disadvantage is that they tend to be highly directional.

An omnidirectional impaction trap described by Wilkening et al. (1981) is both versatile and easy to assemble from commonly available materials (Fig. 4B). This trap consists of two 30 cm plastic funnels, two plexiglass plates, and two collecting vials. The lower chamber typically collects large, fast-flying insects that become stunned and drop upon impact. The upper chamber, however, captures mostly slow-flying insects that crawl upward when their horizontal flight is impeded.

4.1.6. Sticky Traps

Sticky traps work on the principle that airborne insects adhere to sticky substances upon contact (e.g., Service, 1976; Southwood, 1978). Because sticky traps partly make use of wind to catch insects, the airstream itself can influence trap efficiency. Some insects, however, are captured as they contact the sticky material during active flight. The most effective sticky traps are cylindrical in shape (e.g., Heathcote, 1957). These may be constructed from stove pipe, PCV tubing, tin cans, or cylindrical, hardware-cloth frames covered with plastic sheets (e.g., Bradbury and Vehrencamp, 1976;

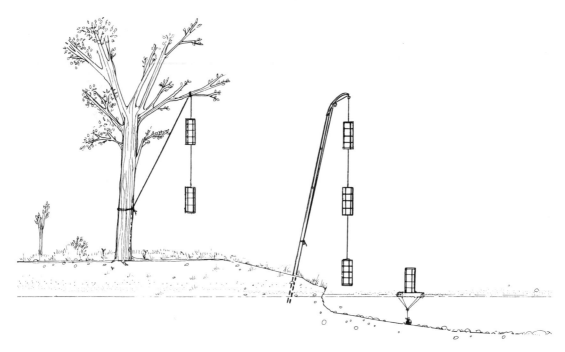

Figure 5. Sticky traps deployed in suspended and floating positions. Suspended traps may be lowered or elevated from the ground level using ropes and O-rings. Floating traps may be buoyed with styrofoam or ABS and should be firmly secured with rope and anchor.

Southwood, 1978; Belwood and Fullard, 1984). Sticky traps with flat surfaces are usually directional and less efficient, unless the surface is mounted perpendicular to a wind vane, or in situations where the two surfaces are mounted perpendicular to each other.

Advantages of using sticky traps to assess the abundance and activity of airborne insects include high versatility and portability, low assembly cost, and ease of operation. These features make it possible to simultaneously sample insects at several sites within the same habitat, in different habitats, and at different heights above the ground or above the water surface (Fig. 5). An improved design for a cylindrical sticky trap (including a carrying case for transporting multiple trap samples) is described in Appendix 2.

The absolute efficiency of cylindrical sticky traps can be estimated by using Service's (1976) corrections for the Johnson-Taylor suction trap and Johnson's (1950b) data on field catches of sticky cylinder and suction traps. Efficiency of sticky traps is almost constant at wind speeds ranging from 3.2 to 16 kmph (Taylor, 1962b). However, because Taylor's (1962b) correction factors (see Southwood, 1978) are based mainly on aerial insects ≤ 6.4 mm in length, caution is advised in extrapolating these corrections to larger insects. Small, cylindrical sticky traps often catch proportionately large numbers of insects than traps with a larger surface area (Heathcote, 1957). Compared to Malaise traps, sticky traps may capture smaller insects (Juillet, 1963). Moreover, large insects may seriously alter the efficiency of sticky traps at all wind speeds by their avoidance and alighting reactions.

Although several kinds of adhesives for sticky traps are available commercially (Ryan and Molyneaux, 1981), some have properties that make them unsuitable for trapping insects. The most effective products are transparent, odorless, easy to spread, resistant to water, long-lasting, do not oxidize to form a "skin," and do not run at warm temperatures or set at cold temperatures. Two commercially available adhesives (Tangletrap and Oecotak) are considered to be the most effective for insect trapping (Ryan and Molyneux, 1981; Kunz, pers. obs.).

A disadvantage of using sticky traps is the relatively poor solubility of most commercial adhesives. Effective and preferred solvents for specimen removal include tolulene, heptane, hexane, xylene, ethyl acetate and various combinations of these (Murphy, 1985). Two effective and commonly available solvents include methylchloroform (1,1,1-trichloroethane), a common household substitute for carbon tetrachloride, and fingernail polish remover (ethyl acetate with other aromatic hydrocarbons). Other effective, but less preferred solvents include petroleum (mineral) spirits, gasoline, and kerosene. Murphy (1985) described a simple procedure for removing sticky material from specimens that involves submerging the sticky trap surface in a shallow pan containing an appropriate solvent. After the sticky material has been dissolved in the solvent, specimens should be washed in ethylene glycol ethyl ether (cellosolve) to remove the solvent. Specimens should then be washed in xylene to remove the cellosolve before they are stored in alcohol. The apparatus and procedure described by Green et al. (1980) for washing insects from sticky traps appears to be unnecessarily complicated.

4.1.7. Emergence Traps

Traps that capture insects as they emerge from the surface of water can be useful for assessing prey available to bats that regularly feed over open water. Emergence traps may be especially valuable for capturing newly emerged "adult" forms of aquatic insects (e.g., Diptera, Trichoptera, Ephemeroptera, etc.). Possible designs include conical or box traps that either float or are anchored to the substrate (e.g., Morgan et al, 1963; Corbet, 1965; Mason and Sublette, 1971; Service, 1976; LaSage and Harrison, 1979). Most

emergence traps can be constructed inexpensively using wood frames covered with fine-mesh netting (Cushman, 1983). Plastic may be used to cover the top one-third of the trap to keep the net dry during rainy periods. Styrofoam may be used for flotation, but ABS tubing offers the advantages of buoyancy and durability. LaSage and Harrison (1979) described an effective trap in which the catch can be processed rapidly to aid in the study of temporal emergence patterns (Fig. 6A). The trap described by Slaff et al. (1984) includes a sticky board that can be exchanged periodically to assess the abundance and emergence patterns of aquatic insects (Fig. 6B).

If emergence traps are to be used they should be designed for portability, convenience, and efficiency. The shape of the trap frame appears to have little bearing on trap efficiency, yet the size of the frame does seem to be important. Morgan et al. (1963) suggested that the optimum frame size for an emergence trap is 0.46 m^2. Emergence traps with interiors exposed to natural illumination appear to catch more insects than darkened varieties. For example, Kimerle and Anderson (1967) found that traps covered with transparent plastic caught 4-5 times more midges (chironomids and chaoborids) than traps covered with black plastic. Emergence traps should always be buoyed so that they consistently sample insects at the same site independent of water level.

4.1.8. Pitfall Traps

Pitfall traps have been used successfully to capture large ground-dwelling arthropods, especially members of the Coleoptera (e.g., Greenslade, 1964). Use of such traps offers a potentially valuable means of assessing the relative abundance of terrestrial arthropods that are regularly eaten by ground-feeding insectivorous bats (e.g., *Myotis myotis*— Bauerova, 1978). When a pitfall trap is properly constructed and used without bait, it often captures most if not all insects that happen to enter.

Pitfall traps can be assembled from glass,

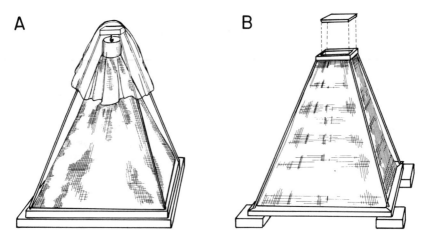

Figure 6. Floating emergence traps. (A) A model designed for temporal sampling (after LaSage and Harrison, 1979). (B) A model that incorporates a sticky board for rapid removal and replacement (after Slaff et al., 1984).

plastic, or metal containers and should be placed into the soil so that the openings are level with the soil surface (Gist and Crossley, 1973; Luff, 1975). Various modifications of this design include rain guards, timing devices, drift fences (Southwood, 1978), and barriers (Reeves, 1980). Because pitfall traps are inexpensive and require little labor, several may be deployed simultaneously in different habitats. Capture success may be doubled by connecting two pitfall traps with a plastic barrier (Durkins and Reeves, 1982).

The efficiency of pitfall traps is influenced by trap shape, trap number, construction material, position with respect to vegetation, and weather conditions (Luff, 1975). Small traps are more efficient at capturing individuals of small species and large traps usually catch larger species. Smooth sided containers (e.g., plastic and glass) are judged better than metal cans (which corrode and allow insects to escape). Small species may escape from traps having large openings or they may be eaten by larger species (Southwood, 1978). Liquid preservatives and killing agents can be used, but these may attract or repel certain species (Luff, 1975). Despite the practical and theoretical difficulties of using pitfall traps (Mitchell, 1963), this method can

provide a useful index for estimating the abundance of terrestrial arthropods in habitats used by bats that capture insects on the ground.

4.2. Attractant Traps

Traps that interfere with an insect's sensory orientation or movements are the most commonly used by entomologists for general collecting (Southwood, 1978). These include chemical (pheromone) and light traps (of various intensity and quality) that interfere with the normal sensory orientation of the insects. Light traps have been extensively used in surveys of insect communities (e.g., Wolda, 1978, 1983) and in less rigorous efforts to estimate prey availability to bats (e.g., Black, 1974, 1979; LaVal and LaVal, 1980). In studies of bat feeding ecology, light traps also have been used for experimental manipulations of insect prey (e.g., Fenton and Morris, 1976; Bell and Fenton, 1984). Because light traps rely on the disturbance of an insect's normal behavior, the variation in response to different kinds of traps, between habitats, and between nights, is a limitation more serious than for most other kinds of traps (but see Bowden, 1982). Diurnally active insects may be attracted to ultraviolet (UV) lights at night (J. J. Belwood, pers. comm.) and this may seriously bias the catch of "available" prey.

Another limitation of light traps is how the effective radius of the trap or "catchment area" (the area in which insects are influenced by the light) is affected by the surrounding environment. The size of the catchment area is determined by the contrast between light from the trap and ambient light from the surroundings. In fact, the amount and intensity of moonlight may have a profound effect on the size of the catchment area (e.g., Bowden, 1973, 1982). Thus, if light traps are to be used, insect catches should be corrected for the phase of the lunar cycle and the duration and intensity of moonlight throughout the night (Bowden and Morris, 1975). In studies where light trap catches of insects have been corrected for moonlight effects, some species appear to be more active on nights with a full moon (e.g., Bidlingmayer, 1964, 1967; Anderson, 1966).

Bearing in mind the influence of the catchment area, light traps set at ground level have the potential to attract insects that normally would not be encountered by many aerially feeding bats. The trap described by Taylor et al. (1982) in which the light source is directed upward restricts the effective location of the catchment area. Because the light from the trap is shielded on the sides, no illumination is visible from below a certain height. This restricts the attraction potential of the trap to those insects already in flight and reduces the number of insects in the catch that may otherwise be attracted.

Intensity and quality (wavelength) of the lamp are two important variables that may influence light-trap effectiveness. Light intensity, more than light quality, may influence the number of insects attracted to traps. Additionally, there are often marked contrasts in the responses of different insect taxa and sexes to light quality. For example, moths (Lepidoptera) and caddisflies (Trichoptera) are more strongly attracted to traps with mercury vapor lamps than to ultraviolet (UV)

lamps, and mayflies (Ephemeroptera) and ichneumonid wasps (Ichneumonidae) are more strongly attracted to the yellow-green bands of the spectrum (Mikkola, 1972). Members of the Diptera and Miridae are attracted in largest numbers to traps with incandescent (tungsten filaments) lamps (Southwood, 1978). However, mercury-vapor lamps equipped with UV-transmitting filters attract more insects from a wider range of taxa than either UV or incandescent lamps alone (Mikkola, 1972).

Despite these limitations, light traps can be valuable for collecting insects as supplements to laboratory diets (Chapter 16), "prey" for feeding experiments (e.g., Goldman and Henson, 1977; Bell and Fenton, 1984), subjects for neurophysiological experiments (e.g., Fullard, 1979, 1982), specimens for reference collections in food habits analysis (Chapter 11), and for estimating energy content of the diet (Chapter 18).

5. RADAR OBSERVATIONS AND REMOTE SENSING

Radar is a powerful tool for assessing the density of insects in the upper air column (e.g., Schaefer, 1976, 1979; Reynolds and Riley, 1979; Riley, 1979) and should be explored for use in conjunction with feeding studies of insectivorous bats. Radar systems adapted from commercial marine equipment or salvaged military hardware have been used successfully to study temporal and spatial patterns of insects at a wide range of altitudes and distances. Some radar systems can detect small insects (the size of aphids) at distances up to 0.2 km and small moths at distances ranging up to 1 km. Generally, insects smaller than one-half wavelength of the radar cannot be detected unless targets are extremely dense and the radar is highly tuned (Farrow and Dowse, 1984). Accurate detection is usually limited to altitudes from 10 to 20 m above open ground or above forest canopies, although it is possible to detect small insects as low as 50 cm above smooth surfaces (e.g., bodies of water). The use of radar to assess airborne insects available to bats may find its greatest utility where bats forage at high altitudes (e.g., *Tadarida brasiliensis*—Williams et al., 1973) and where ground clutter is minimal.

Absolute density of insects may be calculated from radar signals by dividing the number of insects that appear on a radar screen by the volume of air sampled by the radar device (Schaefer, 1976, 1979). It is also possible to obtain density and height profiles of insects by taking standard density measurements at a series of elevation angles. Variations with time can be obtained by making elevation scans with radar at periodic intervals. The major limitation of radar in studying free-flying insects is that detection capabilities are severely limited by ground clutter.

A remote infrared sensing system recently described by Schaefer and Bent (1984) holds considerable promise for assessing airborne insect density at altitudes below the normal detection range of radar. It can be operated day or night and is capable of detecting insects as small as aphids. This system employs a xenon arc source for illumination and the detector itself consists of a 35 mm lens, a narrow band infrared filter, and a 3-stage, cascade image intensifier. An f-1.8 relay lens is used to transfer intensified output to a video camera. Because this system is capable of detecting insects from a few centimeters to a few tens of meters above the ground, it may prove superior to radar signals for assessing insects available to aerial feeding insectivorous bats. Moreover, when compared to radar this system is relatively inexpensive and simple to operate.

6. TREATMENT OF FIELD DATA

6.1.   Enumeration and Transformations

Insect catches can be summarized by reporting actual counts or, alternatively, these numbers may be subjected to various arithmetic transformations. If absolute densities and parametric analyses are of interest, transformations should be made to correct original data for normality, homoscedasticity (equal variances), and additivity. When values are small, a logarithmic transformation [$\log_{10} (n + 1)$], is preferred on theoretical grounds (Zar, 1984). If the assumptions of analysis of variance are met as a result of transformation, one may proceed with parametric testing. When transformed values are used, all variances and confidence limits should be calculated before transforming them back to original units. Only the statistics in the original units should be reported.

Percentages or proportions of captured insects are often presented for comparison with other captured insects or with percentages of taxa observed in diets. Percentages or proportions often are not normally distributed but, when values range from 0 to 30% and 70 to 100%, deviations from normality can often be corrected by using the arcsin transformation. Statistical references (e.g., Zar, 1984) should be consulted for discussions of transformations and analyses of proportions.

6.2.   Prey Selection Analyses

The term "prey selection" has not been used consistently in the literature pertaining to bats. Claims of selective feeding have been commonly made without actually having data on prey availability (e.g., Fenton et al., 1977; Fenton and Thomas, 1980; LaVal and LaVal, 1980). In other situations, selective feeding has been "demonstrated" by using various qualitative and quantitative procedures to compare diet composition and insect prey captured or observed at feeding sites (e.g., Buchler, 1976; Anthony and Kunz, 1977; Bauerova, 1978; Black, 1979; Bell and Fenton, 1984; Belwood and Fullard, 1984; Swift et al., 1985).

When prey selection of free-ranging bats is of interest, special attention should be given to collecting samples of insects at the same place and time that bats are feeding.

Ultimately, the reliability of a prey selection study will depend upon the confidence that one can place on the analysis of gut or fecal contents (or analysis of culled parts) and the reliability of the trapping methods used to assess prey availability. Theoretically, dietary choice may be based on prey size, nutrient quality, energy value, and/or palatability. If the insects that are "reconstructed" from chewed or discarded fragments differ in size or composition from "available" insects, prey selection can then be inferred.

Several forage ratios, including Ivlev's (1961) electivity index, have been used to support evidence of diet choice. Cock (1978) reviewed published forage ratios and indices and concluded that most had major short-comings. The most widely used index (Method 4 of Cock, 1978) may be the most useful. However, it is valid only when the effects of the predator on the prey population are negligible, and it is limited to a considera-tion of two prey types. Ivelev's electivity index has the advantage in that more than two prey types can be considered in an analysis, but it has the shortcoming of being affected by relative prey density.

Graphical analysis of food habits and prey availability can be valuable in assem-bling evidence of prey selection. Of the two types of graphical analyses discussed by Murdoch (1969), the most useful is the one where the proportion of prey in the diet is plotted against the proportion of available prey (Cock, 1978). Graphical methods have been used to gather evidence of prey selection in *Pipistrellus pipistrellus* (Swift et al., 1985) and aerially feeding house martins (Bryant, 1973). When bivariate samples of percent food eaten and percent of available prey fall above or below a line of equality, the predator is judged to have either selected prey items or avoided them. When plotted data fall near or directly on the line of equality, random feeding is assumed. Correlation analysis of original and transformed values also have been used to augment results from graphical analyses (e.g., Bryant, 1973; Swift et al., 1985).

6.3. Insect Biomass and Energy Content

The analysis of insect prey, expressed in units reflecting the goals of a predator, is important in studies of feeding ecology and energetics (Chapter 12). By using estimates of dry mass of prey and suitable conversion factors for energy equivalents (Table 1) insect density estimates can be converted to units of avail-able biomass and energy. Empirically derived estimates of biomass based on measurements of insect length[2] (Janzen, 1973) were used to estimate biomass of prey available to three species of emballonurid bats (Bradbury and Vehrencamp, 1976). More accurate and reli-able estimates of biomass are possible using logarithmic transformations of insect length (e.g., Rogers et al., 1976, 1977; Sage, 1982). Equivalent estimates of insect biomass may be determined by using microvolumetric dis-placement of fluid-preserved specimens (Ciborowski, 1983).

7. SUMMARY AND CONCLUSIONS

In assessing the availability of prey to an insect predator, one should first determine when and where the predator feeds. This knowledge can be used to establish a design for capturing insect prey that might include where, when, what kind, and how many traps are needed. Ideally, several traps should be used to quantify the activity, abundance, and dispersion of insects in any single habitat. If bats feed in several habitats, each should be sampled in such a way so as to permit valid comparisons.

Non-attractant insect traps are usually preferable to attractant traps because they have fewer biases. Non-attractant traps suit-able for assessing insect density and activity include suction traps, tow nets, rotary traps, Malaise traps, impaction (flight) traps, sticky traps, emergence traps, and pitfall traps. Traps that interfere with the normal sensory orientation or movements of insects (e.g., light traps) generally are less suitable for assessing prey availability. Notwithstanding,

Table 1. Average energy equivalents of selected arthropod taxa commonly taken as prey by insectivorous bats. Energy equivalents of stomach contents and feces from *Myotis lucifugus* and a commonly used laboratory diet for bats (*Tenebrio* larvae, pupae, and adults) are given for comparison.

Category	Dry Mass kJ/g	Ash-Free Dry Mass kJ/g	Source
Arachnida	20.19	23.14	Cummins and Wuycheck, 1971
Coleoptera			
Tenebrionidae	24.48	27.83	Cummins and Wuycheck, 1971
Coccinellidae	24.48	—	Cummins and Wuycheck, 1971
Carabidae	—	23.73	Cummins and Wuycheck, 1971
Chrysomelidae	21.85	23.17	Cummins and Wuycheck, 1971
Diptera			
Chironomidae	24.22	22.41	Cummins and Wuycheck, 1971
	21.42	21.92	Maxon and Oring, 1980
	21.25	22.05	Maxon and Oring, 1980
Culicidae	20.65	—	Cummins and Wuycheck, 1971
	23.01	—	Kunz, unpubl
Tipulidae	25.52	—	Kunz, unpubl
Ephemeroptera	22.88	27.42	Cummins and Wuycheck, 1971
	22.09	23.26	Maxon and Oring, 1980
	23.26	24.27	Maxon and Oring, 1980
Hemiptera			
Cerocopidae	23.59	24.13	Cummins and Wuycheck, 1971
Hymenoptera	19.37	—	Cummins and Wuycheck, 1971
Lepidoptera	21.25	—	Kunz, unpubl
Orthoptera	22.18	22.52	Cummins and Wuycheck, 1971
Trichoptera	20.92	24.22	Cummins and Wuycheck, 1971
Insects (mixed)	22.09	—	Cummins and Wuycheck, 1971
Stomach contents of *M. lucifugus*	23.85	—	Kunz, unpubl
Feces of *M. lucifigus*	19.25	—	Kunz, unpubl
Tenebrio larvae	29.71	—	Kunz, unpubl
pupae	28.87	—	Kunz, unpubl
adults	27.61	—	Kunz, unpubl

attractant traps are valuable for collecting insects needed for other purposes (e.g., supplements to laboratory diets, reference collections for food habits analysis, determination of energy equivalents, etc.). Radar offers the potential to gain highly accurate estimates of airborne insect densities at elevations above 10 to 20 m, and recent developments in remote sensing hold promise for assessing aerial insect densities at even lower elevations.

Depending upon the habitat being sampled and the type of sampling device, field data can be converted to absolute or relative densities. In most situations, estimates of relative density can be used for comparative purposes. To gain evidence of prey selection, relative density estimates of prey can be compared with data derived from dietary analysis. Estimates of available and ingested biomass (and energy) can be made using appropriate conversion factors.

8.   ACKNOWLEDGMENTS

I am grateful to J. S. Alexander for preparing the illustrations, and to J. J. Belwood, A.

Kurta, and J. Traniello for reviewing an early draft of this manuscript. The National Science Foundation (BSR-8314821) has generously funded my research.

9. REFERENCES

Anderson, N. H. 1966. Depressant effect of moonlight on activity of aquatic insects. Nature, 209:319-320.

Anthony, E. L. P., and T. H. Kunz. 1977. Feeding strategies of the little brown bat, *Myotis lucifugus,* in southern New Hampshire. Ecology, 58:775-780.

Anthony, E. L. P., M. H. Stack, and T. H. Kunz. 1981. Night roosting and the nocturnal time budget of the little brown bat, *Myotis lucifugus:* Effects of reproductive status, prey density, and environmental conditions. Oecologia, 51:151-156.

Barnard, D. R. 1979. A vehicle-mounted insect trap. Can. Ent., 111:851-854.

Bauerova, Z. 1978. Contribution to the trophic ecology of *Myotis myotis.* Folia Zool., 27:305-316.

Belwood, J. J., and J. H. Fullard. 1984. Echolocation and foraging behavior in the Hawaiian hoary bat, *Lasiurus cinereus.* Can. J. Zool., 62:2113-2120.

Bell, G. P. 1982. Behavioral and ecological aspects of gleaning by a desert insectivorous bat, *Antrozous pallidus* (Chiroptera: Vespertilionidae). Behav. Ecol. Sociobiol., 10:217-223.

Bell, G. P., and M. B. Fenton. 1984. The use of Doppler-shifted echoes as a flutter detection and clutter rejection system: The echolocation and feeding behavior of *Hipposideros ruber* (Chiroptera: Hipposideridae). Behav. Ecol. Sociobiol., 15:109-114.

Bidlingmayer, W. L. 1964. The effect of moonlight on the flight activity of mosquitoes. Ecology, 45:87-94.

Bidlingmayer, W. L. 1967. A comparison of trapping methods for adult mosquitoes: Species response and environmental influence. J. Med. Ent., 4:200-220.

Black, H. L. 1974. A north temperate bat community: Structure and prey populations. J. Mammal., 55:138-157.

Black, H. L. 1979. Precision in prey selection by the trident-nosed bat *(Cleotis percivali).* Mammalia, 43:53-57.

Bowden, J. 1973. The influence of moonlight on catches of insects in light-traps in Africa. Part I. The moon and moonlight. Bull. Ent. Res., 63:113-128.

Bowden, J. 1982. An analysis of factors affecting catches of insects in light-traps. Bull. Ent. Res., 72:535-556.

Bowden, J., and M. G. Morris. 1975. The influence of moonlight on catches of insects in light-traps in Africa. III. The effective radius of a mercury-vapor light-trap and the analysis of catches using effective radius. Bull. Ent. Res., 65:303-348.

Bradbury, J. W., and S. L. Vehrencamp. 1976. Social organization and foraging in emballonurid bats. I. Field studies. Behav. Ecol. Sociobiol., 1:337-381.

Bryant, D. M. 1973. The factors influencing the selection of food by the house martin *Delichon urbica.* J. Anim. Ecol., 42:539-564.

Bryant, D. M. 1975. Breeding biology of the house martin *Delichon urbica,* in relation to aerial insect abundance. Ibis, 117:180-215.

Bryant, D. M., and K. R. Westerterp. 1980. The energy budget of the house martin *(Delichon urbica).* Ardea, 68:91-102.

Bryant, D. M., and K. R. Westerterp. 1983. Short-term variability in energy turnover by breeding house martins *Delichon urbica:* A study using doubly-labelled water (D_2 ^{18}O). J. Anim. Ecol., 52:525-545.

Buchler, E. R. 1976. Prey selection by *Myotis lucifugus* (Chiroptera: Vespertilionidae). Amer. Nat., 110:619-828.

Butler, G. D. 1965. A modified Malaise insect trap. Pan Pacif. Ent., 41:51-53.

Ciborowski, J. J. H. 1983. A simple volumetric instrument to estimate biomass of fluid preserved invertebrates. Can. Ent., 115:427-430.

Cock, M. J. W. 1978. The assessment of preference. J. Anim. Ecol., 47:805-816.

Corbet, P. S. 1965. An insect emergence trap for quantitative studies in shallow ponds. Can. Ent., 97:845-848.

Cushman, R. M. 1983. An inexpensive, floating, insect-emergence trap. Bull. Environ. Contam. Toxicol., 31:547-550.

Cummins, K. W., and J. C. Wuycheck. 1971. Caloric equivalents for investigation in ecological energetics. Mitt. Internat. Verein. Limnol., 18:1-158.

Dwyer, P. D. 1970. Foraging behaviour of the Australian large-footed Myotis (Chiroptera). Mammalia, 34:76-80.

Durkins, T. J., and R. M. Reeves. 1982. Barriers increase efficiency of pitfall traps. Ent. News, 93:25-28.

Farrow, R. A., and J. E. Dowsc. 1984. Mcthod of using kites to carry tow nets in the upper air for sampling migrating insects and its application to radar entomology. Bull. Entomol. Res., 74:87-95.

Fenton, M. B. 1982. Echolocation calls and patterns of hunting and habitat use of bats (Microchiroptera) from Chillagoe, North Queensland. Aust. J. Zool., 30:417-425.

Fenton, M. B., and G. K. Morris. 1976. Opportunistic feeding by desert bats *Myotis* spp. Can. J. Zool., 54:526-530.

Fenton, M. B., and G. P. Bell. 1979. Echolocation and feeding behaviour in four species of *Myotis* (Chiroptera). Can. J. Zool., 57:1271-1277.

Fenton, M. B., and D. W. Thomas. 1980. Dry season overlap in activity patterns, habitat use, and prey selection by sympatric African insectivorous bats. Biotropica, 12:81-90.

Fenton, M. B., N. G. H. Boyle, T. M. Harrison, and D. J. Oxley. 1977. Activity patterns, habitat use, and prey selection by sympatric African insectivorous bats. Biotropica, 9:73-85.

Fullard, J. H. 1979. Behavioral analysis of auditory sensitivity in *Cycnia tenera* Hübner (Lepidoptera: Arctiidae). J. Comp. Physiol., 129:79-83.

Fullard, J. H. 1982. Echolocation assemblages and their effects on moth auditory systems. Can. J. Zool., 60:2572-2576.

Gist, C. S., and D. A. Crossley. 1973. A method for quantifying pitfall trapping. Environ. Ent., 2:951-952.

Glick, P. A. 1939. The distribution of insects, spiders, and mites in the air. U.S. Dept. Agric., Tech. Bull. No. 673, Washington, D.C., 150 pp.

Goldman, L. J., and O. W. Henson, Jr. 1977. Prey recognition and selection by the constant frequency bat *Pteronotus parnellii parnellii*. Behav. Ecol. Sociobiol., 2:411-420.

Goodenough, J. L., P. C. Jank, L. Carroll, W. L. Sterling, E. J. Redman, and J. A. Witz. 1983. Collecting and preserving airborne arthropods in liquid at timed intervals with a Johnson-Taylor-type suction trap. J. Econ. Ent., 76:960-963.

Green, C. L., F. A. McCarty, L. J. Edson, and T. L. Payne. 1980. Apparatus for sticky trap washing and insect recovery. Southwest. Ent., 5:19-21.

Greenslade, P. J. M. 1964. Pitfall trapping as a method for studying populations of Carabidae (Coleoptera). J. Anim. Ecol., 33:301-310.

Gressitt, J. L., J. Sedlacek, K. A. J. Wise, and C. M. Yoshimoto. 1961. A high speed airplane trap for air-borne organisms. Pac. Insects, 3:549-555.

Gressitt, J. L., and M. K. Gressitt. 1962. An improved Malaise trap. Pac. Insects, 4:87-89.

Hardy, A. C., and P. S. Milne. 1938. Studies in the distribution of insects by aerial currents. Experiments in aerial tow-netting from kites. J. Anim. Ecol., 7:199-229.

Heathcote, G. D. 1957. The optimal size of sticky aphid traps. Plant Path., 6:104-107.

Holbrook, R. R., and W. Wuerthele. 1984. A lightweight, hand-portable vehicle-mounted insect trap. Mosq. News, 44:239-242.

Hill, M. N. 1971. A bicycle-mounted trap for collecting adult mosquitoes. J. Med. Ent., 8:108-109.

Holmes, R. T., T. W. Sherry, and S. E. Bennett. 1978. Diurnal and individual variability in the foraging behavior of American redstarts *(Setophaga ruticilla)*. Oecologia, 36:141-149.

Ivlev, V. S. 1961. Experimental ecology of the feeding of fishes. Yale Univ. Press, New Haven.

Janzen, D. H. 1973. Sweep samples of tropical foliage insects: Effects of seasons, vegetative types, time of day and insularity. Ecology, 54:687-709.

Jenkins, C. J. 1981. Kites and meteorology. Weather, 36:294-300.

Johnson, C. G. 1950a. A suction trap for small airborne insects which automatically segregates the catch into successive hourly samples. Ann. Appl. Biol., 37:80-91.

Johnson, C. G. 1950b. The comparison of suction trap, sticky trap, and tow-net for the quantitative sampling of small airborne insects. Ann. Appl. Biol., 37:268-285.

Johnson, C. G. 1969. Migration and dispersal of insects by flight. Methuen, London, 763 pp.

Johnson, C. G., and L. R. Taylor. 1955a. The measurement of insect density in the air. Lab. Pract., 4:187-192, 235-239.

Johnson, C. G., and L. R. Taylor. 1955b. The development of large suction traps for airborne insects. Ann. Appl. Biol., 43:51-62.

Juillet, J. A. 1963. A comparison of four types of traps used for capturing insects. Can. J. Zool., 41:219-223.

Karg, J. 1980. A method of motor-net for estimation of aeroentomofauna. Pol. Ecol. Stud., 6:345-354.

Kimerle, R. A., and N. H. Anderson. 1967. Evaluation of aquatic insect emergence traps. J. Econ. Ent., 60:1255-1259.

Kolb, A. 1976. Funktion und Wirkungsweise der Riechlaute der Mausohrfledermause, *M. myotis.* Z. Saugertierk., 41:226-236.

LaVal, R. K., and M. L. LaVal. 1980. Prey selection by the slit-faced bat *Nycteris thebaica* (Chiroptera: Nycteridae) in Natal, South Africa. Biotropica, 12:241-246.

LaSage, L., and A. D. Harrison. 1979. Improved traps and techniques for the study of emerging aquatic insects. Ent. News, 90:65-78.

Lewis, T. 1965. The effects of artificial windbreaks on the aerial distribution of flying insects. Ann. Appl. Biol., 55:500-512.

Lewis, T. 1970. Patterns of distribution of insects near a windbreak of tall trees. Ann. Appl. Biol., 65:213-220.

Loy, V. A., C. S. Barnhart, and A. A. Therrien. 1968. A collapsible, portable vehicle-mounted insect trap. Mosq. News, 28:84-87.

Luff, M. L. 1975. Some features influencing the efficiency of pitfall traps. Oecologia, 19:345-357.

McClure, E. H. 1938. Insect aerial populations. Ann. Ent. Soc. Amer., 31:504-513.

Malaise, R. 1937. A new insect-trap. Ent. Tidskr., 58:148-160.

Marston, N. 1965. Some recent modifications on the design of Malaise insect traps with a summary of the insects represented in collections. J. Kansas. Ent. Soc., 38:154-162.

Mason, W. T., and S. E. Sublette. 1971. Collecting Ohio River basin Chironomidae (Diptera) with a floating sticky trap. Can. Ent., 103:397-404.

Matthews, R. W., and J. R. Matthews. 1983. Malaise traps: The Townes model catches more insects. Contr. Amer. Ent. Inst., 20:428-432.

Maxson, S. J., and L. W. Oring. 1980. Breeding season time and energy budgets of the polyandrous spotted sandpiper. Behaviour, 74:200-263.

Mikkola, K. 1972. Behavioural and electrophysiological responses of night-flying insects, especially Lepidoptera, to near-ultraviolet visible light. Ann. Zool. Fenn., 9:225-254.

Mitchell, B. 1963. Ecology of two carabid beetles, *Bembidion lampros* (Herbst) and *Trechus quandristriatus* (Schrank). II. J. Anim. Ecol., 32:377-392.

Morgan, N. C., A. B. Wadell, and W. B. Hall. 1963. A comparison of emerging aquatic insects in floating box and submerged funnel traps. J. Anim. Ecol., 32:203-219.

Morris, R. F. 1960. Sampling insect populations. Ann. Rev. Ent., 5:243-264.

Murdoch, W. W. 1969. Switching in general predators: Experiments on specificity and stability of prey populations. Ecol. Monogr., 39:335-354.

Murphy, W. L. 1985. Procedure for the removal of insect specimens from sticky-trap material. Ann. Ent. Soc. Amer., 78:881.

Neuweiler, G. 1984. Foraging, echolocation and audition in bats. Naturwissenschaften, 71:446-455.

Nicholls, C. F. 1960. A portable, mechanical insect trap. Can. Ent., 92:48-51.

Novick, A., and B. A. Dale. 1971. Foraging behavior in fishing bats and their insectivorous relatives. J. Mammal., 52:817-818.

Reeves, R. M. 1980. The use of barriers with pitfall traps. Ent. News, 91:10-12.

Racey, P. A., and S. M. Swift. 1985. Feeding ecology of *Pipistrellus pipistrellus* (Chiroptera: Vespertilionidae) during pregnancy and lactation. I. Foraging behaviour. J. Anim. Ecol., 54:205-215.

Rainey, R. C. 1976. Flight behavior and features of the atmospheric environment. Pp. 75-112, *in* Insect flight. (R.C. Rainey, ed.). Symp. R. Ent. Soc. Lond., No. 7, Blackwell Publ., Oxford, 287 pp.

Reling, D., and R. A. J. Taylor. 1984. A collapsible tow net for sampling arthropods by airplane. J. Econ. Ent., 77:1615-1617.

Reynolds, D. P., and J. R. Riley. 1979. Radar observations of concentrations of insects above a river in Mali, West Africa. Ecol. Ent., 4:161-174.

Riley, J. R. 1979. Radar as an aid to the study of insect flight. Pp. 131-139, *in* A handbook of biotelemetry and radio-tracking. (C. J. Amlaner, Jr., and D. W. MacDonald, eds.). Pergamon Press, Oxford, 804 pp.

Roberts, R. H. 1972. The effectiveness of several types of Malaise traps for the collection of Tabanidae and Culicidae. Mosq. News, 32:542-547.

Rogers, L. E., W. T. Hinds, and R. L. Buschbom. 1976. A general weight vs. length relationship for insects. Ann. Ent. Soc. Amer., 69:387-389.

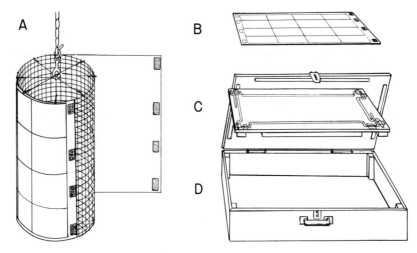

Figure 7. An improved design for a cylindrical sticky trap. (A) Hardware cloth cylinder and vinyl plastic trap surface. (B) Trap surfaces are interchangeable and can be positioned around cylinders with "Velcro" fasteners. (C) Support board for preparing and transporting sticky trap surfaces and for laboratory examination of trap catches. (D) Holding case for temporary storage and transport of trap surfaces in the field.

Rogers, L. E., R. L. Buschbom, and C. R. Watson. 1977. Length-weight relationships of shrub-steppe invertebrates. Ann. Ent. Soc. Amer., 70:51-53.

Ryan, L., and D. H. Molyneux. 1981. Non-setting adhesives for insect traps. Insect Sci. Appl., 1:349-355.

Sage, R. P. 1982. Wet and dry-weight estimates of insects and spiders based on length. Amer. Midl. Nat., 108:407-411.

Schaefer, G. W. 1976. Radar observations of insect flight. Pp. 157-193, in Insect flight. (R. C. Rainey, ed.). Symp. R. Ent. Soc. Lond., No. 7, Blackwell Publ., Oxford, 287 pp.

Schaefer, G. W. 1979. An airborne radar technique for investigations and control of insect pests. Phil. Trans. R. Soc. (B), 287:459-565.

Schaefer, G. W., and G. A. Bent. 1984. An infra-red remote sensing system for the active detection and automatic determination of insect flight trajectories (IRADIT). Bull. Ent. Res., 74:261-278.

Service, M. W. 1976. Mosquito ecology—Field sampling methods. John Wiley and Sons, New York, 586 pp.

Slaff, M., J. D. Haefner, R. E. Parsons, and F. Wilson. 1984. A modified pyramidal emergence trap for collecting mosquitoes. Mosq. News, 44:197-199.

Sommerman, K. M., and R. P. Simmet. 1965. Car-top insect trap with terminal cage in auto. Mosq. News, 25:172-182.

Southwood, T. R. E. 1978. Ecological methods. Chapman and Hall, London, 524 pp.

Steelman, C. D., C. G. Richardson, R. E. Schaefer, and B. H. Wilson. 1968. A collapsible truck-boat trap for collecting blood-fed mosquitoes and tabanids. Mosq. News, 28:64-67.

Swift, S. M., P. A. Racey, and M. I. Avery. 1985. Feeding ecology of Pipistrellus pipistrellus (Chiroptera: Vespertilionidae) during pregnancy and lactation. II. Diet. J. Anim. Ecol., 54:217-225.

Taylor, J., D. E. Padgham, and T. J. Perfect. 1982. A light-trap with upwardly directed illumination and temporal segregation of the catch. Bull. Ent. Res., 72:669-673.

Taylor, L. R. 1951. An improved suction trap for insects. Ann. Appl. Biol., 38:582-591.

Taylor, L. R. 1960. The distribution of insects at low levels in the air. J. Anim. Ecol., 29:45-63.

Taylor, L. R. 1962a. The absolute efficiency of insect suction traps. Ann. Appl. Biol., 50:405-421.

Taylor, L. R. 1962b. The efficiency of cylindrical sticky insect traps and suspended nets. Ann. App. Biol., 50:681-685.

Taylor, L. R., and J. M. P. Palmer. 1972. Aerial sampling. Pp. 189-234, in Aphid technology. (H. F. Van Emden, ed.). Academic Press, New York, 344 pp.

Townes, H. 1962. Design for a Malaise trap. Proc. Ent. Soc. Wash., 64:253-262.

Townes, H. 1972. A light-weight Malaise trap. Ent. News, 83:239-247.

Turner, A. K. 1982. Timing of laying by swallows *(Hirundo rustica)* and sand martins *(Riparia riparia).* J. Anim. Ecol., 51:29-46.

Vaughan, T. A. 1976. Nocturnal behavior of the African false vampire bat *(Cardioderma cor).* J. Mammal., 57:227-248.

Vaughan, T. A. 1977. Feeding behavior of the giant leaf-nosed bat *(Hipposideros commersoni).* E. Afr. Wildl. J., 15:237-249.

Voûte, A. M. 1972. Bijdrage tot de Oecologie van de Merrvleermuis, *Myotis dasycneme* (Boie, 1825). Unpubl. doctoral dissertation, Universiteit Utrecht, Utrecht, 159 pp.

Warnhouse, D. 1980. A portable suction trap for sampling small insects. Bull. Ent. Res., 70:491-494.

Wellington, W. G. 1945. Conditions governing the distribution of insects in the free atmosphere. Can. Ent., 77:7-15, 21-28, 44-49.

Wilkening, A. J., J. L. Foltz, T. H. Atkinson, and M. D. Connor. 1981. An omnidirectional flight trap for ascending and descending insects. Can. Ent., 113:453-455.

Williams, T. C., L. C. Ireland, and J. M. Williams. 1973. High altitude flights of the free-tailed bat, *Tadarida brasiliensis,* observed with radar. J. Mammal., 54:807-821.

Wolda, H. 1978. Seasonal fluctuations in rainfall, food, and abundance of tropical insects. J. Anim. Ecol., 47:369-381.

Wolda, H. 1983. "Long-term" stability of tropical insect populations. Res. Pop. Ecol., Suppl., No. 3:112-126.

Zar, J. H. 1984. Biostatistical analysis. 2nd ed. Prentice-Hall, Englewood Cliffs, New Jersey, 718 pp.

Appendix 1.   Selected Products and Sources for Commercially Available Insect Traps and Accessories

TRAPS

Johnson-Taylor suction trap

Burkard Manufacturing, Limited
Rickmansworth, Hertfordshire WD3 1PJ
England

Malaise trap

BioQuip Products
P.O. Box 61
Santa Monica, California 90406 USA

Marris House Nets
54 Richmond Park Avenue
Bournemouth BH8 9DR England

Pitfall trap

Carolina Biological Supply
2700 York Road
Burlington, North Carolina 27215 USA

Universal light trap (UV)

BioQuip Products

Vehicle mounted tow net

BioQuip Products

STICKY TRAP ADHESIVES

Tangletrap

The Tanglefoot Company
314 Straight Street, S.W.
Grand Rapids, Michigan 49504 USA

BioQuip Products

Oecotak

Oecos Limited
130 High Street
Kimpton, Harpenden
Herts, England

GENERAL ENTOMOLOGY SUPPLIES

BioQuip Products

Appendix 2.   An Improved Design for Cylindrical Sticky Traps and a Portable Holding Case for Transporting Multiple Trap Samples

Hardware cloth cylinders (42 cm high by 16 cm diameter) are assembled and placed at sample locations for repeated use (Fig. 5). White vinyl plastic sheets (42 cm by 52 cm) are used as replaceable trap surfaces (Fig. 7 A and B). Trap surfaces are prepared by sewing small Velcro fasteners along the shortest sides of the vinyl sheet; the Velcro fasteners are used to attach trap surfaces around hardware cloth cylinders. As an aid for enumerating insects, each trap surface should be marked permanently into twenty, 10 x 10 cm squares. A narrow (1 cm) margin should be delineated as an adhesive-free region to facilitate handling when a prepared trap is being set or replaced.

Each trap surface is temporarily attached to a flat support board with metal clips (Fig. 7 C) to enhance portability. Separators (strips of wood 1 cm thick) are affixed to the back of each support board to prevent trap surfaces from adhering to adjacent boards when they are stacked in a carrying case. Before traps are deployed in the field, a thin, uniform coat of adhesive (e.g., Tangletrap) is applied to each trap surface with a putty knife. Support boards with adhesive-prepared trap surfaces are placed into the carrying case and either stored for future use or transported to sampling localities for deployment. Carrying cases (the shape of a small suitcase) can be assembled to transport 6 to 8 holding boards and sticky trap surfaces (Fig. 7 D).

At each sampling site, a sticky-trap surface is removed from its support board and placed securely around a hardware cloth cylinder using the Velcro fasteners. At the end of a trapping session, the sticky-trap surfaces can be quickly and conveniently removed from their cylinders and reattached to support boards and placed into the holding case for transport to the laboratory. This procedure eliminates contamination from "foreign" insects that may otherwise be caught in the adhesive (if trap surfaces are not protected), and obviates the need to apply an adhesive to trap surfaces in the field.

To facilitate enumeration, measurement, and identification of captured insects, trap surfaces are best examined with a dissecting microscope without removing insects individually. If voucher specimens are to be saved, they may be removed individually from the trap surface with a forceps and rinsed with an appropriate solvent (Section 4.1.6).

Chapter 13

Analysis of Diets
of Plant-Visiting Bats

Donald W. Thomas

Département de Biologie
Université de Sherbrooke
Sherbrooke, Québec JIK 2R1
Canada

1. INTRODUCTION

Approximately 250 species of bats in the paleotropical family Pteropodidae and the neotropical family Phyllostomidae regularly visit plants for either fruit or floral resources. Frugivorous bats feed on the fleshy arils, pericarps, or syconia of fruits, often ingesting seeds along with this material. No species, however, is known to actively seek seeds as dietary (nutritional) items. Flower-visiting bats seek nectar and/or pollen, the former being an important source of energy (carbohydrate) and the latter supplying necessary protein (Howell, 1974). Few species are likely to be totally specialized on either fruits or flowers; however, for the sake of simplicity I will refer to plant-visiting bats as either frugivores or nectarivores. In addition, some fruit bats may occasionally ingest leaves or buds (Cunningham von Someren, 1972; Wickler and Seibt, 1976; T. H. Fleming, pers. comm.), but the dietary significance of these items is uncertain.

Studies of the diets of frugivorous and nectarivorous bats can focus on four major questions. What kind of resource does a particular bat species eat (fruit or flowers)? What species of fruits or flowers does it seek? What sizes, stages of ripeness, or parts does it select? What nutrients does it extract during gut passage? In this chapter I will deal exclusively with the first three questions; nutritional approaches are covered in Chapter 15.

Few, if any, techniques for the study of the diets of plant-visiting bats are specialized or technically involved, so in treating this subject I will also consider the biases that may be introduced by sampling with different methods, at different localities, or at different times. Because few published data address this aspect, I will draw on my own data collected during a two year study of the feeding ecology of a pteropodid community in Ivory Coast, West Africa (see Fenton and Thomas, 1984; Thomas, 1982, 1983, 1984a, 1984b; Thomas and Marshall, 1984).

2. DIET ANALYSIS FOR FRUGIVOROUS BATS

The foraging activities of frugivorous bats can be simply described as follows. At dusk a bat leaves its day roost and commutes to some feeding area where it locates a resource tree. From the available fruit crop it selects one fruit which it may eat in situ or which it may carry to a separate feeding roost. During feeding the bat may ingest all or only part of the fruit, leaving the remains as masticated rejecta pellets or uneaten parts below the feeding site. The bat then carries a gut load of fruit pulp and possibly seeds as it continues to forage or undertake other activities. It later voids this and subsequent gut loads during the night. The timing and hence location of defecation relative to feeding is determined by the transit time for material in the gut. At or before dawn the bat returns to its day roost with a final gut load of pulp and/or seeds which it voids beneath the roost during the day. These activities provide at least three convenient windows by which to view the diets of frugivorous bats: by means of feces collected from netted bats at night (net feces), by feces collected below day roosts, or by feces, rejecta pellets, or fruit parts left below feeding roosts.

2.1. Feces from Netted Bats

Bats captured in mist nets commonly defecate under the stress of handling, so feces can be readily collected from bats netted either at fruiting trees or at randomly selected netting sites. In savanna habitats in Ivory Coast, a mean of 23.3% of *Epomops buettikoferi* and *Micropteropus pusillus* (combined n=1224 captures) produced feces during the ca. five

minute handling period. Heithaus et al. (1975) found a similar proportion (19%) in their study of a Costa Rican bat community. The exact proportion of bats that defecate during handling no doubt depends upon the time bats remain in nets and their pre-capture foraging success, so this may vary among habitats and seasons. This proportion (19%-23.3%) compares favorably with the 17.6% of frugivorous phyllostomids that had stomach contents when sacrificed (Fleming et al., 1972) and indicates that killing is unnecessary except when fresh stomach material may be required. The number of fecal samples collected may be increased by placing plastic sheets under nets to collect feces produced before handling. If minimizing the handling time is not a consideration, bats may also be held for about one hour in cloth bags to permit passage of gut loads.

Feces obtained from netted frugivorous bats either contain seeds or consist solely of pulp. Because seeds are relatively easily separated from the pulp, generally have recognizable and distinctive features, can be germinated, and can be kept for long periods if dry-stored, they constitute the primary means of fecal identification. In Ivory Coast, 90.5% of 1825 samples collected from nine species of pteropodids *(Epomops buettikoferi, Eidolon helvum, Hypsignathus monstrosus, Rousettus angolensis, Micropteropus pusillus, Megaloglossus woermanni, Myonycteris torquata, Nanonycteris veldkampi,* and *Scotonycteris zenkeri)* contained seeds. This proportion, however, may be expected to vary both geographically and locally among habitats depending on plant reproductive strategies. Van der Pijl (1957) listed large seed size as one of the characteristics of chiropterophilous (bat dispersed) fruits. His conclusions were based primarily upon studies in Amazonian and Malaysian primary forest where large seed size results from the large energy reserves necessary to maximize seedling survival under the low light levels of closed canopy forest. Ng (1978) indicated that 75% of Malaysian forest trees have seeds over one cm in length. Frugivorous bats foraging in these areas and on these species would be expected to carry seed loads less frequently than bats foraging in successional communities where the mean seed size is smaller.

There are currently no "quick and dirty" means of identifying fecal seeds. I know of no comprehensive keys to the seeds of any tropical plant communities and such keys (if made) would be of only local value. Netolitzky (1926; cited in Corner, 1976) and Corner (1976) present data on seed characters and Corner includes a key to the seeds of dicotyledon families. However, these sources are of limited value since they rely on histological techniques and seeds can only be keyed to the family level. For this reason the identification of fecal seeds must usually be based upon a first hand knowledge of the plant communities where the bats forage. In my study in Ivory Coast, I relied upon weekly "fruit patrols" through samples of all the available habitats in order to gain some idea of which fruits were available and to collect seeds for a reference collection. Heithaus et al. (1975) relied on a similar inventory and reference collection in their study in Costa Rica. Such fruit patrols can be time consuming, and they rarely provide quantitative data on fruit abundance due to the extremely patchy nature of fruiting in space and time (methods of assessing resource availability are considered in Chapter 14). I spent approximately 15 h per week over 12 months on fruit searches before locating and identifying all the major fruits used by the local bat community. Seven species of fruits were never identified; however, none of these were found more than twice in feces and these seven were apparently rare species. The distribution of fruit patrols must necessarily be based upon some knowledge of the foraging movements of the bats in question. Some species may be relatively sedentary, such as *Micropteropus pusillus* in Ivory Coast where a mark-recapture study showed that it was confined to local patches of regenerating unburned savanna (Thomas, 1982), and fruit patrols may be similarly restricted. Other species may be more mobile. In Ivory Coast, *Myonycteris torquata*

relied primarily on *Solanum verbascifolium* (Solanaceae; 89.5% of fecal samples) and it was not until habitats 10 km distant from the netting sites were included that this fruit was identified. Central place foragers such as the colonial *Eidolon helvum* and *Pteropus poliocephalus* (Rosevear, 1965; Nelson, 1965) may commute much farther in a night, making fruit patrols even more difficult.

When fruit availability is assessed, a reference seed collection is made, and fecal seeds are "identified" by comparison with known species, the identification process is still not complete. The seeds of many large genera, such as *Ficus, Solanum,* or *Piper,* are sufficiently similar that final identification should be confirmed by germinating and growing a subsample.

Some feces do not contain seeds and these potentially pose a serious problem for identification. However, due to the relatively short transit time and "gentle" treatment of material in the guts of frugivorous bats, pulp is generally little modified in texture, color, or odor from the fruits themselves. Thus, fresh material can be compared with fresh pulp and so identified. By feeding suspected fruits to captive bats, palatability and fecal characteristics can be assessed. It is difficult to "prove" that a given fecal sample in fact represents a given fruit species; however, palatability to captive bats, similarity of fecal characteristics, and, if possible, observations of bats feeding in the wild should constitute adequate "proof."

In addition to fruit, a variety of other items may be included in the diets of frugivorous bats and so show up in fecal samples. For this reason fecal samples should also be examined at low and high magnification to search for insect parts, moth scales, pollen, and possibly leaf or bud fragments. Insect remains may be from three possible sources: 1) insects that were actively hunted, captured, and ingested, 2) insects that were accidentally ingested along with fruit pulp, and 3) parts rather than whole insects that were incidentally ingested. To date there has been little consideration of these three sources of insect remains in feces of plant-visiting bats, although from a nutritional perspective they may be dramatically different. Phyllostomids may regularly include whole, captured insects in the diet and these may represent a significant nutrient source. Fleming et al. (1972) showed that insects composed up to 25% of the stomach volume of the frugivorous phyllostomids *Artibeus jamaicensis* and *A. lituratus,* and Gardner (1977) provides a comprehensive review of other similar reports. Howell and Burch (1974) reported that insect remains were common in Costa Rican frugivorous bats and that "lepidopteran" parts (probably scales but not specified; see Thomas, 1984a) accounted for 79.7% of those samples with insects. The presence of moth scales does not necessarily indicate the active pursuit and capture of Lepidoptera by frugivorous bats. I found that although moth scales were common in the feces of *Epomops buettikoferi* in Ivory Coast, these could be accounted for statistically by the bats' feeding on fruits that had scales as a surface contaminant (Thomas, 1984a). Thus, scales are not evidence that *E. buettikoferi* (and 79.7% of phyllostomids?) pursues and captures moths so they may not be important dietary and nutritional items.

Similarly, insect exoskeleton fragments may be found in some bats' fig (*Ficus; Moraceae*) feces, but these do not necessarily represent active hunting. The insect parts most commonly found are of agaonid wasps and their hymenopteran parasites which may be ingested incidentally along with fig syconia. These have been proposed as a potentially important source of protein to frugivorous bats (Morrison, 1980); however, this does not appear to be justified. Ripe figs are generally wasp-free (by consuming fruits, frugivores must exert a strong selection against those wasps that remain in ripe syconia). In Ivory Coast I found that only 16% of ripe (orange or red) *Ficus capensis* fruits that I sampled (n=50) had any wasps and those that did had only a mean of 6.4 mg. At a protein level of 18% by fresh mass (Morton, 1973) these wasps could represent a maxi-

mum contribution of only 1.2 mg protein/infested fig and an entire night's foraging would supply only approximately 3% of a frugivorous bat's estimated daily protein requirement (Thomas, 1982, 1984b).

Feces that contain *Ficus* may also include pollen. Due to the unique retention of flower parts inside ripe syconia, pollen may remain and so be ingested incidentally. Such pollen occurs at low density in feces (unquantified pers. obs.) and is unlikely to make an important nutritional contribution.

While the presence of insect parts, moth scales, and *Ficus* pollen in feces does not necessarily indicate active search on the part of fruit bats for these items, neither does the absence of insect parts necessarily indicate a lack of insect hunting. Ayala and d'Alessandro (1973) reported that *Carollia perspicillata* and *Glossophaga soricina* rejected the hard exoskeleton when feeding on some insects and so had no recognizable hard parts in stomach (and presumably fecal) samples. Unfortunately, there appears to be no simple means of resolving these two confounding problems (the possible presence of insect parts without any nutritional input and the possible absence of insect parts despite active hunting and ingestion), and the inclusion of non-fruit or flower items in the diets must continually be questioned before being accepted or rejected.

2.2.   Feces Below Day Roosts

Bats may regularly return to day roosts with gut loads which they later void. This provides an alternate and sometimes more readily accessible source of feces. Feces may be collected from leaf surfaces or on screen, plastic, or paper sheets placed below the roost. How many samples are available, and when they should be collected depends on the roosting behavior of the bat species in question. Some foliage roosting species such as *E. buettikoferi* (a solitary species; Fenton and Thomas, 1984) and *Hypsignathus monstrosus* (roosting in small groups; Bradbury, 1977; Fenton and Thomas, 1984) may use the same roosts for long periods if undisturbed, yet abandon these sites immediately if disturbed (Fenton and Thomas, 1984). In such cases, roosts should be approached and the feces collected at night while the bats are foraging. Colonial species appear to be less sensitive to disturbance. Both *Eidolon helvum* and *Carollia perspicillata* are disturbed by activity below the roost but usually will not abandon the site if approached during the day. In these cases feces can be collected at more convenient times.

Feces collected from below day roosts can be treated and identified in the same fashion as net feces.

2.3. Rejected Pellets and Fruit Parts Below Feeding Roosts

The use of feeding roosts provides yet another means of assessing the diets of frugivorous bats. Although not all species use feeding roosts, those that do leave ample evidence of feeding in the form of rejecta pellets and uneaten fruit parts. These parts are generally easily identified since they include seeds and uneaten parts that are more readily matched with fruits collected in the field than are feces. Feeding roosts potentially provide a large amount of data for a given individual. For example, in Ivory Coast some *Epomops buettikoferi* used the same feeding roosts for up to 79 consecutive days, although individuals often used more than one roost on a given night (Thomas, 1982, 1984b). Sampling from such long-term roosts can provide valuable information on dietary shifts between seasons and inter-individual foraging differences.

Data collected from feeding roosts, however, are not entirely compatible with and additive to data based on net or roost feces (see below). Because bats treat each fruit differently, rejecting more of one species than of another, the use of fruit species cannot be scored on a "percent of total mass" or "percent of rejecta pellets" basis. Unless some means of identifying how many fruits of a given species were consumed and their rela-

tive contribution to the diet on a mass basis is devised, fruits can only be scored on a "presence/absence" basis. This will underestimate the contribution of large or important fruit species and overestimate the contribution of small or rarely used species.

2.4. Sampling Biases

Feces collected from netted bats, feces from below day roosts, and rejecta pellets and/or uneaten fruit parts at feeding roosts all provide information on the diets of frugivorous bats, but it is important to question whether these three sources provide equivalent results. It is unlikely that they do. The most easily evaluated is the difference between data sets based on net feces and rejecta pellets and/or uneaten fruit parts collected from below feeding roosts. During the period of 1 July to 31 October 1979 and 1980, I collected 145 net feces from free-ranging *E. buettikoferi* and also scored the presence or absence of different fruit species below 32 *E. buettikoferi* feeding roosts over a total of 366 roost days. Figure 1 shows the relative abundance of different fruit species in the two samples. Despite the larger sample size from roosts, they had only 37% as many species as net feces. Fruit from *Ficus capensis* was the most common item in each data set, yet was almost twice as common at feeding roosts as in net feces (83.6% at roosts vs 44.8% in net feces). The number two and three ranking species in terms of frequency of use differed between the two data sets (net feces: *Adenia cissampeloides* and *A. miegei* = 15.9%, *Vitex doniana* = 8.2%; feeding roosts: *Psidium guajava* = 8.4%, *Nauclea latifolia* = 4.0%. Clearly the two data sets are not equivalent; apparent dietary breadth and evenness are reduced at feeding roosts. The reasons for this are not entirely clear but are in part related to fruit size. The major difference between the two data sets is the under-representation of small (< 2 cm) fruits at feeding roosts, leaving the large fruits to dominate. Feeding roosts may well be used only for handling large fruits or ones that require relatively long handling

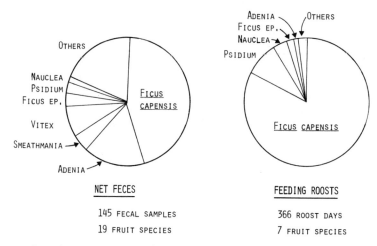

Figure 1. The proportion of *Ficus capensis, Adenia cissampeloides, A. miegei, Psidium guajava, Vitex doniana, Smeathmania pubescens, Nauclea latifolia,* and epiphytic *Ficus* species present in samples of net feces and fruit parts collected from below *Epomops buettikoferi* feeding roosts.

times. This means that feeding roosts will consistently sample only a subset of the total diet of frugivorous bats.

The relatively rapid transit time for food in the guts of fruit bats may also influence the accuracy of fecal samples relative to the true feeding performance of the bats. Both phyllostomid and pteropodid frugivores have transit times of 15-60 min (Fleming and Heithaus, 1981; Wolton et al., 1982), and fecal samples collected at either netting sites or day roosts may be representative of local foraging only. This bias would be most pronounced in samples collected at day roosts. Species such as *Eidolon helvum* may commute over 50 km from day roosts to feeding areas (Rosevear, 1965). If this represents approximately a one hour flight, then fecal samples collected below day roosts may be heavily biased towards the last meal of the night, possibly collected en route away from rather than at the primary feeding area. For other species which forage within minutes of the day roost (e.g., *Artibeus jamaicensis* and *Carollia perspicillata;* Morrison, 1978; Heithaus and Fleming, 1978) this bias may be insignificant.

Rapid food transit times may also affect the conclusions drawn from feces recovered from netted bats. Bats may preferentially forage in one habitat but for some reason (net position, visibility, etc.) they are captured most frequently in another. This would bias fecal samples towards fruit species only occasionally eaten in non-preferred habitats. This problem would be most pronounced in cases where capture and foraging habitats were separated by considerable distances and the bats did not "carry over" gut loads. Fleming and Heithaus (1981) showed that "foreign" feces were common around fruiting trees, creating a diverse seed rain in terms of species and suggesting high "carry over" during foraging. In Ivory Coast I caught *Hypsignathus monstrosus* almost exclusively in nets set at heights of one to four meters, yet fecal samples showed that fruit species associated with the forest canopy 20 m above this level constituted over 47% of the diet (Thomas, 1982). In this case, it appears that foraging areas and capture sites were sufficiently close to minimize the effects of transit times. Similarly, *Solanum verbascifolium* constituted 89.5% of the *Myonycteris torquata* fecal samples despite the fact that no plants were located closer than 10 km from the netting sites. Bats probably move fast enough that "carry over" is high and net feces provide the most accurate measure of the true diet of frugivorous bats.

2.5. Non-Random Fruit Selection

In the eyes of frugivores, not all fruits are equally attractive. Within and between fruit crops there is considerable variability in ripeness, hardness, size, composition, and other physical attributes, and frugivorous bats may select specific fruits on a non-random basis. For example, Bonaccorso (1978) showed that within the "canopy frugivore guild" at Barro Colorado Island, Panama Canal Zone, the mass of *Ficus insipida* fruits that *Artibeus jamaicensis, A. lituratus,* and *Vampyroides caraccioli* carried into nets was significantly correlated with body mass. August (1981) found that the number of bats captured at *Ficus* spp. trees in Venezuela was positively correlated with mean fruit size and negatively correlated with fruit hardness. Fleming et al. (1984) also showed that under captive conditions *Carollia perspicillata, C. subrufa,* and *Glossophaga soricina* selected the ripest fruits of *Muntingia calabura* from the range available. These studies indicate strong selectivity on the part of fruit bats for size (Bonaccorso, 1978; August, 1981), hardness (August, 1981), ripeness (Fleming et al., 1984), or nutritional quality (Fleming et al., 1984).

Non-random fruit selection may be tested by measuring the parameters of interest, marking fruits for individual identification, and monitoring the probabilities of removal in the field. This, however, leaves the identity of the frugivores unknown. Alternately, non-random selection can be tested, possibly in a more controllable fashion, either by presenting bats with fruit arrays in flight cage situations (e.g., Fleming et al., 1984) or by presenting arrays of fruits on display poles in the field (e.g., Fleming et al., 1977). These latter two experiments appear to be the only ones testing fruit selection to date; however, given the extreme importance of non-random selection to studies of fruit intake, nutrition, and foraging decisions, such studies should be stressed in the future.

Once selection of a given fruit has been made, a foraging bat handles the fruit, ingesting some parts and rejecting others. Rarely is the entire fruit consumed. Handling is an important consideration in detailed studies of feeding. The details of handling may be inferred by collecting fruit parts below feeding sites (fruiting trees or feeding roosts) and "reconstructing" fruits. This may be difficult to do if the size, ripeness, or other features of the original fruit are unknown. As with selection experiments, handling may readily be studied by presenting captive bats with known fruits and directly observing their feeding. I believe that such experimental approaches to feeding studies will yield useful results in the future.

3. DIET ANALYSIS FOR NECTARIVOROUS BATS

Foraging nectarivorous bats visit flowers for nectar and/or pollen. In feeding they may: 1) pierce the corolla to extract nectar without contacting the anthers, 2) extract nectar by entering the corolla and contacting the anthers, but without actually feeding on them, or 3) feed directly on pollen with or without ingesting nectar. During a night's foraging, nectarivorous bats may potentially exhibit all or some combination of these feeding modes at a number of different flower species before returning to the day roost. At the day roost bats may void pollen which they ingested directly from the anthers, and/or they may groom pollen from the fur and void this later.

Because nectar-feeding alone (e.g., case 1 above) is undetectable without killing the bats to examine the stomach contents (and nectar in the stomach has few features permitting species identification), pollen is generally used as a "tracer" indicating flower visitation. This limits the recognition of flower visits to cases where the bats contact the anthers (cases 2 and 3) and probably act as legitimate pollinators (e.g., Gould, 1978). Cases where the bats pierce the corolla (e.g.,

Micropteropus pusillus at *Spathodea campanulata;* Ayensu, 1974) would remain undetected.

Pollen used to indicate flower visits may be present either in the feces or on the fur and so may be sampled by collecting feces from netted bats, feces from below day roosts, or by collecting pollen from the fur of netted bats. Fecal samples, whether collected from netted bats or at day roosts, can be moistened, mounted directly on glass slides, dried, and covered for later microscopic examination. Samples of pollen can be collected from the body surfaces by snipping samples of fur from the desired body region, saving this in contamination-free pouches (stamp collectors' glassine envelopes work well), and later mounting the hair on slides for examination. Alternately, pollen can be removed from the hair by swabbing with an adhesive substance. Beattie (1971) published the recipe for a basic fuschin-stained gelatin useful in collecting and mounting pollen. This consists of 175 ml of distilled water, 150 ml of glycerine, 50 g of gelatin, and 5 g of crystalline phenol mixed together and warmed. Crystalline basic fuschin is then added until the desired density of stain is achieved (usually the color of claret, but it is advisable to experiment for the optimal stain density). The gelatin can be cut into small cubes which can be pressed to the bat's fur with forceps, placed on a slide under a coverslip, warmed over an alcohol lamp or cigarette lighter, and stored for later examination. This technique is particularly useful since it both stains and preserves the pollen in a permanent mount. Because small amounts of pollen may contaminate the samples, it is advisable to use some minimum number of pollen grains to indicate a flower visit. Heithaus et al. (1975) used three or more grains as this criterion.

As with seeds, there is no simple means of identifying the pollen of tropical plants from a given area. Although palynologists have developed keys permitting the identification of fossil and subfossil pollen to family and occasionally genus, these keys require considerable familiarity and are unlikely to be of much use to biologists requiring rapid field identification. Generalized searches for flowers in the habitats available to the bats, the construction of a reference collection, and the comparison of unknown samples with this collection will usually form the basis of the identification procedure.

Collecting samples of pollen and assessing the use of different flower species must be subject to several important considerations. Flowers with different morphologies and anther positions may deposit pollen on different body regions of bats. Howell (1977) described how the phyllostomid *Anoura geoffroyi* carried pure *Mucuna* pollen ventrally, *Crescentia* pollen dorsally, and *Inga* and an unidentified Bombacaceae pollen on the face and neck. There may be little or no carry over of pollen between body regions, so surface samples (swabs or hair samples) must be taken from all these sites and either pooled or treated separately.

Because different plant species may invest more or less in pollen production, the relative amounts of different pollen types (i.e., percent species *A* pollen in a sample) in surface samples or feces cannot be used to indicate relative use. Pollen must be scored on a "presence/absence" basis only. Data on the presence of pollen in fecal samples can be grouped with data on the frequency of different fruit types in fecal samples for a given bat species to indicate the relative importance of floral of fruit resources in its diet. However, data based on surface samples is not comparable with data on fecal samples. Pulp, seeds, and pollen will remain in bat guts for only 15-60 min (the transit time), while it is currently unknown how long pollen will remain on the fur. The latter duration is probably at least until the first post-feeding grooming which may be 12 h after feeding. The duration could be even longer if grooming is not 100% effective. Thus, surface pollen may be detectable for longer than gut loads of pollen or fruit, and this would result in a consistent overestimate of flower use if surface samples were compared with feces.

The timing of nectar secretion and hence

flower visitation may also affect sampling. Bat pollinated flowers open and commence nectar secretion at night, but not all species behave in similar ways. In Central America, *Inga marginata* secretes nectar and attracts bats approximately six to eight hours earlier in the night than *Bauhinia ungulata* (Howell, 1977). Fecal samples collected from bats late at night or at the day roosts would be unlikely to contain *Inga* pollen and these samples would be strongly biased toward *Bauhinia.* In general, data sets based on roost feces (e.g., Start and Marshall, 1976) may be strongly biased towards flower species with late night peaks in nectar secretion and so they may show lower diet breadth than surface samples. Due to the longer retention time of pollen on the fur, surface samples would not be expected to be as subject to this bias. Howell (1977), however, showed that the abundance of *Inga* pollen on the fur of *Glossophaga soricina* declined rapidly after peak nectar production, which suggests that the bats groom repeatedly during the night and thus reduce the pollen retention time.

4. SUMMARY AND CONCLUSIONS

In this chapter I have tried to present a general overview of methods used to examine the diets of plant-visiting bats. For frugivores and nectarivores, feces collected from netted bats, feces collected from day roosts, fruit parts found below feeding roosts, and swabs taken from facial, ventral, or dorsal fur may all yield information on fruit or flower species included in the bats' diets. I have stressed, however, that not all data sets provide equivalent and accurate views of the diets and that not all data sets can be combined or compared directly. In any given study a researcher must be clearly aware of the biases that may be introduced by using different sampling methods and so must design the data collection and experiments so as to strive towards the most accurate portrayal of the bats' "real" diets.

5. ACKNOWLEDGMENTS

T. H. Kunz showed extreme patience. T. H. Fleming, F. Bonaccorso, M. B. Fenton, A. G. Marshall, and P. A. Racey provided stimulating discussions and the comments of two anonymous reviewers brought this chapter to ripeness. This work was funded by NSERC postgraduate and post-doctoral fellowships and by a National Geographic Society grant 2220-80.

6. REFERENCES

August, P. V. 1981. Fig fruit consumption and seed dispersal by *Artibeus jamaicensis* in the llanos of Venezuela. Reprod. Bot., Supplement to Biotropica, 13:70-76.

Ayala, S. C., and A. d'Alessandro. 1973. Insect feeding behavior of some Columbian fruit-eating bats. J. Mammal., 54:266-267.

Ayensu, E. S. 1974. Plant and bat interactions in West Africa. Ann. Mo. Bot. Garden, 61:702-727.

Beattie, A. J. 1971. A technique for the study of insect-borne pollen. Pan-Pac. Entomol., 47:82.

Bonaccorso, F. J. 1978. Foraging and reproductive ecology in a Panamanian bat community. Bull. Florida State Mus., Biol. Sci., 24:359-408.

Bradbury, J. W. 1977. Lek mating behavior of the hammer-headed bat. Z. Tierpsychol., 45:225-255.

Corner, E. J. H. 1976. The seeds of dicotyledons. Vol. 1 and 2. Cambridge Univ. Press, Cambridge, 311 pp. and 552 pp.

Cunningham van Someran, R. 1972. Some fruit bats eat leaves. Bull. E. Afr. Nat. Hist. Soc., 1972:24-25.

Fenton, M. B., and D. W. Thomas. 1985. Migrations and dispersal of bats. Pp. 409-424, *in* Migration: Mechanisms and adaptive significance. (M. A. Rankin, ed.). Univ. Texas Marine Sci. Inst., Contr. Marine Science. Suppl., Vol. 27.

Fleming, T. H., E. T. Hooper, and D. E. Wilson. 1972. Three Central American bat communities: Structure, reproductive cycles and movement patterns. Ecology, 53:555-569.

Fleming, T. H., E. R. Heithaus, and W. B. Sawyer. 1977. An experimental analysis of the food location behavior of frugivorous bats. Ecology, 58:619-627.

Fleming, T. H., and E. R. Heithaus. 1981. Frugivorous bats, seed shadows and the structure of tropical forests. Reprod. Bot., Supplement to Biotropica, 13:45-53.

Fleming, T. H., C. F. Williams, F. J. Bonaccorso, and L. H. Herbst. 1985. Phenology, seed dispersal, and colonization in *Muntingia calabura,* a neotropical pioneer tree. Amer. J. Bot. 72:383-391.

Gardner, A. L. 1977. Feeding habits. Pp. 293-350, *in* Biology of Bats of the New World Family Phyllostomatidae. Vol. 2. (R. J. Baker, J. K. Jones, Jr., and D. C. Carter, eds.). Spec. Publ. Mus. Texas Tech. Univ., Lubbock. 364 pp.

Gould, E. 1978. Foraging behavior of Malaysian nectar-feeding bats. Biotropica, 10:184-193.

Heithaus, E. R., T. H. Fleming, and P. A. Opler. 1975. Foraging patterns and resource utilization in seven species of bats in a seasonal tropical forest. Ecology, 56:841-854.

Heithaus, E. R., and T. H. Fleming. 1978. Foraging movements of a frugivorous bat, *Carollia perspicillata* (Phyllostomatidae). Ecol. Monogr., 48:127-143.

Howell, D. J. 1974. Bats and pollen: Physiological aspects of the syndrome of chiropterophily. Comp. Biochem. Physiol., 48A:263-276.

Howell, D. J. 1977. Time sharing and body partitioning in bat-plant pollination systems. Nature, 270:509-510.

Howell, D. J., and D. Burch. 1974. Food habits of some Costa Rican bats. Rev. Biol. Trop., 21:281-294.

Morrison, D. W. 1978. Foraging ecology and energetics of the frugivorous bat, *Artibeus jamaicensis.* Ecology, 59:716-723.

Morrison, D. W. 1980. Efficiency of food utilization by fruit bats. Oecologia, 45:281-294.

Morton, E. S. 1973. On the evolutionary advantages and disadvantages of fruit-eating in tropical birds. Amer. Nat., 107:8-22.

Nelson, J. E. 1965. Movements of Australian flying foxes (Pteropodidae: Megachiroptera). Aust. J. Zool., 13:53-73.

Ng, F. S. P. 1978. Strategies of establishment in Malayan forest trees. Pp. 129-162, *in* Tropical trees as living systems. (P. B. Tomlinson and M. H. Zimmerman, eds.). Cambridge Univ. Press, Cambridge. 675 pp.

Rosevear, D. R. 1965. The bats of West Africa. Trustees Brit. Mus. Nat. Hist., London, 418 pp.

Start, A. N., and A. G. Marshall. 1976. Nectarivorous bats as pollinators of trees in West Malaysia. Pp. 141-150, *in* Tropical Trees: Variation, breeding and conservation. (J. Burley and B. T. Styles, eds.). Linn. Soc. Symp. Ser. 2:243 pp.

Thomas, D. W. 1982. The ecology of an African savanna fruit bat community: Resource partitioning and role in seed dispersal. Unpubl. Ph.D. Dissertation, Univ. of Aberdeen, Aberdeen, Scotland, 206 pp.

Thomas, D. W. 1983. The annual migrations of three species of West African fruit bats (Chiroptera: Pteropodidae). Can. J. Zool., 61:2266-2272.

Thomas, D. W. 1984a. Moth scales in fruit bat feces: Evidence of insectivory or fruit contamination? J. Mammal., 65:484-485.

Thomas, D. W. 1984b. Fruit intake and energy budgets of frugivorous bats. Physiol. Zool., 57:457-467.

Thomas, D. W., and A. G. Marshall. 1984. Reproduction and growth in three species of West African fruit bats. J. Zool., 202:265-281.

Van der Pijl, L. 1957. The dispersal of plants by bats. Acta Bot. Neerl., 6:291-315.

Wickler, W., and U. Seibt. 1976. Field studies of the African fruit bats, *Epomophorus wahlbergi* (Sundevall), with special reference to male calling. Z. Tierpsychol., 40:345-376.

Wolton, R. J., P. A. Arak, H. C. J. Godfray, and R. P. Wilson. 1982. Ecological and behavioural studies of the Megachiroptera of Mount Nimba, with notes on the Microchiroptera. Mammalia, 46:419-448.

Chapter 14

Methods of Estimating Fruit Availability to Frugivorous Bats

Edward R. Stashko[1]

Department of Biology
Boston University
Boston, Massachusetts 02215 USA

and

Eric Dinerstein

Smithsonian/Nepal Terai Ecology Project
Washington, D.C. 20008 USA

1. INTRODUCTION

Fruits differ fundamentally from other food items consumed by small vertebrates in that they are meant to be discovered and eaten (Snow, 1971). Ripe fruits are often conspicuously colored, strong smelling, and clustered at the tips of branches (Howe and Smallwood, 1982). Selection for advertisement rather than concealment suggests that flying vertebrates (bats and birds) should be able to assess local fruit availability quickly and efficiently. The purpose of this chapter is to review the accuracy of field techniques employed by biologists to assess fruit production in diverse tropical forests.

This chapter is written for the individual who is unfamiliar with tropical forest ecology and has little or no knowledge of fruit-bat biology. Our aim is to alert biologists to the limited literature existing on fruit sampling techniques for bats and the biases and potential advantages of such approaches. We stress the need to move beyond descriptive studies and offer a statistical technique for estimating sample variances in fruit production. Finally, we outline the significant commitments in field time which must be devoted to sampling fruits even to answer rather basic questions regarding fruit-bat ecology. As will be observed, any question involving the ecology of fruit bats may require as much time sampling the fruit resource base as the bat fauna itself.

2. BRIEF SYNOPSIS OF FRUIT SAMPLING STUDIES

Until two decades ago, little information existed detailing the extent of the interaction between bats and fruiting plants. Attempts to

[1]Present Address: Brookline Conservation Commission, Town Hall, Brookline, Massachusetts 02146 USA

measure fruit availability for bats were thwarted by ignorance of which fruits to sample. A coherent approach to identifying fruit resources exploited by bats was introduced by van der Pijl (1972) and Vogel (1968, 1969). These authors called attention to a consistent set of morphological traits displayed by fruiting plants whose propagules were ingested by bats. Such traits were popularized into a conceptual framework that became known as "the bat-fruit syndrome." Briefly, fruits adapted for bat dispersal were odiferous, dull-colored, presented at the tips of branches, and ripened during the late afternoon—features which appeared to be designed for dispersal by nocturnal, flying animals that are color-blind and possess a keen sense of smell. Vogel (1968, 1969) provided a list of Neotropical plants that exhibited such characteristics.

The first ecological studies of fruit-eating bats were conducted by Goodwin and Greenhall (1961) in Trinidad. These pioneering studies and others like them emphasized the basic natural history of fruit bats, including partial descriptions of diets (Goodwin, 1970), but they included little or no data on the availability of fruit.

The first attempts to study fruiting activity came directly in the form of plant phenology studies (e.g., McClure, 1966; Medway, 1972; Frankie et al., 1974; Opler et al., 1980). Although these studies were purely descriptive in nature, they provided some indication of the timing of fruit ripening. Particularly influential was the study of Frankie et al. (1974) describing phenology from two forest sites in Costa Rica over a three year period. This study differed from other surveys of phenology by spanning a three year period rather than being a one year sample, although the sampling suffered from having only one or two replicates per species to document changes in fruiting activity. Surveys of phenology by McClure (1966), Medway (1972), and Putz (1979) in Malaysian forests also provided some anecdotal information on potential dispersal agents, including bats. Other phenological data describing fruiting

activity by animal-dispersed plants in the tropics and subtropics can be found in Daubenmire (1972), Howe and van de Kerckhove (1979), Hilty (1980), Milton et al. (1982), and Foster (1982a). Although variable in scope and content, these studies include phenological data on a few species which may be visited by bats.

Heithaus et al. (1975) were the first to report on the fruiting and flowering phenology of plants visited specifically by bats in a tropical dry forest of Costa Rica. Bonaccorso (1979) gave a similar description of bat-visited plants on Barro Colorado Island, Panama. Both of these studies present data from one year of observations.

The first attempt to measure fruit production quantitatively involved the use of seed traps on Barro Colorado Island, Panama (Smythe, 1970; Foster, 1973). This technique involved placing a series of plastic tubs in the forest to catch seeds falling from the canopy. Smythe estimated fruit production by converting the amount of seeds in the tubs to grams of fruit produced/hectare/month. Although this approach purported to be a community-wide study, the sampling technique excluded a number of fruiting species found on the island. Foster (1982a) duplicated Smythe's approach but concentrated more on fruiting patterns among species rather than deriving actual estimates of fruit production.

Two other methods of estimating fruit abundance involved direct counts of ripe fruits produced in study plots over discrete intervals. In one study, plants visited by bats for fruits were mapped within seven one hectare grids (Stashko, 1982). Estimates of fruit availability for bats (in terms of mean number of fruits/night/hectare) were obtained by counting ripe fruits on plants within one of the grids in the late afternoon.

A second approach involved estimating fruit production by counting the number of ripe fruits produced per unit time per unit area along belt transects (Dinerstein, 1985). Monthly fruit production for all bat-visited species was represented as the product of the means of several random variables, namely mean wet mass of fruits, mean crop size/month/resource plant, and mean density of reproductive individuals of a given species. Fruiting plants to be sampled were determined by fecal material obtained from bats caught in mist nets and from others subjected to cafeteria trials. Worthington (1982) estimated fruit availability for manakins on Barro Colorado Island, Panama, using a similar technique.

Several studies have estimated fruit production for only one or a few species of fruiting plants (e.g., Janzen et al., 1976; McDiarmid et al., 1977; Howe and DeSteven, 1979; Howe, 1981). These rely on techniques similar to those used in the transect sampling and mapping studies. Thus, within two decades, studies in which fruit availability has been examined have advanced from lists of species and descriptive phenologies to attempts at quantitative estimates of fruit production.

3. CONCEPTUAL AND PROCEDURAL PROBLEMS

Some of the previous studies, while making valuable contributions, suffer from some basic conceptual and statistical weaknesses. These range from misleading assumptions about the generality of the bat-fruit syndrome to estimates of fruit abundance with no consideration of sample variances. Efforts to increase the accuracy of current techniques must address these problems. We suggest possible solutions to some of these obstacles in the following sections.

3.1. What is a "Bat Fruit"?

The identification of consistent fruit characteristics among animal-dispersed plants has been of considerable heuristic value (Fagri and van der Pijl, 1973). We observe in nature that fruits appear to be designed for dispersal by a specific group of agents such as bats (van der Pijl, 1972), birds (van der Pijl, 1972; McKey, 1975; Snow, 1981), monkeys (Janson, 1983), ants (Horwitz, 1980), and large terrestrial mammals (Janzen, 1981).

Food habit data, however, suggest that strict adherence to assumptions about dispersal modes based solely upon these characteristics can be misleading (Heithaus, 1982). Specifically, preconceived notions of the morphology of a "bat fruit" would lead one to overlook species important in the diets of frugivorous bats.

One example of a fruit inconsistent with the bat-fruit syndrome is the mimosaceous shrub *Acacia cornigera*. Found in the tropical dry forests of Costa Rica, its fruit is an important part of the diet of *Carollia perspicillata* during the dry season, a period of low fruit abundance for frugivores (Stashko, 1982). *Carollia* is an important disperser of the seeds of this tree, yet the showy, bright-yellow pulp of its fruit contrasted against its brown dehiscent pod are characteristics normally associated with bird-disseminated plants.

Other examples of uncharacteristic "bat fruits" include *Allophylus occidentalis* (Sapindaceae) and *Muntingia calabura* (Elaeocarpaceae), two common trees of tropical dry forests which produce small, bright-red fruits. Both of these species figure prominently in the diets of fruit bats (Stashko, 1982). In Monteverde, a premontane cloud forest of Costa Rica, Dinerstein (1985) observed that *Artibeus toltecus* consumed both a bright blue melastome *(Conostegia bernaulliana),* which is dispersed by birds as well as bats, and a bright red fig *(Ficus tuerckheimii),* which is also eaten by birds, white-faced monkeys *(Cebus capuchin),* and kinkajous *(Potos flavus).* In another tropical premontane forest, Howell and Burch (1974) reported that *Acnistus arborescens* (Solanaceae) was a common item in the diets of fruit eating bats. This pasture tree produces large displays of small orange berries and is visited by at least 40 species of fruit-eating birds. Its berries are also relished by captive *Sturnira ludovici* and *C. perspicillata.* These examples of the fruits eaten by bats show that the bat-fruit syndrome is not always valid.

Alternatively, fruits that might seem attractive to bats, based upon fruit morphology, may be ignored by them. Fruit bats avoid the many species of the Lauraceae in Monteverde, even though these large, lipid-rich fruits are aromatic and dark colored, which would ordinarily categorize them as "bat fruit" (Dinerstein, 1985). Finally, many species that figure prominently in bat diets in Monteverde are also seasonally important for frugivorous birds, even though these fruits are dull-colored and strong smelling. We believe that additional data on food habits of frugivores will show considerable overlap in the diets of birds, bats, and other frugivorous mammals.

These observations suggest two major problems: 1) frugivores are opportunistic feeders, therefore, biologists should not dismiss any fleshy fruits as potential food items for bats without specific evidence from bats' diets; 2) there are few instances of fruiting plants that are disseminated exclusively by bats. Approaches to account for these problems are discussed below.

How does one decide on what fruiting species to measure? Some ideas of potential food items can be gleaned from published accounts of bat diets (e.g., Howell and Burch, 1974; Heithaus et al., 1975; Gardner, 1977; Bonaccorso, 1979; Thomas, 1982; Stashko, 1982; Dinerstein, 1985). In many cases genera rather than species of bat-visited plants will overlap between sites. Those species which belong to bat-dispersed genera should be noted and included in initial phenological surveys.

Once in the field, the best method for determining bat diets, and ultimately what fruits to sample, is through direct capture of the bats (see Chapter 1). At the time of capture, bats can be encouraged to pass seeds by gentle palpation of the abdomen. Fecal samples obtained from captured fruit bats should be placed immediately in individual glassine envelopes (see Chapter 13). Time and loca-

tion of capture, species, band number (if applicable), sex, and age should also be noted. Early in the study it would be useful to assemble a reference collection for seeds from all of the fleshy-fruited species in the study area, regardless of fruit color, odor, etc. We recommend that one reference set be stored in alcohol, and one collection be kept dry.

Fruit bats also eat species of fruit that contain seeds too large to swallow, and some species avoid swallowing even small seeds. One method of determining the incidence of such fruits in the diet is through cafeteria trials, in which a variety of potential food species are presented to captive bats. Fruit tissues egested or rejected by captive bats can be compared with pulp egested by free-flying individuals. In addition, olfactory cues that attract bats to fruits can also be used by investigators to identify pulp fragments. Dinerstein (1985) was able to distinguish the presence of *Eugenia acapulcensis* (a member of the eucalypt family) in the feces of bats by its characteristic odor. The same was true for aromatic fruits where bats passed seeds in feces. Bats in Monteverde consumed at least 13 species of fruit in the genus *Piper,* nearly all of which could be distinguished in the feces by either seed characteristics or aroma.

Another method for determining the fruiting plants to be sampled is to examine fecal samples deposited under day roosts (Vasquez-Yanes et al., 1975). The placement of a plastic sheet under the day roost facilitates the collection of fecal material while minimizing disturbance to the bats. Thus, a study design that incorporates direct capture, cafeteria trials, and/or the monitoring of day roosts should provide an idea of the range of species needed to be included in the sampling program.

The second problem, namely how to measure the availability of "bat fruits" when few such fruits are eaten exclusively by bats poses a host of problems for studies on foraging, reproductive patterns, and community organization. This problem is discussed in Section 3.4.

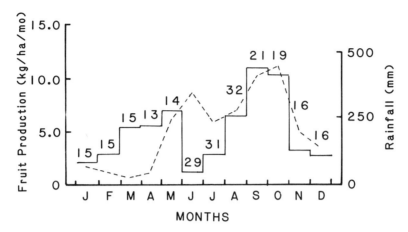

Figure 1. Monthly fruit production and rainfall in study area at Monteverde, Costa Rica. Number above each bar graph refers to the number of species fruiting per month (after Dinerstein, 1983).

3.2.   Fruiting Phenology and Fruit Production

Phenological studies have been popular for assessing resource availability to animals (Foster, 1982a). This popularity can be explained by the ease with which one can document fruiting activity using a rapid survey technique. A major assumption of phenology studies is that temporal changes in fruiting diversity are a good predictor of fruit production. However, the few studies that have actually tested the strength of this relationship have produced contradictory results. In Monteverde, a bimodal pattern of fruit production by bat-visited species was observed (Dinerstein, 1985) (Fig. 1). The first peak was in the mid to late dry season (March-May) when fruiting diversity fell to an annual low. The second peak came in the late wet season (September-October) when fruiting diversity reached intermediate levels. In contrast, fruit production estimates were relatively low between June and August, the period when the number of species fruiting/month reached an annual peak.

Studies from two other sites, a dry tropical forest in Costa Rica (Stashko, 1982) and the moist tropical forest of Barro Colorado Island, Panama (Bonaccorso, 1979), also reported bimodal patterns of fruit production with no correlation between peak fruit production and fruiting diversity. These studies indicate that results obtained from simple descriptions of phenology are probably not reliable as indirect estimates of fruit production.

3.3.   Seed Traps

Seed traps offer the potential of yielding quantitative data on fruit abundance. Methods for establishing seed traps are summarized in Foster (1982a). Basically, a series of plots is randomly located for intense study. Scattered randomly within each plot is a specific number of green polyethylene tubs. Nylon mesh is placed on the bottom of each tub to keep seeds from washing out of drain holes poked through the bottom of each. Tub contents are checked once a week and stored for later analysis. Seeds collected in this fashion have been used to assess both phenological patterns and fruit production. Data collected by Smythe (1970) were quoted by Fleming et al. (1972), Bonaccorso (1979), and Humphrey and Bonnacorso (1979) to advance arguments about the timing of reproductive activity in Neotropical fruit bats and the organization of fruit bat communities.

We have identified many problems with this technique. First, unless traps are checked and emptied daily, it is impossible to avoid loss of seeds to predators. To minimize fruit and seed removal by insects, birds, and mammals, traps must be raised high enough above the ground level to limit their access. This also reduces the probability of such traps capturing the seeds of low shrubs, which also commonly appear in the diets of bats (Dinerstein, 1985; Stashko, 1982). Second, the placement of such traps could bias the results if a disproportionate number were placed under canopy species with spreading crowns that produce large fruit crops. Third, bats eat fruits that contain numerous minute (less than 2 mm long) seeds that might easily be overlooked or lost. Fourth, the heterogeneity of tropical forests and the need for small portable traps implies that variance in seed fall between traps will be extremely high. This could be offset with a large number of samples to reduce the sample variance but would add to the time required to monitor seed rain. Fifth, there appears to be no systematic method for determining the number of traps required to obtain a suitable sample. Sixth, the construction, maintenance, and daily monitoring of a large number of traps implies a heavy investment of research time for several individuals. Unless all field crew members are adept at identifying species of fruits collected in the traps from the seeds present, one person would be completely preoccupied with this part of the project. Seventh, fruits that are carried away by highly mobile frugivores will not appear in the traps. Unless one counts the feces of the animals that eat such fruits, the probability of measuring fruiting plants that are less favored by frugivores would increase. Finally, using the number of seeds/species present to calculate the grams of fruit/species present is likely to introduce large errors. One would also need data to estimate the variance of mean seed number/gram of fruit/species (a time-consuming endeavor for fruits in the genera *Piper, Cecropia,* and *Ficus*). To sum-

marize, the seed trap technique appears to have many potential biases and requires a substantial, and constant time investment.

3.4. Mapping Studies

A detailed mapping study requires a very high initial investment of time on the part of the researcher to establish a grid system. One of the most intensive mapping studies to include ecological considerations was that of Hubbell (1979) in a Costa Rican dry forest. A total of 135 species of trees, shrubs, and vines were mapped in a 13 hectare plot subdivided into 20 m squares. To subsequently map the location of individual plants within the grid system requires a good knowledge of the bats' diet and of the distinguishing characteristics of the plant species (Fleming et al., 1977). Once the plants have been mapped, the sampling interval for estimating fruit production will depend on the questions being asked. Because of the short ripening times of some species, a bimonthly census of fruit crops is often the minimally acceptable interval. In one study of foraging behavior, nightly estimates of fruit production were made during the late afternoon before the grid was sampled for bat activity by mist-netting (Stashko, 1982).

One difficulty encountered by anyone attempting to estimate the availability of fruits for bats is that no fruit species is known to be exclusively bat-dispersed (Fleming, 1979). By censusing fruit crops in the late afternoon, one can minimize the problem of dealing with diurnal frugivores. There is no way to avoid problems with other nocturnal frugivores short of doing time-consuming night-vision scope observations. This could only be reasonably done for a few key plant species.

Another problem with estimating fruit availability for bats is the difficulty in determining the ripeness of fruits. For example, the ripeness of fruits of the common tropical tree, *Cecropia peltata,* is very difficult to determine unless the fruits are in hand. It is important to note that observations of other animals such as birds and monkeys eating fruits are poor indicators of the acceptability of fruits to bats. Feeding experiments have shown that bats are very selective and will only eat ripe fruits, while other animals are often much less selective (Stashko, 1982). One way to assess ripeness is to test a fruit's hardness by measuring the pressure required to rupture the fruit (August, 1981). Unless fruit production occurs over a very long period, it is often possible to gain a rough estimate of the total fruit crop of a plant by making one count just prior to the beginning of ripening.

Several studies have included marking individual fruits on mapped plants and monitoring their removal by bats (Fleming et al., 1977; Fleming, 1981; Stashko, 1982). These studies have provided information concerning the inclusion of particular species in the diets of bats in these areas. Because of the time required by investigators to locate and tag individual fruits, such studies are possible for a few key species but not on a community wide basis.

3.5. Fruit Production Transects

Dinerstein (1985) employed a similar approach to estimate fruit availability for bats in tropical premontane forests. In this procedure, bat-dispersed plants within belt transects of an intensive study area were marked for sampling. The actual length of the 2-3 m wide transects can be determined by species-area curves. To obtain an estimate of grams of fruit for species x/hectare/year (x/ha/yr), it is first necessary to calculate the mean wet mass of the fruit. This number is then multiplied by the mean size of the fruit crop/individual plant of species x/yr. The product of these means is then multiplied by the density of reproductive individuals of species x (obtained from sampling along belt transects) to derive grams of species x/ha/yr. An estimate of grams/ha/month (g/ha/mon) for a given species was calculated by first apportioning the level of fruiting intensity (i.e., the percent of the total fruit crop for species x ripening during month y times the total

fruit crop) to each month of fruiting. The following formula provided an estimate of g/ha/mon: (grams of mean wet mass of ripe fruit of species x) (% of total fruit crop ripening for month y) (density of reproductive individuals /ha) = g/ha/mon. The combined estimate of monthly fruit availability in the study area is the sum of production estimates for all species available to bats in a given month.

Both mapping studies and fruit production transects pose similar methodological problems involving the direct counting of fruits. For bat-dispersed shrubs, counting ripe fruits rarely presents major sampling problems. Fruit crops are generally small and fruits are within easy reach, so determining the state of ripeness is simple. For tree species, acquiring reasonably accurate estimates is considerably more difficult. Some tropical strangling figs produce more than 50,000 fruits/tree/yr (Morrison, 1978). Estimating fruit production often involves determining, with the aid of binoculars, the mean number of fruits/major branch and then multiplying this figure by the number of major branches/tree (August, 1981). Use of tree climbing equipment may provide better estimates, but this method involves considerable time and effort.

3.6. Spatial and Temporal Variation in Fruit Production

Sampling fruit resources in tropical forests is made particularly complex by their high spatial heterogeneity. This is a particular problem on tropical mountains where vegetation gradients tend to shift rapidly with small differences in elevation (Dinerstein, 1985). It is also a problem in dry tropical forests where riparian areas may contain vastly different species than the surrounding drier forest (Stashko, 1982). In both sites the effects of habitat disturbance by humans through clearing, burning, and other activities contributes to overall habitat patchiness. In some areas bordering human settlements, banana and guava patches also serve as food resources for bats and need to be considered in sampling.

In Monteverde, *Carollia brevicauda* feeds mostly on wild fruits but resorts to eating bananas at the end of the rainy season (Dinerstein, 1985). Nevertheless, problems related to habitat patchiness can be overcome to some degree by increasing the sampling effort.

Temporal variation in fruit production looms as a more perplexing problem. Annual variation in fruit production can have a dramatic impact on resident frugivores (Foster, 1977). In a paper entitled "Famine on Barro Colorado Island," Foster (1982b) describes the effects of a fruit crop failure during the late wet season. Fruiting patterns can be drastically altered by delayed onset of rains, short wet seasons, and perhaps most severely by excessive rains out of season. For tropical fruiting trees this is a particularly important problem in that some species fruit every other year (Janzen et al., 1976) or are asynchronous fruiters (e.g., figs) (Foster, 1982a). Annual variation in actual fruit size may also be an important variable to consider, one which has not yet been addressed. Most field studies seldom extend beyond two years, and often fruiting phenology or production is measured intensively for only one year. In community ecology studies, results and conclusions based upon short-term data can be extremely misleading. Thus, we suggest that biologists interested in community-wide phenomena should consider measuring fruit production over a period of several years.

3.7. Statistical Problems

In most studies in which an attempt is made to estimate fruit crop production, sample variances are not considered (but see Worthington, 1982). Estimates of fruit abundance are the result of the product of several random variables (e.g., mean wet mass times percent total fruit crop ripening for a given month times density of reproductive plants/hectare). Since each term includes some variance, the total sample variance for the product of these variables will usually be large. As

pointed out by Travis (1982), biases in estimation will be carried throughout the calculations and can result in very large errors. The need to establish confidence intervals, therefore, is critical to formulate reliable estimates of fruit abundance. The formulas for computing the variance of the product of two or more independent variables and the process for summing these variances as described by Goodman (1962) and Travis (1982) follow.

For the product of the means of two independent random variables X_1 and X_2, (e. g., mean wet mass times mean fruit crop size), an unbiased estimator of the variance is:

$$\text{Vâr}\,(\bar{x}_i \cdot \bar{x}_2) = \frac{s_1^2}{n_1} \cdot \bar{x}_2^2 + \frac{s_2^2}{n_2} \cdot \bar{x}_1^2 + \frac{s_1^2 s_2^2}{n_1 n_2} \quad (1)$$

where s_1 is the estimated variance of X_1, and s_2 that of X_2, and n_1, n_2 are the sample sizes of X_1 and X_2.

For the product of the means of three random variables that are independent,

$$z = \bar{x}_1 \cdot \bar{x}_2 \cdot \bar{x}_3 \quad (2)$$

(e.g., mean wet mass times mean fruit crop size times mean number plants/hectare) the product variance is:

$$V\left(\prod_{i=1}^{3} x_1\right) = E\left\{\sum_{i=1}^{3} x_i^2\right\} - \prod_{i=1}^{3}\left\{E\,(x_i)\right\}^2 \quad (3)$$

$$= \prod_{i=1}^{3}\left(\text{var}\,(x_i) + (E\,x_i)^2\right)$$

$$- \prod_{i=1}^{3}\left(E\,(x_i)\right)^2$$

where E denotes the expectation operator.

If a sample of n observations $(x_{i1}, x_{i2}, \ldots, x_{in})$ is drawn from a population having mean $\bar{x}_i$ and variance v_i, $(i = 1,2,3)$, let $\bar{x}_i$ and v_i be sample mean and sample variance computed from the sample of n_i observations. Then $E\,(\bar{x}_i) = X_i$ and $E\,(v_i) = V_i$.

An unbiased estimator of $V\left(\prod_{i=1}^{3} x_i\right)$ is:

$$V\prod_{i=1}^{3} = \prod_{i=1}^{3}\left(v_i + (\bar{x}_i^2 - \frac{v_i}{n_i})\right) \quad (4)$$

$$- \prod_{i=1}^{3}\left(x_i^2 - \frac{v_i}{n_i}\right), \text{ and}$$

$$V \prod_{i=1}^{3} x_i = \left[(v_1 + \bar{x}_1^2 - \frac{v_1}{n_1})(v_2 + \bar{x}_2^2 - \frac{v_2}{n_2}) \right. \quad (5)$$

$$(v_3 + \bar{x}_3^2 - \frac{v_3}{n_3}) \Big]$$

$$- \left[(\bar{x}_1^2 - \frac{v_1}{n_1})(\bar{x}_2^2 - \frac{v_2}{n_2})(\bar{x}_3^2 - \frac{v_3}{n_3}) \right]$$

It should be noted that not all fruit crop sizes have normal distributions. For these calculations, it is not necessary that x_1, x_2, and x_3 be normally distributed but they must have the same distribution.

The variances for fruit production for all bat-visited plant species in an area over a given unit of time may be summed as long as the time scale is the same for all species (e.g., nightly, monthly, or annually). For example, if

$$B = Z_1 + Z_2 + ... + Z_k, \quad (6)$$

where B = fruit production of all species and z_1 = monthly production of fruit species z_1, z_2 = monthly production of fruit species z_2, zk = monthly production of fruit species z_k; then the variance of total fruit production in a given area may be summed.

$$\text{Var } B = \sum_{i=1}^{k} \text{Var } Z_i \quad (7)$$

Finally, an unbiased estimator of the variance of the product of the means of three random variables which are not independent is given by:

$$V(\prod_{i=1}^{3} x_i) = \prod_{i=1}^{3} (E(x_i))^2 \left\{ E\left\{ \prod_{i=1}^{3} (S_i + 1)^2 \right\} \right. \quad (8)$$

$$\left. - \frac{E\left\{ \prod_{i=1}^{3} x_i \right\}}{\prod_{i=1}^{3} E(x_i)} \right\}$$

The total variances will generally be large in the case of three variables. Therefore, whenever possible, the variables used to calculate fruit production should be reduced to two. The importance of calculating total sample variances is to locate sources of bias and large variation so that efforts can be made in the field to reduce variation and so produce the most reliable estimate of fruit abundance.

4. SUMMARY AND CONCLUSIONS

In this chapter, we have emphasized the limitations of "quick and dirty" techniques to obtain accurate data on fruit availability. The diverse fruit bat fauna in many tropical regions and the exotic and conspicuous nature of "bat fruits" has tempted a number of ecologists to pose the questions: "Are tropical fruit bats food-limited?", "Do they compete for food?" (Fleming, 1979, 1982), and "Does competition for food determine the organization of tropical fruit bat communities?" (McNab 1971). To determine the answer to even the first question requires prolonged sampling and probably some form of major manipulation of fruits. None of these approaches have been used. We suggest that most of these questions are inappropriate given the scale of sampling employed to determine if fruit bats are "resource-limited." No study of tropical fruit bats nor sampling of the fruits they consume has extended beyond a few years.

The most promising direction appears to be single or two species interactions between one fruit bat and one or two species of fruits. Sampling problems are also minimized if the fruiting species are common groundstory shrubs with annual fruit crops of less than 500 fruits per plant.

We suggest that short-term (less than 2 years) research projects would do better to take a small piece of the fruit-bat/bat-fruit interaction and study it in detail. As these pieces of research accumulate, the complex picture of fruit-bat community structure may finally begin to take shape.

This review of fruit sampling techniques illustrates that there are no quick and easy approximations of fruit availability. If a research question demands measures of fruit availability, then significant time, money, and effort must be allocated to do the job properly. Because fruit resource sampling techniques require considerable effort, we suggest that most study designs consider assigning at least one person to the task of measuring fruit production.

5. ACKNOWLEDGMENTS

We wish to thank many people in Santa Rosa National Park and Monteverde, Costa Rica for their generous support. They include, in Monteverde, the Trostle, Wallace, Hoge, and Landers families; and R. K. LaVal and Wolf Guindon of the Tropical Science Center. Jill Zarnowitz helped with bat and fruit sampling in Monteverde. ES thanks Ilona Kemeny for her constant support. This chapter profited from discussions with N. Wheelwright, D. W. Thomas, C. H. Janson, E. R. Heithaus, T. H. Fleming, and T. H. Kunz.

We dedicate this chapter to the conservationists of Costa Rica whose efforts to conserve tropical frugivores and their habitats deserves wide acclaim.

6. REFERENCES

August, P. V. 1981. Fig consumption and seed dispersal by *Artibeus jamaicensis* in the Llanos of Venezuela. Reprod. Bot., Supplement to Biotropica, 13:70-76.

Bonaccorso, F. 1979. Foraging and reproductive ecology in a Panamanian bat community. Bull. Florida State Mus. Biol. Ser., 24:359-408.

Daubermire, R. 1972. Phenology and other characteristics of tropical semi-deciduous forest in northwestern Costa Rica. J. Ecol., 60:147-170.

Dinerstein, E. 1985. Reproductive ecology of fruit bats and seasonality of fruit production in a Costa Rican cloud forest. Biotropica, 18:307-318.

Faegri, K., and L. van der Pijl. 1966. The principles of pollination ecology. Pergamon, Elmsford, 248 pp.

Fleming, T. H. 1979. Do tropical frugivores compete for food? Amer. Zool., 19:1157-1172.

Fleming, T. H. 1981. Fecundity, fruiting pattern and seed dispersal in *Piper amalago* (Piperaceae), a bat-dispersed tropical shrub. Oecologia, 51:42-46.

Fleming, T. H. 1982. Foraging strategies of plant-visiting bats. Pp. 287-325, *in* Ecology of bats. (T. H. Kunz, ed.). Plenum Press, New York, 425 pp.

Fleming, T. H., E. T. Hooper, and D. E. Wilson. 1972. Three Central American bat communi-

ties: Structure, reproductive cycles, and movement patterns. Ecology, 53:653-670.

Fleming, T. H., E. R. Heithaus, and W. B. Sawyer. 1977. An experimental analysis of the food location behavior of frugivorous bats. Ecology, 58: 619-627.

Foster, M. S. 1977. Ecological and nutritional effects of scarcity on a tropical frugivorous bird and its fruit source. Ecology, 58:73-85.

Foster, R. B. 1973. Seasonality of fruit production and seed fall in a tropical forest ecosystem in Panama. Unpubl. Ph.D. dissertation, Duke Univ., Durham, North Carolina, 155 pp.

Foster, R. B. 1982a. The seasonal rhythm of fruitfall on Barro Colorado Island. Pp. 151-172, *in* The ecology of a tropical forest: Seasonal rhythms and long-term changes. (E.G. Leigh, Jr., A. S. Rand, and D. Windsor, eds.). Smithsonian Inst. Press, Washington, D.C., 468 pp.

Foster, R. B. 1982b. Famine on Barro Colorado Island. Pp. 201-212, *in* The ecology of a tropical forest: Seasonal rhythms and long-term changes. (E. G. Leigh, Jr., A. S. Rand, and D. Windsor, eds.). Smithsonian Inst. Press, Washington, D.C., 468 pp.

Frankie, G. H., H. G. Baker, and P. W. Opler. 1974. Comparative phenological studies of trees in tropical wet and dry forests in the lowlands of Costa Rica. J. Ecol., 62:881-919.

Gardner, A. 1977. Feeding habits. Pp. 293-350, *in* Biology of bats in the New World family Phyllostomatidae. Part II. (R. J. Baker, J. K. Jones, Jr., and D. C. Carter, eds.). Spec. Publ. Mus. Texas Tech Univ., Lubbock, Texas, 364 pp.

Goodman, L. A. 1962. The variance of the product of K random variables. J. Amer. Stat. Assoc., 57:54-60.

Goodwin, R. E. 1970. The ecology of Jamaican bats. J. Mammal., 51:571-579.

Goodwin, G. G., and A. M. Greenhall. 1961. A review of the bats of Trinidad and Tobago. Bull. Amer. Mus. Nat. Hist., 122:187-302.

Heithaus, E. R. 1982. Coevolution between bats and plants. Pp. 327-368, *in* Ecology of bats. (T. H. Kunz, ed.). Plenum Press, New York, 425 pp.

Heithaus, E. R., T. H. Fleming, and P. W. Opler. 1975. Foraging patterns and resource utilization in seven species of bats in a seasonal tropical forest. Ecology, 56:841-854.

Hilty, S. L. 1980. Flowering and fruiting periodicity in a premontane rain forest in Pacific Colombia. Biotropica, 12:292-306.

Horwitz, C. C. 1980. Seed dispersal and seedling demography of *Calathea microcephala* and *Calathea ovandensis.* Unpubl. Ph.D. dissertation, Northwestern Univ., Evanston, Illinois, 162 pp.

Howe, H. F. 1981. Dispersal of neotropical nutmeg (*Virola sebifera*) by birds. Auk, 98:88-98.

Howe, H. F., and DeSteven. 1979. Fruit production, migrant bird visitation, and seed dispersal of *Guarea glabra* in Panama. Oecologia, 59:1-12.

Howe, H. F., and G. A. van de Kerckhove. 1979. Fecundity and tree dispersal of a tropical tree. Ecology, 60: 180-189.

Howe, H. F., and J. Smallwood. 1982. Ecology of seed dispersal. Ann. Rev. Ecol. Syst., 13:201-228.

Howell, D. J., and D. Burch. 1974. Food habits of some Costa Rican bats. Rev. Biol. Trop., 21:284-334.

Hubbell, S. P. 1979. Tree dispersion, abundance, and diversity in a tropical dry forest. Science, 203:1299-1309.

Humphrey, S., and F. J. Bonaccorso. 1979. Population and community ecology. Pp. 403-441, *in* Biology of bats in the New World Family Phyllostomatidae. Part III. (R. J. Baker, J. K. Jones, Jr., and D. C. Carter, eds.). Spec. Publ. Mus. Texas Tech. Univ., Lubbock, Texas, 441 pp.

Janson, C. H. 1983. Adaptation of fruit morphology to dispersal agents in a Neotropical forest. Science, 219:187-189.

Janzen, D. H. 1981. Guanacaste tree seed-swallowing by Costa Rican range horses. Ecology, 62:587-592.

Janzen, D. H., G. A. Miller, J. Hackforth-Jones, C. M. Pond, K. Hooper, and D. P. Janos. 1976. Two Costa Rican bat-generated seed shadows of *Andira inermis* (Swartz) HBK, Leguminosae. Ecology, 57:1068-1076.

McClure, H. E. 1966. Flowering, fruiting, and animals in the canopy of a tropical rain forest. Malay. For., 29:182-203.

Medway, L. 1972. Phenology of a tropical rain forest in Malaya. Biol. Jour. Linn. Soc., 4:117-146.

McDiarmid, R. W., R. E. Ricklefs, and M. S. Foster. 1977. Dispersal of *Stemmadenia donnell-smithii* (Apocynaceae) by birds. Biotropica, 9:9-25.

McKey, D. 1975. The ecology of coevolved seed dispersal systems. Pp. 159-191, *in* Coevolution of animals and plants. (L. E. Gilbert, and P. H. Raven, eds.). Univ. Texas Press, Austin, 246 pp.

McNab, B. K. 1971. The structure of tropical bat faunas. Ecology. 52:352-358.

Milton, K. D., M. Windsor, D. W. Morrison, and M. A. Estribi. 1982. Fruiting phenologies of two neotropical *Ficus* species. Ecology, 63:752-762.

Morrison, D. W. 1978. Foraging ecology and energetics of the frugivorous bat, *Artibeus jamaicensis.* Ecology, 59:716-723.

Opler, P. A., G. W. Frankie, and H. G. Baker. 1980. Comparative phenological studies of treelet and shrub species in tropical wet and dry forests in the lowlands of Costa Rica. J. Ecol., 68:167-188.

Putz, F. J. 1979. Aseasonality in Malaysian tree phenology. Malay. For., 42:1-24.

Smythe, N. M. 1970. Relationships between fruiting seasons and seed dispersal methods in a Neotropical forest. Amer. Nat., 104:25-35.

Snow, D. W. 1971. Evolutionary aspects of fruit-eating by birds. Ibis, 113:194-202.

Snow, D. W. 1981. Tropical frugivorous birds and their food plants: A world survey. Biotropica. 13:1-14.

Stashko, E. R. 1982. Foraging ecology of a Neotropical bat, *Carollia perspicillata.* Unpubl. Ph.D. dissertation. Northwestern Univ., Evanston, Illinois, 143 pp.

Thomas, D. W. 1982. The ecology of an African savanna fruit bat community: Resource partitioning and role in seed dispersal. Unpubl. Ph.D. dissertation, Univ. Aberdeen, Aberdeen.

Travis, J. 1983. A method for the statistical analysis of time-energy budgets. Ecology, 63:19-25.

Vogel, S. 1968. Chiropterophilie in der neotrophischen Flora. Neue Mitt. I. Flora Abt., *B*, 157:562-602.

Vogel, S. 1969. Chiropterophilie in der neotrophischen Flora. Neue Mitt. II, III. Flora Abt., *B*, 158:185-222, 289-323.

van der Pijl, L. 1972. Principles of dispersal in higher plants. Springer-Verlag. New York, 161 pp.

Vazquez-Yanes, C., A. Orozco, G. Francois, and L. Trejo. 1975. Observations on seed dispersal by bats in a tropical humid region in Veracruz, Mexico. Biotropica, 7:73-76.

Worthington, A. 1982. Population sizes and breeding rhythms of two species of manakins in relation to food supply. Pp. 213-225, *in* The ecology of a tropical forest: Seasonal rhythms and long-term changes. (E. G. Leigh, Jr., A. S. Rand, and D. M. Windsor, eds.). Smithsonian Inst. Press, Washington, D.C., 468 pp.

Chapter 15

Methods of Nutritional Ecology of Plant-Visiting Bats

Lawrence H. Herbst[1]

Department of Ecology and
  Behavioral Biology
University of Minnesota
Minneapolis, Minnesota 55455 USA

1. INTRODUCTION

Food is a resource from which animals extract energy and nutrients that are necessary for maintenance, growth, and reproduction. The quality of a particular food item depends upon the animal's requirements, the energy and nutrient contents of the item, the types and amounts of non-nutrients that the item contains, and the efficiency with which energy and nutrients can be extracted and allocated to the above functions. The study of nutrition is concerned with all of these factors. The primary goal of nutritional analysis is to divide food into components with similar nutritional properties so that the nutritional quality of a food item can be predicted from its composition and compared to other diets without time-consuming feeding trials (Lucas et al., 1961; Van Soest, 1967, 1982). Besides the practical applications of such information in animal husbandry and wildlife management, nutritional studies are of interest to ecologists who are trying to understand the foraging behavior of animals (e.g., Westoby, 1974; Pulliam, 1975; Belovsky, 1978; and Rapport, 1980; Glander, 1981; Owen-Smith and Novellie, 1982) and the evolution of plant-animal interactions such as herbivory (e.g., Bryant and Kuropat, 1980; Auerbach and Strong, 1981), pollination (e.g., Howell, 1974; Baker and Baker, 1975, 1982), and seed dispersal (e.g., McKey, 1975; Howe and Smallwood, 1982).

The purpose of this paper is to acquaint the reader with some of the techniques used in nutritional analyses, the rationale behind these methods, and the problems associated with them. In keeping with the title of this paper, discussion of these methods is focused on analyses of plant material and on what is

[1]Present Address: 1869 Twain Street, Baldwin, New York 11510 USA

known about the biology of frugivorous and nectarivorous bats. This paper is meant to be a guide in the selection of techniques rather than a detailed cookbook of laboratory procedures. I have restricted the scope of this paper to include methods for measuring digestibility, sample preservation, and techniques for analyzing the major nutritional fractions: minerals, carbohydrates, lipids, and protein. I will also briefly discuss methods for measuring the energy content of food. Some of the techniques presented will yield fractions which can be analyzed in more detail (e.g., essential fatty acids may be studied in the lipid fraction). Techniques for more detailed analyses may be found in *Official Methods of Analysis* (Association of Official Analytic Chemists, 1980). Finally, I will present some schemes of analysis that integrate these basic techniques so that relevant and comparable nutritional data can be gathered from a variety of plant foods. I will not discuss analytical techniques for detecting or measuring plant secondary compounds, although these substances are very important (Freeland and Janzen, 1974; Harborne, 1982; Reese, 1979). Rosenthal and Janzen (1979) provide an excellent introduction to the study of plant secondary compounds.

2. DIGESTIBILITY

The efficiency with which an animal extracts energy and nutrients from food includes both the amount that can be extracted relative to what is initially present and the time it takes to do so. Thus, efficiency includes food handling time, the relative amount of food ingested, gut transit time, and the relative amount of ingested food that is digested and assimilated. An estimate of the digestibility of food (i.e., the relative amount of ingested food that is retained by the gut) is important because it can be used with estimates of energy and nutrient requirements to predict levels of food intake. Digestibility is calculated as follows:

$$\text{Digestibility} = \frac{\text{Ingesta} - \text{Egesta}}{\text{Ingesta}}$$

where Ingesta = the dry mass of food that is ingested

Egesta = the dry mass of feces voided following the meal.

This measure is often referred to as *apparent digestibility* because it measures net retention of material by the gut (the feces contains gut secretions and sloughed tissue as well as undigested material). Apparent digestibility can take on negative values if secretory and abrasive losses exceed gross uptake (Maynard et al., 1979; Van Soest, 1982). Digestibility is usually determined on a dry mass basis to avoid inaccuracies due to evaporation of water from food and feces and variation due to changes in water uptake by the gut. This measure is also known as *dry matter digestibility.*

The net retention of a food component (e.g., nutrient) by the gut is known as *partial apparent digestibility* and is calculated as follows:

$$\text{Partial apparent digestibility} = \frac{\text{Ingesta}\,(A_i) - \text{Egesta}\,(A_f)}{\text{Ingesta}\,(A_i)}$$

where A_i = the relative amount of the component in dry food

A_f = the relative amount of the component in dry feces.

This equation can be simplified to the following:

$$\text{Partial apparent digestibility} = \frac{A_i - A_f(1 - \text{DMD})}{A_i}$$

where DMD = dry matter digestibility.

A measure of the gross uptake of a food component is called *true digestibility* and can be calculated if secretory and abrasive losses (metabolic fecal losses) can be quantified. Such loses can be estimated by feeding component-free diets or by using diets containing different amounts of the component and regressing digested content against food content (Lucas et al., 1961; Fonnesbeck, 1969; Van Soest, 1967, 1982). The Y-intercept is an estimate of metabolic fecal loss (sign is negative) and the slope is an estimate of true digestibility.

Calculations of digestibility are straightforward but the usefulness of the values obtained may be limited. Digestibility results from the interaction of an organism with its food and depends upon the properties of both. Because these properties can vary, digestibility can be highly variable (Drozdz, 1968, 1975; White, 1974; Batzli and Cole, 1979; Sibly, 1981). For example, even within a single individual feeding on a uniform food, digestibility may vary with the animal's health, body temperature, level of physiological excitement, age, the time since last feeding, volume of food ingested, the amount of time it has been eating this food item, and the degree of food preparation (see Kunz, 1980 for references on bats). Digestibilities of mixed diets (containing several food types) may not be equal to the sum of the digestibilities of each food type ingested alone. Given the many factors that can affect digestibility, one must be cautious in extrapolating results.

The most accurate method for measuring digestibility is a total collection procedure carried out under controlled laboratory conditions (Maynard et al., 1979). The procedure requires the careful measurement of all ingested food (mass offered—mass not eaten) and resulting feces. Food should be presented *ad libitum*. The test diet should be fed for a period of time prior to data collection to allow animals to adjust to the diet and to allow their guts to clear of previous foods. Data collection should last several consecutive days in order to determine the relationship between average intake rate and average feces production rate. This method is practical for bats and other small animals that can be maintained in captivity.

Digestibility estimates usually require that feces not be contaminated with urine and that urine be collected and analyzed separately. It is very difficult to collect urine and feces separately with unrestrained bats. Kanthor (1965) demonstrates that some bats

can be catheterized for urine collection. Urine and feces can be collected and analyzed together if one assumes that urine composition and volume are constants.

The total collection procedure is impractical in many field situations. An alternative method eliminates the need to measure ingestion and defecation rates. This method uses a marker that is ingested with the food and quantitatively recovered in the feces. Digestibility would be calculated as follows:

$$DMD = 1 - M_i/M_f$$

where DMD = dry matter digestibility

M_i = the relative amount of marker (M) in dry food

M_f = the relative amount of marker (M) in dry feces.

To yield accurate estimates, the marker must have the following ideal properties: 1) it is ingested in direct proportion to its occurrence in the ingested food; 2) it moves with the food through the gut and does not separate from the food mass; and 3) it is completely recoverable in the feces (neither destroyed nor digested by the gut) (Maynard et al., 1979; Van Soest, 1982).

Marker techniques can be applied to non-captive animals if a food component is used as a marker, but accuracy depends upon one's ability to identify what was eaten from an examination of the feces and is affected by natural variation in the marker content of food. Few naturally occurring food components satisfy all of the criteria for ideal markers. Nevertheless, several natural markers have been used (Kotb and Luckey, 1972). The following may be useful in studies of frugivorous bats: dietary fiber components (e.g., lignin), ash, and specific minerals. Two problems with dietary fiber components are that they may be partly digestible due to microbial activity (Kotb and Luckey, 1972; Servello et al., 1983) and that dietary fiber ingested may be different from dietary fiber defecated due to the differential formation of Maillard reaction products during sample preparation (Van Soest, 1982). Ash content has been used in several field studies (Johnson and Maxell, 1966; Johnson and Groepper, 1970; Soholt, 1973). An assumption of this technique is that the animals are in mineral balance. Correction factors for urinary loss of certain minerals must be determined in the laboratory. Acid insoluble ash has yielded digestibility values that are very close to those determined in total collection trials (Sutton et al., 1977) and this method compares favorably with other marker techniques (Frape et al., 1982). Several specific minerals are excreted primarily in the feces and can be used as indigestible markers (Kaufman et al., 1976).

Marker techniques can also be used to measure food intake rate and gut transit time (see Kotb and Luckey, 1972 for a review of methods). Seeds that are defecated intact by frugivores can be used to measure gut transit times if they remain mixed with the fruit pulp (Herbst, 1983; but see Walsberg, 1975).

Since ecologists are most interested in the digestibility of natural diets, the problems of using natural diets in nutritional studies will be considered. One problem is food availability and one's ability to collect it (see Chapter 14). Another problem is variation in food composition. A third problem is that animals may be more selective or use different selection criteria than humans in collecting suitable food items.

Natural variability in food composition may be eliminated by thoroughly mixing collected food and taking subsamples for feeding and analysis of energy and nutrient content. If discrete food items are used, then samples for analysis and feeding should be randomly selected from the collected total. It is probably impossible to collect food items by the same criteria that animals use and this problem is best approached by letting the animals do the collecting. A comparison of items which are not ingested with random samples of the total collection may estimate the degree of difference in sampling criteria. Items that are carried into mist nets or traps can be compared with human collected items (Morrison, 1978).

3. PRESERVATION AND PREPARATION OF SAMPLES FOR ANALYSIS

Because there is likely to be a time lag between the collection of food samples and their analysis, it is essential that they be preserved properly. Fresh mass should be measured before samples are preserved. Freezing samples in liquid nitrogen is the best method of preservation. The extreme cold (-196°C) allows few chemical changes to occur. Liquid nitrogen can be held in cryogenic tanks for several months (the exact length of time depends primarily upon the tank volume and the number of times the tank is opened). When liquid nitrogen is not available samples may either be dried or preserved in alcohol. The critical factors in drying are drying time and temperature. Drying should be thorough within 24 h to prevent bacterial and fungal growth and temperatures should not exceed 60°C. Higher temperatures result in excessive losses of carbohydrate and protein due to formation of lignin-like Maillard products (Van Soest, 1982) and oxidation of carbohydrates and lipids. Food parts that will be analyzed separately should be separated before drying because this becomes very difficult afterwards. Preservation with alcohol also requires that parts be separated beforehand so that nutrients extracted from different parts are not mixed. Specimens must be kept in leak-proof containers since the alcohol will contain most of the soluble components. Boiling the sample in ethanol (Hladik, 1977) is not recommended because this causes complexing of proteins, nucleic acids, carbohydrates, and polyphenols (Selvendran, 1975; Van Soest, 1982). This may occur to some degree at any temperature and therefore alcohol should only be used if field drying is impractical.

To estimate water content and provide dry material for analysis, preserved samples must be dried to constant mass under uniform conditions. Drying conditions greatly affect the results of subsequent analyses and I urge the use of a standard procedure in all future comparative nutritional studies. For reasons already mentioned drying temperatures should not exceed 60°C.

Samples must be homogenized to obtain a uniform material for quantitative analysis and to break up tissue and cell structure so that extractions can proceed efficiently. Dry material can be ground in a Wiley mill (20-40 mesh is adequate) or ground with a mortar and pestle. Some analyses can be performed on fresh or alcoholic samples provided that fresh mass, water content, and volume of alcohol are known. Wet samples can be homogenized in a tissue homogenizer or a Pascall ball mill (see Selvendran, 1975; Ring and Selvendran, 1978).

4. NUTRITIONAL ANALYSIS OF FOOD COMPONENTS

In this section I present quantitative analytical techniques for measuring the mineral, dietary fiber, available carbohydrate, lipid, protein, and energy content of foods. Before beginning I want to emphasize that the biological relevance of any nutritional analysis depends upon the decision about which food items or parts to analyze. Analyses should be performed on samples that are relevant to the nutrition of the animal. For example, analyses of whole fruits have little meaning if seeds pass undigested through a frugivore's gut (e.g., Janzen, 1983).

4.1. Ash and Mineral Content

A gross measure of the relative amount of minerals in a sample can be obtained by burning a known quantity of dry sample (ca. 0.5 g) in a muffle furnace at 500 C for 5 hrs and weighing the remaining ash. The difference between sample and ash masses gives an estimate of the organic material present. Ashing provides no information about the elemental composition of the sample or about the types of compounds in which these minerals occur

in the original sample. Many minerals are found in several organic and inorganic forms of which only a few may be nutritionally relevant (Maynard et al., 1979). However, ashing is a useful starting point for elemental analyses.

Many elements can be measured using atomic absorption spectrophotometry. A number of colorimetric, photometric, gravimetric, and titrametric techniques are also available for analysis of specific elements (A.O.A.C., 1980). Analyses of the metal-organic compounds require different techniques which are beyond the scope of this paper.

4.2. Dietary Fiber

Dietary fiber can be defined as the lignin and polysaccharide fraction of a food that is not digested by endogenous secretions of the gut (Trowell et al., 1976). Thus, an analysis of dietary fiber must take into account the digestive capabilities of the animal being studied and should separate indigestible carbohydrates and lignin from other indigestible compounds. A problem with most methods is that it is impossible to isolate a pure dietary fiber fraction (see reviews by Southgate et al., 1978 and Selvendran et al., 1979b). By definition fiber includes materials that are degraded by gut microorganisms and therefore available for assimilation. If one is concerned only with available versus unavailable fractions then one may use a technique that does not recover these materials. Since no method can be applied to all animals, I will evaluate several methods in relation to frugivorous bat digestive physiology.

A method long used in feed analysis, but no longer recommended, involves boiling a sample first in sulfuric acid for 30 min and then in sodium hydroxide for 30 min to yield a residue known as crude fiber (Maynard et al., 1979; Van Soest, 1982). This method provides a poor estimate of dietary fiber because many indigestible fiber components such as lignin and hemicellulose are lost under the harsh hydrolysis conditions (Van Soest and Robertson, 1976; Van Soest, 1982).

Two modern methods of fiber analysis are available which can be used in studies of fruit: the detergent method (Goering and Van Soest, 1970) and the unavailable carbohydrate method (Southgate, 1969b). The detergent method involves extracting a food sample (ca. 1 g) with a detergent (sodium lauryl sulfate) and a chelating agent (EDTA). The detergent removes cell contents (soluble carbohydrates, lipids, and protein) and pectins while the chelating agent solubilizes minerals. When the extraction is done at neutral pH, hemicelluloses, cellulose, and lignins are recovered in the residue as neutral detergent fiber (NDF). For most monogastric animals this gives a good estimate of nutritionally unavailable material since pectins, which are usually degraded by gut microflora, are solubilized. However, pectins may be nutritionally unavailable to bats (see Klite, 1965), and a method is needed to measure pectins separately (see Bitter and Muir, 1962; Blumenkrantz and Asboe-Hansen, 1973; Selvendran et al., 1979a; Theander and Aman, 1979).

Neutral detergent fiber may contain bound minerals and nitrogen and these can be measured in the residue to estimate unavailable fractions (Van Soest, 1982). If starchy foods are analyzed, pretreatment of the sample with amylase is recommended (Robertson and Van Soest, 1981).

The unavailable carbohydrate system has several modifications. Basically, a sample is extracted with alcohol and ether to remove soluble carbohydrates, lipids, and proteins (Southgate, 1969b). The residue contains some pectins, hemicellulose, cellulose, and lignin, as well as bound nitrogenous compounds, starch, and minerals (Selvendran, 1975). Because starch becomes modified and proteins complex with polyphenols and carbohydrates during alcohol boiling, protein and starch extraction are recommended before alcohol treatment (Selvendran et al., 1979b, 1981). Protein can be extracted with neutral proteinases (acid proteinases cause

losses of pectins and hemicellulose) or with a solubilizing agent such as sodium deoxycholate.

Selvendran et al. (1979b, 1981) recommend a somewhat different method for unavailable carbohydrates which involves sequential extraction with 1% aqueous sodium deoxycholate, phenol/acetic acid/water (2:1:1, w/v/v), and 90% (v/v) aqueous dimethylsulfoxide (DMSO) (Ring and Selvendran, 1978). The sodium deoxycholate and phenol/acetic acid/water remove cytoplasmic proteins without hydrolyzing them and the DMSO solubilizes starch. For foods containing little starch such as ripe fruits, DMSO can be omitted. This method is thought to yield a relatively pure dietary fiber residue which is free of coprecipitated compounds.

4.3. Total Available Carbohydrates

Total available carbohydrates are defined as those carbohydrates that are readily digestible by endogenous gut secretions. These include mono- and disaccharides, glycogen, dextrin, and starch (Southgate, 1969a). Most fruit pulps and flower nectars contain large amounts of soluble carbohydrates (mono- and disaccharides), primarily glucose, fructose, and sucrose. Therefore, analysis of these foods can exploit the properties of these sugars.

Available carbohydrate content has been routinely estimated as the material remaining after ash, fiber, lipids, and protein have been estimated. This is a very poor estimate of available carbohydrates because analytical errors involved with each of the other determinations accumulate (Southgate, 1969a; Maynard et al., 1979; Van Soest, 1982). Available carbohydrate content is best measured directly.

Refractometry is one method commonly used by field biologists to measure sugar concentrations of liquid samples. A hand held refractometer rapidly gives the concentration by mass of sucrose that has the same refractive index as the sample being measured.

Since fructose and glucose have refractive indices about half that of sucrose the reading is a good estimate of carbohydrate content. However, large errors can occur when other solutes are present in the sample. Refractometry is recommended only where solute components have been characterized (Inouye et al., 1980).

Another group of methods exploits the ability of aldoses and ketoses to reduce various substances, e.g., ferricyanide, hypoiodite, cupric sulfate (Hodge and Hofreiter, 1962). Recommended methods involve using cupric sulfate reagents because these are more specific for reducing sugars and can therefore be applied to food samples. The only major problem with copper reduction techniques is the potential for errors due to back oxidation by air (Hodge and Hofreiter, 1962). Available methods include Lane-Eynon, Munson-Walker, and Shaffer-Somogyi techniques (A.O.A.C., 1980). The first two methods are suitable for determinations of large samples (ca. 100 ml). The Shaffer-Somogyi method is suitable for very small samples (ca. 0.5 g of plant material or as little as 15 μg glucose).

A rapid colorimetric procedure uses the capacity of PAHBAH to react with reducing sugars in aqueous alkali solution to form yellow colored products (Lever, 1972; Lever et al., 1973; Blakeney and Mutton, 1980). This method is preferred because it is less expensive and uses less toxic reagents than some other colorimetric methods (Lever et al., 1973). It is also very sensitive and specific for reducing sugars (Lever, 1972). As with other methods, high protein levels cause interference and preliminary protein precipitation is necessary. Calcium is required for proper color response. When coupled with chromatographic identification of sugars present, this method can yield very specific information (Blakeney and Mutton, 1980).

The widely used anthrone method is not suitable for analyses of unknown or mixed sugar solutions or those containing interfering organic compounds (Dische, 1962; Hodge and Hofreiter, 1962).

Sucrose and starch do not have reducing power because they have no free aldehyde or ketone groups. Starch can be hydrolyzed with weak acid (0.2N HC1) or amylase to yield glucose (Smith et al., 1964) and sucrose can be hydrolyzed to yield fructose and glucose with weak acid or invertase.

4.4. Lipids

Lipids are a heterogeneous group of compounds that, in general, have nearly twice the energy content of carbohydrates. Lipids are defined chemically as "those substances which are a) insoluble in water; b) soluble in organic solvents such as chloroform, ether, or benzene; c) contain long-chain hydrocarbon groups in their molecules; and d) are present in or derived from living organisms" (Kates, 1972). Among the compounds included in this definition are fats, fatty acids, glycolipids, phospholipids, waxes, essential oils, fat soluble vitamins, plant pigments, and sterols. Each of these compounds have their own nutritional properties (some may even be toxic). Nevertheless, a rapid method for determining lipid content is desirable for characterizing food items as lipid-rich or carbohydrate-rich and for deciding whether more detailed lipid analyses are warranted.

Extraction of a dry sample (ca. 2 g) with anhydrous diethyl ether is commonly used to determine the lipid content of feeds (A.O.A.C., 1980). The anhydrous condition minimizes the extraction of soluble carbohydrates, but for materials that contain relatively large amounts of soluble carbohydrates, such as fruits, a preliminary extraction with water may be necessary. Either the loss in dry mass of the sample due to extraction or the mass of the extract after solvent evaporation can be used to estimate lipid content. The two techniques may yield different results because the extract loses volatile components (Van Soest, 1982).

Another method for rapid lipid extraction uses a solvent composed of chloroform, methanol, and water (1:2:0.8, v/v) (Bligh and Dyer, 1959 cited in Kates, 1972). This solvent rapidly extracts lipids and water soluble components. The lipids and water soluble components can be separated by diluting the extract with chloroform and water (lipids remain in the chloroform phase while water soluble components are driven into the aqueous phase). Total lipid content is estimated by evaporating the solvent and weighing the lipid residue.

In digestibility trials, ether extraction may result in an overestimate of lipid digestibility due to the formation of ether insoluble calcium and magnesium soaps in the feces (Van Soest, 1982). Chloroform/methanol/water extraction is recommended because these soaps will dissolve in water and can be recovered in the chloroform phase. Either extraction method may precede more detailed analyses. Detailed lipid analyses can be found in Kates (1972) and in A.O.A.C. (1980).

4.5. Nitrogen and Protein Content

Protein is essential for growth and maintenance of animal tissue. Protein measurements are especially important in plant-visiting bat studies because, with the exception of pollen (Harborne, 1982), plant tissues are among the poorest sources of protein in nature (Mattson, 1980).

Determining the total nitrogen content of a sample is useful because many nitrogenous compounds may be used to synthesize protein. Use of total nitrogen content in comparative studies assumes that useable nitrogenous compounds occur in a constant ratio to unuseable nitrogenous compounds and that no nitrogenous compounds are toxic. A crude estimate of protein content obtained by multiplying total nitrogen content by a factor of 6.25, based on the average nitrogen content of protein, relies on the false assumption that all nitrogen occurs in protein. For more accurate protein estimates, appropriate conversion factors must be determined for each food type (Milton and Dintzis, 1981; Herbst, 1983).

Total nitrogen is determined by the Kjeldahl technique (Bailey, 1967). Basically,

the procedure first involves digestion of a sample in sulfuric acid to release all nitrogen, which is recovered as ammonia sulfate, and then distillation and quantification of the ammonia. The Kjeldahl method has several modifications to accommodate small samples (ca. 0.1 g) and to handle multiple samples rapidly (Lang, 1958; Wall and Gehrke, 1975; Hambreaus et al., 1976; Sylvester-Bradley and Howitt, 1977). Digestion is the slowest step in the analysis and choice of catalyst and digestion time affect recovery (Wall and Gehrke, 1975). Ammonia can be quantified by titration, ammonia electrode, or colorimetry (Weatherburn, 1967; Lang, 1968; Felker, 1977; Nkonge and Ballance, 1982).

Although protein is not the only useable form of nitrogen (nucleic acids and amino sugars), direct measures of protein or amino acid content are good indicators of useable nitrogen for monogastric animals since unuseable nitrogenous compounds (some alkaloids, inorganic nitrogen) are not included in the assay.

Protein can be directly quantified by several methods. Many methods utilize protein-binding dyes. These methods are fast and inexpensive, but they are best for yielding relative data and should be calibrated with total nitrogen analysis (Latkin, 1975). A widely used protein dye technique is that of Lowry et al. (1951) which uses the Folin Phenol Reagent. There are three serious problems with this technique: 1) the amount of color development varies with protein type, 2) color is not strictly proportional to protein concentration, and 3) many substances interfere with the reaction including phenols (Lowry et al., 1951), carbohydrates (Gerhardt and Beevers, 1968; Rosenthal and Sobieszczanska, 1970), EDTA (Neurath, 1966), sulfhydryl and disulfide reagents, and potassium ions (Vallejo and Lagunas, 1970). A preferred dye binding technique uses Coomassie Brilliant Blue (Bradford, 1976). Interference is caused by detergents and strong alkali buffers, but many substances including sucrose have little effect. This method is more sensitive than the Lowry method and gives color development in proportion to concentration.

Several spectrophotometric techniques are available which exploit the capacity of proteins to absorb ultraviolet light (Bailey, 1967; Webster, 1970). A recommended technique uses the difference in measured absorbances at 215 mμ and 225 mμ to estimate protein concentration (Waddell, 1956). At these wavelengths absorbance is primarily due to peptide bonds and there is little difference in response among proteins. Nucleic acids do not interfere at these wavelengths (Wrigley and Webster, 1968) and the results are insensitive to pH. Using the difference in absorbances minimizes error caused by nonprotein compounds. Protein concentrations as low as 20 μg/ml can be measured.

Protein yield by spectrophotometric and colorimetric techniques is heavily influenced by extraction procedures. Ideally extraction should solubilize all unbound protein without hydrolysis. Another method recommended for quantifying protein is amino acid analysis.

Amino acid analysis has three advantages over other protein measures: 1) digestion conditions allow for nearly complete extraction of amino acids, whereas protein extractions are less efficient, 2) free amino acids are measured, and 3) more information about the nature of dietary protein is available from amino acid composition.

Amino acid analysis has been simplified by advances in ion exchange chromatography and amino acids can now be rapidly determined by automated methods. Blackburn (1978) provides an excellent introduction to amino acid analysis techniques. I will briefly discuss some of the problems entailed in sample preparation. Typically a food sample is hydrolyzed in 6N HC1 *in vacuo* at 110°C for 24 h. Extraction time is standardized to optimize amino acid recovery. Some residues are very labile under these hydrolysis conditions, e.g., tryptophan is completely destroyed, and methionine and cystine residues are partially degraded. Different hydrolysis conditions (strong alkali) can be used on a sec-

ond sample to recover these acid labile residues. Recently, techniques have been developed to stabilize the more labile amino acid residues during hydrolysis, allowing for complete amino acid analysis from a single hydrolyzed sample (Felker, 1976; Inglis et al., 1976). Loss of amino acids through artifact formation can occur if the sample contains large amounts of carbohydrates. Dilution of the sample with a sufficient volume of acid minimizes this effect and experiments have shown that no appreciable losses of amino acids occur (Blackburn, 1978; Kunsch and Temperli, 1978). Losses of amino acids can also occur when foods that contain large amounts of tannins are hydrolyzed under acid conditions.

4.6. Energy Content

Ecologists are often interested in measures of food energy content because these relate directly to an organism's energy relations with the environment. The energy content of food can be determined in several ways. Paine (1971) provides an excellent review of calorimetry principles and methods. One method follows from more detailed nutritional analyses and involves multiplying the amounts of available carbohydrate, lipid, and protein by standard energy conversion factors (17.16, 39.56, and 23.65 kJ/g respectively (Kleiber, 1975)). A second method measures energy content directly with a bomb calorimeter (see Chapter 23). Two types of oxygen bomb calorimeters are currently available: the Parr bomb and the Phillipson bomb. A Parr bomb is useful for large samples (ca. 1 g), though some models can handle smaller (50-70 mg) samples. A Phillipson microbomb is valuable for rapid analysis of extremely small samples (10-15 mg) (Paine, 1971; Prus, 1975).

Measurements of the gross energy content of foods that have varying amounts of dietary fiber give poor estimates of available energy unless corrections are made for fiber energy content or digestibility of energy is determined for each food. Available energy

A

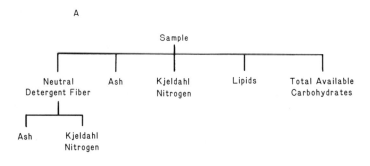

B

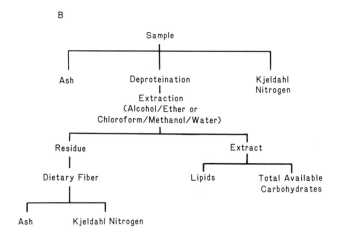

Figure 1. Two schemes for the basic nutritional analysis of plant material.

can be estimated from measurements of gross energy content of food and fiber residue as follows:

$$\text{Available Energy} = E_{food} - E_{fiber}\,(\text{Fiber}_{food})$$

where E_{food} = gross energy content of food
E_{fiber} = gross energy content of dietary fiber
Fiber_{food} = fiber content of food.

Successful application of this method depends upon how fiber is defined and measured.

5. ANALYTICAL SCHEMES

One use of nutritional analysis is to generate comparative data on the nutritional quality of a wide array of foods. To do this, specific techniques must be integrated into a scheme that yields fractions with similar nutritional properties. For example, measures of total nitrogen content are probably not comparable among food types because of varying amounts of soluble versus bound protein, alkaloids, chlorophyll, and other nitrogenous compounds.

The available data on frugivorous bats indicate that they exploit the soluble cytoplasmic components of fruits and that cell wall and fiber bound materials are probably not digested (Klite, 1965; Morrison, 1980; Herbst, 1983). With this knowledge, several schemes might be appropriate. The analysis scheme illustrated in Fig. 1A is commonly used in feed analysis (Van Soest, 1982). In this scheme subsamples of material are analyzed separately and about 5 g dry material is required for a single complete fractionation. Replacement of ether extraction with chloroform/methanol/water extraction would allow determination of lipids and available carbohydrates from the same subsample. Kjeldahl nitrogen determinations of neutral detergent fiber give an estimate of bound (unavailable) nitrogenous compounds. Ashing the fiber residue gives an estimate of unavailable minerals.

A second scheme (Fig. 1B) uses an unavailable carbohydrate method to measure dietary fiber. Less material is needed because available carbohydrates and lipids can be determined from the alcohol/ether extract. This method may fractionate fruits better according to the digestive capabilities of bats because pectins are mostly conserved as part of dietary fiber. Again, nitrogen and ash determinations of the fiber residue give an estimate of unavailable nitrogen and minerals.

There are a variety of modifications to the two schemes presented. Pectins may be analyzed separately in scheme 1 or analyzed in the dietary fiber fraction in scheme 2. The Kjeldahl procedure may be used to estimate the nitrogen content of any of the fractions. I strongly recommend that for all uncharacterized foods, direct protein or amino acid determinations be made along with Kjeldahl nitrogen analyses.

The two schemes presented above provide initial estimates of the nutritional quality of food items. If enough material is available, more detailed analyses may be carried out in order to yield more accurate information or to answer specific questions (e.g., Are foods deficient in certain essential minerals, vitamins, lipids, or amino acids?). However, one must remember that food quality depends upon many factors. Plant material may contain numerous secondary metabolites, some of which are included in certain nutrient fractions but actually lower food quality (e.g., alkaloids, nonprotein amino acids, toxic lipids, and terpenoids). In all

cases, the best indicator of a food's nutritional value will be the performance of animals maintained in feeding trials.

6. ACKNOWLEDGMENTS

I wish to thank C. H. Mallery and D. DiResta for valuable discussions and comments. D. W. Thomas and T. H. Kunz gave me the opportunity to write this paper and provided valuable comments. T. H. Fleming introduced me to frugivorous bat research and provided much encouragement.

7. REFERENCES

Association of Official Analytical Chemists. 1980. Official methods of analysis. 13th ed. (W. Horowitz, ed.). Washington, D.C., 1018 pp.

Auerbach, J., and D. R. Strong. 1981. Nutritional ecology of *Heliconia* herbivores: Experiments with plant fertilization and alternative hosts. Ecol. Monogr., 5:63-83.

Bailey, J. L. 1967. Techniques in protein chemistry. 2nd ed. Elsevier Publ. Co., New York. 406 pp.

Baker, H. G., and I. Baker. 1975. Studies of nectar—constitution and pollinator—plant coevolution. Pp. 100-140, *in* Coevolution of animals and plants. (L. E. Gilbert and P. H. Raven, eds.). Univ. Texas Press, Austin, 263 pp.

Baker, H. G., and I. Baker. 1982. Chemical constituents of nectar in relation to pollination mechanisms and phylogeny. Pp. 131-171, *in* Biochemical aspects of evolutionary biology. (M. H. Nitecki, ed.). Univ. Chicago Press, Chicago, 324 pp.

Batzli, G. O., and F. R. Cole. 1979. Nutritional ecology of microtine rodents: Digestibility of forage. J. Mammal., 60:740-750.

Belovsky, G. E. 1978. Diet optimization in a generalist herbivore: The moose. Theoret. Pop. Biol., 14:105-134.

Bitter, T., and H. M. Muir. 1962. A modified uronic acid carbazole reaction. Anal. Biochem., 4:330-334.

Blackburn, S. (ed.). 1978. Amino acid determination: Methods and techniques. 2nd ed. Marcel Dekker, Inc., New York, 367 pp.

Blakeney, A. B., and L. L. Mutton. 1980. A simple

colorimetric method for the determination of sugars in fruit and vegetables. J. Sci. Fd. Agric., 31:889-897.

Blumenkrantz, N., and G. Aboe-Hansen. 1973. New method for quantitative determination of uronic acids. Anal. Biochem., 54:484-489.

Bradford, M. M. 1976. A rapid and sensitive method for the quantitation of microgram quantities of protein utilizing the principle of protein-dye binding. Anal. Biochem., 72:248-254.

Bryant, J. P., and P. J. Kuropat. 1980. Selection of winter forage by subarctic browsing vertebrates: The role of plant chemistry. Ann. Rev. Ecol. Syst., 11:261-285.

Dische, Z. 1962. Color reactions of hexoses. Pp. 488-494, in Methods in carbohydrate chemistry. Vol. 1. (R. L. Whistler and M. L. Wolfrom, eds.). Academic Press, New York, 589 pp.

Drozdz, A. 1968. Digestibility and assimilation of natural foods in small rodents. Acta Theriol., 8:367-389.

Drozdz, A. 1975. Food habits and food assimilation in mammals. Pp. 325-333, in Methods for ecological bioenergetics. (W. Grodzinski, R. Z. Klekowski, and A. Duncan, eds.). I.B.P. Handbook, No. 24, Blackwell Scientific Publications, Oxford, 367 pp.

Felker, P. 1976. A gas-liquid chromatographic-isotope dilution analysis of cysteine, histidine, and tryptophan in acid hydrolyzed protein. Anal. Biochem., 76:192-213.

Felker, P. 1977. Microdetermination of nitrogen in seed protein extracts with the salicylate-dichloroisocyanurate color reaction. Anal. Chem., 49:1080.

Fonnesbeck, P. V. 1969. Partitioning the nutrients of forage for horses. J. Animal Sci., 28:624-633.

Frape, D. L., M. G. Tuck, N. H. Sutcliffe, and D. B. Jones. 1982. The use of inert markers in the measurement of the digestibility of cubed concentrates and of hay given in several proportions to the pony, horse, and white rhinoceros (Diceros simus). Comp. Biochem. Physiol., 72A:77-83.

Freeland, W. J., and D. H. Janzen. 1974. Strategies in herbivory by mammals: The role of plant secondary compounds. Amer. Nat., 108:269-289.

Gerhardt, B., and H. Beevers. 1968. Influence of sucrose on protein determination by the Lowry procedure. Anal. Biochem., 24:337-352.

Glander, K. E. 1981. Feeding patterns in mantled howler monkeys. Pp. 231-257, in Foraging behavior: Ecological and psychological approaches. (A. C. Kamil and T. D. Sargent, eds.). Garland Press, New York, 534 pp.

Goering, H. K., and P. J. Van Soest. 1970. Forage fiber analysis (apparatus, reagents, procedures, and some applications). U.S.D.A. Agriculture Handbook, No. 379, Washington, D.C., 20 pp.

Hambraeus, L., E. Forsum, L. Abrahamson, and B. Lonnerdal. 1976. Automatic total nitrogen analysis in nutritional evaluations using a block digester. Anal. Biochem., 72:79-85.

Harborne, J. B. 1982. Introduction to ecological biochemistry. 2nd. ed. Academic Press, New York, 278 pp.

Herbst, L. 1983. Nutritional analyses of the wet season diet of Carollia perspicillata (Chiroptera: Phyllostomidae) in Parque Nacional Santa Rosa, Costa Rica. Unpubl. M. S. thesis. University of Miami, Coral Gables, Fl., 80 pp.

Hladik, C. M. 1977. Field methods for processing food samples. Pp. 595-601, in Primate ecology: Studies of feeding and ranging behaviour in lemurs, monkeys, and apes. (T. H. Clutton-Brock, ed.). Academic Press, New York, 631 pp.

Hodge, J. E., and B. T. Hofreiter. 1962. Determination of reducing sugars and carbohydrates. Pp. 380-394, in Methods in carbohydrate chemistry. Vol. 1. (R. L. Whistler and M. L. Wolfrom, eds.). Academic Press, New York, 589 pp.

Howe, H. F., and J. Smallwood. 1982. Ecology of seed dispersal. Ann. Rev. Ecol. Syst., 13:201-228.

Howell, D. J. 1974. Bats and pollen: Physiological aspects of the syndrome of chiropterophily. Comp. Biochem. Physiol., 48A:263-276.

Inglis, A. S., D. T. W. McMahon, C. M. Roxburgh, and H. Takayanagi. 1976. Single analysis for cysteine, cystine, and tryptophan in proteins. Anal. Biochem., 72:86-94.

Inouye, D. W., N. D. Faure, J. A. Lanum, D. M. Levine, J. B. Meyers, M. S. Roberts, F. C. Tsao, and Y. Wang. 1980. The effects of nonsugar nectar constituents on estimates of nectar energy content. Ecology, 61:992-996.

Janzen, D. H. 1983. Dispersal of seeds by vertebrate guts. Pp. 232-262, in Coevolution. (D. J. Futuyma and M. Slatkin, eds.). Sinauer, Sunderland, Massachusetts, 555 pp.

Johnson, D. R., and M. H. Maxell. 1966. Energy dynamics of Colorado pikas. Ecology, 47:1059-1061.

Johnson, D. R., and K. L. Groepper. 1970.

Bioenergetics of north plains rodents. Amer. Midl. Nat., 84:537-548.

Kanthor, H. A. 1965. Indwelling catheters for small bats. J. Applied Physiol., 20:326-327.

Kates, M. 1972. Techniques in lipidology: Isolation, analysis, and identification of lipids. American Elsevier Publ. Co., Inc., New York, 275-610 pp.

Kleiber, M. 1975. Fire of life: An introduction to animal energetics. 2nd ed. Krieger Publ. Co., Huntington, New York, 453 pp.

Kaufman, D. W., M. J. O'Farrell, G. A. Kaufman, S. E. Fuller. 1976. Digestibility and elemental assimilation in cotton rats. Acta Theriol., 21:147-156.

Klite, P. D. 1965. Intestinal bacterial flora and transit time of three neotropical bat species. J. Bacteriol., 90:375-379.

Kotb, A. R., and T. D. Luckey. 1972. Markers in nutrition. Nutr. Abstr. Rev., 42:813-845.

Kunsch, U., and A. Temperli. 1978. Changes in free and protein-bound amino acids in elderberry fruit *(Sambucus nigra)* during maturation. J. Sci. Fd. Agric., 29:1037-1040.

Kunz, T. H. 1980. Daily energy budgets of free-living bats. Pp. 369-392, in Proc. 5th Int. Bat Res. Conf. (D. E. Wilson and A. L. Gardner, eds.) Texas Tech Press, Lubbock, 434 pp.

Lang, C. A. 1958. Simple microdetermination of Kjeldahl nitrogen in biological materials. Anal. Chem., 30:1692.

Latkin, A. L. 1975. The estimation of proteins by dye-binding: Principles and experimental parameters. In Food group symposium: Rapid analysis of food. J. Sci. Fd. Agric., 26:549-558.

Lever, M. 1972. A new reaction for colorimetric determination of carbohydrates. Anal. Biochem., 47:273-279.

Lever, M., J. C. Powell, M. Killup, and C. W. Small. 1973. A comparison of 4-hydroxybenzoic acid hydrazide (PAHBAH) with other reagents for the determination of glucose. J. Lab. Clin. Med., 82:649-655.

Lowry, O. H., N. J. Rosebrough, A. L. Farr, and R. J. Randall. 1951. Protein measurement with the Folin Phenol reagent. J. Biol. Chem., 193:265-275.

Lucas, H. L., Jr., W. W. G. Smart, Jr., M. A. Cipolloni, and H. D. Gross. 1961. Relations between digestibility and composition of feeds and foods. S-45 Report, North Carolina State College (mimeo).

Mattson, W. J., Jr. 1980. Herbivory in relation to plant nitrogen content. Ann. Rev. Ecol. Syst., 11:119-161.

Maynard, L. A., J. K. Loosli, H. F. Hintz, and R. G. Warner. 1979. Animal nutrition. 7th ed. McGraw-Hill Book Co., New York, 602 pp.

McKey, D. 1975. The ecology of coevolved seed dispersal systems. Pp. 159-191, in Coevolution of animals and plants. (L. E. Gilbert and P. H. Raven, eds.). Univ. Texas Press, Austin, 263 pp.

Milton, K., and F. R. Dintzis. 1981. Nitrogen-protein conversion factors for tropical plant samples. Biotropica, 13:177-181.

Morrison, D. W. 1978. Foraging ecology and energetics of the frugivorous bat *Artibeus jamaicensis.* Ecology, 59:716-723.

Morrison, D. W. 1980. Efficiency of food utilization by fruit bats. Oecologia, 45:270-273.

Neurath, A. R. 1966. Interference of sodium ethylenediaminetetra-acetate in the determination of proteins and its elimination. Experientia, 22:290.

Nkonge, C., and C. M. Ballance. 1982. A sensitive colorimetric procedure for nitrogen determination in micro-Kjeldahl digests. J. Agric. Fd. Chem., 30:416-420.

Owen-Smith, N., and P. Novellie. 1982. What should a clever ungulate eat? Amer. Nat., 119:151-178.

Paine, R. T. 1971. The measurement and application of the calorie to ecological problems. Ann. Rev. Ecol. Syst., 2:145-164.

Prus, T. 1975. Measurement of calorific value using Phillipson microbomb calorimeter. Pp. 149-160, in Methods for ecological bioenergetics. (W. Grodzinski, R. Z. Klekowski, and A. Duncan, eds.). I.B.P. Handbook, No. 24, Blackwell Sci. Publ., Oxford, 367 pp.

Pulliam, H. R. 1975. Diet optimization with nutrient constraints. Amer. Nat., 109:765-768.

Rapport, D. J. 1980. Optimal foraging for complementary resources. Amer. Nat., 116:324-346.

Reese, J. C. 1979. Interactions of allelochemicals with nutrients in herbivore food. Pp. 309-330, in Herbivores: Their interaction with secondary plant metabolites. (G. A. Rosenthal and D. H. Janzen, eds.). Academic Press, New York, 718 pp.

Ring, S. G., and R. R. Selvendran. 1978. Purification and methylation analysis of cell wall material from *Solanum tuberosum.* Phytochemistry, 17:745-752.

Robertson, J. B., and P. J. Van Soest. 1981. The detergent system of analysis and its application to human foods. Pp. 123-158, in The analysis of dietary fiber in food. (W. P. T. James and O. Theander, eds.). Marcel Dekker, New York, 276 pp.

Rosenthal, G. A., and D. H. Janzen (eds.). 1979. Herbivores: Their interaction with secondary plant metabolites. Academic Press, New York, 718 pp.

Rosenthal, H. L., and W. A. Sobieszczanska. 1970. Influence of reducing sugars on protein determination by the Lowry procedure. Anal. Biochem., 34:591-598.

Selvendran, R. R. 1975. Analysis of cell wall material from plant tissues: Extraction and purification. Phytochemistry, 14:1011-1017.

Selvendran, R. R., J. F. March, and S. G. Ring. 1979a. Determination of aldoses and uronic acid content of vegetable fiber. Anal. Biochem., 96:282-292.

Selvendran, R. R., S. G. Ring, and M. S. DuPont. 1979b. Assessment of procedures used for analysing dietary fibre and some recent developments. Chemy. Ind., 7 April 1979, pp. 225-230.

Selvendran, R. R., S. G. Ring, and M. S. DuPont. 1981. Determination of the dietary fiber content of the EEC samples and a discussion of the various methods of analysis. Pp. 95-121, *in* The analysis of dietary fiber in food. (W. P. T. James and O. Theander, eds.). Marcel Dekker, New York, 276 pp.

Servello, F. A., K. E. Webb, Jr., and R. L. Kirkpatrick. 1983. Estimation of the digestibility of diets of small mammals in natural habitats. J. Mammal., 64:603-609.

Sibly, R. M. 1981. Strategies of digestion and defecation. Pp. 109-139, *in* Physiological ecology: An evolutionary approach to resource use. (C. R. Townsend and P. Calow, eds.). Sinauer, Sunderland, Massachusetts, 393 pp.

Smith, D., G. M. Paulsen, and C. A. Raguse. 1964. Extraction of total available carbohydrates from grass and legume tissue. Plant Physiol., 39:960-962.

Soholt, L. F. 1973. Consumption of primary production by a population of kangaroo rats *(Dipodomys merriami)* in the Mojave desert. Ecol. Monogr., 43:357-376.

Southgate, D. A. T. 1969a. Determination of carbohydrates in foods I.—Available carbohydrates. J. Sci. Fd. Agric., 20:326-330.

Southgate, D. A. T. 1969b. Determination of carbohydrates in foods II.—Unavailable carbohydrates. J. Sci. Fd. Agric., 20:331-335.

Southgate, D. A. T., G. J. Hudson, and H. Englyst. 1978. The analysis of dietary fibre—the choices for the analyst. J. Sci. Fd. Agric., 29:979-988.

Sutton, E. I., J. P. Bowland, and J. F. McCarthy. 1977. Studies with horses comparing 4N—HC1 insoluble ash as an index material with total collection in the determination of apparent digestibilities. Can. J. Anim. Sci., 57:543-549.

Sylvester-Bradley, R., and S. G. Howitt. 1977. An inexpensive procedure for the rapid determination of total nitrogen in multiple biological samples. J. Sci. Fd. Agric., 28:312-316.

Theander, O., and P. Aman. 1979. Studies on dietary fibres. 1. Analysis and chemical characterization of water-soluble and water-insoluble dietary fibres. Swedish J. Agric. Res., 9:97-106.

Trowell, H., D. A. T. Southgate, T. M. S. Wolever, A. R. Leeds, M. A. Gassull, and D. A. Jenkins. 1976. Dietary fibre redefined. Lancet, 1:967.

Vallejo, C. G., and R. Lagunas. 1970. Interferences by sulfhydryl, disulfide reagents and potassium ions on protein determination by Lowry's method. Anal. Biochem., 36:207-212.

Van Soest, P. J. 1967. Development of a comprehensive system of feed analysis and its application to forages. J. Anim. Sci., 26:119-128.

Van Soest, P. J. 1982. Nutritional ecology of the ruminant. O & B Books, Inc., Corvallis, Oregon, 373 pp.

Van Soest, P. J., and J. B. Robertson. 1976. What is fibre and fibre in food? Nutr. Rev., 35:12-22.

Waddell, W. J. 1956. A simple ultraviolet spectrophotometric method for the determination of protein. J. Lab. Clin. Med., 48:311.

Wall, L. L., and C. W. Gehrke. 1975. An automated total protein method. J. Assoc. Off. Anal. Chem., 58:1221-1226.

Walsberg, G. E. 1975. Digestive adaptations of *Phainopepla nitens* associated with the eating of mistletoe berries. Condor, 77:169-174.

Weatherburn. 1967. Phenol-hypochlorite reaction for determination of ammonia. Anal. Chem., 39:971-974.

Webster, G. C. 1970. Comparison of direct spectrophotometric methods for the measurement of protein concentration. Biochim. Biophys. Acta, 207:371-373.

Westoby, M. 1974. An analysis of diet selection by large generalist herbivores. Amer. Nat., 108:290-304.

White, S. C. 1974. Ecological aspects of growth and nutrition in tropical fruit-eating birds. Unpubl. Ph.D. dissertation. Univ. Pennsylvania, Philadelphia, 145 pp.

Wrigley, C. W., and H. L. Webster. 1968. Spectrophotometric estimation of protein in presence of ultraviolet-absorbing impurities. J. Chromatog., 33:534-536.

Chapter 16

Maintaining Bats for Captive Studies

Don E. Wilson

U.S. Fish & Wildlife Service
National Museum of Natural History
Washington, D.C. 20560, USA

1. INTRODUCTION

Bats enjoy little popularity as pets. In past years the only people who kept bats in captivity were those conducting research and those keeping them for exhibit purposes in zoological parks. Even as zoo animals, bats have been relatively neglected, compared with many other mammals. The taxonomic and ecological diversity found within the order Chiroptera is sufficient to argue for their interest as laboratory animals. Their unique physiological and behavioral adaptations (e.g., heterothermy, flight, and echolocation) offer promise for learning more about a variety of fields from factors regulating reproduction to navigation.

Until the past 10-15 years, the lack of interest in bat husbandry reflected a paucity of published literature dealing with specific problems and techniques associated with keeping bats. Several important reviews were published in the mid-seventies, beginning with Rasweiler's (1975) initial contribution on the subject. Racey (1976) provided a succinct summary of the literature that included a list of species then known to have been kept in captivity. Greenhall (1976) provided a compendium of information on how to keep members of the New World tropical family Phyllostomidae. This was followed by Rasweiler's (1977a) excellent treatise on bats as laboratory animals.

Rasweiler's work cited all of the pertinent earlier literature and provided valuable summaries of maintenance techniques through the mid-1970's. Rasweiler personally devoted years to developing better ways to keep bats in laboratory colonies, and his contributions to maintaining nectar and fruit-eating forms are particularly important.

His diets continue to be used, with minor modifications, in zoos and laboratories around the world. From the standpoint of this review, I have started with Rasweiler (1977a), and for the most part, have cited only those papers that have appeared since.

The most valuable summary since Rasweiler (1977a) is found in the compendium on *Zoo and Wild Animal Medicine* edited by Fowler (1978). Constantine, who has made important personal contributions to our knowledge of bat husbandry, edited a chapter on bats (Constantine, 1978), which contains sections by John J. Rasweiler IV, Roger E. Carpenter, and William A. Wimsatt, all of whom have had considerable experience with bat husbandry.

In an attempt to gather unpublished information from people who are actively involved in maintaining bats in captivity, I circulated a questionnaire to bat researchers and zoological parks in May 1983, requesting information on topics of potential interest to those interested in keeping bats. Of the 200 or so originally mailed, I received some 60-odd completed questionnaires and probably that many more letters from people who believed that they lacked sufficient knowledge to participate in the survey, but who had suggestions that proved useful. Most of the information that follows has been gleaned from the responses to this questionnaire. Without that gratifying response from my colleagues, this chapter would not have been possible.

2. DIET

2.1. Insectivorous Species

2.1.1. Diets for Insectivores

By far the most common food for insectivorous bats in captivity is the larvae of *Tenebrio molitor,* more commonly known as mealworms. These small larvae are easy to grow, clean to keep, and are attractive to most bat species that have been kept in captivity. If mealworms are raised in an enriched medium such as bran fortified with a high protein cereal like turkey starter or chick starter (available from any feed store), they will be completely adequate to maintain the body mass and health of vespertilionids and molossids. The proportions are, by volume, two parts bran to one part protein rich meal. Rasweiler (1977a) suggested that a chow designed for New World monkeys might come closest to providing the necessary vitamins and minerals for bats.

A bin containing this enriched medium should be covered with several layers of newspapers or coarse cloth sacking, which should be kept moist. The mealworms will come up to the moist surface and thus are easier to gather as needed. I have also used pieces of raw potato and apple to provide moisture to the larvae. The larvae will eventually pupate if not used, but they are still perfectly useful as bat food even as pupae. In fact, some species will eat the adult beetles.

It also may be useful to provide vitamin and mineral supplements, such as Vionate vitamin powder, Gevral protein powder, Stuart formula liquid, Pervinal syrup, calcium phosphate, and multivitamins. These supplements may be either dusted on the mealworms as powder, sprinkled on as liquid, or mixed with the drinking water.

Although it is possible to freeze mealworms and other insects, many workers have reported unsatisfactory results with this method. Other kinds of insects may be kept as living cultures to provide larvae, pupae, or adults as live food for bats. If necessary, most insects can be stored under refrigeration, for short periods in order to reduce their metabolic rate and to retard progress through their life cycle.

An intriguing possibility for keeping insectivorous bat species is to use a flight cage with a light to attract insects (Felten, 1956; Griffin, et al., 1960; Gustafson, 1975). This may be done more easily in tropical habitats than in temperate regions. If the favored natural foods are known, it may be possible to collect them in sufficient numbers to keep the bats healthy (see Chapter 12). This method assumes that the bats will reject or avoid distasteful or toxic forms. It is possible to feed insectivorous bats a variety of insect pupae in addition to mealworms. Some workers have used blowfly pupae alone or in combination with other insects. Wasp pupae may prove useful, if large numbers can be obtained easily.

The most common mixed diet for insectivorous species is commonly called bat glop. Although many workers have experimented with a great variety of ingredients for this food, the basic idea for its preparation is to blend a variety of items into a homogeneous mass (Appendix 1), freeze it, and provide it to the bats in small, thawed packages. This is of course more convenient than maintaining live insects, but the convenience is apparently the only advantage. Most workers have found that glop, regardless of the combination, is less satisfactory than using live, enriched mealworms along with a vitamin supplement.

2.1.2. Procedures for Training Bats to Eat

Even though most species of insectivorous bats seem capable of being maintained on a diet of enriched mealworms, frequently the bats must be trained to eat them. The usual approach is to offer the bat a squirming mealworm on the end of a pair of forceps. Most bats will bite at the worm and then will continue to eat once they get a taste of the larva. Recalcitrants may be induced to eat by cutting a mealworm in half and forcing the larva's body fluids onto the bat's lips. Once a bat has learned to accept food offered by hand, it may be helpful to confine it in a jar or glass bowl with a number of mealworms. The mealworms will crawl around and agitate the bat to the point when it should snap at them and thus begin to eat on its own. After a few such sessions, the quick learners will be able to feed freely on mealworms presented in a small dish. Regardless of species, there are always a few individuals that are slow to learn how to eat in captivity, and for such animals,

considerable patience is necessary. There are also species-specific feeding differences in the learning curve (Table 1).

Several workers have stressed the need to maintain the same feeding routine as an important part of the training process (see Chapter 17). Everything should be done exactly the same way, with the same daily routine so that bats become conditioned to meal time. Quiet surroundings with a minimum of disturbance will increase the chance of successful feeding.

2.1.3. Optimum Temperatures for Feeding Bats

There is no clear consensus on the optimal temperatures to insure proper feeding of insectivorous bats. Intuitively, one would expect each animal to do best at temperatures that approximate the normal ambient for that species. This would suggest that temperate species would do well at room temperatures (20-25°C) and that tropical forms might do better at slightly higher (25-30°C). Stones (1965) found that *Myotis lucifugus* required three times as much food at 24°C as they did at a thermoneutral temperature of 33°C.

Body temperature is the key factor. Torpid bats do not eat well when body temperature is low, and it takes time for them to arouse from torpor. Exercise (flight) before feeding facilitates the feeding process. This raises body temperature to homeothermic levels. Another way to keep body temperature high is to allow bats to roost together if possible.

Depending on available cages, it might be possible to provide bats with a range of temperatures in order to determine their preference. A small space heater in one part of the cage might be enough to create a temperature gradient. Even with this type of arrangement, the bats may eat more readily at a warmer temperature than that which they would otherwise select for normal roosting. Perhaps the best suggestion is to use a convenient temperature in the 20-30 range and to increase it if feeding problems are encountered.

Table 1. Summary of selected bat maintenance programs.

Diet Type	Species	Relative Success[1]	Source
Insectivorous	*Antrozous pallidus*	2	John E. Bassett
	Barbastella barbastellus	1	John J. Rasweiler IV
	Chalinolobus morio	3	William R. Phillips
	Eptesicus fuscus	3	Donald R. Clark
	Eptesicus nilssoni	2	John J. Rasweiler IV
	Eptesicus regulus	2	William R. Phillips
	Eptesicus sagittula	2	William R. Phillips
	Eptesicus serotinus	2	Aldo M. Voûte
	Eptesicus tenuipinnis	2	John J. Rasweiler IV
	Euderma maculatum	2	John J. Rasweiler IV
	Hipposideros caffer	1	John J. Rasweiler IV
	Hipposideros cineraceus	2	Adrian G. Marshall
	Hipposideros cyclops	1	John J. Rasweiler IV
	Lasionycteris noctivagans	2	John J. Rasweiler IV
	Lasiurus borealis	2	Robert T. Orr
	Lasiurus cinereus	2	Robert T. Orr
	Lasiurus seminolus	2	John J. Rasweiler IV
	Macrotus waterhousii	3	John J. Rasweiler IV
	Megaderma spasma	1	John J. Rasweiler IV
	Miniopterus medius	2	John J. Rasweiler IV
	Miniopterus schreibersii	2	John J. Rasweiler IV
	Molossus ater	2	Uwe Schmidt
	Molossus molossus	2	Uwe Schmidt
	Myotis austroriparius	1	John J. Rasweiler IV
	Myotis bechsteini	2	John J. Rasweiler IV
	Myotis californicus	2	Robert T. Orr
	Myotis daubentoni	2	John J. Rasweiler IV
	Myotis keenii	2	John J. Rasweiler IV
	Myotis leibii	2	John J. Rasweiler IV
	Myotis lucifugus	3	Donald R. Clark
	Myotis macrotarsus	2	John J. Rasweiler IV
	Myotis myotis	3	Uwe Schmidt
	Myotis mysticinus	2	John J. Rasweiler IV
	Myotis nattereri	1	John J. Rasweiler IV
	Myotis sodalis	2	David Bruce
	Myotis thysanodes	2	Robert T. Orr
	Myotis velifer	2	Richard K. LaVal
	Myotis yumanensis	2	Robert T. Orr
	Noctilio albiventris	3	John J. Rasweiler IV
	Nyctalus leisleri	2	John J. Rasweiler IV
	Nyctalus noctula	2	Paul A. Racey
	Nycteris grandis	2	John J. Rasweiler IV
	Nycticeius humeralis	1	Jacqueline J. Belwood
	Nyctophilus geoffroyi	2	Simon J. Inwards
	Nyctophilus gouldi	2	Simon J. Inwards
	Pipistrellus pipistrellus	3	John J. Rasweiler IV
	Pipistrellus subflavus	1	John J. Rasweiler IV
	Plecotus auritus	1	Ulla M. Norberg
	Plecotus townsendii	3	Clyde M. Senger
	Plecotus rafinesquii	2	John J. Rasweiller IV
	Pteronotus fuliginosus	2	John J. Rasweiler IV
	Pteronotus macleayii	2	John J. Rasweiler IV
	Pteronotus parnellii	3	John J. Rasweiler IV
	Pteronotus personatus	3	John J. Rasweiler IV
	Rhinolophus ferrumequinum	2	John J. Rasweiler IV

Table 1. Continued

Diet Type	Species	Relative Success[1]	Source
	Rhinolophus hipposideros	2	John J. Rasweiler IV
	Rhinolophus subrufus	2	John J. Rasweiler IV
	Rhinopoma hardwickei	1	Uwe Schmidt
	Rhinopoma macrophyllum	0	Uwe Schmidt
	Rhogeessa tumida	1	Timothy J. McCarthy
	Tadarida aegyptiaca	2	Richard K. LaVal
	Tadarida brasiliensis	3	Donald R. Clark
	Tadarida pumila	2	Richard K. LaVal
	Taphozous melanopogon	2	John J. Rasweiler IV
	Taphozous philippinensis	2	John J. Rasweiler IV
	Tylonycteris pachypus	2	John J. Rasweiler IV
	Tylonycteris robustula	2	John J. Rasweiler IV
	Vespertiliio murinus	2	John J. Rasweiler IV
Carnivorous	*Chrotopterus auritus*	3	Timothy J. McCarthy
	Macroderma gigas	3	Roger E. Carpenter
	Megaderma lyra	1	John J. Rasweiler IV
	Nycteris leisleri	1	Adam Krzanowski
	Phylloderma stenops	2	J. David Pye
	Trachops cirrhosus	2	Merlin D. Tuttle
	Vampyrum spectrum	3	Donald R. Griffin
Piscivorous	*Myotis vivesi*	2	Robert T. Orr
	Noctilio leporinus	2	James G. Doherty
Sanguinivorous	*Desmodus rotundus*	3	William A. Wimsatt
	Diaemus youngi	2	John J. Rasweiler IV
	Diphylla ecaudata	1	Richard K. LaVal
Frugivorous	*Artibeus jamaicensis*	2	Richard Mills
	Artibeus lituratus	3	Richard K. LaVal
	Artibeus toltecus	3	Richard K. LaVal
	Carollia brevicauda	3	Richard K. LaVal
	Carollia perspicillata	3	John J. Rasweiler IV
	Cynopterus brachyotis	3	Adrian G. Marshall
	Cynopterus horsfieldi	2	John J. Rasweiler IV
	Dobsonia minor	2	John J. Rasweiler IV
	Eidolon helvum	3	Roger E. Carpenter
	Epomophorous wahlbergi	3	Richard K. LaVal
	Epomops franqueti	2	John J. Rasweiler IV
	Hypsignathus monstrosus	3	Roger E. Carpenter
	Lissonycteris angolensis	2	John J. Rasweiler IV
	Micropteropus pusilus	3	Adrian G. Marshall
	Myonycteris torquata	3	J. David Pye
	Nanonycteris veldkampi	3	Adrian G. Marshall
	Nyctimene albiventer	1	John J. Rasweiler IV
	Nyctimene major	3	John J. Rasweiler IV
	Paranyctimene raptor	1	John J. Rasweiler IV
	Phyllostomus discolor	3	John J. Rasweiler IV
	Phyllostomus hastatus	3	John J. Rasweiler IV
	Pteropus giganteus	3	Bruce Bohmke
	Pteropus gouldi	2	John J. Rasweiler IV
	Pteropus hypomelanus	2	John J. Rasweiler IV
	Pteropus poliocephalus	2	John J. Rasweiler IV
	Pteropus rodricensis	2	J. B. Carrol
	Pteropus vampyrus	2	John J. Rasweiler IV
	Rousettus aegyptiacus	3	Uwe Schmidt
	Rousettus amplexicaudatus	3	Adrian G. Marshall
	Rousettus leachii	2	John J. Rasweiler IV

Table 1. Continued

Diet Type	Species	Relative Success[1]	Source
	Stenoderma rufum	2	John Rasweiler IV
	Sturnira lilium	1	John Rasweiler IV
	Sturnira ludovici	3	Richard K. LaVal
	Vampyrops helleri	3	John J. Rasweiler IV
	Vampyrops lineatus	2	John J. Rasweiler IV
	Vampyrops vittatus	3	Richard K. LaVal
Nectarivorous	*Anoura caudifera*	2	John J. Rasweiler IV
	Anoura geoffroyi	2	John J. Rasweiler IV
	Choeronycteris mexicana	2	John J. Rasweiler IV
	Glossophaga soricina	3	John J. Rasweiler IV
	Eonycteris spelaea	2	Adrian G. Marshall
	Hylonycteris underwoodi	2	John J. Rasweiler IV
	Leptonycteris nivalis	2	John J. Rasweiler IV
	Leptonycteris sanborni	2	Roger E. Carpenter
	Megaloglossus woermanni	2	Roger E. Carpenter
	Syconycteris australis	2	William Z. Lidicker, Jr.

[1]Scale of successful maintenance (0-3), based primarily on experience of listed investigator. If the source given is John J. Rasweiler IV, it is based on the tables in Rasweiler, 1977a, 1977b. 0 indicates no success.

2.2. Carnivorous Species

The most commonly kept carnivorous species are *Vampyrum spectrum* and *Phyllostomus hastatus.* Both are relatively easy to keep in captivity, and learn to eat a variety of foods. *Phyllostomus hastatus* is also frugivorous and nectarivorous, and *Vampyrum spectrum* will accept fruit in captivity. I have found fruit seeds in the feces of wild caught *Phylloderma stenops,* so perhaps this is another omnivore.

Among the food items suggested for carnivorous bats are small chunks of beef, white mice, rats, birds, bats, lizards, chicken meat, rabbit meat, chicks, quail, papaya, mango, melon, and banana. They usually can be taught to accept dead food and some seem to prefer it. Although these foods may be acceptable to the bats, it should be noted that many of these items by themselves, or even in combination, may not provide all of the animals' nutritional needs. For example, meat alone usually has a severely imbalanced Ca/P ratio. Supplementation of the foods listed with well-balanced vitamin and mineral mixes, and in some cases with additional high quality proteins, would seem to be in order.

2.3. Fish-Eating Bats

Various workers have kept *Noctilio leporinus* by feeding them small pieces of fish. The fish need not be alive and can be frozen for later use. Occasional bits of red meat and enriched mealworms will provide a supplement to a fish diet. Where flight facilities are available, this species can be taught to take live fish from the water (House and Doherty, 1975).

2.4. Vampires

Vampires (*Desmodus rotundus*) are popular laboratory animals, due primarily to their unique food habits. They are easily maintained and reared in captivity, and many captive colonies are in existence. Blood from freshly killed cattle frequently is available from local slaughterhouses. Fresh blood should be defibrinated physically by stirring, or chemically treated with sodium citrate or oxalate. It can be kept under refrigeration for about a week, and daily portions can be provided to the bats. At least the equivalent of 50 mg of blood per bat per day is adequate to sustain the animals.

Plastic ice cube trays make convenient

multi-compartmented serving trays, allowing several animals to feed simultaneously. Although such trays have the advantages of being inexpensive and easily procured, their use may promote spillage. Wimsatt (1978) has had good success with inexpensive, gravity-type, bird watering bottles equipped with partially covered feeding troughs. Multivitamin solution can be added to the blood, but probably is not necessary. Free water may be used if provided, but also may not be necessary. Some workers have used frozen defibrinated blood successfully, but others do not recommend it. It has been demonstrated that vampires can be maintained successfully for extended periods on frozen citrated blood (Dickson and Green, 1970; Quintero and Rasweiler, 1974), and clearly it is convenient when one does not have ready access to a supply of fresh blood.

2.5. Frugivorous and Nectarivorous Species

2.5.1. Diets for Megachiroptera

Megachiropterans have been kept by many workers, and frequently are found in zoos. A tremendous variety of foods have been used, with varying degrees of success. Fruits include banana, fig, passion fruit, apple, orange, raisins, grapes, pineapple, papaya, mango, pear, tomato, and breadfruit. Some vegetables, such as lettuce, sweet potato, carrot and various types of flower blossoms are also used as supplements to the fruit diets. Other additions include cottage cheese, cereal, bread, canned primate diet, monkey biscuits, prepared carnivore diet, New World monkey chow, and types of meat. Vitamin and mineral supplements, such as mineral powder (Osteoform), Vi-Daylin, calcium lactate, and a variety of multivitamins have been used as well.

Instant nectar combinations may be an appropriate choice of food for nectarivorous bats; however, some of these products contain primarily sugar. If the bats are to be kept for more than a day or two, investigators should be certain that the instant nectar is well-balanced, or it should be supplemented appropriately.

2.5.2. Diets for Microchiroptera

Phyllostomid bats are becoming more popular both as laboratory animals and zoo exhibits. Although a variety of species have been kept in captivity, the most popular ones have been members of the genera *Artibeus, Carollia,* and *Glossophaga.*

Several diets developed by Rasweiler (1977a, 1977b) have formed the basis for most of the standard diets used in zoos. The extensive summary found in Rasweiler (1977b) is still very much up to date. The nutrition laboratory at the National Zoological Park in Washington, D.C. reviewed Rasweiler's findings and reaffirmed that the diets should be providing a nutritionally balanced diet for the *Artibeus jamaicensis* and *Carollia perspicillata* in their colonies.

Several workers have kept a variety of frugivorous species for short periods of time in the field by feeding them naturally occurring fruits that regularly form a part of the bats' diet. This is probably preferable if sufficient natural fruits are available, but is likely to prove impractical for long-term maintenance, such as in laboratory or exhibit situations. Combinations of chopped and mixed banana, apple, orange, papaya, avocado, pear, grapes, hard boiled eggs, cooked carrots, cooked sweet potatoes, and canned feline diet, along with various vitamin and mineral supplements are used for a variety of species.

2.5.3. Nutrient Content of Foods

The nutrient requirements of fruit bats are unknown. A summary of methods for nutrient analysis appropriate for dietary items of plant-visiting bats is given in Chapter 15. The proper studies to establish quantitative norms have not been done. Theoretically, they should require all of the normal nutrients needed by other mammals—amino acids, essential fatty acids, and energy, as well as vitamins and minerals.

Rasweiler (1977a) provided a useful summary of the chemical composition of a variety of insects and plant parts as well as the content of selected vitamins and minerals in some of them. In constructing special diets for specific species, it would be useful to know which specific food items are either high or low in certain vitamins, minerals, or nutrients.

For example, insects are protein rich, with percentages as high as 46.6 in locusts (Bodenheimer, 1951) and 27.1 in beetles (Morton, 1973). However, they are quite low in carbohydrates, with reported values as low as 0% for crickets and 1.4% for caterpillars (Morton, 1973). Fat content of insects varies widely, with values of 1.3% for flying ants (Morton, 1973) ranging up to 28.3% for termites (Bodenheimer, 1951).

Although fruit and nectar are low in protein and fat (Morrison, 1980), dried fruits may reach 88.6% carbohydrates in the case of bananas (Watt, 1968), and 38.2% in dates (Leung, 1961). From the data given in Rasweiler (1977a) it is clear that bananas, a staple in most diets designed for captive bats, are low in calcium content. Peaches, on the other hand, are high in calcium.

3. NUTRITION

3.1. Nutritional Requirements

3.1.1. Protein

Protein requirements probably vary from species to species. Vogel (1969) provided the following figures on the nutritional content of mealworms, clearly the most used food for captive insectivores: 0.2 g/g protein, 0.03 g/g carbohydrate, and 0.18 g/g fat. Assuming a 10 g bat eats 2 grams of mealworms per day, it is getting 0.4 g protein, 0.06 g carbohydrate, and 0.36 g fat. Studies on daily energy budgets

of free-living bats (Anthony and Kunz, 1977; Kunz, 1980) may provide useful data for estimating energy requirements for captive species.

Blood, analysed on a dry matter basis, is 93% protein, 1% fat, 1% carbohydrate, and 5% ash (Steve Shumake, in litt.). If an average diet for an insectivorous species contained on the order of 10-20% protein, 2-5% carbohydrates, and 2-8% fat, then it is clear that vampires are using one of the most protein-rich diets known.

The protein requirements of most frugivores probably cannot be met by an unsupplemented fruit/vegetable diet. Note that recommended frugivore diets (Rasweiler, 1977a, 1977b) all contain some form of protein supplement.

3.1.2. Carbohydrates

Because frugivorous species are known to consume high-carbohydrate diets in nature (Chapter 13), they commonly are maintained in captivity on simple fruit diets that are rich in carbohydrates and little else. There is a growing body of circumstantial evidence suggesting that some species may consume large amounts of high-carbohydrate foods in order to obtain critical amounts of other nutrients that are in short supply in the normal diet (Fenton, 1983; Chapter 13).

There is also an accumulating body of evidence suggesting that many species previously believed to be strictly frugivorous or nectarivorous are in fact taking occasional insects in their diets (Wilson, 1973; Gardner, 1977). This further suggests that diets based solely on high carbohydrate fruits should be supplemented with protein, fat, mineral, and vitamin sources.

3.1.3. Fat

Although little is known of the fat requirements of any species of bat, presumably there is a requirement for essential fatty acids, much as in other mammals. One method of adding fatty acids to artificial diets is to use

Linatone, a commercial pet product used for birds, cats, and dogs. Rasweiler's (1977a, 1977b, 1978) standard diets for frugivores and nectarivores include corn oil, an inexpensive additive.

3.1.4. Vitamins and Minerals

It seems clear that all bats have specific vitamin and mineral requirements that vary from species to species. Buckland-Wright and Pye (1973) documented a case of calcium and vitamin D deficiency in *Rousettus aegyptiacus.* The afflicted animals showed symptoms of hyperexcitability during handling followed by a tetanic condition in which the wings were partly unfolded, resulting in the death of apparently healthy animals. The problem was solved completely by providing a supplement rich in calcium and vitamin D.

Most recommended artificial diet mixtures include a combination of vitamins and minerals. Rasweiler's (1977a) caveats regarding selection of multivitamins apply here: those concocted for humans or other species may not be suited to the specific requirements of bats.

3.1.5. Dietary Deficiencies

Several workers reported problems with fragile bones of bats, especially in young animals of several frugivorous species. This condition was normally rectified by supplementing the diet with calcium (Buckland-Wright and Pye, 1973). A gelatin diet (Appendix 1) was formulated at the Metropolitan Toronto Zoo in response to a deficiency problem. This zoo reported that during September-November, 1977, they lost four bats, and the remaining six individuals developed a condition characterized by general weakness, poor appetite, loss of mass, and inability to fly. In addition to this, some of them showed soft bony swellings along the wing bones. Their diet was evaluated and found to be deficient in several components: protein, calcium, phosphorus, and vitamin D were particularly low. At that time their diet consisted primarily of a mixture of

fruits plus two vitamin-mineral supplements sprinkled on top of fruits. The gelatin diet was formulated at that time and has been used ever since. The bats were treated with injections of vitamin and mineral supplements. This plus the new diet solved the problem. The swellings disappeared and the bats recovered, including their ability to fly.

3.1.6. Water

Although water balance studies on a variety of bats have demonstrated variability in the need for free water (Geluso, 1980), the safest course would be to provide water *ad libitum* to all captive bats. Fruit and nectar feeders may drink little depending on the diet provided, but they and even vampires may drink free water under certain conditions such as unusually high temperatures and high humidities.

Water may be provided in drinking tubes, which most species can be taught to use, or in a variety of open bowls or containers. The disadvantage of open containers is that they frequently become fouled by food or feces. This problem may be circumvented by covering shallow pans with plexiglass with small openings cut at one edge for access.

3.2. Feeding Requirements

3.2.1. Feeding Schedules

There is a divergence of opinion regarding the proper feeding schedules for different species of bats. One variable that might be important is group size. It may be necessary to provide food at more frequent intervals for large colonies to ensure that each individual receives food, although this procedure might run the risk of disrupting normal circadian rhythms. If only a single daily feeding is provided, the most frequently recommended time is just at the beginning of the bat's night cycle. *Ad libitum* feeding has been suggested for some, but other species, such as *Antrozous pallidus* and *Eptesicus fuscus,* will overeat in captivity to the point of becoming too obese to fly.

3.2.2. Overeating

Overeating problems can occur, and may result in other members of the group being underfed. If individuals can be separated and provided limited rations, the problems are easily solved. In general, bats maintained in flight cages are less likely to overeat. The excess energy can be burned off in exercise if flight is possible.

4. HOUSING

4.1. Cages

4.1.1. Flight Cages

If space is available, all bats do best in cages large enough to permit free flight. A cage with a glass front, rockwork sides, wire mesh top, and pitched concrete floor would provide a good combination of perches, allow good visibility and be easy to clean. The higher the cage, the more secure the bats will feel, but high cages make catching the bats more difficult. If the cages are made of wire, it should be sufficiently small mesh so that the bats cannot push a wing or foot through it, and preferably vinyl coated. A teflon spray can be used on cages to render the mesh smooth and non-irritating. Smaller roosting boxes should be provided somewhere within the cage. Gustafson (1975) provided an excellent design for a flight cage that could be modified for almost any species.

Animals that are deprived of flight for periods of a month or more may lose the ability to fly. They can be re-taught to fly by tossing them to a net or to a human catcher, and increasing the distance a few feet at a time (Carpenter, 1978). A 4 × 4 m plastic or nylon mesh screen tent makes a good flight cage for use in the field.

4.1.2. Small Roost Cages

Permanent cages of almost infinite variety have been used to keep bats for varying

lengths of time. One common type of cage is the wire mesh or welded-wire rodent cages available in a variety of sizes. One possible disadvantage of galvanized iron cages is that the tinned surface metal may be corroded by urine and rendered poisonous.

Small aquaria with mesh tops have been used to maintain individual bats. Some species prefer to roost in a crevice which might have to be added to otherwise simple cages. One of the most popular of small disposable cages is the old fashioned round one- or two-quart ice cream cartons with one end screened and the other with either a water dish or drinking tube.

A simple inexpensive cage for accommodating individual vampire bats was described by Lord (1971, 1981). The cage is made from a one-gallon, cylindrical oil can. The open end of the can is removed completely and replaced with hardware cloth. The bottom is separated by cutting around the sides 50 mm above the base, and the edges of the cut stretched outward slightly to increase the diameter so that the upper part can then be forced down inside the base. Hardware cloth is soldered to one side within the upper half, and a hole is cut into the side of the bottom half to receive a plastic water feeder (normally used for birds). This cage solves the problem of cage cleaning by preparing two bottoms which can be interchanged and cleaned manually or autoclaved. The cages are large enough to hold more than one bat for short periods, and additional feeders can be inserted into the bottom if necessary.

4.1.3. Perches

Smaller cages where the bats spend all of their time hanging put a premium on the type of perches used. The most common type of perch is hardware cloth or wire mesh used in the construction of the roof or sides of the cage. Although many workers report complete satisfaction with this method, others have encountered problems. Ordinary hot-dipped galvanized hardware cloth is rough enough to irritate the wrist area of the bat as it lands and roosts on it. The other common problem is irritation or even loss of claws that are constantly drawn across fine wires. Hardware cloth made of smooth galvanized wire of a heavier gauge would help to minimize these problems, but a variety of other materials can be used as alternative perches. If bats are maintained in cages completely made of wire, the toenails may grow long enough to need clipping (Carpenter, 1978). Providing branches or other sorts of wooden perches should alleviate the problem.

Among successfully-used alternatives are tree branches, burlap, cork board, bark, nylon netting, styrofoam, plywood with small holes and ribs added, string, unfinished wood, textured plaster, or any artificially roughened surface. Regardless of the types of perches provided, bats frequently will congregate at the highest parts of the cage. This suggests that either the roof be designed to provide them with the proper perches, or it should be so smooth as to force them to use the alternatives provided. A similar problem may be encountered with some species that prefer to roost against the wall of the cage, even if it means accepting a poorer-quality perch. For these species, either the walls should be constructed of proper perching materials, or perches should be placed close enough to the wall to allow the bats to roost against it. Sacking or plastic mesh hung an inch or so from the wall and extending well down the side may be attractive to species that normally roost in crevices.

4.2. Lighting

Although studies of the effect of photoperiod on reproduction in captive bats are available, (Racey, 1978; Beasley and Zucker, 1984; Beasley et al., 1984) little is known about the effect of photoperiod on general well-being of bats. Most workers maintain bats on a 12:12 light/dark cycle. These cycles may approximate ambient or may be reversed for exhibit or study purposes. A reverse cycle with lights on at 2000 h and off at 0800 h has been used successfully for the past ten years at the National Zoological Park, and the colony of *Artibeus jamaicensis* kept there has produced young regularly.

Presumably, the best system would be one that closely mimics the natural situation. Outdoor cages in the animals' natural range would be an obvious solution, but they present other problems, especially during the temperate-zone winter. It should be simple enough to vary the photoperiod somewhat by simply providing long days during part of the year and shorter ones during the other part.

4.3. Climate Control

Maintaining bats at natural temperatures is impractical in most instances, and rather than providing a temperature regime that varies daily and seasonally, most workers have opted for either a constant warm temperature for active bats, or a constant cold one for hibernating individuals. For maintaining bats at a constant temperature that allows for normal flight and feeding behavior, 24°C is probably the minimum, even for cold-hearty, temperate zone insectivores. 33°C is likely the maximum, even for tropical species normally occurring in hot climates, and a happy medium for most species might be around 26°C. Stones (1965) recommended keeping *Myotis lucifugus* at thermoneutrality, near 33°C. The proper humidities for maintaining bats have been determined only by trial and error, and no sound data are available to guide one's choice. Once again, the optimum would probably mimic the natural situation as closely as possible, but this is almost never practical. Most people recommended humidities in the range of 60-90% for most kinds of bats. In large cages, the humidity can be increased by watering the cage floor daily or more frequently if necessary.

4.4. Sanitation

4.4.1. Ventilation

A room with fresh air entering at floor level and venting through the roof should be adequate for most captive colonies. Occasionally, odor problems can occur if large colonies are kept in confined spaces inside a building used for other purposes. This may be true particularly for large fruit-eating bats that produce substantial amounts of feces susceptible to rapid bacteriological breakdown. In such cases, air should be ducted to the outside rather than to internal recirculating systems.

4.4.2. Floor Coverings

The ideal floor covering is one that provides maximum sanitation and cleaning ease. Various materials have been used, including cardboard, paper, wood shavings, plastic, stainless steel, newspaper, dried leaves, bark mulch, peat moss, tile, plastic-backed absorbent paper, sand, plexiglass, soil planted with grass clumps and small bushes, sawdust, paper toweling, and fine hay. One problem with many of these materials is that recovery of food dropped to the floor becomes difficult for some bats. Mealworms, for example, disappear rapidly into wood shavings, dried leaves, or other loose or porous coverings.

One simple solution involves the use of wax paper or thin plastic from a large roll passing into the cage at one end and out the other end, allowing it to be cranked through daily with the soiled part then being cut off and disposed of. A similar system was used for the vampire colony at Cornell University, where plastic backed absorbent paper was used, which absorbed the loose feces produced by vampires (William A. Wimsatt, in litt.).

4.4.3. Cage Cleaning

Although no one suggested any particular problems associated with disinfectant use, all disinfectants are potentially harmful, so perhaps cleaning could be accomplished most safely with hot water. For small cages, autoclaving is recommended.

5. MANAGEMENT

5.1. Transportation

Transporting bats is particularly stressful to them, and every precaution should be taken to insure their safety and continued well-being during the trip. Even short distance transportation by automobile can be traumatic. Dehydration can be a serious problem. Using wooden compartments that allow bats to cluster will enable them to stay warm and minimize water loss (Chapter 22). Hibernating animals can be transported in coolers with ice in winter, as long as they are kept dry. On very warm days in summer, adding moist paper to the container will help reduce desiccation, and transportation at night can help to avoid hot, dry summer air.

If cloth bags are used, one or at most a few bats per bag is best, and more than one species should never be put together in a single bag. Double containers are favored by several workers and zoos, especially if it is necessary to ship the animals by air freight. If possible, it is more secure to transport live animals as carry-on luggage. For example, plastic refrigerator boxes with perforations for air circulation, stored in a sturdy outside container, work well. The boxes can be lined with plastic screening for perches. Cedar chips can be placed on the bottom, and covered with burlap. Bats should be shipped only one to a container. The bats need to be protected from temperature extremes, and the containers should be padded to protect against rough handling. Heat in particular may be a problem in tropical areas, and wet newspapers or burlap under and over the cages may help to keep them cool. The container should be small enough to mimimize movement of the animals, either voluntary or involuntary.

5.2. Special Handling Techniques

Because bats are a bit more unusual than are ordinarily encountered mammals, some people are understandably timid about handling them. Unfortunately, this timidity can result in bats being handled too roughly. Common safety precautions dictate using gloves or some sort of hand protection when handling newly caught or skitterish large species; small species and those individuals that have been tamed and are used to being handled often can be handled without gloves. Restraining devices can be used. For example, one-inch-wide velcro strips can be sewn back to back to make a strap that can be used to restrain animals for special handling. Several marking techniques are discussed in Chapter 4.

5.3.   Behavior and Reproduction

5.3.1.   Social Interactions

Bats that are known to be solitary, such as lasiurines, should be housed individually. Frequently, new individuals that are introduced into an already established colony may be ostracized. As with so many other areas of bat husbandry, the more knowledge we have of the natural state of the species in question, the easier it is to maintain them successfully in captivity. This argues not only for more and better field studies, but also for detailed record keeping and observations of captive colonies. Chapter 9 contains additional information on the social structure of bats that may be useful to anyone keeping a captive colony.

5.3.2.   Reproduction

Animals that are not in the best physical, physiological, and psychological condition rarely breed in captivity. Some species may require special handling, such as separation of pregnant females, or removing lone bachelor males. In general, frugivores are easier to breed in captivity than are insectivores. An excellent review of the ecology of reproduction in bats may be found in Racey (1982).

5.3.3.   Raising Young

By far the easiest method of rearing young is to let the parents do it. With almost every species, the success ratio will be higher for infants reared by their natural mothers than for those hand-raised by humans. Unfortunately, there are often cases of infant rejection by the mother, and then hand rearing becomes a necessity. Babies can be fed while hanging upside down and wrapped in a soft cloth. It will be necessary to use a hand-made nipple and a small bottle made from a vial or syringe.

Taylor et al. (1974) used a stomach catheter to hand rear one-week-old *Eptesicus fuscus* and *Antrozous pallidus*. The catheter was made from medical grade (B-D) silastic tubing (0.012 inches I.D., 0.025 inches O.D.) stiffened with #40 stainless steel surgical wire. The tube was inserted through the mouth and esophagus into the stomach, and measured amounts of formula were delivered using a hypodermic syringe. For the first couple of weeks, babies can be fed on any commercially available human baby formula, given in small amounts. Frugivores can be weaned to a combination of mashed banana and baby cereal beginning at three weeks. By nine weeks, they should eat any available diced fruits.

5.4.   Other Laboratory Techniques

Bats that are maintained as research colonies may prove to be useful experimental organisms for a variety of studies. There are a number of laboratory techniques that might be modified for use on bats. In general, the only limitations on using bats is their small size.

5.4.1.   Milk Samples

Milk samples from lactating females are relatively easy to take using microcapillary tubes. Larger species produce large volumes of milk, and when lactating even the smallest have relatively large mammary glands. Separating the mother from the infant will allow the milk to build up in sufficient quantities. Gentle pressure applied around the edges of the mammary tissue will express the milk, which can then be collected in a capillary tube. If necessary, the injection of oxytocin will stimulate milk let-down (Kunz et al., 1983).

5.4.2. Urine Samples

Collecting urine samples from bats is fairly simple, because they almost always urinate when handled (see Chapter 22). If the bat is gently removed from the cage and quickly turned on its back, it usually will urinate within a few seconds. If not, a firm squeeze by the hand holding the bat or a gentle squeeze near the bladder often helps. The urine can be collected in a container, or directly from the urethra with glass capillary tubes 1.5-2.0 millimeters in diameter. These can be immediately sealed with critocaps, labeled, and stored at -20°C until analyzed.

5.4.3. Anesthetics

For a variety of experimental procedures, it may be necessary to anesthetize bats. A wide variety of common anesthetics has been used by investigators, and no consensus exists for which is best. Placing the bat in a glass jar with an ether soaked cotton wad is effective, as is using a nose cone. Ideally, Fluothane should be delivered by an anesthetic machine that enables pure oxygen to be supplied instantly if the bat starts going too far under.

Chloralose can be injected intraperitoneally in a dosage of 110-115 mg/kg body mass. Evipan has been used successfully on vampires (Uwe Schmidt, in litt.). A combination of 11 mg/kg Ketamine hydrochloride and 1.1 mg/kg Acepromazine has been used as well (Carpenter, 1978). Ketamine is probably the safest of the injectants, and if it causes muscle tremors, it can be mixed with Xylazine or Acepromazine to aid in muscle relaxation.

6. HEALTH PRECAUTIONS

6.1. Parasites

6.1.1. Ectoparasites

Ectoparasites disappear from most species after a short time in captivity. If, however, ectoparasites are a problem, the best solution is to remove them by hand. If necessary, bats can be dusted with a commercial flea powder using a cotton swab. This should eliminate the ectoparasites effectively, and once gone, they are unlikely to reinfest the colony unless new bats are added.

6.1.2. Endoparasites

Few problems have been noted with endoparasites in captive bats. Routine medications work well on internal parasites and are probably safe for most species. Ascarids are the most likely, and a worming medicine such as Telmin or Mintezol (Thibendazole) applied to the food should eradicate them.

6.2. Diarrhea

If diarrhea appears suddenly and affects the whole colony, the food should be checked for *Salmonella*. Chronic diarrhea in insectivores may be due to a lack of exoskeleton that they normally get from an insect diet. Feeding them mealworms should solve the problem.

6.3. Hair Loss

Many species of bats suffer hair loss in captivity. Hair loss seems to get progressively worse in some animals the longer they are in captivity. Determining the reasons for the hair loss can be difficult. If bats are fed in such a way that they get the food on the hair, it may exacerbate the problem. The problem may be solved by providing the fruit on better-drained platforms. If the problem is nutritional, the treatment is unclear. The diet should be analyzed to make sure it is balanced nutritionally.

6.4. Sores

Sedentary individuals that cannot fly, or that spend a good deal of time crawling on the floor, often develop sores along the leading edges of the wings. The sores can be treated with any commercially available topical antibiotic.

7. SUMMARY

Because bats are unique among mammals in many respects, they have special requirements for successful maintenance in the laboratory. The roughly 850 species in the order Chiroptera encompass a wide variety of food habits, and their individual nutritional requirements are poorly known. Cage design is important, and most species do better in cages sufficiently large to allow flight. Although maintenance requirements have not been standardized, there is an accumulating body of literature detailing various techniques that can be used to keep and study captive bats. Bats are relatively simple to maintain in a healthy condition, and minor health problems are easily treated.

It would be most useful if future students of captive bats would keep careful records of their management techniques. Most knowledge of bat husbandry is gained through trial and error, and the benefits of shared experience might eliminate many errors. Carefully controlled experiments testing the effects of various diets, housing conditions and handling techniques are needed.

8. ACKNOWLEDGMENTS

I am grateful to the following people for providing information in response to the questionnaire: John E. Bassett, Jacqueline J. Belwood, Johnny Binder, Bruch Bohmke, David Bruce, L. W. Cahill, William Caire, Roger E. Carpenter, J. B. Carrol, Jerry R. Choate, Donald R. Clark, Denny G. Constantine, D. Dekker, James G. Doherty, Mike Dulaney, Heinz Felten, M. Brock Fenton, Theodore H. Fleming, Kenneth N. Geluso, Bryan P. Glass, Donald R. Griffin, Larry Herbst, G. Roy Horst, Simon J. Inwards, Clyde Jones, Henry Kacprzyk, Ken Kawata, Ralph D. Kirkpatrick, Adam Krzanowski, Richard K. LaVal, William Z. Lidicker, Jr., Rexford D. Lord, Adrian G. Marshall, Sumiko Matsumura, Timothy J. McCarthy, George McKey, Dennis Meritt, Richard S. Mills, G. Clay Mitchell, Ulla M. Norberg, Robert T. Orr, William R. Phillips, J. David Pye, Paul A. Racey, Ken Redman, Hubert Roer, Mark Rosenthal, Uwe Schmidt, Clyde M. Senger, Stephen Shumake, Ronnie Sidner, Ray T. Sterner, Eugene H. Studier, Merlin D. Tuttle, Aldo M. Voûte, William A. Wimsatt. Helen Harbett labored long hours preparing and mailing the questionnaire and collating the responses. Alfred L. Gardner, Charles O. Handley, Jr., John J. Rasweiler, IV, and Uwe Schmidt provided helpful comments on the manuscript. Mention of a trade name does not constitute endorsement by the U. S. Government.

9. REFERENCES

Anthony, E. L. P., and T. H. Kunz. 1977. Feeding strategies of the little brown bat, *Myotis lucifugus,* in southern New Hampshire. Ecology, 58:775-786.

Beasley, L. J., and I. Zucker. 1984. Photoperiod influences the annual reproductive cycle of the male pallid bat (*Antrozous pallidus*). J. Reprod. Fert., 70:567-573.

Beasley, L. J., L. Smale, and E. R. Smith. 1984. Melatonin influences the reproductive physiology of male pallid bats. Biol. Reprod., 30:300-305.

Bodenheimer, F. M. 1951. Insects as human food. Junk, The Hague, 352 pp.

Buckland-Wright, J. C., and J. D. Pye. 1973. Dietary deficiency in fruit bats. Int. Zoo Yearbook, 13:271-277.

Carpenter, R. E. 1978. Old World fruit bats. Pp. 495-500, *in* Zoo and Wild Animal Medicine. (M. E. Fowler, ed.). W. B. Saunders Co., Philadelphia, 951 pp.

Constantine, D. G. 1978. Bats (Chiroptera). Pp. 492-521, *in* Zoo and Wild Animal Medicine. (M. E. Fowler, ed.). W. B. Saunders Co., Philadelphia, 951 pp.

Dickson, J. M., and D. G. Green. 1970. The vampire bat (*Desmodus rotundus*): Improved methods of laboratory care and handling. Lab. Anim., 4:37-44.

Felten, H. 1956. Fledermause aus El Salvador. Senckenbergiana Biol., 37:179-212.

Fenton, M. B. 1983. Just Bats. Univ. Toronto Press, Toronto, 165 pp.

Fowler, M. E. (ed.). 1978. Zoo and wild animal medicine. W. B. Saunders, Philadelphia, 951 pp.

Gardner, A. L. 1977. Feeding habits. Pp. 293-350, *in* Biology of bats of the New World family Phyllostomatidae. Part II. (R. J. Baker, J. K. Jones, Jr., and D. C. Carter, eds.). Spec. Publ. Mus. Texas Tech Univ., Lubbock, 364 pp.

Geluso, K. N. 1980. Renal form and function in bats: An ecophysiological appraisal. Pp. 403-414, *in* Proc. 5th Int. Bat Res. Con. (D. E. Wilson and A. L. Gardner, eds.). Texas Tech Press, Lubbock, Texas, 434 pp.

Greenhall, A. M. 1976. Care in captivity. Pp. 89-131, *in* Biology of bats of the New World family Phyllostomatidae. Part I. (R. J. Baker, J. K. Jones, and D. C. Carter, eds.). Spec. Publ. Mus. Texas Tech Univ., Lubbock, Texas, 218 pp.

Griffin, D. R., F. A. Webster, and C. R. Michael. 1960. The echolocation of flying insects by bats. Anim. Behav., 8:141-154.

Gustafson, A. W. 1975. An outdoor flight cage suitable for keeping and maintaining insectivorous bats in captivity. Bat Res. News, 16:23-25.

House, H. B., and J. G. Doherty. 1975. The world of darkness at the New York Zoological Park. Int. Zoo Yearbook, 15:31-34.

Kunz, T. H. 1980. Daily energy budgets of free-living bats. Pp. 369-392, *in* Proc. 5th Int. Bat Res. Conf. (D. E. Wilson and A. L. Gardner, eds.), Texas Tech Press, Lubbock, Texas, 434 pp.

Kunz, T. H., M. H. Stack, and R. Jenness. 1983. A comparison of milk composition in *Myotis lucifugus* and *Eptesicus fuscus* (Chiroptera: Vespertilionidae). Biol. Reprod., 28:229-234.

Leung, W.-T. W. 1961. Food composition table for use in Latin America. Interdepartmental Comm. on Nutrition for Nat. Defense, NIH, Bethesda, Maryland, 145 pp.

Lord, R. D. 1971. A simple inexpensive cage for vampire bats. Zoonosis, 13:225-228.

Lord, R. D. 1981. Comportamiento en cautiverio de murcielagos vampiros en Argentina. An. Inst. Biol. Univ. Nal. Autón. de México, 51:591-604.

Morrison, D. W. 1980. Efficiency of food utilization by fruit bats. Oecologia, 45:270-273.

Morton, E. S. 1973. On the evolutionary advantages and disadvantages of fruit eating in tropical birds. Amer. Nat., 107:8-22.

Quintero, H. F., and J. J. Rasweiler, IV. 1974. Ovulation and early embryonic development in the captive vampire bat, *Desmodus rotundus*. J. Reprod. Fert., 41:265-273.

Racey, P. A. 1976. Bats. Pp. 298-310, *in* UFAW handbook on the care and management of laboratory animals. 5th ed., Churchill Livingstone, Edinburgh, 635 pp.

Racey, P. A. 1978. The effect of photoperiod on the initiation of spermatogenesis in pipistrelle bats, *Pipistrellus pipistrellus*. Pp. 255-258, *in* Proc. 4th Int. Bat Res. Conf. (R. J. Olembo, J. B. Castelino, and F. A. Mutere, eds.). Kenya Nat. Acad. of Arts and Sci., Nairobi, 328 pp.

Racey, P. A. 1982. Ecology of bat reproduction. Pp. 57-104, *in* Ecology of bats. (T. H. Kunz, ed.). Plenum Press, New York, 425 pp.

Rasweiler, J. J., IV. 1975. Maintaining and breeding neotropical frugivorous, nectarivorous, and pollinivorous bats. Int. Zoo Yearbook, 15:18-30.

Rasweiler, J. J., IV. 1977a. Bats as laboratory animals. Pp. 519-617, *in* Biology of bats. Vol. III. (W. A. Wimsatt, ed.). Academic Press, New York, 651 pp.

Rasweiler, J. J., IV. 1977b. Diets for Chiroptera. Pp. 493-533, *in* CRC handbook series in nutrition and food, Section G: Diets, culture media, food supplements. (M. Rechcigl, Jr., ed.). CRC Press, Boca Raton, Florida, 645 pp.

Rasweiler, J. J., IV. 1978. American leaf-nosed bats. Pp. 500-507, *in* Zoo and Wild Animal Medicine. (M. E. Fowler, ed.). W. B. Saunders, Philadelphia, 951 pp.

Stones, R. C. 1965. Laboratory care of little brown bats at thermal neutrality. J. Mammal., 46:681-682.

Taylor, H., E. Gould, A. Frank, and N. Woolf. 1974. Successful hand-raising of one week old bats, *Eptesicus* and *Antrozous,* by stomach catheter. J. Mammal., 55:228-231.

Vogel, V. B. 1969. Vergleichende Untersuchungen uber den Wasserhaushalt von Fledermausen (*Rhinopoma, Rhinolophus,* und *Myotis*). Z. Vergl. Physiol., 76:358-371.

Watt, B. K. 1968. Composition of foods, raw and processed: Plant origin. Pp. 26-47, *in* Metabolism. (P. L. Altman and D. S. Dittmer, eds.). Fed. Am. Soc. Exp. Biol., Bethesda, Maryland, 737 pp.

Wilson, D. E. 1973. Bat Faunas: A trophic comparison. Syst. Zool., 22:14-29.

Wimsatt, W. A. 1978. Vampire bats. Pp. 507-513, *in* Zoo and Wild Animal Medicine. (M. E. Fowler, ed.). W. B. Saunders, Philadelphia, 951 pp.

Appendix 1A. Suggested Ingredients for Bat Glop (Although all of these combinations have been used, none are highly recommended.)

(1) Banana, honey, cottage cheese, and mealworms.
(2) Cottage cheese, mealworms, and vitamins (D. Bruce).
(3) Cottage cheese, canned dog food, hard boiled egg, vionate vitamins, and crickets or mealworms.
(4) Banana, milk powder, hard boiled egg, mealworms, vitamins, and trace elements (A. M. Voûte).
(5) Banana, cheese, egg yolk and vitamins (S. Matsumura).
(6) Mealworms, cream cheese, bananas, and vitamin D (W. Z. Lidicker).
(7) Lean beef, mealworms, tri-vi-sol, linatone, dog vitamins, and calcium lactate (M. B. Fenton).
(8) Cottage cheese, hard boiled egg, banana, and vitamins (P. A. Racey).
(9) Mink chow, Nutriderm, banana, mealworms, and canned feline diet (Brookfield Zoo).
(10) Trout chow, canned dog food, and vitamins.
(11) Banana, egg yolk, cream cheese, and mealworms (M. D. Tuttle).
(12) Cottage cheese, bananas, and cockroaches (R. E. Carpenter).
(13) Banana, boiled eggs, cream cheese, canned dog food, and vitamins (S. J. Inwards and W. R. Phillips).

Appendix 1B. Fruit Bat Diets Used at the Metropolitan Toronto Zoo (courtesy of L. W. Cahill)

a) Egyptian fruit bat (*Rousettus aegyptiacus*)

Diet Ingredients	g/day[1,5]	% composition
Bananas	1,880	41.19
Fruit bat gelatin diet formula[2]	880	19.28
Oranges	530	11.60
Figs	440	9.64
Grapes	440	9.64
Carnivore diet formula[3]	270	5.92
Shrimp meal	50	1.10
Pulverized limestone (39% Ca)	45	0.99
Rogar/STB SA-37 pet supplement	29	0.64
Total	4,564	100.00

[1] Daily ration for 36 animals.

b) Indian flying fox (*Pteropus giganteus*)

Diet Ingredients	g/day[1,5]	% composition
Bananas	1,400	42.04
Gelatin diet formula[2]	550	16.52
Oranges	200	6.00
Figs	210	6.31
Grapes	500	15.02
Apples	350	10.51
Fruit bat supplement[4]	120	3.60
Total	3,330	100.00

[1] Daily ration for 18 animals.

[2] Gelatin Diet Formula	% composition
Water, hot	38.75
Bananas	31.00
Jelly powder-strawberry flavor	6.59
Unflavored gelatin powder	5.81
Granulated sugar	2.33
Pulverized limestone (39% Ca)	0.78
Cyphos-21 (18% Ca, 21% P)	1.55
Rogar/STB SA-37 supplement powder	1.55
Vitamin E supplement powder	0.39
Vitamin C	0.39
Skim milk powder	3.88
Corn oil	2.33
Lean ground beef heart	4.65

[3] Carnivore Diet Formula	% composition
Lean ground horse meat	93.00
Carnivore supplement powder	7.00

[4] Fruit Bat Supplement	% composition
Bone meal, animal feed grade	34.02
Cyphos-21 (18% Ca, 21% P)	22.68
Rogar/STB SA-37 supplement powder	28.87
Pulverized limestone (39% Ca)	6.19
Vitamin C	3.09
Vitamin E (50 IU/g)	5.15

[5] Exact amounts of ingredients are fed every day throughout the year. When increases or reductions are needed, the changes are done proportionally so the percentage composition always remains the same. These quantities allow for approximately 10-15% refusal, although on some days all of the food is eaten.

Chapter 17

Training Bats
for Behavioral Studies

Connie L. Gaudet

Department of Biology
University of Ottawa
Ottawa, Ontario K1N 6N5
Canada

1. INTRODUCTION

In theory, the training of any animal is a straightforward process in which it repeats (learns) responses that are rewarded and fails to repeat responses upon being punished (Broadbent, 1961). If it were really that simple, a chapter on training bats would be little more than a discussion of conditioning techniques. Although conditioning is fundamental to training, other factors are equally important, such as experimental design, motivation, timing, and the species' behavioral and physical limitations.

The role that these factors play in training will vary depending on the experiment and species in question and there is no step-by-step formula that will ensure success. Rather than providing an inflexible set of rules limited to certain situations, the following discussion and examples are intended to impart an understanding of the many factors underlying the training of bats.

2. TRAINING PREREQUISITES

A thorough understanding of conditioning principles and behavioral methodologies is prerequisite to training. The substance of these topics is summarized to provide a framework for discussions and examples, but it is beyond the scope of this chapter to provide a comprehensive review of conditioning theory and behavioral methodology. Extensive references in these areas should be consulted independently (e.g., Gilbert and Sutherland, 1969; Baerenda and Kruijt, 1973; MacIntosh, 1974; Francis, 1975).

2.1. Conditioning

Operant or respondent conditioning is based on the contingency between a behavior and its consequences (Kimble et al., 1974). In essence, when a behavior has a reinforcing consequence, it is more likely to occur again (Skinner, 1974). Operant conditioning can involve behavior-shaping or trial-and-error learning.

Behavior-shaping is a process in which successive approximations to the required behavior are reinforced. When the task is complex, it must be analyzed into appropriate subunits. Trial-and-error learning differs from behavior-shaping in that there is no direct interference from the experimenter. For example, a rat will gradually learn to press a lever for food if accidental pressing of the lever is rewarded immediately with a food pellet (Kimble et al., 1974). It is critical that the desired behavior is one that is likely to occur by accident, and that food reward is immediate upon the response. The application of these techniques is illustrated with examples from the bat literature in Section 3.

2.2. Unconditioned Responses

In some cases, it may be possible to use unconditioned or reflex-like responses that require no training. In bats such responses can be directly elicited by a variety of visual or acoustic cues (e.g., Gaudet, 1982; Fenton et al., 1982). The role of unconditioned responses in training more complex behavior is discussed in Section 3.

2.3. Behavioral Methodologies

Because the intent of this chapter is not to discuss behavioral methodologies, but rather to consider the training process that underlies them, only broad categorizations will be made. The categories are based on methodologies that are commonly used with bats.

2.3.1. Forced Choice Format

The forced choice or Y-maze format has been used extensively to assess sensory capabilities in bats. It is based on the establishment of a response to one stimulus through reinforcement and extinction of generalized responses to other stimuli through nonreinforcement. The reinforced stimulus and a control are presented simultaneously from discrete and randomly alternated positions. A bat indicates an ability to discriminate the stimulus by responding to its location significantly more often than to a control.

This format has been used to test acoustic thresholds (e.g., V. Cucarro, pers. comm.; Poussin and Simmons, 1982), echolocation in discrimination of shapes, distances, depths and angles (e.g., Konstantinov and Akhmarova, 1968; Bradbury, 1970; Peff and Simmons, 1971; Feng et al., 1980; Schnitzler and Flieger, 1983; McCarty and Jen, 1983), and vision (e.g., Suthers et al., 1969; Ellins, 1972; Masterson and Ellins, 1973).

2.3.2. Go No-Go Format

Bats have also been trained to respond to a stimulus presented at random time intervals with no position change. The bat indicates a correct response by performing a critically defined behavior only when the stimulus is presented. This format has been used to test auditory thresholds (Dalland, 1965; Suthers and Summers, 1980) and vision (Childs and Buchler, 1981). Examples for other animals can be found in Schusterman (1980).

2.3.3. Obstacle Avoidance

Sensory capabilities can be tested using a simple obstacle avoidance format that requires limited or no training (e.g., Griffin and Galambos, 1941; Chase and Suthers, 1969; Jen et al., 1980). This format is reviewed in more detail in Schusterman (1980).

2.3.4. Retrieval Format

A large body of experiments using trained bats cannot be clearly assigned to any of the preceding categories. Expansion of Schusterman's (1980) retrieval category (in which an animal picks up a target and returns it to the experimenter for a food reward) to include situations in which the target is itself the food reward will account for many of these experiments. The targets (prey or food items) are presented within a defined area and a positive response is indicated by successful retrieval of the food. The bat's response to changes in prey quality (e.g., sound, movement, size) or environmental conditions (e.g., light level, chamber configuration) is used to assess sensory abilities. Variations on this format have been used to test spatial memory (Mueller and Mueller, 1979) and sensory modality (Fiedler, 1979; Fiedler et al., 1980; Bell, 1982, 1985) as well as other aspects of feeding behavior (e.g., Suthers, 1965; Suthers and Fattu, 1973; Fenton et al., 1982; Vogler and Neuweiler, 1983).

The preceding summarize the major areas of behavioral research using trained bats. They should not be viewed as limits to research possibilities.

3. THE TRAINING PROCESS

3.1. The Preconditioning Period

The first step in training is acclimatizing the bat to captivity. There is no rule for the length of time that should be devoted to this. Some experimenters prefer to limit or even dispense with the acclimatization period so that responses are as natural as possible (M. D. Tuttle, pers. comm.). Others have kept bats in captivity for several weeks or months before the onset of training (e.g., Suthers, 1965; Fiedler, 1979; Mueller and Mueller, 1979). Generally, the more natural the situation is in terms of setting, food type, and cues used, the shorter the period of acclimatization needed.

In my experience, *Nycteris thebaica* required less than one day of acclimatization when experiments were designed around the use of natural prey, whereas *Eptesicus fuscus* required a minimum of one week to acclimatize to captive conditions in a laboratory situation that was characterized by unnatural lighting, temperature, and food.

Species temperament will also influence acclimatization. For example, *Trachops cirrhosus* adapts readily to a captive situation (usually within one day) whereas, under similar conditions, *Pizonyx* sp. requires a prolonged effort even to induce it to eat (M. D. Tuttle, pers. comm.). Generally, when a bat is active and accepts food eagerly from an experimenter, it is ready for training.

3.2. Behavior-Shaping in Practice

Behavior-shaping is a powerful training technique. The following examples from the bat literature illustrate its application in a variety of situations.

3.2.1. Behavior-Shaping in Forced-Choice Formats

A forced-choice format can usually be separated into two discrete stages: training the bat to approach target sites consistently (sites of subsequent stimulus/control presentation) with no discrimination of cues required and secondly, training the bat to respond to a selected cue or stimulus alternated between the target sites.

The first training stage can be further divided into easily learned subunits. For example, *E. fuscus* was trained to fly from a starting platform to either of two landing platforms for a food reward. Training began with the platforms juxtaposed so that the bat could reach the food reward without flying; then they were gradually moved further apart (Simmons and Vernon, 1974). In a similar experiment *Antrozous pallidus* and *E. fuscus* were trained to crawl from a starting position to either of two target sites by initially feeding the bats at the target site and then physically moving them at increasing distances from the target while they were feeding (V. Cucarro, pers. comm.). Behavior can also be shaped by first training the bat to respond to a single target site located in a position between the final target locations (e.g., Gaudet, 1982; McCarty and Jen, 1983). In my experience with *A. pallidus, E. fuscus* and *Myotis lucifugus,* training did not lapse when the single target was replaced with two spatially separated ones.

It is critical that a bat does not develop a strong preference for one position during training (or subsequent experimentation). Random number tables developed for two-choice formats should be used (R. A. Suthers, pers. comm.). If the position effect is not circumvented during training, teaching subsequent discriminations will be difficult.

When working in large chambers, behavior-shaping can be augmented by limiting landing sites (Gaudet, 1982; M. D. Tuttle, pers. comm.). In my work with *E. fuscus, M. lucifugus,* and *A. pallidus,* experiments were conducted in a large 2 m × 2 m chamber entirely lined with acoustic foam. The only suitable landing surfaces were sections of plastic screening attached to walls. Behavior was shaped by gradually reducing the screened areas from an entire coverage of two opposing walls to small 15 cm squares placed at a starting position and two target sites. Merlin D. Tuttle (pers. comm.) similarly limited landing sites in a large mesh cage by hanging plastic in areas where he did not want bats to land. In smaller chambers such as an enclosed Y-maze (e.g., Masterson and Ellins, 1973) the bats' behavior is automatically restricted to certain areas and this kind of manipulation of landing sites is unnecessary.

When a bat consistently approaches the target sites for food reward, the response to a specific stimulus can be conditioned. This is a straightforward process in which the bat is rewarded for approaching a target only if the stimulus is being presented at that site. Food reward is withheld when the bat approaches the control target (positions are randomly alternated). It is important to initiate training with a discrimination that is easily within the grasp of the bat and work gradually up to more difficult discriminations, a type of behavior-shaping termed fading (review in Schusterman, 1980). For example, *M. lucifugus* could not be trained to distinguish differently shaped triangles with the same surface area until bats were first introduced to a simpler discrimination: triangles of different shape and size that gradually approximated the desired discrimination (Simmons and Vernon, 1971).

3.2.2. Behavior-Shaping in Other Experimental Formats

Behavior-shaping can be similarly applied to retrieval, obstacle avoidance, and go no-go formats. In a go no-go format, Suthers and Summers (1980) shaped behavior in *Rousettus* by gradually reducing the size of the platform from which the bat hung until it was facing a speaker through which tone bursts (stimulus) were emitted. Vanda Cucarro (pers. comm.) trained *Artibeus jamaicensis* to fly a complicated route to a target by first training the bat to fly directly to the target and then by gradually placing obstacles in its path. It is evident from these examples that behavior-shaping can be achieved more effectively by a manipulation of the apparatus than the bat.

3.3. Trial-and-Error Learning

Trial-and-error learning can be used exclusively to train a simple behavior or in combination with behavior-shaping to train a more complex behavior. In an experiment assessing the sensory basis of spatial memory (Mueller and Mueller, 1979), trial-and-error learning was used as the sole training technique. Individuals of *E. fuscus* were placed in a small cage and fed each time they happened to crawl on a piece of cloth. Five of six bats consistently approached the cloth for feeding after only two days. Trial-and-error learning is particularly useful if one wishes to limit handling of bats. After finding that *M. lucifugus* was sensitive to handling and difficult to train to approach a target in a large chamber (where handling and the presence of an experimenter were necessary), I successfully used trial-and-error learning to train bats to approach the same target in a smaller chamber. Subsequently, the bats were trained to make target discriminations with behavior-shaping techniques.

3.4. Unconditioned Responses

Training can be minimized through the use of unconditioned responses. For example, *Nycteris thebaica* spontaneously retrieved live fluttering moths held in a forceps (Fenton et al., 1982). Auditory thresholds were assessed for *Macrotus californicus* without training because this species responded reflexively to tone bursts by turning towards the sound (V. Cucarro, pers. comm.). An experiment may be directed at assessing such unconditioned responses (e.g., Fenton et al., 1982; Bell, 1985). In other cases, unconditioned responses may be the key to training a more complex or unnatural behavior. Successful training of *Noctilio labialis* to respond to experimental cues was attributed in part to the bat's spontaneous response to insects that had fallen into an artificial pool (Suthers and Fattu, 1973). *Megaderma lyra* was trained to retrieve mealworms from the floor of a flight chamber by initiating spontaneous feeding behavior through placement of live mice in the chamber. Mice were gradually replaced with smaller and more inanimate food items (V. Cucarro, pers. comm.).

In the absence of live prey, recorded or imitated prey sounds or movements can be used to stimulate responses to target sites. *Myotis lucifugus, A. pallidus* and *E. fuscus* (Gaudet, 1982), *Nycteris grandis* and *N. thebaica* (Fenton et al., 1982), *Megaderma lyra* (Fiedler, 1979), *Tonatia bidens* (J. Belwood, pers. comm.), and *Trachops cirrhosus* (Tuttle and Ryan, 1981) respond to prey sounds varying from specialized calls to general sounds of movement. Such behavior

can be exploited to enhance training. I have found that even scratching noises made by rubbing a forceps against screening will attract *M. lucifugus, A. pallidus, E. fuscus, N. thebaica,* and *N. grandis* to target sites. Once bats respond to the target sites, a natural cue can gradually be replaced with an experimental one.

A final category of unconditioned responses includes cues inherent in the feeding behavior of another bat. *Myotis lucifugus* is attracted to the feeding buzzes of conspecifics in the field and in the laboratory (Barclay, 1982; Gaudet, 1982). Experiments with captive bats indicate that they do not only respond to the location of a feeding bat but can learn a novel feeding behavior through observation of a trained conspecific (Gaudet and Fenton, 1984). Conditioning *A. pallidus, M. lucifugus,* and *E. fuscus* to approach a target site for food reward consistently took an average of two weeks in this experiment, whereas bats learned the behavior through observation of a trained conspecific in an average of about two days. A single *Artibeus jamaicensis* also learned a novel feeding behavior from a trained conspecific (M. B. Fenton, unpublished data), and there is some suggestion that *Macrotus californicus* (G. P. Bell, pers. comm.), *Myotis vivesi* (M. D. Tuttle, pers. comm.), and *Pteronotus parnellii* (R. A. Suthers, pers. comm.) are stimulated by the feeding behavior of other bats. Use of trained bats as "teachers" may be applicable to a range of species.

In the absence of a trained bat, I found that the chewing sounds of another bat restrained at a target stimulated nonfeeding bats and could be used to direct activity to a target area.

4. OTHER CONSIDERATIONS

The preceding sections have dealt with the role of conditioning techniques and unconditioned responses in training bats. The success of training will depend on several additional factors.

4.1. Reinforcement

Selection of an appropriate reinforcement is critical not only to effective training but also for maintaining the health and vigor of the animal. Because bats may receive their entire daily intake of food in the form of reinforcement, it must meet nutritional and energy requirements. Attention to literature on captive diets (Chapter 16) and natural food habits (Chapters 11 and 13) are necessary. Also, the reward must be immediate upon completion of the behavior being conditioned. It is difficult for an animal to learn the connection between present action and reinforcement at some future time (Broadbent, 1961).

In forced choice and go no-go formats, a negative reinforcement can be associated with an undesired response to hasten conditioning (Adcock, 1959; Kimble et al., 1974). Most often, absence of food reward is the only negative reinforcement used (e.g., Simmons and Vernon, 1971; V. Cucarro, pers. comm.) though air blasts (Childs and Buchler, 1981) and quinine added to food to make it distasteful (Suthers et al., 1969) have been effective. Negative reinforcement must be used with caution. The Yerkes-Dodson Law is based on the discovery that a strong negative reinforcement will improve performance on a relatively simple task but in "tricky" situations may actually lead to a deterioration in performance.

4.2. Controls

Rigorous use of controls is critical to ensure that the bat is being trained to respond to the selected stimuli and not to some extraneous cue. Julia Chase (pers. comm.) found that although *Anoura geoffroyi* appeared to have been trained to make a pattern discrimination, a control exercise indicated that the bat had learned to discriminate the food reinforced pattern (sugar and water) through olfaction and was not making a pattern dis-

crimination. Subsequent experimentation corrected for this factor. The acute hearing and olfaction of many bats can lead to the use of an extraneous cue that the experimenter cannot detect, and therefore avoiding sloppiness in experimental design and careful use of controls is imperative.

4.3. Motivation

To avoid erratic behavior that would interfere with training and affect the validity of experimental results, it is essential that a bat be consistently motivated to perform throughout training. Several factors can cause fluctuations in a bat's response to a cue: body mass, time of day, and social condition.

4.3.1. Optimal Training Mass

Food deprivation is cited as a major method of ensuring a consistently high level of motivation in experiments that involve food reward (e.g., Simmons and Vernon, 1971; Suthers and Summers, 1980). Food acts as a strong positive reinforcement when a bat is hungry and is of neutral value to a satiated animal, but extreme food deprivation may also diminish performance due to stress and loss of vigor. To maintain peak motivation, a bat's body mass must be kept within optimal limits. There is no general rule for determining this ideal mass. *Nyctalus noctula* and *Eptesicus serotinus* tended to become obese in captivity (Racey and Kleiman, 1970). These bats were then weighed weekly and food supply regulated to maintain masses comparable to wild animals. Other evidence shows that body mass must be kept below that of wild bats to maintain peak performance. Simmons and Vernon (1971) reduced the mass of *E. fuscus* from 14 - 24 g to 10 - 14 g in preparation for training. In work with *A pallidus,* I found that performance was so critically linked to mass that a 5% gain (1g) caused a profound reduction in performance.

Caution must be exercised when applying these principles to other species. In general, tropical species cannot withstand the same degree of food deprivation as temperate species (M. D. Tuttle, pers. comm.) and may go into rapid decline and die. In the absence of data, it is safest to maintain a bat at its capture mass until a feeding regime can be established through careful interpretation of the bat's response to food availability.

The necessity of controlling daily food intake dictates the duration of training sessions. Once a bat has received its food ration for the day in the form of reinforcement, no further training trials should be conducted.

4.3.2. The Ho-Hum Response

Supplemental feeding outside of training should be avoided. Julia Chase (per. comm.) suggests that if a bat is to receive supplemental feeding, it should occur several hours after a training session to prevent a "ho-hum" response. If a bat anticipates a food reward regardless of its response during training, then it may simply wait this period out. Similarly, if bats are fed in holding cages for several days between training sessions (e.g., weekends), they may show a marked deterioration in motivation when first returned to the experimental or training sessions.

4.3.3. Natural Activity Patterns

Consistency in behavior depends on the timing of the training in relation to the daily light cycle. It is generally best to run training and experimental sessions during the period when the species would normally feed, usually the first few hours after the onset of darkness (e.g., Suthers, 1965; Chase, 1981). Activity can be shifted to suit the experimenter's schedule through a reversal in the Light-Dark cycle (e.g., Suthers and Summers, 1980; V. Cucarro, pers. comm.).

Merlin D. Tuttle (pers. comm.) also suggests that a tropical bat's monthly mass cycle is critical in training. *Trachops cirrhosus* captured in the dark period immediately after a full moon starved to death even when fed more than normal amounts of food. Bats captured during other moon phases endured 2-3

days of reduced food intake while acclimatizing to experimental conditions.

4.3.4. Social Groupings

Behavior can be affected by abnormal groupings of bats during training. Depending on the species, isolation as well as overcrowding may impair learning, induce stress, or affect health (Rasweiler, 1977). My observations of *E. fuscus* (Gaudet, 1982) and *Nycteris grandis* (Fenton et al., 1982) feeding in groups indicated that aggressive interactions reduced the motivation of submissive bats to search for or eat food. On the other hand, *A. pallidus* (Gaudet, 1982), *N. thebaica* (Fenton et al., 1982), *M. californicus* (Bell, 1985), and *Leptonycteris sanborni* (Howell, 1979) respond effectively and even superiorly in group situations. Attention to natural habits and captive behavior is necessary to make a decision as to whether to train bats singly or in groups.

4.4. Accommodating Species Differences

Species differences are profound and the training must reflect this. The species' natural feeding behavior can be particularly important. Attempts to train *Anoura geoffroyi* to discriminate between two patterns were successful only when the food reward was moved from a location immediately below the pattern to a position through the middle of the pattern (J. Chase, pers. comm.). Obviously, the second design was more suited to this nectarivorous bat's instinctive behavior as it more closely resembled the arrangement of a flower. *Macrotus californicus* (Bell, 1985), *N. thebaica,* and *N. grandis* (Fenton et al., 1982) will not crawl after prey, even for short distances, and training and experimentation must be designed to allow free flight in retrieval of food rewards. Other species, *A. pallidus* (Gaudet, 1982), *E. fuscus, M. lucifugus* (Ellins, 1972); Masterson and Ellins, 1973), and *Desmodus rotundus* (Manske and Schmidt, 1976), for example, are more flexible and will adapt to experiments that require either crawling or flying to a target.

All aspects of species differences cannot be covered here. In summary, I would suggest that if a bat seems untrainable, the experimenter should assess natural feeding habits and physical limitations through observation and research and modify the experiment accordingly. The extra work needed to find maintenance and training criteria that will work for a species may be amply rewarded by increasing our understanding of chiropteran behavior.

4.5. Handling

Excessive handling of bats during training should be avoided. Where handling closely follows a correct response (e.g., capturing the bat to return it to a starting position) a situation can be created in which the response has both positive (food) and negative (handling) consequences. This can lead to a state of "neurotic conflict" (Broadbent, 1961) that will adversely affect training. Strategies discussed earlier: limiting landing sites, trial-and-error learning, and use of unconditioned responses to hasten training can be used to minimize handling of particularly sensitive species. *Nycteris thebaica* and *M. californicus* (Bell, 1985) were so intolerant of handling that the entire training procedure had to be designed so that bats were never handled, and all food and cues were introduced from outside the mesh of the flight cage.

4.6. The Training Chamber

There is no "Skinner box" into which bats can be placed for conditioning. The chamber design will vary depending on practical considerations: versatility, expense, and space limitations, as well as the species of bat and the type of experiment. Even a simple Y-maze format can take on many different dimensions varying from open designs in large flight chambers (e.g., Gaudet, 1982) to small enclosed Y-shaped chambers (Masterson and Ellins, 1973). For general training, M. D. Tuttle (pers. comm.) suggests an enclosure

large enough for a person to walk into, but small enough so the bats are never out of reach (3 to 4 m square and no more than 2 m high).

Working in field situations does not limit the use of captive and trained bats. Designs for portable Y-mazes are available (Chase, 1981, 1983). I have used a commercially available screened picnic shelter that can be folded for transport and erected in the same way as a tent when needed.

Certain experiments can require highly specialized chamber design. Artificial pools were incorporated into the design for enclosures for the frog-eating bat *Trachops cirrhosus* (M. D. Tuttle, pers. comm.) and the fish-eating bat *Noctilio leporinus* (Suthers, 1965; Suthers and Fattu, 1973). Determining the response of *E. fuscus* to simulated stars required a special light-proof chamber (Childs and Buchler, 1981).

It is beyond the scope of this chapter to describe all apparatus that has been used for training. The examples provided emphasize the versatility in design. However, all chambers should meet certain minimum requirements.

The visual and acoustic qualities of the chamber are crucial. Some species are attracted to lighted or darkened areas (Chase, 1981, 1983), and inappropriate placement of lights can impede training by causing a bat to concentrate activity in certain areas of the chamber. Within an enclosed flight chamber a bat may use a concentrated light source as a "landmark" in target location (Gaudet, 1982). If the experimenter moves the light to facilitate his/her own activities or removes the light, a significant change in behavior may result when the bat loses this orientation cue. Use of commercial red bulbs does not overcome these problems (Chase, 1981). Centrally located diffuse or dim lighting is recommended.

The acoustic quality of the chamber is important, especially if audition is implicated in the behavior under study. Where the chamber has solid walls, acoustic foam will make the room anechoic to high frequency sound (Suthers and Summers, 1980). Egg cartons have been successfully employed when acoustic foam was not available (G. P. Bell, pers. comm.).

5. IS TRAINING REALLY NECESSARY?

Experiments using trained bats can be the only way to obtain certain kinds of behavioral information, but careful consideration should be given to whether training is really necessary. It is sometimes possible to design experiments that use spontaneous responses of naive bats. Chase (1981, 1983) used the spontaneous escape responses of wild bats in a portable Y-maze to demonstrate vision, and Suthers (1966) used reflexive optomotor responses to measure minimum separable visual angle in untrained bats. Bell (1982) assessed the response of *A. pallidus* to a range of acoustic and visual stimuli without training by attracting a maternity colony of about 150 bats to an area through use of a black light (the light attracted swarms of flying insects which attracted the bats). Certain prey qualities were manipulated and the bats' spontaneous responses were assessed. Webster and Griffin (1962) attracted moths to a porch screen with lights and found that *Lasurius borealis* was not only attracted to the area but learned to pursue moths picked off the screen and tossed into the air, suggesting that Bell's (1982) approach is applicable to other species. The examples cited here only begin to suggest the scope in designing experiments that assess the spontaneity of bats under controlled conditions without training.

6. SUMMARY

Although operant conditioning techniques are fundamental to training bats, other factors are equally important: unconditioned responses, species differences, motivation, and apparatus. Behavior-shaping in which successive approximations to the desired behavior are reinforced is a powerful training technique commonly used for training bats and applicable in a variety of experimental situations. Trial-and-error learning is a less commonly used training technique but can be invaluable when handling of bats must be limited because it requires no direct intervention from the experimenter. Unconditioned responses (instinctive or reflexive responses to prey sounds, movements, and the feeding behavior of other bats) can be valuable aids to conditioning. Forced choice, go no-go, obstacle avoidance, and food retrieval formats are the major categories of behavioral methodologies when using trained bats. These formats are most commonly used to assess sensory capabilities. Maintaining consistent motivation is critical to training bats. Food deprivation is a major technique for maintaining motivation in temperate insectivorous species. Accommodating the training to species differences is important. Natural feeding behavior and physical limitations are the two most important considerations.

7. ACKNOWLEDGMENTS

I would like to thank M. D. Tuttle and Julia Chase for their many valuable contributions to this chapter. I am grateful for the comments of R. J. Suthers and anonymous reviewers on the manuscript and to T. H. Kunz for his patience. Lastly, I would like to thank the bat crew from Carleton University who offered valuable insight into bat training: Vanda Cucarro and G. P. Bell and especially M. B. Fenton, who supervised my work on bats. My research was supported by a Natural Sciences and Engineering Research Council grant.

8. REFERENCES

Adcock, C. J. 1959. Fundamentals of psychology. Purnell and Sons Ltd., Paulton, England.

Baerenda, G. P., and F. P. Kruijt. 1973. Stimulus selection. Pp. 23-50, *in* Constraints on learning: Limitation and predispositions (R. A. Hinde and J. Stevenson-Hinde, eds.). Academic Press, New York.

Barclay, R. M. R. 198. Interindividual use of echolocation calls: Eavesdropping by bats. Behav. Ecol. Sociobiol., 10:271-275.

Bell, G. P. 1982. Behavioral and ecological aspects of gleaning by a desert insectivorus bat, *Antrozous pallidus* (Chiroptera: Vespertilionidae) Behav. Ecol. Sociobiol., 10:217-223.

Bell, G. P. 1985. The sensory basis of prey location by the California leaf-nosed bat *Macrotus californicus* (Chiroptera: Phyllostomidae). Behav. Ecol. Sociobiol., 16:343-347.

Bradbury, J. W. 1970. Target discrimination by the echolocating bat *Vampyrum spectrum*. J. Exp. Zool., 173:23-46.

Broadbent, D. E. 1961. Behaviour. Butler and Tanner, Ltd., London, 215 pp.

Chase, J. 1981. Visually guided escape responses of microchiropteran bats. Anim. Behav., 29:708-713.

Chase, J. 1983. Differential responses to visual and acoustic cues during escape in the bat *Anoura geoffroyi*: Cue preferences and behaviour. Anim. Behav., 31:526-531.

Chase, J. and R. A. Suthers. 1969. Visual obstacle avoidance by echolocating bats. Anim. Behav., 17:201-207.

Childs, S. B., and E. R. Buchler. 1981. Perception of simulated stars by *Eptesicus fuscus* (Vespertilionidae): A potential navigational mechanism. Anim. Behav., 29:1028-1035

Dalland, J. I. 1965. Auditory thresholds in bats: A behavioral technique. J. Aud. Res., 5:95-108.

Ellins, S. R. 1972. Brightness discrimination thresholds in the bat *Eptesicus fuscus*. Brain Behav. Evol., 9:240-263.

Feng, A., J. A. Simmons, S. A. Kick, and B. D. Lawrence. 1980. Neural mechanisms for target ranging in an echolocating bat *Eptesicus fuscus*. Pp. 885-887, *in* Animal sonar systems. (R. G. Busnel and J. F. Fish, eds.). Plenum Press, New York, 1135 pp.

Fenton, M. B., C. L. Gaudet, and M. L. Leonard. 1982. Feeding behaviour of the bats *Nycteris grandis* and *Nycteris thebaica* (Nycteridae) in captivity. J. Zool., 200:347-354.

Fiedler, J. 1979. Prey catching with and without echolocation in the Indian false vampire bat (*Megaderma lyra*). Behav. Ecol. Sociobiol., 6:155-160.

Fiedler, G., J. Habersetzer, and B. Vogler. 1980. Hunting strategies and echolocating performance of bats—quantitative behavioral laboratory analysis. Pp. 889-893, *in* Animal sonar systems. (R. G. Busnel and J. F. Fish, eds.). Plenum Press, New York, 1135 pp.

Francis, R. L. 1975. Behavioral audiometry in mammals: Review and evaluation of techniques. Symp. Zool. Soc. Lond., 37:237-289.

Gaudet, C. L. 1982. Behavioural basis of foraging flexibility in three species of insectivorous bats: An experimental study using captive *Antrozous pallidus, Eptesicus fuscus* and *Myotis lucifugus*. M.Sc. thesis, Carleton University, Ottawa, Ontario, Canada, 144 pp.

Gaudet, C. L., and M. B. Fenton. 1984. Observational learning in three species of insectivorous bats (Chiroptera). Anim. Behav., 32:385-388.

Gilbert, R. M., and N. S. Sutherland. 1969. Animal discrimination learning. Academic Press, New York, 501 pp.

Griffin, D. R., and R. Galambos. 1941. The sensory basis of obstacle avoidance by flying bats. J. Exp. Zool., 86:481-506.

Howell, D. J. 1979. Flock foraging in nectar-feeding bats: Advantages to the bats and to the host plants. Amer. Nat., 114:23-49.

Jen, P. H. S., Y. H. Lee, and R. K. Weidler. 1980. The avoidance of stationary and moving obstacles by little brown bats, *Myotis lucifugus*. Pp. 917-919, *in* Animal sonar systems. (R. G. Busnel and J. F. Fish, eds.). Plenum Press, New York, 1135 pp.

Kimble, G. A., N. Garmezy, and E. Zigler. 1974. Principles of general psychology. 4th ed. Ronald Press, New York.

Konstantinov, A. I., and N. I. Akhmarova. 1968. Object discrimination with the aid of echolocation by bats (*Myotis oxygnathus*). Nauchnye Doklady Vysshei Shkoly, Biol. Naak., 11:22.

MacIntosh, M. J. 1974. The psychology of animal learning. Academic Press, New York.

Manske, U., and U. Schmidt. 1976. Visual acuity of the vampire bat *Desmodus rotundus* and its dependence on light intensity. Z. Tierpsychol., 42:215-221.

Masterson, F. A., and S. R. Ellins. 1973. The role of vision in orientation of the echolocating bat, *Myotis lucifugus*. Behaviour, 51: 88-98.

McCarty, J. K., and P. H. S. Jen. 1983. Bats reject clutter interference for moving targets more successfully than for stationary ones. J. Comp. Physiol., 152:447-454.

Mueller, H. C., and N. S. Mueller. 1979. Sensory basis for spatial memory in bats. J. Mammal., 60:198-201.

Peff, T. C., and J. A. Simmons. 1972. Horizontal-angle resolution by echolocating bats. J. Acoust. Soc. Amer., 51:2063-2065.

Poussin, C., and J. A. Simmons. 1982. Low-frequency hearing sensitivity in the echolocating bat, *Eptesicus fuscus.* J. Acoust. Soc. Amer., 72:340-342.

Racey, P. A., and D. G. Kleiman. 1970. Maintenance and breeding in captivity of some vespertilionid bats, with special reference to the noctule. Int. Zoo. Yearbook, 10:65-70.

Rasweiler, J. J. IV, 1977. Bats as laboratory animals. Pp. 519-617, *in* Biology of bats. Vol. 3. (W. A. Wimsatt, ed.). Academic Press, New York.

Schnitzler, H. U., and E. Flieger. 1983. Detection of oscillating target movements by echolocation in the greater horseshoe bat. J. Comp. Physiol., 153:385-391.

Schusterman, R. J. 1980. Behavioral methodology in echolocation by marine mammals. Pp. 11-41, *in* Animal sonar systems. (R. G. Busnel and J. F. Fish, eds.). Plenum Press, New York, 1135 pp.

Simmons, J. A., and J. A. Vernon. 1971. Echolocation: Discrimination of targets by the bat, *Eptesicus fuscus.* J. Exp. Zool., 176:315-328.

Skinner, B. F. 1974. About behaviorism. Alfred A. Knopf, New York.

Suthers, R. A. 1965. Acoustic orientation by fish-catching bats. J. Exp. Zool., 158:319-348.

Suthers, R. A. 1966. Optomotor responses by echolocating bats. Science, 152:1102-1104.

Suthers, R. A., J. Chase, and B. Braford. 1969. Visual form discrimination by echolocating bats. Biol. Bull., 137:535-546.

Suthers, R. A., and J. M. Fattu. 1973. Fishing behavior and acoustic orientation by the bat *Noctilio labialis.* Anim. Behav., 21:61-66.

Suthers, R. A., and C. A. Summers. 1980. Behavioral audiogram and masked thresholds of the megachiropteran echolocating bat *Rousettus.* J. Comp. Physiol., 136:227-233.

Tuttle, M. D., and M. J. Ryan. 1981. Bat predation and the evolution of frog vocalizations in the Neotropics. Science, 214:677-678.

Vogler, B., and G. Neuweiler. 1983. Echolocation in the noctule (*Nyctalus noctula*) and horseshoe bat (*Rhinolophus ferrumequinum*). J. Comp. Physiol., 152:421-432.

Webster, P. A., and D. R. Griffin. 1962. The role of the flight membrane in insect capture by bats. Anim. Behav., 10:332-340.

Chapter 18

Methods of
Energy Budget Analysis

Thomas H. Kunz

Department of Biology
Boston University
Boston, Massachusetts 02215 USA

and

Kenneth A. Nagy

Laboratory of Biomedical
and Environmental Science
University of California
Los Angeles, California 90024 USA

1. INTRODUCTION

Energy is the currency of living organisms, yet remarkably little is known about how free-ranging animals allocate energy in the course of a day or over longer periods. How animals apportion time and energy ultimately influences their survival and reproductive success. These and other questions are central themes in ecology that are embodied in the concepts of optimal foraging theory, reproductive effort (including parental investment theory), and life history strategies.

The study of energy metabolism and energy allocation by bats is in its infancy (Kunz, 1980). Preliminary estimates of daily energy expenditure (DEE) in free-ranging bats have involved constructing time-activity budgets from field observations and assigning assumed energy costs to each activity (e.g., Howell, 1979; Kunz, 1980; Burnett and August, 1981), estimating daily food intake (Kunz, 1974; Anthony and Kunz, 1977; Morrison, 1978; Kunz, 1980; Funakoshi and Uchida, 1980), and by assessing changes in body composition and energy content (Chapter 23). Doubly labeled water (DLW) has only recently been used to estimate energy expenditure in free-ranging bats (Helversen and Reyer, 1984; Bell et al., 1986).

There are advantages and disadvantages of using one or another method. The time-activity budget method is an intuitively attractive approach to assess individual variation in daily energy expenditure. However, it is often difficult to quantify the amount of time an animal spends in various activities and to apply accurate estimates of metabolism to each activity. This method assumes that costs are additive and they do not substitute (e.g., activity heat for thermoregulatory heat). Field measurements of food ingested can provide a direct estimate of daily energy intake, but this requires knowledge of field diets and measurements of the digestibility of different foods. Moreover, rapid food transit time in bats (e.g., Buchler, 1975; Tedman and Hall, 1985) can lead to underestimates of digestible energy. Laboratory measurements of body composition and energy density of bats are valuable for assessing the allocation of energy to fetal and suckling growth and to seasonal changes in adult growth and fat storage, but these only contribute to a partial assessment of energy investment. The DLW method provides a direct measure of field metabolic rate (FMR) and offers a powerful approach for answering ecological questions related to energy expenditure of individuals. With this method, however, there are several unverified assumptions and potential errors (Lifson and McClintock, 1966; Nagy, 1980; Nagy and Costa, 1980). Energy expenditure and allocation by free-ranging animals can best be understood when several approaches are used concurrently.

The purpose of this chapter is to review methods of energy budget analysis appropriate for the study of free-ranging bats. These include doubly labeled water, food consumption, and time budgets. The schematic diagram of an energy budget (Fig. 1) illustrates major compartments for bats and other small mammals. The analysis of these and other compartments require different methods, equipment, and investment in time and effort. Other methods needed for energy budget analysis, including observational techniques, radiotelemetry, respirometry, body composition and calorimetry, and microclimate analysis, only briefly discussed here, are treated elsewhere in this volume.

2. DOUBLY LABELED WATER METHOD

2.1. Rationale

The DLW method works by measuring CO_2 production via the differential washout rates

of injected isotopes of hydrogen and oxygen. This method, developed over 30 years ago, is based on the observation that the oxygen of respiratory CO_2 is in isotopic equilibrium with the oxygen of body water (Lifson et al., 1949). Most of the hydrogen isotope (deuterium, ^2H, or tritium, ^3H) is lost from the body as water, whereas the oxygen isotope (^{18}O) is lost both as water and as respiratory CO_2 (Lifson and McClintock, 1966; Nagy, 1980). This makes it possible to determine CO_2 production by labeling both types of atoms of the body water in an animal and monitoring the relative turnover of the two isotopes. CO_2 production can then be converted to units of energy metabolism (field metabolic rate) using an appropriate equation and corrections made for diet composition and digestibility (see Nagy, 1980).

2.2. Field Metabolic Rate (FMR)

Doubly labeled water measurements of FMR integrate all metabolic costs, including basal metabolism, thermoregulation, metabolism of food (specific dynamic action), activity, and reproduction. Several authors have used the term "average daily metabolic rate" (ADMR) in studies using DLW in free-ranging animals (e.g., Hails and Bryant, 1979; Turner, 1983; Westerterp and Bryant, 1984), but we suggest that this practice be discontinued. ADMR as originally conceived (see Grodzinski and Gorecki, 1967), was based on metabolic measurements taken on animals confined to large chambers at temperatures similar to the natural environment.

2.3. Assumptions and Potential Errors

Assumptions and potential errors inherent in the DLW method have been reviewed (Lifson and McClintock, 1966; Mullen, 1973; Hails, 1977; Hails and Bryant, 1979; Nagy, 1980; Nagy and Costa, 1980). The major assumptions are: 1) body water volume remains constant during the measurement period, 2) rates of water flux and CO_2 production are constant through time, 3) isotopes label only the H_2O and CO_2 in the body, 4) isotopes leave the

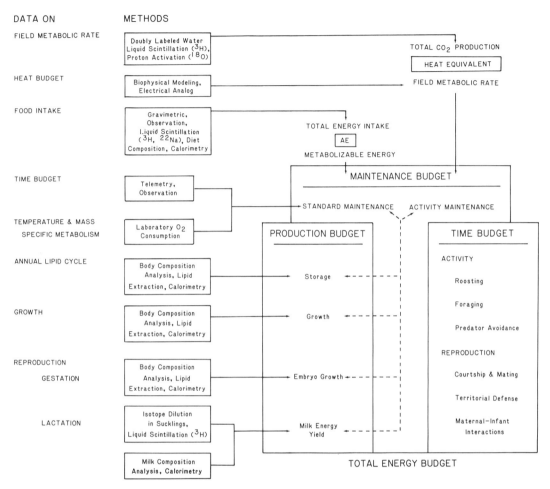

Figure 1. Schematic diagram of a generalized mammalian energy budget illustrating major compartments and methods of analysis.

body only as H_2O and CO_2, 5) specific activities of the isotopes in H_2O and CO_2 leaving the body are the same as in body water, and 6) labeled or unlabeled water or CO_2 in the environment does not enter the animal via respiratory or skin surfaces.

The magnitude of errors associated with the above assumptions is small in most situations, and can be avoided by careful choice of equations, animals, and sampling times (Nagy, 1980). Under some circumstances the errors may be unacceptably high. For example, if labeled animals breathe air containing unusually high concentrations ($>1\%$) of unlabeled CO_2, this CO_2 may equilibrate with body fluids and be measured by the isotopes. Thus, DLW values may be falsely high because they include exogenous as well as endogenous sources of CO_2.

Potential errors particular to communal bats include high humidity and high levels of unlabeled CO_2 found in natural roosts, such as reported in some caves and mines (see Chapter 29 and Kunz, 1982). Theoretically, these conditions could introduce large errors in the calculations of CO_2 production and water flux (Lifson and McClintock, 1966; Nagy, 1980). Although ^{3}H turnover gave an accurate estimate of water flux for pocket gophers confined to simulated burrow condi-

DOUBLY LABELED WATER METHOD

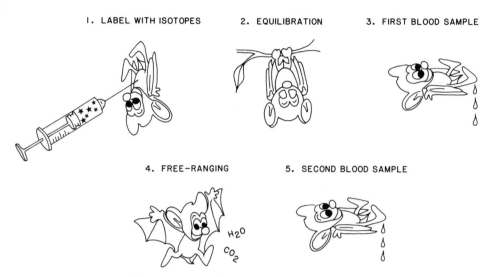

Figure 2. Field protocol for doubly labeled water studies on free-ranging bats: 1) intraperitoneal injection, 2) equilibration, 3) initial blood sample, 4) free-ranging activity, and 5) final blood sample (see text for details).

tions with 75% relative humidity (RH) (Gettinger, 1983), the RH of some bat roosts may be as high as 100% (Kunz, 1982). Studies are encouraged to determine the effects of high CO_2 levels and high humidity on results using the DLW method on bats that are normally exposed to these conditions.

2.4. Practical Considerations

There are several practical considerations when using DLW. These concern the choice of the study organism, field protocol (Fig. 2), isotope costs, and isotope analyses (see Mullen, 1973; Nagy, 1980; Nagy and Costa, 1980; Bryant and Westerterp, 1980; Nagy, 1983).

2.4.1. Choice of Organism

Aside from the biological significance of the results, the most important criterion in selecting bats for DLW studies is recapturability of the animals. Accessibility, high site fidelity, and high tolerance to disturbance all increase capturability and recapturability. Species that roost in protected shelters (Kunz, 1982) and form highly structured social groups (Bradbury, 1977) offer the best choices of animals for study. Their roost locations are predictable and adequate sample sizes can usually be obtained. Roost fidelity and recapture success are often linked to an animal's reproductive condition and social behavior. Lactating females are more likely to be recaptured at a maternity roost than are pregnant and non-reproductive females. Also, harem males are more likely to be recaptured than harem females, and harem members are more likely to be recaptured than members of non-harem (bachelor) groups (T. H. Kunz, unpubl.).

Flightless young are especially suitable subjects for study (e.g., Kunz and Anthony, 1982; Burnett and Kunz, 1982). High recapture success offers the potential for quantifying FMR and milk energy intake during the suckling period (Kunz and Nagy, unpubl.).

Although nursing females may transport neonates to alternate roosts following disturbance, they are less likely to move older sucklings, especially as they approach weaning size.

2.4.2. Capture and Blood Sampling Time

The time of day that bats are captured, injected, and bled can affect the amount of disturbance and bleeding success, and ultimately the error associated with calculating FMR. A consistent capture and processing time insures comparable values of body mass and minimizes overall disturbance to the colony. For best results adults and flying young should be captured in their roosts between 1100 h and 1300 h for initial processing. By 1100 h bats have voided most, if not all, of their feces from a previous meal, thus their body masses should have stabilized. Moreover, returning bats to their roost site immediately following treatment allows labeled individuals to reestablish social contacts with other members of the colony. This protocol allows enough time to process bats and return them for settling before the onset of nightly departure. State of hydration may affect the success of bleeding. Because adult bats, especially lactating females, are maximally dehydrated at the end of the day-roosting period, attempts to obtain blood samples at this time are less likely to be successful.

Flightless young are best captured and processed as soon as possible following the nightly departure of adults (e.g., Kunz, 1973; Kunz and Anthony, 1982). This protocol not only eliminates direct disturbance to roosting adults but also minimizes disturbance to the young. Dehydration is less likely to be a problem for sucklings at this time, particularly if they have recently nursed from their mother. Moreover, captures at this time eliminate the need to remove a suckling from its mother, and it is easier to locate marked individuals that might otherwise be difficult to find when adult bats are present. Young bats should be captured and processed as soon as possible after the departure of adults, since very young

bats may enter torpor, making it difficult, if not impossible, to draw a sufficient sample of blood.

2.4.3. Injection Procedures

Detailed procedures for preparing and calibrating injection solutions of $^3HH^{18}O$ are given in Nagy (1983). We prefer an injection solution consisting of 25 mCi/ml enrichment of ^3HHO and a 90-99 atom % enrichment of $H_2^{18}O$. After this tritium enrichment is mixed with the $H_2^{18}O$ enriched water, the tritium dose is about 1 mCi/kg body mass. Using this level of enrichment, injection volumes consist of about 3 ml/kg of animal. This volume is small enough so as not to overly increase the animal's total body water (TBW). A 30 µl sample of each injection solution should be flame-sealed in a microcapillary tube (Section 2.4.8) to be used in the preparation of standards (Nagy, 1983). Procedures for using deuterium instead of tritium are discussed by Mullen (1973) and Hails (1977). The amount of deuterium administered will depend on the sensitivity and accuracy of the spectrometer being used for deuterium analysis. Selected commercially available sources of isotopes for DLW studies are given in Nagy (1983).

In the field, a calibrated glass syringe (e.g., Hamilton microliter syringe) is filled to the desired volume, and constant pressure is applied to the plunger during injection. We pull the skin of the abdomen to the side before injection to reduce leakage when the needle is withdrawn. Special care should be taken to avoid contamination of the syringe with blood or dirt.

Subcutaneous, intramuscular, and intraperitoneal injections have been used on bats, but we prefer the intraperitoneal route. Intravenous injections should be avoided and may prove fatal to small animals, and subcutaneous injections are slow to equilibrate. The size of syringe that is used depends upon the enrichment of the injection solution, the mass of the bat, and the volume of the injection solution to be used. Accurate, careful, and reproducible injections can be made by using the same syringe and same volume of injection solution for each animal in a given experiment. The person who does the field injections also should calibrate the syringe volume in the laboratory, using distilled water (mass = volume) instead of the heavier injection solution.

2.4.4. Effects on Normal Behavior

The effects of isotope labeling on normal behavior (apart from disturbances caused by capture, handling, weighing, etc.) have not been investigated. Suter and Rawson (1968) found that the circadian rhythm of *Peromyscus leucopus* was temporarily altered when given drinking water containing highly-enriched deuterium oxide (^2HHO), although it has generally been assumed that such effects are minimal (but see Sutton and Nielson, 1974). Our observations indicate that some bats abandon roost sites after being captured, injected, and bled, but this response is influenced by such factors as species, sex, age, reproductive condition, and/or social behavior (see Bell et al., 1986). The DLW protocol most certainly involves some disturbance to animals, but this method is probably less subject to investigator bias and disturbance than some field estimates of time-activity budgets and related laboratory measurements of metabolism (see Congdon et al., 1982).

2.4.5. Measuring Body Mass

Precise and accurate measurements of body mass are extremely important in making calculations of FMR and water flux. Body mass should be taken as near as possible to the time of injection. Mass measurements taken at other times may cause errors in calculated TBW values, hence errors in FMR. Body mass should also be determined at the time of final bleeding. For bats having a body mass less than 100 g, we suggest that it be recorded to the nearest 0.01 g. This can be accom-

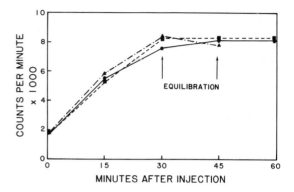

Figure 3. Equilibration times of tritiated water injected intraperitoneally into three little brown bats *(Myotis lucifugus).*

plished using a portable field balance (e.g., Ohaus, model 7401-02 or Torsion Balance, model DLM-2). Hand-held spring scales (e.g., Pesola) are less precise and often yield inconsistent and unreliable results. For bats weighing over 100 g, body mass measurements with a precision of 0.1 g are usually adequate.

2.4.6. Isotope Equilibration

To determine the amount of time required for isotope equilibration, individuals are injected with ^3HHO, and serial blood samples are taken at regular intervals (e.g., 15 min) following injection. When several bats are being tested, we suggest they be housed individually to minimize the time needed to search for and process each animal and to avoid isotope exchange between animals. An injection solution consisting of ^3HHO is used instead of one containing ^3H and ^{18}O since only one isotope (the least expensive) is needed. We microdistill blood samples and determine the specific activity of ^3H with a liquid scintillation counter (Section 2.6). The specific activity (CPM) of ^3H is plotted against time following injection, and equilibration time is determined as the beginning of the asymptote on the plot (Fig. 3).

Results from our analysis (Kunz and Nagy, unpubl.) indicate that ^3HHO equilibra-

BLEEDING PROCEDURES

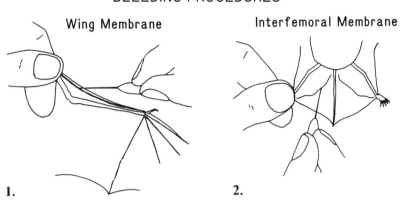

Figure 4. Suggested procedures for bleeding bats in doubly labeled water studies: 1) venous puncture of cardiac vein in propatagium and 2) venous puncture of major vein in interfemoral membrane.

tion occurs within 30-45 min following intra-peritoneal injection in adult *Myotis lucifugus* (7-10 g), *Eptesicus fuscus* (15-18 g), *Carollia perspicillata* (18-22 g), and *Phyllostomus hastatus* (70-90 g). This time is consistent with results from adult birds having a similar body mass (e.g., Hails and Bryant, 1979; Williams and Nagy, 1984) but is shorter than reported for similar size rodents (e.g., Mullen, 1971).

Time required for isotope equilibration may vary with body mass, route of injection, metabolic rate, and state of hydration. Isotopes injected into small animals (<5 g) are likely to equilibrate sooner than in larger individuals. If the initial blood sample is taken before isotopes have equilibrated, TBW will be underestimated because of falsely low isotope measurements. If isotopes reach equilibrium before the first blood sample is taken, some of the $^3HH^{18}O$ will be lost via normal routes of water loss, and input of unlabeled water from energy metabolism and ambient water vapor may combine to slowly lower the isotope concentration. This will lead to an overestimate of TBW. Because isotope equilibration takes longer when animals are dehydrated (Richmond et al., 1962), equilibration experiments should be conducted at the same time of day as the experiments to

determine FMR and water flux in the field (Section 2.4.5).

2.4.7. Blood Sampling Procedures

Several procedures for bleeding bats have been described, including cardiac puncture (LaMotte, 1958), rupture of the infraorbital sinus (Baer, 1966), puncture of wing veins (Baer and McClean, 1972; Keegan, 1979; Gustafson and Demassa, 1985), puncture of the jugular vein (Baer and McClean, 1972), puncture of veins in the interfemoral membrane (Black and Wiederhielm, 1976), and the use of starved hemophagous bugs (Helversen and Reyer, 1984). The procedures described by Keegan (1979) and Gustafson and Demassa (1985) are valuable modifications for bleeding bats, but they may prove to be unnecessarily cumbersome for taking blood samples in the field.

Depending upon the species and size (age) of the animal, we have had good success bleeding bats using two relatively simple procedures (Fig. 4). We use 25-gauge needles to puncture veins in the interfemoral membrane or in the wings. Small surgical needles are less effective and lances should be avoided. For most small vespertilionid bats (young and

Temporary Seal   Flame Seal

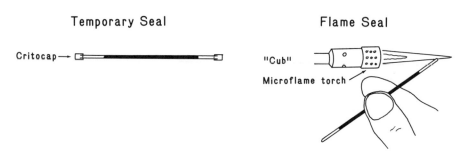

Figure 5. Procedures for temporarily and permanently sealing glass microcapillary tubes: (A) Critocaps should be inserted firmly into both ends of the tube. (B) Flame seals can be successfully made by holding the capillary tube horizontally, but at an angle to the flame, so that the opening of the tube is directed away from the source of the flame. The capillary tube should be rolled between the thumb and forefinger until a small bead forms at the tip of the tube. Repeat procedure at other end.

adults ranging from 2-15 g), we have successfully taken blood from veins that run semi-parallel to the tail in the interfemoral membrane. In the field we accomplish this by first transilluminating the interfemoral membrane with a small incandescent light source (e.g., MineSpot Cap Lamp or Koehler Wheat Lamp; see Chapter 1). We then usually puncture only one vein in the first bleeding session, saving the other vein for when the bat is recaptured. The lamp allows one to easily see the vein, but it also produces a small amount of heat that stimulates venous dilation and blood flow. Rhythmic flexing of the leg on the side where blood is being taken often promotes the flow of blood. In larger species (>15 g), and those lacking an interfemoral membrane, we have successfully taken blood from the cardiac vein located near the leading edge of the propatagium. Attempts to draw blood from other veins in the wings should be avoided because of the risks of causing a hematoma (blood blister).

When the animal has been inactive or torpid, blood is commonly shunted away from the wing membrane. Blood flow can be stimulated by placing the bat's body against a hot water bottle or other heat source. During the equilibration and processing periods we have successfully kept bats warm by allowing them to form small clusters (5-6 individuals) in small wooden roosts (see Chapter 1). Bats held in this manner usually remain warm,

equilibrate sooner, and are thus easier to bleed than if housed alone or in cloth holding bags. Extremely small bats can be warmed by holding them in cupped, bare hands. Light etherization may be used to promote vasodilation and blood flow to peripheral veins before attempts are made to bleed bats (see Gustafson and Demassa, 1985).

Blood samples are routinely collected in 70 µl heparinized, glass microcapillary tubes. A minimum of 35 µl (activation analysis) or 10 µl (mass analysis) of blood is needed for routine analysis in DLW studies. If possible, 45 µl (activation analysis) should be collected in each of two tubes so that one can be used as a backup sample (Nagy, 1983). These volumes of blood can be drawn successfully from most full-grown bats, but one must be willing to accept smaller volumes from neonates and other immature bats. Holding the capillary tube at a slightly downward angle from the drop of blood should promote adequate filling.

The flow of blood from a punctured vein of a bat usually ceases soon after a sample has been taken; however, some animals may bleed profusely. Slight upstream pressure from the fingers, combined with blowing air on the wound, is often sufficient to stop the bleeding. If the animal continues to bleed, an application of powdered "Gelfoam" (sterile gelatin powder) at the place of bleeding may stop the flow of blood. Application of ice to the wound may also reduce or stop the flow of blood in profuse bleeders. It is important to note that excessive bleeders may loose as much as 3-5% of TBW in a few minutes and this can lead to serious errors when calculating FMR and water flux.

When animals are very small and the taking of an initial blood sample would be harmful or might interfere with normal behavior, this step can be eliminated and isotope activity (from initial samples) can be estimated rather than measured (Nagy, 1983; Nagy et al., 1984a). In this procedure, animals are released immediately after being marked, injected, and weighed. A small sample of bats of comparable age, sex, and reproductive condition are weighed and injected, and blood is taken after the period of equilibration. These animals can then be killed and used to verify TBW and to quantify body composition. Ricklefs and Williams (1984) proposed a field protocol for eliminating initial blood samples and the potentially traumatic equilibration period by estimating initial isotope ratios (not absolute concentrations) from other animals that were injected and sampled initially. This procedure is suitable for determining FMR, but it cannot be used for determining water flux because the latter requires knowledge of absolute ^3H activity after equilibration.

2.4.8. Sample Preparation

Capillary tubes containing blood samples should be sealed temporarily or permanently in the field (Fig. 5), labeled, and refrigerated to prevent samples from spoiling. Decayed samples usually produce contaminated water upon distillation, and this will cause errors in activation analysis. Blood should be centered in the microcapillary tube before sealing both ends. Critocaps provide temporary seals and are suitable when field conditions make flame-sealing hazardous or difficult. Critocaps should be removed and the ends of the tubes flame-sealed before transporting samples overland or by air. Flame seals are permanent, prevent loss of samples by evaporation,

isotopic fractionation during evaporation, and dilution of samples by instillation of water from ambient humidity. Flame-sealed microcapillary tubes containing blood should not be frozen as this may cause the tubes to fracture when the water in blood expands (Nagy, 1983).

Lack of suitable field-refrigeration may pose problems until samples can be transported to the laboratory. We have successfully used blocks of ice or sealed, gel coolants (available in many sporting goods stores) to keep samples cold in the field. Gel coolants have an advantage in that they can be frozen in advance and kept at cold temperatures in small picnic coolers for up to 48 h in the field. They also can be used many times and without causing an accumulation of water in a cooler from melted ice. When it becomes necessary to keep samples cold for longer periods without access to ice or refrigeration, we have used a supply of instant catalytic coolants (available at many sporting goods stores) which, when activated and kept insulated, will keep samples cool for up to 24 h. Sealed blood samples should be distilled following the procedures described in Wood et al. (1975) and Nagy (1983). Undistilled, flame-sealed blood samples can be stored safely under refrigeration for several months.

2.4.9. Costs

Oxygen-18 labeled water is the most expensive of the isotopes involved in DLW studies. At current (1986) prices, this isotope costs about U.S. $180/kg of animal body mass to be injected, for studies involving ^{18}O measurement by activation analysis or conventional mass spectrometry. Tritium and deuterium are much less expensive. For a bat weighing 20 g, total costs for isotopes are about $200/kg ($4 per bat). Analysis of isotopes in blood samples costs about $0.75 per sample for tritium and about $14 per sample for ^{18}O using proton activation analysis (Nagy, 1983). Deuterium analysis is best done using isotope-ratio mass spectrometry, but the cost is high (about $45/sample). Isotope-ratio mass spectrometry can also be used to measure ^{18}O in samples, but this method is expensive (about $40/sample). Because isotope-ratio mass spectrometric analysis is more accurate than proton activation analysis, animals can be injected with one-tenth, or less, of the ^{18}O needed for proton activation analysis, thus reducing isotope costs. The total cost of a project depends mainly on the body mass of the animal to be studied, and is about the same with either ^{18}O analysis method when individual animals weigh 1 to 5 kg. For smaller animals, the activation analysis method is less expensive overall, but for larger animals the mass spectrometer method is less costly.

2.5.   Validation Experiments

The DLW method for measuring CO_2 production has been validated for several groups of vertebrates, including reptiles (e.g., Congdon et al., 1978; Nagy, 1980), rodents (Mullen, 1970; Gettinger, 1983), and birds (e.g., Utter and LeFebvre, 1971; Hails, 1977; Hails and Bryant, 1979; Williams and Nagy, 1984). Results from these and other studies indicate errors averaging less than 10% (also see Weathers et al., 1984).

A simple and reliable method of validation is to simultaneously measure CO_2 production from isotope turnover and from gravimetric measurements (e.g., Kendeigh, 1939; Williams and Nagy, 1984) or gas analysis using a CO_2 analyzer (e.g., Hails and Bryant, 1979). For active bats, we have successfully used a gravimetric approach by confining individual animals to small metal or plexiglass metabolic chambers, which include a hollowed-out wood block (a simulated roost). Validation methods based on food consumption in the laboratory (e.g., Karasov, 1981; Gettinger, 1983) are less suitable for bats because of the difficulties in getting captive bats to eat and maintain a stable body mass, and associated problems with the quantitative collection of urine and feces.

Gravimetric measurement of CO_2 production can be accomplished by determining the mass increase of a CO_2 absorbent (NaOH-coated silica) after excurrent air from a metabolic chamber has passed through a tube of anhydrous $CaSO_4$ (Kendeigh, 1939). Williams and Nagy (1984) found that Ascarite (a CO_2 absorbent) gave off water after it had been used for a while. Thus, the mass of Ascarite did not increase in proportion to the CO_2 absorbed. This problem can be minimized by adding a small band of H_2O absorbent (anhydrous $CaSO_4$) at the end of the column of CO_2 absorbent.

2.6.   Isotopes and Isotope Analysis

Several isotopes and analytical methods can be used in DLW studies, and the choices among these can affect costs and convenience. The hydrogen isotope can be either tritium or deuterium. Tritiated water is inexpensive both to purchase and to analyze. Liquid scintillation vials and chemicals cost about $0.75 per sample (Nagy, 1975, 1983) and liquid scintillation counters are available at many institutions. Scores of tritium samples can usually be analyzed in one day. However, a drawback of using tritiated water is that its radioactivity requires users to obtain permits for its use in the field and laboratory.

For tritium analysis, 5 or 10 µl aliquants of water distilled from blood samples are placed in 10 ml of scintillation fluid for counting. A common scintillation cocktail consists of 3.6 g 2,5-diphenyloxazole (PPO), 250 ml Triton X-100, and 1 liter scintillation-grade toluene (Nagy, 1983). Plasma, urine, or saliva samples may be pipetted without distilling them first, but the results will contain larger errors due to variable quenching and variations in dry matter content between samples (which reduces the amount of water per unit volume of sample). In general, these methodological errors translate into large errors in calculated FMR, thus distillation is recommended (Nagy, 1980; Nagy and Costa, 1980).

Deuterium is a stable (non-radioactive) isotope of hydrogen, consequently no permits are needed for its use. Deuterated water also is inexpensive to purchase, but analysis of this isotope may be costly and time-consuming. Higher concentrations of ^2H (above about 0.1%) can be measured directly in water distilled from biological samples by means of infrared absorbence (Zweens et al., 1980). This requires an infrared spectrophotometer with dual, temperature-controlled sample chambers. Conventional mass spectrometers can also be used to measure deuterium at higher concentrations (Mullen, 1973), and isotope-ratio mass spectrometers, being much more sensitive, can measure deuterium at low concentrations (Schoeller et al., 1980; Matthews and Bier, 1983). For mass spectrometry, it is necessary to convert the hydrogen in samples into hydrogen gas for measurement of the mass 3 to mass 2 ratio. This requires a high vacuum line, and is relatively more time consuming.

There are two isotopes of oxygen, ^{17}O and ^{18}O, that can be used in DLW studies. Oxygen-17 is very expensive, but its natural abundance is so low that only small enrichments, and hence small doses are required. Unfortunately, no procedures for measuring ^{17}O in biological samples have been developed, although mass-spectrometry should work. Oxygen-18 is a stable isotope, as is ^{17}O, and ^{18}O has been the isotope used in all DLW studies to date. Like deuterium, ^{18}O can be used at both high and low concentrations. At higher levels (0.05 atom % excess and above), proton activation analysis (Wood et al., 1975) provides relatively inexpensive (ca. $15 per sample) measurements, and large numbers of samples (40 per day) can be processed routinely. In this procedure, blood samples are first distilled, then 8 µl aliquants (in triplicate) are sealed in glass microcapillary tubes, bombarded with protons which convert ^{18}O to gamma-emitting (radioactive) ^{18}F, and counted in a gamma spectrometer.

Oxygen-18 can also be analyzed by mass spectrometry. This analysis requires one to 5 ml of blood, but techniques requiring smaller volumes of sample are being developed in several laboratories. The oxygen in water is transferred to CO_2, either by isotopic exchange with CO_2 added to the container holding the sample (Schoeller et al., 1980), or by reacting the sample with guanidine hydrochloride (Mullen, 1973) or with BrF_5 and carbon (Hails, 1977) to produce CO_2 from water. For samples containing higher ^{18}O enrichments (0.05 to 1.8 atom % excess), the ratio of mass 44 (CO_2) to mass 46 ($CO^{18}O$) can be measured with a conventional mass spectrometer (Mullen, 1973). Lower ^{18}O enrichments (0.002 to 0.02 atom % excess) can be measured using the newer, isotope-ratio mass spectrometers (Schoeller et al., 1980; Matthews and Bier, 1983). This procedure reduces costs for ^{18}O purchase, because much lower doses are required to obtain measurable enrichments, yet analytical costs are higher.

3. FOOD CONSUMPTION

3.1. Gravimetric Methods

Methods for estimating food consumption of bats based on gravimetric measurements were summarized by Kunz (1980). Methods appropriate for energy budget analysis of free-ranging bats include those involving mass increments from feeding, recording the volume (or size) and number of prey items eaten, or measuring the amount of feces produced from food consumed. To insure that total nightly consumption can be determined, the number and duration of feeding bouts should be known. Knowledge of water content, energy density, and the assimilation efficiencies of different foods are needed to convert prey or fecal mass to metabolizable energy.

3.1.1. Ingesta

One approach that has been used with moderate success for some species is to weigh individuals before and after each feeding period (Wimsatt, 1969; Kunz, 1974; Anthony and Kunz, 1977; Funakoshi and Uchida, 1975,

1980; Wilkinson, 1985). Ideally, it would be valuable to weigh the same individuals before and after each feeding period, but recapture success of marked individuals on the same night is often extremely poor. This method of estimating nightly food consumption is usually made by comparing average mass increments from samples of the same cohorts (e.g., age, sex, reproductive condition, etc.) for a given species. A major assumption is that the bats captured after having fed have the same mean mass (without food) as those actually weighed at the time of emergence (Wimsatt, 1969). This assumption is likely to be violated especially during pregnancy when females (carrying embryos) exhibit a wide range of developmental stages, and pregnant females in the pre- and post-feeding samples may differ in their average stages of pregnancy (Kunz, 1980).

If bats have two feeding periods, the prefeeding mass for the second period can be determined by weighing bats upon emergence from their night roost. Alternatively, this prefeeding mass can be estimated by subtracting the amount of feces and water lost during the night-roosting period from the body mass of bats as they enter the night roost (e.g., Anthony et al., 1981). The mass increment from the second feeding period (using the actual or adjusted mass at the end of the night-roosting period) is added to the increment from the first feeding period to estimate total nightly wet mass consumption. This procedure assumes that body mass losses due to evaporation and urination during the foraging period are balanced by water intake, or can be corrected for by measuring mass losses of bats that did not feed (i.e., caged animals over the same period).

Mean or individual mass increments from each feeding period can be converted to dry mass equivalents and multiplied by the energy density (kJ/g) of the food consumed. Energy equivalents of field diets or stomach contents are determined by calorimetry. Energy density for some insect prey and stomach contents of *Myotis lucifugus* are summarized in Chapter 12. Metabolizable energy is

determined as the product of the dry mass energy equivalent and the percent assimilation efficiency. When possible, it is advisable to determine energy density of prey items that were captured at the same time and place where bats were observed feeding.

Direct observations of bats that transport food items to feeding roosts can sometimes yield data on amounts of food eaten (e.g., Morrison, 1978; Vehrencamp et al., 1977; Bell, 1982), but caution should be exercised in determining what is actually consumed. Some items transported to feeding roosts may be partly culled before being eaten (see Chapter 11). In some instances only the juices of fruits and leaves are ingested and pulp is rejected as fibrous pellets (Gardner, 1977). In other situations only parts of insects are ingested and wings and head capsules are culled by the bats (Chapter 11). Nutrient analysis (Chapter 15) and energy density should be determined only for those parts or items of food known to be ingested.

Some potential errors in estimating energy intake can be avoided by feeding bats in captive situations. Thomas (1984) calculated the amount of fruit eaten as the difference between the mass of fruit offered at the beginning of an *ad libitum* feeding period and the rejected fruit at the end of a designated feeding period (after correcting for the amount of water that evaporated from the fruit). It should be emphasized, however, that some bats in captivity may overeat (see Chapter 16). Moreover, energy expended on activity in captive situations is likely to be lower than under free-ranging conditions. However, thermoregulatory costs may be higher in captivity unless bats are maintained at temperatures near thermoneutrality (Chapter 20).

3.1.2. Egesta

Daily metabolizable energy of individual bats can be estimated from the nightly production of feces. By knowing the dry mass and energy density of feces produced on a given night, and correcting this for assimilation efficiency of field diets, one can estimate the amount of metabolizable energy available to a bat (e.g., Kunz, 1980; Kurta, 1986). This approach has also been used to estimate energy intake in brooding House Martins (e.g., Bryant and Westerterp, 1983).

Collecting feces from insectivorous bats in the field may be accomplished by capturing individuals as they return from feeding and holding them individually in separate containers until all feces have been voided (e.g., Anthony and Kunz, 1977; Anthony et al., 1981; Swift et al., 1985; Kurta, 1986). The number of separate feeding periods can be determined from direct observations (Chapter 4), trapping (Chapter 1), or by monitoring the activity of bats with radio-transmitters (Chapters 4 and 7, and Section 4.3). To insure that all feces are voided from a given feeding period, individual bats should be held in containers until the normal departure time on the following evening. If one or more feeding periods have been documented, feces should be collected from two different cohorts, one captured upon return from the first feeding period and the other captured after the second feeding period. The sum of the total dry mass is used to establish nightly energy intake. For example, if a bat produced a total of 0.20 g of dry feces and the assimilation efficiency was 0.88, the total dry mass of food would be 1.66g or [1/(1 − 0.88)] 0.20. Assuming that the energy density of feces was 19.25 kJ/day, the nightly ingested energy available to this bat would be (1.66 × 19.25 = 31.95 kJ).

There are advantages and disadvantages in using this method to estimate daily energy intake. An important advantage is that energy intake may be estimated for individual bats. A disadvantage, as with the ingesta method, is that it may yield less than complete estimates of energy intake (see Kurta, 1986). This would occur if bats are captured before a feeding period has been completed or captured after some of the digested meal has already passed as feces. The former situation is avoided if bats return to their roost (and are captured) immediately after having fed.

Owing to high rates of food passage in some species (e.g., Buchler, 1975; Kunz, 1980; Funakoshi and Uchida, 1980), some fecal loss can be expected during feeding flights and before bats return to a roost. Kunz (1980) estimated that nightly fecal loss by insectivorous bats in flight was approximately 5% of total daily fecal production for species that return to a night roost after an early feeding bout. It may be higher for other species that feed continuously or intermittently throughout the night and do not use communal night roosts. The egesta method is not suitable for most frugivorous, nectarivorous, and sanguivorous bats because there is little or no easily "identifiable" fraction of digested material in the feces as there is with insectivorous bats. Rapid food passage time and fecal loss also is higher in frugivorous and nectarivorous species (Klite, 1965; Wolton et al., 1982), making it difficult to collect feces from a single feeding period.

3.2. Isotope Dilution

Isotope dilution methods hold considerable promise for estimating food intake in bats. When an animal is labeled with an isotope (^{2}H, ^{3}H, or ^{22}Na) its specific activity will decline exponentially with time owing to the respiratory and/or excretory loss of isotopes, and the simultaneous dilution of isotopes through the gain of unlabeled water or mineral from food, drink, and metabolic water production. The rate of decline of specific activity of an isotope can be related to food intake (e.g., Nagy, 1975; Green, 1978). Isotope dilution can also be used to estimate daily milk input to suckling young (see Section 3.3.1).

3.2.1. Estimates from ^{3}H Turnover

Because the DLW water method allows the determination of gross water flux by measuring the turnover of ^{3}HHO (Section 2.1), it may be used to determine the daily food intake (e.g., Nagy, 1975; Shoemaker et al., 1976; Helversen and Reyer, 1984; Bell et al.,

1986). This method is valid if the source of ingested water comes only from the food eaten (no drinking of water), or if the rate of consumption of free-standing water is known. In these cases, the portion of total water influx due to dietary water (preformed and metabolically-formed) can be determined. Helversen and Reyer (1984) used this method to estimate nectar intake by *Anoura caudifer*. Other bats that obtain water from their food (e.g., frugivorous, sanguivorous, and some insectivorous species) should be suitable subjects for estimating food intake using this method. Bell et al. (1986) estimated nightly food intake in the desert bat, *Macrotus californicus,* which gains its water from the insects it eats and from metabolic water.

If the water content of the food is known, one can determine how much dry mass of food is needed to equal the measured amount of dietary water gain (equation 2 of Nagy, 1975). The metabolic water yield of the food can be determined by knowing the chemical composition and metabolizability of the ingested food. Alternatively, metabolic water production can be estimated from DLW measurements of energy metabolism in the field.

3.2.2. Estimates from Doubly Labeled Water ($^3HH^{18}O$)

The rate of food consumption required to provide the metabolizable energy for an animal can be calculated from its FMR (Section 2.4) and knowledge of its diet. This approach requires an assumption that the animal eats no more and no less food than it needs to satisfy metabolic expenditures (i.e., it was in energy balance, or steady-state). Rates of CO_2 production are then converted to energy units based on chemical composition of the diet (Nagy, 1983).

3.2.3. Sodium Dilution

A technique described by Green (1978) to estimate food intake in the dingo (*Canis familiaris dingo*) is based on the turnover of ^{22}Na. This approach has not been tried but

should work with bats. An important assumption is that there is no major source of Na intake (e.g., salt water) during the experiment. This technique is based on observations that an animal has two Na compartments, a non-exchangeable compartment (metabolically inert) and an exchangeable compartment containing about 75% Na. An animal is given an injection containing 20 μCi $^{22}NaCl$ and the isotope is allowed to equilibrate. Weighing, injection, bleeding, equilibration, blood sampling, and sample preparation procedures are as described above (Section 2.4). The specific activity of ^{22}Na is determined using a liquid scintillation counter. The ^{22}Na turnover rates and rates of food intake are calculated using equations in Green (1978). Knowledge of Na content (mg/kg) in the diet is required to calculate food intake. Sodium content of food items can be determined by using atomic absorption spectrophotometry (see Green and Eberhard, 1984).

3.3. Milk Yield and Energy Intake by Sucklings

Several methods have been used to quantify milk production in wild and domesticated mammals. These include mass differences of sucklings before and after feeding, timed milking, isotope dilution, and isotope transfer (reviewed in Oftedal, 1984a). For bats and most other small, free-ranging mammals, the first two methods are impractical. Isotope dilution and transfer methods (e.g., Macfarlane et al., 1969; Green and Newgrain, 1979) have been used successfully to estimate milk yield by lactating females and milk intake of sucklings in a variety of marsupial and placental mammals (Oftedal, 1984a, 1986). These methods hold considerable promise for studies on free-ranging bats (Kunz and Nagy, unpubl.).

3.3.1. Tritium Dilution

This method requires that milk is the only source of exogenous water to sucklings. Although this method is limited to sucklings before they begin to take solid food, it can yield valuable information on maternal investment and energy intake during the early postnatal growth period. Tritium is injected into suckling bats and milk consumption is measured from the exponential decline of isotopes in the body fluid of the suckling. The use of $^3HH^{18}O$ is an improvement over using ^3HHO, because TBW can be estimated from the ^{18}O dilution space instead of ^3H (see Nagy, 1980). This makes it possible to determine FMR as well as water flux of the suckling.

Sources of error associated with estimating milk intake from ^3HHO dilution in suckling mammals were reviewed by Oftedal (1984a, 1986). These include: 1) incorporation of isotopes into non-exchangeable hydrogen sites in newly synthesized tissue, 2) reduction of isotope concentration due to increasing size of the body water pool (Dove and Freer, 1979), 3) recycling of isotopes from suckling to mother (via maternal ingestion of urine and feces of sucklings) and from the mother back to the suckling by uptake of the isotope in milk (Baverstock and Green, 1975), and 4) entry of water into the body water pool from sources other than milk (e.g., ingested whole food and metabolized fat). Because young bats grow rapidly, the first source of error could be large (Lewis and Phillips, 1972). Error 2 can be eliminated by use of appropriate flux equations (Nagy and Costa, 1980). Equations to correct for error 3 have been suggested (Baverstock and Green, 1975; Dove and Freer, 1979).

A protocol to control for isotope recycling using one pup from a litter as an unlabeled control was suggested by Baverstock and Green (1975). This would work for bats with litters of two or more, but most species only produce a single offspring. In situations where suckling young begin to feed on solid food (or regurgitated blood) before they are weaned (e.g., Wilkinson, 1985), alternative isotope transfer methods may be more appropriate (Holleman et al., 1975). One such method involves the use of two isotopes (tritium and deuterium); first by measuring the transfer of tritium from milk of the mother to the suckling and then by determining the turnover of deuterium oxide (^2HHO) in the suckling (Holleman et al., 1975; Wright and Wolff, 1976). Other methods, involving the combined use of ^3HHO and ^2HHO (or some other isotope) in which both mother and suckling are labeled, are difficult to use with free-ranging bats because they require the simultaneous capture and recapture of the mother and sucklings. Under most circumstances capture and recapture of the mother and suckling together is extremely difficult in communal roosts, especially as the suckling matures and spends less time attached to its mother.

3.3.2. Sodium Dilution

Green and Newgrain (1979) described a method that relates the rate of ^{22}Na turnover in sucklings with milk consumption. Animals are injected with $^{22}NaCl$ (5 µCi ^{22}Na is diluted in 100 µl NaCl solution). Animals are bled and the samples are processed as described above (Section 2.4). Sodium-22 activity is determined with a liquid scintillation counter, and total Na content of blood is determined with an atomic absorption spectrometer.

The major advantage of using ^{22}Na for estimating milk intake is that it avoids potential errors associated with pulmocutaneous exchange between litter mates and the mother (Friedman and Bruno, 1976). Use of ^{22}Na instead of ^3HHO also avoids the problem of the isotope being incorporated into milk solids during milk synthesis. Moreover, considerably less ^{22}Na is recycled to the suckling via milk secretion (Green and Newgrain, 1979) as compared to ^3H when ^3HHO is used (Baverstock and Green, 1975).

3.3.3. Milk Energy Output

If age-specific milk intake (Section 3.3) and energy density of milk are known (e.g., Kunz et al., 1983), total milk energy output of lactating females can then be calculated for different stages of lactation. This latter value can be used as a measure of maternal investment (e.g., Trivers, 1972) and reproductive effort (e.g., Williams, 1966). It should be noted that energy estimates will be in error if the analyzed milk samples are not representative. Data that do not distinguish stages of lactation are not sufficiently accurate for energy calculations (Oftedal, 1984b).

3.3.4. Predictions from Allometric Equations

When it is impractical to estimate milk energy input-output using isotope turnover, an estimate may be derived for peak lactation using an appropriate allometric equation. Prediction of milk energy yield derived from metabolic mass ($m^{0.83}$) of sucklings in kilograms (Oftedal, 1984a) appears to be an improvement over most previously published equations (e.g., Brody, 1945; Blaxter, 1961; Linzell, 1972; Hanwell and Peaker, 1977). One should be reminded, however, of the potential errors in allometric equations derived from the analysis of different taxa (see Harvey and Mace, 1982; Huesner, 1982).

4. TIME-BUDGET METHOD

4.1. Rationale and General Procedures

The time-budget method for estimating energy expenditure in animals is derived from observed daily activity budgets and averages of laboratory-derived estimates of energy expenditure for various activities. Time budgets are often difficult to estimate accurately, and many are commonly subdivided into only crude categories. Recent efforts to examine the reliability and sensitivity of time budgets in relation to variation in their major components (Travis, 1982; Weathers et al., 1984) have shown that time-budget estimates can vary markedly, depending on the model chosen and the kind of data that are used. Timed signals are best analyzed

using an instantaneous time-sampling method (e.g., Altmann, 1974; Jacobsen and Wiggens, 1982).

The time-budget method has become increasingly used in the study of birds (e.g., King, 1974; Kendeigh et al., 1977; Walsberg, 1983) and several species of medium to large, diurnal mammals but there have been few such studies on small mammals. The secretive and nocturnal behavior of most small mammals has generally hampered time-budget studies on this group. Notwithstanding, many bat species are ideal subjects for time-budget analyses. Their synchronous nightly departure and return behavior (reviewed in Erkert, 1982), combined with communal roosting behavior (in several species), potentially allows the establishment of time budgets from direct observations (Kunz, 1980). In some situations it is necessary to determine time budgets from a composite assessment of colony behavior (e.g., Burnett and August, 1981), including mean emergence and return times (Kunz, 1980), and the amount of time that day and night roosts are occupied (Anthony et al., 1981; Barclay, 1982). Moreover, observations of individually marked bats are possible using night vision devices, light tags (Chapter 4), and radiotelemetry (Chapter 7).

4.2. Roosting Activity

Time budgets of roosting bats may include time allocated to different behaviors, including grooming, crawling, resting, and intraspecific interactions (e.g., Burnett and August, 1981), as well as account for the energetic consequences of clustering and torpor (e.g., Trune and Slobodchikoff, 1976; Kunz, 1980; Kurta, 1986). Ideally, a roosting time-budget should integrate animal characteristics with radiative and convective properties of the environment (see Chapter 19). Meteorological sensors (including taxidermic mounts) can be used to measure the T_e (operative temperature) of natural roosts. For bats that roost in protected shelters (e.g., caves, tree cavities, buildings), time-budget models that include heat-transfer parameters can be simplified by omitting measurements of forced convection and direct solar radiation.

Estimates of roosting costs require laboratory-derived measurements of metabolic expenditure for each activity, but few such measurements have been made for bats. Exceptions include costs of thermoregulation at different temperatures and energy conserved by clustering. Metabolic costs for roost activities such as grooming and crawling continue to be based on unverified estimates from other taxa (Kunz, 1980).

4.3. Foraging Activity

Most energy budget studies of bats (e.g., Kunz, 1980; Burnett and August, 1981; Helversen and Reyer, 1984; Kurta et al., 1987) have used Thomas' (1975) allometric equation 36 to estimate flight costs. Despite the attractiveness of this equation, caution is urged in applying it uncritically to estimate flight costs in species having different foraging strategies. At best Thomas' equation predicts minimum power required for level flight; it does not include flight costs associated with aerial insect pursuit, hovering, obstacle avoidance, and other activities associated with different modes of flight. Moreover, extrapolation of estimates to animals having a body mass less than empirically measured estimates (<60 g) is questionable.

The development of miniature (<1 g) radio-transmitters (Chapter 7) has made it possible to quantify the amount of time individuals of some species spend on the wing. Nightly time budgets based on signals from radio-tagged bats can be quantified using one of several methods. Continuous records from one individual can yield the most accurate time budgets, but this approach is extremely time-intensive and yields only a minimum amount of data. Automated data logging of signals over short intervals (less than one

min) can essentially provide a continuous record for several individuals. Cooper and Charles-Dominique (1985) described a microcomputer data acquisition system for use in monitoring the flight activity of radio-tagged bats. This system allows data collection in the field with a portable cassette tape recorder and can be easily adapted to ordinary radio-tracking equipment.

With the possible exception of aerial insectivores, foraging time should not be interpreted as "flight time." Even some insectivorous species pause intermittently to ingest prey in the course of their nightly foraging activity (Kunz, 1982), and some species are known to capture their prey on the ground (Chapters 11 and 12). Moreover, the foraging activity of some insectivorous, frugivorous, carnivorous, and sanguivorous bats may involve little actual time in flight, except for commutes between roosts and feeding areas.

A procedure that we have used for estimating foraging costs combines time-budget data from radio-tagged bats and estimates of FMR from DLW. Foraging costs are determined by regressing FMR of radio-tagged bats against time spent in flight. This approach also has been used to estimate flight costs for birds (Hails, 1980; Turner, 1983; Flint and Nagy, 1984b) and swimming costs for penguins (Nagy et al., 1984).

Foraging costs may also be estimated by subtracting roosting time-energy budgets from daily energy expenditure (Section 3.1). This indirect method should be suitable for species whose roosting time and energy budgets can be determined from direct observation (Burnett and August, 1981), where roosting metabolism can be measured (Stack, 1985; Bell et al., 1986; Kurta, 1986) and where species are too small to carry radio-transmitters. This approach has been used successfully in studies of aerial feeding swallows and martins (Turner, 1983). It may underestimate foraging requirements of lactating females, however, since it does not take into account energy requirements associated with milk energy output.

5. RATES AND EFFICIENCIES OF ENERGY TRANSFER

5.1. Integration of Complete and Partial Energy Budgets

Rates and efficiencies of energy transfer derived from complete and partial energy budgets are useful for describing daily and seasonal patterns of energy expenditure (see Brody, 1945). More importantly they can be used to test predictions from life-history theory (e.g., optimal foraging, reproductive effort, and parental investment). Integration of partial and complete energy budgets are made possible when a combination of time-budget, body composition, food consumption, and isotope methods are used. Even when energy investment is measured in terms of biomass, data on transfer efficiencies and costs of producing these tissues are often difficult to obtain. In calculating energy transfer efficiencies it is important to specify what category of efficiency (gross or net) and what category of food (gross, digestible, or metabolizable) is being used.

5.2. Feeding Rates and Foraging Efficiencies

Feeding rates can be estimated as the ratio of FMR to the metabolizable energy content of the diet (Section 3.2.2). These rates can be converted from units of dry mass to units of wet mass using appropriate conversion factors for different food items in field diets. Feeding rates calculated in this manner are those needed to meet maintenance costs and do not include the allocation to, or metabolism, of stored energy reserves.

If the total energy expenditure of an animal is known and the assumption is made that an individual is in energy balance (metabolizable energy = expended energy), foraging efficiency needed to achieve a balanced energy budget can be calculated as the ratio of metabolizable energy gained while foraging to the energy expended while foraging (Wolf et al., 1975; Nagy and Shoemaker, 1984). Foraging efficiency calculated in this manner indicates how much more metabolizable energy is acquired from foraging than is expended in the process of food acquisition. Foraging expenditures can be determined as described in Section 4.3. Metabolizable energy gained while foraging can be determined by using results from DLW (Section 2), nightly food intake (Section 3), or time-budget methods (Section 4).

5.3. Parental Investment

An important part of the daily energy budget of an animal is the amount of energy allocated to reproduction. Some of this energy is expended on courtship and mating but, for female bats, most is spent on the actual production of young and on parental care. The concepts of parental investment and reproductive effort have been of considerable theoretical interest, but empirical data from free-ranging animals needed to test predictions lag far behind the theory. Methods described here and elsewhere in this volume can help to bridge this gap.

5.3.1. Fetal Production

The net cost of fetal production can be estimated from sequential measurements of energy density of embryo(s) during the pregnancy period. The cost of gestation theoretically can be determined by subtracting the daily energy expenditure of non-reproductive females from that of pregnant females at different times during pregnancy. However, because most females at maternity roosts are pregnant, opportunities to measure daily energy expenditure in non-reproductive individuals are rare. In temperate regions pregnant females also replace tissue depleted during hibernation; thus, a complete analysis of energy partitioning during pregnancy requires body composition analysis of females and their embryo(s) (Stack, 1985; Pierson et al., in prep.).

5.3.2. Lactation Costs

The most complete and direct analysis of energy expenditure during lactation can be derived from data on FMR and milk energy output of lactating females. However, attempts to compare the costs of lactating females with non-reproductive females are plagued by the same problem noted for pregnant females. At best, estimates of daily energy expenditure for lactating females can be compared with those for pregnant females. Available estimates based on metabolizable energy during pregnancy and lactation for *Myotis lucifugus* indicate that energy expenditure during lactation increases by 20-50% (Anthony and Kunz, 1977; Kurta et al., 1987).

5.3.3. Gross Efficiency of Milk Production

The efficiency of converting energy of food consumed to the milk energy produced by lactating females can be estimated as the ratio of milk energy yield (kJ/day) to the total food intake (kJ/day). Milk energy yield from females is assumed to equal the milk energy intake of sucklings (Section 3.3). Estimates of gross efficiency (including maintenance costs) of milk production have not been determined for bats. For dairy cows and goats (Brody, 1945), laboratory rats (Romero et al., 1976), and shrews (Dryden and Anderson, 1978), gross efficiency of milk production is on the order of 33% (range 28 to 40%). If similar values are found for bats this would suggest that approximately one-third of the energy consumed by a lactating female should be recovered in milk. The net efficiency of milk production in domestic animals (expressed as a percentage of metabolizable energy, excluding maintenance costs) is nearly double that of gross efficiency (Brody, 1945).

5.3.4. Efficiency of Growth

The literature on growth efficiency is confusing and ambiguous. In part, this reflects the fact that categories of dietary energy (gross, digestible, or metabolizable) are not always specified, the stage of growth may not be defined, or because appropriate conversion factors have not been used. It is also confusing unless a distinction is made between trophic level production (growth) efficiencies and individual growth efficiencies.

We follow Brody (1945) in referring to gross growth efficiency as the term for individuals converting metabolizable energy (ME) to new tissue during postnatal growth (G), expressed as the ratio G/ME. This is comparable to the term energetic growth efficiency as expressed by Ricklefs (1983). Thus, for suckling bats and other mammals, gross growth efficiency is expressed as the ratio of age-specific energy density of sucklings to the metabolizable energy of ingested milk. Net growth efficiency is expressed as the ratio of G/(ME - M), where G and ME are defined above and M is maintenance energy. Because measurement of maintenance costs in growing animals is problematical (see Millward and Garlick, 1976), estimates of net growth efficiency in free-ranging bats (and other mammals) remain elusive.

During postnatal growth, gross (energetic) growth efficiency decreases with increasing age because the amount of energy allocated to new tissue decreases in comparison to the size of the maintenance expenditure component. The greatest growth efficiencies have been observed shortly after birth, followed by a steady decrease as more energy is allocated to heat production (Brody, 1945).

No estimates of gross or net growth efficiencies have been reported for bats. Gross growth efficiencies reported for domestic mammals average 0.35 during early postnatal growth (Brody, 1945). Estimates of gross growth efficiency range from 0.12 to 0.37 for five species of captive rodents [reported as net growth (production) efficiency by McClure and Randolph, 1980]. Net growth efficiency as determined for several species of captive-reared mammals ranges from 0.59 to 0.78 (Millard and Garlick, 1976).

5.4. Energetics of Fat and Protein Deposition

The energy cost of fat and protein deposition is the increment of dietary energy (here expressed as metabolizable energy) required to promote an increment in fat or protein (Puller and Webster, 1977). Most bats deposit fat when energy input exceeds demand (e.g., during postnatal growth and in preparation for migration and/or hibernation) and mobilize it when energy demand exceeds energy input (e.g., at weaning and during hibernation). The most dramatic fluctuations in fat deposition occur in hibernating species (McNab, 1974), although tropical species also undergo seasonal changes in body fat (McNab, 1976) associated with reproductive events and periodic food shortages. The most rapid rates of protein deposition occur in the pre- and postnatal growth periods.

5.4.1. Fat Deposition

There are no published cost estimates of fat deposition for bats. Rates of fat deposition in bats may be estimated from data derived from *in vitro* or *in vivo* methods of body composition analysis (Chapter 23). Attempts to estimate the *costs* of fat deposition in bats are complicated by factors such as molt, migration, courtship, and daily torpor, each of which may occur simultaneously with fat deposition. Investigations of food consumption, body composition analysis, and energy metabolism offer challenging opportunities to partition the costs of fat deposition and its mobilization in bats. Reported values for growing rats (1.4 kJ of metabolizable energy per kJ of fat deposited) may be used as a first approximation for the cost of fat deposition in growing bats. The net efficiency of fat deposition (70 to 79%) in growing rats and pigs (Pullar and Webster, 1977; van Es, 1977) could be used as a testable prediction.

5.4.2. Protein Deposition

No cost estimates of protein deposition have been reported for bats. Estimates of protein deposition can be derived from nitrogen balance studies or body composition analysis (Thorbek, 1977). Reported costs of protein deposition in laboratory and domestic animals, which average 2.3 kJ of metabolizable energy per kJ protein deposited (Pullar and Webster, 1977), could be used as a first order prediction for growing bats. The net efficiency of protein deposition in growing rats and pigs (36 to 77%) (Pullar and Webster, 1977; Thorbek, 1977) varies considerably with age, but is the highest during the early period of growth.

6. COMPARISON OF METHODS

A time-budget model that incorporated occupied roost temperatures, energy conserved by clustering, and times spent foraging and roosting, indicated that daily energy expenditure in *Myotis lucifugus* was only 5.5% less than an estimate of metabolizable energy derived from nightly food intake (Kunz, 1980). Although differing considerably in methods and assumptions, this close agreement lends confidence to both methods for estimating daily energy expenditure in free-ranging bats.

There have been no independent assessments of daily energy expenditure in free-ranging bats, where DLW was one of the methods. Apparent discrepancies in estimates of daily energy expenditure for bats derived from DLW (Helversen and Reyer, 1984) and predictions based on Kunz's (1980) allometric equation could reflect different methods, different life histories, and biases characteristic of interspecific allometric equations (Harvey and Mace, 1982; Huesner, 1982; Calder, 1984). Weathers et al. (1984) and Williams and Nagy (1984) reported that estimates of daily energy expenditure for birds derived from time budgets were 20 to 40% lower than those derived from DLW measurements. Helversen and Reyer (1984) suggested that differences between estimates of daily energy expenditure derived from DLW turnover for the nectar feeding bat *Anoura caudifer* and the allometric equation for bats (Kunz, 1980) could reflect a higher pace of life for flower-visiting bats. It is certainly reasonable that the costs associated with high speed flight and aerial maneuvers, during flower visitation, could explain the higher estimated daily energy expenditure (Helversen and Reyer, 1984), since Kunz's equation was based on limited data and included only one flower-visiting bat (*Leptonycteris sanborni*—Howell, 1979).

Relationships between food availability and food demand are important for understanding the ecological energetics and evolution of a species. Efforts should be made to include measurements of food availability in studies of energy expenditure (Chapters 12 and 14). This can be especially important in assessing individual variability in energy turnover. Moreover, failure to acknowledge the effect of food availability may account for discrepancies in estimates of daily energy expenditure derived from time-budget and DLW studies (Bryant and Westerterp, 1983).

analysis may involve direct observations, radiotelemetry, microclimate analysis, and laboratory-derived estimates of the energy expenditure for different activities. This approach is limited by the sensitivity of animals to direct observation, the imprecision in establishing time budgets for individuals, and the difficulty in quantifying energy costs for various activities.

Isotope methods offer considerable potential for estimating energy budgets of free-ranging bats. Use of DLW can yield direct estimates of daily energy expenditure, foraging costs, and changes in total body water (including estimates of milk intake of sucklings and milk output of lactating mothers). When estimates of daily milk output/input are combined with estimates of energy content of milk, it becomes possible to quantify the energetics of lactation and postnatal growth. In the final analysis, energy budget studies of bats can best be accomplished by using a combination of methods, including time-budgets, food consumption, and doubly labeled water.

7. SUMMARY

In this chapter we review methods of analyzing energy budgets of free-ranging bats. These include the use of doubly labeled water (DLW), food consumption, and time-budget analysis. For the DLW method, practical considerations include choice of appropriate subjects, decisions on cost of isotopes and their analyses, and verification of underlying assumptions. Potential errors associated with this method can be as high as $\pm$ 70%, although careful choice of the study animal and the sampling period can reduce the overall error to less than 10%. Estimates of food consumption include gravimetric and isotope methods. Limitations of the gravimetric method include low recapture rates after feeding, rapid food passage, and difficulties in establishing the number of feeding periods. Isotope methods for determining food intake are limited to animals that obtain their water from food and metabolic water. Time-budget

8. ACKNOWLEDGMENTS

We thank the National Science Foundation (BSR-8314821) and the U.S. Department of Energy (Contract DE-AC03-76-SF00012) for funding our research. We are grateful to G. P. Bell, A. Kurta, P. A. Racey, and J. Speakman for reviewing the manuscript and making helpful comments.

9. REFERENCES

Altmann, J. 1974. Observational study of behaviour: Sampling methods. Behaviour, 49:227-267.

Anthony, E. L. P., and T. H. Kunz. 1977. Feeding strategies of the little brown bat, *Myotis lucifugus,* in New Hampshire. Ecology, 58:775-786.

Anthony, E. L. P., M. H. Stack, and T. H. Kunz. 1981. Night roosting and the nocturnal time-budget of the little brown bat, *Myotis lucifugus*: Effects of reproductive status, prey density, and environmental conditions. Oecologia, 51:151-156.

Baer, G. M. 1966. A method for bleeding small bats. J. Mammal., 47:340.

Baer, G. M., and R. G. McLean. 1972. A new method of bleeding small and infant bats. J. Mammal., 53:231-232.

Baverstock, P., and B. Green. 1975. Water recycling in lactation. Science, 187:657-658.

Bell, G. P. 1982. Behavioral and ecological aspects of gleaning by a desert insectivorous bat, *Antrozous pallidus* (Chiroptera: Vespertilionidae). Behav. Ecol. Sociobiol., 10:217-223.

Bell, G. P., G. A. Bartholomew, and K. A. Nagy. 1986. The roles of energetics, water economy, foraging behavior, and geothermal refugia in the distribution of the bat, *Macrotus californicus*. J. Comp. Physiol., B, 156:441-450.

Black, L. L., and C. A. Wiederhielm. 1976. Plasma oncotic pressure and hematocrit in the intact, unanesthetized bat. Microv. Res., 12:55-58.

Blaxter, K. L. 1961. Lactation and the growth of young. Pp. 305-361, *in* Milk: The mammary gland and its secretion. (S. K. Kon and A. T. Cowie, eds.). Academic Press, New York, 423 pp.

Bradbury, J. 1977. Social organization and communication. Pp. 1-72, *in* Biology of bats. Vol. 3. (W. A. Wimsatt, ed.). Academic Press, New York, 651 pp.

Brody, S. 1945. Bioenergetics of growth. Reinhold, Baltimore, 1023 pp.

Bryant, D. M., and K. R. Westerterp. 1980. The energy budget of the house martin (*Delichon urbica*). Ardea, 68:91-102.

Bryant, D. M., and K. R. Westerterp. 1983. Short term variability in energy turnover by breeding House Martins *Delichron urbica*: A study using doubly-labeled water (D_2 ^{18}O). J. Anim. Ecol., 52:525-543.

Buchler, E. R. 1975. Food transit time in *Myotis lucifugus* (Chiroptera: Vespertilionidae). J. Mammal., 56:252-255.

Burnett, C. D., and P. V. August. 1981. Time and energy budgets for dayroosting in a maternity colony of *Myotis lucifugus*. J. Mammal., 62:758-766.

Calder, W. A., III, 1984. Size, function, and life history. Harvard Univ. Press, Cambridge, Massachusetts, 431 pp.

Congdon, J. D., W. W. King, and K. A. Nagy. 1978. Validation of the HTO-18 method for determination of CO_2 production of lizards (Genus *Sceloporus*). Copeia, 1978:360-362.

Congdon, J. D., A. E. Dunham, and D. W. Tinkle. 1982. Energy budgets and life histories of reptiles. Pp. 233-271, *in* Biology of the Reptilia. Vol. 13. Physiological ecology. (C. Gans and F. H. Pough, eds.). Academic Press, New York, 345 pp.

Cooper, H. M., and P. Charles-Dominique. 1985. A microcomputer data acquisition-telemetry system: A study of activity in the bat. J. Wildl. Manage., 49:850-854.

Dove, H., and M. Freer. 1979. The accuracy of tritiated water turnover rate as an estimate of milk intake in lambs. Aust. J. Agr. Res., 30:725-739.

Dryden, G. L., and R. R. Anderson. 1978. Milk composition and its relation to growth rate in the musk shrew *Suncus murinus*. Comp. Biochem. Physiol., 60A:213-216.

Erkert, H. G. 1982. Ecological aspects of bat activity rhythms. Pp. 201-242, *in* Ecology of bats. (T. H. Kunz, ed.). Plenum Press, New York, 425 pp.

Es, A. J. H. van. 1977. The energetics of fat deposition during growth. Nutr. Metab., 21:88-104.

Flint, E. N., and K. A. Nagy. 1984. Flight energetics of free-living sooty terns. Auk, 101:288-294.

Friedman, M. I., and J. P. Bruno. 1976. Exchange of water during lactation. Science, 191:409-410.

Funakoshi, K., and T. A. Uchida. 1975. Studies on the physiological and ecological adaptation of temperate insectivorous bats. I. Feeding activities in the Japanese long-fingered bats, *Miniopterus schreibersi fuliginosus*. Jap. J. Ecol., 25:217-235. (in Japanese with English summary.)

Funakoshi, K., and T. A. Uchida. 1980. Feeding activity during the breeding season and postnatal growth in the Namie's frosted bat, *Vespertilio superans superans*. Jap. J. Ecol., 31:67-77.

Gardner, A. L. 1977. Feeding habits. Pp. 293-350, *in* Biology of bats of the New World family Phyllostomatidae. Part II. (R. J. Baker, J. K. Jones, Jr., and D. C. Carter, eds.). Spec. Publ. Mus., Texas Tech Univ., Lubbock, 364 pp.

Gessaman, J. A. 1973. Methods of estimating the energy cost of free existence. Pp. 3-31, *in* Ecological energetics of homeotherms. (J. A. Gessaman, ed.). Monogr. Ser., Vol. 20, Utah State Univ. Press, Logan, 155 pp.

Gettinger, R. D. 1983. Use of doubly-labeled water ($^3HH^{18}O$) for determination of H_2O flux and CO_2 production by a mammal in a humid environment. Oecologia, 59:54-57.

Green, B. 1978. Estimation of food consumption

in the dingo, *Canis familiaris dingo,* by means of ^{22}Na turnover. Ecology, 59:207-210.

Green, B., and K. Newgrain. 1979. Estimation of the milk intake of sucklings by means of ^{22}Na. J. Mammal., 60:556-559.

Green, B., and I. Eberhard. 1984. Water and sodium intake and estimated food consumption in free-living eastern quolls *Dasyurus viverrinus.* Aust. J. Zool., 31:871-880.

Grodzinski, W., and A. Gorecki. 1967. Daily energy budgets of small rodents. Pp. 295-314, *in* Secondary productivity of terrestrial ecosystems. (K. Petruzewicz, ed.). Polish Acad. Sci., Warsaw.

Gustafson, A. W., and D. A. Demassa. 1985. Repetitive blood sampling from small peripheral veins in bats. J. Mammal., 66:173-177.

Hails, C. J. 1977. Energetics of free-living house martins (*Delichon urbica*) during breeding. Unpubl. Ph.D. dissertation, Univ. Stirling, Scotland.

Hails, C. J. 1980. A comparison of flight energetics in hirundines and other birds. Comp. Biochem. Physiol., 63A:581-585.

Hails, C. J., and D. M. Bryant. 1979. Reproductive energetics of a free-living bird. J. Anim. Ecol., 48:471-482.

Harvey, P. H., and G. M. Mace. 1982. Comparisons between taxa and adaptive trends: Problems of methodology. Pp. 342-361, *in* Current problems in sociobiology. (King's College Sociobiology Group, ed.). Cambridge Univ. Press, Cambridge.

Hanwell, A., and M. Peaker. 1977. Physiological effects of lactation on the mother. Symp. Zool. Soc. Lond., 41:297-312.

Helversen, and H.-U. Reyer. 1984. Nectar intake and energy expenditure in a flower visiting bat. Oecologia, 63:178-184.

Heusner, A. A. 1982. Energy metabolism and body size. II. Dimensional analysis and energetic non-similarity. Respir. Physiol., 48:13-25.

Howell, D. J. 1979. Flock foraging in nectar feeding bats: Advantages to the bats and to the host plants. Amer. Nat., 114:23-49.

Holleman, D. F., R. G. White, and J. R. Luick. 1975. New isotope methods for estimating milk intake and yield. J. Dairy Sci., 58:1814-1821.

Jacobsen, N. K., and A. D. Wiggins. 1982. Temporal and procedural influences on activity estimated by time sampling. J. Wildl. Manage., 46:313-324.

Jenness, R., and E. H. Studier. 1976. Lactation and milk. Pp. 201-218, *in* Biology of bats of the New World family Phyllostomatidae. Part II.

(R. J. Baker, J. K. Jones, Jr., and D. C. Carter, eds.). Spec. Publ. Mus. Texas Tech Univ., Lubbock, 218 pp.

Karasov, W. H. 1981. Daily energy expenditure and the cost of activity in a free-living mammal. Oecologia, 51:253-259.

Keegan, D. J. 1979. Restraining cage and methods for bleeding fruit bats (*Rousettus aegyptiacus*). Lab Anim. Sci., 29:402-403.

Kendeigh, S. C. 1939. The relation of metabolism to the development of temperature regulation in birds. J. Exp. Zool., 82:403-416.

Kendeigh, S. C., V. R. Dol'nik, and V. M. Gavrilov. 1977. Avian energetics. Pp. 127-204, *in* Granivorous birds in ecosystems. (J. Pinowski and S. C. Kendeigh, eds.). Cambridge Univ. Press, New York.

King, J. R. 1974. Seasonal allocation of time and energy resources in birds. Pp. 4-70, *in* Avian energetics. (R. A. Paynter, Jr., ed.). Publ. Nuttall Ornithol. Club. No. 15, Cambridge, Massachusetts, 334 pp.

Klite, P. D. 1965. Intestinal bacterial flora and transit time of three neotropical bat species. J. Bact., 90:375-379.

Kunz, T. H. 1973. Population studies of the cave bat (*Myotis velifer*): Reproduction, growth, and development. Occas. Pap. Mus. Nat. Hist. Univ. Kansas, 15:1-43.

Kunz, T. H. 1974. Feeding ecology of a temperate insectivorous bat (*Myotis velifer*). Ecology, 55:693-711.

Kunz, T. H. 1980. Daily energy budgets of free-living bats. Pp. 369-392, *in* Proc. 5th Int. Bat Res. Conf. (D. E. Wilson and A. L. Gardner, eds.). Texas Tech Press, Lubbock, 434 pp.

Kunz, T. H. 1982. Roosting ecology of bats. Pp. 1-55, *in* Ecology of bats. (T. H. Kunz, ed.). Plenum Press, New York, 425 pp.

Kunz, T. H., and E. L. P. Anthony. 1982. Age estimation and post-natal growth in the bat *Myotis lucifugus*. J. Mammal., 63:23-32.

Kunz, T. H., M. H. Stack, and R. Jenness. 1983. A comparison of milk composition in *Myotis lucifugus* and *Eptesicus fuscus* (Chiroptera: Vespertilionidae). Biol. Reprod., 28:229-234.

Kurta, A. 1985. External insulation available to a non-nesting mammal, the little brown bat (*Myotis lucifugus*). Comp. Biochem. Physiol., 82A:413-420.

Kurta, A. 1986. Insulation, thermoregulation, and metabolic rates of the little brown bat (*Myotis lucifugus*) under simulated roost conditions. Unpubl. Ph.D. dissertation, Boston Univ., Boston, Massachusetts, 283 pp.

Kurta, A., K. A. Johnson, and T. H. Kunz. 1987. Oxygen consumption and body temperature of female little brown bats (*Myotis lucifugus*) under simulated roost conditions. Physiol. Zool., 60:386-397.

LaMotte, L. C., Jr. 1958. Japanese B encephalitis in bats during simulated hibernation. Amer. J. Hyg., 67:101-108.

Lewis, L. D., and R. W. Phillips. 1972. Volume and kinetics of a slow tritium-hydrogen exchange in neonatal calves. Amer. J. Physiol., 223:74-76.

Lifson, N., and R. McClintock. 1966. Theory of use of the turnover rates of body water for measuring energy and material balance. J. Theoret. Biol., 12:46-74.

Lifson, N., G. B. Gordon, M. B. Vissher, and A. O. Nier. 1949. The fate of utilized molecular oxygen and the source of the oxygen of respiratory carbon dioxide, studied with the aid of labeled water. Amer. J. Chem., 180:803-811.

Linzell, J. L. 1972. Milk yield, energy loss in milk, and mammary gland weight in different species. Dairy Sci. Abstr., 34:352-360.

Macfarlane, W. V., B. Howard, and B. D. Siebert. 1969. Tritiated water in the measurement of milk intake and tissue growth of ruminants in the field. Nature, 221:578.

McNab, B. K. 1974. The behavior of temperate bats in a subtropical environment. Ecology, 55:943-958.

McNab, B. K. 1976. Seasonal fat reserves in two tropical environments. Ecology, 57:332-338.

Matthews, D. E., and D. M. Bier. 1983. Stable isotope methods for nutritional investigation. Ann. Rev. Nutr., 3:309-339.

Morrison, D. W. 1978. Foraging ecology and energetics of the frugivorous bat *Artibeus jamaicensis*. Ecology, 59:716-723.

Mullen, R. K. 1970. Respiratory metabolism and body water turnover rates of *Perognathus formosus* in its natural environment. Comp. Biochem. Physiol., 32:259-265.

Mullen, R. K. 1971. Energy metabolism and body water turnover rates of two species of free-living kangaroo rats, *Dipodomys merriami* and *Dipodomys microps*. Comp. Biochem. Physiol., 39A:379-390.

Mullen, R. K. 1973. The $D_2{}^{18}O$ method of measuring the energy metabolism of free-living animals. Pp. 23-43, *in* Ecological energetics of homeotherms: A view compatible with ecological modeling. (J. A. Gessaman, ed.). Monogr. Ser. 20, Utah State Univ. Press, Logan, 155 pp.

Nagy, K. A. 1975. Water and energy budgets of free-living animals: Measurement using isotopically labeled water. Pp. 227-245, *in* Environmental physiology of desert organisms. (N. F. Hadley, ed.). Dowden, Hutchinson, and Ross, Inc., Stroudsburg, Pennsylvania.

Nagy, K. A. 1980. CO_2 production in animals: Analysis of potential errors in the doubly labeled water method. Amer. J. Physiol., 238:R466-R473.

Nagy, K. A. 1983. The doubly labeled water (^3HH ^{18}O) method: A guide to its use. Univ. California Los Angeles Publ., No. 12-1417, 45 pp.

Nagy, K. A., and D. P. Costa. 1980. Water flux in animals: Analysis of potential errors in the tritiated water method. Amer. J. Physiol., 238: R454-R465.

Nagy, K. A., and V. H. Shoemaker. 1984. Field energetics and food consumption of the Galapagos marine iguana, *Amblyrhynchus cristatus*. Physiol. Zool., 57:281-290.

Nagy, K. A., R. B. Huey, and A. F. Bennett. 1984a. Field energetics and foraging mode of Kalahari lacertid lizards. Ecology, 56:588-596.

Nagy, K. A., W. R. Siegfried, and R. P. Wilson. 1984b. Energy utilization by free-ranging jackass penguins, *Spheniscus demersus*. Ecology, 65:1648-1655.

Oftedal, O. T. 1984a. Milk composition, milk yield and energy output at peak lactation: A comparative review. Symp. Zool. Soc. Lond., 51:33-85.

Oftedal, O. T. 1984b. Body size and reproductive strategy as correlates of milk energy output in lactating mammals. Acta Zool. Fenn., 17:183-186.

Oftedal, O. T. 1986. Pregnancy and lactation. Pp. 215-238, *in* Bioenergetics of wild herbivores. (R. Hudson and R. White, eds.). CRC Press, Boca Raton, Florida, 314 pp.

Pierson, E. D., W. Rainey, and T. H. Kunz. In preparation. Changes in body composition during pregnancy and lactation in the little brown bat, *Myotis lucifugus*.

Pullar, J. D., and A. J. F. Webster. 1977. The energy cost of fat and protein deposition in the rat. Br. J. Nutr., 37:355-363.

Richmond, C. R., W. H. Langham, and T. T. Trujillo. 1962. Comparative metabolism of tritiated water by mammals. J. Cell Comp. Physiol., 59:45-53.

Ricklefs, R. E. 1983. Avian postnatal development. Pp. 1-83, *in* Avian biology. Vol. VII. (D.

S. Farner, J. R. King, and K. C. Park, eds.). Academic Press, New York, 542 pp.

Ricklefs, R. E., and J. B. Williams. 1984. Daily energy expenditure and water-turnover rate of adult European Starlings (*Sturnus vulgaris*) during the nesting cycle. Auk, 101:707-711.

Romero, J. J., R. Cañas, R. L. Baldwin, and L. J. Koong. 1976. Lactational efficiency complex of rats: Provisional model for interpretation of energy balance data. J. Dairy Sci., 59:57-67.

Schoeller, D. A., E. van Santen, D. W. Peterson, W. Dietz, J. Jaspan, and P. D. Klein. 1980. Total body water measurement in humans with ^{18}O and ^{2}H labeled water. Amer. J. Clin. Nutr., 33:2686-2693.

Shoemaker, V. H., K. A. Nagy, and W. R. Costa. 1976. Energy utilization and temperature regulation by jack rabbits (*Lepus californicus*) in the Mojave Desert. Physiol. Zool., 49:364-375.

Stack, M. H. 1985. Energetics of reproduction in the big brown bat (*Eptesicus fuscus*). Unpubl. Ph.D. dissertation, Boston Univ., Boston, Massachusetts, 283 pp.

Swift, S. M., P. A. Racey, and M. I. Avery. 1985. Feeding ecology of *Pipistrellus pipistrellus* (Chiroptera: Vespertilionidae) during pregnancy and lactation. II. Diet. J. Anim. Ecol., 54:217-225.

Suter, R. B., and K. S. Rawson. 1968. Circadian activity rhythm of the deer mouse, *Peromyscus*: Effect of deuterium oxide. Science, 160:1011-1014.

Sutton, S. P., R. Damm, and M. K. Neilsen. 1974. Biological effects of D_2O administration to *Coturnix japonica*. Life Sci., 15:2097-2108.

Tedman, R. A., and L. S. Hall. 1985. The morphology of the gastrointestinal tract and food transit time in the fruit bats *Pteropus alecto* and *P. poliocephalus* (Megachiroptera). Aust. J. Zool., 33:625-640.

Thomas, D. W. 1984. Fruit intake and energy budgets of frugivorous bats. Physiol. Zool., 57:457-467.

Thomas, S. P. 1975. Metabolism during flight in two species of bats, *Phyllostomus hastatus* and *Pteropus gouldii*. J. Exp. Biol., 63:273-293.

Thorbek, G. 1977. The energetics of protein deposition during growth. Nutr. Metab., 21:105-118.

Travis, J. 1982. A method for the statistical analysis of time-energy budgets. Ecology, 63:19-25.

Trivers, R. L. 1972. Parental investment and sexual selection. Pp. 136-179, *in* Sexual selection and the descent of man. (B. G. Campbell, ed.). Aldine Publ. Co., Chicago, 378 pp.

Trune, D. R., and C. N. Slobodchikoff. 1976. Social effects of roosting on metabolism of the pallid bat (*Antrozous pallidus*). J. Mammal., 57:656-663.

Turner, A. K. 1983. Time and energy constraints on the brood size of swallows, *Hirundo rustica,* and sand martins, *Riparia riparia.* Oecologia, 59:331-338.

Utter, J. M., and E. A. Lefebvre. 1970. Energy expenditure for free flight by the purple martin (*Progne subis*). Comp. Biochem. Physiol., 35:713-719.

Vehrencamp, S. L., F. G. Stiles, and J. W. Bradbury. 1977. Observations on the foraging behavior and avian prey of the Neotropical carnivorous bat, *Vampyrum spectrum*. J. Mammal., 58:469-478.

Walsberg, G. E. 1983. Avian ecological energetics. Pp. 161-220, *in* Avian biology. Vol. VII. (D. S. Farner, J. R. King, and K. C. Parkes, eds.). Academic Press, New York, 542 pp.

Weathers, W. W., and K. A. Nagy. 1980. Simultaneous doubly labeled water ($^{3}HH^{18}O$) and time-budget estimates of daily energy expenditure in *Phainopepla nitens*. Auk, 97:861-867.

Weathers, W. W., W. A. Buttemer, A. M. Hayworth, and K. A. Nagy. 1984. An evaluation of time-budget estimates of daily energy expenditure in birds. Auk, 101:459-472.

Westerterp, K. R., and D. M. Bryant. 1984. Energetics of free existence in swallows and martins (Hirundinidae) during breeding: A comparative study using doubly-labelled water. Oecologia, 62:376-381.

Williams, G. C. 1966. Natural selection, the cost of reproduction, and a refinement of Lack's Principle. Amer. Nat., 100:687-692.

Williams, J. B., and K. A. Nagy. 1984. Validation of the doubly labeled water technique for measuring energy metabolism in savannah sparrows. Physiol. Zool., 57:325-328.

Wimsatt, W. A. 1969. Transient behavior, nocturnal activity patterns, and feeding efficiency of vampire bats (*Desmodus rotundus*) under natural conditions. J. Mammal., 50:233-244.

Wolf, L. L., F. R. Hainsworth, and F. B. Gill. 1975. Foraging efficiencies and time budgets in nectar feeding birds. Ecology, 56:117-128.

Wolton, R. J., P. A. Frak, C. J. Godfrey, and R. P. Wilson. 1982. Ecological and behavioral studies of the Megachiroptera of Mount Nimba,

Liberia, with notes on the Microchiroptera. Mammalia, 46:419-448.

Wood, R. A., K. A. Nagy, N. S. MacDonald, S. T. Wakakuwa, R. J. Beckman, and H. Kaaz. 1975. Determination of oxygen-18 in water contained in biological samples by charged particle activation. Anal. Chem., 47:646-650.

Wright, D. E., and J. E. Wolff. 1976. Measuring milk intake of lambs suckling grazing ewes by a double isotope method. Proc. N. Z. Soc. Prod., 36:99-102.

Wunder, B. A. 1975. A model for estimating metabolic rate of active or resting animals. J. Theoret. Biol., 49:345-354.

Zweens, J., H. Frankena, A. Reicher, and W. G. Zylstra. 1980. Infrared spectrophotometric determination of D_2O in biological fluids. Pflugers. Arch., 38:71-77.

Chapter 19

Microclimate Methods

George S. Bakken

Department of Life Sciences
Indiana State University
Terre Haute, Indiana 47809 USA

and

Thomas H. Kunz

Department of Biology
Boston University
Boston, Massachusetts 02215 USA

1. INTRODUCTION

Knowledge of the thermal environment of an animal is essential to understanding energy and water use. The selection of warm roosts by bats during active periods promotes digestion, gestation, and growth of young. In both temperate and tropical regions bats utilize daily and/or seasonal torpor to economize in energy use. Thus, in active and torpid states energy and water use are sensitive to temperature. This can be seen (Fig. 1) as a generalized plot of metabolic rate, M (watts/animal) vs. standard operative temperature, T_{es} (Scholander et al., 1950; Bakken, 1980). Symbols and units are listed in Appendix 1. The upper curve, corresponding to the endothermic state, shows a thermal neutral zone (TNZ) where M is independent of T_{es}. Above the

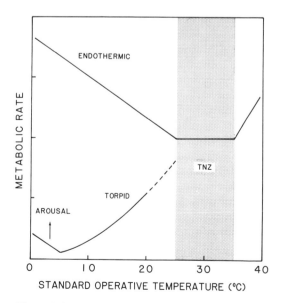

Figure 1. Schematic plot of metabolic rate of a bat as a function of standard operative temperature.

TNZ, M increases as energetically expensive means of increasing evaporative cooling are used. Below the TNZ, M increases to balance increased heat loss as temperature decreases. The lower curve, corresponding to the torpid state, shows an ectothermic Q_{10} response, with M declining as T_b (roughly equivalent to T_e) falls. However, near 0°C, M rises to prevent freezing. Evaporative water loss (EWL) increases rapidly for thermoregulation in the upper part of the TNZ and above. EWL typically rises or remains constant as air temperature decreases below the TNZ. In the ectothermic state, EWL falls markedly with ambient temperature.

Presently, no published studies have detailed the complexities of the roost microclimate of bats. Most studies report little more than daily, weekly, or monthly average or extreme temperatures. A few studies have recorded hourly or continuous temperatures in occupied and unoccupied roosts (e.g., Licht and Leitner, 1967; Dwyer and Harris, 1972; Voûte, 1972; Kunz, 1973, 1974, 1980; Vaughn and O'Shea, 1976; Humphrey et al., 1977; Burnett and August, 1981).

Temperatures recorded in crevices and cavities occupied by active bats are typically warmer than unoccupied sites. Bats may contact the probes, causing incorrect readings, but generally metabolic heat appears to warm the immediate environment (e.g., Voûte, 1972; Kunz, 1974, 1980). Solar radiation can produce marked temperature differences within hollow trees and other above-ground roosts. Estimated energy expenditures are sensitive to these effects. For example, Burnett and August (1981) found the estimated energy expenditure during roosting was twice as great in cool, unoccupied roosts as in warm, occupied roosts. Clearly, spatial temperature variations in roosts, solitary vs. group roosting, and the position of a bat in the interior or on the edge of a cluster may strongly affect energy and water use.

Future studies that address daily activity, energy, and water budgets should consider quantifying the thermal environment of solitary and clustered bats. Particular attention

should be paid to spatial variation in temperature produced by solar heating of aboveground roosts or by bat metabolism. Heat transfer by radiation, conduction, convection, and evaporation must all be considered, using combinations of thermal modeling and experimental measurements (Bakken, 1976; Bakken et al., 1981; Weathers et al., 1984). This chapter is intended to give a brief guide to the rationale and appropriate methods needed to characterize bat roost microclimates.

2. BIOPHYSICS OF THERMOREGULATION

The physics of heat and mass transport can be used to estimate the body temperature and/or the energy and water needs of free-ranging animals in various microclimates. These estimates can then be used to address questions of ecological interest. Relevant theory and methods developed to date are detailed by Birkebak (1966), Rose (1966), Monteith (1973), Bakken (1976, 1981), Campbell (1977), and Gates (1980). Published studies have emphasized lizards, insects, birds, and ground squirrels (e.g., Bartlett and Gates, 1967; Porter and Gates, 1969; Porter et al., 1973; Morhardt and Gates, 1974; Casey, 1981; Chappell and Bartholomew, 1981; Christian and Tracy, 1981; Biedenweg, 1983; Chappell, 1983a, 1983b; Christian et al., 1983; Crawford et al., 1983; Rollo et al., 1983; Bennett et al., 1984). No studies of bats have included rigorous heat transfer and microclimate analysis. Thus, while the theory and methods described below have applicability to various taxa, they have not been tested on bats.

2.1. Heat Transfer Analysis

2.1.1. Animal Model

The calculation of T_b and/or energy and water use is based on the principle of conservation of energy. Most studies have considered the animal as a unit. This is generally invalid, especially for bats which can vasodilate or vasoconstrict the uninsulated membranes for thermoregulation (Kluger and Heath, 1970), and where there may be large regional differences in T_b, especially during arousal (e.g., Rauch and Haywood, 1970; Rauch, 1973).

Birkebak (1966) and Bakken (1981) present a more realistic analysis. The animal is divided into a number of volumes that are assumed to be at constant temperature. The algebraic sum of heat flow to and from each volume, heat produced by metabolism, heat stored by a change in temperature, and heat removed by evaporation must be zero. Bakken's model (1981) assumes the animal to be composed of a single isothermal core with a heat capacitance C (J °C^{-1}animal^{-1}), metabolic rate M (W/animal), and body temperature T_b surrounded by an insulating shell (includes appendages and the flight membrane) divided into n elements. Figure 2 shows a possible division of a bat. Each element is composed of a layer of skin and subcutaneous fat of conductance K_{si} (W °C^{-1} area element^{-1}). The subscript i is used to identify a parameter of a particular surface element of an animal. The absence of the i subscript means the parameter refers to the whole animal. Appendages are included by defining suitable equivalent conductances. Although not strictly valid, the heat capacitance of the surface elements is included with that of the core to facilitate an analytic solution. Areas of naked skin have K_{fi} infinite, because the fur thickness is zero. Heat is transferred to the environment by convection, radiation, evaporation, and (to roost surfaces) by conduction. Evaporative cooling is considered separately for the respiratory (core), skin, and fur surfaces, respectively E_b, E_{si}, E_{fi} (W/element), because different fractions of the heat come from the animal (Fourt and Harris, 1949; Eyal, 1963; Bakken, 1976). The heat of vaporization, λ, is about 2.45 MJ/kg, and varies somewhat with evaporating surface and air temperatures (Kerslake, 1972; Campbell, 1977).

Another notation is also in common use. Agricultural meteorologists (Monteith, 1973; Campbell, 1977) use resistance r (sec/m) in place of conductance, K, with the reciprocal relation $K = \rho c_p A/r$. Here, ρ and c_p are the density and specific heat of air, and A is the area of the surface. The notation we use is more com-

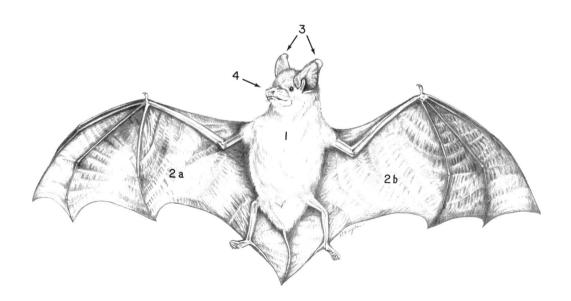

Figure 2. A possible division of a bat into surface elements for a two-dimensional heat-transfer analysis.

pact and more convenient for analyzing the parallel heat flow paths found in animals.

2.1.2. Energy Conservation Equations

The heat flows to the core sum to zero at the core-skin interface to give

$$M - \lambda E_b - C\,(dT_b/dt) - \sum_{i=1}^{n} K_{si}\,(T_b - T_{si}) = 0 \quad (1)$$

The skin temperature of the i-th element of skin and fat is T_{si}. The heat flows to the skin-pelage interface sum to zero to give n equations of the form:

$$K_{si}\,(T_b - T_{si}) - K_{fi}\,(T_{si} - T_{fi}) - \lambda E_{si} = 0 \quad (2)$$

The outer fur surface temperature of the i-th element is T_{fi}. Similarly, the outer surface gives n equations of the form:

$$K_{fi}\,(T_{si} - T_{fi}) - H_i\,(T_{fi} - T_{ai}) + Q_{ai,eff}$$
$$- A_{ei}\,\sigma\varepsilon\,(T_{fi} + 273)^4 - \lambda E_{fi} = 0 \quad (3)$$

Here, H_i (W K^{-1} element^{-1}) is the convective conductance. The emitted thermal radiation is $A_{ei}\,\sigma\varepsilon(T_{fi} + 273)^4$, where A_{ei} is the effective radiating area of the i-th element, the thermal emittance $\varepsilon \simeq 0.95-0.98$, and the Stefan-Boltzmann constant is $\sigma = 5.67 \times 10^{-8}$ W m^{-2}K^{-4}. The pelage of an animal does not have a well-defined outer surface. Walsberg et al. (1978) assume that solar radiation penetrates the pelage, but that thermal radiation and convection act at the outer surface. They define a corrected absorbed radiation term

$$Q_{ai,eff} = A_{ei}\,\varepsilon\,I + [A_{si}\,S + A_{ei}\,\{s + r\}]$$
$$[a_{si} + \{(H_i + R_i)/K_{fi}\}\,\{(2 - a_{si})/p_i\}] \quad (4)$$

where ε is the thermal radiation absorptance (= emittance), I is thermal irradiance (W/m^2), A_{si} is the area normal to the solar beam (m^2). Direct solar irradiance is S, s is sky irradiance, and r is reflected irradiance (all W/m^2). The average solar absorptance of the pelage is a_{si} (dimensionless, range 0 to 1), and p_i is the projected area of pelage fibers per unit skin area (dimensionless). The equivalent radiation conductance is $R = 4A_e\,\sigma\varepsilon\,(T_{ai} + 273)^3$ (W animal^{-1}K^{-1}). More details on heat transfer in fur can be found in Davis (1972),

Davis and Birkebak (1975), Cena and Monteith (1975a,b,c), Kowalski (1978), and Webb and King (1984).

The quadratic dependence of heat flow on T_{fi} (equation 3) makes an analytic solution difficult. Several effectively identical series expansions can be used to linearize this term. The most useful is an expansion about T_{ai} (Gagge and Hardy, 1967). The effect of wind and radiation are combined to define a temperature increment, ΔT_{ri}. This is added to air temperature to define a pseudo-temperature, T_e, called operative temperature.

$$T_{ei} = T_{ai} + \Delta T_{ri} \quad (5)$$
$$\Delta T_{ri} = (Q_{ai,eff} - A_{ei}\,\sigma\varepsilon(T_{ai} + 273)^4/$$
$$(H_i + R_i) \quad (6)$$

The overall thermal conductance between the core of the animal and the environment at temperature T_{ei} through the i-th element, K_{ei}, is then

$$K_{ei} = K_{sfi}\,(H_i + R_i)/(K_{sfi} + H_i + R_i) \quad (7)$$

where K_{sf} (W animal^{-1}°C^{-1}) is the combined conductance of skin and any external insulation or the equivalent overall conductance of appendages. In general, $K_{sf} = [K_s K_f/(K_s + K_f)]$; however, K_{sf} reduces to K_s for naked surfaces.

Whole-animal values are defined as:

$$K_e = \sum_{i=1}^{n} K_{ei} \quad (8)$$

$$T_e = (1/K_e)\sum_{i=1}^{n} K_{ei} T_{ei} \quad (9)$$

Note that the overall conductance of the whole animal is found by summing the local conductances, not by averaging the parameters used to calculate local conductances. Also, T_e is influenced by the relative distribution of shell conductance as well as by the overall size, shape, and color of the animal.

The heat of vaporization of water evaporated at the skin and pelage surfaces comes partly from the environment, and a correction must be made in arriving at the effective total evaporation rate, E:

$$E = \lambda E_b + \lambda \sum_{i=1}^{n} \frac{E_{fi} + E_{si}[1 + (R_i + H_i)/K_{fi}]}{[1 + (R_i + H_i)/K_{sfi}]} \quad (10)$$

The differential equation for $(M - \lambda E)$ is then:

$$(M - \lambda E) = K_e (T_b - T_e) + C (dT_b/dt) \quad (11)$$

and the differential equation for T_b is

$$(C/K_e) \, dT_b/dt + T_b = T_e + \triangle T_p \quad (12)$$

$$\triangle T_p = (M - \lambda E)/K_e \quad (13)$$

The first term on the right in equation (12), T_e, primarily specifies physical heat transfer effects. The physiological offset temperature, $\triangle T_p$ (Bakken and Gates, 1975), primarily specifies physiological processes. This separation of physical and physiological processes, while imperfect, is the basis for the utility of T_e (Gagge, 1940).

2.2. OPERATIVE (T_e) AND STANDARD OPERATIVE (T_{es}) TEMPERATURES

Operative temperature, T_e, provides a precise definition of the intuitive concept of "environmental temperature." It and the related standard operative temperature may be understood by analogy with ordinary temperature. T_e uses a physical or mathematical model of the animal of interest as the "thermometer" and the net sensible heat flow between the animal and its environment as the "mercury column." Environments resulting in the same net heat flow are considered to be thermally equivalent (i.e., "have the same temperature"). The numerical temperature scale is defined by the thermodynamic temperature of an equivalent isothermal blackbody enclosure with specified convection (wind) conditions.

Operative temperature, T_e (Eq. 5), assumes identical convection in the field and the enclosure defining the temperature scale. Standard operative temperature, T_{es}, uses a fixed convection condition (usually still air). The mathematical expression for T_{es} is:

$$T_{es} = T_b - (K_e/K_{es})(T_b - T_e)$$
$$= T_b - (M - \lambda E)/K_{es} \quad (14)$$

where K_e is the overall thermal conductance of the whole animal in the general environment, K_{es} is the value in the standard environment, and T_e is the operative temperature for the whole animal in the general environment. Note that, while T_e is an index of thermal potential and requires K_e to specify heat flow (Eq. 11), T_{es} incorporates K_e and specifies heat flow directly. This is because the fixed convection condition sets up a unique relation between the temperature of the standard environment and the sensible heat flow to or from a specific animal.

3. MEASUREMENT OF THE THERMAL ENVIRONMENT

3.1. Direct Integrated Measurement of T_e and T_{es} with Test Bodies

3.1.1. Operative Temperature

Operative temperature, T_e, can be measured with a suitable model or taxidermic mount of the animal of interest (Bakken and Gates, 1975). Eq. 11 shows that when $(M - \lambda E) = 0$ and T_{bm} has equilibrated ($dT_{bm}/dt = 0$), $T_{bm} = T_{em}$. (The subscript m indicates a parameter of a model or mount.) The mount or model should have low heat capacitance to maintain T_{bm} near equilibrium, which can be done by using a hollow copper electroform (Bakken and Gates, 1975; Bakken et al., 1981; Bakken et al., 1983). The increase in absorption of solar radiation in pelage (Eq. 4) and the effect of regional differences in insulation thickness (Eq. 9) must be duplicated by using taxidermic mounts made by mounting pelts on hollow copper electroformed cores (Bakken, 1976; Bakken et al., 1981; Bakken et al., 1983). This is because Eq. 9 only requires that the relative distribution of conductance, K_{ei}/K_e, over the animal be duplicated (but not the actual values of K_{ei}). Substantial errors can result if simpler models are used (Bakken et al., 1985).

3.1.2. Standard Operative Temperature

There are two approaches for measuring T_{es}. The first uses an electrically-heated taxidermic mount of the animal of interest; the mount is maintained at T_b and the power supplied to the heater recorded (Bakken, 1976, 1983; Bakken et al., 1981, 1983). Equating $M - \lambda E$ with heater power (Eq. 14), this determines T_{es} for the mount, because T_b and K_{es} are constants. The $M - \lambda E$ of a live animal in the standard environment at this T_{es} should equal that of a live animal in the environment occupied by the model. This assumes that the response of K_e/K_{es} to sun and wind is similar for the model and the live animal (cf. Eq. 14), but the similarity need not be precise (Bakken et al., 1981). The most common problem is that the mount of a poorly-insulated animal is more sensitive to wind than is the live animal.

Alternatively, an unheated mount measures T_e and a nearby anemometer measures wind speed (Chappell and Bartholomew, 1981). Assuming that wind is the only environmental factor (other than T_{es}) that affects K_e/K_{es}, laboratory relations of K_e/K_{es} to wind speed may be used to estimate K_e/K_{es}. Then T_{es} is calculated using Eq. 14.

3.1.3. Application to Bats

Bakken et al. (1985) discuss and compare the accuracy of the various methods of determining T_e and T_{es}, including calculations, mounts, and models. One source of error noted is that mounts do not necessarily duplicate the conductance of a live animal (Bakken et al., 1981). This may be a particular problem with bats, because the thermoregulatory vasodilation of the flight membrane (Kluger and Heath, 1970) and regional T_b gradients (Rauch, 1973) cannot be duplicated. The practical importance of this problem is yet to be evaluated. It is nonetheless important to include a taxidermic mount or similar test body in field studies to provide a control over microclimate measurements and calculations. If the temperature of an inanimate test object cannot be calculated within 1 or 2°C, significant problems exist in measurements, extrapolations, or calculations (Bakken et al., 1985).

3.2. INDIVIDUAL MEASUREMENTS OF MICROCLIMATE AND ANIMAL PARAMETERS

3.2.1. General

Kurta and Fujita (Chapter 20) review instruments commonly used in laboratory thermoregulation studies, and so we will consider primarily field instruments and procedures.

Many instruments are available for measuring and recording microclimate data and animal temperatures. Appendix 2 lists selected suppliers of instruments. Unwin (1980) describes easily constructed instruments, although his discussion of calibration and sources of error is often inadequate. Fritschen and Gay (1979) and WMO (1981) provide more extensive discussions of instruments and measurement theory. Microclimate is the subject of a number of excellent books (Geiger, 1965; Sellers, 1965; Rose, 1966; Munn, 1970; Monteith, 1973; Campbell, 1977; Oke, 1978; Gates, 1980) and the reader is referred to these for theory.

3.2.2. Data Recording

Manual recording or the reduction of graphical recorder charts is a heroic project for more than a few sensors or a few days' worth of data. A fairly complete microclimate study requires 12 to several hundred sensors and many days of data collection (e.g., Daan and Wichers, 1968; Daan, 1973; Porter et al., 1973; Sluiter et al., 1973). Digital recorders for field use are now available that scan one to several hundred sensors from once a second to once a day, and store data in semiconductor memory or on magnetic tape. Even in remote areas, a portable microcomputer can read a tape, apply calibrations, calculate T_e and T_{es}, and prepare plots and statistical summaries (Case, 1984).

The frequency at which microclimate parameters are sampled should be at least twice the frequency of animal observations or behavioral changes of interest. Alternatively, data should be averaged over the interval between samples. Byrne (1970) and Fuchs (1971) discuss sampling theory for microclimate studies.

3.3. Temperature Measurement

Field measurements of temperature are subject to two frequently-ignored sources of error. First, direct solar radiation on sensors or the recorder produces heating errors. Air temperature sensors should be <1mm in diameter and painted white, shielded, or shaded (Christian and Tracy, 1985) to minimize radiation errors. Second, heat may be conducted to the sensor along the wires connecting it to the recorder if a temperature gradient exists near the sensor. Surface temperature sensors should be in contact with the surface for 5–10 cm to minimize this error (Molnar and Rosenbaum, 1963).

The most useful temperature sensors are PVC-insulated type "T" (copper-constantan) thermocouples. Sensors are small (<1mm diameter), moisture-resistant, and easily cut to size in the field. The cost is low enough that sensors may be considered disposable. This facilitates permanent mounting techniques such as attaching sensors to rock walls using rapid (5-min) setting epoxy which will bond to wet rock. Thermocouples made from one roll of wire are usually consistent, and a calibration is needed only for the roll. Splices and kinks in thermocouple wire should be avoided. Insulation must be intact and the exposed metal junction electrically insulated and waterproofed to avoid ground-loop and galvanic voltage errors (American Society for Testing and Materials, 1976, 1977, 1980).

Thermistors can also be used. Each thermistor must be calibrated individually. The recording instrument can be less expensive than that used for thermocouples. However, this is rapidly negated by the greater cost of the thermistor sensors, which discourages permanent mounting techniques. Field damage can impose large costs. Damage can be minimized by protecting the thermistors in a metal tube and using heavy connecting wire. This may increase the radiation and conduction errors discussed above.

General above-ground microclimate studies should include ground surface temperature and air temperature at two heights (e.g., 0.5 and 3 m). Soil temperature should be measured at two depths (e.g., 10 and 30 cm). These measurements are needed for the logarithmic extrapolation equations developed for agricultural and similar simple habitats. A large number of temperature measurements of surfaces facing roosts or roosting bats and within roost sites may be useful.

Caves, tree cavities, and other enclosed roost sites are difficult to generalize. Air warmed by the bats (or the investigator) can be trapped in domes in the ceiling to produce substantial temperature differences between air and substrate temperatures near roosting bats. McNab (1974) used measurements on the floor surface, roosting substrate, and various points 2 cm from the roosting surface. The effect of metabolic heating and dome heat traps can be explored by comparing roost and non-roost sites (e.g., Licht and Leitner, 1967; Dwyer and Harris, 1972; Kunz, 1974; Voute, 1972; Burnett and August, 1981; Anthony et al., 1981). Sensors should be positioned when bats are out of the roost to minimize disturbance. Cementing thermocouple leads to the wall until they are well out of the roost area also minimizes disturbance. Continuous recording can provide temporal information on roost utilization and movement within the roost as well as thermal data (Dwyer and Harris, 1972; Anthony et al., 1981; Burnett and August, 1981; Kunz, 1974).

Roosts in buildings, hollow trees, under leaves or exfoliating rock or bark may display large regional temperature differences (e.g., Humphrey et al., 1977). These often result from solar heating. The hottest and coolest areas may shift position during the day. Sensors should be positioned on both shaded and sunlit surfaces. Thicker walls and/or beams will heat more slowly than thin areas, and so sensors should be placed on both thin and massive areas. Air temperature should be measured at several points, with careful attention given to potential traps for hot or cool air and sources of ventilation.

Non-contact infrared thermometers sense thermal radiation emitted by surfaces. The energy emitted by the surface, q, is converted to an apparent surface temperature, T, by the Stefan-Boltzmann law, $q = \sigma\varepsilon (T + 273)^4$. A possible source of error is that an emittance, ε, of around 0.95 is assumed in the conversion. Most instruments sense only a narrow wavelength band (7–14 micrometers) of the total thermal radiation spectrum, and some surfaces have ε different from 0.95 in this region. Also, errors may result from solar radiation reflected from the surface to the sensor. Infrared thermometers allow surface temperature measurement with little disturbance to the animal. Different types give spot measurements (Gates, 1968) or an image of the scene with brightness proportional to temperature (Cena and Clark, 1973; Hill et al., 1980). Some new types are compact, portable, and less expensive than earlier models (Huband, 1985a,b).

3.4. Radiation Measurement

Bats typically occupy protected roosts and rarely receive direct solar radiation (Kunz, 1982). In the still air conditions typical of such roosts, thermal radiation can account for as much heat transfer as convection. Solar radiation data may be needed for a heat transfer analysis of bats in foliage roosts and for predictions of temperatures within roosts heated by the sun, such as hollow trees, buildings, or under exfoliating rock or bark.

Gates (1965, 1980) and World Meteorological Organization (1981) discuss the physics of radiation, the natural radiation environment, and instruments used for radiation measurements. The radiant environment can be conveniently divided into thermal and solar components. Short-wave or solar radiation has wavelengths from 0.3 to 3 micrometers. The solar radiation field is usually divided into one directional and two hemispherical diffuse components: direct beam, scattered skylight and light reflected from terrestrial surfaces. Long-wave or thermal radiation has wavelengths from about 3 to 50 µm, and is emitted and absorbed by all surfaces in the environment. The thermal radiation field is diffuse, and outdoors is usually divided into hemispherical diffuse sky radiation and hemispherical diffuse ground radiation. In enclosed roosts (buildings, caves, hollow trees, etc.) the distribution follows the surface temperatures facing the animal. Solitary bats hanging in a cave receive thermal radiation from the surrounding walls, ceiling and floor. The cave floor may be cooler than the walls (McNab, 1974), and hence emit less radiation. Bats in roosts heated by solar radiation or bats roosting in clusters experience complex thermal radiation environments. The temperatures of sunlit and shaded walls may differ by 20°C or more. A bat in the center of a cluster will receive radiation primarily from other bats, while a bat on the periphery will receive radiation from both other bats and roost walls. The investigator must be alert to these complexities.

3.4.1. Radiation Properties of Animals

The fraction of incident radiation that is absorbed by a surface varies with the wavelength, λ (micrometers), of the radiation. In the thermal infrared region, natural materials are usually black, i.e., absorptance = emittance = 0.95–0.97 (Hammel, 1956; Birkebak et al., 1964). However, some variation is present in the $\lambda = 7$–14 micrometer region used by radiation thermometers. Bartlett and Gates (1967) and Hill et al. (1980) give thermal radiation absorptance spectra of some animal surfaces.

Spectral absorptance, $a(\lambda)$ (dimensionless), is highly variable in the solar region, and must be measured. The spectral irradiance of the light source, $E(\lambda)$ (W $m^{-2}\lambda^{-1}$), also varies greatly with wavelength. Thus, the effective absorptance, a, of an animal for a particular light source is a weighted average:

$$a = \sum_{\lambda=0.3}^{3} a(\lambda)\, E(\lambda)\, \triangle\lambda \,/\, \sum_{\lambda=0.3}^{3} E(\lambda)\, \triangle\lambda \qquad (15)$$

Birkebak (1966) describes an apparatus that uses the sun as the light source to measure the effective a for solar radiation directly. Spectral measurement and calculation is more generally useful, as the spectral irradiance of the direct solar beam, skylight, light transmitted through clouds or vegetation, and artificial sources are all different, and the spectral distribution of natural sources varies with altitude, atmospheric conditions, and time of day (Gates, 1965, 1966).

The spectral absorptance of bats (or the surface of their roost) is best measured with an integrating sphere spectroreflectometer (Dunkle, 1960). The reflectance of the sample is compared with a pressed $BaSO_4$ reflectance standard (Grum and Luckey, 1968; American Society for Testing and Materials, 1966). The absolute reflectance of the standard given by the manufacturer is usually adequate. Procedures for absolute reflectance measurement are available (Gobel et al., 1966; Van den Akker et al., 1966; American Society for Testing and Materials, 1971). Gates et al. (1965) and Gates (1980) give some spectra and effective solar absorptances of biological surfaces.

Spectral irradiance measurement is possible but impractical in the field. The spectral irradiances of some natural sources are given by Gates (1965, 1966), McCullough and Porter (1971), Thekaekara (1975), Bird and Hulstrom (1983), and Bird et al. (1983).

3.4.2. Solar Radiation Instruments

Solar radiation measurements are needed when studying foliage roosting bats or the influence of sun on temperatures inside hol-low trees, buildings, etc. The best field instrument is a black-and-white pyranometer. The sensor consists of a radially-symmetric pattern of black and white paint. Temperature differences between the black and white areas are proportional to solar irradiance. Accuracy is 3–5%. Calibration is an exacting procedure (see American Society for Testing and Materials, 1981a, 1981b) and the only method available to the typical user is a side-by-side comparison with an instrument known to be accurate.

Silicon photoelectric detectors are less accurate, but less expensive and somewhat more rugged. They do not respond to the full solar spectrum, and the calibration for direct sunlight is not valid for light reflected from or transmitted through vegetation. This limits their use in bat studies, although they might be calibrated for various radiation sources.

Standard short-wave measurements require three sensors. Their sensing surfaces must be level within 1° to correct for solar zenith angle. One horizontal sensor records global radiation, i.e., direct solar radiation plus scattered skylight, and a second sensor is inverted and supported horizontally in a position similar to that of a roosting animal to measure reflected solar radiation. Diffuse skylight is recorded by a third horizontal sensor shielded from direct solar radiation by a strip of black-painted metal adjusted to shade the sensor all day (called a shade ring or shadowband). The ring blocks a substantial part of the sky, and sensor output must be multiplied by a correction factor. The empirical correction is found by periodically shading the global sensor with a 10–cm disk on the end of a rod. The global sensor then reads true diffuse radiation. This correction will vary with vegetation around the site, cloud cover, and possibly time of day.

Solar irradiance measurement within vegetation is more complex, and requires spatial and temporal averaging (Reifsnyder et al., 1971; Hutchison and Matt, 1977). Various instruments have been devised for such measurements (Gutschick et al., 1985).

3.4.3.   Thermal Radiation Instruments

Various instruments are available for measuring thermal radiation. The choice of instruments depends on the type of study.

Inside enclosed roosts, infrared thermometers (see Section 3.3) are most useful in evaluating the thermal radiation environment. Field-portable imaging types are useful, but are not often available because of cost. Some of the newer spot-measurement types are relatively inexpensive and highly portable. Detached sensing heads small enough to use inside larger tree cavities are available.

The investigator must estimate the thermal radiation reaching a bat from measurements of the temperatures of all surfaces surrounding the bat (except those in direct contact) and the solid angle (steradians) subtended by the surfaces surrounding the bat as seen from the bat. Temperatures are best measured using a radiation thermometer, but fine thermocouples cemented to the surface will do (Molnar and Rosenbaum, 1963). For rough calculations, an average radiation temperature can be calculated by weighting the temperature of each surface by the solid angle subtended, summing, and dividing the sum by the sum of the solid angles. The sum of the solid angles will range from 2π steradians for a bat closely pressed to a wall, to nearly 4π steradians for a bat hanging freely from the ceiling. More exact calculations may be needed if the temperatures of surfaces surrounding the bat vary by more than 5 or 10°C. These are too complex to discuss here, and the reader is referred to a text covering radiative heat transfer (e.g., Kreith, 1965; Love, 1968).

Studies of foliage-roosting bats or heat-transfer modeling of hollow trees, buildings, etc. may use standard micrometeorological sensors. Most measure net radiation, i.e., the difference between solar plus thermal radiation falling on the top of a horizontal plane, and thermal plus reflected solar radiation falling on the bottom. Sky and ground hemi-spherical thermal radiation are calculated by subtracting the solar components. The most useful sensor for field use is the Funk-Fritschen net radiometer (Funk, 1962; Fritschen, 1963, 1965). This consists of a black-painted plastic plate shielded from the wind by 0.05 mm thick hemispherical polyethylene domes on top and bottom. The temperature difference between top and bottom is proportional to net radiation. Water vapor inside the dome is a frequent problem, and often causes large (200% +) errors. The polyethylene dome is permeable to water vapor, and a very slow inflow of dried air is needed to maintain dryness (Funk, 1962). The theory and calibration of net radiometers is described by Tanner et al. (1960) and Idso (1970, 1971a). Suomi and Kuhn (1958) and Tanner et al. (1960) describe an awkward but very inexpensive version of interest to the impoverished researcher.

Standard measurements require two carefully-leveled sensors placed near the solar radiation instruments. One measures net irradiance, N. The other uses a modified lower dome with a thermocouple to measure the temperature of the lower dome, T_d (Idso, 1971b, 1972a). Then the net irradiance of the modified instrument, N, can be corrected using T_d to give the total hemispherical irradiance, R_h (global irradiance plus sky thermal irradiance), falling on the upper surface:

$$R_h = N + \sigma\varepsilon\,(T_d + 273)^4 \qquad (16)$$

3.4.4.   Calculation of Radiation Components

Unlike the thermal radiation field inside caves, buildings, etc., irradiance (W/m²) components needed for heat-transfer calculations on bats roosting in foliage or on roosts in hollow trees, buildings, etc. are not directly measured (except for scattered sunlight, s, and reflected sunlight, r). Direct solar irradiance normal to the sun's rays, S, is

$$S = (G - s)/\cos(\theta_z) \qquad (17)$$

where G is global irradiance and θ_z is the zenith angle of the sun. Thermal irradiance from the atmosphere, I_s, is

$$I_s = R_h - G \tag{18}$$

where total hemispherical irradiance from the sky is R_h (Eq. 16). Total hemispherical thermal irradiance from the ground, I_g, is

$$I_g = R_h - r - N = \sigma\varepsilon\,(T_g + 273)^4 \tag{19}$$

where N is net radiation and T_g is average ground or vegetation surface temperature.

3.4.5. Estimation of Radiation Components

Although much less satisfactory than direct measurements, some radiation terms may be estimated from other meteorological parameters. Solar radiation estimation has been reviewed by Tracy et al. (1983). Swinbank's (1963) formula can be used to estimate thermal radiation from the sky, I_s. Weiss and Norman (1985) and National Climatic Data Center (1979) discuss methods for estimating other radiation components as well.

3.5. Wind Measurement

Convective heat transfer studies have a long history (Eckert, 1981). The reader is referred to Vogel (1981), Prandtl and Tietjens (1934), standard engineering texts (e.g., Kreith, 1965) and review articles (Kestin, 1966; Morgan, 1975) for details and experimental methods.

Heat is transferred from an object to the air at a rate $H(T_f - T_a)$ (see Eq. 3). The convective conductance, H, is sensitive to both the size and shape of the animal and to wind speed. For rough calculations, the formula for a sphere may be used (Mitchell, 1976).

$$H = 6.84\,A\,D^{-0.4}u^{0.6} \tag{20}$$

where A is the total surface area (m²) of the animal, D (m) is the cube root of the volume (m³) of the animal, and u is the wind speed (m/sec). This equation gives a minimum

value which is increased by turbulent flow and/or mixed convection conditions. These effects are common in natural environments (Cionco, 1972), including caves (Tuttle and Stevenson, 1977).

Turbulence increases convective transport 50 to 100% (Kestin, 1966; Pearman et al., 1972; Nobel, 1974; Mitchell, 1976; Morgan, 1975). Mitchell (1976) suggests multiplying H by a value of 1.5 when an animal is resting on a surface.

Mixed convection may occur at wind speeds less than 0.5 m/sec, and is probably typical of caves, buildings, and other cavity roosts. In mixed convection, the buoyancy of heated air generates additional air motion (Morgan, 1975; Churchill, 1977). Free convection occurs when there is no wind, and all air motion is generated by buoyancy. It is rarely found in natural environments, but might occur in small caves and cavities. Gates (1980) suggests using a minimum $u = 0.1$ m/sec to allow for free and/or mixed convection in calm conditions. This is most easily done by adding 0.1 m/sec to the measured wind speed.

It is possible to check for turbulence and mixed convection effects by measuring convection coefficients in the field with gold-plated models of the animal (Porter et al., 1973; Bakken and Gates, 1975). Measurements of T_e from taxidermic mounts can be used to check for problems with both convection and radiation in complex habitats (Bakken et al., 1985).

3.5.1. Convective Conductance of Animals

Briefly, convective conductance can be measured in the laboratory by recording the cooling rate of gold-plated or black-painted metal casts or models of the animal in a wind tunnel, and correcting for thermal radiation (Bartlett and Gates, 1967; Porter et al., 1973; Bakken and Gates, 1975; Mitchell, 1976). The surface of the model should be rough (textured). Smooth models are excessively sensitive to turbulence (Farrell et al., 1977), and live animals are aerodynamically-rough. The area blockage (ratio of cross-section of the animal model to the cross section of the tunnel) should be less than 0.1. Blockage alters air velocity and flow patterns over the animal or animal model (Farrell et al., 1977), and thus *H*. As metabolism chambers with simulated wind must be as small as possible for gas exchange measurement, blockage may be unavoidable. Pederson and Sparrow (1977) and Farrell et al. (1977) discuss blockage effect corrections.

Accurate measurements of *H* require air flow across the section of the tunnel to be uniform, and turbulence to be known and minimized. Loehrke and Nagib (1976) discuss methods for reducing turbulence. A hot wire anemometer should be used to detect turbulence and measure the root-mean-square value of the longitudinal turbulence intensity, $(\Delta u/u)$. Comings et al. (1948) describe another method for measuring turbulence that uses simple equipment. Vogel (1981) and Prandtl and Tietjens (1934) present wind tunnel designs.

3.5.2. Wind Speed Measurement

3.5.2.1. Calibration

All anemometers suitable for field use require individual calibration in a wind tunnel. Factory calibrations may be 200% in error. A Prandtl-design (Prandtl and Tietjens, 1934) pitot-static tube is the usual reference instrument, as it is self-calibrating when properly constructed. Low wind velocities of biological interest require an extremely sensitive water manometer (≤ 0.0025 mm). An electronic manometer is adequate, but differential manometers can be more sensitive and can be constructed inexpensively (Stong, 1969; Vogel, 1981). Both devices respond to tilting—do not rest your arm on the supporting bench, and make measurements sitting on a fixed stool. An alternative approach uses a sharp-edged orifice in a cylindrical wind tunnel. Flow is calculated (within a few %) from standard tables using the pressure difference across the orifice and dimensions of the ori-

fice and pipe (American Society of Mechanical Engineers, 1971). Precise construction is essential.

3.5.2.2. Thermal Anemometers

Thermal anemometers measure convective heat loss from a heated bead thermistor, wire, or sphere. They are very sensitive to low wind speeds, as is convective heat transfer from animals. The need for heater power may present a problem in field sites. All are sensitive to contamination, and need regular checking and cleaning in the field.

Hot wire anemometers (Freymuth, 1980) use a short piece of fine platinum wire or platinum-coated quartz fiber as a sensor. These are usually expensive research instruments. It is possible to construct the electronics (Miller, 1976; Simpson et al., 1979), but probes are best purchased. The fast response (5,000 to 50,000 Hz) and very small probe size make them ideal for measuring turbulence and velocity uniformity in wind tunnels.

Heated thermistor anemometers are easily constructed and are also available commercially. Vogel (1981) and Bergen (1971) give some designs. Calibration is temperature-dependent (Bergen, 1971). Response (1 to 10 Hz) is not rapid enough for turbulence studies, but is fast enough that some form of averaging is needed for field use.

A third type uses relatively large-diameter (5 to 30 mm) spheres or cylinders for sensors. An identical pair, one electrically heated, are mounted a few cm apart. The temperature difference, measured with a thermocouple or thermopile, is inversely proportional to the effective (i.e., including turbulence effects) value of *u*. The heat capacitance of the large sensor provides time-averaging. The calibration is somewhat temperature sensitive, and solar heating may produce errors. Roer and Kjolsvik (1973) present a useful design. Their design may be simplified by using 12 to 20 mm aluminum spheres as sensors. A hole is drilled in the sphere to hold a 1/8 W resistor used as the heater. The spheres should be white-painted or gold-plated to minimize radiation errors.

3.5.2.3. Dynamic Anemometers

These anemometers all use the dynamic force of moving air, which is proportional to the square of wind speed. Thus, most designs are insensitive in sheltered habitats (e.g., in foliage, buildings, or caves). Furthermore, most of the change in convective heat transfer with wind occurs from 0 to 1 m/sec. Some ultra-sensitive cup (Bradley, 1969) and styrofoam propeller anemometers (Gill, 1975) respond down to 0.1–0.2 m/sec. These are the only type that may be of value in the field. All use photoelectric sensors and require external power. The main advantages are the lack of temperature and radiation errors and minimal maintenance.

3.5.2.4. Flow Tracers

Smoke, kerosene vapor (flammable and explosive), or titanium chloride (corrosive, toxic), and small soap bubbles (adjusted to neutral buoyancy by using a helium-air mixture) can be used to visualize air flow. Twente (1955) and Daan (1973) used cigarette smoke as a flow tracer in caves.

Flow tracers may also be used to measure wind speed. Time-distance measurements of velocity are possible with bubbles by measuring streaks on photographs taken with a within-lens shutter and known exposure time (e.g., Moen, 1974). The sonic anemometer and the ion anemometer use sound and charged air molecules, respectively, as flow tracers. The laser anemometer uses dust particles in the air as a tracer. The ion anemometer is potentially useful in bat studies; the others are primarily suitable for laboratory or specialized agricultural meteorology studies.

3.6. Conduction to Roosting Surface

Heat transfer by conduction to the roosting surface may be significant for bats (e.g., Twente, 1955; McNab, 1974). Davis (1970) reported condensation on roosting bats with a body temperature below air temperature, possibly due to conduction to the roost wall. Others have reported behavior patterns such as pressing the body against large (hence cool) beams in roosts in buildings during the heat of a summer day (e.g., Licht and Leitner, 1967; Kunz, 1974; Kunz, pers. obs.).

Twente (1955) asserted that the temperature of clustered bats during hibernation assumed temperatures close to that of the cave ceiling on which they roosted. McNab (1974) argued that the body temperatures of bats more closely approximated the radiative temperature of the cave floor beneath the roost. However, similarity of temperatures does not necessarily mean that the correlated environmental temperature determines body temperature. Rather, the correlations may mean the animal and the adjacent substrate integrate convective and radiative heat flow similarly (e.g., Bartholomew and Dawson, 1979; Crawford et al., 1983).

3.6.1. Conductive Heat Flow Measurement

The usual method for measuring conductive heat flux, q (W/m²), is a heat flow plate embedded in the medium conducting heat (here, the roosting surface). This is a sheet of material of known thickness, $\triangle x$ (m) and known thermal conductivity, k (W m^{-1} °C^{-1}). A multi-junction thermopile measures the average temperature difference across the sheet, $\triangle T$ (°C), which is proportional to q by the Fourier equation:

$$q = k \triangle T/\triangle x \qquad (21)$$

Construction and calibration of heat flow plates are discussed by Fuchs and Tanner (1968), Mogensen (1970), Idso (1972b), Biscoe et al. (1977), and Fritschen and Gay (1979). The heat flow plate alters the heat flow through the medium unless k for the medium and plate are identical (Mogensen, 1970; Phillip, 1961).

3.6.2. Application to Bats

Measurement of the total heat conducted to or from a solid is straightforward, provided that the sensor is smaller than the area of contact, the contact area is known, and heat flow is uniform over the contact area. These assumptions hold for studies of large animals on artificial surfaces (Bond et al., 1952; Spillman and Hinkle, 1971; Beckett and Barron, 1972; Restrepo et al., 1977; Ohata and Whittow, 1974; Gatenby, 1977; Kimball, 1983). Because of small size and tendency to roost on walls and ceilings, the skin of a bat is not pressed as firmly to the substrate as that of a large animal. As a result, the contact area is uncertain and heat flow may be uneven. Some bats roost in holes or crevices where they are in close contact with the substrate (Kunz, 1982). Others roost in compact clusters with considerable contact between individuals. Many roosting bats hang pendant from the roosting surface, often by one foot, which may minimize conductive heat loss to the cool substrate (Kunz, 1982). Conductive heat loss measurement from bats thus presents an interesting challenge, as there are few appropriate precedents.

In most cases, the contact area of a bat is smaller than or comparable to the area of typical sensors, and therefore heat flow plate measurements may include air-wall as well as bat-wall heat flow. A heat flow plate larger than a single bat but smaller than a cluster, constructed as for a gradient layer calorimeter (e.g., Benzinger and Kitzinger, 1963; Hammel and Hardy, 1963), might be used to average heat flow to the substrate occupied by a dense cluster of bats. A solitary bat might be studied with a heat flow plate with an active area larger than the contact area of the animal by partitioning total heat flow into heat flow from the animal, heat flow from the environment, and changes in heat flow from the environment due to the effect of the animal on convection and radiation.

In addition to posture and the cluster configuration, experimental setups must consider the surface texture, thermal properties, and thickness of the roosting surface. Each of these variables influences the time course of heat flow between the bat and its roosting surface.

Heat flow is greatest when a bat first establishes good thermal contact with a surface. Surface texture may influence the thermal conductance between the bat and the surface, and hence heat flow. As heat is stored in the surface material, the temperature near the animal changes with time and approaches animal temperature (see Dwyer and Harris, 1972; Voûte, 1972; Kunz, 1974). Consequently, the heat flow rate normally decreases with time. Because stored heat is important, heat flow depends on the thermal diffusivity, $k/\rho c$ (m²/sec), of the roosting surface material, where ρ is the density (including the effect of porosity) kg/m³, and c is the specific heat (J kg^{-1} °C^{-1}). The thickness of the roosting surface may limit the total heat storage capacity. Heat transfer texts (e.g., Kreith, 1965) discuss the relevant theory.

The heat capacitance of material between the bat and the sensor also requires attention when the heat transferred during the initial contact of the bat with the roosting surface is important. Any heat transferred from the bat that was stored in the volume between the heat flow plate and the animal will not be measured by the heat flow plate. The plate must be placed as near the surface as possible to minimize this error. However, the variation in $\triangle T$ over the heat flow plate is then increased, and may not be correctly averaged by the thermopile junctions.

4. HUMIDITY AND MASS TRANSPORT

4.1. Evaporative Water Loss

The evaporative water loss (EWL) from an animal is important in two respects. First, desiccation may be a serious threat when ELW cannot be easily replaced, e.g., during hibernation or in hot, arid regions. Second, the evaporation of water requires heat, and thus has thermoregulatory significance. Heat of vaporization may be utilized for cooling under hot conditions. Under cold conditions, it imposes an additional requirement for metabolic heat production.

Water vapor is transported between the animal and the environment by convection. The rate of mass transport is given by

$$E = H_m (\rho_s - \rho_a) \qquad (22)$$

where E is the rate of mass transport (kg/sec), ρ_s is the water vapor density at the evaporating surface (g/m³), and ρ_a is the water vapor density of the air. The process is sufficiently similar to heat convection that the Lewis rule can be used to estimate (to about 10%) the convective mass conductance, H_m, from the convective heat conductance, H:

$$H_m = H/\rho \, cp \qquad (23)$$

where ρ is the density of air and cp is the specific heat ($\rho cp = 1200 \, J \, m^{-3} \, °C^{-1}$ at 20°C). The associated rate of latent heat transport (W) is found by multiplying E by the latent heat of vaporization, λ, (cf. Eq. 1).

Terrestrial animals other than wet-skinned amphibians have considerable control over EWL. The permeability of the skin is often adjustable, and introduces a variable conductance in series with H_m. Countercurrent heat exchange in the respiratory tract reduces the temperature of the effective evaporating surface, and consequently ρ_s. The environmental vapor density does set upper and lower limits on EWL where it is of greatest ecological importance. The substantial literature on EWL is reviewed for birds by Calder and King (1974) and Dawson (1982); for reptiles by Minnich (1982), Lillywhite and Maderson (1982), Mautz (1982), and Nagy (1982); for bats by McNab (1982) and chapter 22 in this volume. Some important details have been discussed by Welch (1980, 1984), Pinshow et al. (1982), and Webster et al. (1985).

4.2. Measurement of Vapor Density

Water vapor density is probably the most difficult environmental variable to measure accurately and automatically at reasonable cost. Thus, there is no clearly preferred method for all studies. Instruments and theory are discussed by Fritschen and Gay (1979).

The dewpoint (temperature at which water condenses on a surface) is accurately related to water vapor density through standard tables (Goff and Gratch, 1946). It is easily measured by observing the temperature at which a "fog" appears on a mirror finish surface as it cools through the dewpoint. The dewpoint hygrometer is simple and self-calibrating. Automatic instruments sense the "fog" on the mirror photoelectrically, and use the output to regulate the mirror temperature with a Peltier-effect cooler. Although expensive, this is the most accurate (to 0.1 °C) and reliable instrument. The need for 25–200 W electrical power limits its field use. Machin (1970) described a microprobe dewpoint hygrometer which allows dewpoint measurement in very confined spaces (e.g., between densely roosting bats). The effect of the roosting bats on their immediate environment is thus measurable.

The sling and fan-ventilated psychrometers are commonly used instruments. A sling psychrometer cannot be operated in a confined space. Numerous sources of error affect wet-bulb readings, including insufficient duration and rate of ventilation, contamination of the wick or water used on the wet bulb, and heat conducted along the temperature sensor or from a water reservoir. These errors are large when relative humidity is below 30%, and a fan-ventilated unit that allows readings while the wet bulb is being ventilated is essential. Electric fans impose heavy battery drains which can be avoided by using spring-drive fans.

The popular spring-drive direct-recording hair hygrograph and hygrothermograph are bulky and require frequent care and recalibration (Cotton, 1970). For low-power automatic recording, various sensors use electrical properties that vary with humidity (and usually temperature as well). Many of these use lithium chloride or other salts. These sensors are destroyed by high humidity or wetting, and are *not* field instruments. Some thin-film capacitor sensors are resistant to wetting and can be used for low-power data-logging (Teel and Fleetwood, 1982).

5. NATIONAL METEOROLOGICAL SERVICE DATA

Most nations now collect standardized meteorological data for synoptic weather forecasts. Instruments, site selection and procedures are detailed by the World Meteorological Organization (1971). The utility of these data for thermoregulation studies is limited. Synoptic data are usually taken every 3 hours with at least 100 km between stations. Solar radiation data are rarely available. The relevance to the experimental site depends on distance and terrain, but is generally poor. In flat, open country, solar radiation data can typically be extrapolated only 15 km with ± 10% accuracy for daily totals, and less for hourly data (Suckling, 1982). Air temperature, humidity, and wind are greatly influenced by vegetation and topography. In hilly or forested terrain, extrapolation over 100 m may give poor results (Geiger, 1965; Barry, 1981; Barry and Chorley, 1982). Data from the nearest weather station are often of limited utility for microclimate studies and comparison with simultaneous field observations of animals. However, meteorological station data are useful for studies of statistical climate patterns, historical, and large-scale (100 km) geographical effects on populations (e.g., Burnett, 1983). Meteorological theory allows conditions at the study site to be modeled using input data from surrounding meteorological stations. Oke (1978), Porter et al. (1973), Barry (1981), and Barry and Chorley (1982) introduce the principles and provide guides to a voluminous literature.

Locating suitable data sets can be a problem. The World Meteorological Organization (1981) lists addresses of worldwide national meteorological services, but not all meteorological services are helpful in providing data (for financial or national security reasons).

The U.S. National Climatic Data Center, Asheville, North Carolina 28801, U.S.A., is very helpful in locating worldwide data sources. The National Climatic Data Center can provide data for the U.S. and many other areas in print and/or magnetic tape format (Hatch, 1983).

Few meteorological data records include the accurate solar irradiance data needed for heat transfer calculations of conditions in above-ground roosts (buildings, hollow trees, etc.). The most useful data source has been compiled as part of a U.S. Department of Energy solar energy research program. The National Climatic Data Center "SOLMET" file provides hourly data for global, direct, and diffuse radiation, cloud cover, wind speed and direction, air temperature, humidity, and descriptive weather codes in a common format on magnetic tape. The "SOLMET" file (National Climatic Data Center, 1978, 1979) covers the period 1952–1976, with a supplement for 1977–1980. Actual data, corrected for instrument errors, are given for 27 sites in the U.S. Estimates based on cloud cover and visibility data are given for another 222 sites. All data for one site are on one tape. The "TMY" file abstracts the "SOLMET" file to form a synthetic year typical of each site. Each tape covers several sites in a region.

Other meteorological data are available from the National Climatic Data Center, but are not readily usable. Solar radiation data in the U.S. are available for the period since 1980 from the 26-station NOAA Solar Radiation Network data files. The associated synoptic meteorological data are available in the Surface Airways Observation Network files. However, the investigator must pay to have the raw data synthesized into useful "SOLMET-like" files containing all parameters for one site. The investigator could also apply radiation estimation procedures as for "SOLMET" (National Climatic Data Center, 1979) to sites with hourly or synoptic data but no solar radiation. The Surface Airways Observation Network provides hourly or synoptic data for the U.S. Worldwide synoptic data, primarily from U.S. military bases, are also available from the National Climatic Data Center, at a high cost, in the "Synoptic Data File—Surface Land" and U.S. Air Force "DATSAV" files.

6. SUMMARY

As is evident from the definitions of T_e and T_{es}, the animal and its thermal environment must be considered together. Direct measurement of T_e and T_{es} with taxidermic mounts or models allow inexpensive thermal measurement and mapping at the size scale of the animal. Conventional instrumentation is too large to examine the thermal variation often present at the size scale of small bats, and usually too expensive to replicate for mapping.

Standard microclimate measurements and animal properties can be used in equations (1)–(14) to find T_e and T_{es}. Equations developed for crop fields allow extrapolation of microclimate data from the instrument site to occupied sites in simple habitats such as deserts and grassland (e.g., Porter et al., 1973). These relations do not accurately apply to more complex habitats typical of bat roosts. However, heat transfer analysis described above can be applied to the roost itself to estimate thermal conditions in roost sites such as hollow trees or branches, bamboo culms, under leaves or palm fronds, and beneath exfoliating rock and bark (e.g., Derby and Gates, 1966; Thorkelson and Maxwell, 1974; Lewis and Nobel, 1977). T_e and T_{es} measurements with mounts or models aid in developing and testing extrapolations and calculations.

Meteorological records are usually the only source of data for study of annual cycles, statistical distribution of severe climate conditions, and historical influences on distribution and abundance. However, it cannot be substituted for local microclimate measurements. Meteorological service data are taken in open situations atypical of roost environments and usually some distance away. Slope, topography, elevation, and vegetation differ-

ences substantially alter thermal conditions. Radiation data are often absent. Thus, considerable computer modeling of uncertain accuracy is needed to relate the data to roost site conditions.

7. ACKNOWLEDGMENTS

This work has been supported by NSF Grants DEB 8300651 to G.S.B. and DEB 8314821 to T.H.K. The National Climatic Data Center and the instrument suppliers listed in Appendix 2 have been most helpful in supplying information on data files and currently-available instruments, respectively. We thank Michael T. Murphy for reading and commenting on the manuscript and Laura Bakken for editing and typing the manuscript.

8. REFERENCES

American Society of Mechanical Engineers. 1971. Fluid meters—their theory and application. 6th ed. American Society of Mechanical Engineers, New York.

American Society for Testing and Materials. 1966. Preparation for reference white reflectance standards. ASTM Standard E 259-66. ASTM, Philadelphia.

American Society for Testing and Materials. 1971. Standard method for absolute calibration of reflectance standards. ASTM Standard E 306-71. ASTM, Philadelphia.

American Society for Testing and Materials. 1976. Standard recommended practice for preparation and use of freezing point reference baths. ASTM Standard E 563-76. ASTM, Philadelphia.

American Society for Testing and Materials. 1977. Standard temperature-electromotive force (EMF) tables for thermocouples. ASTM Standard E 230-77. ASTM, Philadelphia.

American Society for Testing and Materials. 1980. Standard method for calibration of thermocouples by comparison techniques. ASTM Standard E 220-80. ASTM, Philadelphia.

American Society for Testing and Materials. 1981a. Standard methods for calibration of secondary reference pyrheliometers and pyrheliometers for field use. ASTM Standard E 816-81. ASTM, Philadelphia.

American Society for Testing and Materials. 1981b. Standard method for transfer of calibration from reference to field pyranometers. ASTM Standard E 824-81. ASTM, Philadelphia.

Anthony, E. L. P., M. H. Stack, and T. H. Kunz. 1981. Night roosting and the nocturnal time budget of the little brown bat, *Myotis lucifugus*: Effects of reproductive status, prey density, and environmental conditions. Oecologia, 51:151-156.

Bakken, G. S. 1976. A heat-transfer analysis of animals: Unifying concepts and the application of metabolism chamber data to field ecology. J. Theor. Biol., 60:337-384.

Bakken, G. S. 1980. The use of standard operative temperature in the study of the thermal energetics of birds. Physiol. Zool., 53:108-119.

Bakken, G. S. 1981. A two-dimensional operative-temperature model for thermal energy management by animals. J. Thermal Biol., 6:23-30.

Bakken, G. S. 1983. A battery-powered three-mode temperature-controller circuit. J. Thermal Biol., 8:297-299.

Bakken, G. S., and D. M. Gates. 1975. Heat-transfer analysis of animals: Some implications for field ecology, physiology, and evolution. Pp. 255-290, *in* Perspectives of biophysical ecology. (D. M. Gates and R. B. Schmerl, eds.). Springer-Verlag, New York, 609 pp.

Bakken, G. S., W. A. Buttemer, W. R. Dawson, and D. M. Gates. 1981. Heated taxidermic mounts: A means of measuring the standard operative temperature affecting small animals. Ecology, 62:311-318.

Bakken, G. S., D. J. Erskine, and W. R. Santee. 1983. Construction and operation of heated taxidermic mounts used to measure standard operative temperature. Ecology, 64:1658-1662.

Bakken, G. S., W. R. Santee, and D. J. Erskine. 1985. Operative and standard operative temperature: Tools for thermal energetics studies. Amer. Zool., 25:933-943.

Barry, R. G. 1981. Mountain weather and climate. Methuen, New York, 313 pp.

Barry, R. G., and R. J. Chorley. 1982. Atmosphere, weather, and climate. 4th ed. Methuen, London, 407 pp.

Bartholomew, G. A., and W. R. Dawson. 1979. Thermoregulatory behavior during incubation in Heerman's gulls. Physiol. Zool., 52:422-437.

Bartlett, P. N., and D. M. Gates. 1967. The energy budget of a lizard on a tree trunk. Ecology, 48:315-322.

Beckett, F. E., and R. F. Barron. 1972. Heat transfer from a pig to the floor. Trans. Amer. Soc. Agric. Eng., 15:700-703.

Bennett, A. F., R. B. Huey, H. John-Alder, and K. A. Nagy. 1984. The parasol tail and thermoregulatory behavior of the cape ground squirrel *Xerus inauris*. Physiol. Zool., 57:57-62.

Benzinger, T. H., and C. Kitzinger. 1963. Gradient layer calorimetry and human calorimetry. Pp. 87-109, *in* Temperature—its measurement and control in science and industry. Vol. 3. (J. D. Hardy, ed.). Reinhold, New York, 683 pp.

Bergen, J. D. 1971. An inexpensive heated thermistor anemometer. Agric. Meteorol., 8:395-405.

Biedenweg, D. W. 1983. Time and energy budgets of the mockingbird (*Mimus polyglottos*) during the breeding season. Auk, 100:149-160.

Bird, R. E., and R. L. Hulstrom. 1983. Availability of the Soltran 5 solar spectral model. Solar Energy, 30:379.

Bird, R. E., R. L. Hulstrom, and L. J. Lewis. 1983. Terrestrial solar spectral data sets. Solar Energy, 30:563-573.

Birkebak, R. C. 1966. Heat transfer in biological systems. Internat. Rev. Gen. Exp. Zool. 2:269-344.

Birkebak, R. C., R. C. Roland, and D. W. Warner. 1964. Total emittance of animal integuments. J. Heat Trans., 86:287-288.

Biscoe, P. V., R. A. Saffell, and P. D. Smith. 1977. An apparatus for calibrating soil heat flux plates. Agric. Meteorol., 18:49-54.

Bond, T. E., C. F. Kelley, and H. Heitman, Jr. 1952. Heat and moisture loss from swine. Agric. Eng., 33:148-153.

Bradley, E. F. 1969. A small, sensitive anemometer system for agricultural meteorology. Agric. Meteorol., 6:185-193.

Burnett, C. D. 1983. Geographic and climatic correlates of morphological variation in *Eptesicus fuscus*. J. Mammal., 64:437-444.

Burnett, C. D., and P. V. August. 1981. Time and energy budgets for day roosting in a maternity colony of *Myotis lucifugus*. J. Mammal., 62:758-766.

Byrne, G. F. 1970. Data logging and scanning rate considerations in micrometeorological experiments. Agric. Meteorol., 7:415-418.

Calder, W. A., and J. R. King. 1974. Thermal and caloric relations of birds. Pp. 259-413, *in* Avian Biology, Vol. 4. (D. S. Farner and J. R. King, eds.). Academic Press, New York, 504 pp.

Campbell, G. S. 1977. An introduction to environmental biophysics. Springer-Verlag, New York, 159 pp.

Case, R. P. 1984. Microcomputers in the field. Byte, 9:243-250.

Casey, T. M. 1981. Behavioral mechanisms of thermoregulation. Pp. 79-114, in Insect thermoregulation. (B. Heinrich, ed.) Wiley, New York.

Cena, K. and J. A. Clark. 1973. Thermographic measurements of the surface temperatures of animals. J. Mammal., 54:1003-1007.

Cena, K., and J. L. Monteith. 1975a. Transfer processes in animal coats I. Radiative transfer. Proc. R. Soc. Lond. B, 188:377-393.

Cena, K., and J. L. Monteith. 1975b. Transfer processes in animal coats II. Conduction and convection. Proc. R. Soc. Lond. B, 188:395-411.

Cena, K., and J. L. Monteith. 1975c. Transfer processes in animal coats III. Water vapor diffusion. Proc. R. Soc. Lond. B, 188:413-423.

Chappell, M. A. 1983a. Metabolism and thermoregulation in desert and montane grasshoppers. Oecologia, 56:126-131.

Chappell, M. A. 1983b. Thermal limitations to escape responses in desert grasshoppers. Anim. Behav., 31:1088-1093.

Chappell, M. A., and G. A. Bartholomew. 1981. Standard operative temperatures and thermal energetics of the antelope ground squirrel *Ammospermophilus leucurus.* Physiol. Zool., 54:83-91.

Christian, K. A., and C. R. Tracy. 1985. Measuring air temperature in field studies. J. Thermal Biol., 10:55-56.

Christian, K. A., and C. R. Tracy. 1981. The effect of the thermal environment on the ability of hatchling Galapagos land iguanas to avoid predation during dispersal. Oecologia, 49:218-223.

Christian, K., C. R. Tracy, and W. P. Porter. 1983. Seasonal shifts in body temperature and use of microhabitats by Galapagos land iguanas (*Conolophus pallidus*). Ecology, 64:463-468.

Churchill, S. W. 1977. A comprehensive correlating equation for laminar, assisting, forced and free convection. Amer. Inst. Chem. Eng. J., 23:10-16.

Cionco, R. M. 1972. Intensity of turbulence within canopies with simple and complex roughness elements. Boundary-Layer Meteorol., 2:453-465.

Comings, E. W., J. T. Clapp, and J. F. Taylor. 1948. Air turbulence and transfer processes. Indust. Eng. Chem., 40:1076-1082.

Cotton, R. F. 1970. Calibration and adjustment of hair hydrographs. Agric. Meteorol., 7:45-58.

Crawford, K. M., J. R. Spotila, and E. Standora. 1983. Operative environmental temperatures and basking behavior of the turtle *Pseudemys scripta.* Ecology, 64:989-999.

Daan, S. 1973. Activity during natural hibernation in three species of vespertilionid bats. Netherlands J. Zool., 23:1-71.

Daan, S., and H. T. Wichers. 1968. Habitat selection of bats hibernating in a limestone cave. Z. Saugetierk., 33:262-287.

Davis, L. B. 1972. Energy transfer in fur. Unpubl. Ph.D. dissertation, University of Kentucky, Lexington. UKY BU-101 Office of Research and Engineering Services, University of Kentucky, Lexington.

Davis, L. B., and R. C. Birkebak. 1975. Convective energy transfer in fur. Pp. 525-548, *in* Perspectives of biophysical ecology. (D. M. Gates and R. B. Schmerl, eds.). Springer-Verlag, New York, 609 pp.

Davis, W. H. 1970. Hibernation: Ecology and physiological ecology. Pp. 265-300, *in* Biology of bats. Vol 1. (W. A. Wimsatt, ed.) Academic Press, New York, 406 pp.

Dawson, W. R. 1982. Evaporative losses of water by birds. Comp. Biochem. Physiol., 71A:495-510.

Derby, R. W., and D. M. Gates. 1966. The temperature of tree trunks—calculated and observed. Amer. J. Botany, 53:580-587.

Dunkle, R. V. 1960. Spectral reflectance measurements. Pp. 117-137, *in* Surface effects on spacecraft materials, (F. J. Clauss, ed.). John Wiley and Sons, New York.

Dwyer, P. D. and J. A. Harris. 1972. Behavioral acclimatization to temperature by pregnant *Miniopterus* (Chiroptera). Physiol. Zool., 45:14-21.

Eckert, E. R. G. 1971. Pioneering contributions to our knowledge of convective heat transfer. ASME J. Heat Trans., 103:409-414.

Eyal, E. 1963. Shorn and unshorn Awassi sheep IV. Skin temperature and changes in temperature and humidity in the fleece and its surface. J. Agric. Sci., 60:183-193.

Farell, C., S. Carrasquel, O. Guven, and V. C. Patel. 1977. Effect of wind-tunnel walls on the flow past circular cylinders and cooling tower models. ASME J. Fluids Eng., 99:470-479.

Fourt, L., and M. Harris. 1949. Physical properties of clothing fabrics. Pp. 291-319, *in* Physiology of heat regulation and the science of clothing. (L. H. Newburgh, ed., reprinted 1968). Hafner, New York, 457 pp.

Freymuth, P. 1980. Review: A bibliography of thermal anemometry. ASME J. Fluids Eng. 102:152-159.

Fritschen, L. J. 1963. Construction and evaluation of a miniature net radiometer. J. Appl. Meteorol., 2:165-172.

Fritschen, L. J. 1965. Miniature net radiometer improvements. J. Appl. Meteorol., 4:528-532.

Fritschen, L. J., and L. W. Gay. 1979. Environmental instrumentation. Springer-Verlag, New York, 216 pp.

Fuchs, M. 1971. Data logging and scanning rate considerations in micrometeorological experiments—a discussion. Agric. Meteorol., 9:285-286.

Fuchs, M., and C. B. Tanner. 1968. Calibration and field test of soil heat flux plates. Soil Sci. Soc. Amer. Proc., 32:326-328.

Funk, J. P. 1962. A net radiometer designed for optimum sensitivity and a ribbon thermopile used in a miniaturized version. J. Geophys. Res., 67:2753-2760.

Gagge, A. P. 1940. Standard operative temperature. A generalized temperature scale applicable to direct and partitional calorimetry. Amer. J. Physiol., 131:93-103.

Gagge, A. P., and J. D. Hardy. 1967. Thermal radiation exchange of the human by partitional calorimetry. J. Appl. Physiol., 23:248-258.

Gatenby, R. M. 1977. Conduction of heat from sheep to ground. Agric. Meteorol., 18:387-400.

Gates, D. M. 1965. Radiant energy, its receipt and disposal. Meteorol. Mon., 6:1-26.

Gates, D. M. 1966. Spectral distribution of solar radiation at the earth's surface. Science, 151:523-529.

Gates, D. M. 1968. Sensing biological environments with a portable radiation thermometer. Appl. Optics, 7:1803-1809.

Gates, D. M. 1980. Biophysical ecology. Springer-Verlag, New York, 611 pp.

Gates, D. M., H. J. Keegan, J. C. Schleter and V. R. Weidner. 1965. Spectral properties of plants. App. Optics, 4:11-20.

Geiger, R. 1965. The climate near the ground. Harvard University Press, Cambridge, 611 pp.

Gill, G. C. 1975. Development and use of the Gill UVW anemometer. Boundary-Layer Meteorol., 8:475-495.

Goebel, D. G., B. P. Caldwell, and H. K. Hammond, III. 1966. Use of an auxiliary sphere with a spectroreflectometer to obtain absolute reflectance. J. Optical Soc. Amer., 56:783-788.

Goff, Z. A., and S. Gratch. 1946. Low-pressure properties of water from −160 to 212°F. Trans. Amer. Soc. Heat. Vent. Engr., 52:95-122.

Grum, F., and G. W. Luckey. 1968. Practical sphere paint and a working standard of reflectance. Appl. Optics, 7:2289-2295.

Gutschick, V. P., M. H. Barron, D. A. Waechter, and M. A. Wolf. 1985. Portable monitor for solar radiation that accumulates irradiance histograms for 32 leaf-mounted sensors. Agric. For. Meteorol., 33:281-290.

Hammel, H. T. 1956. Infrared emissiveness of some arctic fauna. J. Mammal., 37:375-381.

Hammel, H. T., and J. D. Hardy. 1963. A gradient layer calorimeter for measurement of thermoregulatory responses in the dog. Pp. 31-42, *in* Temperature—its measurement and control in science and industry. Vol. III. (J. D. Hardy, ed.). Reinhold, New York, 683 pp.

Hatch, W. L. 1983. Selective guide to climatic data sources (Key to Meteorological Records Documentation No. 4.11). National Climatic Data Center, Asheville, N. C., 338 pp.

Hill, R. W., D. L. Beaver, and J. H. Veghte. 1980. Body surface temperatures and thermoregulation in the black-capped chickadee (*Parus atricapillus*). Physiol. Zool., 53:305-321.

Huband, N. D. S. 1985a. An infra-red radiometer for measuring surface temperature in the field. Part I. Design and construction. Agric. For. Meteorol., 34:215-226.

Huband, N. D. S. 1985b. An infra-red radiometer for measuring surface temperature in the field. Part II. Calibration and performance. Agric. For. Meteorol., 34:227-233.

Humphrey, S. R., and A. R. Richter, and J. B. Cope. 1977. Summer habitat and ecology of the endangered Indiana bat *Myotis sodalis*. J. Mammal., 58:334-346.

Hutchison, B. A., and D. R. Matt. 1977. The distribution of solar radiation within a deciduous forest. Ecol. Monogr., 47:185-207.

Idso, S. B. 1970. The relative sensitivities of polyethylene shielded net radiometers for short and long wave radiation. Rev. Sci. Inst., 41:939-943.

Idso, S. B. 1971a. A simple technique for the calibration of long-wave radiation probes. Agric. Meteorol., 8:235-243.

Idso, S. B. 1971b. Transformation of a net radiometer into a hemispherical radiometer. Agric. Meteorol., 9:109-121.

Idso, S. B. 1972a. Simplifications in the transformation of net radiometers into hemispherical radiometers. Agric. Meteorol., 10:473-476.

Idso, S. B. 1972b. Calibration of soil heat flux plates by a radiation technique. Agric. Meteorol., 10:467-471.

Kerslake, D. McK. 1972. The stress of hot environments. Cambridge University Press, London, 316 pp.

Kestin, J. 1966. The effect of free-stream turbulence on heat transfer rates. Pp. 1-32, *in* Advances in heat transfer, Vol. 3. (T. F. Irvine, Jr. and J. P. Hartnett, eds.). Academic Press, New York.

Kimball, B. A. 1983. Conduction transfer functions for predicting heat fluxes into various soils. Trans. Amer. Soc. Agric. Eng., 26:211-218.

Kluger, M. J., and J. E. Heath. 1970. Vasomotion in the bat wing: A thermoregulatory response to internal heating. Comp. Biochem. Physiol., 32:219-226.

Kowalski, G. J. 1978. An analytical and experimental investigation of the heat loss through animal fur. Unpubl. Ph.D. dissertation, University of Wisconsin, Madison, 294 pp.

Kreith, F. 1965. Principles of heat transfer, 2nd ed. International Textbook Co., Scranton, Pennsylvania, 620 pp.

Kunz, T. H. 1973. Population studies of the cave bat (*Myotis velifer*): Reproduction, growth, and development. Occas. Pap. Mus. Nat. Hist. Univ. Kansas, 15:1-43.

Kunz, T. H. 1974. Feeding ecology of a temperate insectivorous bat (*Myotis velifer*). Ecology, 55:693-711.

Kunz, T. H. 1980. Daily energy budgets of free-living bats. Pp. 369-392, *in* Proc. 5th Int. Bat Res. Conf. (D. E. Wilson and A. L. Gardner, eds.). Texas Tech Press, Lubbock, 434 pp.

Kunz, T. H. 1982. Roosting ecology of bats. Pp. 1-55, *in* Ecology of bats. (T. H. Kunz, ed.). Plenum Press, New York, 425 pp.

Lewis, D. A., and P. S. Nobel. 1977. Thermal energy exchange model and water loss of a barrel cactus, *Ferocactus acanthoides*. Plant Physiol., 60:609-616.

Licht, P., and P. Leitner. 1967. Behavioral responses to high temperature in three species of California bats. J. Mammal., 48:52-61.

Lillywhite, H. B., and P. F. A. Maderson. 1982. Skin structure and permeability. Pp. 397-442, *in* Biology of the Reptilia. Vol. 12. (C. Gans and F. H. Pough, eds.). Academic Press, New York, 536 pp.

Loehrke, R. I., and H. M. Nagib. 1976. Control of free-stream turbulence by means of honeycombs: A balance between suppression and generation. ASME J. Fluids Engr., 98:342-353.

Love, T. J. 1968. Radiative heat transfer. Merrill Publ. Company, Columbus, Ohio, 287 pp.

McCullough, E. C., and W. P. Porter. 1971. Computing clear day solar radiation spectra for the terrestrial ecological environment. Ecology, 52:1008-1015.

McNab, B. K. 1974. The behavior of temperate cave bats in a subtropical environment. Ecology, 55:943-958.

McNab, B. K. 1982. Evolutionary alternatives in the physiological ecology of bats. Pp. 151-200, *in* Ecology of bats. (T. H. Kunz, ed.). Plenum Press, New York, 425 pp.

Machin, J. 1970. The study of evaporation from small surfaces by the direct measurement of water vapour pressure gradients. J. Exp. Biol., 53:753-762.

Mautz, W. J. 1982. Patterns of evaporative water loss. Pp. 443-481, *in* Biology of the Reptilia. Vol. 12, Physiology C—Physiological Ecology. (C. Gans and F. H. Pough, eds.). Academic Press, New York, 536 pp.

Miller, J. A. 1976. A simple linearized hot-wire anemometer. ASME J. Fluids Engr., 98:749-752.

Minnich, J. E. 1982. The use of water. Pp. 325-395, *in* Biology of the Reptilia. Vol. 12, Physiology C—Physiological Ecology. (C. Gans and F. H. Pough, eds.). Academic Press, New York, 536 pp.

Mitchell, J. W. 1976. Heat transfer from spheres and other animal forms. Biophys. J., 16:561-569.

Moen, A. N. 1974. Turbulence and the visualization of wind flow. Ecology, 55:1420-1424.

Mogensen, V. O. 1970. The calibration factor of heat flux meters in relation to the thermal conductivity of the surrounding medium. Agric. Meteorol., 7:401-410.

Molnar, G. W., and J. C. Rosenbaum, Jr. 1963. Surface temperature measurement with thermocouples. Pp. 5-11, *in* Temperature—its measurement and control in science and industry. (J. D. Hardy, ed.). Reinhold, New York, 683 pp.

Monteith, J. L. 1973. Principles of environmental physics. American Elsevier, New York, 241 pp.

Morgan, V. T. 1975. The overall convective heat transfer from smooth circular cylinders. Pp. 199-264, *in* Advances in heat transfer. (T. F. Irvine, Jr. and J. P. Hartnett, eds.). Academic Press, New York.

Morhardt, S. S., and D. M. Gates. 1974. Energy exchange analysis of the Belding ground squirrel and its habitat. Ecol. Monogr., 44:17-44.

Munn, R. E. 1970. Biometeorological methods. Academic Press, New York, 336 pp.

National Climatic Data Center. 1978. SOLMET Volume 1—user's manual. Technical Document TD-9724. National Climatic Data Center, Asheville, North Carolina, 8 + appendices.

National Climatic Data Center. 1979. SOLMET Volume 2—final report. Technical Document TD-9724. National Climatic Data Center, Asheville, North Carolina, 165 pp.

Nagy, K. A. 1982. Field studies of water relations. Pp. 483-501, *in* Biology of the Reptilia. Vol. 12: Physiology C—Physiological Ecology. (C. Gans and F. H. Pough, eds.). Academic Press, New York, 536 pp.

Nobel, P. S. 1974. Boundary layers of air adjacent to cylinders. Plant Physiol., 54:177-181.

Ohata, C. A., and G. C. Whittow. 1974. Conductive heat loss to sand in California sea lions and a harbor seal. Comp. Biochem. Physiol., 47A:23-26.

Oke, T. R. 1978. Boundary layer climates. Methuen, London, 372 pp.

Pearman, G. I., H. L. Weaver, and C. B. Tanner. 1972. Boundary layer heat transport coefficients under field conditions. Agric. Meteorol., 10:83-92.

Pederson, R. J., and E. M. Sparrow. 1977. Heat transfer from a cylinder in crossflow situated in a turbulent pipe flow. ASME J. Heat Trans., 99:425-432.

Phillip, J. R. 1961. The theory of heat flux meters. J. Geophys. Res., 66:571-579.

Pinshow, B., M. H. Bernstein, G. E. Lopez, and S. Kleinhaus. 1982. Regulation of brain temperature in pigeons: Effects of corneal convection. Amer. J. Physiol., 242:R577-R581.

Porter, W. P., and D. M. Gates. 1969. Thermodynamic equilibria of animals with environment. Ecol. Monogr., 39:227-244.

Porter, W. P., J. W. Mitchell, W. A. Beckman, and C. B. DeWitt. 1973. Behavioral implications of mechanistic ecology. Oecologia, 13:1-54.

Prandtl, L., and O. G. Tietjens. 1934. Applied hydro- and aerodynamics. Reprinted 1957 by Dover, New York, 311 pp.

Rauch, J. C. 1973. Sequential changes in regional distribution of blood in *Eptesicus fuscus* (big brown bat) during arousal from hibernation. Can. J. Zool., 51:973-981.

Rauch, J. C., and J. S. Hayward. 1970. Regional distribution of blood flow in the bat (*Myotis lucifugus*) during arousal from hibernation. Can. J. Physiol. Pharmacol., 48:269-274.

Reifsnyder, W. E., G. M. Furnival, and J. L. Horowitz. 1971. Spatial and temporal distribution of solar radiation beneath forest canopies. Agric. Meteorol., 9:21-37.

Restrepo, G., M. D. Shanklin, and L. Hahn. 1977. Heat dissipation from growing pigs as a function of floor and ambient temperature. Trans. Amer. Soc. Agric. Eng., 20:145-147.

Roer, P., and M. Kjolsvik. 1973. Equipment for measuring low air velocity. Agric. Meteorol., 12:281-296.

Rollo, C. D., I. B. Vertinsky, W. G. Wellington, W. A. Thompson, and Y. Kwan. 1983. Description and testing of a comprehensive simulation model of the ecology of terrestrial gastropods in unstable environments. Pop. Ecol., 25:150-179.

Rose, C. W. 1966. Agricultural physics. Pergamon Press, London, 230 pp.

Scholander, P. F., R. Hock, V. Walters, F. Johnson, and L. Irving. 1950. Heat regulation in some arctic and tropical mammals and birds. Biol. Bull., 99:237-258.

Sellers, W. D. 1965. Physical climatology. University of Chicago Press, Chicago, 272 pp.

Simpson, R. L., K. W. Heizer, and R. E. Nasburg. 1979. Performance characteristics of a simple linearized hot-wire anemometer. ASME J. Fluids Engr., 101:381-382.

Sluiter, J. W., A. M. Voûte, and P. F. van Heerdt. 1973. Hibernation of *Nyctalus noctula*. Period. Biol., 75:181-188.

Spillman, C. K., and C. N. Hinkle. 1971. Conduction heat transfer from swine to controlled temperature floors. Trans. Amer. Soc. Agric. Eng., 14:301-303.

Stong, C. L. 1969. The amateur scientist. Sci. Amer., 221:128-132.

Suckling, P. W. 1982. An assessment of the adequacy of the solar radiation data network for the contiguous United States. Phys. Geogr., 3:49-57.

Suomi, V. E., and P. M. Kuhn. 1958. An economical net radiometer. Tellus, 10:160-163.

Swinbank, W. C. 1963. Longwave radiation from clear skies. Quart. J. Royal Meteorol. Soc., 89:339-348.

Tanner, C. B., J. A. Businger, and P. M. Kuhn. 1960. The economical net radiometer. J. Geophys. Res., 65:3657-3667.

Teel, P. D., and S. C. Fleetwood. 1982. An integrated sensing and data acquisition system designed for unattended continuous monitoring of microclimate relative humidity and its use to determine the influence of vapor pressure deficits on tick (Acari: Ixodoidea) activity. Agric. Meteorol., 27:145-154.

Thekaekara, M. P. 1975. Alternate methods in solarimetry: remote sensing and computer models. Presented at the Solarimetry Workshop, February 24-28, 1975, Brazilian National Academy of Sciences. Paper plus data tape. NSSDC 21A, National Space Science Data Center, Goddard Space flight Center, Greenbelt, Maryland.

Thorkelson, J., and R. K. Maxwell. 1974. Design and testing of a heat transfer model of a raccoon (*Procyon lotor*) in a closed tree den. Ecology, 55:29-39.

Tracy, C. R., K. A. Hammond, R. A. Lechleitner, W. J. Smith, II, D. B. Thompson, A. D. Whicker, and S. C. Williamson. 1983. Estimating clear-day solar radiation: An evaluation of three models. J. Thermal Biol., 8:247-251.

Tuttle, M. D., and D. E. Stevenson. 1978. Variation in the cave environment and its biological implications. Pp. 108-121, *in* Proc. Natl. Cave Manage. Symp. (R. Zuber, J. Chester, S. Gilbert, and D. Rhodes, eds.). Adobe Press, Albuquerque, New Mexico, 140 pp.

Twente, J. R., Jr. 1955. Some aspects of habitat selection and other behavior of cavern dwelling bats. Ecology, 36:706-732.

Unwin, D. M. 1980. Microclimate measurement for ecologists. Academic Press, New York, 97 pp.

Van Den Akker, J. A., L. R. Dearth, and W. M. Shillcox. 1966. Evaluation of absolute reflectance for standardization purposes. J. Optical Soc. Amer., 56:250-252.

Vaughan, T. A., and T. J. O'Shea. 1976. Roosting ecology of the pallid bat, *Antrozous pallidus*. J. Mammal., 57:19-42.

Vogel, S. 1981. Life in moving fluids: The physical biology of flow. Princeton University Press, Princeton, New Jersey, 352 pp.

Voûte, A. M. 1972. Bijdrage tot de Oecologia van de Meervleermuis, *Myotis dasycneme* (Boie, 1825). Unpubl. doctoral dissertation, Universiteit Utrecht, Utrecht, 159 pp.

Walsberg, G. E., G. S. Campbell, and J. R. King. 1978. Animal coat color and radiative heat gain: A re-evaluation. J. Comp. Physiol., 126:211-222.

Weathers, W. W., W. A. Buttemer, A. M. Hayworth, and K. A. Nagy. 1984. An evaluation of time-budget estimates of daily energy expenditure in birds. Auk, 101:459-472.

Webb, D. R., and J. R. King. 1984. Effects of wetting on insulation of bird and mammal coats. J. Thermal Biol., 9:189-191.

Webb, D. R., and R. R. Schnabel. 1983. Functions of fat in hibernators: Thermal aspects. J. Thermal Biol., 8:369-374.

Webster, M. D., G. S. Campbell, and J. R. King. 1985. Cutaneous resistance to water-vapor diffusion in pigeons and the role of the plumage. Physiol. Zool., 58:58-70.

Weiss, A., and J. M. Norman. 1985. Partitioning solar radiation into direct and diffuse, visible and near-infrared components. Agric. For. Meteorol., 34:205-213.

Welch, W. R. 1980. Evaporative water loss from endotherms in thermally and hygrically complex environments: An empirical approach for interspecific comparisons. J. Comp. Physiol. B, 139:135-143.

Welch, W. R. 1984. Temperature and humidity of expired air: Interspecific comparisons and significance for loss of respiratory heat and water from endotherms. Physiol. Zool., 57:366-375.

World Meteorological Organization. 1971. Guide to meteorological instruments and observing practices, 4th edn. WMO, Geneva (loose leaf ca. 200 pp.).

World Meteorological Organization. 1981. Meteorological aspects of the utilization of solar radiation as an energy source. WMO Technical Note No. 172; WMO Publication No. 557. WMO, Geneva, Switzerland, 298 pp.

Appendix 1.   Mathematical Symbols and Units

Symbol	Definition	Units
A	Area through which heat flows	m^2
A_e	Effective radiation area	m^2
A_s	Area normal to the solar beam	m^2
a	Effective absorptance relative to a specific source	dimensionless
a_s	Average solar absorptance of the outer surface	dimensionless
$a(\lambda)$	Spectral absorptance of the outer surface	dimensionless
C	Heat capacitance of the body	$J\,°C^{-1}animal^{-1}$
c	Specific heat of a solid	$J\,°C^{-1}kg^{-1}$
c_p	Specific heat of air	$J\,°C^{-1}kg^{-1}$
D	Characteristic dimension of the animal for convection	m
d	Derivative operator	
E	Effective whole-animal evaporation rate	$kg\,s^{-1}animal^{-1}$
E_b	Evaporation from respiratory surfaces	$kg\,s^{-1}animal^{-1}$
E_s	Evaporation from skin surfaces	$kg\,s^{-1}animal^{-1}$
E_f	Evaporation from outer surface of fur	$kg\,s^{-1}animal^{-1}$
$E(\lambda)$	Spectral irradiance	$W\,u^{-1}m^{-2}$
G	Global (direct + scattered solar) irradiance	W/m^2
H	Convective heat conductance	$W\,animal^{-1}°C^{-1}$
H_m	Convective water vapor conductance	m/sec
I_s	Thermal irradiance from sky	W/m^2
I_g	Thermal irradiance from ground	W/m^2
i	Subscript denoting a surface area element in a two-dimensional calculation	
K	Thermal conductance (general)	$W\,°C^{-1}animal^{-1}$
K_e	Overall thermal conductance	$W\,°C^{-1}animal^{-1}$
K_{es}	Overall thermal conductance under standard conditions	$W\,°C^{-1}animal^{-1}$
K_f	Thermal conductance of fur layer	$W\,°C^{-1}animal^{-1}$
K_s	Thermal conductance of skin + fat layers	$W\,°C^{-1}animal^{-1}$
K_{sf}	Thermal conductance of skin + fat + fur layers	$W\,°C^{-1}animal^{-1}$
k	Thermal conductance of solid material	$W\,°C^{-1}\,m^{-1}$
M	Metabolic rate	$W/animal$
m	Subscript denoting a parameter of a taxidermic mount	
N	Net thermal + solar irradiance	W/m^2
N'	Net thermal irradiance	W/m^2
n	Number of surface elements used in a two-dimensional calculation	

Symbol	Definition	Units
p	Projected hair area index of fur	dimensionless
$Q_{a,\,eff}$	Effective solar irradiance, including fur structure effects	W/m^2
q	Heat flux per unit area	W/m^2
R	Linearized thermal radiation conductance	$W\,°C^{-1}animal^{-1}$
R_h	Total hemispherical irradiance	W/m^2
r	Transport resistance (section 2.1.1 only)	sec/m
r	Reflected solar irradiance (elsewhere)	W/m^2
S	Direct solar irradiance on a plane normal to the solar beam	W/m^2
s	Scattered solar irradiance on a horizontal surface	W/m^2
T	Temperature (general)	°C
T_a	Air temperature	°C
T_b	Body core temperature	°C
T_d	Lower dome temperature of modified net radiometer	°C
T_e	Operative temperature	°C
T_{es}	Standard operative temperature	°C
T_g	Ground or vegetation temperature	°C
T_s	Skin temperature	°C
T_f	Fur surface temperature	°C
t	Time	sec
u	Wind velocity	m/sec
x	Thickness	m
$\triangle$	Finite difference operator	
$\triangle T_{ri}$	Increase in T_e above T_a due to radiation	°C
$\triangle T_p$	Difference between T_b and T_e due to metabolism and evaporation	°C
ε	Thermal emittance (ca. 0.95)	dimensionless
λ	Latent heat of vaporization of water (humidity context)	J/kg
λ	Wavelength of light (radiation context)	m
ρ	Density of roosting surface (section 6.3.2 only)	kg/m^3
ρ	Density of air	kg/m^3
ρ_s	Partial density of water vapor in saturated air	kg/m^3
ρ_a	Partial density of water vapor in ambient air	kg/m^3
σ	Stefan-Boltzmann constant, 5.67×10^{-8}	$W\,m^{-2}K^{-4}$
θ_z	Zenith angle of sun	radians

Appendix 2. U. S. Suppliers of Instruments for Microclimate and Heat Transfer Studies

Legend. The suppliers are listed alphabetically. The instrument classification codes are arranged in columns for easy identification of suppliers of a given class of instrument. The codes are: IR = non-contact infrared thermometers; Tcw = thermocouple wire; Tc = thermocouple thermometers; Tm = thermistor thermometers; Tg = mechanical thermographs; SR = solar radiation sensors; NR = net radiation sensors; TR = total radiation sensors; ThR = thermal radiation sensors; Ad = dynamic anemometer; Ath = thermal anemometers; HF = heat flow plates; Hg = mechanical hygrograph; DPH = chilled-mirror dewpoint hygrometers; EH = electronic hygrometers using other sensors; Ps = wet and dry bulb psychrometers; DDL = digital data loggers with thermocouple capability.

	IR	Tcw	Tc	Tm	Tg	SR	NR	TR	ThR	Ad	Ath	HF	Hg	DPH	EH	Ps	DDL	
Abbeon Cal 123 Gray Ave. Santa Barbara, CA 93101	IR	Tcw	Tc	Tm	Tg					Ad	Ath	HF	Hg		EH	Ps		
Alnor Instrument 7301 N. Caldwell Niles, IL 60648											Ath							
Atkins Technical 3314 SW 40 Blvd. Gainesville, FL 32608				Tm											EH	Ps		
Bacharach Instrument 301 Alpha Dr. Pittsburgh, PA 15238																Ps		
Bellfort Instrument Co. 727 S. Wolfe Rd. Baltimore, MD 21231					Tg					Ad			Hg		EH	Ps		
Barnes Engineering 44 Commerce Rd. Stamford, CT 06904	IR																	Includes imaging types
Ben Meadows Co. P.O. Box 80549 Atlanta, GA 30366				Tm	Tg					Ad			Hg			Ps		
Bruel & Kjaer Instruments 185 Forest St. Marlborough, MA 01752																		Human T_e and T_{es} meters

	IR	Tcw	Tc	Tm	Tg	SR	NR	TR	ThR	Ad	Ath	HF	Hg	DPH	EH	Ps	DDL	
C & M Meteorological Supply Box 5723 Riverside, CA 92517																		Livingston atmometers
Campbell Scientific, Inc P.O. Box 551 Logan, UT 84321						SR				Ad							DDL	Portable data loggers for microclimate data
Climatronics 140 Wilbur Pl. Bohemia, NY 11716						SR	NR			Ad			Hg		EH		DDL	
Cole-Parmer Instrument 7425 N. Oak Park Ave. Chicago, IL 60648	IR		Tc	Tm	Tg	SR	NR			Ad	Ath		Hg	DPH	EH	Ps	DDL	
Crodata Corporation 255 Bear Hill Road Waltham MA 02154																	DDL	Data logger for field use
DISA Elec. 779 Susquehanna Ave. Franklin Lakes, NJ 07417											Ath							
Dwyer Instrument Co. P.O. Box 373 Michigan City, IN 46360										Ad								Also Pitot tube and electronic hook gauge
EG&G Envir. Equipment 151 Bear Hill Rd. Waltham, MA 02154														DPH				
Epic 150 Nassau St. New York, NY 10038					Tg	SR	NR			Ad			Hg			Ps		
Eppley Laboratory 12 Sheffield Ave. Newport, RI 02840						SR		TR	ThR									
Extech International 114 State St. Boston, MA 02109	IR	Tcw	Tc	Tm	Tg						Ath		Hg		EH	Ps		

	IR	Tcw	Tc	Tm	Tg	SR	NR	TR	ThR	Ad	Ath	HF	Hg	DPH	EH	Ps	DDL	
John Fluke Box C9090 Everett, WA 98206																	DDL	
Fisher Scientific Co., Allied Corp. 711 Forbes Avenue Pittsburgh, PA 15219					Tg										EH	Ps		
General Eastern 50 Hunt St. Watertown, MA 02172														DPH	EH	Ps		
Honeywell 1100 Virginia Dr. Fort Washington, PA 19034																	DDL	
IMC Instruments 6659 N. Sidney Pl. Glendale, WI 53209				Tm														
Inframetrics 25 Wiggins Ave. Bedford, MA 01730	IR																	Field portable imaging in standard TV format
Interactive Microware Inc. P.O. Box 139 State College, PA 16804																	DDL	Uses Apple II computer
Kahl Scientific Instrument Box 1166 El Cajon, CA 92022					Tg	SR	NR	TR	ThR	Ad		HF	Hg			Ps	DDL	
Kahn & Co., Inc. 885 Wells Rd. Weathersfield, CT 06109														DPH	EH			
Kipp & Zonen Div. Einraf-Norius Co. 390 Central Ave. Bohemia, NY 11716						SR												

	IR	Tcw	Tc	Tm	Tg	SR	NR	TR	ThR	Ad	Ath	HF	Hg	DPH	EH	Ps	DDL	
Li-Cor Box 4425 Lincoln, NE 68504																		
Markson Science 7815 S. 46 St. Phoenix, AZ 85040	IR		Tc	Tm	Tg	SR							Hg		EH	Ps	DDL	
Matrix 537 S. 31 St. Mesa, AZ 85204						SR												
Meriam Instrument 10920 Madison Ave. Cleveland, OH 44102										Ad								Pitot tube
Omega Engineering Box 4047 Stamford, CT 06907	IR	Tcw	Tc	Tm	Tg										EH			
Omnidata International Box 3489 Logan, UT 84321				Tm		SR				Ad					EH		DDL	Data logger for field use
Phys-Chemical Research 36 W 20 St. New York, NY 10011															EH			
RdF Corporation 23 Elm Avenue Hudson, NH 03051												HF						
Sargent-Welch 7300 N. Linder Ave. Skokie, IL 60077					Tg					Ad						Ps		
Science Associates 230 Nassau St. Princeton, NJ 08540				Tm	Tg					Ad			Hg	DPH	EH	Ps		
ScienceMart Box 8149 La Jolla, CA 92038				Tm	Tg								Hg					

	IR	Tcw	Tc	Tm	Tg	SR	NR	TR	ThR	Ad	Ath	HF	Hg	DPH	EH	Ps	DDL	
Solomat 65 Rowayton Ave. Rowayton, CT 06853				Tm							Ath				EH			
Teledyne Hastings-Raydist Box 1275 Hampton, VA 23661											Ath							
Thermo-Electric Saddle Brook, NJ 07662		Tcw	Tc															
Thunder Scientific 623 Wyoming SE Albuquerque NM 87123														DPH	EH			
C.W. Thornthwaite Associates Route 1, Centerton Elmer, NJ 08318						SR	NR			Ad		HF						
TSI Box 43394 St. Paul, MN 55164											Ath							Includes field and high-precision lab instruments
Wescor 459 S. Main St. Logan, UT 84321			Tc	Tm											EH			
Westberg Mfg. 3400 Westach Way Sonoma, CA 95476										Ad								
Robert E. White Instruments 64 Commercial Wharf Boston, MA 02110					Tg					Ad						Ps		
Yellow Springs Instrument Box 279 Yellow Springs, OH 45387				Tm				TR							EH			
R.M. Young Co. 2801 Aero-Park Dr. Traverse City, MI 49684										Ad								Sensitive cup and propeller types for micrometeorology

Chapter 20

Design and Interpretation of Laboratory Thermoregulation Studies

Allen Kurta and Marty S. Fujita[1]

Department of Biology
Boston University
Boston, Massachusetts 02215 USA

1. INTRODUCTION

Energy is a central theme in much of the ecological and evolutionary literature. From the trophic-dynamic approach of Lindeman (1942) and Slobodkin (1960) through today's emphasis on optimality (Pyke et al., 1977; Townsend and Hughes, 1981) and reproductive effort (Millar, 1977; Ricklefs, 1977; Stearns, 1980), measurements of energy intake, output, and transfer have been essential to testing relevant hypotheses. There is a growing trend in ecology to estimate daily and seasonal energy budgets and, more importantly, to decide how different organisms successfully partition their available energy (Gessaman, 1973; King, 1974; Calow, 1977). Bat biologists are no exception (Kunz, 1980). The Chiroptera, with its large number of species and diverse habits and habitats, will undoubtedly play a critical role in future studies of mammalian energy partitioning.

An important component of any mammalian energy budget is thermoregulation. The cost of maintaining a high body temperature (T_b) at ambient temperatures (T_a) below the thermoneutral zone can be extremely large (Studier, 1981; Robinson et al., 1983). This is true for small animals in general, with their relatively great surface-to-volume ratio, and for bats in particular, with their large and usually uninsulated flight membranes. Although early workers described bats as poikilothermic (Hock, 1951; Hanuš, 1959a) or hemipoikilothermic (Cowles, 1947; Reeder and Cowles, 1951; Bradley and O'Farrell, 1969), more recent studies indicate that many bats are capable of maintaining large T_b to T_a differentials within their own range of ecologically relevant T_a's. A realistic energy budget for any chiropteran must con-

---

[1]Present Address: Museum of Comparative Zoology, Harvard University, Cambridge, Massachusetts 02138 USA

sider the level, duration, and frequency of high T_b.

The purpose of this chapter is threefold:

1) To briefly describe techniques used in bat thermoregulation studies and to provide more detailed references.
2) To point out the drawbacks and benefits of various approaches. This will hopefully allow for realistic interpretation of previous work as well as aid in designing future studies from an ecological perspective.
3) To indirectly point out many relatively new published works on chiropteran thermoregulation. The thorough reviews by Davis (1970), Henshaw (1970), and Lyman (1970) contain no references later than 1968. The paper by McManus (1977) was restricted to the phyllostomids with the latest citation being 1972.

2. TEMPERATURE SENSORS

2.1. Thermocouples

A thermocouple (TC) consists of two wires made of dissimilar metals and joined at both ends to form a complete circuit. Heating one of the junctions generates an electromotive force (EMF) within the circuit. The EMF is proportional to the temperature difference between the two points where the wires are joined. If the temperature of one of the junctions, the "reference junction," is known, the temperature of the other, the "measuring junction," may be determined by placing a potentiometer within the circuit and measuring the EMF. For a detailed discussion, consult American Society for Testing and Materials (ASTM, 1970) or Benedict (1977).

Thermocouples are classified by the types of metal which compose the measuring junction. Type T thermocouples (copper and constantan) are most frequently used in thermoregulation studies, although Type J (iron and constantan) is occasionally employed (e.g., Morrison, 1959). With proper measuring devices, both types are sensitive to ± 0.1°C. However, type J thermocouples are more brittle and susceptible to oxidation, and therefore are not suitable for T_b studies requiring chronic implantation.

The measuring junction of a thermocouple is made by twisting the uninsulated ends of two dissimilar wires and soldering or welding the twists together, or by butt-welding the two ends (ASTM, 1970; Platt and Griffiths, 1964). To obtain T_b's that most closely approximate a "point" measurement, the length of wire over which the twists occur must be minimized. Three to four twists, leaving a small exposed tip of no more than 2 to 5 mm is sufficient. To avoid injury to the animal and to shield the sensor from moisture, the measuring junction may be dipped in quick-drying epoxy glue to form a smooth tip (L. C. H. Wang, pers. comm.). The insulated wire leads extending from the thermocouple junction may then be threaded through a narrow diameter piece of polyethylene tubing which adds rigidity and facilitates rectal T_b measurements (e.g., Bartholomew et al., 1964, 1970). Enclosing the wires also reduces the possibility of moisture penetrating to the wires and affecting the EMF (galvanic error; see Platt and Griffiths, 1964). Insertion length can be marked on the tubing to ensure that repeated measurements are taken at the same depth.

Instruments designed for use with TC's automatically measure the circuit EMF and convert this to a temperature estimate of the measuring junction. The reference junction theoretically must be at a known temperature. In the past, this was often accomplished by immersing the reference junction in an ice bath. If reference junction temperature is not fixed, the circuit EMF will change and the indicated temperature for the measuring junction will be incorrect. Most modern instruments electronically compensate for a variable reference junction temperature; however, rapid fluctuations in T_a near the indicating unit can lead to spurious results since all parts of the circuitry may not be at exactly the same temperature. This is particularly true for large, recording potentiometers designed for laboratory use. Careful investigators point out whether their recorders were kept in temperature-controlled areas (e.g., Hill, 1972) or frankly admit the potential inaccuracies (e.g., Lindstedt, 1980). Newly designed, smaller, portable instruments are apparently less susceptible to this type of error (e.g., Bailey Instruments, BAT-12; or the low cost thermocouple amplifier of Analog Devices, AD595). Other potential errors associated with TC use are discussed in Platt and Griffiths (1964), ASTM (1970), Benedict (1977), and Omega Engineering, Inc. (1983).

2.2. Thermistors

A thermistor (TM) is a temperature-sensitive resistor composed of semiconductor material (Benedict, 1977; Bloor and Lee, 1982). An increase in temperature results in a proportional decrease in the resistance of the thermistor. An external power source passes a current through the thermistor and the resulting voltage is measured and transformed into a temperature reading. In general, TM's are more sensitive than TC's, i.e., a given change in temperature will result in extremely large changes in TM resistance but relatively small changes in TC EMF. The increased sensitivity of TM's and the absence of a reference junction have, in general, allowed for the construction of smaller and more rugged indicating units for use with TM's (Platt and Griffiths, 1964). This is one reason why, in the past, TC's were relegated to the laboratory and only TM's were used in the field.

Today both TC's and TM's have fast response times and can be used in the laboratory or the field with recording or non-recording units capable of accepting single or multiple inputs. Accuracy to within ± 0.1°C is possible with either sensor; however, thermistor sensors are more difficult to construct (Swift, 1979, 1981), more susceptible to mechanical damage, and generally more expensive to replace than homemade TC's. A wide range of commercially supplied sensors of either type are available for specific uses such as measuring surface temperatures or

tissue temperatures (see Chapter 19). Choice of sensor and indicating unit is most likely to be based on cost and the exact needs of the investigator.

2.3. Radiotransmitters

The field of biotelemetry has grown tremendously in recent years (see also Chapters 4 and 7). Techniques currently exist for remote monitoring of various physiological parameters such as blood pressure, heart rate, pH, and T_b. The most complete and readable introduction to the subject is still the book by Mackay (1970; see also Caceres, 1965; Fryer and Sandler, 1974; Ysenbrandt et al., 1976; Fryer et al., 1976; Amlaner and MacDonald, 1980; Fryer, 1981). The T_b of a wide variety of mammals has been successfully monitored using telemetry (Baldwin, 1973; Wang, 1978; Gessaman, 1980; Andrews, 1981; Chappell and Bartholomew, 1981; Vogt and Lynch, 1982; Müller et al., 1983) including two studies on bats (Weigold, 1973; Noll, 1979a.).

In simplest form, telemetric units consist of a thermistor, an oscillating circuit, a transmitting antenna, and a battery. The oscillator causes the unit to be constantly turned on and off; the frequency of oscillation is determined by the temperature of the thermistor. The unit emits radio waves which are detected by a nearby receiver and are heard as a series of clicking sounds. The rate of clicking is proportional to the temperature of the thermistor. Click frequency may be timed with a stopwatch or by automatic methods; an observer can time the clicks as they occur, or the sounds may be recorded for future analysis (Wang, 1972, 1973; Adams et al., 1973; Langman, 1973; Pivorun, 1976; Jacobsen and Stuart, 1982; Müller et al., 1983). Battery life varies from a few days to a few months or more depending on circuit design and temperature (Ko, 1980). Minimum mass of present day transmitters ranges from 0.75 g (Reinertsen, 1982) to about 1.2 g (Andrews, 1978; Paladino and King, 1984) with a precision of about 0.1°C.

Temperature-sensitive radiotransmitters are commercially available or can be made in the laboratory using published schematic diagrams (Mackay, 1970; Langman, 1973; Southwick, 1973; Pivorun, 1976; Lund et al., 1980; Riley et al., 1980). Since the electronics are moisture-sensitive, the units are "potted," or waterproofed, before implanting in a test animal. Potting material is chosen for its waterproofing ability, non-toxicity to tissue, and if appropriate, plasticity over a wide range of temperatures. Numerous potting substances exist (Mackay, 1965, 1970; Fryer, 1981; Reinertsen, 1982), but many investigators use paraffin in combination with beeswax or a synthetic rubber or vinyl compound (e.g., Pivorun, 1976; Riley et al., 1980; H. R. Smith, 1980). After potting, a calibration curve is established by placing the transmitter in different water baths of known temperature and counting the resulting clicks. The unit is then sterilized and implanted (for a concise, yet detailed example, see H. R. Smith, 1980).

Biotelemetric techniques have been developed to a point where thermoregulation studies using implanted thermocouples are almost entirely outmoded (see discussion in Boyd and Sladen, 1971). The use of transmitters totally avoids the problem of entangling wires and irritating metal leads that protrude through the animal's skin. The main drawback to this new technique is transmission range. In general, transmission distance is inversely proportional to the size of the telemeter (Fryer, 1980; E. N. Smith, 1980). With small units ($<$ 2 g), transmission distance is about 1.0 m. This does not present a problem with confined animals and the effective range may be increased somewhat through the use of multiple receiving antennae (e.g., Bartholomew and Rainy, 1971; Saint Girons and Bradshaw, 1981; see also Amlaner, 1980). Larger units ($>$ 12 g), with a greater transmission range ($>$ 25 m), have been used on medium-sized, free-ranging mammals (Wang, 1978; Gessaman, 1980; Lund et al., 1980; Chappell and Bartholomew, 1981). Colonial bats, with their strong attachment to the home roost, may be ideal subjects in which to

combine small telemetry units with field studies.

2.4. Mercury Thermometers

Thermometers generally consist of a reservoir of mercury in a bulb and a capillary tube within a glass stem. Thermal expansion of mercury in the bulb forces the fluid up the capillary tube and temperature is read off the marked stem. Thermometers are available with 0.1°C gradations. For use in thermoregulation studies, "quick-registering" or "rapid-reading" thermometers are desirable. These thermometers contain only a small amount of mercury in the reservoir and the bulb is cylindrical rather than spherical. The cylindrical shape provides a larger surface area for heat transfer from the animal to the mercury, thus resulting in a rapid response. Advantages of mercury thermometers over TC's, TM's, and their indicating units are that thermometers are smaller, cheaper, immune to moisture damage and electrical interference, do not need a power source, and are readily understood and used by the novice. Disadvantages of thermometers include the lack of recording capability, generally slower response time, and ease of breakage; and they are obviously inappropriate for studies requiring remote monitoring.

3. METHODOLOGICAL CONSIDERATIONS

3.1. Site of Measurement

Body temperatures can be measured by 1) surgically implanted devices, by 2) touching the surface of the animal, or by 3) inserting an instrument into natural body openings. Both thermocouples (e.g., Stones and Wiebers, 1965; Leitner, 1966), and temperature-sensitive radiotransmitters (Noll, 1979a) have been surgically implanted. If a device is implanted, an important question is how long to wait after surgery before using the animal in experiments. Leitner (1966) tested *Eu-*

mops perotis only one hour after recovery from anesthesia (see also Licht and Leitner, 1967; Heldmaier, 1970). In contrast, Stones and Wiebers (1965, 1967) waited a minimum of three days before testing *Myotis lucifugus*. Although immediate testing minimizes acclimation and captivity effects (see below), it ignores the possibility of inflammatory reactions and physical irritation due to non-habituation to the sensor. The investigator must decide which drawback is the most serious.

In many cases surface temperature is recorded instead of core T_b. This is accomplished by cementing a sensor to the subject's body (Weigold, 1973; Riedesel and Williams, 1976), by simply touching an individual with the sensor (Kulzer, 1965; Cena and Wołoszyn, 1966; Weigold, 1973; Funakoshi and Uchida, 1978; Noll, 1979b; Kulzer and Storf, 1980), or by constructing a cage in such a way that a bat consistently rests on a sensor (Sluiter et al., 1973). Body temperatures have also been estimated by inserting a probe into a cluster of bats (Twente, 1955; Hall, 1962; Herreid, 1963a; Vaughan and O'Shea, 1976).

Unfortunately it is difficult to translate a surface or cluster temperature into an estimate of core temperature. Morhardt (1975) showed that in small rodents surface temperature is generally below rectal T_b. Vaughan and O'Shea (1976) assumed that cluster temperature approximated rectal T_b in *Antrozous pallidus*. Cluster temperature of non-torpid *M. lucifugus* is usually about 4 to 5 degrees lower than rectally measured T_b (Kurta, 1986a; see also Brenner, 1974). In contrast, Herreid (1963a) found that cluster temperature varied with depth in the cluster and that it was possible for core T_b to be lower than cluster temperature in *Tadarida brasiliensis*. In addition, the site of the surface measurement is important. For example, Cena and Wołoszyn (1966) showed that surface temperature of the chest area exceeded that of the carpus by 2.1°C in *Myotis dascyneme* and by 3.0°C in *Barbastellus barbastellus* (see also Kürten and Schmidt, 1982). The relationship between core temperature and surface temperature must be independently determined (e.g., Kulzer, 1963; Kurta et al., 1987).

Core T_b is often measured esophageally in neonatal rodents (e.g., Casey, 1981) and occasionally in small adult bats (Reeder, 1949; Hartung, 1981). Hughes (1968) took vaginal measurements of T_b in *Plecotus townsendii*. Most commonly, however, bat biologists have reported rectal measurements of T_b. Depending on the depth of insertion, many of these reported "rectal" T_b's are actually colonic T_b's. Temperature sensors are often coated with a lubricant, such as petroleum jelly or glycerine (McManus and Nellis, 1972), to facilitate penetration.

Although rectal temperatures are easily obtained, they may not always be comparable between studies. Lomax (1966) showed that the depth to which a sensor is introduced can lead to significant differences in reported T_b of small mammals. Table 1 lists a number of bat thermoregulation studies to illustrate the variety of depths used in these mammals. Note, for example, that Carpenter and Graham (1967), working with the 22-g *Leptonycteris sanborni*, inserted their sensor 25 mm, while Janský and Hájek (1961), using the 22-g *Myotis myotis*, inserted theirs only 10 mm. O'Farrell and Bradley (1977) inserted a quick-registering mercury thermometer 8 mm into a number of species ranging in size from the 4-g *Pipistrellus hesperus* to the 25-g *A. pallidus*. Clearly, size of the bat and insertion depth are factors to consider when making interspecific comparisons or comparisons between different reports.

Besides depth, the type of sensor may also affect the actual rectal T_b obtained. A well-made thermocouple with the two metals fused only at their ends (i.e., butt-welded) may yield a slightly different reading from one in which the wires are twisted together for 5 mm or more. Twisting results in continual contact between the two metals and gives an "average" temperature over a 5 mm span of the rectum rather than a "point" measurement. A similar problem results from using mercury thermometers. In general, only the

Table 1. Body mass and insertion depth of rectal temperature sensors.

Species	Mass (g)	Depth (mm)	Sensor Type[1]	Reference
Pteropus poliocephalus	550–1100	≥50	TC	Bartholomew et al., 1964
Pteropus scapulatus	330–550	≥50	TC	Bartholomew et al., 1964
Macroderma gigas	150	≥30	TC	Leitner and Nelson, 1966
Rousettus aegyptiacus	146	21	TM	Noll, 1979a
Dobsonia minor	87	25	TC	Bartholomew et al., 1970
Eumops perotis	50–65	30	TC	Leitner, 1966
Antrozous pallidus	20–31[2]	8	Hg	O'Farrell and Bradley, 1977
Leptonycteris sanborni	22	25	TC	Carpenter and Graham, 1967
Myotis myotis	22	10	TC	Janský and Hajek, 1961
Paranyctimene raptor	21	25	TC	Bartholomew et al., 1970
Tadarida brasiliensis	13–16	15	TM	Pagels, 1972
Tadarida brasiliensis	9–12[3]	20	TM	Herreid, 1967
Glossophaga soricina	9–12	15	TC	Rasweiler, 1973
Myotis lucifugus	7–10	10–12	TC	Reite and Davis, 1966
Myotis lucifugus	7–10[4]	20	TM	Studier and O'Farrell, 1972
Pipistrellus hesperus	4–8	8	Hg	Bradley and O'Farrell, 1969

[1] TC=Thermocouple; TM=Thermistor; Hg=Mercury.
[2] Trune and Slobodchikoff, 1976.
[3] Herreid, 1963c.
[4] Reite and Davis, 1966.

mercury reservoir, approximately 8 mm in length, is inserted into the rectum. This does not give a point estimate of T_b 8 mm within the body, but instead yields an average T_b of the surrounding tissue from the anal sphincter to the tip of the mercury reservoir.

3.2. Continuous Measurements and Restraints

Devices implanted in the animal or attached to the surface are often preferred because they allow for continuous, remote monitoring of T_b. In addition to T_b, metabolic rate (MR) or other physiological parameters can be simultaneously measured. Continuous recordings of T_b have also been made using rectally positioned thermocouples or thermistors; however, these probes must be maintained in the same position throughout an experiment. This is accomplished by clipping the wires to the animal's fur (Bartholomew et al., 1964), taping them to the interfemoral membrane (Herreid and Schmidt-Nielsen, 1966; Davis and Reite, 1967; Studier and Wilson, 1970), cementing them to hairs around the anus

(Bradley and O'Farrell, 1969), or by other more sophisticated means (Henshaw and Folk, 1966). Unfortunately the attached sensors often "tend to irritate the bats excessively" (Licht and Leitner, 1967) with the result that the probes are pulled out or chewed off.

To prevent disturbance of the probes many investigators resort to the use of restraints. Types of restraints include nets (Hanuš, 1959a; Mejsnar and Janský, 1967), screens (Kluger and Heath, 1970), plastic holders (Studier and O'Farrell, 1972), cloth (Noll, 1979a), wire cages (Herreid and Schmidt-Neilsen, 1966; Hurst, 1966), and more elaborate devices (Chew and White, 1960; Menaker, 1961). Unfortunately restraints can affect T_b and MR by inducing the animal to struggle. Although measurements taken during obvious periods of unrest are generally discarded, it is often difficult to determine whether the eventual "steady state" is that of rest or of exhaustion. Many studies compound this problem by the use of EKG leads that are clipped to or hooked through the subject's skin.

An additional question raised by the use of restraints is if and how such devices affect the thermal conductance, and therefore the heat loss characteristics, of the test animal. Some restraints may actually act as extra insulation, while others may increase heat loss by disrupting the integrity of the pelage or by compressing it (see Davis and Birkebak, 1975). If laboratory data are used to estimate energy budgets of free-ranging individuals, potential effects of restraining devices must be considered. Bat biologists rarely compare energetic parameters of restrained versus unrestrained animals (for an exception, see Lyman and Wimsatt, 1966).

3.3. Noncontinuous Measurements

In studies concerned strictly with T_b, biologists often make rectal measurements at one time during the day (Stones and Wiebers, 1967) or take a series of recordings on the same animal at pre-determined time intervals (Bartholomew et al., 1970; Pagels, 1975; Howell, 1976; Trune and Slobodchikoff, 1976). This experimental design obviously requires handling the animal while the sensor is inserted. Heat flow to or from the investigator's hands may interfere with accurate T_b measurements because of the high thermal conductance of bats (Bradley and Deavers, 1980) and the low heat capacity of the smaller species. Gloves are often worn to reduce the possibility of heat transfer (Menaker, 1962; Hughes, 1968; Wolverton and Edgar, 1969; Rausch, 1973).

In noncontinuous experiments, the investigator generally makes successive measurements on a series of subjects (Herreid, 1967; Wolverton and Edgar, 1969; Pagels, 1972, 1975; Rasweiler, 1973; Howell, 1976). Unfortunately the order of measurement may affect the final T_b reading. One of us (Kurta, 1986b; unpubl. data) conducted a study in which individually caged *M. lucifugus* were placed in an incubator at 0600 h at a starting T_a of 12°C. Ambient temperature was slowly raised to 32°C by 1330 h, and rectal T_b was finally taken at 1600 h. Body temperature was correlated with the order of measurement (Figure 1). A significant correlation was less obvious at lower test temperatures but was detectable through the use of multivariate statistical techniques. Presumably the disturbance involved in taking cages out of the incubator excited the remaining bats, resulting in a higher T_b. This methodological error probably cannot be eliminated if multiple subjects are used; however, its effect can be statistically minimized by proper randomization of the order among treatments and/or by the use of covariance procedures (Kleinbaum and Kupper, 1978).

3.4. Nutritional State

Proper nutrition is essential if a normal thermoregulatory or metabolic response is expected (Stones and Wiebers, 1966). Much of the variation in bat thermoregulatory patterns may be explained by inadequate energy intake or improper diet. Racey and Swift (1981) demonstrated that captive, well-fed *P. pipistrellus* maintain high T_b, while those deprived of food for only 24 h become torpid. Besides the insectivorous *P. pipistrellus,* similar data exist for the frugivorous *Carollia perspicillata* (Arata and Jones, 1967; see also Arata, 1972), nectarivorous *Glossophaga soricina* (Rasweiler, 1973), and the sanguinivorous *Desmodus rotundus* (McNab, 1973). Large species, with their greater capacity for fat storage (Calder, 1974; Peters, 1983), may not be as easily affected. Leitner and Nelson (1967), for example, were unable to obtain a lowered T_b in the 150-g *Macroderma gigas* by withholding food.

The potential for large differences in T_b with only slight food deprivation is extremely important in interpreting the literature on chiropteran energetics. Many thermoregulation studies have been done in conjunction with MR measurements. To avoid the complicating effects of specific dynamic action, researchers often use animals in the "post-absorptive" state. This means that the bats were starved for 12 to 36 h before measurements were begun (Hanuš, 1959a; Stones and

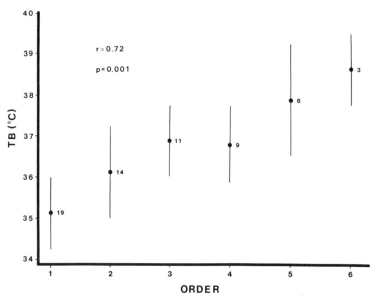

Figure 1. The effect of order of measurement on body temperature in adult female *Myotis lucifugus*. All bats were caught between 14 May and 18 August 1982, individually caged, and tested on the day of capture (see text). Error bars encompass ± one standard deviation. Dots represent mean values; numbers indicate sample size. Total time between measurements averaged 57.5 sec (SD=9.1; N=11).

Wiebers, 1965, 1967; Herreid and Schmidt-Nielsen, 1966; Lyman and Wimsatt, 1966; Pagels, 1975). In the wild, bats seldom go more than 15 h without feeding. Studies using "post-absorptive" animals may not actually reflect the bat's "normal" thermoregulatory pattern. The detrimental effects of mild food deprivation may partially explain why different reports on the same or similar species can result in widely disparate conclusions (see McNab, 1973, 1982; Studier and O'Farrell, 1980).

3.5. Body Water and Environmental Moisture

Low T_b is either an energy-saving mechanism or a water-saving mechanism (Chew and White, 1960; Herreid and Schmidt-Nielsen, 1966). Unless bats are fully hydrated at the beginning of an experiment, anomalous results are possible. *Myotis lucifugus,* for example, will maintain T_b 2 to 3°C higher over a

12-h period if allowed to drink after feeding than if water is denied (Geluso, 1975). Availability of water is easily controlled in animals maintained in captivity; however, many researchers test bats only on the day of capture. If test animals are caught while foraging they may not have had time to obtain adequate water. This potential problem is easily avoided by only capturing bats as they return to their roost (e.g., Studier and O'Farrell, 1972) or by providing water prior to testing (e.g., Studier and Wilson, 1970).

Moisture level in the air is also an important consideration. High relative humidity combined with high T_a will lessen a bat's ability to use evaporative heat loss to prevent its T_b from rising to lethal levels (Licht and Leitner, 1967; see also Lasiewski et al., 1966). Conversely, low ambient vapor pressure can greatly increase the rate of evaporative water loss (Procter and Studier, 1970). Thermoregulation studies done in conjunction with MR measurements frequently surround the animal with "dry" air, despite the fact that many bats roost in extremely humid environments. Can evaporative water loss during such measurements increase to the point that a heterothermic bat will reduce T_b in order to conserve water? To our knowledge, no study has specifically examined the effect of different water vapor pressures on T_b in any species of Chiroptera (but see Ewing and Studier, 1973).

3.6. Transport from Field to Laboratory

Animals are often tested on the day of capture to avoid acclimation and captivity effects (see below). Transport time to the laboratory and type of holding cage may affect results later in the day. Juvenile *M. lucifugus,* transported for about two hours, responded differently upon cold exposure than those tested at a site only 15 min from the roost (M. Fujita, unpubl. data). Transport time should be kept as low as possible, and holding cages should attempt to simulate the normal roosting conditions of the species.

Our laboratory has had great success in transporting active *M. lucifugus* in wooden holding cages. The bats are confined in one of a series of small compartments approximately 5 x 5 x 12 cm (see Chapter 1). Each compartment has a removable wooden top and a hardware cloth floor. Up to 10 bats can be placed in each compartment where they quickly form a compact cluster. The bats rapidly settle down, compared to our experiences with screen cages or cloth bags, and rarely appear disturbed by incidental movements of the investigator. This type of cage simulates the animals' normal roost site; it helps to retain heat and moisture and apparently minimizes psychological and physiological stress.

3.7. Simulated Roosts as Experimental Chambers

Although some bats, especially the larger Megachiroptera, may hang totally exposed

"to the direct impact of climatic conditions" (Bartholomew et al., 1964), most species seek shelter in an amazing variety of roost sites (Kunz, 1982; Bell et al., 1986). What are the energetic or thermoregulatory benefits of domed cave ceilings, hollow trees, the "tents" of *Uroderma bilobatum,* or the tunnels of *Mystacina tuberculata*? Although potential benefits are frequently alluded to and supported by field observations (e.g., Maeda, 1974; Daniel, 1979; Hall, 1982), there has been virtually no experimental work done along these lines. Sluiter and co-workers (Sluiter and van Heerdt, 1960; van Heerdt and Sluiter, 1965; Sluiter et al., 1973) reported on the insulative value of hollow trees for hibernating *Nyctalus noctula,* and recently Kurta (1985, 1986a) quantified the energetic benefits available to active *M. lucifugus* roosting in wooden cavities. The energetics of rodents and insectivores are greatly affected by the presence of nesting material (Hart, 1971; Casey, 1981; Vogt and Lynch, 1982). If laboratory data on bats are to be useful in formulating energy budgets of free-ranging animals, we should abandon the use of hardware-cloth cages, cardboard cartons, metal cans, and glass jars. Experimental chambers should be designed to simulate the animal's natural environment as closely as possible (e.g., Sluiter and van Heerdt, 1960; Stack, 1985; Kurta et al., 1987).

4. PHYSIOLOGICAL CONSIDERATIONS

4.1. Acclimation and the "Captivity Effect"

Acclimation is a change in physiological state resulting from long-term adjustments to controlled laboratory conditions (Hart, 1957, 1964; Hill, 1976). Although some investigators maintain experimental animals at constant temperatures prior to testing (Stones and Wiebers, 1965, 1967, Trune and Slobodchikoff, 1976), the results from such studies may not be broadly applicable since thermoregulatory ability may change with acclimation temperature. Holyoak and Stones (1971), for example, examined thermoregulation in *M. lucifugus* that had been maintained at 10, 20, or 30°C for four to six weeks. They found that thermoregulatory ability was inversely related to acclimation temperature (but see Noll, 1979a).

Studies using acclimated animals may provide little ecological insight. The T_a and other environmental factors that an animal is exposed to in its day-to-day activities probably fluctuate much more than those within a normal laboratory setting. Stones and Wiebers (1967) maintained their bats at 30°C. In the wild, this species would experience daily T_a fluctuations of 20°C or more during the reproductive season. If data from laboratory animals are extrapolated to the field environment, then at least a minimal attempt should be made to compare freshly captured specimens with those from the laboratory colony (e.g., Lyman and Wimsatt, 1966).

A phenomenon related to acclimation is the "captivity effect" (Studier and Wilson, 1979). In some cases a bat's thermoregulatory and metabolic responses change quickly after the animal is first captured. Stones and Wiebers (1965) showed that *M. lucifugus,* taken from hibernation and kept in the laboratory, showed a progressive change both in the time needed for arousal and the level of T_b attained (see also Menaker, 1969). Studier and Wilson (1979) reported that *Artibeus jamaicensis* actually increased both oxygen consumption and T_b level after only a few days in captivity. The rapid changes in thermoregulation shown by some species after very brief periods of captivity make one question the ecological relevance of classical laboratory studies using animals held captive for weeks or months (Hock, 1951; Hanuš, 1959a,b; Herreid and Schmidt-Nielsen, 1966; Mejsnar and Janský, 1967; Trune and Slobodchikoff, 1976; see also Bruce and Wiebers, 1970). Studier and O'Farrell (1980)

provide additional discussion on this topic.

4.2. Daily and Seasonal Rhythms

Many bats display circadian patterns of T_b change, both in the field (Brosset, 1969), and in the laboratory (Menaker, 1961; Kulzer, 1963, 1965; Cena and Wołosczyn, 1966; Leitner, 1966; Morrison and McNab, 1967; Heldmaier, 1970; Noll, 1979a; see also Aschoff, 1981). Much of the daily change in T_b is probably the result of differences in activity level, since even small increases in activity lead to an increase in a bat's T_b (Morrison, 1959; Leitner, 1966; Morrison and McNab, 1967; Wolverton and Edgar, 1969). Unless T_b is continuously monitored, any experimental design must consider the possibility of circadian rhythms so that T_b is consistently measured during the same part of the daily cycle. An additional complication is that patterns of circadian activity may change with acclimation temperature (Erkert and Rothmund, 1981).

Physiological adjustments resulting from an animal adapting to seasonal changes in its environment are called acclimatization (Hart, 1957, 1964). Henshaw and Folk (1966) documented changes in thermoregulation and MR in *M. lucifugus* and *M. sodalis* as the hibernation season progressed (see also Hurst, 1966; Kurta, 1986b). Based on laboratory experiments and on field observations, Leitner (1966) showed that *E. perotis* will undergo daily torpor in winter but not in summer. A number of other papers have reported seasonal changes in T_b (Pohl, 1961; Mejsnar and Janský, 1967), arousal patterns (Menaker, 1962; Wolverton and Edgar, 1969; Pagels, 1972, 1975), and insulation (Shump and Shump, 1980). The previous thermal environment of the test animal is extremely important, and comparisons between studies and species should only be made using animals tested during similar periods of their annual cycle. Hanuš (1959a) made a similar statement more than 25 years ago, yet inappropriate comparisons and extrapolations still appear in the literature.

4.3. Reproductive Condition

Reproductive condition can affect thermoregulation in thermolabile mammals such as sloths (Morrison, 1945) and tenrecs (Nicoll, 1982). Does thermoregulatory ability change as a female bat progresses through pregnancy, lactation, and into post-lactation? Studier and O'Farrell (1972) concluded that lactating *Myotis thysanodes* showed the poorest thermoregulatory ability compared to pregnant and post-lactating individuals (see also Kurta, 1986b). In contrast, Brosset (1969) reported that pregnant and lactating *Hipposideros commersoni* (= *gigas*) maintain T_b 2 to 3°C higher than non-reproductive adults. Qualitative field observations also indicate T_b differences depending on reproductive condition in temperate rhinolophids (Gaisler, 1963; Saint Girons et al., 1969; Ransome, 1973). Racey (1982) provides an excellent critique of this topic. Obviously reproductive condition is another factor to consider when designing or comparing thermoregulatory studies and when formulating energy budgets.

4.4. Sexual Differences

The majority of chiropteran thermoregulatory studies neither state what sex was used nor attempt intersexual comparisons. Stones and Wiebers (1966), however, noted that the thermoregulatory patterns of torpid *M. lucifugus* were correlated with body mass in males but not in females. Trune and Slobodchikoff (1976) saw no difference in T_b among their laboratory-acclimated *A. pallidus*. O'Farrell and Bradley (1977) found no sexual differences in flight T_b of seven vespertilionids and one molossid. Hanuš (1959b) noted a significant sexual difference in thermoregulatory ability of winter-captured *M. myotis* but not in *M. nattereri*, *Plecotus auritus*, or *B. barbastellus*.

Based on qualitative field observations, Gaisler (1963) believes that adult male *Rhinolophus hipposideros* enter torpor more frequently in summer than do adult females.

Saint Girons et al. (1969) reported similar observations on *R. ferrumequinum*. Keen and Hitchcock (1980) and Hitchcock et al. (1984) reported that male survivorship is greater in three species of Nearctic vespertilionids, and they suggest that more frequent torpor by males in summer is a contributing factor.

Unfortunately, most detailed reports on chiropteran thermoregulation have been done on the common temperate species which are sexually segregated for large portions of the year. Males are generally solitary and difficult to locate during the spring and summer reproductive season. For this reason, many studies have used only adult females taken from maternity colonies. A study of male thermoregulatory and metabolic patterns in summer would be quite interesting in terms of intersexual differences in energy partitioning, reproductive effort, and survivorship. The potential effects of torpor on longevity are discussed more fully in Herreid (1964), McNab (1982), and Lyman et al. (1981) (see also Boddington, 1978; Lindstedt and Calder, 1981).

5. BEHAVIORAL CONSIDERATIONS

5.1. Clustering

Bats are perhaps the most gregarious of mammals. The strong tendency to cluster by many species has often been claimed to have thermoregulatory and/or energetic significance (Henshaw, 1970; Davis, 1970; Lyman, 1970). Despite the commonness of clustering, few attempts have been made to measure the energetic benefits to bats (Herreid, 1963b, 1967; Riedesel and Williams, 1976; Trune and Slobodchikoff, 1976; Storf, in Kulzer, 1979; Hartung, 1981), although an extensive literature exists for other mammals (reviewed in Hart, 1971; Martin et al., 1980). We are aware of only a few experimental studies which have investigated the effect of clustering on steady state T_b or arousal in bats.

Howell (1976) compared the T_b of captive *G. soricina* in groups of one and eight. Unfortunately, her small sample size, and the large variance in her data, apparently precluded any statistical comparison. She provided no means or error estimates and was careful to point out that the data only "suggests" that clustering results in a higher T_b. Herreid (1963a) compared the T_b of *T. brasiliensis* in groups of 1, 5, and 10. His data "indicate that there was no large difference in body temperature among groups of different size." McNab (1969) examined clusters of one to four *Phyllostomus discolor*, and he also could not unequivocally demonstrate a significant relationship between T_b and cluster size. Brenner (1974) could show no differences between grouped or single *M. lucifugus* and *M. sodalis* in torpor in the laboratory, nor could he show a difference in arousal states. Funakoshi and Uchida (1978), in contrast, actually found a lower T_b in clustered *Miniopterus schreibersii* than in singles.

Demonstrable effects of clustering on T_b in bats seem to be very elusive. Part of this difficulty may be in the extreme thermolability of many species (see Kulzer, 1965, and Kulzer et al., 1970, for numerous examples). Bats tested as singles tend to show highly variable T_b between individuals, while bats taken from clusters show less variation (Brenner, 1974; Howell, 1976). For example, the coefficient of variation of T_b for singly caged adult female *M. lucifugus* was generally 25-30 percent greater than for bats taken from clusters under similar conditions (Kurta, 1986a). The apparently unpredictable T_b of singles makes it difficult to obtain statistical differences between individuals and clusters because of the resulting large variance term. The only way to overcome this problem is to greatly increase sample size (e.g., Kurta, 1986b) or, perhaps, resort to a non-parametric categorical analysis (e.g., Holyoak and Stones, 1971; Pagels, 1972). The experimental T_a may also be a factor; at lower T_a, a wider range in T_b is possible, and, therefore, a larger variance term may result.

5.2. Social Facilitation

The extreme gregariousness of many bats also raises the possibility of social facilitation. Social facilitation is a complex phenomenon often invoked to explain enhanced learning, increased feeding rates, or more successful foraging of groups as opposed to individuals (Zajonc, 1965; Wilson, 1975; Kurta, 1982). Recent attempts have been made to demonstrate that simply the presence of a conspecific, with no possibility of physical contact, is enough to reduce MR in some rodents (Herreid and Schlenker, 1980; Martin et al., 1980; but see Contreras, 1984).

Although no bat study has specifically addressed this question, Trune and Slobodchikoff (1976) claim that clustering in *A. pallidus* results in a lower mass-specific MR compared to individuals. They believe that the lower MR is not caused by an increase in insulation due to clustering, but that "the sociality of the cluster exerts a calming effect on the bats allowing them to lower their metabolic rate." These authors did not directly test this hypothesis, but formulated it *a posteriori* after they demonstrated no difference in T_b between bats in the center of a cluster and those on the edge. (They did not address the possibility that bats on the edge had a slightly higher MR than centrally positioned bats; this could potentially compensate for any increased heat loss compared to central bats.) Social facilitation of T_b or MR appears to be an interesting area for future research using well-planned experiments such as those of Herreid and Schlenker (1980). Since many chiropterans cluster in the wild, any laboratory study designed to examine thermoregulatory patterns under simulated natural conditions must consider the potential physical (insulative) and psychological effects of living in groups.

5.3. Social Stress

Although some evidence exists that conspecifics may have a calming influence on mammals, other evidence points in the opposite direction. Andrews (1978, 1981) has shown that *Microtus* and *Peromyscus* exposed to strange conspecifics may raise core T_b by 1 or 2°C. Similar data exist for birds (Myhre et al., 1981). This suggests that if clusters of bats are tested, all bats should be from the same roost or, at least, have been exposed to one another in the laboratory prior to testing. Also along these lines, Rasweiler (1977) provides an interesting discussion of the potential benefits and dangers of housing captive bats as singles or in groups.

6. SUMMARY

Biologists most often measure body temperature using thermocouples, thermistors, and mercury thermometers; temperature-sensitive radio transmitters are relatively new but will undoubtedly see greater use in the future. These different temperature sensors are readily available from commercial sources, and many can be made in the laboratory. Although measuring body temperature is a simple procedure, the interpretation of that temperature must be tempered by a number of physiological, methodological, and behavioral considerations. Body temperature of bats can vary with nutritional state, water balance, sex, reproductive condition, time of day, and seasonal acclimatization. In addition, mode of transport between field and laboratory, acclimation conditions, and the use of restraints may affect thermoregulatory patterns. The potential physiological and psychological effects of social roosting and the potential use of external insulation have not been adequately investigated. Past studies of chiropteran thermoregulation have concentrated on the physiological capabilities of a particular species; hopefully, this chapter will act as a stimulus for future research that will be carried out within an ecological framework.

7. ACKNOWLEDGMENTS

R. H. Baker, G. P. Bell, K. A. Johnson, T. H. Kunz, C. P. Lyman, E. H. Studier, C. R. Taylor, L. C. H. Wang, and an anonymous reviewer provided helpful comments and references. K. A. Johnson and J. A. Molenkamp provided German and Dutch translations, respectively.

8. REFERENCES

Adams, L., R. E. Wetmore, R. L. Limes, and H. J. Hauer. 1973. Radio telemetry and computers used in automated analysis of heart rate in ground squirrels. Pp. 55-66, *in* Ecological energetics of homeotherms: A view compatible with ecological modeling. (J. A. Gessaman, ed.). Utah State Univ. Press, Logan, 155 pp.

Amlaner, C. J., Jr. 1980. The design of antennas for use in radio telemetry. Pp. 251-262, *in* A handbook on biotelemetry and radio tracking. (C. J. Amlaner, Jr. and D. W. MacDonald, eds.). Pergamon Press, Oxford, 804 pp.

Amlaner, C. J., Jr., and D. W. MacDonald (eds.). 1980. A handbook on biotelemetry and radio tracking. Pergamon Press, Oxford, 804 pp.

American Society for Testing and Materials. 1970. Manual on the use of thermocouples in temperature measurement. American Society for Testing and Materials, Philadelphia, 249 pp.

Andrews, R. V. 1978. Incremental changes in deer mouse *(Peromyscus maniculatus)* core temperatures during behavioral challenges. Comp. Biochem. Physiol., 59A:45-48.

Andrews, R. V. 1981. Comparison of incremental temperature responses of deer mice and voles to behavioral alarm stimuli. Comp. Biochem. Physiol., 70A:23-26.

Arata, A. A. 1972. Thermoregulation in Colombian *Artibeus lituratus* (Chiroptera). Mammalia, 36:86-92.

Arata, A. A., and C. Jones. 1967. Homeothermy in *Carollia* (Phyllostomatidae: Chiroptera) and the adaptation of poikilothermy in insectivorous northern bats. Lozania, 14:1-10.

Aschoff, J. 1981. Thermal conductance in mammals and birds: Its dependence on body size and circadian phase. Comp. Biochem. Physiol., 69A:611-619.

Baldwin, H. A. 1973. Instrumentation for remote observation of physiology and behavior. Pp. 67-76, *in* Ecological energetics of homeotherms: A view compatible with ecological modeling. (J. A. Gessaman, ed.). Utah State Univ. Press, Logan, 155 pp.

Bartholomew, G. A., and M. Rainy. 1971. Regulation of body temperature in the rock hyrax, *Heterohyrax brucei*. J. Mammal., 52:81-95.

Bartholomew, G. A., P. Leitner, and J. E. Nelson. 1964. Body temperature, oxygen consumption, and heart rate in three species of Australian flying foxes. Physiol. Zool., 37:179-198.

Bartholomew, G. A., W. R. Dawson, and R. C. Lasiewski. 1970. Thermoregulation and heterothermy in some of the smaller flying foxes (Megachiroptera) of New Guinea. Z. Vergl. Physiol., 70:196-209.

Bell, G. P., G. A. Bartholomew, and K. A. Nagy. 1986. The roles of energetics, water economy, foraging behavior, and geothermal refugia in the distribution of the bat, *Macrotus californicus*. J. Comp. Physiol. B, 156:441-450.

Benedict, R. P. 1977. Fundamentals of temperature, pressure, and flow measurements. Wiley-Interscience, New York, 517 pp.

Bloor, B. C., and A. St. J. Lee. 1982. Linearizing the thermistor: A reminder that the thermistor can be tamed. J. Clin. Eng., 7:301-304.

Boddington, M. J. 1978. An absolute metabolic scope for activity. J. Theor. Biol., 75:443-449.

Boyd, J. C., and W. J. Sladen. 1971. Telemetry studies of the internal body temperatures of Adelie and Emperor Penguins at Cape Crozier, Ross Island, Antarctica. Auk, 88:366-380.

Bradley, S. R., and D. R. Deavers. 1980. A reexamination of the relationship between thermal conductance and body weight in mammals. Comp. Biochem. Physiol., 65A:465-476.

Bradley, W. G., and M. J. O'Farrell. 1969. Temperature relationships of the western pipistrelle *(Pipistrellus hesperus)*. Pp. 85-96, *in* Physiological systems in semi-arid environments. (C. C. Hoff and M. L. Riedesel, eds.). Univ. New Mexico Press, Albuquerque.

Brenner, F. J. 1974. Body temperature and arousal rates of two species of bats. Ohio J. Science, 74:296-300.

Brosset, A. 1969. Recherches sur la biologie de chiroptères troglophiles dans le nord-est Gabon. Biol. Gabonica, 5:93-116.

Bruce, D. S., and J. E. Wiebers. 1970. Body weight of *Myotis lucifugus* under natural and laboratory conditions. J. Mammal., 51:823-824.

Caceres, C. A., ed. 1965. Biomedical telemetry. Academic Press, New York, 392 pp.

Calder, W. A., III. 1974. Consequences of body size in avian energetics. Pp. 86-151, *in* Avian energetics. (R. A. Paynter, Jr., ed.). Publ. Nuttall Ornithol. Club, 15:1-334.

Calow, P. 1977. Ecology, evolution and energetics: A study in metabolic adaptation. Adv. Ecol. Res., 10:1-61.

Carpenter, R. E., and J. B. Graham. 1967. Physiological responses to temperature in the long-nosed bat, *Leptonycteris sanborni*. Comp. Biochem. Physiol., 22:709-722.

Casey, T. M. 1981. Nest insulation: Energy savings to brown lemmings using a winter nest. Oecologia, 50:199-204.

Cena, K., and B. W Wołoszyn. 1966. Investigations on the diurnal changes of the skin temperature in bats. Folia Biol., 14:195-203.

Chappell, M. A., and G. A. Bartholomew. 1981. Activity and thermoregulation of the antelope ground squirrel *Ammospermophilus leucurus* in winter and summer. Physiol. Zool., 54:215-223.

Chew, R. M., and H. E. White. 1960. Evaporative water losses of the pallid bat. J. Mammal., 41:452-458.

Contreras, L. C. 1984. Bioenergetics of huddling: Test of a psycho-physiological hypothesis. J. Mammal., 65:256-262.

Cowles, R. B. 1947. Vascular changes in the wings of bats. Science, 105:362-363.

Daniel, M. J. 1979. The New Zealand short-tailed bat, *Mystacina tuberculata;* a review of present knowledge. New Zealand J. Zool., 6:357-370.

Davis, L. B., Jr., and R. C. Birkebak. 1975. Convective energy transfer in fur. Pp. 525-548, *in* Perspectives of biophysical ecology. (D. M. Gates and R. B. Schmerl, eds.). Springer-Verlag, New York, 609 pp.

Davis, W. H. 1970. Hibernation: Ecology and physiological ecology. Pp. 266-300, *in* Biology of bats. Vol. 1. (W. A. Wimsatt, ed.). Academic Press, New York, 406 pp.

Davis, W. H., and O. B. Reite. 1967. Responses of bats from temperate regions to changes in ambient temperature. Biol. Bull., 132:320-328.

Erkert, H. G., and E. Rothmund. 1981. Differences in temperature sensitivity of the circadian systems of homeothermic and heterothermic Neotropical bats. Comp. Biochem. Physiol., 68A:383-390.

Ewing, W. G., and E. H. Studier. 1973. A method for control of water vapor pressure and its effect on metabolism and body temperature in *Mus musculus*. Comp. Biochem. Physiol., 45A:121-125.

Fryer, T. B. 1980. The advantages of short range telemetry through the intact skin for physiological measurements in both animals and man. Pp. 21-32, *in* A handbook on biotelemetry and radio tracking. (C. J. Amlaner, Jr. and D. W. MacDonald, eds.). Pergamon Press, Oxford, 804 pp.

Fryer, T. B. 1981. Survey of implantable telemetry. Biotelem. Pat. Monit., 8:125-130.

Fryer, T. B., and H. Sandler. 1974. A review of implant telemetry systems. Biotelemetry, 1:351-374.

Fryer, T. B., H. A. Miller, and H. Sandler (eds.). 1976. Biotelemetry III. Academic Press, New York, 381 pp.

Funakoshi, K., and T. A. Uchida. 1978. Studies on the physiological and ecological adaptations of temperate insectivorous bats. II. Hibernation and winter activity in some cave-dwelling bats. Japanese J. Ecol., 28:237-261.

Gaisler, J. 1963. The ecology of the lesser horseshoe bat (*Rhinolophus hipposideros hipposideros* Bechstein, 1800) in Czechoslovakia. Part I. Acta Soc. Zool. Bohemoslov., 27:211-233.

Geluso, K. N. 1975. Urine concentration cycles of insectivorous bats in the laboratory. J. Comp. Physiol., 99:309-319.

Gessaman, J. A. (ed.). 1973. Ecological energetics of homeotherms: A view compatible with ecological modeling. Utah State Univ. Press, Logan, 155 pp.

Gessaman, J. A. 1980. Heart rate and body temperature of the Uinta ground squirrel in the field. Comp. Biochem. Physiol., 66A:707-710.

Hall, J. S. 1962. A life history and taxonomic study of the Indiana bat, *Myotis sodalis*. Sci. Publ., Reading Pub. Mus. Art Gallery, 12:1-68.

Hall, L. S. 1982. The effect of cave microclimate on winter roosting behaviour in the bat, *Miniopterus schreibersii blepotis*. Aust. J. Ecol., 7:129-136.

Hanuš, K. 1959a. Body temperature and metabolism in bats at different environmental temperatures. Physiol. Bohemoslov., 8:250-259.

Hanuš, K. 1959b. K otázce thermoregulace netopýrů (To the question of thermoregulation in bats). Acta Soc. Zool. Bohemoslov., 23:307-327.

Hart, J. S. 1957. Climatic and temperature induced changes in the energetics of homeotherms. Rev. Can. Biol., 16:133-174.

Hart, J. S. 1964. Insulative and metabolic adaptations to cold in vertebrates. Symp. Soc. Exp. Biol., 18:31-48.

Hart, J. S. 1971. Rodents. Pp. 1-149, *in* Comparative physiology of thermoregulation. Vol. 2. (G. C. Whittow, ed.). Academic Press, New York, 410 pp.

Hartung, J. D. 1981. The effect of clustering on the metabolic rate of hibernating little brown bats, *Myotis lucifugus*. Unpubl. M.S. thesis. Michigan Tech. Univ., Houghton, 26 pp.

Heldmaier, G. 1970. Variations of body temperatures and metabolism during entrance into cold lethargy in the bat, *Myotis myotis*. Bijdragen tot de Dierkunde, 40:45-50.

Henshaw, R. E. 1970. Thermoregulation in bats. Pp. 188-232, *in* About bats: A chiropteran symposium. (B. H. Slaughter and D. W. Walton, eds.). Southern Methodist Univ. Press, Dallas, 339 pp.

Henshaw, R. E., and G. E. Folk, Jr. 1966. Relation of thermoregulation to seasonally changing microclimate in two species of bats *(Myotis lucifugus* and *M. sodalis)*. Physiol. Zool., 39:223-236.

Herreid, C. F., II. 1963a. Temperature regulation of Mexican free-tailed bats in cave habitats. J. Mammal., 44:560-573.

Herreid, C. F., II. 1963b. Temperature regulation and metabolism in Mexican freetail bats. Science, 142:1573-1574.

Herreid, C. F., II. 1963c. Metabolism of the Mexican free-tailed bat. J. Cell. Comp. Physiol., 61:201-207.

Herreid, C. F., II. 1964. Bat longevity and metabolic rate. Exp. Gerontol., 1:1-9.

Herreid, C. F., II. 1967. Temperature regulation, temperature preference and tolerance, and metabolism of young and adult free-tailed bats. Physiol. Zool., 40:1-22.

Herreid, C. F., II, and E. H. Schlenker. 1980. Energetics of mice in stable and unstable social conditions: Evidence of an air-borne factor affecting metabolism. Anim. Behav., 28:20-28.

Herreid, C. F., II, and K. Schmidt-Nielsen. 1966. Oxygen consumption, temperature, and water loss in bats from different environments. Amer. J. Physiol., 211:1108-1112.

Hill, R. W. 1972. The amount of maternal care in *Peromyscus leucopus* and its thermal significance for the young. J. Mammal., 53:774-790.

Hill, R. W. 1976. Comparative physiology of animals: An environmental approach. Harper and Row, New York, 656 pp.

Hitchcock, H. B., R. Keen, and A. Kurta. 1984. Survival rates of *Myotis leibii* and *Eptesicus fuscus* in southeastern Ontario. J. Mammal., 65:126-130.

Hock, R. J. 1951. The metabolic rates and body temperatures of bats. Biol. Bull., 101:289-299.

Holyoak, G. W., and R. C. Stones. 1971. Temperature regulation of the little brown bat, *Myotis lucifugus*, after acclimation at various ambient temperatures. Comp. Biochem. Physiol., 39A:413-420.

Howell, D. J. 1976. Weight loss and temperature regulation in clustered versus individual *Glossophaga soricina*. Comp. Biochem. Physiol., 53A:191-199.

Hughes, S. E. 1968. Temperature of the bat, *Plecotus townsendii*, during arousal. J. Mammal., 49:140-142.

Hurst, R. N. 1966. Seasonal physiological responses of the bat *Myotis lucifugus*. Unpubl. Ph.D. dissertation, Purdue Univ., West Lafayette, 153 pp.

Jacobsen, N. K., and J. L. Stuart. 1982. A field-portable, microprocessor-controlled, data processing and storing cardiotachometer. Biotelem. Pat. Monit., 9:80-88.

Janský, L., and L. Hájek. 1961. Thermogenesis of the bat *Myotis myotis* Borkh. Physiol. Bohemoslov., 10:283-289.

Keen, R., and H. B. Hitchcock. 1980. Survival and longevity of the little brown bat *(Myotis lucifugus)* in southeastern Ontario. J. Mammal., 61:1-7.

King, J. R. 1974. Seasonal allocation of time and energy resources in birds. Pp. 4-85, *in* Avian energetics. (R. A. Paynter, Jr., ed.). Publ. Nuttall Ornithol. Club, 15:1-334.

Kleinbaum, D. G., and L. L. Kupper. 1978. Applied regression analysis and other multivariable methods. Duxbury Press, North Scituate, Massachusetts, 556 pp.

Kluger, M. J., and J. E. Heath. 1970. Vasomotion in the bat wing; A thermoregulatory response to internal heating. Comp. Biochem. Physiol., 32:219-226.

Ko, W. H. 1980. Power sources for implant telemetry and stimulation systems. Pp. 225-246, *in* A handbook on biotelemetry and radio tracking. (C. J. Amlaner, Jr. and D. W. MacDonald, eds.). Pergamon Press, Oxford, 804 pp.

Kulzer, E. 1963. Die Regelung der Körpertemperatur beim Indischen Riesenflughund. Natur und Mus., 93:1-11.

Kulzer, E. 1965. Temperaturregulation bei Fledermäusen (Chiroptera) aus verschiedenen Klimazonen. Z. Vergl. Physiol., 50:1-34.

Kulzer, E. 1979. Physiological ecology and geographical range in the fruit-eating cave bat genus *Rousettus* Gray 1821—A review. Bonn. Zool. Beitr., 30:233-275.

Kulzer, E., J. E. Nelson, J. L. McKean, and F. P. Möhres. 1970. Untersuchungen über die Temperaturregulation australischer Fledermäuse (Microchiroptera). Z. Vergl. Physiol., 69:426-451.

Kulzer, E., and R. Storf. 1980. Schlaf-lethargie bei dem afrikanischen Langzungenflughund *Megaloglossus woermanni* Pagenstecher, 1885. Z. Saugetierk., 45:23-29.

Kunz, T. H. 1980. Energy budgets of free-living bats. Pp. 369-392, *in* Proc. 5th Int. Bat Res. Conf. (D. E. Wilson and A. L. Gardner, eds.). Texas Tech Press, Lubbock, 434 pp.

Kunz, T. H. 1982. Roosting ecology of bats. Pp. 1-56, *in* Ecology of bats. (T. H. Kunz, ed.). Plenum Press, New York, 425 pp.

Kurta, A. 1982. Social facilitation of foraging behavior by the hermit crab, *Coenobita compressus*, in Costa Rica. Biotropica, 14:132-136.

Kurta, A. 1985. External insulation available to a non-nesting mammal, the little brown bat *(Myotis lucifugus)*. Comp. Biochem. Physiol., 82A:413-420.

Kurta, A. 1986a. Insulation, thermoregulation, and metabolic rates of the little brown bat *(Myotis lucifugus)* under simulated roost conditions. Unpubl. Ph.D. dissertation, Boston University, Boston, Massachusetts, 283 pp.

Kurta, A. 1986b. Factors affecting the resting and postflight temperature of little brown bats, *Myotis lucifugus*. Physiol. Zool., 59:429-438.

Kurta, A., K. A. Johnson, and T. H. Kunz. 1987. Oxygen consumption and body temperature of female little brown bats (*Myotis lucifugus*) under simulated roost conditions. Physiol. Zool., 60:386-397.

Kürten, L., and U. Schmidt. 1982. Thermoperception in the common vampire bat *(Desmodus rotundus)*. J. Comp. Physiol., 146:223-228.

Langman, V. A. 1973. A radio-biotelemetry system for monitoring body temperature and activity levels in the Zebra Finch. Auk, 90:375-383.

Lasiewski, R. C., A. L. Acosta, and M. H. Bernstein. 1966. Evaporative water losses in birds—I. Characteristics of the open flow method of determination, and their relation to estimates of thermoregulatory ability. Comp. Biochem. Physiol., 19:445-457.

Leitner, P. 1966. Body temperature, oxygen consumption, heart rate, and shivering in the California mastiff bat, *Eumops perotis.* Comp. Biochem. Physiol., 19:431-443.

Leitner, P., and J. E. Nelson. 1967. Body temperature, oxygen consumption and heart rate in the Australian false vampire bat, *Macroderma gigas.* Comp. Biochem. Physiol., 21:65-74.

Licht, P., and P. Leitner. 1967. Physiological responses to high environmental temperatures in three species of microchiropteran bats. Comp. Biochem. Physiol., 22:371-387.

Lindeman, R. L. 1942. The trophic dynamic aspect of ecology. Ecology, 23:399-418.

Lindstedt, S. L. 1980. Regulated hypothermia in the desert shrew. J. Comp. Physiol., 137:173-176.

Lindstedt, S. L., and W. A. Calder, III. 1981. Body size, physiological time, and longevity of homeothermic animals. Quart. Rev. Biol., 56:1-16.

Lomax, P. 1966. Measurement of 'core' temperature in the rat. Nature, 210:854-855.

Lund, G. F., R. M. Westbrook, and T. B. Fryer. 1980. Heart rate, multiple body temperature, long-range and long-life telemetry system for free-ranging animals. Biotelem. Pat. Monit., 7:137-177.

Lyman, C. P. 1970. Thermoregulation and metabolism in bats. Pp. 301-330, *in* Biology of bats. Vol. 1. (W. A. Wimsatt, ed.). Academic Press, New York, 406 pp.

Lyman, C. P., and W. A. Wimsatt. 1966. Temperature regulation in the vampire bat, *Desmodus rotundus.* Physiol. Zool., 39:101-109.

Lyman, C. P., R. C. O'Brien, G. C. Greene, and E. D. Papafragos. 1981. Hibernation and longevity in the Turkish hamster *Mesocricetus brandti.* Science, 212:668-670.

Mackay, R. S. 1965. Telemetering from within the body of animals and man: Endoradiosondes. Pp. 148-236, *in* Biomedical telemetry. (C. A. Caceres, ed.). Academic Press, New York, 392 pp.

Mackay, R. S. 1970. Bio-medical telemetry: Sensing and transmitting information from animals and man. John Wiley and Sons, New York, 532 pp.

Maeda, K. 1974. Éco-éthologie de la grande noctule, *Nyctalus lasiopterus,* a Sapporo, Japon. Mammalia, 38:461-487.

Martin, R. A., M. Fiorentini, and F. Connors. 1980. Social facilitation of reduced oxygen consumption in *Mus musculus* and *Meriones ungulatus.* Comp. Biochem. Physiol., 65A:519-522.

McManus, J. J. 1977. Thermoregulation. Pp. 281-292, *in* Biology of bats of the New World family Phyllostomatidae. Part II. (R. J. Baker, J. K. Jones, Jr., and D. C. Carter, eds.). Spec. Publ. No. 13, Mus. Texas Tech Univ., 364 pp.

McManus, J. J., and D. W. Nellis. 1972. Temperature regulation in three species of tropical bats. J. Mammal., 53:226-227.

McNab, B. K. 1969. The economics of temperature regulation in Neotropical bats. Comp. Biochem. Physiol., 31:227-268.

McNab, B. K. 1973. Energetics and the distribution of vampires. J. Mammal., 54:131-144.

McNab, B. K. 1982. Evolutionary alternatives in the physiological ecology of bats. Pp. 151-200, *in* Ecology of bats. (T. H. Kunz, ed.). Plenum Press, New York, 425 pp.

Mejsnar, J., and L. Janský. 1967. Seasonal changes of temperature regulation in the bat *Myotis myotis* Borkh. Physiol. Bohemoslov., 16:147-152.

Menaker, M. 1961. The free running period of the bat clock: Seasonal variations at low body temperature. J. Cell Comp. Physiol., 57:81-86.

Menaker, M. 1962. Hibernation-hypothermia: An annual cycle of response to low temperature in the bat *Myotis lucifugus.* J. Cell. Comp. Physiol., 59:163-174.

Menaker, M. 1969. Heat acclimation of summer bats. Amer. Midl. Nat., 82:289-290.

Millar, J. S. 1977. Adaptive features of mammalian reproduction. Evolution, 31:370-386.

Morhardt, J. E. 1975. Preferred body temperature of small birds and rodents: Behavioral and physiological determinations of variable set points. Pp. 475-490, *in* Perspectives of biophysical ecology. (D. M. Gates and R. B. Schmerl, eds.). Springer-Verlag, New York, 609 pp.

Morrison, P. R. 1945. Acquired homiothermism in the pregnant sloth. J. Mammal., 26:272-275.

Morrison, P. R. 1959. Body temperatures in some Australian mammals. I. Chiroptera. Biol. Bull., 116:484-497.

Morrison, P., and B. K. McNab. 1967. Temperature regulation in some Brazilian bats. Comp. Biochem. Physiol., 21:207-221.

Müller, E. F., J. M. Z. Kamau, and G. M. O. Maloiy. 1983. A comparative study of basal metabolism and thermoregulation in a folivorous *(Colobus guereza)* and an omnivorous *(Cercopithecus mitis)* primate species. Comp. Biochem. Physiol., 74A:319-322.

Myhre, G., H. Ursin, and I. Hanssen. 1981. Corticosterone and body temperature during acquisition of social hierarchy in the captive willow ptarmigan *(Lagopus l. lagopus)*. Z. Tierpsychol., 57:123-130.

Nicoll, M. E. 1982. Reproductive ecology of *Tenrec ecaudatus* (Insectivora: Tenrecidae) in the Seychelles. Unpubl. Ph.D. dissertation, University of Aberdeen, 327 pp.

Noll, U. G. 1979a. Body temperature, oxygen consumption, noradrenaline response and cardiovascular adaptations in the flying fox, *Rousettus aegyptiacus*. Comp. Biochem. Physiol., 63A:79-88.

Noll, U. G. 1979b. Postnatal growth and development of thermogenesis in *Rousettus aegyptiacus*. Comp. Biochem. Physiol., 63A:89-93.

O'Farrell, M. J., and W. G. Bradley. 1977. Comparative thermal relationships of flight for some bats in the southwestern United States. Comp. Biochem. Physiol., 58A:223-227.

Omega Engineering, Inc. 1983. 1984 Temperature measurement handbook and encyclopedia. Omega Engineering, Inc., Stamford, Connecticut.

Pagels, J. F. 1972. The effects of short and prolonged cold exposure on arousal in the free-tailed bat, *Tadarida brasiliensis cynocephala* (Le Conte). Comp. Biochem. Physiol., 42A:559-567.

Pagels, J. F. 1975. Temperature regulation, body weight and changes in total body fat of the free-tailed bat, *Tadarida brasiliensis cynocephala* (Le Conte). Comp. Biochem. Physiol., 50A:237-246.

Paladino, F. V., and J. R. King. 1984. Thermoregulation and oxygen consumption during terrestrial locomotion by white-crowned sparrows *Zonotrichia leucophrys gambelii*. Physiol. Zool., 57:226-236.

Peters, R. H. 1983. The ecological implications of body size. Cambridge University Press, New York, 329 pp.

Pivorun, E. B. 1976. A biotelemetry study of the thermoregulatory patterns of *Tamias striatus* and *Eutamius minimus* during hibernation. Comp. Biochem. Physiol., 53A:265-271.

Platt, R. B., and J. F. Griffiths. 1964. Environmental measurement and interpretation. Reinhold, New York, 235 pp.

Pohl, H. 1961. Temperaturregulation und Tagesperiodik des Stoffwechsels bei Winterschläfern. Z. Vergl. Physiol., 45:109-153.

Procter, J. W., and E. H. Studier. 1970. Effects of ambient temperature and water vapor pressure on evaporative water loss in *Myotis lucifugus*. J. Mammal., 51:799-804.

Pyke, G. H., H. R. Pulliam, and E. L. Charnov. 1977. Optimal foraging theory: A selective review of theory and tests. Quart. Rev. Biol., 52:137-154.

Racey, P. A. 1982. Ecology of bat reproduction. Pp. 57-104, *in* Ecology of bats. (T. H. Kunz, ed.). Plenum Press, New York, 425 pp.

Racey, P. A., and S. M. Swift. 1981. Variations in gestation length in a colony of pipistrelle bats *(Pipistrellus pipistrellus)* from year to year. J. Reprod. Fert., 61:123-129.

Ransome, R. D. 1973. Factors affecting the timing of births of the greater horseshoe bat *(Rhinolophus ferrumequinum)*. Period. Biol., 75:169-175.

Rasweiler, J. J., IV. 1973. Care and management of the long-tongued bat, *Glossophaga soricina* (Chiroptera: Phyllostomatidae), in the laboratory, with observations on estivation induced by food deprivation. J. Mammal., 54:391-404.

Rasweiler, J. J., IV. 1977. The care and management of bats as laboratory animals. Pp. 519-617, *in* Biology of bats. Vol. 3. (W. A. Wimsatt, ed.). Academic Press, New York, 651 pp.

Rausch, J. C. 1973. Sequential changes in regional distribution of blood in *Eptesicus fuscus* (big brown bat) during arousal from hibernation. Can. J. Zool., 51:973-981.

Reeder, W. G. 1949. Hibernating temperature of the bat, *Myotis californicus pallidus*. J. Mammal., 30:51-53.

Reeder, W. G., and R. B. Cowles. 1951. Aspects of thermoregulation in bats. J. Mammal., 32:389-403.

Reinertsen, R. E. 1982. Radio telemetry measurements of deep body temperature of small birds. Ornis Scand., 13:11-16.

Reite, O. B., and W. H. Davis. 1966. Thermoregulation of bats exposed to low ambient temperatures. Proc. Soc. Exp. Biol. Med., 121:1212-1215.

Ricklefs, R. A. 1977. On the evolution of reproductive strategies in birds. Amer. Nat., 111:453-478.

Riedesel, M. L., and B. A. Williams. 1976. Continuous 24-hour oxygen consumption studies of *Myotis velifer*. Comp. Biochem. Physiol., 54A:95-99.

Riley, J. L., J. R. Thurston, C. L. Egemo, and H. L. Elliott. 1980. A radio transmitter for transmitting temperatures from small animals. J. Appl. Physiol., 45:1016-1018.

Robinson, W. R., R. H. Peters, and J. Zimmerman. 1983. The effects of body size and temperature on metabolic rate of organisms. Can. J. Zool., 61:281-288.

Saint Girons, H., and S. D. Bradshaw. 1981. Preliminary observations of behavioural thermoregulation in an elapid snake, the dugite, *Pseudonaja affinis* Gunther. J. Royal Soc. West. Australia, 64:13-16.

Saint Girons, H., A. Brosset, and M. C. Saint Girons. 1969. Contribution à la connaissance du cycle annuel de la chauve-souris *Rhinolophus ferrumequinum* (Shreber, 1774). Mammalia, 33:357-470.

Shump, K. A. Jr., and A. U. Shump. 1980. Comparative insulation in vespertilionid bats. Comp. Biochem. Physiol., 66A:351-354.

Slobodkin, L. B. 1960. Ecological energy relationships at the population level. Amer. Nat., 95:213-236.

Sluiter, J. W., and P. F. van Heerdt. 1960. Winterslaap-proeven met de rosse vleermuis. De Levende Natuur, 63:231-240.

Sluiter, J. W., A. M. Voûte, and P. F. van Heerdt. 1973. Hibernation of *Nyctalus noctula*. Period. Biol., 75:181-188.

Smith, E. N. 1980. Physiological radio telemetry of vertebrates. Pp. 45-56, *in* A handbook on biotelemetry and radio tracking. (C. J. Amlaner, Jr. and D. W. MacDonald, eds.). Pergamon Press, Oxford, 804 pp.

Smith, H. R. 1980. Intraperitoneal transmitters in suckling white-footed mice, *Peromyscus leucopus*. Biotelem. Pat. Monit., 7:221-230.

Southwick, E. E. 1973. Remote sensing of body temperature in a captive 25-g bird. Condor, 75:464-466.

Stack, M. H. 1985. The energetics of reproduction in the big brown bat, *Eptesicus fuscus*. Unpubl. Ph.D. dissertation, Boston Univ., Boston, Massachusetts, 283 pp.

Stearns, S. C. 1980. A new view of life-history evolution. Oikos, 35:266-281.

Stones, R. C., and J. E. Wiebers. 1965. Body temperature cycling of winter little brown bats in the cold following heat exposure. Experientia, 21:1-6.

Stones, R. C., and J. E. Wiebers. 1966. Body weight and temperature regulation of *Myotis lucifugus* at a low temperature of 10°C. J. Mammal., 47:520-521.

Stones, R. C., and J. E. Wiebers. 1967. Temperature regulation in the little brown bat, *Myotis lucifugus*. Pp. 97-109, *in* Mammalian hibernation III. (K. C. Fisher, A. R. Dawe, C. P. Lyman, E. Schönbaum and F. E. South, Jr., eds.). American Elsevier, New York, 535 pp.

Studier, E. H. 1981. Energetic advantages of slight drops in body temperature in little brown bats, *Myotis lucifugus*. Comp. Biochem. Physiol., 70A:537-540.

Studier, E. H., and M. J. O'Farrell. 1972. Biology of *Myotis thysanodes* and *M. lucifugus* (Chiroptera: Vespertilionidae)—I. Thermoregulation. Comp. Biochem. Physiol., 41A:567-595.

Studier, E. H., and M. J. O'Farrell. 1980. Physiological ecology of *Myotis*. Pp. 415-424 *in* Proc. 5th Int. Bat Res. Conf. (D. E. Wilson and A. L. Gardner, eds.). Texas Tech Press, Lubbock, 434 pp.

Studier, E. H., and D. E. Wilson. 1970. Thermoregulation in some Neotropical bats. Comp. Biochem. Physiol., 34:251-262.

Studier, E. H., and D. E. Wilson. 1979. Effects of captivity on thermoregulation and metabolism in *Artibeus jamaicensis* (Chiroptera: Phyllostomatidae). Comp. Biochem. Physiol., 62A:347-350.

Swift, C. S. 1979. Designing a simple, inexpensive digital thermometer. J. Clin. Eng., 4:113-120.

Swift, C. S. 1981. Improved digital thermometer design. J. Clin. Eng., 6:227-229.

Trune, D. R., and C. N. Slobodchikoff. 1976. Social effects of roosting on metabolism of the pallid bat *(Antrozous pallidus)*. J. Mammal., 57:656-663.

Townsend, C. R., and R. N. Hughes. 1981. Maximizing net energy returns from foraging. Pp. 86-108, *in* Physiological ecology: An evolutionary approach to resource use. (C. R. Townsend and P. Calow, eds.). Sinauer Press, Sunderland, Massachusetts, 393 pp.

Twente, J. W. Jr., 1955. Some aspects of habitat selection and other behavior of cavern-dwelling bats. Ecology, 36:706-732.

van Heerdt, P. F., and J. W. Sluiter. 1965. Notes on the distribution and behaviour of the noctule bat *(Nyctalus noctula)* in the Netherlands. Mammalia, 29:463-477.

Vaughan, T. A., and T. J. O'Shea. 1976. Roosting

ecology of the pallid bat, *Antrozous pallidus*. J. Mammal., 57:19-42.

Vogt, F. D., and G. R. Lynch. 1982. Influence of ambient temperature, nest availability, huddling, and daily torpor on energy expenditure in the white-footed mouse *Peromyscus leucopus*. Physiol. Zool., 55:56-63.

Wang, L. C. H. 1972. Circadian body temperature of Richardson's ground squirrel under field and laboratory conditions: A comparative radio-telemetric study. Comp. Biochem. Physiol., 43:503-510.

Wang, L. C. H. 1973. Radiotelemetric study of hibernation under natural and laboratory conditions. Amer. J. Physiol., 224:673-677.

Wang, L. C. H. 1978. Energetic and field aspects of mammalian torpor: The Richardson's ground squirrel. Pp. 109-145, *in* Strategies in cold: Natural torpidity and thermogenesis. (L.

C. H. Wang and J. W. Hudson, eds.). Academic Press, New York, 715 pp.

Weigold, H. 1973. Jugendentwicklung der Temperaturregulation bei der Mausohrfledermaus, *Myotis myotis* (Borkhausen, 1797). J. Comp. Physiol., 85:169-212.

Wilson, E. O. 1975. Sociobiology. Belknap Press, Cambridge, Massachusetts, 697 pp.

Wolverton, C., and A. L. Edgar. 1969. Temperature regulation of migrating and hibernating bats in Gratiot County, Michigan. Bios, 40:147-153.

Ysenbrandt, H. J. B., T. A. L. Selten, J. J. M. Verschuren, T. Kock, and H. P. Kimmich. 1976. Biotelemetry, literature survey of the past decade. Biotelemetry, 3:145-250.

Zajonc, R. B. 1965. Social facilitation. Science, 149:269-274.

Chapter 21

Methods of Measuring Metabolic Rate: Respirometry

M. Holly Stack[1]

Department of Biology
Boston University
Boston, Massachusetts 02215 USA

and

David J. Rossi[2]

Department of Electrical Engineering
    and Computer Science
Massachusetts Institute of Technology
Cambridge, Massachusetts 02139 USA

[1] Present Address: Muséum National d'Histoire Naturelle, Laboratoire d'Anatomie Comparée, 55 Rue Buffon, 75005 Paris, France

[2] Present Address: Etudes et Productions Schlumberger, 26 rue de la Cavée, 92140 Clamart, France

1. INTRODUCTION

Estimates of energy metabolism are important in answering questions concerning the physiology of an organism and its role in the ecosystem. The metabolic costs of activities such as foraging, reproduction, and thermoregulation provide answers to ecological questions of strategies for survival, energy balance, and reproductive success (Aspey and Lustick, 1980). Considerable research has focused on rates of energy metabolism because it is one measurement that embraces many underlying processes, and likely "integrates more aspects of animal performance than any other single physiological parameter" (Bartholomew, 1972). Measurement of the metabolic cost of various activities combined with daily time budgets for those activities allows estimates of daily energy budgets (Chapter 18).

Numerous factors, both biotic and abiotic, affect metabolic rate: biotic factors include body mass, age, reproductive condition, nutritional status, food habits, stress, and activity level; abiotic factors include ambient temperature, relative humidity, ambient light, and CO_2 concentration (Gessaman, 1973; Grodzinski and Wunder, 1975). An important consideration in ecological studies of metabolism is to provide a natural environment in the laboratory for such measurements—maintaining abiotic factors within ecologically meaningful levels, while investigating the influence of biotic factors on metabolic rate. The purpose of this chapter is to review the means by which metabolism can be measured, and to describe in detail gas analysis methods for measuring metabolic rate.

2. DIRECT VS. INDIRECT CALORIMETRY

Metabolic rate, the rate of energy consumption or the rate of conversion of chemical energy to heat and external work, can be determined by either direct or indirect calorimetry. Direct calorimetry measures the heat dissipated from an animal at rest. A calorimeter of this type is an insulated animal chamber, in which the heat generated by the animal is determined by measuring the increase in temperature of the surrounding medium, or by measuring the amount of heat that must be removed to maintain a constant chamber temperature. The techniques of direct calorimetry which have been used recently include gradient-layer calorimetry, in which the rate of heat loss from an animal is measured by thermocouples lining the insulated chamber (Benzinger et al., 1958; Pivorun, 1976); air circuit calorimetry, in which the increase in the energy content of the air is measured by differential thermometry and hygrometry between incurrent and excurrent air (Tschegg et al., 1981; Snellen et al., 1983); and heat-exchange calorimetry, in which heat produced by an animal is removed by a continuously flowing coolant within the chamber (Pickwell, 1968). All of these direct calorimetric methods have the advantage that metabolic rate is measured directly as heat energy. However, calibration and operation of these systems is inconvenient, and they impose severe restrictions on the environmental and behavioral conditions possible during experimentation. Although the technique is rarely used, an advantage of direct calorimetry is that total metabolism is measured, and the anaerobic metabolism of an exercising animal can be determined by combining the techniques of direct calorimetry and indirect calorimetry (O_2 consumption).

Indirect calorimetric methods for measuring energy metabolism are almost universally used in metabolism studies because they allow considerable flexibility in experimental design. The principal indirect methods include measurement of O_2 consumption,

CO_2 production, quantity of food utilized, and the turnover rate of doubly labeled water ($^3HH^{18}O$ or $^2HH^{18}O$). Gas analysis methods require confinement or the use of a mask; food consumption and doubly labeled water studies permit estimates under natural conditions, but each has its own particular set of difficulties and assumptions [see Blaxter, 1971; Kunz, 1980 (food consumption); Nagy, 1980; Randolph, 1980 (doubly labeled water); and Chapter 18 for further discussion]. Gas analysis methods will be considered in detail here, including set-up, calibration, and operation of an open-flow system, the method by which $\dot{V}_{O_2}$ (the rate of O_2 consumption) equations are derived, and determination of evaporative water loss (EWL).

3. METABOLIC TERMINOLOGY

There are several terms that are used to describe experimentally measured metabolic rates, and distinctions can be made among them based on experimental conditions, including ambient temperature (T_a), level of activity, recency of feeding of the animal, and duration of measurement (Grodzinski, 1975; Hill, 1976).

1) Basal metabolic rate (BMR), the most commonly measured metabolic value, is the minimal normothermic rate of energy metabolism, or equivalently, the rate of metabolism, measured at thermoneutrality, of a post-absorptive adult awake and at rest, with all factors eliminated which might cause stress. Because of the ambiguity of the term "basal metabolism," especially with regard to poikilotherms and heterotherms, comparative physiologists often prefer to use standard metabolic rate (SMR).

2) Standard metabolic rate (SMR) is the rate of energy metabolism of a post-absorptive animal at rest for a prevailing body temperature. This term is more appropriate than BMR when dealing with bats.

3) Resting metabolic rate (RMR) is the rate of energy metabolism of a resting animal that is not post-absorptive and may be at a T_a below thermoneutrality.

4) Average daily metabolic rate (ADMR) is the mean value of metabolic measurements over a 24-h period at a temperature regime close to natural conditions. This value includes the BMR, the energy of the specific dynamic action of food (SDA), metabolic equivalents of activity and thermoregulation, and the influence of pregnancy or lactation (Randolph, 1980).

BMR is a useful measurement in that it allows comparisons over a wide range of taxa. However, it is the most limited view of metabolism, and under natural conditions BMR may rarely occur. ADMR may be more difficult to measure and more subject to error, but ADMR, as well as RMR, are inherently more meaningful values in ecological studies. Also, there are well-documented diurnal rhythms in energy metabolism for many mammals (Aschoff and Pohl, 1970), including bats (Pearson, 1947). When measuring metabolic rate, the animal's normal circadian rhythm with regard to the sleep-wake cycle should be taken into account, and the time of measurement planned accordingly and reported. Another aspect in measuring metabolism is the animal's microclimate. Although it will not be discussed in detail in this chapter, the "climate space" within which the animal functions thermodynamically, including the primary factors of radiation, humidity, air temperature, and air velocity, influences the metabolic rate and should also be considered (Porter and Gates, 1969; Gates, 1980; Chapter 19).

The respiratory quotient, RQ, is the volume ratio of CO_2 produced to O_2 consumed, and is used to convert the rate of O_2 consumption to a metabolic rate. If the RQ is known, the types of food being oxidized can be determined (carbohydrate, protein, or fat) and the energy equivalent calculated in terms of calories or joules (1 cal = 4.148 joules). For example, if carbohydrates are being used, the volumes of CO_2 produced and O_2 consumed during catabolism are equal, RQ = 1, and energy production is 21.13 J/ml O_2 consumed. If fats are being oxidized exclusively, more O_2 is consumed compared to the CO_2 produced, RQ = 0.71, and energy production is 19.83 J/ml O_2 consumed. If the diet composition or RQ is unknown, an energy conversion factor of 20.08 J/mlO_2 is commonly used (Kleiber, 1975; Hill, 1976). The degree of error in using this value can be estimated by calculating the metabolic rate (see Section 5.1.3) using the extremes of an all-carbohydrate diet (21.13 J/ml O_2) and an all-protein diet (18.66 J/ml O_2), and examining the deviation of the results away from the rate obtained, assuming a value of 20.08 J/ml O_2. Other conditions may result in larger errors when RQ is estimated. Hyperventilation or acidosis leads to an elevated RQ which can reach values as high as 1.7 (Brody, 1945; Knoebel, 1971). Conversely, the RQ may fall below 0.70 during hypoventilation or alkalosis. Synthesis of fat from carbohydrate may also result in RQ values greater than one. Fattened geese have exhibited RQ values as large as 1.47 (Swan, 1974). Synthesis of carbohydrate from fat, as occurs in hibernating mammals, may be the cause of RQ values below 0.70 (Kleiber, 1975).

An infrequently used technique for assessing metabolic rate is the measurement of CO_2 production alone. Using this technique, if the type of food is unknown and the RQ is estimated (assuming an energy conversion factor of 20.08 J/ml O_2), relatively large errors in the metabolic rate (as much as 15-20%) may result (Hill, 1976), since the energy equivalent for CO_2, unlike that for O_2, differs markedly among the three food types. Another drawback to the use of CO_2 production for measuring metabolic rate is the assumption that a steady state exists between CO_2 elimination in the lungs and CO_2 production at the cellular level. Sudden exercise or hyperventilation, for example, can disrupt the steady state (for O_2 consumption also), resulting in larger error in the estimation of CO_2 production than in O_2 consumption due to the greater solubility of CO_2 in body fluids.

There are two general methods of gas analysis that will be discussed in the following sections. In the closed system technique, an animal is sealed into a closed chamber where it consumes O_2 and produces CO_2. The CO_2 is absorbed (by a suitable compound placed within the chamber), resulting in either a drop in pressure or volume according to the type of system used. In the open-flow or open-circuit technique, air flows through the animal chamber, and the outflow and inflow gases are analyzed to calculate O_2 consumption or CO_2 production.

4. CLOSED SYSTEM

The simplest system for the measurement of O_2 consumption is the closed system. The closed system relies on the ideal gas law

$$PV = nRT \qquad (1)$$

which states that at constant temperature, the amount of any gas (n in moles) is directly proportional to the product of pressure and volume. During respiration, O_2 is consumed and CO_2 is produced, and in a closed system the expired CO_2 is absorbed (usually by NaOH or KOH). If either pressure (volumetric system) or volume (manometric system) is held constant, the change in the other term will indicate the amount of O_2 consumed (Morrison and West, 1975). In a manometric system, for instance, the chamber volume is held constant, and since CO_2 is absent, any decrease in overall chamber pressure is due to a decrease in the partial pressure of O_2, regardless of the value of RQ.

A closed system is relatively inexpensive and easy to operate, and may be more reliable than an open-flow system when measuring very small O_2 consumption rates, as with bats under hibernating conditions. However, the use of a closed system may present difficulties with large animals or animals having high metabolic rates, in which case O_2 may be rapidly depleted below physiologically accepta-

ble levels. Also, the oxygen in the chamber must be replenished during the course of a lengthy experiment by either manual or automated means, and the chamber must be airtight and maintained at a constant temperature. Closed-system respirometers that have been widely used are the automated Morrison respirometer (Morrison and Grodzinski, 1975) and the Kalabukhov-Skvortsov respirometer (Gorecki, 1975). An automated digitally-controlled electrolytic respirometer has been described by Gutmann (1983). Several studies of bat metabolism have utilized closed-system respirometry (e.g., Morrison, 1948; Hock, 1951; Herreid, 1963, 1967; Bartholomew et al., 1964; Hayward and Ball, 1966; Leitner and Nelson, 1967; Morrison and McNab, 1967; Stones and Wiebers, 1967; Holyoak and Stones, 1971; McNab, 1974).

5. OPEN SYSTEM

In open-circuit or open-flow respirometry, air is allowed to flow through the animal chamber. The concentration of O_2 in the gas exiting the chamber is compared to the O_2 concentration in the incurrent gas, and the difference is used to calculate O_2 consumption. The most obvious advantage of open-flow respirometry is that a constant flow of O_2 is supplied to the animal; also, ambient temperature need not be precisely controlled, and an airtight chamber is not necessarily required. Measurement of the O_2 content of the chamber excurrent gas is accomplished through the use of an oxygen analyzer (e.g., paramagnetic type, such as those made by Beckman, or electrochemical type, such as those made by Applied Electrochemistry) which allows continuous and accurate measurements of oxygen consumption over extended periods of time. Most studies of bat metabolism have employed open-system respirometry (Henshaw and Folk, 1963; Herreid and Schmidt-Nielsen, 1966; Leitner, 1966; Carpenter and Graham, 1967; Licht and Leitner, 1967; Carpenter, 1968, 1969, 1975; McNab, 1969, 1980; Bartholomew et al., 1970; O'Farrell and Studier, 1970; Studier and O'Farrell, 1972, 1976; Thomas and Suthers, 1972; Thomas, 1975, 1981; Riedesel and Williams, 1976; Trune and Slobodchikoff, 1976; Noll, 1979; Studier and Wilson, 1979; Studier, 1981; Thomas et al., 1984; Stack, 1985).

Less frequently, CO_2 production is also determined either gravimetrically (Kendeigh, 1939; Withers, 1977; Williams and Nagy, 1984) or by means of an infrared CO_2 analyzer (e.g., Applied Electrochemistry, Beckman). Gravimetric measurement of CO_2 production is performed by passing excurrent air through a water absorbent (e.g., $CaSO_4$, Drierite), followed by a CO_2 absorbent [e.g., NaOH-impregnated asbestos (Ascarite)] and a second stage of water absorbent. The chemical reaction occurring in the CO_2 absorbent is

$$2\,NaOH + CO_2 \rightarrow Na_2CO_3 + H_2O \qquad (2)$$

and the water produced is partially absorbed by the CO_2 absorbent, with the remainder absorbed by the last stage of H_2O absorbent. The mass of absorbed CO_2 may be inferred by measuring the mass change of the CO_2 absorbent *and* the second H_2O absorbent over a fixed time interval; denote this mass change as M grams. The volume of CO_2 at STP may be calculated by solving equation (1) for the volume of CO_2, $V = nRT/P$. Here, n is M/44 moles (44 is the molecular weight of CO_2), R is 8.31×10^7 (dyne cm)/(mole °K), T is 273 °K, and P is 1.01×10^6 dynes/cm². This leads to a conversion factor of 510.5 ml CO_2/g CO_2. The gravimetric method was validated by Kendeigh (1939), with an error of less than 1%. With the availability of both O_2 and CO_2 measurements, for a non-active animal, a value of RQ can be estimated.

The following is a description of the open-flow respirometry system, including discussions of the system hardware, calibration and operating procedures, and a derivation of the appropriate equations to calculate $\dot{V}_{O_2}$. The single-channel apparatus is discussed first due to its simplicity. In practice, to increase the amount of collectable data and to measure the metabolic rates of animals under varying conditions (e.g., solitary vs. clustered bats, male vs. female, pregnant vs. non-reproductive female), a single set of O_2 and CO_2 measuring equipment is often sequentially shared among several animal chambers, and a representative multichannel system is also presented.

5.1. Single-Channel Open-Flow System

5.1.1. System Description

A variety of configurations of the open-flow gas analysis system may be used for determining an animal's rate of oxygen consumption (and possibly CO_2 production). In every case, these systems contain pressure and flow regulating and measuring components, as well as the oxygen (and possibly CO_2) analyzer. Since the removal of CO_2 and water from the air sample simplifies the calculation of oxygen consumption, a CO_2 absorbent and a water absorbent are often used prior to the introduction of the gas to the analyzer. Because wet air tends to hydrate the CO_2 absorbent, and because water is generated during CO_2 absorption [see equation (2)], the CO_2 absorbent is always preceded and followed by a water absorbent.

The principal differences between various configurations of open-flow systems involve the following.

Placement of the pump—In some systems, the pump is placed at the chamber inlet (or a source of pressurized air is used) and air is pumped into the chamber, which is well sealed and operated at a slight positive pressure (positive pressure system). More often, the pump is situated downstream from the chamber exhaust port and air is pulled through the chamber, which is operated at a slight negative pressure or vacuum (negative pressure system) and does not have to be tightly sealed.

Conditioning of the animal chamber incurrent gas—The chamber inflow gas may or may not have CO_2 and/or H_2O removed, and the type of inflow gas-conditioning is a matter of choice. The removal of CO_2 and H_2O prior to passage through a flow meter makes the calculation of the rate of O_2 consumption ($\dot{V}_{O_2}$) somewhat easier but is not required. Water may be removed prior to flow measurement, and the air rehumidified before entering the animal chamber. However, in practice it may not always be possible to condition the chamber incurrent gas, particularly with a poorly-sealed chamber, as in field measurement, or with use of an open mask.

Placement of the flow meters—Gas flow rates are measured and controlled at appropriate points in the system using rotameters, mass flow controllers, high precision null-type flow measuring instruments such as a hot-wire anemometer (Doebelin, 1975), or similar flow measuring devices. The flow meter measuring the chamber flow rate may be situated either before or after the chamber, the former case requiring a well-sealed chamber.

Several types of chambers are used in open-flow respirometry and are most commonly fashioned from paint cans, glass jars, or lucite containers. The environmental radiative properties of the walls of the metabolism chamber should be considered, particularly when using shiny paint cans (flat black paint is often used to coat the inside of the chamber; true optically black paint, i.e., of high emissivity over a broad range of infrared wavelengths, is available). Hardware cloth, window screen, or rough-cut wood attached vertically in the chamber allows the bats to hang in a natural position. A layer of mineral oil on the bottom of the chamber, beneath a platform of hardware cloth or coarse screening, prevents evaporation from urine and feces. For ecological studies, simulation of a natural roost for the metabolism chamber is recommended. For example, with barn-dwelling bats, mortices cut in beams of dry wood and covered with lucite make appropriate metabolism chambers (Fig. 1). With this type of chamber, however, evaporation from urine and feces may influence the measurement of EWL. Some creativity is required to make simulated natural roosts in metabolism

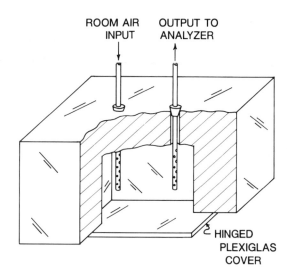

ROOM AIR INPUT   OUTPUT TO ANALYZER

HINGED PLEXIGLAS COVER

Figure 1. Cutaway section of a mortice in a wooden beam modified as a metabolic chamber.

chambers suitable for bats with varied roosting habits, such as cave-dwelling species or foliage roosters. To maintain a controlled temperature, the metabolism chamber can be housed in a constant-temperature cabinet or, if the chamber is airtight, submerged in a water bath. The open-flow method assumes the sampling of well-mixed chamber air. This may be accomplished by placing the incurrent and excurrent ports at opposite ends of the chamber. Mixing may be further enhanced by use of a small fan or a magnetic stirrer, or by diffusing incurrent and excurrent air with multiple outlet manifolds.

No single open-flow respirometer design is optimal for all metabolism experiments, so four representative systems are presented, all of which have the pump situated downstream from the chamber, but they differ in flow meter placement and incurrent gas conditioning. In each of the four cases, the equation for calculating $\dot{V}_{O_2}$ from the measured quantities is presented. The method for deriving the equation for $\dot{V}_{O_2}$ is illustrated for the first case; the general approach toward the derivation is the same for other system configurations.

A basic system with incurrent gas stream conditioning is shown in Fig. 2. In this system, CO_2 and H_2O are removed from the incurrent gas, and a flow meter is situated at the chamber input. The chamber flow rate, monitored with the *chamber flow meter*, is adjusted using the needle valve labeled *chamber flow adjust*. In order to maintain an appropriate chamber O_2 level, the chamber flow rate is generally larger than the recommended O_2 analyzer flow rate, and only a fraction of the chamber outflow gas is passed through the analyzer. The remainder is vented to room air (at a point distant from the animal chamber and room air inlet) and the analyzer flow rate, monitored with the *analyzer flow meter,* is adjusted using the *bleed valve.*

The appropriate chamber flow rate to be used during respirometry depends on the size, number, and the level of activity of animals in the metabolism chamber. An excessive flow rate results in a small measured deflection away from the ambient air baseline, and causes high rates of EWL. Too low of a flow rate causes a depletion in the levels of chamber O_2 and a build-up of the levels of chamber CO_2 and humidity, which may affect normal respiration. The flow rate (and the resultant chamber humidity level) also influences an animal's ability to dissipate metabolic heat by evaporative cooling (Lasiewski et al., 1966). Normally, the concentration of O_2 in dry, CO_2-free excurrent air should not fall below 19%, and is usually above 20%; the level of chamber CO_2 should not exceed 1%.

In addition to the measurement of chamber O_2 concentration, the CO_2 content of the chamber outflow may be measured by several means, including the introduction of a CO_2 analyzer as shown in Fig. 2. The O_2 and CO_2 content measured by these analyzers are gen-

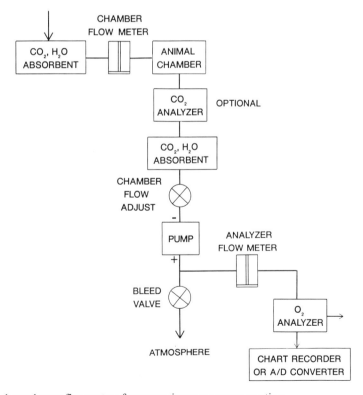

Figure 2. A single-channel open-flow system for measuring oxygen consumption.

erally available as electrical voltages, which can either be displayed on most analog chart recorders or transferred to a computer or magnetic storage medium via an analog-to-digital converter (ADC).

The simple system shown in Fig. 2 can be modified or improved as desired. Analyzer flow and pressure must be maintained at a constant level throughout the experiment; if these quantities tend to drift with time, long term stability of the measurement system may be improved by the addition of a mass flow controller or a pressure regulator. This is particularly desirable in cases where the pressure at the output of a conventional pump (measured using a manometer) has a tendency to decrease over extended periods of time. This decrease results in a decreased pressure and flow rate at the analyzer input port, which (because the instrument is calibrated at a fixed pressure/flow setting) leads to a shift in the instrument calibration point and an erroneous indication of O_2 content. The addition of a pressure regulator to this system may be achieved by removing the bleed valve and inserting a pressure regulator after the pump output; in this case the pressure is adjusted to achieve the desired analyzer flow rate.

During system construction, care should be taken to design a system that responds quickly and accurately to changes in the chamber O_2 level. Temperature readings from thermocouples in the chamber are effectively instantaneous, whereas air sampled from the chamber must pass through tubing and various other components before oxygen or humidity can be measured. This creates a time delay in the results which cannot be ignored. This delay can be controlled to some extent by minimizing the volume of the system, by limiting the diameter and length of the tubing, and using small chambers and drying tubes. If good, constant-pressure air pumps or mass flow controllers are used, then the time lag of a system can be accurately measured using a timed pulse of N_2 or CO_2 introduced into the chamber with a syringe. This is particularly important when attempting to relate discrete behavioral or temperature events to oxygen consumption patterns, using instantaneous oxygen consumption techniques (Bartholomew et al., 1981).

5.1.2. Calibration and Operating Procedure

Precise calculation of oxygen consumption rates depends upon stable flow rates. Prior to system construction all system flow meters should be calibrated using a gas mass flow meter or a volume meter (e.g., Tylan Mass Flow Controller, Brooks Vol-U-Meter). If instantaneous rates of oxygen consumption are required, the effective volume of the system (respirometer, downstream tubing, and apparatus) must be accurately measured. This is easily done by injecting N_2 or CO_2 into the chamber to reduce the O_2 content, and by plotting the washout curve for the system (see Bartholomew et al., 1981).

Checking for system leaks and ensuring complete drying of the air before it reaches the oxygen analyzer can be accomplished by watching for condensation in a glass tubing coil placed in ice water or a dry ice bath. This is particularly advisable if water-loss measurements are to be made gravimetrically.

System operation is straightforward: 1) *close* the chamber flow valve and *open* the bleed valve, 2) turn on the pump, 3) open the chamber flow valve to obtain the desired chamber flow rate as displayed on the chamber flow meter, and 4) close the bleed valve to obtain the recommended flow rate through the analyzer as displayed on the analyzer flow meter. Care should be exercised in adjusting the rate of flow to paramagnetic analyzers, as excessive flow may damage the analyzer.

Once the flow rates are established, paramagnetic O_2 analyzers must be calibrated (Applied Electrochemistry analyzers do not require calibration since oxygen measurement is relative to an arbitrary baseline). This is typically accomplished by using two gases of precisely-known O_2 content (the upscale gas may be dry, CO_2-free room air, taken to be 20.953% O_2) (Hitchcock, 1966).

The calibration gases are introduced sequentially into the sample stream and the instrument span and zero are adjusted; the exact calibration procedure is instrument-dependent, and may be found in the analyzer operating manual. An alternate calibration technique utilizing only one gas involves N_2 dilution (Fedak et al., 1981). Paramagnetic oxygen analyzers may also be calibrated manometrically, by closing off the system and varying the pressure (and thus the partial pressure of O_2). After the analyzer is calibrated, the animal(s) is introduced into the chamber, and experiments are commenced after the appropriate acclimation interval, usually one to two hours.

One assumption implicit in use of the open-flow technique is that barometric pressure remains constant throughout the duration of an experiment, since changes in barometric pressure result in changes in the volume and partial pressure (but not concentration) of oxygen in the air. However, since the calculation of O_2 consumption depends only on the deflection of the O_2 content away from the ambient air baseline, errors due to barometric pressure variations may be minimized by frequent monitoring of the ambient air baseline. Also, at the end of experimentation, the system should be recalibrated to establish any change in analyzer span.

In addition to O_2 content, several other measurements are typically made. Barometric pressure and relative humidity should be recorded for each experiment, as well as the water content of incurrent air if no conditioning of this air is performed. Before and after each experiment, body mass is measured and either the mean or minimum value is used in calculating mass-specific $\dot{V}_{O_2}$. Body temperature is usually either recorded before and after each experiment by taking a rectal temperature with a quick-registering thermometer, or continuously monitored telemetrically, by a thermocouple inserted rectally or implanted in the body (Chapter 20). While the invasive techniques greatly increase the amount of temperature data obtained, consideration should be given to the risk of alter-

ing the normal metabolism due to discomfort or physical restraints on the animal.

5.1.3. Derivation of $\dot{V}_{O_2}$ Equations

This section is concerned with the calculation of oxygen consumption ($\dot{V}_{O_2}$) from the quantities that are measured during experimentation. In general, we have used symbols (Table 1) defined by Depocas and Hart (1957) and Hill (1972). Notationally, the ′ symbol denotes a CO_2-free condition, the subscript I indicates incurrent gas, the subscript E denotes excurrent or exhaust gas, $\dot{V}$ indicates a rate of gas flow, and all volumes of gases are corrected to standard temperature and pressure (STP). The oxygen consumption rate $\dot{V}_{O_2}$ is usually calculated in units of ml O_2 g^{-1} h^{-1} (STP). If the RQ or the precise diet composition is unknown, an energy equivalent of 20.08 J/ml O_2 is used to convert rates of oxygen consumption to metabolic rates.

For the system illustrated in Fig. 2, the gases present at each important point in the

Table 1. Definition of symbols used for calculating oxygen consumption.

$\dot{V}_{O_2}$ = the oxygen consumption of the animal in volume of dry oxygen per unit time, corrected to STP

$\dot{V}_I$ = the volume of dry ambient air flowing into the animal chamber per unit time, corrected to STP

$\dot{V}'_I$ = the volume of dry, CO_2-free ambient air flowing into the animal chamber per unit time, corrected to STP

$\dot{V}'_E$ = the volume of dry, CO_2-free ambient air flowing out of the animal chamber per unit time, corrected to STP

$\dot{V}_{I,W}$ = the volume of ambient air flowing into the animal chamber per unit time, corrected to STP (water not removed)

$F_{I_{O_2}}$ = the volume fractional concentration of oxygen in dry inlet air; = 0.20946 (Hitchcock, 1966)

$F'_{I_{O_2}}$ = the volume fractional concentration of oxygen in dry, CO_2-free inlet air; = 0.20953 (Hitchcock, 1966)

$F_{I_{H_2O}}$ = the volume fractional concentration of water in inlet air

$F'_{E_{O_2}}$ = the volume fractional concentration of oxygen in dry, CO_2-free outlet air

$F_{I_{CO_2}}$ = the volume fractional concentration of CO_2 in dry inlet air; = 0.0003 (Hitchcock, 1966)

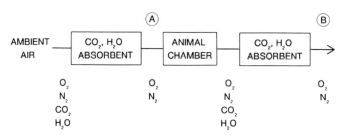

Figure 3. Schematic representation of the gases present at various points in the system shown in Fig. 2.

system are shown schematically in Fig. 3. The measured or available quantities are $\dot{V}'_I$ (measured at point A by the chamber flow meter), $F'_{I_{O_2}}$ and $F'_{E_{O_2}}$ (measured at point B by the O_2 analyzer).

The general approach toward deriving an equation for $\dot{V}_{O_2}$, the rate of O_2 consumption by the animal, is based on the fact that O_2 within the system is conserved (what flows into the animal chamber either leaves the chamber or is consumed by the animal). First, expressions are developed for the oxygen flow rate into and out of the chamber, written in terms of measured or available quantities. Then, the difference between excurrent and incurrent O_2 rates is set equal to $\dot{V}_{O_2}$.

To illustrate this approach, consider the system shown in Fig. 3; this system configuration and the corresponding equations were originally given by Depocas and Hart (1957). At the chamber inlet point A, only O_2 and N_2 are present, and the total flow rate is $\dot{V}'_I$; the O_2 flow rate is then equal to $\dot{V}'_I F'_{I_{O_2}}$. At the input to the analyzer, point B, again only O_2 and N_2 are present, and by the conservation of oxygen, the total flow rate at point B is $\dot{V}'_I - \dot{V}_{O_2}$; the O_2 flow rate at point B is then equal to $(\dot{V}'_I - \dot{V}_{O_2}) F'_{E_{O_2}}$.

By the conservation of system O_2, the difference between the outflow and the inflow rates of O_2 is equal to the O_2 consumption of the animal:

$$\dot{V}_{O_2} = \dot{V}'_I F'_{I_{O_2}} - (\dot{V}'_I - \dot{V}_{O_2}) F'_{E_{O_2}}$$
$$= \dot{V}'_I F'_{I_{O_2}} - \dot{V}'_I F'_{E_{O_2}} + \dot{V}_{O_2} F'_{E_{O_2}}$$

Rearranging,

$$\dot{V}_{O_2} = \frac{\dot{V}'_I [F'_{I_{O_2}} - F'_{E_{O_2}}]}{1 - F'_{E_{O_2}}} \qquad (4)$$

which is equation 2 of Hill (1972).

As discussed previously, a variety of open-flow respirometer system configurations are possible, depending on the type of incurrent gas conditioning (CO_2 and H_2O removal) and the location of chamber flow meters. Three alternative system configurations are shown in Fig. 4, each of which may have certain advantages for particular types of experimentation.

The system illustrated in Fig. 4A is similar to that in Fig. 2, except that CO_2 is not absorbed from the chamber incurrent gas; this system and the $\dot{V}_{O_2}$ equation are described as condition B by Hill (1972). In this system, the measured or available quantities are $\dot{V}_I'$ (measured by the chamber flow meter), $F'_{I_{O_2}}$, $F_{I_{CO_2}}$, and $F'_{E_{O_2}}$ (measured by the O_2 analyzer).

The general approach toward deriving an equation for $\dot{V}_{O_2}$, the rate of O_2 consumption by the animal, is identical to that described for the system in Fig. 2, and leads to the following expression [equation 4 of Hill (1972)],

$$\dot{V}_{O_2} = (1 - F_{I_{CO_2}}) \dot{V}_1 \left\{ \frac{F'_{I_{O_2}} - F'_{E_{O_2}}}{1 - F'_{E_{O_2}}} \right\} \qquad (5)$$

It is known that the removal of water from the chamber incurrent gas may cause

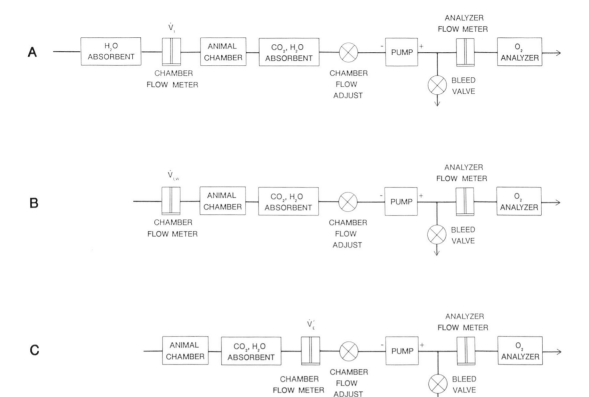

Figure 4. Three alternative system configurations with different inflow gas conditioning and chamber flow meter locations. (A) Chamber flow meter situated at chamber inflow; only water is removed from inflow gas. (B) Chamber flow meter situated at chamber inflow; no conditioning of inflow gas. (C) Chamber flow meter situated at chamber outflow; no conditioning of inflow gas.

water stress in the animal under study, which in turn can affect the metabolic rate (Reese and Haines, 1978). Because of this, it may be desirable to perform no conditioning of the incurrent gas, as shown in Fig. 4B. An alternative approach is to dry the input air, measure the flow rate, and then rehumidify the air before it enters the animal chamber [equation (5) is used in this case]. Because the flow meter is situated at the chamber inflow, however, the chamber must be well sealed. In this system, the measured or available quantities are $\dot{V}_{I,W}$ (measured by the chamber flow meter) $F'_{I_{O_2}}$, $F_{I_{CO_2}}$ and $F'_{E_{O_2}}$ (measured by the O_2 analyzer).

The general approach toward deriving an equation for the rate of O_2 consumption by the animal, $\dot{V}_{O_2}$, is identical to that described for the system in Fig. 2, and leads to the following expression,

$$\dot{V}_{O_2} = (1 - F_{I_{CO_2}})(1 - F_{I_{H_2O}})\dot{V}_{I,W}\left\{\frac{F'_{I_{O_2}} - F'_{E_{O_2}}}{1 - F'_{E_{O_2}}}\right\}(6)$$

It is not always possible, particularly in field studies or with use of an open mask, to insure that the animal chamber (or mask) is well sealed. In this case the chamber flow meter may be situated on the chamber outflow, as shown in Fig. 4C (also, this arrangement has the advantage that it requires the connection of only one line to the chamber). As pointed out by Depocas and Hart (1957), $\dot{V}_{O_2}$ may be calculated without knowledge of the animal's RQ, provided the chamber excurrent rate is measured after CO_2 removal. For the configuration shown in Fig. 4C, the available or measured quantities are $\dot{V}_E$ (measured by the chamber flow meter), $F'_{I_{O_2}}$, and $F'_{E_{O_2}}$ (measured by the analyzer). Analysis leads to the following expression

$$\dot{V}_{O_2} = \dot{V}_E \left\{ \frac{F'_{I_{O_2}} - F'_{E_{O_2}}}{1 - F'_{I_{O_2}}} \right\} \qquad (7)$$

Other system configurations are possible in addition to those shown in Figs. 2 and 4. See Fedak et al. (1981) and Withers (1977) for a discussion of alternative configurations, including systems with the flow meter, followed by the H_2O and CO_2 absorbents, situated downstream from the chamber, and systems in which no absorbents are used.

In practice, the value of $F'_{E_{O_2}}$ recorded by the analyzer during chamber sampling varies continuously. A representative value of $F'_{E_{O_2}}$ is usually calculated periodically (e.g., every 5 min), and is determined during each interval by fitting the best horizontal line to the recorded data. For the interval between time t_0 and t_1, this is achieved by integrating the area A under the curve between times t_0 and t_1, and using the average value $A/(t_1 - t_0)$.

Instantaneous rates of oxygen consumption (departure events from steady-state $\dot{V}_{O_2}$) can be measured by taking the first derivative of the $F'_{E_{O_2}}$ between t_0 and t_1. Consult Bartholomew et al. (1981) for details.

5.1.4. Evaporative Water Loss Determination

Evaporative water loss (EWL), that is, the rate at which H_2O is lost from cutaneous and respiratory surfaces by the animals, is a major source of water loss in bats or any small mammal (Chapter 22). Rates of EWL are important in dealing with questions of water flux,

and can be studied concurrently with rates of metabolism determined by open-flow respirometry.

Two techniques commonly used in estimating EWL in an open-flow system are gravimetric and electronic sensor methods. Evaporative water loss may be determined gravimetrically by introducing a pre-weighed quantity of H_2O absorbent into the excurrent air flow at the chamber outlet for a known amount of time, prior to the air flow passing through the system H_2O and CO_2 absorbents. (A pair of electronic solenoids may be arranged to control the air flow, which either totally bypasses the EWL water absorbent, or passes completely through it.) If H_2O is removed from the chamber incurrent air or the water content of incurrent air is known, the difference between the chamber excurrent and incurrent water mass flow rates represents the EWL. Alternatively, electronic humidity sensors such as dew point hygrometers (e.g., EG&G or Yellow Springs Instruments) are introduced in the chamber incurrent and excurrent air flows, and from knowledge of the air flow rate and the difference between the two sensors (or the difference between the outlet sensor and reference air humidity), the EWL may be estimated. EWL, usually expressed in g H_2O/h or normalized for body mass, is easily calculated using dew point temperature/vapor pressure conversions from meteorological tables (Goff and Gratch, 1946; List, 1966). Bernstein et al. (1977) give simpler approximations for calculating water loss from dew point hygrometry, but if a computer or programmable calculator is available one can most easily employ the original, and more accurate, conversion formulae. Estimates of EWL will be affected by evaporation from urine and feces if they are not trapped in the metabolic chamber by a layer of oil.

5.2. Multiple-Channel Open-Flow System

In practice, in order to increase the amount of data that can be collected, multiple chambers are often run simultaneously, using, for exam-

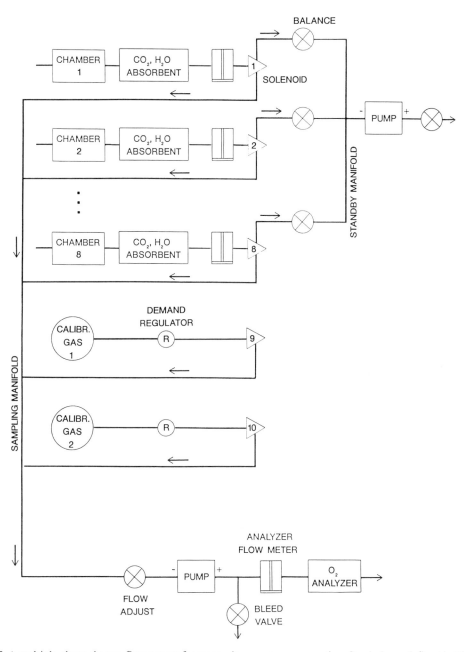

Figure 5. A multiple-channel open-flow system for measuring oxygen consumption. Symbols are defined in Fig. 2.

ple, the multiple channel system shown in Fig. 5. This system has two negative pressure (or vacuum) manifolds: 1) a *sampling* manifold through which the sequentially selected gas is fed to the gas analysis system, and 2) a *standby* manifold driven by a single large pump, which maintains chamber flow rates during nonsampling or standby intervals. The gas sampling apparatus, which at any time samples from one of the multiple sources (ten in this example), is controlled by an automatic 10-channel stream selector (e.g.,

Beckman). This selector sequentially activates designated electronic solenoids, providing for the sampling of up to 8 animal chambers (fewer may be selected) and two calibration gases, with programmable sampling dwell times that are typically multiples of 5 min. The calibration gases are metered to the system through demand regulators.

Each of the channels in Fig. 5 is virtually identical to the single-channel system shown in Fig. 4C. Each channel has its own flow meter, and a *balance* needle valve which is used to equalize the chamber flow rate during sampling and nonsampling intervals, so that respiratory gas equilibrium is maintained. Aside from these changes, the system, its operation, and the $\dot{V}_{O_2}$ calculation are identical to that of the single-channel system described above. The sampling manifold is switched among different chambers, and it is important to minimize the time it takes for the system to respond to a newly-selected channel. This is accomplished by keeping tubing diameter and length as small as possible, particularly downstream from the solenoids, and, as shown in Fig. 5, by placing the CO_2 and water absorbents upstream from the solenoids. If the chamber flow rates tend to drift with time, it may be necessary to include pressure regulation in the standby manifold.

5.3. Computerized Data-Gathering and Analysis

Respirometry is a technique that lends itself well to computerized data gathering methods. In the simplest case, this might entail gathering oxygen analyzer and thermocouple amplifier outputs at a set interval over a period of time. However, the greatest advantage in computerization comes from the ability to handle large quantities of raw data and to rapidly manipulate it through otherwise laborious equations.

Computerized data gathering involves interfacing electronic analyzers or other analog transducers with a computer using an analog-to-digital converter (ADC). Some degree of signal conditioning may be required to bring the voltage input of the device into the analysis range of the ADC, by multiplying, dividing, or inverting the signal with a small amplifier circuit. The resolution of such a system, which is much greater than manual plotting techniques, is determined by the resolution of the ADC.

One such data acquisition system, costing about $2,000, is available from John Lighton at UCLA. It requires little knowledge of digital or analog electronics, and setting-up time is minimal. The system is based on the Acorn BBC Microcomputer, which is an innovative 8-bit machine with a built-in, 4-channel, 12-bit ADC. It can measure voltages, count impulses, and control external devices simultaneously. The software is designed for respirometry, but can be adapted for most laboratory applications involving input from analog devices. It includes programs for calculating regression equations for analog devices, determining effective volume of a respirometry system, and for interfacing with other computers via a serial link. The main program collects data from the 4-channel ADC at intervals ranging from 0.25 seconds to several hours, while displaying the data on-screen in calibrated, graphic form. Analysis programs allow manipulation of the data file on-screen, calculating time delays, offsets, and corrections for temperature, pressure, and flow meter placement. It then applies standard equations including integration to calculate $\dot{V}_{O_2}$ and derivation for instantaneous calculations. For more information contact the sources listed in Appendix 1.

6. SUMMARY

There are a number of techniques for determining an animal's metabolic rate, i.e., the rate of energy consumption. Direct methods of calorimetry have the advantage of determining the metabolic rate directly as heat energy, but they tend to involve complex systems, and severe constraints are imposed on the experimental measurement conditions. Indirect methods of calorimetry based on respirometry are more often used to determine metabolic rate. These methods do not measure metabolic rate directly, but infer metabolic rate from measurements of O_2 consumption and/or CO_2 production, using either a closed- or an open-flow system. Closed system respirometry is inexpensive, simple to operate, and potentially useful in measuring small O_2 consumption rates. The open-flow system, considered in detail in this chapter, has the advantages of continuous ventilation of the chamber and considerable flexibility in system design. Gravimetric methods may be used in conjunction with open-flow systems measuring O_2 consumption to determine CO_2 production (and thus the respiratory quotient) and evaporative water loss. Open-flow systems are also easily configured, with the addition of a multichannel stream selector, to monitor several metabolic chambers sequentially.

7. ACKNOWLEDGMENTS

Support for equipment used in the design of open-flow systems and the computerized data-gathering system came from National Science Foundation grants (SER-14984 and BSR-831482) to T. H. Kunz. We thank G. P. Bell, R. W. Hill, T. H. Kunz, E. H. Studier, and two anonymous reviewers for many useful suggestions, and we are grateful to R. W. Hill for valuable discussions.

8. REFERENCES

Aschoff, J., and H. Pohl. 1970. Rhythmic variations in energy metabolism. Fed. Proc., 29:1541-1552.

Aspey, W. P., and S. I. Lustick, eds. 1980. Behavioral energetics: The cost of survival in vertebrates. Ohio State Univ. Press, Columbus, 300 pp.

Bartholomew, G. A. 1972. Energy metabolism. Pp.

44-72, *in* Animal physiology: Principles and adaptations. (M. S. Gordon, ed.). Macmillan, New York, 592 pp.

Bartholomew, G. A., W. R. Dawson, and R. C. Lasiewski. 1970. Thermoregulation and heterothermy in some of the smaller flying foxes (Megachiroptera) of New Guinea. Z. Vergl. Physiol., 70:196-209.

Bartholomew, G. A., P. Leitner, and J. E. Nelson. 1964. Body temperature, oxygen consumption, and heart rate in three species of Australian flying foxes. Physiol. Zool., 37:179-198.

Bartholomew, G. A., D. Vleck, and C. M. Vleck. 1981. Instantaneous measurements of oxygen consumption during pre-flight warm-up and post-flight cooling in sphingid and saturniid moths. J. Exp. Biol., 90:17-32.

Benzinger, T. H., R. G. Huebscher, D. Minard, and C. Kitzinger. 1958. Human calorimetry by means of the gradient principle. J. Appl. Physiol., 12:S1-S24.

Bernstein, M. H., D. M. Hudson, J. M. Stearns, and R. W. Hoyt. 1977. Measurement of evaporative water loss in small animals by dew-point hygrometry. J. Appl. Physiol.: Resp. Environ. Exer. Physiol., 43:302-385.

Blaxter, K. L. 1971. Methods of measuring the energy metabolism of animals and interpretation of results obtained. Fed. Proc., 30:1436-1443.

Brody, S. 1945. Bioenergetics and growth. Reinhold, New York, 1023 pp.

Carpenter, R. E. 1968. Salt and water metabolism in the marine fish-eating bat, *Pizonyx vivesi*. Comp. Biochem. Physiol., 24:951-964.

Carpenter, R. E. 1969. Structure and function of the kidney and the water balance of desert bats. Physiol. Zool., 42:288-302.

Carpenter, R. E. 1975. Flight metabolism of flying foxes. Pp. 883-890, *in* Swimming and flying in nature. Vol. 2. (T. Y. -T. Wu, C. J. Brokaw and C. Brennen, eds.). Plenum Press, New York, 1005 pp.

Carpenter, R. E., and J. B. Graham. 1967. Physiological responses to temperature in the long-nosed bat, *Leptonycteris sanborni*. Comp. Biochem. Physiol., 22:709-722.

Depocas, F., and J. S. Hart. 1957. Use of the Pauling oxygen analyzer for measurement of oxygen consumption of animals in open-circuit systems and in a short-lag, closed-circuit apparatus. J. Appl. Physiol., 10:388-392.

Doebelin, E. O. 1975. Measurement systems:

Application and design. McGraw-Hill, New York, 772 pp.

Fedak, M. A., L. Rome, and H. J. Seeherman. 1981. One-step N_2-dilution technique for calibrating open-circuit $\dot{V}_{O_2}$ measuring systems. J. Appl. Physiol.: Resp. Environ. Exer. Physiol., 51:772-776.

Gates, D. M. 1980. Biophysical ecology. Springer-Verlag, New York, 611 pp.

Gessaman, J. A., ed. 1973. Ecological energetics of homeotherms: A view compatible with ecological modeling. Utah State Univ. Monographs Series, 20:1-155.

Goff, J. A., and S. Gratch. 1946. Low-pressure properties of water from −160 to 212°F. Trans. Amer. Soc. Heat. Vent. Engr., 52:95-122.

Gorecki, A. 1975. Kalabukhov-Skvortsov respirometer and resting metabolic rate measurement. Pp. 309-313, in Methods for ecological bioenergetics. (W. Grodzinski, R. Z. Klekowski and A. Duncan, eds.). IBP Handbook No. 24. Blackwell Sci. Publ., Oxford, 367 pp.

Grodzinski, W. 1975. Energy flow through a vertebrate population. Pp. 65-94, in Methods for ecological bioenergetics. (W. Grodzinski, R. Z. Klekowski, and A. Duncan, eds.). IBP Handbook No. 24. Blackwell Sci. Publ., Oxford, 367 pp.

Grodzinski, W., and B. A. Wunder. 1975. Ecological energetics of small mammals. Pp. 173-204, in Small mammals: Their productivity and population dynamics. (F. B. Golley, K. Petrusewicz, and L. Ryszkowski, eds.). Cambridge Univ. Press, Cambridge, 451 pp.

Gutmann, K. 1983. Measuring oxygen consumption with an all-electronic multi-range digital respirometer. Oecologia, 56:140.

Hayward, J. S., and E. G. Ball. 1966. Quantitative aspects of brown adipose tissue thermogenesis during arousal from hibernation. Biol. Bull., 131:94-103.

Henshaw, R. E., and G. E. Folk, Jr. 1963. Measurement of standard metabolism, water loss and body temperature of the little brown bat. Proc. Iowa Acad. Sci., 70:472-478.

Herreid, C. F., II. 1963. Temperature regulation and metabolism in Mexican freetail bats. Science, 142:1573-1574.

Herreid, C. F., II. 1967. Temperature regulation, temperature preference and tolerance, and metabolism of young and adult free-tailed bats. Physiol. Zool., 40:1-22.

Herreid, C. F., II, and K. Schmidt-Nielsen. 1966.

Oxygen consumption, temperature, and water loss in bats from different environments. Amer. J. Physiol., 211:1108-1112.

Hill, R. W. 1972. Determination of oxygen consumption by use of the paramagnetic oxygen analyzer. J. Appl. Physiol., 33:261-263.

Hill, R. W. 1976. Comparative physiology of animals: An environmental approach. Harper and Row, New York, 656 pp.

Hitchcock, F. A. 1966. Characteristics and composition of the atmosphere. Pp. 269-270, in Environmental biology. (P. L. Altman and D. S. Dittmer, eds.). Fed. Amer. Soc. Exp. Biol., Bethesda, Maryland, 694 pp.

Hock, R. J. 1951. The metabolic rates and body temperatures of bats. Biol. Bull., 101:289-299.

Holyoak, G. W., and R. C. Stones. 1971. Temperature regulation of the little brown bat, Myotis lucifugus, after acclimation at various ambient temperatures. Comp. Biochem. Physiol., 39A:413-420.

Kendeigh, S. C. 1939. The relation of metabolism to the development of temperature regulation in birds. J. Exp. Zool., 82:419-438.

Kleiber, M. 1975. The fire of life: An introduction to animal energetics. Krieger, Huntington, New York, 453 pp.

Knoebel, L. K. 1971. Energy metabolism. Pp. 635-650, in Physiology. (E. E. Selkurt, ed.). Little Brown, Boston, 860 pp.

Kunz, T. H. 1980. Daily energy budgets of free-living bats. Pp. 369-392, in Proc. 5th Int. Bat Res. Conf. (D. E. Wilson and A. L. Gardner, eds.). Texas Tech Press, Lubbock, 434 pp.

Lasiewski, R. C., A. L. Acosta, and M. H. Bernstein. 1966. Evaporative water loss in birds—I. Characteristics of the open flow method of determination, and their relation to estimates of thermoregulatory ability. Comp. Biochem. Physiol., 19:445-457.

Leitner, P. 1966. Body temperature, oxygen consumption, heart rate and shivering in the California mastiff bat, Eumops perotis. Comp. Biochem. Physiol., 19:431-443.

Leitner, P., and J. E. Nelson. 1967. Body temperature, oxygen consumption and heart rate in the Australian false vampire bat, Macroderma gigas. Comp. Biochem. Physiol., 21:65-74.

Licht, P., and P. Leitner. 1967. Physiological responses to high environmental temperatures in three species of microchiropteran bats. Comp. Biochem Physiol., 22:371-387.

List, R. J. 1966. Smithsonian meteorological

tables. Smithsonian Institution, Misc. Coll., No. 114, Washington, D.C.

McNab, B. K. 1969. The economics of temperature regulation in Neotropical bats. Comp. Biochem. Physiol., 31:227-268.

McNab, B. K. 1974. The behavior of temperate cave bats in a subtropical environment. Ecology, 55:943-958.

McNab, B. K. 1980. Food habits, energetics, and the population biology of mammals. Amer. Nat., 116:106-124.

Morrison, P. R. 1948. Oxygen consumption in several small wild mammals. J. Cell Comp. Physiol., 31:69-96.

Morrison, P., and W. Grodzinski. 1975. Morrison respirometer and determination of ADMR. Pp. 300-309, *in* Methods for ecological bioenergetics. (W. Grodzinski, R. Z. Klekowski, and A. Duncan, eds.). IBP Handbook No. 24. Blackwell Sci. Publ., Oxford, 367 pp.

Morrison, P., and B. K. McNab. 1967. Temperature regulation in some Brazilian phyllostomid bats. Comp. Biochem. Physiol., 21:207-221.

Morrison, P., and G. C. West. 1975. Methods of measuring respiratory exchange in terrestrial vertebrates. Pp. 293-300, *in* Methods for ecological bioenergetics. (W. Grodzinski, R. Z. Klekowski, and A. Duncan, eds.). IBP Handbook No. 24. Blackwell Sci. Publ., Oxford, 367 pp.

Nagy, K. A. 1980. CO_2 production in animals: Analysis of potential errors in the doubly labeled water method. Amer. J. Physiol., 238:R466-R473.

Noll, U. G. 1979. Body temperature, oxygen consumption, noradrenaline response and cardiovascular adaptations in the flying fox, *Rousettus aegyptiacus.* Comp. Biochem. Physiol., 63A:79-88.

O'Farrell, M. J., and E. H. Studier. 1970. Fall metabolism in relation to ambient temperatures in three species of *Myotis.* Comp. Biochem. Physiol., 35:697-703.

Pearson, O. P. 1947. The rate of metabolism of some small mammals. Ecology, 28:127-145.

Pickwell, G. V. 1968. An automatically compensating heat-exchange calorimeter for metabolic studies. Med. Biol. Eng., 6:425-431.

Pivorun, E. B. 1976. A gradient calorimeter study of normothermic and hibernating eastern chipmunks, *Tamias striatus.* Comp. Biochem. Physiol., 54A:259-261.

Porter, W. P., and D. M. Gates. 1969. Thermodynamic equilibria of animals with environment. Ecol. Monogr., 39:227-244.

Randolph, J. C. 1980. Daily energy metabolism of two rodents (*Peromyscus leucopus* and *Tamias striatus*) in their natural environment. Physiol. Zool., 53:70-81.

Reese, J. B., and H. Haines. 1978. Effects of dehydration on metabolic rate and fluid distribution in the jackrabbit, *Lepus californicus.* Physiol. Zool., 51:155-165.

Riedesel, M. L., and B. A. Williams. 1976. Continuous 24-hour oxygen consumption studies of *Myotis velifer.* Comp. Biochem. Physiol., 54A:95-99.

Snellen, J. W., K. S. Chang, and W. Smith. 1983. Technical description and performance characteristics of a human whole-body calorimeter. Med. Biol. Eng. Comput., 21:9-20.

Stack, M. H. 1985. Energetics of reproduction in the big brown bat, *Eptesicus fuscus.* Unpubl. Ph.D. dissertation, Boston University, Boston, 283 pp.

Stones, R. C., and J. E. Wiebers. 1967. Temperature regulation in the little brown bat, *Myotis lucifugus.* Pp. 97-109, *in* Mammalian hibernation III. (K. C. Fisher, A. R. Dawe, C. P. Lyman, E. Schönbaum, and F. E. South, Jr., eds.). American Elsevier, New York, 535 pp.

Studier, E. H. 1981. Energetic advantages of slight drops in body temperature in little brown bats, *Myotis lucifugus.* Comp. Biochem. Physiol., 70A:537-540.

Studier, E. H., and M. J. O'Farrell. 1972. Biology of *Myotis thysanodes* and *M. lucifugus* (Chiroptera: Vespertilionidae)—I. Thermoregulation. Comp. Biochem. Physiol., 41A:567-595.

Studier, E. H., and M. J. O'Farrell. 1976. Biology of *Myotis thysanodes* and *M. lucifugus* (Chiroptera: Vespertilionidae)—III. Metabolism, heart rate, breathing rate, evaporative water loss and general energetics. Comp. Biochem. Physiol., 54A:423-432.

Studier, E. H., and D. E. Wilson. 1979. Effects of captivity on thermoregulation and metabolism in *Artibeus jamaicensis* (Chiroptera: Phyllostomatidae). Comp. Biochem. Physiol., 62A:347-350.

Swan, H. 1974. Thermoregulation and bioenergetics: Patterns for vertebrate survival. American Elsevier, New York, 430 pp.

Thomas, S. P. 1975. Metabolism during flight in two species of bats, *Phyllostomus hastatus* and *Pteropus gouldii.* J. Exp. Biol., 63:273-293.

Thomas, S. P. 1981. Ventilation and oxygen extraction in the bat *Pteropus gouldii* during rest and steady flight. J. Exp. Biol., 94:231-250.

Thomas, S. P., and R. A. Suthers. 1972. The physiology and energetics of bat flight. J. Exp. Biol., 57:317-335.

Thomas, S. P., M. R. Lust, and H. J. Van Riper. 1984. Ventilation and oxygen extraction in the bat *Phyllostomus hastatus* during rest and steady flight. Physiol. Zool., 57:237-250.

Trune, D. R., and C. N. Slobodchikoff. 1976. Social effects of roosting on the metabolism of the pallid bat (*Antrozous pallidus*). J. Mammal., 57:656-663.

Tschegg, E., A. Sigmund, V. Veitl, and K. Irsigler. 1981. A whole-body calorimeter for long-term measurements in man. J. Physics E: Sci. Instrum., 14:550-554.

Williams, J. B., and K. A. Nagy. 1984. Validation of the doubly labeled water technique for measuring energy metabolism in savannah sparrows. Physiol. Zool., 57:325-328.

Withers, P. C. 1977. Measurement of $\dot{V}_{O_2}$, and $\dot{V}_{CO_2}$, and evaporative water loss with a flow-through mask. J. Appl. Physiol.: Resp. Environ. Exer. Physiol., 42:120-123.

Appendix 1. Selected Commercially Available Instruments for Respirometry Studies

PRODUCT

O₂ analyzers
CO₂ analyzers

Applied Electrochemistry, Inc.
AMETEK
Thermox Instruments Division
150 Freeport Rd.
Pittsburgh, Pennsylvania 15238 USA

O₂ analyzers
CO₂ analyzers
Stream selectors

Beckman Industrial Corporation
Process Instruments Division
600 South Harbor Blvd.
La Habra, California 90631 USA

Flow meters
Mass flow controllers
Volume meters

Brooks Instruments Division
Emerson Electric Co.
407 W. Vine St.
Hatfield, Pennsylvania 19440 USA

Hot wire anemometers

Datametrics
Dresser Instrument Division
Dresser Industries, Inc.
340 Fordham Rd.
Wilmington, Massachusetts 01887 USA

Dew point hygrometers

EG&G, Inc.
Environmental Equipment Division
151 Bear Hill Rd.
Waltham, Massachusetts 02254 USA

Flow meters

Gilmont Instruments, Inc.
401 Great Neck Rd.
Great Neck, New York 11021 USA

Analog and digital recorders

Honeywell Test Instruments Division
Honeywell, Inc.
P.O. Box 5227
Denver, Colorado 80217 USA

Houston Instruments Division
Bausch and Lomb, Inc.
8500 Cameron Rd.
Austin, Texas 78753 USA

Mass flow controllers
Pressure regulators
Flow meters

Matheson Instruments
430 Caredean Dr.
Horsham, Pennsylvania 19044 USA

Flat black paint

Minnesota Mining and Manufacturing (3M) Co.
3M Center
St. Paul, Minnesota 55144 USA

Dew point hygrometers

> Yellow Springs Instrument Co., Inc.
> Box 279
> Yellow Springs, Ohio 45387 USA

Analog-to-digital converters
Thermocouple amplifiers

> Analog Devices
> P.O. Box 280
> Norwood, Massachusetts 02062 USA

> John Fluke Manufacturing Co., Inc.
> P.O. Box C9090
> Everett, Washington 98206 USA

Acorn microcomputers

> Berry Associates
> 28 Berry St.
> Danvers, Massachusetts 01923 USA

Data-gathering software

> John Lighton
> Department of Biology
> University of California
> Los Angeles, California 90024 USA

Chapter 22

Methods for Determining Water Balance in Bats

John E. Bassett

Department of Neurological Surgery
Harborview Medical Center
University of Washington
Seattle, Washington 98104 USA

and

Eugene H. Studier

Biology Department
University of Michigan—Flint
Flint, Michigan 48503 USA

1. INTRODUCTION

Water balance and the components of water economy in mammals are simply stated and understood in theory, but the mechanics of partitioning the components of overall water balance remain elusive. Water is gained by drinking, from food, and by metabolic water production. Water is lost by both pulmonary and cutaneous evaporation as well as by urinary and fecal routes. Milk production is a further source of water loss in lactating females.

Before reviewing theories and methods which may be useful in estimating the various components involved in water balance, a word of caution is needed. Most published methods for the study of water balance require at least one live capture and handling of the study animals, and most methods include the use of caged individuals maintained in the laboratory. Among small mammals, capture and caging for either brief or extended time periods can markedly affect renal function (Bakko, 1977; Studier and Rimle, 1980) and metabolic rate (MR) (Holyoak and Stones, 1971; Studier and Wilson, 1979). Short term changes result from the stress of capture, and longer term changes result from acclimation to the laboratory environment. Data collected from captured or caged animals, therefore, provide information that can delimit the physiologically adjustable range of function but may not represent normal function in free-ranging individuals. Acclimated bats exposed to quasi-natural conditions in the laboratory may not respond in the same manner as free-ranging individuals. Ideal methods of study, therefore, would be those in which the study animals are never captured, handled or

caged, i.e., conditions in which the animal is
unaware that it is being studied. With this in
mind, appropriate controls should be devised
whenever possible to determine whether capture, handling or acclimation have significant
effects on the parameter being investigated.
At least in regard to renal function, brief (less
than 12 h) periods of confinement seem to
have no appreciable effect on bats (Studier
and Rimle, 1980; Studier et al., 1983a).

In this paper we review theories and
methods that have been or might be useful in
quantifying aspects of water balance in bats.
Use of isotopic water to measure water flux is
discussed in Chapter 18. We begin with those
parameters, metabolic water production and
evaporative water loss (EWL), which occur
continuously, albeit not at constant rates, and
parameters that occur discontinuously (i.e.,
water intake from drinking and food and
water loss in urine and feces).

2. CONTINUOUS PARAMETERS

2.1. Metabolic Water Production

Production of metabolic water by reoxi-
dation of reduced coenzymes in the electron
transport system is easily estimated using the
stoichiometry of balanced equations for the
aerobic oxidation of carbohydrates and fatty
acids. Glucose, for example, is aerobically
metabolized as follows:

$$C_6H_{12}O_6 + 6\,O_2 \rightarrow 6\,CO_2 + 6\,H_2O + \text{heat}$$

Thus for each mole (180 g) of glucose
catabolized, 6 moles (108 g) of metabolic
water are formed, or for each mole (22.4 l) of
O_2 consumed or CO_2 produced, one mole
(18 g) of metabolic water is formed. Similar
calculations can be made for a typical fatty
acid, palmitic, as follows:

$$C_{16}H_{32}O_2 + 23\,O_2 \rightarrow 16\,CO_2 + 16\,H_2O + \text{heat}$$

Metabolic water equivalents can therefore be constructed for glucose or fatty acid
depletion and O_2 consumption or CO_2 pro-

Table 1. Metabolic water equivalents for calculating water production from nutrient use or gas exchange.

Parameter Measured	Metabolic Water Formed For Carbohydrate	For Fatty Acid
Glucose depletion	0.600 g/g	—
Fatty acid	—	1.125 g/g
O_2 utilized	0.804 g/l	0.559 g/l
CO_2 produced	0.804 g/l	0.804 g/l

duction which are as accurate as the investigator's ability to measure gas exchange or
nutrient use. These equivalents are summarized in Table 1. Because metabolic water
equivalents for O_2 consumption differ for fats
and carbohydrates, it is necessary to know
which nutrient is being metabolized for accurate conversion of O_2 use to water production.
If both gases are measured, the ratio of CO_2
production to O_2 consumption (= respiratory
quotient or RQ) can be used to determine if
fats (RQ = 0.7) or carbohydrates (RQ = 1.0)
are being catabolized. If only O_2 consumption
is measured, one can assume an RQ of 0.8 to
0.9 for dayroosting, sedentary animals
(Thomas and Suthers, 1972; Noll, 1979) and
an RQ of 0.75 to 0.80 for animals during sustained flight (Carpenter, 1975; Thomas,
1975).

Inactive animals metabolize a mixture of
nutrients from their diet, whereas bats in sustained flight metabolize fat for energy. Flight
muscles in bats contain predominately oxidative fibers (e.g., Armstrong et al., 1977;
Strickler, 1980), indicating that these muscles
use fatty acids as their primary energy source.
In addition, fat provides the most efficient
metabolic fuel for sustained flight activity
when energy reserves are limiting (Carpenter,
1975). When *Phyllostomus hastatus* and
Pteropus gouldii begin to fly in the laboratory,
RQ declines from 1.0 to 0.8 (Thomas, 1975).
Carbohydrate appears to be the preferred
metabolic fuel at the onset of flight; however,
as exercise continues and glycogen stores are
depleted, these bats draw upon fat reserves
for energy, and RQ declines. The rate of

change of this RQ shift when a bat begins to fly in the field has not been determined.

Metabolic rate and the rate of metabolic water production of animals vary over the daily cycle. Metabolic rates of bats vary with the time of day in laboratory studies (e.g., Pearson, 1947; Riedesel and Williams, 1976), and activity levels and their associated MR vary with time of day in the laboratory (Bassett, 1977) and in the field (Kunz, 1980; Burnett and August, 1981). Changes in MR during the daily cycle coupled with changes in RQ with type of activity performed will affect the amount of metabolic water produced.

Water obtained by bats from the oxidation of nutrients can be calculated from knowledge of MR and RQ. Metabolic water production can also be estimated from knowledge of the amount of food consumed, nutrient content of that food and MR. Such an approach has been used to estimate metabolic water production in bats by McFarland and Wimsatt (1969), Vogel (1969), and Bassett (1977) in laboratory studies. The assumptions required to estimate water production by this approach are more numerous and tenuous than those required for the use of an assumed RQ and MR. Therefore, the preferred method for estimation of metabolic water would be that based on MR and RQ.

Metabolic water production by bats in the field has been estimated for periods ranging from 12 to 24 h, based upon MR data acquired in the laboratory and a knowledge of the nutrient content of the diet for a particular species. Metabolic water production by insectivorous (Carpenter, 1969; Vogel, 1969; O'Farrell et al., 1971; Bassett, 1977), piscivorous (Carpenter, 1968), sanguinivorous (McFarland and Wimsatt, 1969), nectarivorous (Carpenter, 1969) and frugivorous (Studier et al., 1983a) bats has been estimated in this manner. Most of these studies did not consider daily fluctuations in MR and activity and thus only represent first approximations of actual metabolic water production.

To our knowledge, there are no reports of nutrient use in the intact organism which can be used to calculate metabolic water production. The relative difficulty of repeatedly measuring nutrient disappearance in a whole animal compared with the relative ease of repeatedly measuring gas exchange suggests that such an approach is impractical.

2.2. Pulmocutaneous Water Loss

Evaporation of water from body surfaces occurs continuously and represents a major route of water loss in small mammals. Evaporative water loss occurs from both the integument and respiratory tract and is under physical, physiological and behavioral control. The primary physical control is determined by the water vapor pressure difference (WVPD) between the evaporating surface and the adjacent air. Air temperature (T_a), temperature of the evaporating surface, and concentration of water at each location, in turn, determine the water vapor pressure (WVP). Water, which moves from areas of higher WVP to areas of lower WVP, evaporates from the skin and lungs when WVP in the air is less than WVP at the body surfaces. Conversely, water condenses on body surfaces when WVP in the air is greater than at the surfaces. Two commonly used measures of the potential for EWL, relative humidity and saturation deficit, express the amount of water held by air in relation to the maximum amount that can be held at a constant temperature. As indicators of EWL by animals, these measures ignore the animal entirely. Further discussion of the physical determinants of EWL can be found in Thornthwaite (1940), Lowry (1969), and Hill (1976).

2.2.1. Cutaneous Water Loss

Integumentary EWL can, in theory, occur both insensibly (transepidermal) and sensibly (sweat), although significant EWL by sweating has not been reported for bats. Bat skin contains sweat (sudoriparous) glands (Sisk, 1957), but instead of producing water for evaporative cooling, these structures appear to produce secretions which lubricate and condition the skin. The extremely large surface area to volume ratio of bats increases the effectiveness of conduction, convection, and radiation as avenues of heat loss.

Insensible evaporation represents the primary route of integumentary EWL. Except when heat-stressed, flight membrane temperatures of bats approach T_a owing to peripheral vasoconstriction (Bartholomew et al., 1964). The temperature of furred skin varies between body temperature (T_b) and T_a depending on MR, activity, and degree of peripheral vasoconstriction. Because flight membranes comprise 85% of total body surface area in bats (Baker, 1966), at least 85% of the skin surface is at a temperature approaching T_a. Thus, EWL from the skin appears to be (as a first approximation) inversely proportional to the WVP of ambient air. The engorgement of surface vessels which occurs when bats are experimentally heat-loaded (Reeder and Cowles, 1951; Bartholomew et al., 1964; Licht and Leitner, 1967b; Kluger and Heath, 1970) increases flight membrane temperatures which facilitates heat dissipation and increases WVPD and integumentary EWL. Wetting of fur with saliva during heat stress also increases water loss by evaporation. The lipid layer and hair of skin inhibit EWL acting as a water impermeable barrier and creating dead air space. It is important to note, however, that bats behaviorally avoid marked heat stress through appropriate roost selection (e.g., Studier et al., 1970; Henshaw, 1970; Humphrey, 1975) and daily intraroost movement (e.g., Licht and Leitner, 1967a; Burnett and August, 1981; Watkins and Shump, 1981).

Two methods have been used to estimate cutaneous water loss in bats. Hattingh (1972a, 1972b) measured transepidermal (cutaneous) water loss in two bat species by an unventilated capsule technique. Airtight chambers filled with hygroscopic material of known mass were sealed over a known area of skin for a designated period of time. After removal from the skin, the hygroscopic material was reweighed and the gain in mass was used to represent water loss from a measured

area of skin. Rates of cutaneous water loss in bats ranged from about one to three times those of other small mammals.

Cutaneous water loss also has been estimated by using open-flow systems designed for measuring total EWL (see Chapter 21). Attempts can then be made to partition total EWL into respiratory and cutaneous loss. Chew and White (1960) partitioned total EWL in *Antrozous pallidus* by calculating respiratory loss from MR and by making assumptions about respiratory gas exchange rate. Cutaneous water loss was determined as the difference between total and respiratory water losses. Laburn and Mitchell (1975) measured total EWL in *Rousettus aegyptiacus* and then measured respiratory water loss by placing a plastic bag over the body with only the head exposed. Because water lost from the skin cannot be recorded using this system, the difference between total and respiratory water loss is considered equal to cutaneous loss. This protocol, however, overestimates respiratory loss because the plastic bag elevates T_b and consequently the respiratory rate and water loss. Cutaneous water loss was also underestimated owing to an increased WVP around the animal, thereby decreasing the normal WVPD between the animal and its environment. The decreased WVPD reduced cutaneous water loss from what it would have been without the plastic bag.

Vogel (1969) used a modified version of this method to partition total EWL in bats. She simultaneously used two open-flow systems to measure EWL from the head (respiratory) and trunk (cutaneous) in *Rhinopoma, Rhinolophus,* and *Myotis* at a given T_a. To our knowledge, no other attempts have been made to measure cutaneous water loss in bats.

2.2.2. Respiratory Water Loss

Respiratory EWL is often the major route of water loss in bats (Vogel, 1969). Bats have exceptionally large lungs in comparison to similar-sized, nonflying mammals (Jürgens et al., 1981; Maina et al., 1982). Bat lungs also exhibit finely divided air spaces with a large surface area of tissue barrier for the exchange of O_2 and CO_2. Air at the respiratory membrane is water vapor saturated, and most of that water derived from the respiratory tract is exhaled. The primary determining factors in respiratory EWL are WVPD and minute respiratory volume. Secondary factors known to modify these primary factors include T_b or lung temperature (which can modify WVPD and breathing rate) and breathing depth (which can modify the volume of air that becomes humidified). As lung temperature approaches T_a, WVPD decreases and water is conserved. As minute respiratory volume or MR decreases, the water needed to saturate inhaled air also decreases.

2.2.3. Total Evaporative Water Loss

Methods used to estimate EWL include trapping the water vapor that passes out of an exposure chamber or measuring the rate of mass loss of an animal over time. The former method is often employed in conjunction with studies of MR in the laboratory (see Chapter 21). Both MR and EWL can be measured simultaneously with "open-flow" systems which draw air through a holding chamber and subsequently measure the amount of water vapor added to the air by the animal and either the amount of O_2 removed or CO_2 added to the air. Simultaneous measurement of MR and EWL is of value in thermoregulatory studies where it is desirable to know what proportion of metabolic heat production is dissipated by evaporative cooling. Water in urine and feces will not interfere with EWL measurement as long as these wastes are trapped with a layer of oil on the bottom of the chamber so the water they contain cannot evaporate into the air stream.

Two variations of the open-flow system are commonly employed in studies of bats. In the first variation, totally dry air, obtained by drawing air through a desiccant (Drierite), or air of known water content, obtained by bub-

bling air through an appropriate saturated salt solution (Winston and Bates, 1960) or water held at an appropriate temperature (Ewing and Studier, 1973) is drawn through the exposure chamber and then through either a chemical absorbent such as calcium chloride or a freezing bath. The amount of water collected from the air leaving the chamber in excess of that known to have entered represents the EWL of the animal in the chamber, assuming fecal and urinary water losses have been masked. After removing the water, air can be drawn through an oxygen analyzer to measure MR. Studies employing this type of open-flow system on bats include the work of Herreid and Schmidt-Nielsen (1966), Carpenter and Graham (1967), Docter (1967), Carpenter (1968, 1969), Holt (1969), Vogel (1969) and Studier and O'Farrell (1976).

A modification of this method, where air is drawn through a mask fitted to the face of a bat, has been used to measure respiratory EWL and metabolic rate during flight (Thomas and Suthers, 1972; Carpenter, 1975; Thomas, 1975; Thomas et al., 1984).

The second variation of the open-flow system draws room air into the chamber through an electronic moisture sensor, usually a dew point hygrometer. Air leaving the chamber is drawn through a second electronic sensor, and EWL is calculated from the difference in readings of the two sensors combined with the rate of air flow through the chamber. Studies employing this technique include Laburn and Mitchell (1975) and Licht and Leitner (1967b). As with the first variation of the open-flow system, urine and feces must be trapped under oil to obtain an accurate estimate of EWL.

Rate of air flow through the exposure chamber of an open-flow system affects the WVP of air in the chamber, which can influence the EWL response recorded for an animal at a given T_a (Lasiewski et al., 1966a). At low flow rates, the WVP of air in the chamber can increase, especially at high T_a, to the point where the WVPD between the animal and surrounding air is lower than normally encountered in the field. EWL measured in this situation would be lower than that measured at the same T_a in a field situation.

Two solutions to this problem have been proposed. The first solution (Welch, 1980) employs electronic moisture sensors at the inflow and outflow of the exposure chamber to estimate actual WVP of air in the chamber at a given flow rate. With this knowledge, the true WVPD experienced by the animal can be determined and related to the observed EWL. WVPD is varied by changing air flow rate at a given T_a, and statistical techniques are then employed to relate EWL to T_a and WVPD.

The second solution proposed by Lasiewski et al. (1966b) directly measures rate of loss of body mass. This method does not allow for simultaneous determination of EWL and MR as does the open-flow system. However, with the gravimetric method, T_a and WVP can be varied independently of each other in the laboratory, air flow rate can be kept constant, and respiratory rate of the experimental animal can be measured. With an open-flow system, these goals are difficult if not impossible to achieve.

The gravimetric method provides precise measurements of EWL only during periods when defecation and urination do not occur. At times when defecation and urination occur, however, loss of body mass may provide information about total water loss if fecal production can be measured or estimated. Loss of body mass corrected for the mass of fecal solids can approximate values for total water loss over a given time period. Estimated total water loss rate may also be related to EWL with reasonable accuracy since both O'Farrell et al. (1971) and Bassett (1980) found EWL to be 90% of total water loss in bats. Thus, even in situations where fecal production can only be estimated, a reasonable first approximation of EWL can be obtained.

The gravimetric method also fails to take into account potential continuous mass change due to metabolic gas exchange. The CO_2 produced in aerobic metabolism is of greater mass than the O_2 consumed on an equal volume basis. Thus, when metabolizing glucose (RQ = 1.0), continuous loss of body mass will occur. When metabolizing fats (RQ = 0.7), the volume of O_2 consumed per mole of fatty acid catabolized is greater than the volume of CO_2 produced, and a small continuous gain of body mass will occur. For example, a 10 g bat with a MR of 1.0 cc $O_2 \cdot g^{-1}h^{-1}$, when metabolizing glucose, loses mass at a rate of 5.36 mg/h, and when metabolizing fatty acids, gains mass at a rate of 0.54 mg/h. Mass changes due to gas exchange are small relative to the mass loss due to EWL, ranging from 0.5% when RQ = 0.7 to 5% when RQ = 1.0, and have routinely been ignored.

Gravimetric estimates of EWL have the advantage that they can be obtained from caged animals in their natural habitat (Studier, 1970; Studier et al., 1970; Howell, 1976; Watkins and Shump, 1981). This method requires simple equipment (a balance and a cage) in contrast to the extensive temperature control and electronic equipment required for an open-flow system. The elaborate nature of the open-flow system also makes it difficult to use in the field. Evaporative water loss in bats has been determined with the gravimetric method in both the laboratory and field as affected by T_a and WVP (Kallen, 1964; Procter and Studier, 1970; Studier et al., 1970), clustering behavior (Kallen, 1964; Studier, 1970; Studier et al., 1970; Howell, 1976; Trune and Slobodchikoff, 1976), food and water consumption (Kallen, 1964; McFarland and Wimsatt, 1969; Studier et al., 1970; Geluso, 1975; Howell, 1976; Bassett, 1980; Bassett and Wiebers, 1980), and flight (Carpenter, 1968).

3. DISCONTINUOUS PARAMETERS

Discontinuous parameters such as water drunk, water in food, and water in urine and feces could, in theory, be determined by mass gain or loss and corrected for continuous mass flux, if mass differentials can be obtained for any single parameter in the absence of the others. The usefulness of mass change methods, then, depends on sufficient prior knowledge of specific behavioral and activity patterns to delimit times during which only one of the discontinuous patterns occurs.

3.1. Drinking

Other than direct laboratory measurements, there appear to be no published methods for the determination of daily water intake. In the laboratory, water consumption can be quantified by either measuring body mass gain after each drinking session (O'Farrell et al., 1971; Bassett, 1980) or measuring the quantity of water removed from a calibrated container (Vogel, 1969). Quantification of free water consumption in the field remains elusive and difficult.

3.2. Preformed Water in Food

Water derived from food by bats includes preformed water in the food and metabolic water produced from oxidation of nutrients. Determining the contribution of preformed water to the bat's total intake is limited by the ability to determine total food consumption. Knowledge of total food consumption also allows estimation of metabolic water production by an animal on a specific diet as mentioned previously. Periodic feeding behavior of bats aids greatly in measuring food consumption by narrowing the portion of the animal's daily cycle during which the investigator must be alert for feeding (e.g., Anthony and Kunz, 1977).

Foods consumed by bats generally contain large amounts of free water. Insects contain 60% water (Carpenter, 1969; Vogel, 1969; Geluso, 1975; Anthony and Kunz, 1977; Bassett, 1977), marine invertebrates contain 75% water (Carpenter, 1968), and vertebrates generally contain 70-90% water (Altman and Dittmer, 1974). In contrast, blood contains 80% water (McFarland and Wimsatt, 1969). Fruit contains 70-90% water (Altman and Dittmer, 1968), while nectar contains 80% water (Carpenter, 1969; Ho-

well, 1974). The amount of water consumed by bats depends upon the specific items and quality of food eaten. The particular parts of the food item consumed also influence the amount of preformed water gained. The water content of various foods represents total water content; by consuming selected parts of its food, the bat may enhance its preformed water gain.

Food consumption has been measured in the laboratory by measuring either mass gain with feeding or the quantity of food consumed (e.g., Carpenter, 1968, 1969; McFarland and Wimsatt, 1969; Vogel, 1969; O'Farrell et al., 1971; Vogel and Vogel, 1972; Howell, 1974; Geluso, 1975; Bassett, 1977; Noll, 1979; Bassett and Wiebers, 1979a). Food consumption of laboratory-maintained bats is easily quantified when studying water balance.

Determination of food consumption in the field, however, presents the investigator with more of a challenge (see Chapter 18). Two methods of measuring food intake in the field are discussed by Kunz (1980) with regard to their application, assumptions and limitations. The first, the ingesta method, measures increase in body mass during a feeding period by a field population of animals. This population-based technique employs statistical sampling of body mass upon emergence from and return to the roost during each foraging period. The average gain in body mass subject to certain assumptions represents the food intake of a typical member of the population during the feeding period.

The second method, the egesta method, measures fecal production by bats collected after their normal feeding period in the wild. Total fecal production can be related to food consumed from the results of laboratory studies. Before the egesta method is routinely used, however, the assumed equality of assimilation efficiency of both captive and free-ranging bats must be verified. The egesta method has the advantages compared to the ingesta method of having to handle the animal only once after feeding and of yielding data from individual animals (but see Chapter 18).

3.3. Fecal Water Loss

Water lost in feces is easily measured by collecting all feces produced during a given time interval, drying this material to a constant mass, and calculating the water loss by correcting the mass of dry feces with the known water content of fresh feces. Previous laboratory studies of insectivorous bats have estimated fecal water loss by assuming a fresh water content of 50% (O'Farrell et al., 1971; Bassett, 1977). These workers underestimated fecal water loss since Vogel (1969) found fresh laboratory-collected feces of insectivorous bats to contain 70% water. Carpenter (1968) found that fresh feces of *Pizonyx vivesi,* which consumes marine invertebrates, contained 73% water. McFarland and Wimsatt (1969) also found laboratory-collected feces of the sanguinivore *Desmodus rotundus* to contain 64% water. To our knowledge, neither fecal water content nor total water loss has been measured in bats that consume diets other than invertebrates or blood.

3.4. Milk Production

The impact of milk production on water balance in female bats rearing young has not been investigated. Racey (1982) reviewed work done on lactation in bats which has emphasized daily timing, length in relation to postnatal growth, and energetics of the process. The effects of this additional route of water loss on the physiology of the mother or of the large water intake from a milk diet on the water balance of the animal during postnatal growth have not been studied.

Kunz et al. (1983) present a technique for collecting milk from lactating animals by injection of oxytocin to stimulate milk letdown. While this technique works well for collection of samples for qualitative analysis, it is unsuitable for quantifying milk yield.

Kunz et al. (1983) suggested the use of tritiated or deuterated water to quantify milk production by measuring the buildup of tritium or deuterium in young bats nursing from labeled mothers. The rate of buildup in the offspring can be related to milk production by the mother and thus to the water loss resulting from lactation. Alternatively, a preferred method is to measure the dilution of isotope in total body water of labeled nursing young. These techniques are discussed further in Chapter 18.

3.5. Urinary Water Loss

Modification of volume and concentration of urine appears, for most mammals, to be the parameter of water loss under greatest physiological control. Three distinct experimental approaches are employed to study renal function in bats and its influence on water balance. These complementary approaches include traditional laboratory studies of renal physiology which determine the physiological abilities of bats, studies on anatomy of the kidney to determine maximum ability to concentrate urine (and thus conserve urinary water), and studies of renal function in free-ranging animals as influenced by their daily activity cycles.

Laboratory studies of the physiological abilities of bats maintained in captivity have explored several questions of importance to water balance in the field. The ability of bats with stressful dietary habits (Carpenter, 1968; McFarland and Wimsatt, 1969) or from arid habitats (Carpenter, 1969) to physiologically regulate when given dietary salt and/or protein loads has been explored. The ability of insectivorous bats to conserve urinary water following feeding when either normally hydrated or dehydrated also has been explored (Vogel and Vogel, 1972; Geluso, 1975; Bassett and Wiebers, 1979a, 1979b). Bats in the field are often exposed to the greatest water stress during the dayroosting period which they enter having just completed their daily feeding period. Finally, urine production rate as affected by T_b (10-40° C) and state of hydration has been determined by Kallen and Kanthor (1967).

3.5.1. Urine and Plasma Samples

To determine renal function in any mammal, both urine and plasma samples must be obtained and the concentration of several chemical species in these samples must be determined. Bats which range in body mass from 5 g to 1 kg present special problems in collecting physiological samples. Small urine volumes, especially from small bats, require either techniques for collecting, storing, and analyzing small samples or pooling of urine samples to obtain sufficient volumes for standard analytical techniques. Urine samples from bats are usually obtained by collecting voided urine. This technique in any of its many variations works well in both the laboratory (e.g., Carpenter, 1968, 1969; McFarland and Wimsatt, 1969; Vogel, 1969; Vogel and Vogel, 1972; Geluso, 1975; Bassett and Wiebers, 1979a) and the field (e.g., Geluso and Studier, 1979; Studier and Rimle, 1980; Studier et al., 1983a; Studier and Wilson, 1983). Kanthor (1965) described a bladder catheter technique for collecting urine from small bats, but the tedious nature of the technique and restriction to the laboratory have limited its use.

Problems arising from small physiological sample size are even more pronounced when plasma or serum must be collected. Bats, like other mammals, contain 6.5 ml of plasma per 100 g of body mass (Kallen, 1960). Thus, bats with body mass near 10 g contain only 650 μl of plasma. In studies of renal physiology, it is often desirable to obtain repeated plasma samples of sufficient size for analysis from the same animal. In small bats, this cannot be accomplished without disrupting the animal's physiology (i.e., inducing hypovolemia). For some analyses, sufficient sample size can only be obtained by sacrificing the animal. For example, Studier and Ewing (1971) were able to do either $Na^+ - K^+$

or Cl^- analysis with the serum sample from a single *Myotis lucifugus,* but not both.

Plasma samples from bats of body mass near 10 g have been obtained by rapid decapitation of the animal (Vogel and Vogel, 1972; Bassett and Wiebers, 1979a). This acute procedure yields only one sample per animal. Another potentially useful technique for blood sampling in small bats, suborbital canthal sinus puncture, is described by Lee and Brown (1970) for rodents. This technique, which has never been used in published work on bats, may require that the animal be anesthetized and also traumatizes the animal such that subsequent release in a field study may not be possible.

Blood samples have been obtained from bats with body masses between 10-30 g by cardiac puncture (McFarland and Wimsatt, 1969) and by severing a peripheral artery (Studier and Ewing, 1971). Cardiac puncture, which often requires anesthesia, may or may not be a fatal procedure depending on the skill of the investigator and the size of the sample obtained, while severing a major artery is usually fatal. Sample size requirements often make these techniques acute procedures for collection of a single sample from a given animal. Venipuncture techniques which allow repeated plasma sample collections have been described for bats (Black and Wiederhielm, 1976; Studier et al., 1983a; Gustafson and Damassa, 1985). The number of repeated samples is limited by the size of each sample in relation to the total blood volume of the bat. Techniques described above for blood collection may not be equally useful in the laboratory and the field (see Chapter 18).

3.5.2. Osmolality

Chemical species of interest in plasma and urine are usually Na^+, K^+, urea, and total osmotic concentration. Flame photometry is the method of choice to quantify Na^+ and K^+ (Carpenter, 1968; McFarland and Wimsatt, 1969; Studier and Ewing, 1971; Vogel and

Vogel, 1972; Studier and Wilson, 1983; Studier et al., 1983a), while spectrophotometric determination of NH_4^+ enzymatically hydrolyzed from urea is the method of choice to quantify urea (McFarland and Wimsatt, 1969; Vogel and Vogel, 1972). The introduction of vapor pressure osmometry has provided a powerful tool for total osmolality determination in small samples produced by small bats (Carpenter, 1969; Bassett and Wiebers, 1979a, 1979b; Studier et al., 1983a). These instruments have increased accuracy and ease of osmolality determination by eliminating the need to pool or dilute samples.

3.5.3. Renal Anatomy

Renal medullary anatomy in mammals reflects the maximum urine concentration that the kidney is capable of producing. Geluso (1978) demonstrated that this relationship is valid for insectivorous bats and presented a regression equation to predict maximum concentrating ability of the kidney from its anatomy. Studier et al. (1983b) extended this relationship to bats with dietary habits other than insects. Such an approach has great appeal since the histological procedures needed to quantify anatomy are easier and less expensive than the physiological procedures needed to obtain the same information. Animals do not have to be maintained in the laboratory with the histological approach, and animals can be collected in remote areas for later study. Also, material collected previously and appropriately preserved in spirits (Chapter 24) can be used for this procedure.

Renal anatomy has been used to predict maximum urinary water conservation as influenced by habitat aridity both between species (Geluso, 1980; Lu and Bleier, 1981; Studier et al., 1983b) and among populations of a species (Bassett, 1982). Dietary habits and body size have been studied as they affect maximum renal water conservation (Geluso, 1980; Studier et al., 1983b). Maximum urine concentrations obtained from bats in the field have also been compared to those predicted from renal anatomy (Studier and Wilson, 1983).

3.5.4. Renal Function

Renal function of free-ranging bats has also been investigated. These studies are usually conducted during portions of the animal's daily cycle when they are easily captured. Animals are typically sampled during the dayroosting period (Studier and Ewing, 1971; Geluso and Studier, 1979; Studier and Rimle, 1980) or during the foraging period when they can be captured in mist nets or caught in night roosts (Studier et al., 1983a).

Physiological techniques needed to study renal function in free-ranging bats are similar to those required in the laboratory. Studies of renal function in the field on freshly captured animals yield information on "normal" function. The investigator, however, often has only a general idea what the animal did or what environment it was exposed to immediately before capture. This lack of experimental control should be kept in mind when interpreting field studies.

Studies of renal function in bats reported to date have explored the functioning of the kidney, with kidney output the variable of interest. The focus of these studies has been urine concentration, Na^+ conservation, urea excretion, etc. The mechanics of how the kidney accomplishes these tasks was assumed to be similar to that in other mammals. We would like to present a few techniques which may expand knowledge of how the bat kidney conserves urinary water and whether bats have evolved unusual renal mechanisms. These techniques may be applicable only in the laboratory since most employ radionuclides; however, they may also be used with animals confined in large, simulated-natural enclosures which allow a near-normal existence.

Knowledge of glomerular filtration rate (GFR) and renal plasma flow (RPF) within the kidney are essential to understand the interaction of the kidney and the circulatory system. Techniques now available to measure these parameters in intact, unanesthetized, uninfused mammals have been applied to small mammals, mainly rodents. GFR can be measured with endogenous creatinine clearance (Hewitt, 1982), a technique which does not use radioactive materials. The validity of this technique in bats must, however, be determined with laboratory studies. GFR and RPF may also be measured with techniques employing ^{3}H-para-aminohippurate (RPF) and ^{3}H-inulin or ^{14}C-creatinine (GFR) (Hewitt et al., 1981). A potentially useful technique for chronic administration of radioactively labeled tracers to bats with an Alzet osmotic minipump is described by Anderson (1980). The effects of diet, habitat, activity and age on these physiological parameters in bats have not been explored.

Estimates of daily urinary water loss by bats with various diets have been made in studies conducted in the laboratory by various techniques (Kallen and Kanthor, 1967; Vogel, 1969; O'Farrell et al., 1971; Carpenter, 1968, 1969; McFarland and Wimsatt, 1969; Bassett and Wiebers, 1979a). In all cases, data obtained in the laboratory were extrapolated to the field. To date, no estimates of urinary water loss for bats in the wild have been done based upon data acquired in the field.

4. SUMMARY

We have presented both the theory and practice of quantifying the components of water economy in bats. As mentioned initially, collection of data is often disruptive to the animal's normal life style both in the laboratory and the field. All techniques described here for studying water balance require at least one capture of the animal, most require experimental manipulation, and several require maintenance of the animal in the laboratory. All techniques described, however, are useful in quantifying a particular component of water economy. In addition, as the investigator attempts to simultaneously measure more than one component of water balance, both complexity of the experimental protocol

required and disruption of the bat's routine increase.

The least intrusive technique available to assess overall water economy of captive or free-ranging animals is measurement of water turnover with tritiated or deuterated water. Measurement of any component of water economy by methods outlined here in conjunction with measurement of water turnover provides an excellent method for relating that particular component to the animal's total water economy. Water economy of bats can be quantified with reasonable ease in both laboratory and field settings, as long as the investigator remains cognizant of the assumptions and limitations inherent in the techniques employed and of the disruption caused by these experimental manipulations.

5. ACKNOWLEDGMENTS

We thank T. H. Kunz for the opportunity to contribute to this book. J. E. Bassett was supported during preparation of this chapter by USPHS NIH grants HL-28497-01 and HL-16910-09.

6. REFERENCES

Altman, P. L., and D. S. Dittmer. 1968. Metabolism. Fed. Amer. Soc. Exp. Biol. Bethesda, Maryland, 737 pp.

Altman, P. L., and D. S. Dittmer. 1974. Biology Data Book. Vol. III. Fed. Amer. Soc. Exp. Biol., Bethesda, Maryland, 2133 pp.

Anderson, G. L. 1980. Kidney function and postrenal modification of urine in desert quail. Unpubl. Ph.D. dissertation, Univ. Arizona, Tucson, 200 pp.

Anthony, E. L. P., and T. H. Kunz. 1977. Feeding strategies of the little brown bat, *Myotis lucifugus,* in southern New Hampshire. Ecology, 58:775-786.

Armstrong, R. B., C. D. Ianuzzo, and T. H. Kunz. 1977. Histochemical and biochemical properties of flight muscle fibers in the little brown bat, *Myotis lucifugus.* J. Comp. Physiol., 119:141-154.

Baker, R. E. 1966. Body composition of the winter and summer *Myotis lucifugus* (LeConte) (Mammalia: Chiroptera). Unpubl. M.S. thesis, Purdue Univ., Lafayette, Indiana, 79 pp.

Bakko, E. B. 1977. Influence of collecting techniques on estimate of natural renal function in red squirrels. Amer. Midl. Nat., 97:502-504.

Bartholomew, G. A., P. Leitner, and J. E. Nelson. 1964. Body temperature, oxygen consumption, and heart rate in three species of Australian flying foxes. Physiol. Zool., 37:179-198.

Bassett, J. E. 1977. Water metabolism and urine concentrating ability of the little brown bat, *Myotis lucifugus lucifugus,* during dehydration stress. Unpubl. Ph.D. thesis, Purdue Univ., Lafayette, Indiana, 155 pp.

Bassett, J. E. 1980. Control of postprandial water loss in *Myotis lucifugus lucifugus.* Comp. Biochem. Physiol., 65A:497-500.

Bassett, J. E. 1982. Habitat aridity and intraspecific differences in the urine concentrating ability of insectivorous bats. Comp. Biochem. Physiol., 72A:703-708.

Bassett, J. E., and J. E. Wiebers. 1979a. Urine concentration dynamics in the postprandial and the fasting *Myotis lucifugus lucifugus.* Comp. Biochem. Physiol., 64A:373-379.

Bassett, J. E., and J. E. Wiebers. 1979b. Subspecific differences in the urine concentrating ability of *Myotis lucifugus.* J. Mammal., 60:395-397.

Bassett, J. E., and J. E. Wiebers. 1980. Effect of food consumption on water loss in *Myotis lucifugus.* J. Mammal., 61:744-747.

Black, L. L., and C. A. Wiederhielm. 1976. Plasma oncotic pressures and hematocrit in the intact, unanesthetized bat. Microvasc. Res., 12:55-58.

Burnett, C. D., and P. V. August. 1981. Time and energy budgets for dayroosting in a maternity colony of *Myotis lucifugus.* J. Mammal., 62:758-766.

Carpenter, R. E. 1968. Salt and water metabolism in the marine fish-eating bat, *Pizonyx vivesi.* Comp. Biochem. Physiol., 24:951-964.

Carpenter, R. E. 1969. Structure and function of the kidney and the water balance of desert bats. Physiol. Zool., 42:288-302.

Carpenter, R. E. 1975. Flight metabolism of flying foxes. Pp. 883-890 *in* Swimming and flying in nature. Vol. 2. (T. Y.-T. Wu, C. J. Brokaw, and C. Brennen, eds.), Plenum Press, New York, 1005 pp.

Carpenter, R. E., and J. B. Graham, 1967. Physiological responses to temperature in the long-

nosed bat, *Leptonycteris sanborni.* Comp. Biochem. Physiol., 22:709-722.

Chew, R. M., and H. E. White. 1960. Evaporative water losses of the pallid bat. J. Mammal., 41:452-458.

Docter, P. J. 1967. Physiological responses of the bat *Myotis lucifugus* to heat stress. Unpubl. Ph.D. dissertation, Purdue Univ., Lafayette, Indiana, 221 pp.

Ewing, W. G., and E. H. Studier. 1973. A method for control of water vapor pressure and its effect on metabolism and body temperature in *Mus musculus.* Comp. Biochem. Physiol., 45A:121-125.

Geluso, K. N. 1975. Urine concentration cycles of insectivorous bats in the laboratory. J. Comp. Physiol., 99:309-319.

Geluso, K. N. 1978. Urine concentrating ability and renal structure of insectivorous bats. J. Mammal., 59:312-323.

Geluso, K. N. 1980. Renal form and function in bats: An ecophysiological appraisal. Pp. 403-414, *in* Proc. 5th Int. Bat Res. Conf. (D. E. Wilson and A. L. Gardner, eds.). Texas Tech Press, Lubbock, Texas, 434 pp.

Geluso, K. N., and E. H. Studier. 1979. Diurnal fluctuation in urine concentration in the little brown bat, *Myotis lucifugus,* in a natural roost. Comp. Biochem. Physiol., 62A:471-473.

Gustafson, A. W., and D. A. Damassa. 1985. Repetitive blood sampling from small peripheral veins in bats. J. Mammal., 66:173-177.

Hattingh, J. 1972a. A comparative study of transepidermal water loss through the skin of various animals. Comp. Biochem. Physiol., 43A:715-718.

Hattingh, J. 1972b. The correlation between transepidermal water loss and the thickness of epidermal components. Comp. Biochem. Physiol., 43A:719-722.

Henshaw, R. E. 1970. Thermoregulation in bats. Pp. 188-232, *in* About Bats. (B. H. Slaughter and D. W. Walton, eds.). Southern Methodist University Press, Dallas, Texas, 339 pp.

Herreid, C. F. II, and K. Schmidt-Nielsen. 1966. Oxygen consumption, temperature, and water loss in bats from different environments. Amer. J. Physiol., 211:1108-1112.

Hewitt, S. 1982. Method for the micro-assay of endogenous creatinine in blood and urine of small murid rodents. Lab. Anim., 16:201-203.

Hewitt, S., J. F. Wheldrake, and R. V. Baudinette. 1981. Water balance and renal function in the Australian desert rodent *Notomys alexis:* The effect of diet on water turnover rate, glomerular filtration rate, renal plasma flow and renal blood flow. Comp. Biochem. Physiol., 68A:405-410.

Hill, R. W. 1976. Comparative physiology of animals: An environmental approach. Harper and Row, New York, 656 pp.

Holt, E. J. 1969. Physiological response of the bat *Eptesicus fuscus* to thermal stress. Unpubl. Ph.D. dissertation, Purdue University, 190 pp.

Holyoak, G. W., and R. C. Stones. 1971. Temperature regulation of the little brown bat *Myotis lucifugus* after acclimation at various ambient temperatures. Comp. Biochem. Physiol., 39A:413-420.

Howell, D. J. 1974. Bats and pollen: Physiological aspects of the syndrome of chiropterophily. Comp. Biochem. Physiol., 48A:263-276.

Howell, D. J. 1976. Weight loss and temperature regulation in clustered versus individual *Glossophaga soricina*. Comp. Biochem. Physiol., 53A:197-199.

Humphrey, S. R. 1975. Nursery roosts and community diversity of nearctic bats. J. Mammal., 56:321-346.

Jürgens, K. D., H. Bartels, and R. Bartels. 1981. Blood oxygen transport and organ weights of small bats and small non-flying mammals. Resp. Physiol., 45:243-260.

Kallen, F. C. 1960. Plasma and blood volumes in the little brown bat. Amer. J. Physiol., 198:999-1005.

Kallen, F. C. 1964. Some aspects of water balance in the hibernating bat. Ann. Acad. Sci. Fenn., A.IV. 71/18:259-267.

Kallen, F. C., and H. A. Kanthor. 1967. Urine production in the hibernating bat. Pp. 280-294 *in* Mammalian hibernation III. (K. C. Fisher, A. R. Dawe, C. P. Lyman, E. Schönbaum and F. E. South, Jr., eds.). American Elsevier, New York, 534 pp.

Kanthor, H. A. 1965. Indwelling catheters for small bats. J. Appl. Physiol., 20:326-327.

Kluger, M. J., and J. E. Heath. 1970. Vasomotion in the bat wing: A thermoregulatory response to internal heating. Comp. Biochem. Physiol., 32:219-226.

Kunz, T. H. 1980. Daily energy budgets of free-living bats. Pp. 369-392 *in* Proc. 5th Int. Bat Res. Conf. (D. E. Wilson and A. L. Gardner, eds.), Texas Tech Press, Lubbock, Texas, 434 pp.

Kunz, T. H., M. H. Stack, and R. Jenness. 1983. A comparison of milk composition in *Myotis*

lucifugus and *Eptesicus fuscus* (Chiroptera: Vespertilionidae). Biol. Reprod., 28:229-234.

Laburn, H. P., and D. Mitchell. 1975. Evaporative cooling as a thermoregulatory mechanism in the fruit bat, *Rousettus aegypticaus*. Physiol. Zool., 48:195-202.

Lasiewski, R. C., A. L. Acosta, and M. H. Bernstein. 1966a. Evaporative water loss in birds.—I. Characteristics of the open flow method of determination and their relation to estimates of thermoregulatory ability. Comp. Biochem. Physiol., 19;445-457.

Lasiewski, R. C., A. L. Acosta, and M. H. Bernstein. 1966b. Evaporative water loss in birds.—II. A modified method for determination by direct weighing. Comp. Biochem. Physiol., 19:459-470.

Lee, A. K., and J. H. Brown. 1970. Variations in the hemoglobin concentrations of Great Basin rodents. J. Mammal., 51:669-674.

Licht, P., and P. Leitner. 1967a. Behavioral responses to high temperatures in three species of California bats. J. Mammal., 48:52-61.

Licht, P., and P. Leitner. 1967b. Physiological responses to high environmental temperatures in three species of microchiropteran bats. Comp. Biochem. Physiol., 22:371-387.

Lowry, W. P. 1969. Weather and life: An introduction to biometeorology. Academic Press, New York, 305 pp.

Lu, S. L., and W. J. Bleier. 1981. Renal morphology of *Macrotus* (Chiroptera, Phyllostomatidae). J. Mammal., 62:181-182.

Maina, J. N., A. S. King, and D. Z. King. 1982. A morphometric analysis of the lung of a species of bat. Resp. Physiol., 50:1-11.

McFarland, W. N., and W. A. Wimsatt. 1969. Renal function and its relation to the ecology of the vampire bat, *Desmodus rotundus*. Comp. Biochem. Physiol., 28:985-1006.

Noll, U. G. 1979. Body temperature, oxygen consumption, noradrenaline response and cardiovascular adaptations in the flying fox, *Rousettus aegyptiacus*. Comp. Biochem. Physiol., 63A:79-88.

O'Farrell, M. J., E. H. Studier, and W. G. Ewing. 1971. Energy utilization and water requirements of captive *Myotis thysanodes* and *Myotis lucifugus* (Chiroptera). Comp. Biochem. Physiol., 39A:549-552.

Pearson, O. P. 1947. The rate of metabolism of some small mammals. Ecology, 28:127-145.

Procter, J. W., and E. H. Studier. 1970. Effects of ambient temperature and water vapor pressure on evaporative water loss in *Myotis lucifugus*. J. Mammal., 51:799-804.

Racey, P. A. 1982. Ecology of bat reproduction. Pp. 57-104 *in* Ecology of Bats. (T. H. Kunz, ed.). Plenum Press, New York, 425 pp.

Reeder, W. G., and R. B. Cowles. 1951. Aspects of thermoregulation in bats. J. Mammal., 32:389-403.

Riedesel, M. L., and B. A. Williams. 1976. Continuous 24-hour oxygen consumption studies of *Myotis velifer*. Comp. Biochem. Physiol., 54A:95-99.

Sisk, M. O. 1957. A study of the sudoriparous glands of the little brown bat, *Myotis lucifugus*. J. Morph., 101:425-456.

Strickler, T. L. 1980. Downstroke muscle histochemistry in two bats. Pp. 61-68, *in* Proc. 5th Int. Bat Res. Conf. (D. E. Wilson and A. L. Gardner, eds.). Texas Tech Press, Lubbock, Texas, 434 pp.

Studier, E. H. 1970. Evaporative water loss in bats. Comp. Biochem. Physiol., 35:935-943.

Studier, E. H., and W. G. Ewing. 1971. Diurnal fluctuation in weight and blood composition in *Myotis nigricans* and *Myotis lucifugus*. Comp. Biochem. Physiol., 38A:129-139.

Studier, E. H., and M. J. O'Farrell. 1976. Biology of *Myotis thysanodes* and *M. lucifugus* (Chiroptera: Vespertilionidae)—III. Metabolism, heart rate, breathing rate, evaporative water loss and general energetics. Comp. Biochem. Physiol., 54A:423-432.

Studier, E. H., and D. A. Rimle. 1980. Concentration and composition of natural urine of some Michigan small mammals. Comp. Biochem. Physiol., 67A:163-165.

Studier, E. H., and D. E. Wilson. 1979. Effects of captivity on thermoregulation and metabolism in *Artibeus jamaicensis* (Chiroptera: Phyllostomatidae). Comp. Biochem. Physiol., 62A:347-350.

Studier, E. H., and D. E. Wilson. 1983. Natural urine concentrations and composition in neotropical bats. Comp. Biochem. Physiol., 75A:509-515.

Studier, E. H., J. W. Procter, and D. J. Howell. 1970. Diurnal body weight loss and tolerance of weight loss in five species of *Myotis*. J. Mammal., 51:302-309.

Studier, E. H., B. C. Boyd, A. T. Feldman, R. W. Dapson, and D. E. Wilson. 1983a. Renal function in the neotropical bat, *Artibeus jamaicensis*. Comp. Biochem. Physiol., 74A:199-209.

Studier, E. H., S. J. Wisniewski, A. T. Feldman, R. W. Dapson, B. C. Boyd, and D. E. Wilson, 1983b. Kidney structure in neotropical bats. J. Mammal., 64:445-452.

Thomas, S. P. 1975. Metabolism during flight in two species of bats, *Phyllostomus hastatus* and *Pteropus gouldii*. J. Exp. Biol., 63:273-293.

Thomas, S. P., and R. A. Suthers. 1972. The physiology and energetics of bat flight. J. Exp. Biol., 57:317-335.

Thomas, S. P., M. R. Lust, and H. J. Van Riper. 1984. Ventilation and oxygen extraction in the bat *Phyllostomus hastatus* during rest and steady flight. Physiol. Zool., 57:237-250.

Thornthwaite, C. W. 1940. Atmospheric moisture in relation to ecological problems. Ecology, 21:17-28.

Trune, D. R., and C. N. Slobodchikoff. 1976. Social effects of roosting on the metabolism of the pallid bat (*Antrozous pallidus*). J. Mammal., 57:656-663.

Vogel, V. B. 1969. Vergleichende Untersuchungen über den Wasserhaushalt von Fledermäusen (*Rhinopoma, Rhinolophus* und *Myotis*). Z. Vergl. Physiol., 64:324-345.

Vogel, V., and W. Vogel. 1972. Über das Konzentrationsvermögen der Nieren zweier Fledermausarten (*Rhinopoma hardwickei* und *Rhinolophus ferrum-equinum*) mit unterschiedlich länger Nierenpapille. Z. Vergl. Physiol., 76:358-371.

Watkins, L. C., and Shump, Jr., K. A. 1981. Behavior of the evening bat *Nycticeius humeralis* at a nursery roost. Amer. Midl. Nat., 105:258-268.

Welch, W. R. 1980. Evaporative water loss from endotherms in thermally and hygrically complex environments: An empirical approach for interspecific comparisons. J. Comp. Physiol., 139:135-143.

Winston, P. W., and D. H. Bates. 1960. Saturated solutions for the control of humidity in biological research. Ecology, 41:232-237.

Chapter 23

Methods of Body Composition Analysis

Elizabeth D. Pierson[1]

and

M. Holly Stack[2]

Department of Biology
Boston University
Boston, MA 02215, USA

1. INTRODUCTION

The purpose of this chapter is threefold: 1) to provide investigators with a practical guide to techniques used in body composition analysis; 2) to offer a critical review of these techniques; and 3) to summarize the type of research for which body composition analysis is useful.

Although body composition analysis has been used in community and ecosystem studies (e.g. Golley, 1968; French et al., 1976) the emphasis in this chapter is on its application to population and species-level inquiries. In avian research the focus has been on the energetics of reproduction (e.g., Ricklefs, 1974; Walsberg, 1983), growth and development (Ricklefs, 1983; O'Conner, 1984), and fat deposition for migration (e.g., Odum et al., 1964, 1965; Rogers and Odum, 1964; King et al., 1965; Helms et al., 1967, Yarbrough, 1970; Berthold, 1975; Holmes, 1976; McLandress and Raveling, 1981; Pilo and George, 1983; McEwan and Whitehead, 1984).

Small mammal (rodent and shrew) research has focused on variation in body composition with such factors as season, habitat, and geographic locality (Jameson and Mead, 1964; Hayward, 1965; Myrcha, 1969; Blake, 1972; Evans, 1973; Fleharty et al., 1973; Lynch, 1973; Scarth et al., 1973; Morton, 1975; Schreiber and Johnson, 1975; Galster and Morrison, 1976; Zegers and Williams, 1977; Millar, 1981; Rickart, 1982). Energetics studies have emphasized seasonal and species-level variation in energy content (Gorecki, 1965, 1975a; Myrcha, 1969; Golley, 1969/70; Fleharty et al., 1973; Kaufman et al., 1975a; Schreiber and Johnson, 1975; Bergeron, 1976; Newman, 1977;

[1] Present Address: Museum of Vertebrate Zoology, University of California, Berkeley, California 94720, USA

[2] Present Address: Museum d'Histoire Naturelle, Laboratoire d'Anatomie Comparée, 55 Rue Buffon, 75005 Paris, France

Gyug and Millar, 1980; Lochmiller et al., 1983). There has also been interest recently in the energetics of reproduction (Millar, 1975; Randolph et al., 1977; Judd et al., 1978; Kiell and Millar, 1980), growth and development (Myrcha and Walkowa, 1968; Sawicka-Kapusta, 1970; Morton et al., 1974; Kaufman and Kaufman, 1975a; Millar, 1978; Gyug and Millar, 1981; Cameron and Spencer, 1983).

For bats, body composition analysis has been used primarily to document seasonal changes in fat content for migratory or hibernating species (Hayward and Ball, 1966; Baker et al., 1968; Ewing et al., 1970; Weber and Findley, 1970; Krulin and Sealander, 1972; Esher et al., 1973; Pagels, 1975; O'Farrell and Schreiweis, 1978; Wilson et al., 1978; Tidemann, 1982). There have been few studies on seasonal changes in total body composition (O'Farrell and Studier, 1976) or on the energetics of reproduction, growth and development (O'Farrell and Studier, 1973, Studier et al., 1973; Stack, 1985; Kunz, 1987; Pierson et al., unpubl.).

In this chapter we discuss five components: water, lipids, proteins, carbohydrates, and inorganic constituents. Based on our review, we recommend a step-wise procedure for analysis as outlined in Fig. 1 and discussed in Sections 2-7. Whenever possible *in vivo* as well as *in vitro* techniques are described. Although previous research has relied mostly on *in vitro* methods, recent technology has made *in vivo* procedures possible. Given the frequent need for repeat sampling, and the importance of protecting many wild populations, it is becoming increasingly necessary to develop *in vivo* methods. It is hoped that researchers will, whenever possible, use the techniques described here and, by experimentation and ingenuity, add to this meagre repertoire.

The procedural discussions provided below are intended as a guide, not a "cookbook," and are usually offered as a supplement to already published methods for which relevant citations are given. The most thorough, current review of available methods appears in Gordzinski et al. (1975). For an excellent discussion of applications for body composition analysis to ecological energetics, see Paine (1971).

2. DATA COLLECTION AND ANALYSIS

2.1. Conditions of Capture

Techniques for capturing bats are discussed in detail in Chapter 1, but it is important to add a few cautionary remarks pertinent to body composition analysis. Body composition can be exceedingly labile (Licht and Leitner, 1967b; Studier and Ewing, 1971; Okon et al., 1978; Okon and Ekanem, 1979; Bassett, 1980). *When* (time of day, time of year) animals are captured, and *how* they are handled prior to experimentation can significantly affect results. Animals held in the laboratory can, with minor changes in exercise or diet, show alterations in fat stores which would not occur in a free-ranging animal (Pond, 1981). Thus it is exceedingly important to use consistent and expeditious collecting methods (e.g., for serial samples, always collect them at the same time of day; for all samples, process them as quickly as possible).

2.2. Data Recording and Analysis

Our review of the literature has revealed a notable lack of consistency in how results are reported and analyzed. Although bivariate ratios are most frequently used to report the distribution of body components, they may take several forms: a percentage of total mass, a percentage of fat-free mass, and an index (e.g., grams of water, lipids, or ash over grams of lean dry mass). It may at times be necessary to use all these measures for comparative purposes, but the index, because it factors both water and fat (the two most variable components) out of the denominator, is the most informative.

There are two serious problems with ratios, however, as they have often been used in biological research (Blem, 1984). First, the assumption is frequently made that ratios remove the effect of size. Atchley et al. (1976) argue very convincingly that this is not the case, since one cannot assume that variance in the numerator (e.g., lipids, water, or ash) is independent of variance in the denominator (e.g., lean dry mass, fat-free mass, or total mass). In fact, a ratio may, in some cases, compound the effect of size. Secondly, ratios are often subjected to parametric tests, the assumption being that ratios, like their component parts, are normally distributed. Atchley et al. (1976) have demonstrated that this is incorrect, and to perform parametric tests ratios must be log-transformed (Atchley and Anderson, 1978; Hills, 1978). Most importantly, however, they argue that covariance analysis be used instead of ratios. It is a far more powerful analytical tool, and avoids the two problems mentioned above.

This issue is far from resolved in the literature (see Atchley et al., 1976; Albrecht, 1978; Atchley, 1978; Atchley and Anderson, 1978; Dodson, 1978; Hills, 1978; Blem, 1984; Prothero, 1986), but we generally accept the position of Blem (1984) and suggest the following: that raw data always be reported (this enables the reader to manipulate data for comparative purposes), that covariance analysis be used in place of ratios, but that past research using ratios not be disregarded. In an analysis of nine data sets on lipid content, Blem (1984) found that covariance analysis was more sensitive, but every effect deemed significant by ratio analysis was also found to be significant by covariance analysis.

2.3. Computing Energy Values

Three body components (lipids, proteins, and carbohydrates) are often considered for their energy value in bioenergetics research. These three tissues have characteristic energy values, which on an ash-free gram basis average 39.56 kJ for lipids, 23.65 kJ for proteins, and 17.16 kJ for carbohydrates (Paine, 1971). These values may, however, show developmental (Pierson et al., unpubl.), interspecific (Schreiber and Johnson, 1975), or seasonal

variation. Thus it is often desirable to compute the energy values on lipids and lean dry tissue directly using bomb calorimetry (see Section 8).

There are two units of energy commonly used in bioenergetics research: the calorie and the joule. Although the joule is the standard S.I. energy unit, many studies on body composition continue to use the calorie (cal) or kilocalorie (kcal) as the unit of energy (1 cal = 4.184 joules). In compliance with the S.I. standard, we recommend the joule or kilojoule (kJ).

Energy values are generally reported on a per gram—calorie or joules per gram wet mass, dry mass, lean dry mass (LDM), or ash-free lean dry mass (AFLDM). Our cautionary remarks regarding ratios (see Section 2.2) apply here also, but if a ratio must be used, we recommend kJ/g AFLDM (the denominator least complicated by widely varying components).

3. WATER CONTENT

Water is the predominant component in all living organisms, usually comprising approximately 66% (Grubbs, 1980) of the total body mass in adult mammals. It can fluctuate markedly in small mammals, however, with changes in season, environmental conditions, and reproductive status, varying (in the literature surveyed) from 53.5 to 74.2% of total body mass (Gorecki, 1965; Myrcha, 1969; Fleharty et al., 1973; Schreiber and Johnson, 1975). Water content is of special interest in animals like desert rodents that deal with extreme environmental conditions (Grubbs, 1980), or in others like sloths that show atypical metabolic rates (Nagy and Montgomery, 1980). Maintaining water balance is a particular challenge to bats, whose small size and large surface to volume ratio lead to high evaporative water loss (see Chapter 22). Temperate zone bats, that may roost without access to water for at least 14 h, often at exceedingly high ambient temperatures (Licht and Leitner, 1967a), may lose up to

16.0% of their body mass in water per day (Chew and White, 1960; Licht and Leitner, 1967b; Studier, 1970; Studier et al., 1970; Studier and Ewing, 1971; Bassett, 1980).

Information on water content is also important in developmental studies. Embryos have a much higher water content than adults, and the rate at which the young achieve adult water levels provides information on their maturation (Pierson et al., unpubl.). Water content at birth, for example, has often been used as an altriciality-precociality index for young (Adolph, 1970; Adolph and Heggeness, 1971).

3.1. *In Vitro* Methods

The first steps in a multi-step tissue analysis (see Fig. 1) are the accurate determinations of total wet and dry mass. Absolute water content can then be calculated as the difference between these two measurements.

The most precise wet mass values are obtained by sacrificing the animal upon capture, and weighing it immediately with an electronic balance, accurate to 0.01 g. If such a balance (e.g., a compact, battery-operated model) is unavailable in the field, then the best procedure is to sacrifice the animal, seal it tightly in a tared plastic bag, and keep it cool (refrigerated, on ice, or frozen) until an accurate weight can be taken. If this cannot be done within 12 to 24 h, then a wet mass should be determined using a high precision mechanical scale (e.g., Ohaus, Model #1010-10).

To provide adequate tissue preservation for subsequent steps in the analysis, animals should be chilled as soon as they are sacrificed, and frozen within 24 h. Gut contents should be removed prior to analysis, and for pregnant females, separate measurements can be useful for the embryo, placenta, and mammary glands. Unless tissue can be stored in liquid nitrogen or an ultracold ($-70°C$) freezer, analysis should be done within six months. Prolonged storage at normal freezer temperatures ($-10°C$ to $-15°C$) desiccates tissue and alters its energy content (Sisula and

Virtanen, 1977; Strong et al., 1980). Some studies require that individual tissues or organs (e.g., skin, liver, spleen) be weighed and examined separately. Frozen specimens should be partially thawed before dissection, and tissues weighed as soon as they are dissected. Since small tissue samples are especially prone to desiccation, they should be placed in weighing pans and covered with damp paper towels.

Dry mass is determined by drying the carcass to a constant mass. Small animals ($<$ 15 g) can be dried whole, but larger animals should be chopped into 10-15 g pieces. Unfortunately there is no standardized procedure for this drying process. Recommended drying temperatures range from $30°C$ to $125°C$ (Kerr et al., 1982), and drying methods include the use of air-dry ovens, vacuum ovens, and freeze-drying (Kerr et al., 1982). The challenge is to find a temperature that will dry tissue to constant mass without altering the composition or energy content of lipids and proteins. Paine (1971) contends he had difficulty achieving a constant mass below $80°C$. Yet various authors have cautioned that high temperatures (usually meaning in excess of $60°C$) will alter the chemical composition of proteins (Kerr et al., 1982) or cause volatilization of fatty acids (Gorecki, 1975b; Blem, 1976). Kerr et al. (1982), however, found no evidence for the latter claim. The safest option is freeze-drying. It is faster than low temperature drying, and causes no change in tissue composition (Gorecki, 1975b; Kerr et al., 1982). If an oven must be used, vacuum ovens are preferable to air-dry ovens because drying time is shorter, and thus the risk of altering lipids and proteins is less. Probably the safest, compromise oven temperature, and the one most often recommended, is $60°C$ (Dowgiallo, 1975b; Sisula and Virtanen, 1977).

If whole body composition is to be studied, the dried carcass should be ground to a uniform homogenate using a food chopper (large species) or Wiley mill (small species). This homogenate can then be used for further steps in body composition analysis—fat, pro-

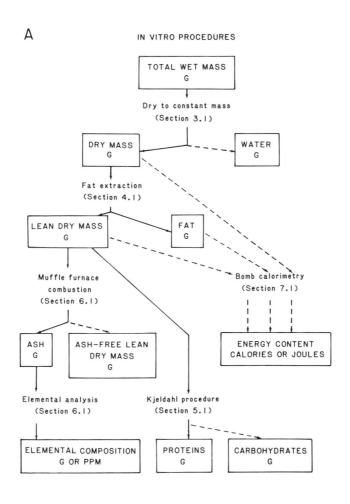

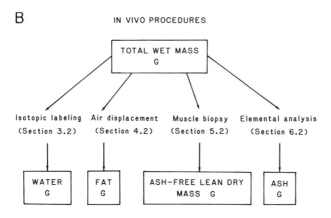

Figure 1. Schematic diagram illustrating stepwise procedures for (A) *in vitro* and (B) *in vivo* body composition analysis. Solid lines indicate that methods yield direct results; lines with short dashes indicate that results are determined indirectly by calculation; lines with long dashes are used for bomb calorimetry procedures. See text for discussion.

tein, or ash determination (see Fig. 1), but should be redried to constant mass and reweighed before being used in any of these procedures.

Total water content is then estimated by taking the difference between the total wet mass and the constant dry mass.

3.2. *In Vivo* Methods

There are also methods, using isotopically-labeled water, to estimate body water volume *in vivo* (Nagy and Costa, 1980). These methods are discussed elsewhere (Chapter 18) in conjunction with the use of doubly-labeled water to estimate energy expenditure and water flux in free-ranging bats. In brief, deuterium- (or tritium-) enriched water or water doubly enriched with deuterium (or tritium) and oxygen-18 is injected into an animal. After an appropriate equilibration period (approximately 45 min in small bats), a small sample of blood is taken by venipuncture. Water is microdistilled from each blood sample and isotope activity is determined. Body water volume is calculated from isotope dilution space. Tritium dilution space tends to overestimate total body water volume, whereas oxygen-18 dilution space more closely approximates values derived from drying a carcass to constant mass (Nagy and Costa, 1980).

4. FAT CONTENT

Fat is the primary energy-storage tissue in mammals. As such, its patterns of fluctuation reveal how an animal manages its energy budget—how it copes with variations in food supply or how it accomplishes such energetically demanding tasks as growth, reproduction, migration, and hibernation. Thus, it is not surprising that many studies concerned with these phenomena have examined patterns of lipid deposition and utilization in considerable detail—see the citations in Introduction, plus Schemmel (1976), Young (1976) and Pond (1981). To date, the primary

work on bats has focused on energy storage for hibernation (Baker et al., 1968; Ewing et al., 1970; Weber and Findley, 1970; Krulin and Sealander, 1972; Esher et al., 1973; O'Shea, 1976), and an examination of the role of brown adipose tissue in non-shivering thermogenesis (Hayward and Ball, 1966; O'Farrell and Schreiweis, 1978; Tidemann, 1982).

Equally interesting is the role of fat as an energy reserve for the tasks of reproduction. This has been examined extensively in birds (reviewed in Ricklefs, 1983), but only scantily in free-ranging mammals: the Grey Seal (Fedak and Anderson, 1982), several rodents (Blake, 1972; Randolph et al., 1977; Kiell and Millar, 1980; Rickart, 1982), and three species of bats (O'Farrell and Studier, 1976; Stack, 1985; Pierson et al., unpubl.). Likewise, patterns of development, particularly fat deposition in pre- and postnatal young (O'Farrell and Studier, 1973; Wilson et al., 1978, Stack, 1985; Fujita, 1986; Pierson et al., unpubl.), have received little attention in bats.

4.1. *In Vitro* Methods

The most common technique for extracting fat from tissue utilizes the Soxhlet apparatus, whose component parts and set-up are described in chemical analysis handbooks (Sawicka-Kapusta, 1975). A single unit consists of three parts: a flask for the solvent, an extractor with a porous extraction thimble to hold the tissue, and a water-cooled condenser. A hot plate supplies heat. The apparatus is available in a range of sizes, but for most bats a flask capacity of 250 to 500 ml is sufficient. Numerous solvents can be used for extraction (Sawicka-Kapusta, 1975). Those most commonly recommended are petroleum ether, ethanol, or petroleum ether plus another solvent (Kerr et al., 1982; Dobush et al., 1985). Although chloroform is often used (Blem, 1976), we advise against it (it extracts non-lipids along with the fat and is carcinogenic). We use a 3:1 mixture of 95% ethanol and petroleum ether.

Assuming one does not wish to recover individual fat samples, it is possible to extract numerous samples simultaneously by wrapping each one separately in labeled filter paper, and placing packets together in the same extraction thimble. Sawicka-Kapusta (1975) recommends soaking samples in 95% ethanol for 30 min prior to extraction to denature proteins. This step should be omitted, however, if protein analysis is of subsequent interest. When starting, the flask should be two-thirds full of solvent, and the thimble one-half full. Any lubricant used on ground-glass connections should be insoluble to the solvent if the extraction solution is to be used later to recover the extracted fat.

The solvent goes through extraction cycles in the apparatus. The number of cycles required depends upon the fat content of the tissue, but 25 cycles are usually sufficient. The solvent should be replaced after the tenth and twentieth cycles, and the cycles should run until the samples reach a constant dry mass. The solvent, yellow in the presence of fat, will appear clear when extraction is complete. For samples containing very large amounts of fat (e.g., pre-hibernating bats), up to 40 cycles may be required. Samples may be stored in a desiccator after extraction, awaiting further analysis.

An alternative method for fat extraction in the "tea-bag" method (Child, 1969), in which a carcass is macerated, placed in a sealed, tared acetate rayon bag, and submerged in boiling petroleum ether (with adequate ventilation). The solvent is replaced at 45 min intervals until no visible fat is left, and the tissue reaches a constant dry mass.

Fat content is determined by taking the difference between the dry mass of a sample prior to and following extraction. The extracted fat can be air-dried in a ventilated hood until the solvent has evaporated, analyzed for caloric value using bomb calorimetry (see Section 7), or analyzed for fatty acid and lipid phosphorus content by gas-liquid and thin-layer chromatography (Christopherson and Glass, 1969). For a review of the numerous biochemical procedures available for analysis of lipids, see Allen (1976).

4.2. *In Vivo* Methods

Kodama and Pace (1963) describe a method (complete with schematic drawings) for *in vivo* determination of body fat in small mammals. This procedure relies on measuring air-displacement in a simple, easily constructed decompression chamber. Although we know of no use of this procedure with bats, it is potentially useful for many kinds of studies (e.g., monitoring changes in lipid content in reproductive females and growing young).

Another possible technique, muscle biopsy, is discussed in the section on AFLDM (Section 5.2).

5. ASH-FREE LEAN DRY MASS (PROTEINS AND CARBOHYDRATES)

The non-fat organic constituent is usually considered as a single component, ash-free lean dry mass, but is, in fact, composed of both proteins—approximately 83% of fat-free lean dry mass (Robbins, 1983), and carbohydrates—less than 1% of total body (Robbins, 1983). Lean dry mass, like fat, is energy-rich, and thus of considerable interest in bioenergetic studies. Although its levels tend to remain relatively constant in adult animals (Odum et al., 1964; Robbins, 1983), it does show important variation with season, age and reproductive condition. In fact, small but important changes occur even on a daily basis. (Okon et al., 1978; Okon and Ekanem, 1979).

Although it is possible to analyze proteins and carbohydrates separately, most ecological studies utilizing body composition analysis consider the two components together as AFLDM.

5.1. *In Vitro* Methods

AFLDM is estimated indirectly by calculating the difference between the LDM obtained through fat extraction and the ash mass determined by combustion (Section 6).

Separate protein determination is traditionally done by the Kjeldahl procedure. This is an indirect method for calculating protein concentrations, via a conversion factor (empirically derivable, but usually 6.25 for animal tissue), from measurable nitrogen content. Descriptions of this procedure are readily available in a number of handbooks (e.g., Dowgiallo, 1975a). Also see Chapter 15.

Carbohydrate content is usually taken to be the difference between the protein fraction and the total AFLDM, but a separate determination is also possible. Various methods are again reviewed by Dowgiallo (1975a; 1975b).

5.2. *In Vivo* Methods

We know of no established procedures for protein and carbohydrate determination *in vivo*. Using the composition of certain tissues, however, to predict total body content, an established *in vitro* technique for large mammals (Anderson et al., 1972; Robbins et al., 1974; Finger et al., 1981) has potential *in vivo* application. Ringberg et al. (1981) recently found they could use indicator muscles to predict total carcass composition in reindeer, and suggest that the required information could be obtained by non-destructive muscle biopsy. Such a technique was used by McCracken (1984) on 10-12 g *Tadarida brasiliensis* to obtain tissue for electrophoresis. Thus, if it could be determined that the ratio of fat to AFLDM in certain muscles accurately predicts their proportions in the body as a whole, a muscle biopsy technique could be used to determine both fat and AFLDM. Failure to account for large deposits of fat in concentrated areas, however, could make this approach unreliable.

6. ASH CONTENT

The inorganic (ash) component of a vertebrate organism forms only a small fraction of the total body mass (about 4% in bats), and is composed largely of calcium and phosphorus, the two major elements in bone (Moss and Moss-Salentijn, 1979; Robbins, 1983), plus a small proportion of numerous trace elements and mineral salts. Most ecologically oriented studies of mammals treat ash as a single component, examining total ash levels in relation to some biological or environmental parameter (e.g., age, reproductive status or seasonal change [Gorecki, 1965; Sawicka-Kapusta, 1970; Fleharty et al., 1973; Kaufman and Kaufman, 1975b; Kaufman et al., 1975; O'Farrell and Studier, 1976; Stack, 1985; Pierson et al., unpubl.]).

It is also possible, however, to determine the elemental composition of ash. This approach has been widely used in ecological studies to look for naturally occurring or introduced elements, which may be toxic or nutritionally limiting: in agriculture to document the elemental content of soil and plants (Walsh and Beaton, 1973), in wildlife research to investigate animal nutrition (Robbins, 1983), and in ecosystems studies to examine nutrient cycling (Pomeroy, 1970). Although elemental analysis has been used in relatively few small mammal studies (Beyers et al., 1971; Briese, 1973; Nabholz, 1973; Sella, 1973; Kaufman and Kaufman, 1975b; Wiener et al., 1975; Wiener et al., 1977), valuable information has been gained on differences in elemental concentrations, within species and between species, in relation to such variables as season, habitat, age, sex, body size, and reproductive condition (Gentry et al., 1975).

Elemental analysis has rarely been used in bat research but would be of particular interest in reproductive and developmental studies. Kwiecinski (1984, 1985), for example, using histology and biochemical assays for plasma levels of calcium and phosphorus, has documented changes in bone composition of *Myotis lucifugus* during pregnancy and lactation.

Elemental analysis can also be used to examine effects of pesticides on bats (Clark, 1981). Such analysis is generally done on the liver, brain, whole carcasses (Clark, 1981), or guano (Clark et al., 1982), not just ash, and includes assays for organic chemicals.

6.1. *In Vitro* Methods

Inorganic constituents are generally considered equal to the ash residue remaining after high temperature combustion of dry or lean dry tissue samples. This ash residue can be generated in two ways: by combustion in a bomb calorimeter or in a muffle furnace.

We recommend the muffle furnace. Reiners and Reiners (1972), in comparing oxygen bomb combustion with the muffle furnace technique, found that the muffle furnace gave highly predictable results, whereas bomb combustion was subject to a systematic error of underestimation which increased with increasing ash content. Paine (1971) also demonstrated that the exceedingly high operating temperatures of the bomb calorimeter caused many salts to decompose and certain elements to be lost via colloidal particles or volatilization.

To use a muffle furnace, predried, preweighed tissue samples are placed in ceramic crucibles and held at high temperature until all the organic material has been volatilized. There is little agreement in the literature as to the best regime of time and temperature for this procedure. Recommended time regimes range from two (Schreiber and Johnson, 1975) to four (Paine, 1971;

Kaufman and Kaufman, 1975a; Kaufman et al., 1975), eight (Ewing et al., 1970) or 12 h (O'Farrell and Studier, 1973, 1976). Despite substantial evidence that many inorganic salts are volatilized above 500°C (Paine, 1971; Dowgiallo, 1975b), recommended temperature regimes vary from 450°C (Kaufman and Kaufman, 1975a; Kaufman et al., 1975) to 500°C (Paine, 1971), 550°C (Holmes, 1976) or 620°C (Ewing et al., 1970; O'Farrell and Studier, 1973, 1976).

In an attempt to establish an optimum time and temperature regime for bats, one of us (E. D. Pierson) used 10 tissue samples from *Myotis lucifugus* (1.0 g each, predried at 60°C to a constant mass) and ran 10 subsamples (0.5 g each) at 500°C, plus 10 identical subsamples at 620°C [the temperature used in most other bioenergetics studies of *Myotis* (O'Farrell and Studier, 1973, 1976)], weighing the samples after 4, 5, 8 and 12 h. There were significant differences between the two temperature regimes (see Table 1). The lower ash values at 620°C substantiate the claims of Paine (1971) and Dowgiallo (1975b) that material is lost at high temperatures. Although Paine (1971) suggests a time regime of 4 h (at 500°C), it took 5 h for our samples to reach stable ash values at this temperature. Thus our conclusion was that bat tissue should be ashed for 5 h at 500°C.

There are two sources of error in the muffle furnace technique that deserve men-

Table 1. Mean ash mass values for 0.5 g lean dry tissue samples taken from pregnant *Myotis lucifugus* specimens and run at two temperature regimes.

Ashing Time[a] (Hours)	Temperature[b]	
	500°C (n=10)	620°C (n=10)
4	0.098[c]	0.084
5	0.089	—
8	0.085	0.087
12	0.083	0.079

[a] The same samples were used throughout the experiment, and weighed in their ceramic vials after 4, 5, and 8 hours. For the final weighing at 12 h each sample was placed on weighing paper. See Section 6.1 of text for discussion.

[b] An F-Test, using SAS PROC GLM Repeated Measures Design, indicated highly significant differences between the two temperature regimes (F = 12.18, p < 0.001).

[c] Pair-wise t-tests comparing all ash volumes at 500°C showed significant differences (p < 0.05 to p < 0.001) between the 4 h value and all others, and no differences between any pair of values for hours 5, 8, or 12.

tion. One is temperature variation in different areas of the furnace (Reiners and Reiners, 1972). This can be avoided by using relatively few vials at once, and placing them all in the center of the furnace. Another problem arises in the final determination of ash mass. Because the sample begins to absorb moisture rapidly upon removal from the furnace, it is important to take mass measurements as quickly as possible. We found, however, that more accurate results could be obtained by taking extra time to transfer the sample to weighing paper, since it was impossible to obtain consistent tare masses for the relatively larger, extremely porous ceramic vials.

The muffle furnace will yield a reliable estimate of ash mass, but provides no data on ash composition. For such information a number of analytical techniques are available. It is outside the scope of this chapter to discuss them in detail, but for an overview, see Jones and Steyn (1973) and Gentry et al. (1975). The four most important are: atomic absorption spectrometry, nuclear activation (IAEA, 1972), x-ray fluorescence, and emission spectrometry (Jones and Warner, 1969). Each has advantages and limitations which should be considered with specific research questions in mind. Atomic absorption is the most advanced of these technologies (Horlick, 1984), but is subject to inter-laboratory calibration errors of up to 20% (W. E. Rainey, pers. comm.), and requires that each element be analyzed independently. The other three can scan one sample for numerous elements, but may have various difficulties dealing with calcium or phosphorus. These methods usually operate with less than 1.0% error (Budlinger et al., 1972; J. Cate, pers. comm.), and the last two (x-ray fluorescence and emission spectrometry) are rapidly growing technologies that hold great promise for wider application to biological problems (Keliher et al., 1984; Marcowicz and Van Grieken, 1984). X-ray fluorescence is particularly attractive because it is nondestructive to the sample, and can be coupled with a scanning electron microscope to examine microscale elemental distribution in tissues. The latest developments in these fields are reviewed every two years in a special edition of *Analytical Chemistry* (see *Anal. Chem.,* April 1984).

If elemental analysis is to include identification of metals, then care must be taken at every stage not to contaminate the samples (Gentry et al., 1975). Animals should not be held in metal cages. Tissues should be processed with teflon or plastic dissecting tools and homogenized in an all-agate mechanical ball mill (Jones and Steyn, 1973).

6.2. *In Vivo* Methods

Radionuclide tracers have been used in numerous ecological studies (Bailey et al., 1973; Schultz and Whicker, 1982) to estimate elemental concentrations *in vivo*. These markers work most readily for elements like hydrogen and oxygen which have rapid equilibration times. Radioactive calcium has been used to follow mineral transfer from mothers to young in cottontail rabbits (Rongstad, 1965) but, because it does not mix rapidly with body pools, it is not practical for measuring bone content (Cohn and Dombrowski, 1971).

Various radiographic techniques can yield estimates of calcium concentration by measuring bone density (Chamberlain et al., 1968), but transmission densitometry is far more sensitive—detecting changes of 3-4% in bone density (Cameron and Sorenson, 1963) than x-ray densitometry—which requires a 30% density change (Nelp et al., 1970).

Several technologies have already found application in human medicine and could be used in small mammal research: neutron activation to measure bone calcium (Chamberlain et al., 1968; Nelp et al., 1970, 1972), Cohn and Dombrowski, 1971; Cohn et al., 1972), nuclear magnetic resonance (NMR) to estimate organic and inorganic phosphorus (Dwek et al., 1977; Jardetzky and Roberts, 1981), and x-ray fluorescence to identify numerous elements—provided tissue is no thicker than a human finger, e.g., bat wing, leg or tail bones (J. Cate, pers. comm.). Neutron activation has already been applied to some *in vivo* work with mammals—hair analysis in ungulates (Kennington and Ching, 1966), and the other techniques deserve serious consideration.

7. ENERGY CONTENT

There are basically four approaches for studying energy budgets of living organisms: analysis of metabolic rate—by respirometry (Chapter 21) or, more recently, by doubly-labeled water (Chapter 18); microclimate analysis (Chapter 19); input-output, nutritional analysis (Kunz, 1980); and analysis of body composition. The first three are appropriate for studies concerned with daily energy utilization. Body composition analysis provides information on how energy is stored. By determining the value of energy-rich substances (fats, proteins, and carbohydrates), and by observing the shifting levels of these substances in the body, it is possible to gain considerable insight into the energy strategy of an organism. Because fat has about twice the energy content of the non-fat components combined, an organism's energy content serves as a kind of "barometer" with increases indicating upcoming energy demands (e.g., the well documented increase in fat levels in pre-migratory birds and pre-hibernating bats)(Odum et al., 1965; Baker et al., 1968, Ewing et al., 1970; O'Shea, 1976), and decreases revealing periods of energetic stress (during hibernation or lactation). Just how great the energetic challenge or how severe the stress can often be inferred from the patterns of change in energy content.

The energy content of tissue is determined by oxygen bomb or microbomb calorimetry. The principle for both techniques is the same: samples of known mass are combusted in an oxygen-pressurized steel container. The heat released by this process provides an indirect but accurate measure of the energy value of the original sample.

There are two types of bomb calorimeters in common use: the Phillipson-type (microbomb) and the Parr-type. The Phillipson-type measures the heat transferred to a copper ring, and the Parr-type, the heat transferred to a water jacket. The Phillipson model has a faster running time (8 to 10 min per sample vs. 18 min for the Parr-type), but which bomb is preferred depends on the size of individual samples. The Phillipson microbomb takes samples ranging from 5 to 50 mg; the Parr semimicrobomb (Model No. 1411), samples between 40 and 70 mg; and the Parr Model No. 1341, samples from 0.25 to 1.1 g.

Material must be dried and ground before combustion. Whole bodies of animals and large tissues can be ground in a Wiley mill with a 20-mesh screen (for large animals with heavy bones, grind in a Waring blender first). Small tissues (e.g., mammary glands, liver, small embryos) can be ground, with little loss of material, in an electric mortar, such as the type used by dentists (e.g., Wig-L-Bug).

This homogenized material is then compressed into pellets (in a pellet maker) for combustion. Pellets should be 10-15 mg for the Phillipson microbomb, 40-70 mg for the Parr semimicrobomb, and 0.75-1.0 g for the standard Parr model. Tissues with high ash content (like bone) are difficult to combust and may have to be mixed with a known amount of benzoic acid before forming the pellet. Benzoic acid can also be used to fill out samples that are below minimum size (e.g., less than 5 mg for the Phillipson microbomb, or 0.25 g for the Parr Model No. 1341). This works best by making a benzoic acid sandwich around the sample. A drop of water may be helpful in forming a pellet, but all pellets should be redried and reweighed before combustion. To insure accurate results, two or three samples from any tissue should be run, and the system should be calibrated using benzoic acid pellets of known energy values.

The manuals that accompany these calorimeters provide detailed directions for their operation. For discussion of sources of error associated with calorimetry, see Paine (1971) and Schroeder (1977).

8. SUMMARY

This chapter discusses ecological applications of body composition analysis to bat research. A step-wise procedure (Sections 3-7) is suggested for analyzing five components: water, lipids, proteins, carbohydrates, and ash (inorganic materials). For each one, both *in vivo* and *in vitro* methods are described. Special attention is given to bioenergetics research and techniques for determining energy values of organic components (fats and ash-free lean dry mass)(Section 7). Section 2 is devoted to recommended methods for recording and analyzing data.

9. ACKNOWLEDGMENTS

We acknowledge National Science Foundation Grants SP177-83465 and SER 14984 to T. H. Kunz for partial support in the preparation of this paper. Our thanks to I. L. Brisbin, Jr., T. H. Kunz, J. L. Patton, O. P. Pearson, and W. E. Rainey for their critical review of the manuscript, to R. Culter and M. Kirkpatrick for their advice on statistics, and to J. Cate, J. M. Lowenstein, H. V. Michel and G. Shalimoff for providing information on elemental analysis techniques.

10. REFERENCES

Adolph, E. F. 1970. Physiological stages in the development of mammals. Growth, 34:113-124.

Adolph, E. F., and F. W. Heggeness. 1971. Age changes in body water and fat in fetal and infant mammals. Growth, 35:55-63.

Albrecht, G. H. 1978. Some comments on the use of ratios. Syst. Zool., 27: 67-71.

Allen, W. V. 1976. Biochemical aspects of lipid storage and utilization in animals. Amer. Zool., 16:631-647.

Anderson, A. E., D. E. Medin, and D. C. Bowden. 1972. Indices of carcass fat in a Colorado mule deer population. J. Wildl. Manage., 36:579-594.

Atchley, W. R. 1978. Ratios, regression intercepts, and the scaling of data. Syst. Zool., 27:78-83.

Atchley, W. R., and D. Anderson. 1978. Ratios and the statistical analysis of biological data. Syst. Zool., 27:71-78.

Atchley, W. R., C. T. Gaskins, and D. Anderson. 1976. Statistical properties of ratios. I. Empirical results. Syst. Zool., 25:137-148.

Bailey, G. N. A., I. J. Linn, and P. J. Walker. 1973. Radioactive marking of small mammals. Mammal. Rev., 3:11-23.

Baker, W. W., S. G. Marshall, and V. B. Baker. 1968. Autumn fat deposition in the evening bat (*Nycticeius humeralis*). J. Mammal., 49:314-317.

Bassett, J. E. 1980. Control of postprandial water loss in *Myotis lucifugus lucifugus*. Comp. Biochem. Physiol., 65A:497-500.

Bergeron, J. M. 1976. Caloric values of small mammals of southeastern Quebec. Acta Theriol., 21:157-163.

Berthold, P. 1975. Migration: Control and metabolic physiology. Pp. 77-128, *in* Avian Biology. Vol. 5. (D. S. Farner, J. R. King, and K. C. Parkes, eds.). Academic Press, New York, 523 pp.

Beyers, R. J., M. H. Smith, J. B. Gentry and L. L. Ramsey. 1971. Standing crops of elements and atomic ratios in a small mammal community. Acta Theriol., 16:203-211.

Blake, B. H. 1972. The annual cycle and fat storage in two populations of golden-mantled ground squirrels. J. Mammal., 52:157-167.

Blem, C. R. 1976. Patterns of lipid storage and utilization in birds. Amer. Zool., 16:671-684.

Blem, C. R. 1984. Ratios in avian physiology. Auk, 101:153-155.

Briese, L. A. 1973. Variations in elemental composition and cycling in the cotton rat, *Sigmodon hispidus*. Unpubl. M.S. Thesis, Univ. Georgia, Athens.

Brisbin, I. L., Jr. 1968. A determination of the caloric density and major body components of large birds, Ecology, 49:792-794.

Brisbin, I. L., Jr. 1969. Bioenergetics of the breeding cycle of the ring dove. Auk, 86:54-74.

Brisbin, I. L., Jr., and L. J. Tally. 1973. Age-specific changes in the major body components and caloric value of growing Japanese quail. Auk, 90:624-635.

Budinger, T., B. Moyer, H. V. Michel, F. Asaro, and I. Perlman. 1972. Quantitative neutron activation analysis of human tissues. Pp. 331-333, *in* LBL Annual Report, Lawrence

Berkeley Laboratory Publ. No. 1666, Univ. Calif., Berkeley, 444 pp.

Cameron, G. N. and S. R. Spencer. 1983. Field growth rates and dynamics of body mass for rodents on the Texas coastal prairie. J. Mammal., 64:656-665.

Cameron, J. R., and J. Sorenson. 1963. Measurement of bone mineral *in vivo:* An improved method. Science, 142:230-232.

Chamberlain, M. J., J. H. Fremlin, D. K. Peters, and H. Phillip. 1968. Total body calcium by whole body neutron activation: New technique for study of bone disease. Br. Med. J. 2:581-585.

Chew, R. M. and H. E. White. 1960. Evaporative water losses of the pallid bat. J. Mammal., 41:452-458.

Child, G. I. 1969. A study of nonfat weights in migrating Swainson's Thrushes (*Hylocichla ustulata*). Auk, 86:327-338.

Christopherson, S. W., and R. L. Glass. 1969. Preparation of milk fat methyl esters by alcoholysis in an essentially non-alcoholic solution. J. Dairy Sci., 52:1289-1290.

Clark, D. R., Jr. 1981. Bats and environmental contaminants: A review. Special Scientific Report—Wildlife No. 235. U.S. Dept. Int., Fish Wildl. Ser., Washington, D. C., 27 pp.

Clark, D. R., Jr., R. K. LaVal, and M. D. Tuttle. 1982. Estimating pesticide burdens of bats from guano analysis. Bull. Environ. Contam. Toxicol., 29:214-220.

Cohn, S. H., T. J. Cinque, C. S. Dombrowski, and J. M. Letteri. 1972. Determination of body composition by neutron activation analysis in patient with renal failure. J. Lab. Clin. Med., 79:978-994.

Cohn, S. H., and C. S. Dombrowski. 1971. Measurement of total-body calcium, sodium, chlorine, nitrogen, and phosphorus in man by *in vivo* neutron activation analysis. J. Nucl. Med., 12:499-505.

Dobush, G. R., C. D. Ankney, and D. G. Krementz. 1986. The effect of apparatus, extraction time, and solvent type on lipid extractions of snow geese. Can. J. Zool., 63:1917-1920.

Dodson, P. 1978. On the use of ratios in growth studies. Syst. Zool., 27:62-67.

Dowgiallo, A. 1975a. Appendix: Proposed methods for estimating the excreted non-protein nitrogenous waste products in mixed urinary-faecal material (rejects). Pp. 185-199, *in* Methods for ecological bioenergetics. (W. Grodzinski, R. Z. Klekowski, and A. Duncan, eds.). IBP Handbook No. 24. Blackwell Sci. Publ., Oxford, 367 pp.

Dowgiallo, A. 1975b. Chemical composition of an animal's body and of its food. Pp. 160-185, *in* Methods for ecological bioenergetics. (W. Grodzinski, R. Z. Klekowski, and A. Duncan, eds.). IBP Handbook No. 24. Blackwell Sci. Publ., Oxford, 367 pp.

Dwek, R. A., I. D. Campbell, R. E. Richards, and R. J. P. Williams. 1977. NMR in biology. Academic Press, New York, 381 pp.

Esher, R. J., A. I. Fleischman and P. H. Lenz. 1973. Blood and liver lipids in torpid and aroused little brown bats. *Myotis lucifugus.* Comp. Biochem. Physiol. 45A:933-938.

Evans, D. M. 1973. Seasonal variations in the body composition and nutrition of the vole *Microtus agrestis.* J. Anim. Ecol., 42:1-18.

Ewing, W. G., E. H. Studier, and M. J. O'Farrell. 1970. Autumn fat deposition and gross body composition in three species of *Myotis.* Comp. Biochem. Physiol., 36:119-129.

Fedak, M. A., and S. S. Anderson. 1982. The energetics of lactation: Accurate measurements from a large wild mammal, the Grey seal (*Halichoerus grypus*). J. Zool., 198:473-479.

Finger, S. E., I. L. Brisbin, Jr., and M. H. Smith. 1981. Kidney fat as a predictor of body condition in white-tailed deer. J. Wildl. Manage., 45:964-968.

Fleharty, E. D., M. E. Krause and D. P. Stinnett. 1973. Body composition, energy content, and lipid cycles of four species of rodents. J. Mammal., 54:426-438.

French, N. R., W. E. Grant, W. Grodzinski, and D. M. Swift. 1976. Small mammal energetics in grassland ecosystems. Ecol. Monogr., 46:201-220.

Galster, W., and P. Morrison. 1976. Seasonal changes in body composition of the arctic ground squirrel, *Citellus undulatus.* Can. J. Zool., 54:74-78.

Gentry, J. B., L. A. Briese, D. W. Kaufman, M. H. Smith, and J. G. Wiener. 1975. Elemental flow and standing crops for small mammal populations. Pp. 205-221, *in* Small mammals: Their productivity and population dynamics. (F. B. Golley, K. Petrusewicz, and L. Ryszkowski, eds.). IBP 5. Cambridge Univ. Press, Cambridge, 451 pp.

Golley, F. B. 1968. Secondary productivity in terrestrial communities. Amer. Zool., 8:53-59.

Golley, F. B. 1969/70. Caloric value of cotton rats (*Sigmodon hispidus*). Pp. 143-147, *in* Energy flow through small mammal populations. (K. Petrusewicz, and L. Ryszkowski, eds.). Polish Sci. Publ., Warsawa, 298 pp.

Gorecki, A. 1965. Energy values of body in small mammals. Acta Theriol., 10:333-352.

Gorecki, A. 1975a. Calorimetry in ecological studies. Pp. 275-281, in Methods for ecological bioenergetics. (W. Grodzinski, R. Z. Klekowski, and A. Duncan, eds.). IBP Handbook No. 24. Blackwell Sci. Publ., Oxford, 367 pp.

Gorecki, A. 1975b. The adiabatic bomb calorimeter. Pp. 281-288, in Methods for ecological bioenergetics. (W. Grodzinski, R. Z. Klekowski, and A. Duncan, eds.). IBP Handbook No. 24. Blackwell Sci. Publ., Oxford, 367 pp.

Grodzinski, W., R. Z. Klekowski, and A. Duncan (eds.). 1975. Methods for ecological bioenergetics. IBP Handbook No. 24. Blackwell Sci. Publ., Oxford, 367 pp.

Grubbs, D. E. 1980. Tritiated water turnover in free-living desert rodents. Comp. Biochem. Physiol., 66A:89-98.

Gyug, L. W. and J. S. Millar. 1980. Fat levels in a subarctic population of Peromyscus maniculatus. Can. J. Zool., 58:1341-1346.

Gyug, L. W. and J. S. Millar. 1981. Growth of seasonal generations in three natural populations of Peromyscus. Can. J. Zool., 59:510-514.

Hayward, J. S. 1965. The gross body composition of six geographic races of Peromyscus. Can. J. Zool., 43:297-308.

Hayward, J. S. and E. G. Ball. 1966. Quantitative aspects of brown adipose tissue thermogenesis during arousal from hibernation. Biol. Bull., 131:94-103.

Helms, C. W., W. H. Aussiker, E. B. Bower, and S. D. Fretwell. 1967. A biometric study of major body components of the slate-colored junco, Junco hyemalis. Condor, 69:560-578.

Hills, M. 1978. On ratios—a response to Atchley, Gaskins and Anderson. Syst. Zool., 27:61-62.

Holmes, R. T. 1976. Body composition, lipid reserves and caloric densities of summer birds in a northern deciduous forest. Amer. Midl. Nat., 96:281-290.

Horlick, G. 1984. Atomic absorption, atomic fluorescence, and flame emission spectrometry. Anal. Chem., 56:278R-292R.

International Atomic Energy Agency. 1972. Nuclear activation techniques in the life sciences. Proc. Symp., Bled, Yugoslavia, 10-14 April 1972. International Atomic Energy Agency, Vienna, 664 pp.

Jardetzky, O. and G. C. K. Roberts. 1981. NMR in molecular biology. Academic Press, New York, 681 pp.

Jameson, E. W., Jr., and R. A. Mead. 1964. Seasonal changes in body fat, water and basic weight in Citellus lateralis, Eutamias speciosus and E. amoenus. J. Mammal., 45:359-365.

Jones, J. B., and W. J. A. Steyn. 1973. Sampling, handling and analyzing plant tissue samples. Pp. 249-267, in Soil testing and plant analysis. (L. M. Walsh, and J. D. Beaton, eds.). Soil Sci. Soc. Amer., Madison, Wisconsin, 491 pp.

Jones, J. B., and M. H. Warner. 1969. Analysis of plant-ash solutions by spark emission spectroscopy. Devel. Appl. Spectrosc., 7A:152-160.

Judd, F. W., J. Herrera, and M. Wagner. 1978. The relationship between lipid and reproductive cycles of a subtropical population of Peromyscus leucopus. J. Mammal., 59:669-676.

Kaufman, D. W., and G. A. Kaufman. 1975a. Caloric density of the old field mouse during postnatal growth. Acta Theriol., 20:83-95.

Kaufman, G. A., and D. W. Kaufman. 1975b. Effects of age, sex, and pelage phenotype on elemental composition of the old-field mouse. Pp. 518-527, in Mineral cycling on southeastern ecosystems (F. G. Howell, J. B. Gentry and M. H. Smith, eds.). U.S. ERDA Symposium Series (Conf-740513). Technical Information Center, ERDA, Springfield, Virginia, 898 pp.

Kaufman, D. W., G. A. Kaufman, and J. G. Wiener. 1975. Energy equivalents for sixteen species of xeric rodents. J. Mammal., 56:946-949.

Keliher, P. N., W. J. Boyko, J. M. Patterson, III, and J. W. Hershey. 1984. Emission spectrometry. Anal. Chem., 56:133R-156R.

Kennington, G. S., and C. F. T. Ching. 1966. Activation analysis of ungulate hair. Science, 151:1085-1086.

Kerr, D. C., C. D. Ankney, and J. S. Millar. 1982. The effect of drying temperature on extraction of petroleum ether soluble fats of small birds and mammals. Can. J. Zool., 60:470-472.

Kiell, D. J., and J. S. Millar. 1980. Reproduction and nutrient reserves of arctic ground squirrels. Can. J. Zool., 58:416-421.

King, J. R., D. S. Farner, and M. L. Morton. 1965. The lipid reserves of white-crowned sparrows on the breeding ground in central Alaska. Auk, 82:236-252.

Kodama, A. M. 1971. *In vivo* and *in vitro* determinations of body fat and body water in the hamster. J. Appl. Physiol., 31:218-222.

Kodama, A. M., and N. Pace. 1963. A simple decompression method for *in vivo* body fat estimation in small animals. J. Appl. Physiol., 18:1272-1276.

Krulin, G. S., and J. A. Sealander. 1972. Annual lipid cycle of the gray bat, *Myotis grisescens.* Comp. Biochem. Physiol., 42A:537-549.

Kunz, T. H. 1980. Daily energy budgets of free-living bats. Pp. 369-392, *in* Proc. 5th Int. Bat Res. Conf. (D. E. Wilson and A. L. Gardner, eds.). Texas Tech Press, Lubbock, 434 pp.

Kunz, T. H. 1987. Post-natal growth and energetics of suckling growth in bats. Pp. 395-420, *in* Recent advances in the study of bats. (M. B. Fenton, J. M. V. Rayner, and P. A. Racey, eds.). Cambridge Univ. Press, Cambridge.

Kwiecinski, G. G. 1984. Some factors regulating skeletal homeostasis in the little brown bat, *Myotis lucifugus,* with particular reference to pregnancy and lactation. Unpubl. Ph.D. dissertation, Cornell Univ., Ithaca, New York, 257 pp.

Kwiecinski, G. G. 1985. Bone remodeling and its regulation in *Myotis lucifugus.* Pp. 45-48, *in* Proc. Int. Symp. Vert. Morph. (H.-R. Duncker and G. Fleischer, eds.). Gustav Fischer Verlag, Stuttgart, 752 pp.

Licht, P., and P. Leitner. 1967a. Behavioral responses to high temperatures in three species of California bats. J. Mammal., 48:52-61.

Licht, P., and P. Leitner. 1967b. Physiological responses to high environmental temperatures in three species of microchiropteran bats. Comp. Biochem. Physiol., 22:371-387.

Lochmiller, R. L., J. B. Whelan, and R. L. Kirkpatrick. 1983. Body composition and reserves of energy of *Microtus pinetorum* from southwest Virginia. Amer. Midl. Nat., 110:138-144.

Lynch, G. R. 1973. Seasonal changes in thermogenesis, organ weights, and body composition in the white-footed mouse, *Peromyscus leucopus.* Oecologia, 13:363-376.

Markowicz, A. A., and R. E. Van Grieken. 1984. X-ray spectrometry. Anal. Chem., 56:241R-250R.

McCracken, G. 1984. Communal nursing in Mexican free-tailed bat maternity colonies. Science, 223:1090-1091.

McEwan, E. H., and P. M. Whitehead. 1984. Seasonal changes in body weight and composition of dunlin (*Calidris alpina*). Can. J. Zool., 62:154-156.

McLandress, M. R., and D. G. Raveling. 1981. Changes in diet and body composition of Canada geese before spring migration. Auk, 98:65-79.

Millar, J. S. 1975. Tactics of energy partitioning in breeding *Peromyscus.* Can. J. Zool. 53:967-976.

Millar, J. S. 1978. Energetics of reproduction in *Peromyscus leucopus*: The cost of lactation. Ecology, 59:1055-1061.

Millar, J. S. 1981. Body composition and energy reserves of northern *Peromyscus leucopus.* J. Mammal., 62:786-794.

Morton, M. L. 1975. Seasonal cycles of body weights and lipids in Belding ground squirrels. Bull. South. Calif. Acad. Sci., 74:128-143.

Morton, M. L., C. S. Maxwell, and C. E. Wade. 1974. Body size, body composition, and behavior of juvenile Belding ground squirrels. Great Basin Nat., 34:121-134.

Moss, M. L., and L. Moss-Salentijn. 1979. Mineral metabolism and bone. Pp. 77-102, *in* Chemical zoology. XI: Mammalia. (M. Florkin and B. T. Scheer, eds.). Academic Press, New York, 341 pp.

Myrcha, A. 1969. Seasonal changes in caloric value, body water and fat in some shrews. Acta Theriol., 14:211-227.

Myrcha, A., and W. Walkowa. 1968. Changes in the caloric value of the body during the postnatal development of white mice. Acta Theriol., 13:391-400.

Nabholz, J. V. 1973. Small mammals and mineral cycling on three Coweeta watersheds. Unpubl. M. S. thesis, Univ. Georgia, Athens.

Nagy, K. A., and D. P. Costa. 1980. Water flux in animals: Analysis of potential errors in the tritiated water method. Amer. J. Physiol., 238:R454-R465.

Nagy, K. A., and G. G. Montgomery. 1980. Field metabolic rate, water flux, and food consumption in three-toed sloths (*Bradypus variegatus*). J. Mammal., 61:465-472.

Nelp, W. B., J. D. Denney, R. Murano, G. M. Hinn, and C. H. Chestnut. 1972. Quantitative and serial studies of total body calcium (bone mass) in man by *in vivo* activation analysis. Pp. 627-638, *in* Nuclear activation techniques in the life sciences. Proc. Symp., Bled, Yugoslavia, 10-14 April 1972. Int. Atomic Energy Agency, Vienna, 664 pp.

Nelp, W. B., H. E. Palmer, R. Murano, K. Pailthorp, G. M. Hinn, C. Rich, J. L. Williams, T. G. Rudd, and J. D. Denney. 1970. Measurement of total body calcium (bone mass) *in vivo* with the use of total body neutron activation analysis. J. Lab. Clin. Med., 76:151-161.

Newman, J. R. 1977. Energy value of the shrew, *Sorex ornatus.* Acta Theriol., 22:274-275.

O'Conner, R. J. 1984. The growth and development in birds. John Wiley and Sons, Somerset, New Jersey, 305 pp.

Odum, E. P., S. G. Marshall, and T. G. Marples. 1965. The caloric content of migrating birds. Ecology, 46:901-904.

Odum, E. P., D. T. Rogers, and D. L. Hicks. 1964. Homeostasis of the nonfat components of migrating birds. Science, 143:1037-1039.

O'Farrell, M. J., and D. O. Schreiweis. 1978. Annual brown fat dynamics in *Pipistrellus hesperus* and *Myotis californicus* with special reference to winter flight activity. Comp. Biochem. Physiol., 61A:423-426.

O'Farrell, M. J., and E. H. Studier. 1973. Reproduction, growth, and development in *Myotis thysanodes* and *M. lucifugus* (Chiroptera: Vespertilionidae). Ecology, 54:18-30.

O'Farrell, M. J., and E. H. Studier. 1976. Seasonal changes in wing loading, body composition, and organ weights in *Myotis thysanodes* and *M. lucifugus* (Chiroptera: Vespertilionidae). Bull. Calif. Acad. Sci., 75:258-266.

Okon, E. E., and R. J. Ekanem. 1979. Diurnal variations of the glycogen and fat stores in the liver and breast muscle of the insect bat, *Tadarida nigeriae.* Physiol. Behav., 23:659-661.

Okon, E. E., R. M. Umukoro, and A. Ajudua. 1978. Diurnal variations of the glycogen and fat stores in the liver and breast muscle of the fruit bat, *Eidolon helvum* (Kerr). Physiol. Behav., 20:121-123.

O'Shea, T. J. 1976. Fat content in migratory central Arizona Brazilian free-tailed bats, *Tadarida brasiliensis* (Molossidae). Southwest. Nat., 21:321-326.

Pagels, J. F. 1975. Temperature regulation, body weight and changes in total body fat of the free-tailed bat, *Tadarida brasiliensis cynocephala* (LeConte). Comp. Biochem. Physiol., 50A:237-246.

Paine, R. T. 1971. The measurement and application of the calorie to ecological problems. Ann. Rev. Ecol. Syst., 2:145-164.

Pierson, E. D., W. E. Rainey, and T. H. Kunz. Unpubl. Changes in body composition during pregnancy and lactation in the little brown bat (*Myotis lucifugus*).

Pilo, B., and J. C. George. 1983. Diurnal and seasonal variation in liver glycogen and fat in relation to metabolic status of liver and *M. pectoralis* in the migratory starling, *Sturnus roseus,* wintering in India. Comp. Biochem. Physiol., 74A:601-604.

Pomeroy, L. R. 1970. The strategy of mineral cycling. Ann. Rev. Ecol. Syst., 1:171-190.

Pond, C. M. 1981. Storage. Pp. 190-219, *in* Physiological ecology: An evolutionary approach to resource use. (C. R. Townsend and P. Calow, eds.). Sinauer, Sunderland, Massachusetts, 393 pp.

Prothero, J. 1986. Methodological aspects of scaling in biology. J. Theoret. Biol., 118:259-286.

Randolph, P. A., J. C. Randolph, K. Mattingly, and M. M. Foster. 1977. Energy costs of reproduction in the cotton rat, *Sigmodon hispidus.* Ecology, 58:31-45.

Reiners, W. A., and N. M. Reiners. 1972. Comparison of oxygen-bomb combustion with standard ignition techniques for determining total ash. Ecology, 53:132-136.

Rickart, E. A. 1982. Annual cycles of activity and body composition in *Spermophilus townsendii mollis.* Can. J. Zool., 60:3298-3306.

Ricklefs, R. E. 1974. Energetics of reproduction in birds. Pp. 152-292, *in* Avian energetics. (R. A. Paynter, Jr., ed.). Nuttall Ornithological Club, Publication No. 15, Cambridge, Massachusetts, 334 pp.

Ricklefs, R. E. 1983. Avian postnatal growth. Pp. 1-83, *in* Avian biology. Vol. VII. (D. S. Farner, J. R. King, and K. C. Parkes, eds.). Academic Press, New York, 542 pp.

Ringberg, T. M., R. G. White, D. F. Holleman, and J. R. Luick. 1981. Prediction of carcass composition in reindeer (*Rangifer tarandus tarandus* L.) by use of selected indicator muscles. Can. J. Zool., 59:583-588.

Robbins, C. T. 1983. Wildlife feeding and nutrition. Academic Press, New York, 343 pp.

Robbins, C. T., A. N. Moen, and J. T. Reid. 1974. Body composition of white-tailed deer. J. Anim. Sci., 38:871-876.

Rogers, D. T., Jr., and E. P. Odum. 1964. Effect of age, sex, and level of fat deposition on major body components in some wood warblers. Auk, 81:505-513.

Rongstad, O. J. 1965. Calcium-45 labeling of mammals for use in population studies. Health Phys., 11:1543-1556.

Sawicka-Kapusta, K. 1970. Changes in the gross body composition and the caloric value of the common voles during their postnatal development. Acta Theriol., 15:67-79.

Sawicka-Kapusta, K. 1975. Fat extraction in the Soxhlet apparatus. Pp. 288-292, *in* Methods for ecological bioenergetics. (W. Grodzinski, R. Z. Klekowski, and A. Duncan, eds.). IBP Handbook No. 24. Blackwell Sci. Publ., Oxford, 367 pp.

Scarth, R. D., C. O. Leverett, L. L. Scarth, M. H. Smith, and J. L. Carmon. 1973. Effects of temperature, radiation and sex on body composition in *Peromyscus polionotus*. Growth, 37:311-321.

Schemmel, R. 1976. Physiological considerations of lipid storage and utilization. Amer. Zool., 16:661-670.

Schreiber, R. K., and D. R. Johnson. 1975. Seasonal changes in body composition and caloric content of Great Basin rodents. Acta Theriol., 20:343-364.

Schroeder, L. A. 1977. Caloric equivalents of some plant and animal material. Oecologia, 28:261-267.

Schultz, V., and F. W. Whicker. 1982. Radioecological techniques. Plenum Press, New York, 298 pp.

Sella, L. D. 1973. Trace elements in the cotton rat, *Sigmodon hispidus*, on the Piedmont in Georgia. Unpubl. M. S. thesis, Univ. Georgia, Athens.

Sisula, H., and E. Virtanen. 1977. Effects of storage on the energy and ash content of biological material. Ann. Zool. Fenn., 14:119-123.

Stack, M. H. 1985. Energetics of reproduction in the big brown bat, *Eptesicus fuscus*. Unpubl. Ph.D. dissertation, Boston University, Boston, 283 pp.

Strong, K. W., R. M. Ward, and V. L. Sinclair. 1980. The effect of storage on the energy values of some plant and animal material. Proc. Nova Scotia Inst. Sci., 30:65-67.

Studier, E. H. 1970. Evaporative water loss in bats. Comp. Biochem. Physiol., 35:935-943.

Studier, E. H., and W. G. Ewing. 1971. Diurnal fluctuation in weight and blood composition in *Myotis nigricans* and *Myotis lucifugus*. Comp. Biochem. Physiol., 38A:129-139.

Studier, E. H., V. L. Lysengen, and M. J. O'Farrell. 1973. Biology of *Myotis thysanodes* and *M. lucifugus* (Chiroptera: Vespertilionidae). II. Bioenergetics of pregnancy and lactation. Comp. Biochem. Physiol., 44A:467-471.

Studier, E. H., J. W. Procter, and D. J. Howell. 1970. Diurnal body weight loss and tolerance of weight loss in five species of *Myotis*. J. Mammal., 51:302-309.

Tidemann, C. R. 1982. Sex differences in seasonal changes of brown adipose tissue and activity of the Australian vespertilionid bat, *Eptesicus vulturus*. Aust. J. Zool., 30:15-22.

Walsberg, G. E. 1983. Avian ecological energetics. Pp. 161-220, *in* Avian biology. Vol. VII. (D. S. Farner, J. R. King, and K. C. Parkes, eds.). Academic Press, New York, 542 pp.

Walsh, L. M., and J. D. Beaton. 1973. Soil testing and plant analysis. Soil Sci. Soc. Amer., Madison, Wisconsin, 491 pp.

Weber, N. S., and J. S. Findley. 1970. Warm-season changes in fat content of *Eptesicus fuscus*. J. Mammal., 51:160-162.

Wiener, J. G., I. L. Brisbin, Jr., and M. H. Smith. 1975. Chemical composition of white-tailed deer: Whole-body concentrations of macro- and micro-nutrients. Pp. 536-541, *in* Mineral cycling in southeastern ecosystems. (F. G. Howell, J. B. Gentry, and M. H. Smith, eds.). ERDA Symposium Series (Conf-740513). Technical Information Center, ERDA, Springfield, Virginia, 898 pp.

Wiener, J. G., D. W. Kaufman, G. A. Kaufman, J. B. Gentry, M. H. Smith, and P. R. Ramsey. 1977. Chemical composition of rodents: Use of whole body concentrations for estimation of standing crops of elements. Southwest. Nat., 22:77-88.

Wilson, D. E., K. N. Geluso, and J. S. Altenbach. 1978. The ontogeny of fat deposition in *Tadarida brasiliensis*. Pp. 15-19, *in* Proc. 4th Int. Bat Res. Conf. (R. J. Olembo, J. B. Castelino, and F. A. Mutere, eds.). Kenya National Acad. Arts Sci., Nairobi, 328 pp.

Yarbrough, C. G. 1970. Summer lipid levels of some subarctic birds. Auk, 87:100-110.

Young, R. A. 1976. Fat, energy and mammalian survival. Amer. Zool., 16:699-710.

Zegers, D. A., and O. Williams. 1977. Seasonal cycles of body weight and lipids in Richardson's ground squirrel, *Spermophilus richardsonii elegans*. Acta Theriol., 22:380-383.

Preparation and Fixation of Tissues for Histological, Histochemical, Immunohistochemical, and Electron Microscopical Studies

G. Lawrence Forman

Department of Biology, Rockford College, Rockford, Illinois 61101 USA

and

Carleton J. Phillips

Department of Biology, Hofstra University, Hempstead, New York 11550 USA

1. INTRODUCTION

The increasingly sophisticated nature of behavioral and ecological studies of bats often has generated circumstances that require examination of cells and tissues. Studier et al. (1983) used quantitative renal histology to assess the ecophysiology of Neotropical Microchiroptera. These authors used hematoxylin and eosin-stained sections to determine relationships among renal morphology, diet, and environmental dehydration pressure. Changes in a variety of cellular constituents occur as consequences of hibernation in bats and in other small mammals. Many of these chemical changes can be visualized using histochemical techniques. Documented changes in kidney constituents, for example, include lipid in Henle's loop, secretory granules in the collecting tubules in *Rhinolophus,* and changes in cytochrome oxidase activity (Yoshimura, 1951). The important role of histomorphology and histochemistry in ecological and behavioral studies also is well-illustrated by work on integumentary secretions such as those elaborated by sudoriferous glands (Quay, 1970), by studies of the pituitary gland in hibernating and non-hibernating bats (Nunez et al., 1981; Anthony and Gustafson, 1984), and by comparative histology of the digestive tract (Forman, 1972, 1974a, 1974b).

Quay (1970), for example, reviewed studies of the distribution and morphology of many integumentary glands. Sexual dimorphism occurs in some glands in some species suggesting a possibly important role in behavior. Additionally, Sokolov and Dzhemukhadze (1982) used histochemical reactions to document changes in integumentary enzyme activity before and during hibernation in

Erinaceus and similar studies on bats should prove interesting.

The purpose of this chapter is to provide an introduction to preparation and preservation of tissues that may be of value to ecological or behavioral studies of bats. We have assumed that most of our readers need technology that can be used under field conditions and that most are in need of a starting point because histology and histochemistry are not their fields of expertise. Our approach therefore has been to select from a great body of information some aspects that our experience suggests would be most helpful. With few exceptions (see especially the review by Brown and Hilton, 1979) most of the excellent, comprehensive, accounts of cell and tissue preparatory technique mirror the perspective of pathologists or other specialists not directly concerned with studies of wild mammals (e.g., Pearse, 1968-72; Chayen et al., 1973; Culling, 1974; Lillie and Fullmer, 1976; Humason, 1979).

Preservation of tissues under field conditions traditionally has involved employment of chemical fixation. Other types of fixation and preservation (discussed later) might be more or less desirable than chemical fixation, but often are less practical. Regardless of the method of preservation used, fixation serves several purposes, the most important of which is stabilization of tissue components as close as possible to the *in vivo* condition.

Fixation also has additional important functions including: 1) prevention of microbial decay, 2) inactivation of autolytic enzymes, 3) insolubilization of components that would otherwise move from the tissue during processing, 4) reduction or prevention of shrinkage or swelling during processing by alteration of membranes, and 5) modification of tissue (e.g., mordanting) and alteration of indices of refraction (to make possible or improve its stainability).

Many of these considerations also apply to the requirements of transmission electron microscopy. However, electron microscopy requires more critical attention to preservation of structure so that the list of acceptable fixation procedures is considerably shorter and the worker has less of a margin for error.

2. PREPARATION AND HANDLING OF TISSUES FOR FIXATION

For light level studies little or no prefixation treatment of tissue is required, although some prefer a rinse in isotonic saline. A few fixatives (see Methacarn in Table 1) work best if tissues are not rinsed. Some hints for immersion fixation, which may be helpful, are summarized below.

1) Fix as small a piece of tissue as possible ($\sim$ 1 cm^3 for light microscopy; 1 mm^3 for transmission electron microscopy). Briefly fix large pieces of very soft tissues (15-30 min) until they harden enough to be sliced without unduly compressing them.

2) Very soft tissues (e.g., bone marrow) can be wrapped in porous paper (filter paper) prior to immersion.

3) Tissues or organs with lumina should be opened; thin or tubular pieces that may roll or invert should be attached to paper against their outer walls.

4) Intratracheal injection of a fixative fluid is essential for lung tissue if perfusion is not performed.

5) Tissues should never be so large as to be compressed or bent by the container and fixative volume should be at least 20x that of the tissue.

6) The rate of penetration of tissue by fixatives varies proportionally with temperature; however, low temperature retards or arrests autolytic changes and therefore may actually result in the best fixation.

7) Plastic or other non-metallic instruments must be used when handling tissues in fixatives containing $HgCl_2$.

8) Finally, it must be remembered that although high quality fixation is possible even under the most adverse field conditions, it nevertheless is difficult to achieve

and the investigator must use care even with routine procedures. In the end, fixation quality limits the real value of extensive laboratory analysis.

3. IMMERSION, PERFUSION, AND VAPOR FIXATION

Most tissues (excluding perhaps hemopoietic tissue, or smears of gametes) can be adequately preserved by immersion in fluid or by vascular perfusion of part or all of the animal. Perfusion is highly desirable because: 1) the quality of fixation usually is excellent since the fixative reaches virtually all cells within a few minutes, 2) all organs are fixed and may be held *in situ* as "museum" preparations for later use, and 3) tissues that deteriorate soon after death (e.g., brain) are preserved with few artifacts.

Perfusion of bats with fixative can be done simply, without elaborate equipment. Large syringes with needles of varying sizes (Quay, 1974, recommends #22-24 for small bats, #14-18 for large specimens) may be used. A five-minute perfusion will require 100 ml or more of perfusate. A major vein such as the jugular is opened after anesthetizing the animal and fixative then is injected into the left ventricle of the heart. The needle should either be clamped or glued (a drop of "crazy glue" works very well) to the wall of the heart. Nearly all accounts of perfusion technique with which we are familiar recommend a "washing out" of blood before the fixative is introduced. Ringer's solution, or 0.85% saline, can be injected into the left ventricle until the venous effluent is clear. Caution should be taken not to inject these solutions into the animal under high pressure as this may introduce artifacts into the tissues.

Kiernan (1981) describes a slightly more elaborate apparatus for perfusion of small mammals that should be readily adaptable to field conditions. Two containers, one with normal saline and one with fixative, are placed a meter or so above the specimen to be preserved. Tubes exiting from the bases of the containers are closed with pinch clamps and joined by a Y-connector which leads to a needle (hypodermic). Saline solution is allowed to flow first into the heart. When the outgoing liquid (from the jugular) is clear, the valve to the fixative is opened and that to the saline is closed simultaneously. This procedure prevents the serious problem of introducing air into the cardiovascular system, which may occur when syringes are used. Excessive pressure can damage capillaries and create unwanted artifacts that would limit studies involving transmission electron microscopy. In large measure, experimentation and practice are required for consistent success with perfusion of any small mammals. The investigator thus should practice these techniques before attempting them in the field. Tissues or organs with lumina (such as the digestive tract) can be fixed by direct injection into the lumen; gastric intubation of anesthetized bats has been used for both light and electron microscopic studies and is relatively easy to do (Phillips et al., 1984; Phillips, 1985). The digestive tract tissues absorb the fixative quickly and most cell types are well preserved when death occurs. Lung, liver, and kidney should be perfused directly via their vasculature.

In theory, any fluid fixative could be used for perfusion, but 10% neutral buffered formalin (prepared with paraformaldehyde, see Table 1) is the fixative of choice for general histology and histochemistry. Quay (1974) provides ample visual evidence that excellent histological results can be obtained by perfusing bats in this way.

Immersion fixation is used when perfusion is impractical, or where particular organs or tissues must be fixed in special fixatives. Some procedures call for cold fixative, but this is not always so and the investigator should be selective. With immersion fixation, penetration is critical; addition of a carrier such as dimethyl sulfoxide (DMSO) should be considered. Lastly, large volumes of fixative should always be used, regardless of the size of tissue blocks.

Vapor fixation (fixation in the atmo-

Table 1. Selected fixative mixtures for preservation of mammalian tissues.

Fixative Mixture	Constituents	Application(s)	Special Instructions
Alcoholic-formalin	10 ml 10% formalin; 10 ml distilled H_2O; 80 ml ETOH	Glycogen; parasites *in situ*	
Aoyama	85 ml H_2O; 15 ml 40% formalin; 1 g $CdCl_2$	Mitochondria; Golgi; lipids	
Baker's formol	10 ml 40% formalin; 90 ml H_2O; 1 g anhydrous $CaCl_2$	Phospholipids; thyroid (colloid)	Fix 2–3 days
Bodian's	5 ml 40% formalin; 5 ml glacial acetic acid; 90 ml 80% ETOH	Axons; mucosubstances; nucleic acids; thyroid	Mix immediately before using; fix 12–24 h
Bouin's	25 ml 40% formalin; 75 ml sat. aqueous picric acid; 5 ml glacial acetic acid	General purpose; reproductive tracts; skin; connective tissue; G.I.	Fix 24 h; store in 70% ETOH
Carnoy II	60 ml 100% ETOH; 30 ml chloroform; 10 ml glacial acetic acid	Bone; cartilage (chondroitin sulfates); nuclei; carbohydrates; fibrous proteins; mast cells (histamine); histochemistry of proteins	Fix 6–8 h; 2–3 hour wash in 100% ETOH (remove chloroform)
DeFano	15 ml 40% formalin; 1 g cobalt nitrate; 100 ml H_2O	Golgi	
Formal-ammonium bromide	15 ml 40% formalin; 2 g NH_4Br; 100 ml H_2O	Brain; spinal cord; neurolgia	Mix immediately before use
Gendre's	80 ml sat. alcoholic picric acid; 15 ml 40% formalin; 5 ml glacial acetic acid	Glycogen	Fix 16–20 h; wash in 80–95% ETOH
Glutaraldehyde + formalin (NBF)	90 ml NBF (referred to elsewhere in table); 10 ml 25% glutaraldehyde	Cytoplasmic inclusions; esterases (some); phosphatases; AMP, ADP, ATPases; aminopeptidases; glucose—6 phosphatase; succinic dehydrogenase?; noradrenaline	
*Helly's	5 g $HgCl_2$; 2.5 g $K_2Cr_2O_7$; 1 g $Na_2SO_4.10H_2O$; 100 ml H_2O	Hemopoietic; hypothalamic; neurosecretory material (NSM); mitochondria; myelin; endocrine organs (secretory granules); intercalated discs; bone marrow	Fix 12–24 h
Kolmer's	20 ml 5% $K_2Cr_2O_7$; 20 ml 10% formalin;	Eyes; nervous tissue	Mix just before use; 6 h wash in running

Table 1. Continued

Fixative Mixture	Constituents	Application(s)	Special Instructions
	5 ml glacial acetic acid; 5 ml 50% aqueous trichloro-acetic acid; 5 ml 10% aqueous uranyl acetate		H_2O; 6 h each in 35, 50, 70, 95, 100% ETOH; embed
Methacarn	60 ml 100% methanol; 30 ml chloroform; 10 ml glacial acetic acid	As with Carnoy II	No H_2O or saline wash of tissues; after fixation transfer to methanol, methyl benzoate, methyl benzoate-xylene, xylene; embed (see Humason, 1979)
NBF	1000 ml H_2O; heat to boiling – add 40 g paraformaldehyde; cool; add 4 g $NaH_2PO_4.H_2O$ and 6.5 g Na_2HPO_4	General purpose; argentaffin granules; adrenal glands; enzymes (frozen section); lipids (general)	Progressive fixation; fix at 4°C
Regaud's	80 ml 3% $K_2Cr_2O_7$; 20 ml % formalin	Bacteria; rickettsiae; cytoplasmic detail	Add formalin just before use; wash in running H_2O overnight
Sanfalice	80 ml 1% CrO_3; 40 ml % formalin; 5 ml glacial acetic acid	General purpose; nuclei; chromosomes	Mix immediately before use; fix 24 h; wash thoroughly in running water
Petrunkewitsch's	Part A: 100 ml H_2O; 12 ml nitric acid; 8 g cupric nitrate Part B: 100 ml 80% ETOH; 4 g phenol; 6 ml ethyl ether	General purpose (where $HgCl_2$ fixatives are incon-venient)	Mix 1:3 = Parts A:B just before use
*Susa (Heidenhain's)	45 g $HgCl_2$; 5 g NaCl; 20 g trichloroacetic acid; 40 ml glacial acetic acid; 200 ml 40% formalin; 1000 ml H_2O	General microanatomy; mitochondria; connective tissue; myelin; neurosecretory material	Fix 24 h; transfer to 95% ETOH
Trialdehyde	5 g paraformaldehyde dissolved in 25 ml H_2O with a drop of NaOH; add 15 ml 50% glutaraldehyde, 6.25 ml DMSO, 0.25 ml of 0.1 N $CaCl_2$, 2.5 ml acrolein, and dilute to 250 ml with 0.05 M cacodylate buffer with 0.1 M sucrose (makes 250 ml; use fresh daily)	Ultrastructure; organelles; cell membrane; also good for light-level histochemistry	Fix 10–24 h; replace fix with 3% glutaraldehyde and store at 4–5°C or, in field, store at ambient temperature in 0.05 M cacodylate buffer with 0.01 M sucrose

Table 1. Continued

Fixative Mixture	Constituents	Application(s)	Special Instructions
*Zenker's	Stock: 2.5 g $K_2Cr_2O_7$; 5 g $HgCl_2$; 1 g Na_2SO_4; 100 ml H_2O; add 5 ml glacial acetic acid just before use	General microanatomy; cell organelles	

* For long-term storage of tissues fixed with Hg salts, Lillie and Fullmer (1976) recommend "thin cedar oil" following alcohol dehydration.

sphere above the fluid) may have little application for field biologists. However, formalin vapor fixation of tissues at 60°C has been used to capture some labile materials that otherwise would be lost. Some amines, such as adrenaline, are caused to fluoresce after such treatment. Behaviorists interested in neurotransmitter substances (e.g., during torpor or arousal in bats) may wish to investigate vapor fixation in more detail, but generally speaking, buffered 47% paraformaldehyde is adequate.

4. SELECTION AND USE OF FIXATIVES

Investigators who expect to examine tissues of bats histologically or histochemically should thoroughly review collection and storage procedures as they pertain to their particular project well before animals are sacrificed. Routine histological studies generally present few problems with regard to selection of a preservation technique and, indeed, numerous histochemical methods are possible with tissues fixed in "traditional" fixative solutions. However, many other histochemical methods require the use of fresh tissue, or tissue preserved by freeze-drying or freeze substitution. Some classes of compounds (e.g., lipids and enzymes) may be destroyed or removed by some fixative solutions and yet be preserved or unaffected by others. Various methods of visualization of a particular tissue component may or may not be possible

depending upon the method of preservation. One or more of the references listed at the end of this chapter should be consulted if questions arise with respect to specific staining or histochemical procedures.

To investigators who intend to do comparative studies among individuals of a species or between different species, we strongly recommend consistency in choice of a fixative for any particular method of visualization. This same recommendation would apply when comparing normal with diseased tissues, experimental with controls, and so forth. The ability of tissues to take certain stains often is strongly influenced by the fixative. Consistency in fixation and dehydration is extremely important when quantitative data (cellular or tissue dimensions) are to be obtained. Primary fixatives and fixative mixtures may cause shrinkage or swelling, changes in membrane dimensions, and intercellular spaces.

Some available data (reviewed in Lillie and Fullmer, 1976) demonstrate that optimal fixation times can vary among species for particular organs and fixatives. No data are available for species of wild mammals, or bats in particular, so we can only recommend at this point that fixation times should be consistent.

In their review of histological techniques, Brown and Hilton (1979) made an important point regarding the names of fixative solutions. Simply because Altmann or Zenker may have their names associated with more than one fixative mixture does not mean that these fluids necessarily are substitutes for one another. Developers of fixatives often use the name of another worker to identify a fluid, or use their own name for a fluid subsequent to its being used for something else. A careful review of the fluid's ingredients should be made before using any fixative.

5. FIXATIVES FOR LIGHT MICROSCOPY

Fixatives discussed and recommended here are but a few drawn from a pool of many hundreds of published formulae. No attempt is made to comprehensively review fixatives and their applications. Our recommendations for fixatives (those summarized in Table 1) are based upon the following considerations: 1) recommendations by those who have published on preservation techniques they felt were useful to mammalogists (especially those of Brown and Hilton, 1979), 2) personal experience with certain of the fixatives, 3) a desire to provide an array of fixatives, which collectively includes as many of the "simple" fixative agents as possible (see section which follows on primary fixatives), and 4) our list of tissues and inclusions that may be important to behaviorists and ecologists.

5.1. "Primary" Fixatives and Their Actions

Fixation of proteins is of prime importance and is accomplished by coagulants (e.g., picric acid, $HgCl_2$, CrO_3) or non-coagulants (e.g., aldehydes, acetic acid, $K_2Cr_2O_7$). Coagulants produce a coarse matrix (desirable for wax embedding), whereas non-coagulants are better for fine histological detail. These substances may fix non-proteinaceous cellular contents (e.g., OsO_4-lipids), preserve but not fix them (e.g., formaldehyde-lipids), or remove them (ethyl alcohol-lipids). Some may severely shrink tissue (picric acid); others counteract shrinkage (acetic acid). These

and many other variables have led to the development of fixative mixtures in which the defects of one component are compensated for by others. Because acids (such as acetic acid) are good fixatives for nuclei, general purpose fixatives often combine an acid, a coagulant, and a non-coagulant (the familiar Bouin's fluid is an example). Some primary fixatives may react with one another to a greater or lesser degree (e.g., dichromate-formaldehyde) requiring mixing of the ingredients just before use.

Some good features and problematic characteristics of primary fixative agents are listed below.

1) *Formalin*: fixation of structure is good; a "soft fixative" so some cell structures are not adequately hardened (e.g., cellular brush borders).

2) *Mercuric chloride*: enhances "brightness" of staining reactions; good preservation of proteins; forms a precipitate that must be removed from the tissue.

3) *Chromium salts* ($-Cr_2O_7$): fair preservation of proteins; penetrates tissue rapidly; converts catecholamines to a brown pigment; may form green pigment with ETOH.

4) *Picric acid*: avoid if interested in histochemistry of DNA or RNA; causes considerable tissue swelling when used alone.

5) *Ethanol* and *methanol*: organelles destroyed; lipids extracted.

6) *Trichloroacetic acid*: causes relatively little shrinkage.

7) *Acetic acid*: rapid penetration; excellent for nuclei; poor cytoplasmic preservation.

Some researchers may prefer to rely upon commercially available preservatives and decalcifiers (see Appendix) for routine histological studies rather than to make up their own. "Perfix" is an alcohol-formalin-acid type of mixture with broad applications in histology and histochemistry. "Histocan" is for temporary storage of tissues (0-40°C) prior to fixation. The manufacturer claims that it will prevent autolysis and that ". . . cellular inclusions and structural components . . . are preserved."

5.2. Aldehydes

Aldehydes are so extensively used for fixation that they deserve special attention. The most commonly used aldehydes are formaldehyde (used as a formalin solution), glutaraldehyde, and acrolein. For general histological purposes and for preservation of whole museum specimens, neutral buffered formalin (NBF) is highly recommended. Formalin, as obtained in commercial form (40% by weight) contains methanol, which tends to inhibit polymerization. Methanol may not be desirable as a component of a fixative solution. Also, formalin deteriorates with time and formic acid is produced; the resultant lowering of pH adversely affects subsequent azure-eosin staining methods frequently employed in histological studies. Lillie and Fullmer (1976) recommended depolymerization of paraformaldehyde (heat to 80°-90°C) in neutral buffer solutions to be used as a 4% (2-5%) concentration (by mass). In the field, we have found that 4% paraformaldehyde in 0.1% M cacodylate buffer and sucrose (pH 7.2), mixed fresh daily, is an excellent general fixative for bat tissues. Preparation requires a source of heat; in remote locations we carry a back-packer's light-weight stove. When paraformaldehyde flakes are added to hot water they generally will not dissolve until the buffer solution is added. Alternatively one can add a few drops of NaOH to the solution to promote the depolymerization of the paraformaldehyde. We carry a small squeeze bottle (5 ml) in our field kit. In addition to avoiding unwanted effects from formic acid and methanol, this mixture also prevents the occurrence of brown pigments in tissues that may occur with formalin solutions. Additionally, we often find that it is much easier to transport small pre-weighed vials of paraformaldehyde and ingredients for making buffer than to carry containers of commercial formalin into the field.

Tissues fixed in buffered 4% paraformaldehyde can be transferred to buffer alone or left in the fixative for weeks without loss of many antigenic sites, so this fixative is ideal for immunohistochemistry as well as for routine histology and pathology.

5.3. General Fixatives

Table 1 contains formulae for several fixatives broadly useful for studies of microanatomy. Bouin's fluid remains in wide use although Gray (1964) feels that its only advantage may be that tissues can remain in it for lengthy periods (even so, immediate storage in 70% ETOH is desirable), and it may have the disadvantage of causing formation of vacuoles in cells. Additional general microanatomical fixatives (Table 1) that we believe will meet the needs of most investigators are Zenker's, Sanfalice, Heidenhain's Susa, and Helly's. An investigator can select one or more of these depending upon which ingredients are beneficial or disadvantageous for his or her study. As with any fixative, attention should be given to fixation times and wash and storage procedures. Mercuric chloride must be removed following fixation, a simple procedure discussed in most textbooks of technique. Where rapid penetration is important (large pieces, considerable rapid autolysis), Carnoy II and Methacarn should be employed. Another mixture that is widely recommended for large pieces because it penetrates rapidly is Stieve's fluid (76 ml saturated aqueous $HgCl_2$; 20 ml concentrated formalin; 4 ml glacial acetic acid).

5.4. Histochemistry

5.4.1. Lipids

Numerous histochemical procedures are available for the visualization of lipids and lipid-like compounds. Kiernan (1981) provided a useful review of the types of lipids that may be distinguished collectively or individually. Brown (1979) gave an excellent general account of the methodology of lipid histochemistry, along with some useful guidelines as to what mammalogists may or may not be able to visualize in their material. Unlike other reviews of histochemical methods, Brown sometimes makes specific references to mammalian groups (e.g., lipofuscins in the marking substances elaborated by preputial glands of voles). Mammalogists likely will find techniques for staining the following of greatest value: cholesterol and its esters, phospholipids, fatty acids, hydrophobic vs. hydrophilic lipids, and unsaturated fats. Some lipids of considerable biological interest, such as cholesterol and prostaglandins (fatty acids), may be difficult to stain as they are stored in normal tissues in extremely small quantities. A comprehensive review of specific procedures for lipid staining can be found in Lillie and Fullmer (1976). For general studies of lipids, tissues can be fixed in any one of several formalin fixatives, but Aoyama's fluid (see Table 1) is recommended by Brown and Hilton (1979), and fomal-calcium (10 g $CaCl_2$; 100 ml 40% formalin; 900 ml distilled water) or formal-calcium-cadmium (add 10 g $CdCl_2$ to formalin-calcium mixture) is widely recommended. Some lipids will be retained in paraffin sections provided the proper fixation is employed (e.g., those with Ca^{++} added), however, frozen sections prepared on a cryostat generally are required for detailed qualitative and quantitative study.

5.4.2. Carbohydrates and Glycoproteins

Mammalian tissues elaborate a rich diversity of carbohydrate-containing products collectively referred to as mucosubstances. They are especially noteworthy in connective tissues as glycosaminoglycans, or as so-called mucins in epithelia. The latter group of substances likely will be of the most prospective interest to behaviorists as they are elaborated by tissues and organs subject to environmental influence. Examples would include surface gastro-intestinal mucins, products of salivary glands, epithelia of the female reproductive tract, and thyroid gland colloid (see Forman, 1972; Pinkstaff et al., 1982).

With the use in recent years of dyes such as Alcian Blue, one can classify mucosubstances within a hierarchy that reflects physi-cal and chemical properties of the constituents (e.g., sulfated—non-sulfated; resistance to enzyme digestion; stainability at differing pH's). A comprehensive review of categorization and visualization of these mucosubstances may be found in Lillie and Fullmer (1976). The review of Brown (1979) should be consulted by any investigator contemplating a detailed study of mammalian mucopolysaccharides and mucins.

Mucosubstances are preserved by most fixatives, although those with ingredients that act as oxidizing agents should be avoided. Furthermore, $HgCl_2$ in fixatives may induce production of aldehydes in tissues. This is problematic as it may result in staining artifacts with the familiar and most widely used technique in carbohydrate histochemistry, the periodic acid-Schiff reaction (PAS). Glycogen is best preserved by alcoholic fixatives and Table 1 includes several in wide use (Gendre's, Bodian's, alcohol-formalin).

For general histochemical studies of glycoproteins in bat tissues, we have found that 4% paraformaldehyde, 1% cetylpyridinium chloride (1 g/100 ml), and 0.1 M cacodylate buffer works very well and easily can be used in the field.

5.4.3. Amines

Kiernan (1981) observed that biogenic amines (dopamine, noradrenaline, adrenaline, serotonin, and histamine) are one of the few groups of low molecular weight, soluble organic compounds for which suitable methods are available for histochemical demonstration. The recognized importance of these chemicals in the nervous and endocrine functions of mammals warrants their inclusion in an account dealing with techniques in animal behavior. Some of these amines may be found in relatively large quantities in intracellular secretory granules (in endocrine organs), whereas others are present in much smaller quantities (e.g., central and peripheral neurons). Techniques for preserving them *in situ* vary accordingly.

Amines in endocrine organs (e.g., serotonin-containing argentaffin cells of the gut and noradrenaline and adrenaline "chromaffin" cells of the adrenal medulla) often are preserved by chemical fixation. Kiernan (1981) outlines a number of methods of visualization and recommends for them the following fixation regimes: 1) formalin fixation for argentaffin cells (azo-coupling method) and 2) Carnoy II for histamine in most cells.

Noradrenaline-containing cells can be visualized directly using a buffered 25% glutaraldehyde followed by OsO_4 treatment. Frozen sections are cut several hours after placement in glutaraldehyde. This technique may prove to be difficult under field conditions, but hardly is impossible. Kiernan (1981) should be consulted for details.

The "chromaffin" reaction, which demonstrates the presence of adrenaline- and noradrenaline-containing granules, results from an interaction between $K_2Cr_2O_7$ and the amines. It occurs to varying degrees in the adrenal medulla and in enterochromaffin cells of the stomach and intestine. Kiernan (1981) described a procedure that will distinguish these two amines (on the basis of staining intensity); however, fresh tissue and a special chromate-dichromate fixative are required. The procedure is not rigorous and should be readily suited to field conditions. Lillie and Fullmer (1976) reported a satisfactory chromaffin reaction following fixation of tissues in Regaud's solution (Table 1). These authors reviewed a number of procedures which permit specific visualization of adrenaline or noradrenaline or both, and this source should be consulted for more complex, more precise methodology. Aldehyde-induced autofluorescence of amines is discussed by Kiernan (1981). More precise localization is possible with antiserum and immunohistochemical techniques.

5.4.4. Enzymes and Other Proteins

Enzymes and enzyme activity are subject to alteration as a result of environmental changes or extreme environmental conditions. Considering the environmental extremes to which bats must adapt, and the considerable tolerance of bats to extremes, these animals may represent especially useful models for studies of enzymes.

Among the numerous enzymes that can be visualized histochemically are hydrolytic ones such as phosphatases, esterases, proteinases, as well as oxidoreductases such as dehydrogenases, oxidases, and peroxidases. Brown (1979) provided an excellent review of methods in enzyme histochemistry that might be of importance to mammalogists. He noted that there were, at that time, published methods for visualizing about 80 of the 400 known enzymes in vertebrate tissues. Most of these methods were for either oxidoreductases or hydrolases. Kiernan (1981) noted that wax procedures are not possible with the oxidoreductases. With those enzymes small blocks of fresh tissue (less than 2 mm square) are fixed five to ten minutes in NBF (4°C), and sectioned on a cryostat.

Generally speaking, cyrostat (frozen) sections are preferred or required for *in situ* visualization of enzyme activity. The enzyme is caused to react with one or more substrates which form a colored or electron dense product which marks the location of the enzyme. Hydrolytic enzymes usually are reacted with an artificial substrate which yields a visible product when hydrolyzed. Oxidoreductases are reacted with natural substrates which yield colored products after one or more reactions. Sections of unfixed tissue often are most desirable because the least amount of enzyme loss or degradation will occur with fresh frozen material. However, many field mammalogists will find this approach obviously unworkable. Nevertheless, tissues can be preserved in the field in ways so that distinctive enzyme activity can be demonstrated weeks or even months after collection; and "wax" procedures are possible in a few cases (see Lillie and Fullmer, 1976, for enzyme procedures that may be carried out with material embedded in paraffin).

Lillie and Fullmer (1976) discuss in

detail the use of aldehydes as fixatives for enzyme histochemistry. Formaldehyde, glutaraldehyde, and acrolein are used most frequently. In practice, formaldehyde or a mixture of formaldehyde and glutaraldehyde (see Table 1) will probably best serve the needs of field mammalogists. For field collection of tissues fixative should be cooled to 0-4°C, and provision should be made to store tissues within this range. Fixation is for 24 h or longer, and tissue pieces should be 1-2 mm in thickness.

Storage of tissue in cold buffer is possible for up to several months (Lillie and Fullmer, 1976). These authors also cite Hopsu and Glenner (1964), who successfully stored small blocks of tissue in 50% glycerol in water at -20°C. A considerable variety of enzymes could be visualized after 9 months of storage.

Occasions may arise where one wishes to demonstrate the presence of a particular protein or proteins in a tissue, or desires to visualize a material that is rich in particular amino acids. Some, but not all, reactive groups of amino acids can be utilized for histochemical visualization. In general, proteins must be bound to tissue in order to be histochemically defined. For this reason, the soluble globulins generally are not available for study, whereas fibrous and conjugated ones may often be stable and reactive. Usually, the amino group of simple (fibrous) proteins is the histochemically reactive site—a few amino acids (five) are exceptions to this (see Brown, 1979, for a detailed account of theoretical considerations in protein histochemistry). In the case of conjugated ones (lipo-, glyco-, muco-, and nucleoproteins), they most often are histochemically distinguished by way of the non-protein component of the molecule (glycoproteins often are considered within the framework of carbohydrates in histochemistry texts).

Fixation is an important consideration if studies of proteins are anticipated. Kiernan (1981) treats the matter of tissue fixation for protein study with particular clarity. He recommends Carnoy's fluid (we concur based upon our experience) for histochemical studies of proteins, although formalin may be used as well. Picric acid and $HgCl_2$ may be used as fixatives unless cysteine is the acid of interest. There may be some partial inhibition of staining with these latter agents. For demonstration of particular amino acids Kiernan provides specific suggestions as regards fixation, and references such as his (see list of selected histochemistry texts) should be consulted if specific peptides or endgroups are of interest. For the investigator who, at the time of collection and preservation of tissue, is unsure of the course to be followed in examining proteins histochemically, alcohol-acetic acid and NBF would seem to be the fixatives of choice.

6. IMMUNOHISTOCHEMISTRY

Until recently, immunohistochemical techniques remained beyond the technical reach of scientists studying wild species. Mainly this was due to the fact that antisera (both polycolonal and monoclonal antibodies) to a variety of molecules were not readily available. An investigator thus would be required to isolate and purify a substance of interest and then raise antibodies and test their specificity even before applying the technology to a particular problem. This drawback for investigators lacking expertise and time to undertake the preparation necessary for immunohistochemistry has been largely eliminated in recent years. A great variety of antisera now is commercially available and a number of companies are willing to raise antibodies to specific molecules or fragments of molecules. Moreover, several companies also now sell "kits" that can be used very easily by an investigator seeking to monitor particular molecules in bats. Lastly, several recent general references are available (e.g., Heimer and Robards, 1981; Cuello, 1983).

Basically, immunohistochemistry enables *in situ* localization of particular molecules or compounds. A good example of the technique at the light microscopic level can be

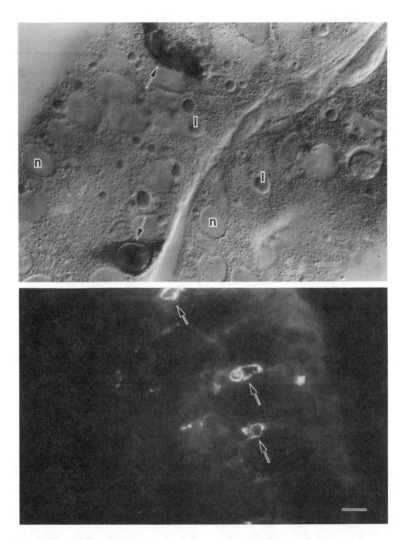

Figure 1. Top: Peroxidase-anti-peroxidase (PAP) method demonstrating gastrin-like immunoreactivity in G-cells (arrows) in the pyloric gland of the stomach in *Ariteus flavescens*. Abbreviations are: I, lipid inclusions; n, nuclei. (Scale bar equals 5 μm.) Bottom: FITC-conjugated anti-cholecystokinin (CCK 10-20) immunoreactivity in perivascular nerves (arrows) in the gastric mucosa in *Erophylla sezekorni*. (Scale bar equals 10 μm.)

found in Anthony and Gustafson (1984). These authors used an antibody to the β subunit of human luteinizing hormone (anti-hLHβ) to study pituitary gland gonadotropes in male and female little brown bats (*Myotis lucifugus*). In order to demonstrate the presence of the hormone (actually considered as hLHβ-like immunoreactivity) they used a popular "indirect" method known as the PAP (peroxidase-anti-peroxidase) technique,

which was developed by Sternberger et al. (1970). This process involves three main steps: 1) attachment of a primary antibody (anti-hLHβ raised in rabbits in this example) to the antigen, 2) attachment of unconjugated (goat) anti-rabbit IgG to the primary antibody, and 3) attachment of the PAP complex (peroxidase-anti-peroxidase with rabbit IgG) to the free binding site on the goat anti-rabbit globulin. These three "bridged" layers provide a very sensitive, intense reaction that can be easily visualized in the light microscope. An example is given in Figure 1, which shows gastrin 17-like immunoreactivity in the pyloric tube of the stomach in a fruit bat, *Ariteus flavescens*. This example was prepared by using a PAP kit (see Appendix).

A second useful approach is the fluorescence method, which employs fluorchrome labeling of antibodies (see Haaijman, 1983; Moore, 1981). One commonly used label is fluorescein isothiocyanate (FITC), which can be purchased and used relatively easily with commercially available antisera. Unlike the PAP method, however, visualization of immunoreactivity requires a light microscope with fluorescence attachments and the slides are not permanent. On the other hand, some molecules are best localized by FITC (depending on antibody sensitivity and dilutions available). An example of FITC-labelling is shown in Fig. 1; cholecystokinin (CCK 10-20)-like immunoreactivity is demonstrated in fine nerve fibers in the fundic mucosa of the stomach in *Erophylla sezekorni*.

A third method, also easily adapted to studies of bats, is the avidin-biotin (ABC) method that results in a sensitive three layer label (see Polak and Van Noorden, 1983). The first layer is the rabbit primary antibody; the second is biotinylated goat anti-rabbit IgG; and the third is an avidin-biotin complex. Kits for ABC immunohistochemistry also are available commercially (see Appendix).

Fixation for light-level microscopic immunohistochemistry, in our experience, is relatively easy and can be done under the most extreme field conditions. In the field we use 4% paraformaldehyde with 0.1 or 0.2 M cacodylate buffer and sucrose; tissues are fixed for at least 24 h (we have left them in fixative, without loss of antigenicity, for up to six months) before being rinsed and transferred to 0.2 M cacodylate buffer and stored at 4°C (we have no evidence that storage up to 2 weeks at tropical ambient temperatures harms the tissues, at least with antisera used by us). It seems important to avoid transfer-ring tissues to ethyl alcohol if they are to be used in immunohistochemistry because we have not had consistent success to date with traditional museum specimens of bats. Sections can be prepared by either paraffin-embedding or by cutting them on a cryostat; again, in our experience frozen sections generally work better. The individual investigator thus will need to determine which technique (PAP, FITC, or ABC) and preparation techniques are best for localizing a particular hormone, neuropeptide, or other molecule or compound in a particular tissue.

7. FIXATION FOR TRANSMISSION ELECTRON MICROSCOPY

Glutaraldehyde has been widely recommended to field collectors who wish to fix tissues for later study with transmission electron microscopy (scanning electron microscopy can be readily accomplished with formalin-fixed specimens and, insofar as field work is concerned, does not require special procedures). Unfortunately, in our experience, glutaraldehyde by itself simply is not an adequate field fixative for quality transmission electron microscopy (Phillips, 1985) and although it is relatively simple to obtain and handle, it is not recommended for field use. The most common problems appear to be: 1) osmolarity (causing destruction of certain cellular organelles) and 2) slow penetration. Fortunately, however, there is available a trialdehyde-DMSO fixative (first described by Kalt and Tandler, 1971) that is outstanding even under the most rigorous field conditions (Phillips, 1985; Feldman and Phillips, 1984; Nagato et al., 1984). This fixative makes possible the routine collection of tissue samples that can be stored for later analysis at the ultrastructural level (Phillips, 1985; Phillips et al., in press).

The fixative consists of 3% glutaraldehyde, 1% paraformaldehyde (mixed fresh), 0.5% acrolein, 2.5% DMSO and 1 mM $CaCl_2$ in 0.05 M cacodylate buffer at pH 7.2. To prepare 250 ml (the amount that we prepare each

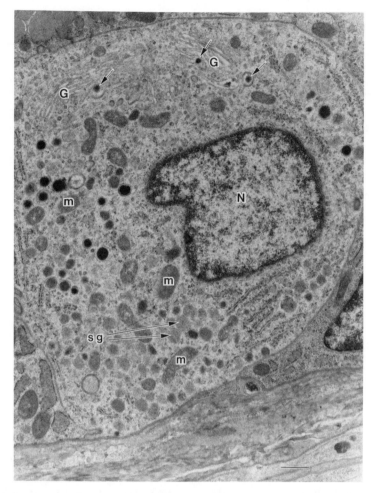

Figure 2. Transmission electron micrograph of a D-cell in the gastric mucosa of *Pteronotus parnellii*. This tissue sample was fixed with trialdehyde-DMSO under field conditions in South America. (Scale bar equals 0.5 μm.)

day in the field), one should first dissolve 5 g of paraformaldehyde powder in 25 ml of distilled water (using heat and a few drops of NaOH). Next add 15 ml of 50% (stock) glutaraldehyde, 6.25 ml of DMSO, 0.25 ml of 0.1 M $CaCl_2$ and, lastly, 2.5 ml of stock acrolein (remember that the acrolein is a dangerous poison and must be handled carefully). Finally, dilute this solution up to 250 ml with 0.05 M cacodylate buffer with 0.1 M sucrose.

In practice, we have found that minced tissues should be left overnight in this trialdehyde fixative; in the morning the fixative is replaced with 0.05 M cacodylate buffer with 0.1 M sucrose. Tissues can be left in buffer, even at tropical ambient temperatures, for at least one month. When refrigeration is available, the tissues should be transferred to fresh 3% glutaraldehyde and stored at 4°C. The results of this entire procedure are remarkable (see Fig. 2).

The acrolein used in the trialdehyde fixative can pose a problem under some circumstances. This is a potentially dangerous chemical and although we have taken it by light

aircraft and helicopters to remote field locations, the investigator should be aware of the
risk involved. Furthermore, international
transportation of acrolein sometimes is difficult. An alternative fixative, which is not
quite as good as the trialdehyde, can be tried
in such instances. We have successfully used a
modified Karnovsky fix as follows: 5%
glutaraldehyde, 4% paraformaldehyde, and
0.2 M cacodylate buffer with 0.4 mM $CaCl_2$
and 0.1 M sucrose are diluted 1:1 in 5%
DMSO prepared in 0.2 M cacodylate buffer.
This fixative is prepared fresh each day and
used at ambient temperatures. Tissues are
treated in the same way as described for the
trialdehyde.

8. PRESERVATION BY FREEZING

For most histological and histochemical
work, unfixed frozen tissues are not as desirable as fresh ones. Unless freezing is accomplished quickly, deep portions of large pieces
are destroyed or ice crystals form which disrupt tissues.

Brown and Stoddart (1977) reviewed
freeze-preparation of mammalian tissues and
noted that small pieces of tissue, cell suspensions, fluids, and small organs may sometimes be successfully frozen for later study.
Ideally, any tissue to be frozen should be
"quenched" in something like liquid nitrogen
to remove water, the source of ice crystals.
Brown and Stoddart (1977) describe a low
temperature "refrigerator" originally described by Hugh-Jones et al. (1972) that will
keep small quantities of tissue at -77°C for
several months and is adaptable to field conditions. This unit employs solid carbon dioxide (dry ice) in liquid nitrogen in a Dewar
flask. Hugh-Jones et al. (1972) reported that
the 10.4 liter flask that they used would hold
250 7-ml samples for four months. A spring
balance was used to periodically weigh the
flask in order to determine the amount of
coolant mixture that remained. In any case, if
preservation of otherwise unfixed tissue by
freezing is contemplated, the investigator

should at least use a cryoprotectant such as
phosphate-buffered saline with sucrose.
Although cytological features will be disrupted, such tissues might be suitable for
enzymatic analysis.

9. SPECIAL APPLICATIONS

9.1 Tissue Smears and Spreads

In some cases, tissues are more efficiently and
more quickly examined by preparing a smear
of associated cells rather than by embedding
and sectioning. In addition to the familiar
blood smear, those of bone marrow, spleen,
spermatozoa, exudates from conditions that
result from infections, and pathogens such as
protozoans can be prepared easily in the
field.

Generally, tissue smears must be fixed at
the time that they are prepared. A 2-3 minute
fixation in 100% methanol will permit smears
of blood and marrow to be stained when convenient (for up to several weeks). Several
commercial cytological fixatives (sprays, aerosols) work well. For preservation of cytological smears on slides, "Spray-Cyte" and "Pro-
Fixx" are available in aerosols or aspirator
bottles (see Appendix).

Spermatozoa can be observed without
sectioning the testes or epididymides after
preparation of either a wet mount (suspension) or dry smear. Smears work best in practice and can be prepared from fresh material
(preferred) or from preserved specimens.
Short segments of tubules from fresh material
are macerated in a solution of isotonic
sodium citrate. A drop or two each of the
sperm suspension and buffer are placed on a
clean slide and allowed to air dry. Spermatozoa on slides are subsequently fixed in mixture of glacial acetic acid and 100% methanol
(1:4) for 15 seconds and air dried. If only
information about presence or absence of
sperm is desired, slides can be simply stained
in a 0.01-0.1% Toludine Blue 0 for 15-30 minutes followed by an acetone, then acetone-
xylene rinse before mounting a cover slip. A

more elaborate staining procedure useful for detailed study of sperm morphology appears in Forman and Genoways (1979).

Tubules from previously field-fixed epididymides also may be used to prepare smears. The following fixative mixture is recommended for preservation of spermatozoa: 2 parts methanol (100%), 4 parts ethanol (95%), 1 part acetone, 2 parts chloroform, and 1 part propionic acid. Tissue should be refrigerated if long term storage is anticipated. Smears are prepared by macerating sections of tubules on a slide, removal of large pieces of tissue, and the addition of more fixative before preparation of a smear which then can be air dried. The Toludine Blue stain mentioned above is suitable for these smears as well. An additional staining procedure for smears of spermatozoa that may be useful for studies using light microscopy is the so-called Tianese method (cited by Baccetti in Gray, 1973). The staining solution consists of 0.1 g acid fuchsin, 0.5 g Malachite green, 50 ml ethanol, and 150 ml distilled water. Squash techniques have been of considerable importance in studies of chromosomes, but these are discussed elsewhere in Chapter 25.

9.2.   Fixation of Embryonic Tissues

Mammalian embryos may be fixed *in toto* or in pieces. Perfusion generally is impractical for embryos, and those larger than 2-3 mm should have the body wall opened before immersion. The tissues of embryos usually are rather pliable so that rapid fixation is desirable in order to avoid artifacts. Some workers recommend the use of fixatives with reduced hypertonicity that may help overcome these problems (Kalt and Tandler, 1971).

Formalin is highly desirable as a primary fixative for embryos because it penetrates tissues fairly rapidly. Although Bouin's fluid also may be used, other fixatives are more widely recommended, particularly Tellyesniczky's fluid (3g $K_2Cr_2O_7$; 5 ml glacial acetic acid; 100 ml distilled H_2O). Eichler (1973) recommends Lavdowsky's fluid (10 ml com-

mercial formalin; 30 ml 95% alcohol; 10 ml glacial acetic acid; 50 ml distilled H_2O) specifically for mammalian embryos, as it penetrates very rapidly. Eichler (1973) also suggests for mammalian embryos a mixture of 10 ml 1% platinum chloride (stored as stock in the dark), 20 ml saturated picric acid, and 70 ml distilled water.

Studies of skeletal differentiation in mammalian embryos often make use of techniques which allow visualization of ossified and cartilaginous tissue. One popular procedure is that of Williams (1941).

1) Fix in formalin (NBF).
2) 24 h in 70% ETOH + ammonium hydroxide (few drops).
3) One week in 0.25% Toluidine blue in 70% ETOH (100 ml) with 2 ml 0.5% HCl.
4) 95% ETOH (4 changes) for 3 days.
5) 2% KOH, approximately one week.
6) 2% KOH (fresh) with saturated alcoholic Alizarin Red S added drop by drop until KOH turns deep red.
7) Stain approximately 24 h in second solution.
8) Destain in 90% ETOH (acidified with 1% sulfuric acid).
9) Dehydration in alcohol series followed by 3 changes of benzene; clear and store in methyl salicylate.
10) Results: cartilage dark blue; ossified tissues red; intermediate stages red-blue; degree of ossification proportional to intensity of stain.

9.3.   Decalcification

Hard tissues, those containing Ca^{++} salts and other "hard" materials such as chitin, must be "softened" before they can be sectioned. Brown and Hilton (1979) provide an excellent review of methods available for decalcification of hard materials such as enamel, dentin, cementum, and bone. Formalin-based fixatives such as NBF are the fixatives of choice. Removal of calcium salts may be accomplished using 1) mineral acids such as nitric or chromic acid, 2) organic acids (formic acid is "gentler" than nitric acid but its action is slower), 3) organic buffers (citric acid-citrate buffers), or 4) chelating agents (these often are the procedures of choice and are good both for histology and histochemistry of tissues).

Chelating agents such as EDTA (disodium salt of ethylene diamine tetra-acetic acid) are slow to work but result in excellent preservation of structures when used at "room" temperatures and at an adjusted pH of approximately 7.2. Days to weeks are required. Much longer times (weeks) may be required for large pieces of tissue. Several commercially produced decalcifying solutions have proved effective (see Appendix). They include "Cal-Ex" and "Decal", both of which employ a chelating agent. Brown and Hilton (1979) note that numerous enzymes "and other labile substances" persist after formalin fixation and decalcification in a 5.5% EDTA in 10% formalin.

For enzyme studies, frozen sections can be prepared directly from small pieces of decalcified tissue on a freezing microtome. A variety of enzymes, for example, dehydrogenases, acid and alkaline phosphatases, and esterases, can be visualized. Decalcification in 1N formic acid solution (15°-25°C) is said to yield excellent staining. Lillie and Fullmer (1976) recommended the use of 25 ml of fluid per gram of bone with two changes of fluid daily. If the purpose of processing bone in this way is to study sections of bone marrow, some attention to fixation should be given. Chromate fixatives, such as Helly's, or those with formalin, such as Regaud's, are fixatives of choice.

Phillips et al. (1982) recently evaluated the value of incremental lines in secondary dentin and cementum of teeth in bats as indices of age (see also Chapter 3). EDTA (adjusted to pH 7.2) and Decal were used as decalcifiers following fixation in non-buffered 10% formalin (recommended for teeth). The procedures worked well and permitted the staining of tooth sections with a considerable diversity of staining methods. We have

no reason to believe that more elaborate procedures, or those which affect tissues more severely, are superior for these types of studies.

Kiernan (1981) provides many useful suggestions for the use of decalcifying agents. Specimens to be treated must be thoroughly fixed followed by complete removal of the fixative agents. Decalcifying agents should be used in a volume that is at least 20 times that of the tissue. Acid decalcifiers should be replaced with fresh solutions each day or two, and chelating agents (such as EDTA) should be replaced every 3-5 days. Other authors have recommended daily changes of EDTA solutions.

Physical and chemical changes in tissue such as those caused by hydrolysis and swelling may be a problem when acids are used for decalcification. Gray (1964) recommended Haug's solution (70 ml 95% ETOH, 30 ml H_2O, 1 g phloroglucinol, 5 ml nitric acid), claiming superior results with its use. The solution is warmed slightly under running water before use.

The endpoint of decalcification may be determined several ways. Kiernan (1981) suggests the following method. For the last change of decalcifier, reduce the volume to five times that of the tissue (to concentrate any calcium that may remain). To 5 ml of the Decal solution add NH_4OH (S.G. 0.9) at pH 7, then to this add 5 ml of saturated ammonium oxalate. A white precipitate will form within 30 minutes if Ca^{++} is present.

10. SUMMARY

A variety of microscopic techniques now are available for use by investigators interested in ecology, eco-morphology, and eco-physiology of bats. Some of these (standard histology and histochemistry) have been available for many years but only recently have been incorporated into field research. Others, especially immunohistochemistry and transmission electron microscopy, either were seemingly impossible under field conditions or were at least impractical until relatively recently. However, these latter techniques now can be widely used, and both promise to provide significant new data about bat biology.

11. ACKNOWLEDGMENTS

Support for this project was provided by a Summer Research Grant from the Mary Ashby Cheek Research Fund of Rockford College. Some of the field techniques described herein were developed with support from the Research Corporation (grants C-1251 and C-1855 to Phillips) and Hofstra University (HCLAS grants). Special thanks are extended to Albert Mennone, Keith M. Studholme, Marjean Silberhorn, and Brenda Forman. Linda Cossen of the Hofstra University Special Secretarial Services typed our manuscript.

12. REFERENCES

Anthony, E. A., and A. N. Gustafson. 1984. Seasonal variations in pituitary LH-gonadotrophes of the hibernating bat *Myotis lucifugus:* an immunohistochemical study. Amer. J. Anat., 170:101-115.

Baccetti, B. 1973. Spermatozoa. Pp. 545-547, *in* Encyclopedia of microscopy and microtechnique. (P. Gray, ed.). Van Nostrand Reinhold Co., New York, 638 pp.

Brown, J. C. 1979. Techniques in mammalogy. Ch. 9. Microscopical examination: Histochemical methods. Mammal Review, 9:96-141.

Brown, J. C., and A. J. Hilton. 1979. Techniques in mammalogy. Ch. 8. Microscopical examination: Histological technique. Mammal Review, 9:53-95.

Brown, J. C., and D. M. Stoddart. 1977. Techniques in mammalogy. Ch. 7. Killing mammals and general post-mortem methods. Mammal Review, 7:64-94.

Chayen, J., L. Bitensky, and R. G. Butcher. 1973. Practical histochemistry. Wiley, New York, 271 pp.

Cuello, A. C., ed. 1983. Immunohistochemistry. John Wiley and Sons, New York, 501 pp.

Culling, C. F. A. 1974. Handbook of histopathological and histochemical techniques (including museum techniques). Butterworths, London, 712 pp.

Eichler, V. B. 1973. Embryological techniques. Pp. 127-139, *in* Encyclopedia of microscopy and microtechnique. (P. Gray, ed.). Van Nostrand Reinhold Co., New York, 638 pp.

Feldman, J. L., and C. J. Phillips. 1984. Comparative retinal pigment epithelium and photoreceptor ultrastructure in nocturnal and fossorial rodents: the eastern woodrat, *Neotoma floridana,* and the plains pocket gopher, *Geomys bursarius.* J. Mammal., 65:231-245.

Forman, G. L. 1972. Comparative morphological and histochemical studies of stomachs of selected American bats. Univ. Kansas Sci. Bull., 49:591-729.

Forman, G. L. 1974*a*. Comparative studies of organized gut-associated lymphoid tissue in mammals with diverse food habits. Distribution, size, and organization of Peyer's patches in New World bats. Trans. Illinois Acad. Sci., 67:152-156.

Forman, G. L. 1974*b*. The structure of Payer's patches and their associated nodules in New World bats in relation to food habits. J. Mammal., 55:738-746.

Forman, G. L., and H. H. Genoways. 1979. Sperm morphology. Pp. 177-204, *in* Biology of bats of the New World family Phyllostomatidae. Part III. (R. J. Baker, J. K. Jones, Jr., and D. C. Carter, eds.). Spec. Publ. Mus., Texas Tech Univ., 16:1-441.

Gray, P. 1964. Handbook of basic microtechnique. 3rd. ed., McGraw-Hill, New York, 302 pp.

Gray, P. (ed.). 1973. The encyclopedia of microscopy and microtechnique. 3rd. ed., Van Nostrand Reinhold Co., New York, 638 pp.

Haaijman, J. J. 1983. Labeling of proteins with fluorescent dyes: Quantitative aspects of immunofluorescence microscopy. Pp. 47-85, *in* Immunohistochemistry. (A. C. Cuello, ed.). John Wiley and Sons, New York, 501 pp.

Heimer, L., and M. J. Robards, eds. 1981. Neuroanatomical tract-tracing methods. Plenum Press, New York, 567 pp.

Hopsu, V. K., and G. G. Glenner. 1964. Characterization of enzymes hydrolyzing acyl naphthylamides. I. Mono- and dihalogen derivatives. J. Histochem. Cytochem., 12:674-686.

Hugh-Jones, P. et al. 1972. Medical studies among Indians of upper Xingú. British J. Hosp. Med., 3:317-334.

Humason, G. L. 1979. Animal tissue techniques. W. H. Freeman and Co., San Francisco, 661 pp.

Kalt, M. R., and B. Tandler. 1971. A study of fixation of early amphibian embryos for electron microscopy. J. Ultrastruct. Res., 36:633-645.

Kiernan, J. A. 1981. Histological and histochemical methods: theory and practice. Pergamon Press, New York, 344 pp.

Lillie, R. D., and H. M. Fullmer. 1976. Histopathologic technique and practical histochemistry. 4th ed., McGraw-Hill, 942 pp.

Moore, R. Y. 1981. Fluorescence histochemical methods: Neurotransmitter histochemistry. Pp. 441-482, *in* Neuroanatomical tract-tracing methods. Plenum Press, New York, 567 pp.

Nagato, T., B. Tandler, and C. J. Phillips. 1984. Unusual smooth endoplasmic reticulum in submandibular acinar cells of the male round-eared bat, *Tonatia sylvicola.* J. Ultrastruc. Res., 87:275-284.

Nunez, E. A., M. D. Gershon, and A.-J. Silverman. 1981. Uptake of 5-hydroxytryptamine by gonadotrophs of the bat's pituitary: A combined immunocytochemical radioautographic analysis. J. Histochem. Cytochem., 29:1336-1346.

Pearse, A. G. E. 1968-72. Histochemistry: Theoretical and applied. 3rd. ed., Williams and Wilkins Co., Baltimore, 1518 pp. (2 vols.).

Phillips, C. J. 1985. Field fixation and storage of museum tissue collections suitable for electron microscopy. Acta. Zool. Fenn., 170:87-90.

Phillips, C. J., B. Steinberg, and T. H. Kunz. 1982. Dentin, cementum, and age determination in bats: A critical evaluation. J. Mammal., 63:197-207.

Phillips, C. J., T. Nagato, and B. Tandler. In press. Comparative ultrastructure and evolutionary patterns of acinar secretory product of parotid salivary glands in Neotropical bats. Fieldana: Zoology.

Phillips, C. J., K. M. Studholme, and G. L. Forman. 1984. Results of the Alcoa Foundation Suriname Expeditions. VIII. Comparative ultrastructure of gastric mucosae in four genera of bats (Mammalia: Chiroptera), with comments on gastric evolution. Ann. Carnegie Mus., 53:71-117.

Pinkstaff, C. A., B. Tandler, and R. P. Cohan. 1982. Histology and histochemistry of the parotid and the principal and accessory submandibular glands of the little brown bat. J. Morphol., 172:271-285.

Polak, J. M., and S. Van Noorden, eds. 1983. Immunocytochemistry: Practical applications in pathology and biology. J. Wright Psg. Inc., Littleton, Mass.

Quay, W. B. 1970. Integument and derivatives. Pp. 1-56, *in* Biology of bats, Vol. I. (W. A. Wimsatt, ed.). Academic Press, New York, 477 pp.

Quay, W. B. 1974. Bird and mammal specimens in fluid—objectives and methods. Curator, 17:91-104.

Sokolov, V. E., and N. K. Dzhemukhadze. 1982. Enzyme histochemistry in specific cutaneous glands of *Erinaceus europaeus* during hibernation. Doklady Akademii Nauk SSR, 264 (6):1492-1494 (English Translation).

Sternberger, L. A., P. H. Hardy, Jr., J. J. Cuculis, and H. G. Meyer. 1970. The unabled antibody enzyme method of immunohistochemistry: Preparation and properties of soluble antigen-antibody complex (horseradish peroxidase-antihorseradish peroxidase) and its use in identification of spirochetes. J. Histochem. Cytochem., 18:315-333.

Studier, E. H., S. J. Wisniewski, A. T. Feldman, R. W. Dapson, B. C. Boyd, and D. W. Wilson. 1983. Kidney structure in Neotropical bats. J. Mammal., 64:445-452.

Williams, T. W., Jr. 1941. Alizarin Red S and Toluidine Blue for differentiating adult or embryonic bone and cartilage. Stain Technol., 16:22-25.

Yoshimura, F. 1951. On the specialties of the chiropteran kidney. J. Fac. Med. Shinshu Univ., 1:45-50.

Appendix 1.   Commercially Available Products Mentioned in Text

PRODUCTS

ABC Kit

Vector Laboratories
1429 Rollins Road
Burlingame, California
94010 USA

Cal-Ex
Perfix

Fisher Scientific
711 Forbes Avenue
Pittsburgh, Pennsylvania
15219 USA

Decal
Pro-fixx

>American Scientific Products
>1210 Waukegan Road
>McGaw Park, Illinois
>60085 USA

Histocan

>Lipshaw Corporation
>7446 Central Avenue
>Detroit, Michigan
>48120 USA

PAP KIT

>Dako Corporation
>22 North Milpas Street
>Santa Barbara, California
>93103 USA

Spray-Cyte

>Clay Adams
>Division of Becton,
>Dickinson and Company
>2990 Webro Road
>Parsippany, New Jersey
>07054 USA

Chapter 25

Methods in Chiropteran Mitotic Chromosomal Studies

Robert J. Baker

and

Mazin B. Qumsiyeh

The Museum and the Department of
  Biological Science
Texas Tech University
Lubbock, Texas, 79409 USA

1. INTRODUCTION

Karyotypic information is one of the valuable data sets used in systematic and genetic studies of bats. It is important in assessing relationships between taxa (Patton and Baker, 1978; Baker et al., 1979, 1982, 1984; Haiduk and Baker, 1982; Koop et al. 1984), identifying undescribed species (Baker, 1984), and in studying the processes of speciation and evolution (Bickham and Baker, 1978; Baker and Bickham, 1980; Baker, 1981; Baker et al., 1982; Greenbaum, 1981; Baker et al., 1987).

This paper explains the techniques used for obtaining karyotypic preparations from both bone marrow and primary cell cultures.

2. BONE MARROW PREPARATIONS

The best sources of bone marrow from bats are the humeri. For bone marrow preparations, live bats can be processed without prior treatments such as with mitotic inhibitors and mitogens. However, good health of the bat is important in order to achieve a sufficiently high mitotic index for study. For medium and large bats one humerus is sufficient, for small bats (less than 15 g), both humeri should be used. The humerus should be quickly dissected from the sacrificed animal by clipping through the humerus near the elbow and removing the proximal portion with the head and tuberosity intact (Fig. 1A). Muscle is cleaned from the humerus and the proximal end is removed (Fig. 1B). At least 1-2 mm of the shaft and the trochlear region of the humerus should be left articulating with the radius and ulna, as removal of the entire humerus from the specimen affects the length of the forearm, which can be critical in

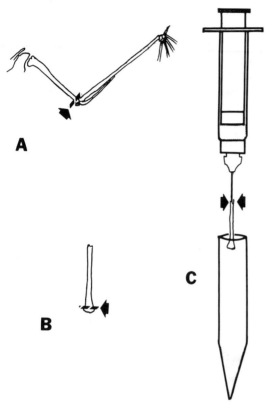

A

B

C

Figure 1. Method of extracting bone marrow from the humerus of a bat. (A) The humerus is cut and dissected out of freshly killed bat. (B) Then the proximal tuberosity is chipped. (C) The bone marrow is forced out of the humerus using a needle full of the hypotonic solution. The thumb and the index finger are used to seal the area around the needle tip and bone (arrows) when forcing the hypotonic solution through the shaft.

remaining small amount of hypotonic solution. The treatment of the cells at this stage is extremely critical and care must be taken to avoid rupturing the mitotic cells. Five milliliters of Carnoy's fixative (one part glacial acetic acid: three parts absolute methanol) is gently introduced down the side of the centrifuge tube. It is important that the fixative be prepared fresh each time (we generally make 40 ml in a 50 ml graduated cylinder) and that the methanol and acetic acid are absolutely free of water. The cells are very gently suspended and the tube centrifuged as before. This time all the supernatant is decanted or removed with a Pasteur pipette, and the cells are gently resuspended in new fixative and are recentrifuged. After one more washing with fixative, the cells are suspended in a small amount of fixative (0.5-3.0 mm depending on the number of cells), and a slide is made as described below. The slide is then either scanned with phase contrast microscopy or, if phase is not available, it can be Giemsa stained and observed with bright field microscopy. Under phase contrast, fixed chromosomes look black and contrast with the background, but if yellowish or surrounded by a bright yellow haze, they should be fixed one or more times as described above. Under bright field microscopy, well fixed cells appear to have little or no cytoplasm, which will appear as purplish haze, remaining associated with the chromosomes. At this stage, slides can be made, or the cell suspension can be frozen in liquid nitrogen (Baker et al., 1982). Freezing in liquid nitrogen is particularly useful on long field trips where bats cannot be transported alive to the laboratory. Cell suspensions can then be thawed after returning to the laboratory. We have made slides for G- and C-banding in the field and transported them to the laboratory, but these efforts generally produce poor G-bands and also pose some problems in transporting large numbers of slides on sustained field trips. Conical eppendorf or microcentrifuge tubes work well for storing cell suspensions and for additional fixation of cells by centrifugation, thus avoiding loss of

identifying the specimen. The bone marrow is flushed into a centrifuge tube with a syringe containing a 0.075 M KCl hypotonic solution (see Appendix 2) at 37°C (Fig. 1C). The bone marrow is gently aspirated with a Pasteur pipette until all the cells are dispersed in the hypotonic solution, then incubated for 27 min at 37°C.

Following incubation in hypotonic solution, the suspension is centrifuged at 1000 rpm for 1 min and the supernatant is gently decanted, leaving two or three drops of liquid in the centrifuge tube. The pellet should be *very gently* but thoroughly resuspended in the cells in larger glass tubes. If a microcentrifuge is not available, eppendorf or NUNC tubes can be used by placing them directly inside larger glass tubes.

2.1. Standard Karyotypes

For each specimen, it is desirable to have a standard karyotype for reference, and air dried slides generally do not provide the best quality spreads for determining centromere position on the chromosomes. Therefore, for each specimen, we prepare one or more slides by the blaze dry technique (Scherz, 1962). This technique consists of dropping three or four drops of the cell suspension onto a slide and immediately igniting the fixative. After the fire extinguishes itself, the residue solution on the slide is removed by tapping the slide gently on its side on a paper towel. Blotting the material with filter paper may destroy some of the cells so this technique is not generally recommended.

2.2. Preparations of Air-dried Slides for Banding

Two, three, or more drops of the cell suspension are dropped from a distance of two feet into water on a slide. The method is illustrated in Baker et al. (1982). Slides are then drained of excess water and can be used for the various banding techniques. For a review of the available banding techniques see Pathak (1976).

2.3. Problems

2.3.1. Low Mitotic Index

Even with healthy animals, the mitotic index may be too low. Yeast stress (Lee and Elder, 1980), however, significantly increases the mitotic index. A subcutaneous injection of 0.1 ml/10 g body mass of the yeast solution (3 g yeast: 2 g dextrose: 12 ml H_2O) is given to the animal on two or three consecutive days before sacrificing. We inject the specimen subcutaneously on the dorsal part of the fore-

arm because too often individuals died when injected on the main body areas. It is important to keep the bats in good condition for the duration of the treatment. This will allow the animals to respond fully to the yeast infection. Although an injection with a mitotic inhibitor (e.g., Velban or Colchicine) causes an increase in the number of cells in the metaphase stage, this also results in shorter chromosomes which are not desirable for the banding techniques. When we do use a mitotic inhibitor, we add it to the hypotonic solution (see Baker et al., 1982) rather than injecting the animal. We have found that for some species of bats it is very difficult to obtain banded chromosomes from bone marrow preparations because of the very low mitotic index. This is true for very small and/or less hardy species of bats, as well as bats taken from hibernation. For such bats, cell cultures can be initiated to obtain the needed data.

2.3.2. Inadequate Spreading of Chromosomes

If a high number of prophase and early metaphase cells are observed, but the chromosomes are not spread sufficiently so that each chromosome is separate, this can be corrected by increasing the time in hypotonic solution. Incubation time is critical because cells will rupture if incubated for too long a time, and the chromosomes will not be spread enough if the incubation time is too short. For most bats the optimum time is around 27 min. Some adjustment of this time may be in order and our times generally range from 25-40 min. The temperature of the hypotonic solution is also critical, and if room temperature is too cool, we keep the temperature elevated by keeping the centrifuge tube inside a belt next to the body, where it is warmed by body heat or in an incubator if available.

2.3.3. Improper Fixation

The stage of fixation also affects the spreading of cells as well as quality of banding. If chromosomes appear under-fixed (see above) and the chromosomes are not well spread on the slide, then one or more additional washes in new fixative is appropriate. However, each time that cells are washed in fixative, some of the best cells may be ruptured during handling. If additional washes do not provide adequate fixation, this may indicate that a new supply of absolute methanol and glacial acetic acid should be obtained.

2.3.4. Clumping after Fixation

For some species, cells may become clumped after centrifugation in hypotonic solution. Aspirating the clump until it dissociates can cause the fragile mitotic cells to rupture. Clumping can be reduced by introducing a few drops of fixative to the hypotonic solution and gently mixing the solutions immediately prior to the initial centrifugation.

3.   G-BANDING PROCEDURE

G-bands are useful tools for identifying and matching homologous chromosomes (Fig. 2) even between distant taxa (see as examples Patton and Baker, 1978; Dutrillaux, 1979; Baker et al., 1982, 1983; Haiduk and Baker, 1982, 1984; Koop et al., 1984; Yunis and Prakash, 1982; Qumsiyeh and Baker 1985). Preparation of G-banded chromosomes is not easily done in the field and requires some experience before the material can be used in systematic or genetic studies. The following procedure is a modification of the techniques used by Seabright (1971) as modified in Patton and Baker (1978).

1) Place slides on a 60°C slide warmer for 12-24 h.
2) The G-banding set-up consists of 6 Copeland jars as follows:
   A. 7 ml of 0.25% trypsin solution and 43 ml Hanks buffer (see Appendix 2).
   B. 50 ml of Hanks buffer
   C. 70% ethanol
   D. 95% ethanol
   E. 95% ethanol

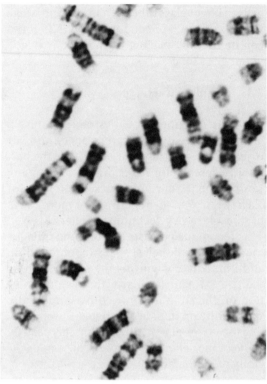

Figure 2. A partial spread of correctly banded chromosomes of a bat *(Uroderma bilobatum).*

   F. 2% Giemsa stain in phosphate buffer (see Appendix 2).
   One slide at a time is prepared and then studied for the quality and stage of banding.
3) Place the slide in the trypsin solution (jar A) for 4-8 min. If the slides have been on a warmer for less than 20 h, then start at 4 min. Rinse in each of the next four jars and allow the slide to dry.
4) Stain in Giemsa for 7-8 min.
5) Dry and scan under light microscope for spreads then check under oil for the quality of the G-bands. If the chromosomes are fuzzy, faint, and destroyed (see Fig. 4), then decrease the time in trypsin. The slides can be left on the slide warmer longer if the chromosomes are still too soft or the bands are not sharp. If, on the other hand, the spreads look like standards by showing no banding or little banding (Fig. 3), more time is needed in trypsin.

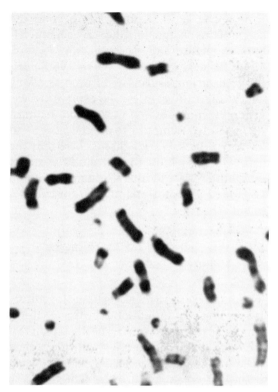

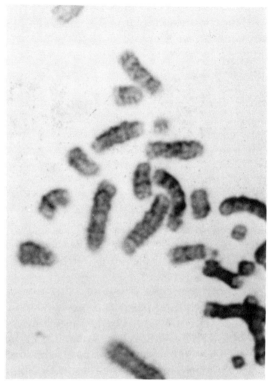

Figure 3. A partial spread of chromosomes showing their appearance when undertreated in trypsin (*Rhinolophus* sp.).

Figure 4. A partial spread of chromosomes showing their appearance when overtreated in trypsin (*Rhinolophus* sp.).

Usually 4-6 slides are adequate to get good G-band preparations using these techniques.

4. C-BANDING PROCEDURE

When chromosomes are treated in acid and the chromatin material is dissociated (usually in barium hydroxide) followed by a reassociation, a characteristic banding pattern can be observed. The bands are usually localized around the centromeres or in some cases elsewhere on the arms. Such bands represent heterochromatin material (usually highly repetitive DNA). Following is a modification of the techniques described by Stefos and Arrighi (1971) for obtaining C-bands.

1) Air dried slides are stored in covered slide boxes at room temperature generally for 1-8 weeks before treatment. However, we have obtained consistently adequate results from slides aged for up to five months.

2) Treat in 0.1 molar HCl for 20 min.

3) Rinse in distilled water and air dry.

4) Incubate individual slides in saturated Ba(OH)$_2$ at 46°C for 0.5, 1, 2, and 3 min. There is a direct correlation between how long slides have been aged and the proper treatment time in barium hydroxide (older slides require longer treatment times). If more slides are available, then more times can be covered (between 0.5-4 min). This will give one or more slides that are at the correct dissociation time.

5) Immediately rinse in 0.1 molar HCl, give two rinses in distilled water and let air dry.

6) Set up humidity chambers (these can be

Figure 5. A petri dish with a filter paper lining and slide supporters used as a humidity chamber for C-banding.

tories. The general process is beyond the scope of this chapter and there are general references (Kruse and Patterson, 1973; Paul, 1975; Pollack, 1973 and Adams, 1980) dealing with various aspects of the process. Many colleges and universities offer courses in these general techniques and they should be mastered before attempting to use cell cultures to karyotype bats. We will discuss here only the aspects of cell culture that are modified in our laboratory or are unique to obtaining G- and C-banded chromosomal data from cultures of bat cells.

5.1. Procedures for Taking Tissue for Culture

The major concern in taking tissue for culture is avoiding contamination. The tissue sample should be taken under a sterile hood or, if this is not available (in the field), inside a clear plastic bag that has been sprayed thoroughly with 70% ethanol. All instruments used to take the sample should be sterilized with alcohol and, if possible, flamed before use. We usually place instruments in a Copeland jar of 70% ethanol. Plastic disposable centrifuge tubes containing 10 ml of sterile medium are taken to the field to keep biopsy samples alive until returned to the laboratory. Once aseptic procedures have been followed, the bat is sacrificed and the tissues are obtained immediately as follows:

simply constructed out of petri dishes lined with filter paper and provided with slide supporters, see Fig. 5). Put 4-8 drops of 2X SSC solution (see Appendix 2) on the slide and cover with a cover slip and soak the filter paper well with 2X SSC. Cover and incubate overnight (or 10-14 h) at 60°C. Make sure that the humidity chamber remains moist and does not dry out during the incubation. If needed, more layers of moist filter paper can be added.
7) Rinse slides in water to remove coverslips.
8) Rinse in 70% then 95% ethanol then air dry.
9) Stain for 10-12 min in 2% Giemsa.

If the chromosomes do not take up the stain, and both the chromosomes and the non-mitotic cells show faint (ghost) images, then the slides have been overtreated in the barium hydroxide. If the chromosomes are dark and look like standard (nondifferentially banded) chromosomes, then the slides have been under-treated and a longer time in barium hydroxide is needed.

5. CELL CULTURE AND HARVESTING TECHNIQUES

Cell culture is a complex technique commonly used in hospital and university labora-

1) Spray entire animal with 70% ethanol until soaked.
2) To take ear biopsies, saturate a piece of cheesecloth with 70% ethanol and clean the ear thoroughly by rubbing with the cloth, even to the extent of removing outer layers of skin. Hold ear out with forceps and clip with scissors. Place in tube containing media as below (see step 8 below).
3) To take lung biopsies, slit skin along chest with scissors, peel back, and secure (hemostats work well for this).
4) Spray chest and dip scissors in ethanol before opening chest cavity.
5) Open chest cavity to expose lungs.

6) With sterile forceps, bring one lobe of the lung into a position that makes it easy to remove a small portion of tissue from the outer rim.

7) Clip a small piece (approximately 5 mm²) of tissue from this area of the lung.

8) Remove cap from media tube and drop tissue sample into it with forceps. Be careful not to touch the lip of the tube with your hands or the forceps. Replace the cap immediately, being careful not to pass your hand over the open mouth of the tube.

9) Take a second sample as above but place the tissue in a separate tube of media.

10) Label all samples immediately as to sex, tissue type, species, specimen number and locality. Voucher specimens of all bats should be preserved in the usual ways (in formalin, alcohol, or as skins and skeletons) for reference (see Chapter 26).

11) If possible, immediately mail tissue samples with proper permits and instructions to customs officials identifying the contents, asking them not to open the tubes. In the United States permits available from the Center for Disease Control (Atlanta, Georgia) should be obtained so that customs officials will not open the containers in transit.

Contamination usually arises from handling the tubes, from the original specimen itself, and from air if the medium or sample receive prolonged exposure to it. It is best to open the culture tube only briefly and with one hand hold the cap on top of the tube while introducing the sample with sterile forceps in the other hand to the inside of the tube.

5.2. Procedure for Initiating Primary Cultures

The following is a summary of techniques used in our laboratory. For a more detailed and alternate techniques of cell and tissue culture see Pollack (1973), Paul (1975) and Adams (1980). Most of the cell culture work is done under a horizontal laminar flow hood equipped with HEPA (high efficiency partic-

ulate air) filters. Spray the inside walls of the hood with 70% ethanol, wipe, and turn the hood on to allow the airflow to stabilize for one-half hour before proceeding.

HAMS F-10 (or HAMS F-12) supplemented with 15-20% fetal bovine serum (FBS) is a good medium for growing primary cell cultures of mammals. HAMS F-10 is best purchased in powdered form, which occupies little space in the freezer. It is diluted into a 10X stock solution and then sterilized by filtration (see Adams, 1980). The 1 X solution is prepared by introducing 50 ml of the sterile 10X solution into a bottle containing 450 ml sterile deionized water. Next, 75-100 ml of fetal calf serum are added aseptically, and a small sample of the medium is poured into a T-25 flask for a sterility check. Antibiotics are not generally used in this procedure because they can result in lax aseptic procedures and selection for resistant bacterial and fungal strains that could spread extensively to other flasks. However, if a particularly important cell line becomes contaminated, it can be cleared by washing the monolayer with Hanks buffer several times (see steps 1-3 below) and then introducing a medium that contains antibiotics. Antibiotics that are commonly used and their recommended concentrations are listed in Table 1.

Bacteria and fungi can be easily recognized both microscopically and macroscopically (cloudiness or colonies in flasks). Mycoplasmas are harder to detect but they cause a slowdown in cell growth and can be tested for by using PPLO agar gels (see Adams, 1980).

Table 1. Antibiotics commonly used against culture contaminants and their optimum concentrations in the culture medium (from Paul, 1975).

Antibiotic	Concentration (μg/ml)	Contaminant
Penicillin-Streptomycin	50	Bacteria
Gentamycin	50	Bacteria
Mycostatin	20	Fungi
Fungizone (Amphotericin B)	2.5	Fungi
Kanamycin	100–200	Mycoplasmas
Gentamycin	200	Mycoplasmas

5.3. Initiating and Maintaining Primary Cell Lines

It is important that all equipment and material that will touch the tissue or medium be absolutely sterile. Forceps and scalpels are placed in a Copeland jar with 70% ethanol and flamed lightly before use. The contents of the tube with the animal explant are poured into a petri dish, then the explant is transferred to another petri dish (or the petri dish cover). The explant may be rinsed quickly by dipping it into some fresh medium. The tissue is then minced into small pieces using a sterile scalpel. The chopped tissue is then transferred to a growing flask for initiating the culture with cell culture medium. There are many kinds of culture vessels on the market; the easiest to use are disposable T-25 or T-75 flasks (size of surface area available for cell growth) which are designed for best attachment of cells. For mammalian cells, 5 ml of HAMS F-10 are required for the T-25 flasks and 15 ml are required for the T-75 flasks. Flasks containing tissue are then incubated horizontally at 37°C. Generally pieces of explants will attach to the surface and begin explanting fibroblast cells in 2-10 days. Fibroblast type cells are not the only type of cells that will be initiated, but they generally outgrow epithelial and other types of cells.

The flasks can be rapped after the initial growth to allow explants to resettle and initiate new colonies of cells. Once 5-10 colonies of rapidly growing cells are initiated, the cells must be dispersed. To disperse cells in medium, proceed as follows:

1) Gently pour medium into a T-25 flask and save for possible growth of other explants or as a bacterial check.
2) Add 10 ml of sterile Hanks buffer (see Appendix 2), close the flask, and let it sit horizontally for 10 min.
3) Decant and repeat step 2 two more times.
4) Decant and introduce 1-2 ml of 0.25% sterile trypsin (see Appendix 2), cover and let sit horizontally for 1-2 min.
5) Scan using inverted microscopy for the number of cells detaching from the substrate. If cells are not responding very well, then rap the flask gently. If this does not work, incubate for 5-15 min at 37°C. For some bat cell lines, longer periods of trypsin treatment may be required, but for most, 5-15 minutes are sufficient. Selection for cells that are more resistant to the action of trypsin can be done if the cell line is kept for several generations.

Trypsin acts as a proteolytic enzyme by dissociating glycoproteins of cell membranes, making cells separate from one another and from the substrate. Action of trypsin is inhibited by calcium and magnesium ions which are present in most cell culture media. Accordingly, it is essential to wash the attached cells with Hanks buffer (Ca^{++} and Mg^{++} free) before adding the trypsin. It should be emphasized here that if cells respond to trypsin, by rounding up and then detaching from the surface, the next step should be performed quickly by not allowing cells to remain any longer in the trypsin. Over-exposure to the trypsin can destroy cellular membranes and result in cell death.

6) Introduce fresh culture medium when about 80% of cells are in suspension in the trypsin. This will inhibit further trypsin action.
7) To subculture dispersed cells, simply add double the amount of medium (i.e., 30 ml for T-75 flasks) and then remove half the medium with cells into a new flask. Some rapidly growing cells can be subcultured using a split ratio of 1:3 (i.e., one flask is subcultured into 3 flasks) or even higher.

5.4. Karyotyping from Cultured Cells

Generally we karyotype a cell line only if three or more flasks of the same animal are apparently confluent. To reduce the risk that all cells from the same animal are contaminated, we do not feed or treat all flasks from the same animal at the same time. Flasks that show an abundance of cells undergoing mitosis are chosen for karyotyping. An active culture should show a number of cells rounded up, and many of those should be in the telophase stage. Proceed to disperse the cells as described above for maintaining cell lines, but save all media (F-10 and Hanks) and centrifuge for 5 minutes to collect any floating cells. When cells have dispersed into the trypsin, pour out the suspension into a tube and centrifuge. Before centrifugation, one or two drops of Velban (0.00025%) can be added to the tubes if the chromosomes are long and thin and as such show much overlap. After centrifugation for 5 min at 1000 rpm, decant the supernatant leaving but 2-3 drops in which the cells are resuspended. A hypotonic solution of one part medium: four parts deionized water is added, and the tube is incubated for 25 min at 37°C. After this step, follow the procedure as for fixing and making slides from bone marrow. Cells obtained from culture are generally more fragile than bone marrow cells, and are obviously less in volume. These disadvantages are outweighed by the higher mitotic index obtained in cell culture preparations. Flasks may be saved after harvesting cells for karyotyping by simply adding new media.

Living cells may be frozen in liquid nitrogen and revived when needed again (Baker and Haiduk, 1984). For freezing, cells are dispersed as above but in a small amount of sterile medium rather than the hypotonic solution. Suspended cells are introduced into sterile vials (NUNC tubes), and Dimethyl Sulfoxide (DMSO) is added to a concentration of 7%. The vials are closed tightly and correctly labeled. Slow freezing and fast thawing of cells gives best results. Vials ready to freeze are put on ice for 30 min, then into a -70°C freezer overnight, and then into the liquid nitrogen (-196°C).

6. SUMMARY

Methods for obtaining mitotic chromosomal preparations from bone marrow or cultured cells for systematic and evolutionary studies of bats are presented. We discuss methods for nondifferentially stained, G-, and C-banded chromosomal preparations. G-bands are produced on chromosomes treated with trypsin and stained in giemsa. C-bands are obtained by subsequent treatments in hydrochloric acid, saturated barium hydroxide, reassociation in humidity chambers with 2x SSC buffer, and stained with giemsa.

Problems of low mitotic index, inadequate spreading of chromosomes, improper fixation, and clumping after fixation are addressed and possible solutions presented. Procedures are presented for obtaining samples, initiating and maintaining primary cell cultures, and karyotyping from cultured cells. We also present formulas for making growth media, buffers, trypsin, and hypotonic solution, and provide the names and addresses of sources for the chemicals and supplies.

7. ACKNOWLEDGMENTS

We would like to thank John W. Bickham, Karen McBee, Craig S. Hood, Frederick B. Stangl, Jr., and Robert R. Hollander for their helpful comments. The development and use of many of these techniques took place while the senior author was supported by NSF grants DEB-76 20580 and DEB-80 04293.

8. REFERENCES

Adams, R. L. P. 1980. Cell culture for biochemists. Elsevier/North Holland Biomedical Press, Amsterdam, 292 pp.

Baker, R.J. 1981. Chromosomal flow between chromosomally characterized taxa of a volant mammal, *Uroderma bilobatum* (Chiroptera: Phyllostomatidae). Evolution, 35:296-305.

Baker, R. J. 1984. An example of sympatric, cryptic species: A new species of *Rhogeessa* (Chiroptera: Vespertilionidae). Syst. Zool., 33:178-183.

Baker, R. J., and J. W. Bickham. 1980. Karyotypic evolution in bats: Evidence of extensive and conservative chromosomal evolution in closely related taxa. Syst. Zool., 29:239-253.

Baker, R. J., and M. W. Haiduk. 1984. Collections

of cell lines suspended by freezing. Acta Zool. Fenn., In Press.

Baker, R. J., R. A. Bass, and M. A. Johnson. 1979. Evolutionary implications of chromosomal homology in four genera of stenodermatine bats (Phyllostomatidae, Chiroptera). Evolution, 33:220-226.

Baker, R. J., M. W. Haiduk, L. W. Robbins, A. Cadena, and B. Koop. 1982. Chromosomal studies of South American bats and their systematic implications. Pp. 303-327, *in* Mammalian Biology in South America (M. A. Mares and H. H. Genoways, eds.). Pymatuning laboratory of Ecology, Vol. IV, Pymatuning, Pennsylvania, 539 pp.

Baker, R. J., B. F. Koop, and M. W. Haiduk. 1983. Resolving systematic relationships with G-bands: A study of five genera of South American cricetine rodents. Syst. Zool., 32:403-416.

Baker, R. J., M. B. Qumisyeh, and C. S. Hood. 1987. Role of chromosomal banding patterns in understanding mammalian evolution. Pp. 67-96, *in* Current Mammalogy, Vol. 1 (H. H. Genoways, ed.). Plenum Press, New York.

Bickham, J. W. and R. J. Baker. 1978. Canalization model of chromosomal evolution. Bull. Carnegie Mus. Nat. Hist., No. 13, pp. 70-84.

Dutrilaux, B. 1979. Chromosomal evolution in primates: Tentative phylogeny from *Microcebus murinus* (Prosimian) to man. Hum. Gen., 48:251-314.

Greenbaum, I. F. 1981. Genetic interactions between hybridizing cytotypes of the tent-making bat *(Uroderma bilobatum).* Evolution, 35:306-321.

Haiduk, M. W., and R. J. Baker. 1982. Cladistical analysis of the G-banded chromosomes of nectar-feeding bats (Glossophaginae: Phyllostomidae). Syst. Zool. 31:252-265.

Haiduk, M. W., and R. J. Baker. 1984. Scientific method, opinion, phylogenetic reconstruction, and nectar-feeding bats: A response to Griffiths and Warner. Syst. Zool., 33:343-350.

Koop, B. F., R. J. Baker, M. W. Haiduk, and M. D. Engstrom. 1984. Cladistical analysis of the primitive G-band sequences for the karyotype of the Cricetidae complex of rodents. Genetica, 64:199-208.

Kruse, P. F., Jr., and M. K. Patterson, Jr. 1973. Tissue culture: Methods and Applications. Academic Press, New York and London, 868 pp.

Lee, M. R., and F. F. B. Elder. 1980. Yeast stimulation of bone marrow mitosis for cytogenetic investigations. Cytogen. Cell Gen., 26:36-40.

Patton, J. C. and R. J. Baker. 1979. Chromosomal homology and evolution of phyllostomatoid bats. Syst. Zool., 27:449-462.

Pathak, S. 1976. Chromosome banding techniques. J. Reprod. Med., 17:25-28.

Paul, J. 1975. Cell and Tissue Culture. Churchill Livingstone, Edinburgh, London, and New York, 5th ed., 484 pp.

Pollack, R. (ed.). 1973. Readings in mammalian cell culture. Cold Spring Harbor Laboratory, New York, 864 pp.

Qumsiyeh, M. B., and R. J. Baker. 1985. G- and C-band karotypes of the Rhinopomatidae (Microchiroptera). J. Mammal., 66:541-544.

Scherz, R. G. 1962. Blaze drying, by igniting the fixative, for improved spreads of chromosomes in leucocytes. Stain Technology, 37:386.

Seabright, M. 1971. A rapid banding technique for human chromosomes. Lancet, ii:971-972.

Stefos, K., and F. E. Arrighi. 1971. Heterochromatic nature of the W chromosome in birds. Expl. Cell Res., 68:228-231.

Yunis, J. J., and O. M. Prakash. 1982. The origin of man: A chromosomal pictorial legacy. Science, 215:1525-1530.

Appendix 1. Chemicals, Equipment, and Their Suppliers

This list gives only the supplies that are not commonly available in universities (i.e., it does not include the common chemicals). This list gives only the most common American suppliers. For European suppliers, see Adams (1980).

Chemicals and Media

Nutrient F-10 medium (Ham's)
Penicillin-Streptomycin
  (10,000 mcg/ml each)
Neomycin-Sulfate
  (10,000 mcg/ml)
Hanks base
Fetal Bovine or Fetal Calf Serum
Trypsin
        Chemicals and media
        can be obtained from one of
        the following suppliers:
        KC Biological, Irvine
        Scientific, Grand Island
        Biological Company

Equipment and Supplies

Plastic petri dishes, 100x20 mm

Falcon, Corning, NUNC

15 mm Polystyrene conical tubes
with screw caps

Falcon, Corning, NUNC

25 cm and 75 cm culture flasks

Falcon, Corning, NUNC

Filtration set-up with 0.22 μ pore
size, 47 mm filter size

Millipore

Addresses of Suppliers

Corning Glass Works
Corning, New York 14830

Falcon
Cockeysville, Maryland 21030

Grand Island Biological Company
Grand Island, New York 14072

Irvine Scientific
2511 Daimler Street
Santa Ana, California 92705

KC Biological, Inc.
Lenexa, Kansas 66215

Millipore Corporation
Bedford, Massachusetts 01730

NUNC (Denmark) distributed by
Southland Cryogenics, Inc.
1212 Tappan Circle, Box 627
Carrollton, Texas 75006

Appendix 2. Media and Recipes for Chromosomal Studies

Standard F-10 Medium
450 ml sH$_2$O (sterile water)
50 ml 10 X F-10 medium
75 ml FBS (Fetal bovine serum)
adjust pH with sterile NaHCO$_3$ to golden amber,
and refrigerate

Field F-10 medium
as above but use 100 ml FBS and add
2 ml Penicillin-Streptomycin
2 ml Neomycin-Sulfate
0.25 ml Fungizone
Hanks Buffer
450 ml sH$_2$O
25 ml 20 X Hanks Salts
25 ml 20 X Glucose
0.5 ml Phenol
Adjust pH to red with sterile NaHCO$_3$
20 X Hanks Salts
80 g NaCl
5 g KCl
0.6 g Na$_2$HPO$_4$
0.6 g KH$_2$PO$_4$
Mix in 500 ml dH$_2$O (distilled water) and
auto clave
20 X Hanks Glucose
20 g glucose in 500 ml dH$_2$O and autoclave
Phosphate buffer for Giemsa stain
0.469 g NaH$_2$PO$_4$
0.937 g Na$_2$HPO$_4$
1000 ml dH$_2$O
pH=7
Phenol Red
1 gm Phenol Red
100 ml H$_2$O
Autoclave
0.075 M Potasium Chloride (Hypotonic
Solution)
2.79 g KCl
500 ml dH$_2$O
2X SSC (for C-banding)
5.47 g NaCl
4.32 g Sodium Citrate
500 ml H$_2$O
0.25% Trypsin
10 ml Stock 2.5% Trypsin
90 ml Hanks Solution
adjust pH with sterile NaHCO$_3$ until color is
pinkish.
For G-banding we use 8 ml of this Trypsin
solution and dilute it further by adding 42 ml
of Hanks solution (to a Copeland jar, jar A in
page 428)

Chapter 26

Specimen Preparation

Charles O. Handley, Jr.

Division of Mammals
National Museum of Natural History
Smithsonian Institution
Washington, D.C. 20560 USA

1. INTRODUCTION

Subjects of behavioral and ecological studies usually are studied alive, so there should be few opportunities for specimen preservation. However, some species of bats are so slightly differentiated externally that they may be confused easily or they may be difficult, if not impossible, to identify with confidence alive in the field. Consequently, voucher specimens of subject animals are essential for verifying identifications. Some studies are consumptive—they require deliberate sacrifice of animals for the examination of internal parasites, stomach contents, organs, or collection of tissues (Chapters 11, 13, 24, 25). Even in studies where every effort is made to keep animals alive and healthy, accidental deaths do occur. In some areas the chiropteran fauna has not been completely or thoroughly documented, so new and undescribed species or rare species easily confused with more common ones could be among throwaways. Animals deliberately or accidentally killed should be salvaged as specimens whenever possible. Representative samples of common species and all specimens of rare species should be saved.

Fortunately, preservation of bats is neither difficult nor time consuming. No other mammal is as easily prepared. The stuffed skin of a bat requires no wires for arms, legs, or tail, and routine preservation in fluid is an acceptable procedure. However, few publications have described or illustrated the techniques for preparation of bats (Peterson, 1965, and Barbour and Davis, 1969 are exceptions), and no complete guide has dealt exclusively with bats. Usually mention of bats has been incidental to the detailed description of techniques of preservation of other mammals (e.g., Hall, 1962; Setzer, 1968; Nagorsen and Peterson, 1980; DeBlase and Martin, 1983).

2. SUPPLIES AND EQUIPMENT

Preservation of bats requires few supplies and little equipment. Needed materials can be obtained from biological supply houses, university stock rooms, or from museums willing to exchange supplies for specimens (Dowler and Genoways, 1976). If supplies are destined for an overseas project, check prevailing regulations before preparing an air shipment. Rather stringent regulations apply to air shipment of chemicals.

In the following lists, items required for dry preservation are marked with an asterisk. Those needed for both wet and dry preservation are italicized. The others are for wet preservation only.

2.1. Tools

Dissecting scissors (one or both points acute)
Syringe [fine needle (ca. 22 gauge) for injections; *heavy needle (ca. 16 gauge) for flushing brains]
Sewing needles (large eyed, embroidery, or small, curved surgical suturing)
Pencil (no. 1 or no. 2)
Pen and waterproof black ink
Metric rule or tape (preferably metal, since plastic and fiberglass distort easily)
Metric (gram) balance or spring scale (e.g., triple beam balance or Pesola scale, 50 and 100 g capacity)
Bottle forceps
*Dissecting forceps
*Scalpel

2.2. Supplies

Formaldehyde (37–40%, buffers optional—see Nagorsen and Peterson, 1980:37, 67-68)
Cheesecloth

String (for tying cheesecloth specimen pouches)
Container (for fixing specimens in fluid)
Plastic bags (1 pint to 1 gallon in size and a few garbage bags; a bag approximately 12.5 x 45 cm is most useful)
Shipping containers
Rubber bands
Cotton (any kind will do, but the best for specimen preparation is a long staple, resilient, non-absorbent variety)
Labels [labels for dry skins printed on 100% rag paper; small waterproof (vulcanized) labels for wet specimens and skulls]
Looseleaf or bound notebooks (looseleaf is most desirable because of its versatility; a 15 x 24 cm page size is recommended for a field catalog and journal and an 8 x 13 cm page size is recommended for a field notebook)
*Absorbent (hardwood sawdust—never softwood, *white* cornmeal, magnesium carbonate; borax should not be used because of its potential for altering coloration of the pelage and because it renders skulls and carcasses unpalatable to the beetles used for cleaning them)
*Thread (no. 30 cotton preferred)
*Pins (any sharp-pointed pins are suitable, but glass headed or T-pins are preferred)
*Pinning board (any flat surface that will take and hold a pin is usable; the corrugated paper of packing cartons and styrofoam are universally available)
*No-pest strips (an insecticide) or naphthalene flakes or paradichlorobenzene crystals (insect repellent and fungicide to protect dry skins)
*Arsenic (Arsenic trioxide, As_2O_3—optional, for insect-proofing skins)

3. SACRIFICING AND STORAGE BEFORE PRESERVATION

If animals are to be intentionally sacrificed there are several ways that it can be accom-

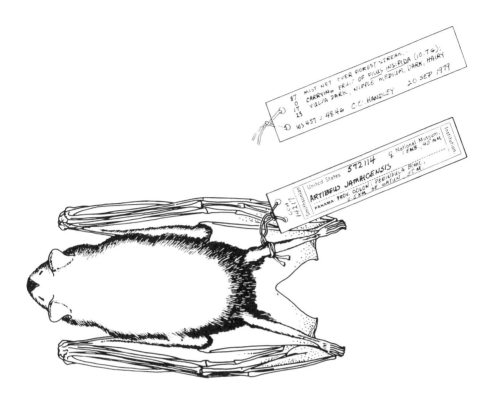

Figure 1. Specimen label, Smithsonian style, showing both sides of a skin label.

plished neatly. Whichever method is employed, it should be humane and should not damage the specimen.

The simplest and quickest procedure is to break the animal's neck. With small bats this can be accomplished by holding the animal with the forefinger under its throat and the thumbnail of the same hand on the back of its neck. Pressure from the thumbnail will easily separate the neck vertebrae. The more heavily muscled necks of larger bats may require bone snips or wire-cutter pliers. The jaws of these tools must be padded with tape to eliminate the danger of severing the head or cutting the skin. A bat also can be killed by injecting its heart with nicotine or an anesthetic such as novocain or nembutal. Or, the bat can be overanesthetized with chloroform, ether, or a similar drug.

The appearance and often the value of a specimen are directly correlated with its freshness at the time of preservation. Tissue deterioration begins soon after death and proceeds rapidly. Both rotting and dehydration result. Thus, it is advisable to begin specimen preparation as soon as possible. Ideally, the bat should be kept alive until preservation can be performed. Otherwise, seal the dead specimen in a plastic bag to retard dehydration and store it, labeled, in a freezer. For short term storage, depending upon field conditions, and for a few hours at most, place the plastic-bagged bat in a refrigerator, roll it up in a wet burlap bag exposed to a breeze, or place it in the coolest available spot, such as on the ground in the shade or on a concrete floor in a house. Of course the specimen must be protected from scavenging birds, mammals, and arthropods such as ants and roaches.

4. DATA

4.1. Labeling

Bats must be measured and labeled before they can be preserved. Those preserved dry must be individually labeled, but those preserved in fluid may be labeled individually or in daily lots.

A field catalog is necessary for dry specimens with multiple parts (e.g., skin and skull). Actually, it is desirable to use a catalog for all specimens. The catalog includes a series of collector's numbers to be assigned to individual specimens. Each catalog entry should include at least the tentative identification of the specimen, locality, date, and nature of the specimen (i.e., skin and skull, skull only, fluid, etc.). It may include other label data. Format and content of the catalog should satisfy the needs of the individual collector. Hall (1962) and Nagorsen and Peterson (1980) have illustrated several styles. Catalog entries and labels of dry specimens ought to be inscribed with waterproof black ink. Labels of wet specimens can be in waterproof black ink or medium (no. 2) pencil.

For specimens preserved dry, label information should include locality, date of collection, sex and reproductive data, external measurements, name of collector, and collector's number (Fig. 1). If fluid specimens are individually cataloged and full data are in the catalog, only the collector's initials and number are necessary on the specimen labels. In the absence of a catalog, labels of such specimens must include at least locality, date, and name of collector.

The collecting locality should be defined as precisely as possible. Relate it to a locality that can be found on most maps (e.g., Panamá, Prov. Bocas del Toro, Boca de Río Risco, 8 km WSW Almirante). If the distance between points is not a straight line map distance, specify "by road," "by trail," "estimate," or whatever. Give latitude and longitude if they are known, and note the elevation as precisely as possible.

4.2. Reproductive Data

The determination of sex and reproductive status are rather straight forward on most bats (see Chapter 2). Males of most species have an easily recognized pendulous penis and females have characteristic labiae and vagina. Bats of two families, however, require closer scrutiny. In the Emballonuridae the genitalia are oddly cone-shaped in both sexes, and in the Noctilionidae the labiae are elongated and superficially resemble a penis. Determination of sex should be based always on examination of the genitalia and not on observation of the mammae. The males of many bats have well developed nipples. Indeed, in the Stenodermatinae mammae are quite similar in the young of both sexes.

In addition to sex, several other sorts of reproductive data should be noted on specimen labels. Length and width of a testis and coloration of the skin over the testes provide clues to age and reproductive condition of males. Size of nipples, status of hair on their areolae, and color of the vulva are similarly informative about females. Record the length and width of a nipple and whether its areola is naked, clothed with old hair, or covered with new hair. Note lactation or a state of postlactation. Record the number and crown-rump length of embryos and any that are being resorbed. Note transport of young and measure the forearm length (and body mass if possible) of each baby. Also note the lack of evidence of reproduction, for negative information is useful too.

4.3. Other Data

If circumstances and diligence permit, numerous other data which would enhance the value of a specimen can be collected. Most notable are information on ecology and natural history of the specimen. Habitat, life zone, roost characteristics, and method of capture could be recorded. Often a specimen comes with evidence of feeding, including stomach contents, fecal contents, food in the mouth, stains on the pelage, or pollen grains lodged in the fur. Broken bones (healed or not), punctures, cuts, tears, sores, scars, and other wounds, hair loss, blindness, and unusual infestations of parasites all warrant notes. Three categories of age can be recognized in the field: 1) Juvenile.—Epiphyses of the fingers open (not ossified). 2) Subadult (post-juvenile but pre-reproductive).—Epiphyses closed (ossified), nipples tiny and testes small. 3) Adult (reproductive).—Epiphyses closed, nipples at least slightly enlarged, and testes large (also see Chapters 2 and 3). Invariably these features are more noticeable and can be more accurately recorded in a fresh specimen than in a preserved one.

4.4. External Measurements

External measurements of a fresh specimen are recorded in millimeters on the specimen label, preferably with black waterproof ink. Measurements are always straight line distances, never following body contours. Precision is essential. Four standard external measurements always are recorded: total

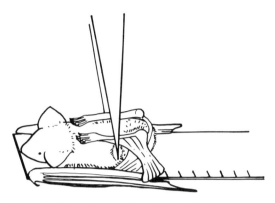

Figure 3. Measuring total length of a tailless bat.

length, length of tail vertebrae, length of hind foot, and length of ear from notch. Since they are always listed in the same order, they need not be identified on the label. They may be listed in vertical columnar format or consecutively (horizontally). Measurements that are incomplete or that the collector feels are inaccurate should be enclosed in brackets. The standard measurements are taken as follows.

Total length.—This is the distance from the tip of the snout to the tip of the last caudal vertebra, measured with the bat lying belly down on the ruler, or as some preparators prefer, belly up. The body of the specimen should first be flexed gently to relax it. Place the snout at zero and gently press down the head and back of the specimen so that its underparts are flat against the ruler. Grasp the terminal tail vertebra securely with forceps. When the tail is fully extended read the total length (Fig. 2).

If the bat is a tailless species, lay it belly down on the ruler. Fold its legs forward against its flanks while grasping its waist with forceps. Legs and waist can be grasped simultaneously with the forceps if the bat is small. In this posture the ischia of the pelvis protrude as the posteriormost parts of the skeleton. Flatten the back so that the snout of the bat rests on zero of the ruler. Read the total length at the hind edge of the pelvis (Fig. 3).

Length of tail vertebrae.—This is the dis-

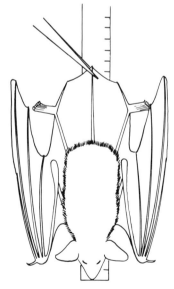

Figure 2. Measuring total length of a bat with a tail.

tance from the base of the tail to the tip of the last caudal vertebra. Grasp the terminal vertebra securely with forceps. Hold the tail at right angles to the backbone. Place zero of the ruler at the angle of the tail and the backbone. Read the length at the tip of the tail (Fig. 4).

Length of hind foot.—Greatest length of the fully extended, flattened foot, measured from the tip of the claw of the longest toe to the inner (anterior) edge of the calcar at its junction with the tibia. Flatten the foot on the ruler with the inner edge of the calcar at zero. Read the length at the tip of the longest claw (Fig. 5).

Length of ear from notch.—This is the distance from the notch at the base of the ear to the tip of the ear. Grasp the forward edge of the ear with thumb and forefinger and extend (but do not stretch) the ear to its greatest length. Place zero of the ruler in the notch at the base of the ear and read length at the tip of the ear (Fig. 6).

Two other measurements sometimes taken at the time of preservation are wingspread and length of the tragus. Since these are not standard measurements, they should be identified on the label with the abbreviations *ws* and *tr.*

Wingspread.—This is the distance between the tips of the fully extended wings. With the bat lying belly down on the ruler, grasp the forward edge of each wing near its tip, extend wings, and read distance between the tips (Fig. 7).

Length of tragus.—Since this can measured in two ways, the method of measurement should be stated (Fig. 8).

1) The preferred measurement is the distance from the anterior (dorsal) insertion of the tragus to its tip—actually the *length of the tragus blade.*

2) A less frequently used alternative is the *total length of the tragus*—blade plus basal foliations. This is measured from the lowest point of the basal foliations to the tip of the tragus.

Several other external dimensions of bats, all measurements of bones, should be taken only on preserved specimens. Because of shrinkage in preservative or in drying,

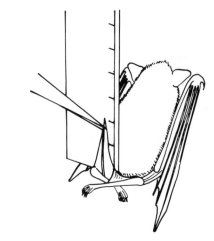

Figure 4. Measuring length of the tail.

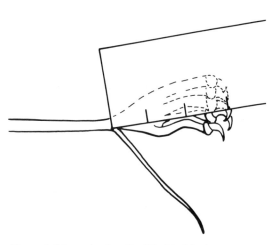

Figure 5. Measuring length of the hind foot.

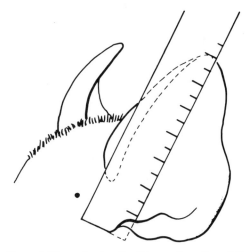

Figure 6. Measuring length of the ear from the notch.

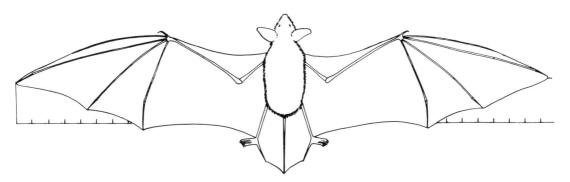

Figure 7. Measuring the wingspread.

measurements taken on fresh specimens are not exactly comparable to the same measurements taken on preserved specimens. Thus, it is a waste of time and needlessly clutters the specimen label to measure the forearm, metacarpals, phalanges, tibia, and calcar at the time of preservation.

A nonlinear dimension that should be taken is body mass. Record in grams if possible, and note whether the measurement includes stomach contents. When correlated with reproductive condition and age, body mass can be a useful measurement. There are no published body masses for many species of bats.

parasitological studies. Also, their skulls can be removed and cleaned, if necessary, more easily than those of many other mammals. Most museums welcome collections of fluid preserved bats in exchange for identifications.

A variety of fluids can be used effectively for wet preservation, but because it can be expanded so much by dilution and because it is such a good fixative, formaldehyde is probably the most widely used in field situations. The stock formaldehyde (37 to 40 percent) should be diluted 10 parts water to one of formaldehyde. Formaldehyde is also available in a powdered form. This is especially conve-

5. PREPARING SPECIMENS

5.1. Wet Preservation

As a rule wet specimens of most mammals are used for dissection and not much else. One wet rat looks very much like any other wet rat. It must be dried and probably its skull must be extracted and cleaned before it can be identified with certainty. The same can be said of a wet marsupial or a wet lagomorph.

Bats, however, are very useful as wet specimens. Their ears, lips, snout, wings, tail, and feet may be so distinctive that most specimens can be readily identified when they are wet. Museums commonly maintain large collections of bats preserved in fluid. They are useful for taxonomic studies, dissections, and

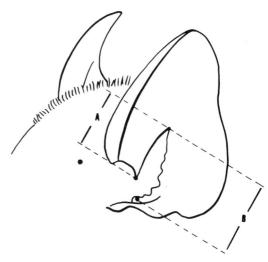

Figure 8. Two methods of measuring the tragus. (A) Length of the tragus blade. (B) Total length of the tragus.

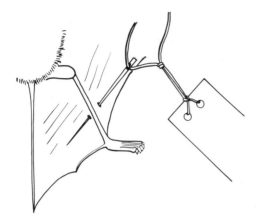

Figure 9. Attaching the skin label to the tibia with a sewing needle.

nient for foreign travel where airlines do not permit liquid formaldehyde in baggage. Make sure that the formaldehyde is fresh. Old formaldehyde produces a whitish precipitate, making the solution weak and acidic and harmful to specimens. Several buffers are available which counteract the acid that is present even in fresh formalin. Make sure that the buffer does not leave a residue in the tissue.

Bats can be individually labeled with a waterproof tag sewed through the membranes and tied around the tibia (Fig. 9). Never tie a tag to the ankle. Permanent distortion of the calcar and membrane attachment to the foot results. Several bats can be preserved together with a single label in a pouch formed from a square of cheesecloth. This should be done only when the bats all have the same data. If collector's numbers are being assigned they should be attached to each individual. To insure uniform fixing, the number of bats in each cheesecloth pouch should be kept small—10 or less depending upon the size of the bats. The pouch should be draped loosely around the bats to insure good circulation of fixative.

The container for fixing specimens should be wide-mouthed and, depending upon the number of specimens to be preserved, it may vary from a small glass or plastic jar to a 10-gallon polypropylene-lined "Liquipak" drum. The container should not be overfilled with specimens. The volume of fixative should be twice the volume of the specimens to allow for adequate circulation of fixative.

Bats should be processed as follows:

1) Record the essential data (locality and date) on the label and in the field catalog. If time permits, also record measurements and body mass. Use waterproof ink or a medium (no. 2) pencil.

2) Sew the label through the membranes and tie with a square knot around the tibia (if the specimens are individually labeled).

3) Open the mouth to the widest gape and stuff it full with a substantial wad of cotton. With the mouth fixed open, the teeth, palate, and tongue later can be examined easily. With the mouth closed it is necessary to dissect out the skull in order to examine the teeth, palate, and tongue—unnecessarily destructive and time consuming.

4) Carefully inject the thorax with the preservative (perfuse through the arteries if detailed dissections are the objective).

5) With scissors, open an incision into the abdomen through the skin and muscles without disturbing the viscera.

6) Wet the fur with water so the bat will sink readily into the preservative.

7) Drop the bat or the cheesecloth pouch of bats into the preservative.

8) Keep the specimens in the preservative for at least 3-5 days, until the body is relatively rigid to the touch. If it takes longer to fix the specimens, the formalin solution must be weak, or the volume of bats is too great for the amount of formalin. If the formalin seems weak, pour it out and start again. Keeping the solution at about 10 percent is very important. If it is weaker, specimens will rot. If it is stronger, specimens will become hard and brittle from dehydration and teeth and bones will become rubbery from leaching of calcium. Specimens will suffer the same consequences if they are left too long in 10 percent formalin. Never store them for more than 30 days in formalin. After that, rinse them

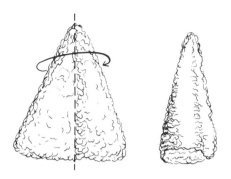

Figure 10. Forming a cone-shaped body from a triangular sheet of cotton.

briefly in water (do not soak) and store in 70% ethanol. The alcohol should be changed after about 30 days to eliminate any residual formalin which might be contaminating it. Formalin is an excellent fixative, but a poor preservative. Ethanol is an excellent preservative, but other alcohols—isopropyl, denatured alcohol, and alcohol intended for personal consumption— are not, but they can be used temporarily if ethanol is not available. From such substitutes, transfer the specimens to ethanol as soon as possible. The volume of both fixative and preservative should be at least twice that of the specimens.

5.2. Dry Preservation

If time permits, a few specimens of each species might be preserved dry. There are several forms of dry preservation: skin and skull; skin, skull, and skeleton; skull only; and skeleton only.

Premature drying of the skin and membranes is a problem in preparation of bats; so the process of skinning and stuffing must move along rapidly. To facilitate this, several things should be done before skinning is begun. First, measure and sex the specimen. Record these and all associated data on the specimen label and in the field catalog (*on the label first,* then in the catalog; the label is the primary data source) with waterproof black ink.

Next, prepare a body from a thin, clean, triangular sheet of cotton (Fig. 10) in which there are no lumps. The length of the cotton, from apex to base, should approximate the length of the body of the bat. Lay small pieces of cotton neatly on one-half of the cotton triangle to approximate the bulk of the bat and to give the body compactness, then fold (don't roll) the triangle into halves, with a little edge lap, to form a flattish cone.

5.2.1. Skin and Skull

Break the humerus of each wing close to the body (Fig. 11). Make an incision from the middle of the chest to the genitals with scissors or scalpel. Take care not to cut through the abdominal wall into the viscera (if this happens hold the bat with the incision down and remove the viscera with the forceps before proceeding (Fig. 12). Blot moisture by dipping belly into sawdust or other absorbent). Work on top of a handfull of sawdust. Use it liberally. The working surface of the specimen should never be wet and shiny.

Grasp the skin at the edge of the incision and peel it away from the body all around the sides and the front of the incision by pushing the body away from the skin with the scissor tips or the handle of the forceps, the scalpel or

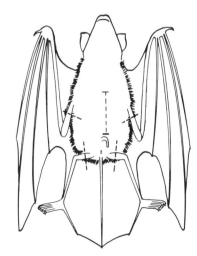

Figure 11. Breaking the humeri and femora and making the initial incision on the belly.

Figure 14. Clipping muscle masses on the leg.

Figure 12. Dumping viscera onto a pile of sawdust.

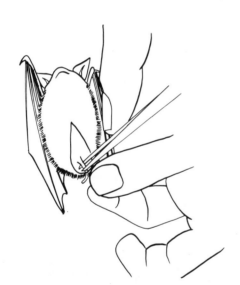

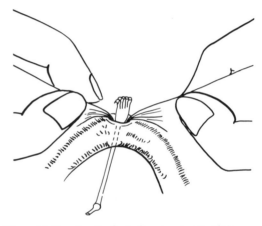

Figure 15. Everting the foot after cleaning the tibia.

Figure 13. Clipping the genital tube inside the skin.

character of its tip can be examined later in the dry specimen.

fingernails. Always work at the point of separation of skin and carcass. Otherwise the skin will stretch or tear. Use sawdust!

Posteriorly, lift the edge of the skin and cut through the genital tube and the rectum (Fig. 13). Evert the penis of the males so that it later can be clipped from the study skin to salvage the baculum, if one is present. Peel the skin back over the pelvis. Clip the tail, if there is one, at the base, close to the body. *Leave the tail vertebrae in the skin* so that the tail and the

Grasp the pelvis with the fingers of one hand, peel the skin down over the femur to the knee with the other. Break the femur close to the body with fingernails (Fig. 11); clip through the muscles at the break with the scissors. Peel the distal muscle remnants down to the knee and clip. Peel the skin down over the knee and the tibia to the ankle. Clip the tendons at each end of the tibia and remove the muscle (Fig. 14). *Leave the tibia intact* so its length can be measured later on the dry specimen. Turn the skin back over the leg (Fig. 15). Repeat on the other leg.

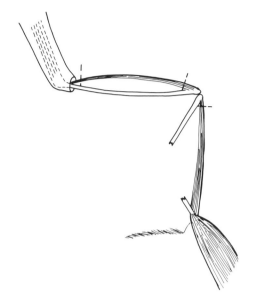

Figure 16. Clipping muscles from the forearm and the broken stump of the humerus; freeing the wing from the body.

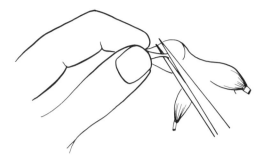

Figure 18. Clipping the tube of the ear with the scissors close to the skull.

dust! Expose the broken humerus of one wing and snip through the distal muscle insertion, freeing the wing from the body. Be wary of the broken ends of the humerus. They have sharp, knifelike edges. Carefully turn the skin of the wing down over the forearm (radius and ulna); snip the muscles loose at both ends (Fig. 16). Turn the skin back over the arm (Fig. 17). Try not to disturb the ulna when cutting the proximal muscle origins on the forearm. The proximal head of the ulna is large and forms the elbow; but its abbreviated shaft is thin and fragile. If cut, it leaves a sharp stub, hazardous to the preparator's fingers and likely to snag and tear the skin of the wing when it is turned back over the elbow. Repeat the same skinning procedure on the other wing.

The neck is short, so the base of the skull is soon exposed as the skin is turned back over the anterior portion of the body. With fingernails or butt of forceps carefully peel the skin away from the back of the skull. Expose the tube of each ear and sever it *close to the skull* (Fig. 18). With further peeling, the thin black lines of the eye lids can be seen through the skin. Pinch up the skin at an eyelid to create tension and cut, with scissors or scalpel, between the eyelid and the skull (Fig. 19). Continue to cut until the eyelid is completely free all around its circumference. Repeat on the other eye. Below the eye pinch up the gape of the mouth on one side and cut through into the mouth. Do the same on the other side. Cut along the edges of the upper and lower lip to

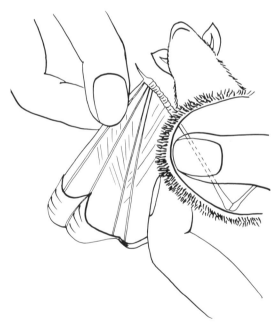

Figure 17. Pulling the skin back over the forearm.

Peel the body loose from the skin of the flanks and back, and pull it out through the incision to the level of the armpits. Use saw-

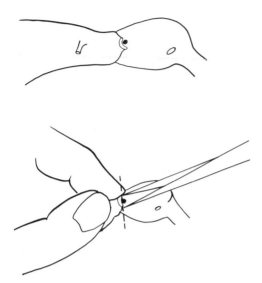

Figure 19. Cutting the eyelid free from the skull.

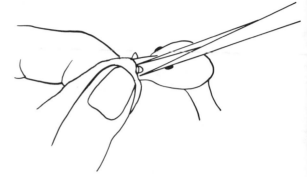

Figure 21. Freeing muzzle glands from the skin.

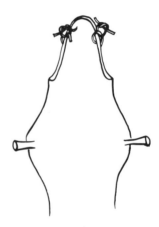

Figure 22. Lips tied shut with thread.

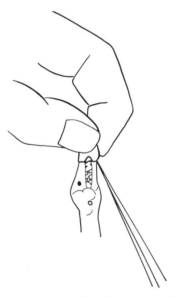

Figure 20. Cutting the lips free from the mandibles.

free them, taking care, especially with smaller bats, not to damage teeth or bones (Fig. 20). Scissors or scalpel will cut such delicate bone easily. If there are muzzle glands, carefully clip them free from the skin (Fig. 21). Any glandular material left on the skin will later shed its oily exudate. Finally, carefully clip

through the nasal cartilage to complete the skinning procedure.

Close the mouth on the inverted skin with a stitch in each side, close to the edges of the lips, about two-thirds of the way out from the gape. Knot each stitch *loosely,* so as not to distort the lips excessively (Fig. 22). Sew up any holes created accidentally during skinning. Examine the original incision in the belly. If there are rips in its margin, sew the edges together.

Remove *every* vestige of fat from the skin. Especially remove fat from around the genitalia, mammary glands, snout, and edges of the belly incision. Any fat that is overlooked will soon manifest itself in the dry skin as grease on the fur.

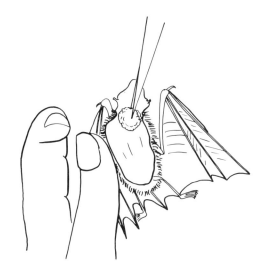

Figure 23. Dusting inside of the skin with arsenic.

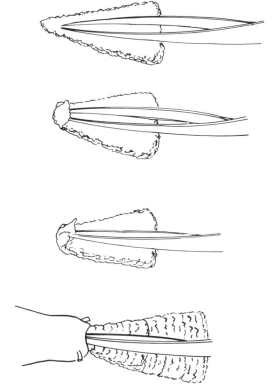

Figure 24. Grasping a cotton body with forceps and everting the skin over it.

If the skin is to be treated with arsenic, dust the inner surface thoroughly (Fig. 23). This is a desirable field procedure, for it renders the skin permanently immune to insect attack. There is an element of risk of poisoning for the preparator. However, since arsenic is a cumulative poison the infrequent preparator has little reason to fear it and is unlikely to suffer ill effects from it. The risk is negligible, particularly if the preparator has no open cuts on fingers, grasps the cotton dusting swab with forceps, and washes hands after preparing specimens. Arsenic in open cuts can cause painful and long-lasting sores.

Examine the fur. If there is crusted blood, remove it by rubbing with sawdust between the fingers. Remove other soils by swabbing with cotton dampened with cold water and drying with sawdust. Never use a brush of any kind on the fur of a specimen. Invert the skin again (fur side in). If it has dried even slightly, restore moisture by patting the inside (bare side) of the skin with droplets of water on a fingertip. Then roll the moistened skin gently between thumb and forefinger.

Lay the inverted skin on a flat surface, belly up. Turn back the tip of the cotton body cone, grasp the now blunt tip firmly with the forceps, press against the nose of the skin, and

roll the skin over the cotton body, restoring it to the right-side-out position (Fig. 24). Still holding the cotton snout firmly with the forceps, tug *gently* on the skin of the neck to orient the head symmetrically on the cotton and to remove any folds or creases in the skin. Tug again at shoulder level, and then at the flanks. Release the forceps, then grasp and lay the specimen on a hard surface. Carefully tear off surplus cotton from the large end of the body cone and tuck the posterior of the body into the skin, again taking care to orient the back and rump symmetrically over the cotton cone.

Next, with needle and thread, attach thread to the front edge of the belly incision with an overhand knot, and work back along the incision with a loose criss-cross stitch to close the opening. At the final stitch, in the genital area, make an overhand knot in the

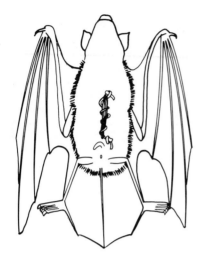

Figure 25. Stitching up the ventral incision.

thread, place the needle point through it, press down carefully against the skin, and tighten the knot as the needle is withdrawn (Fig. 25). Clip the thread close to the knot. Blow off (never brush) any lingering sawdust or debris from the fur and make final adjustments to symmetry.

Note reproductive condition on the specimen label. Thread one label string on a needle and sew through the wing membrane, under the middle of the right tibia, out through the interfemoral membrane, and tie securely around the tibia with three square knots (Fig. 9). Clip off the string ends, half an inch from the knots. The specimen is ready to pin.

Some important points to remember:

1) The specimen label is always tied to the *right* tibia to reduce tangling when several specimens are placed side by side (Fig. 1). The label is sewn through the membranes so it can be tied at mid-tibia (Fig. 9), to avoid distortion of characters at the ankle which could occur if the label were tied there.

2) There are *no* wires in the specimen—no wire in the tail, no wire in the legs, and no wire in the wings. Not only are wires unnecessary in bats, their use actually lessens the value of the specimen by obscuring the character of the tail and making it difficult or impossible to take accurate measurements of the forearm and tibia.

3) The distal part of the humerus is left attached to the forearm (Fig. 11). Later when the forearm is measured on the dry specimen, it is reassuring to be able to feel the stump of the humerus, guaranteeing that the forearm is complete. For the same reason, the distal portion of the femur is left attached to the tibia.

4) The cotton body should be firm, but not hard or lumpy, and should be designed to fit the skin. The resulting specimen is neither under-stuffed nor over-stuffed. Actually, to say "stuffed" in this context is misleading. The cotton is not stuffed into the skin. The skin is carefully rolled back over the cotton and the cotton is gently tucked into the rear of the skin as the belly skin is pulled up over it. A properly prepared skin should not look "stuffed."

Pinning completes the job of skin preparation. Lay the specimen belly down on the pinning board. Take time to pin properly and use forceps for positioning and grooming the specimen. Arrange the wings and the legs in desired positions. Be sure that the fingers are orderly and curled inward, and that each of the feet extends back the same distance (Fig. 26). Thumbs should be pinned back if necessary. The objective of pinning should be a neat, symmetrical, and reasonably compact specimen.

The first pin, at the base of the tail or interfemoral membrane, anchors the specimen. If the bat has a tail, the second pin is placed *near* the end of the tail (but not actually in the tail tip, which could cause distortion). The next pins are placed in the angle between calcar and tibia, anchoring the feet and spreading the interfemoral membrane. Chances are the membrane cannot be extended to its fullest without placing legs and feet in a rakish attitude. There must be a compromise between leg position and membrane expansion by pinning so that the tibiae diverge only a little from a position parallel to one another. Furthermore, each foot should have its sole flat on the pinning surface to facilitate later measuring when it is dry. The

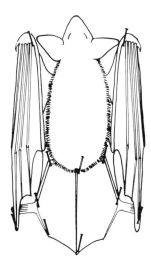

Figure 26. Pins holding the wings and legs in place for drying.

calcar should extend from the tibia at an angle of about 90° and, if necessary, should have a pin *near* its distal end (but not *at* the end, which would make it difficult later to locate the exact tip of the calcar). Pin through the interfemoral membrane in the bend of each knee if necessary.

The next pin should be placed between the forearm and the fingers near the wrist to anchor the wings. The wrist should be positioned close to the head or neck, depending upon the length of the forearm, but should not extend beyond the snout in any case. The forearms may parallel one another or diverge slightly posteriorly. The fingers may be bunched close to the forearm or they may be spaced a little apart from one another. The wingtip should be pinned near the feet. In long-winged bats it is necessary to fold back the terminal phalanges against the metacarpals. Thumbs should be folded back against the metacarpals, restrained by pins if necessary (this will greatly reduce snagging and tangling when several specimens are stored together). In species with a noseleaf, a final pin may be placed in front of the snout (never through the snout) to hold the noseleaf erect.

Make a last inspection for symmetry by sighting down the specimen head-on. If the head, body, and tail are not in line, or if the feet and wings are unevenly placed, make necessary adjustments with the pins.

The skin preparations should be dried in an air conditioned room, dry cabinet, near a heat source such as lamp or stove, or in a well-ventilated place. Drying too rapidly (cabinet too warm, or specimen too close to heat source) has the undesirable consequences of shrinking ears and membranes and warping the body. A specimen can also dry too slowly, allowing fungus growths, particularly on the belly. The order of drying usually is skin, ears, wings, and feet. When the feet are dry and can no longer be moved with finger pressure, the specimen can be unpinned.

To complete the preparation of skin and skull, the skull must be processed (Fig. 27). Clip along the inner edge of the mandibles to the chin. Lift the tongue up and back, and carefully peel out the trachea and esophagus with it, back to the thorax. Take care not to damage the palate, pterygoid processes, and

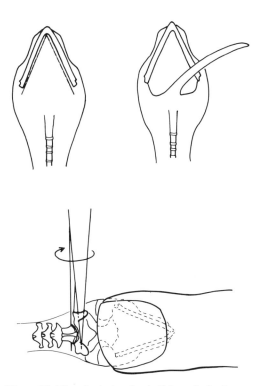

Figure 27. Disarticulating the skull from the body.

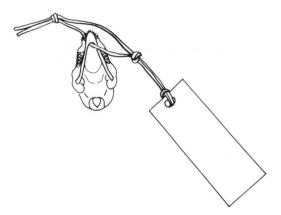

Figure 28. Labeled skull.

auditory bullae. Place the scissor blades across the neck, as though to sever the head. However, do not cut. Rather, catch the upper blade on the anterior dorsal edge of the atlas and, with the thumbnail of the other hand resting firmly on the basioccipital, dislocate the neck by pressing back the atlas with the scissors. Cut the neck muscles and spinal cord. Snip through the temporal muscles if they are large (to facilitate drying), but do not attempt to remove flesh from the skull (once dried it protects the skull from damage until it can be properly cleaned). Tie the skull label loosely (secured with an overhand knot formed with the string ends held together as one) through the mandibles (Fig. 28) and dunk the skull in water for a few minutes to soften the brain. Fill the syringe with water; insert the large needle through the foramen magnum; carefully stir up the brain, and inject water forcefully into the cranium to flush out the brain (Fig. 29). Removal of the brain facilitates drying, markedly reduces odor, and reduces staining of sutures in cleaned skulls. After the brain is out, wash off sawdust still adhering to the skull (dermestid beetles, used later to clean the skull, disdain sawdust-coated skulls); shake it free of water, and hang it to dry in an airy, shady place where it will be safe from scavengers. It will have little odor and, although flies may lay

eggs on it, the maggots should soon die from dryness. If flies are a problem, the skull can be made unpalatable to them (without affecting its future attractiveness to dermestid beetles) by soaking it overnight in alcohol before hanging it to dry. Quick drying is important. Rotting must be prevented. The teeth inevitably fall out of the jaws of a rotted skull when it is cleaned, and the sutures on skulls of young animals open and the bones fall apart.

5.2.2. Skin, Skull, and Skeleton

With only a little more effort than goes into preparing a conventional skin and skull, a specimen can be made more useful by extracting the bones from the leg and wing on one side of the body along with the trunk skeleton. The result is a study skin and skull *and* a complete half skeleton. The skin with its free wing folded under it, can be stored and used like a conventional study skin. It has the additional potential for study of wing size, shape, and texture.

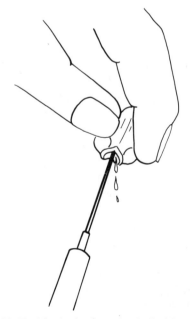

Figure 29. Flushing brains from the skull with a syringe.

To successfully extract the leg and wing bones without damage to the skeleton or membranes it is imperative that the membranes be not at all desiccated. If the specimens have been properly handled before preparation, satisfactory results can be obtained from bats that have been frozen as well as from those that are fresh.

Most of the procedure is exactly the same as for preparation of the conventional skin and skull. Differences are as follows: Break the humerus and the femur *on the right side only.* On the left side pull out the leg, calcar, foot, and toes, much as the tail would be pulled on a rodent. With the nails of the thumb and forefinger of one hand grasping the bones close to the skin, successively grasp and pull the femur, tibia, and foot with the thumb and forefinger of the other hand, taking special care not to bend and break any of the bones in the process. At the end, pull the toes (with claws) loose from the skin. The whole limb is now inverted. Immediately turn it right side out, again by gently tugging simultaneously on the interfemoral membrane and wing on either side of the leg. This will leave the toes still inverted, but they usually can be turned by pricking them with a needle from the outside.

The procedure for pulling the bones from the wing is similar. After the skin has been inverted beyond the wrist, however, the digits are so long that they must be treated individually. Eventually, when all bones have been pulled, the entire wing is inverted. Immediately restore it to normal relationships by pulling on the wingtip from the outside. Turning the wing right side out is an easy matter—easier than turning the foot.

The next procedural differences appear in pinning (Fig. 30). Begin as usual by pinning the hind extremities and right wing. Now place a pin in the left wing at the elbow and set it close to the body (so that the body lies lax). Stretch out the forearm skin to its full extent and pin the wrist so it is even with the right wrist. Now place pins at finger two, at the wing tip, and at the ends of fingers four and

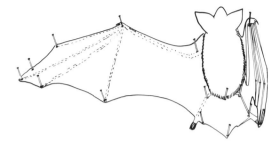

Figure 30. Skin, with skeleton of left appendages removed, pinned for drying.

five, stretching the wing to its fullest extent at each pin.

Disarticulate and label the skull as usual. Now rough out the skeleton. Eviscerate the body carcass; slice through the diaphragm and remove heart and lungs; remove tongue, larynx, and esophagus, and more or less cut off the pectoral muscles (a neat dissection is not necessary—just get most of the muscles off). Fold the legs forward; fold the phalanges back against the metacarpals, and the metacarpals against the forearm; and wrap a thread several times around the skeleton to form a compact bundle (Fig. 31). Tie a label loosely around the lumbar vertebrae ("small of the back"). Hang the skeleton to dry in the manner suggested for skulls. Several skulls

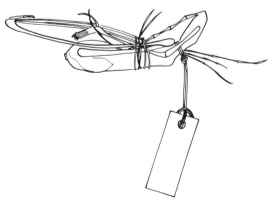

Figure 31. Labeled skeletal bundle.

and skeletons can be strung together on a wire loop and hung on a line to dry.

5.2.3. Skull Only

The simplest form of preservation is the "skull only" specimen. This often is prepared with minimum data—date, locality, and sex—but if time permits it is worthwhile to make the standard measurements and to record reproductive condition.

After the label has been prepared, expedite skull removal by making an incision in the skin of the nape and crown. Grasp the edges of the incision together with the ears, and peel down and forward. Snip the skin away from the skull at the chin and nose (being careful not to mar the bone), and proceed as outlined for skull processing in the "skin and skull" preparation section of this chapter.

5.2.4. Skeleton Only

To process a bat as a "skeleton only" (actually "skull and skeleton"), prepare two skull-type labels as usual, then make an incision in the skin from the middle of the back to the crown. Peel out the head, and pull the skin back down the neck to the thorax. Next peel the skin of the shoulder down over the elbow and pull out the bones of the wing; repeat for the other wing. Finally, peel the skin back over the rump and belly and pull out the legs and feet. Disarticulate the skull from the skeleton; complete preparation of the skeleton as outlined above, and attach the labels.

6. PROTECTING SPECIMENS FROM INSECTS AND FUNGUS

The intrinsic value of the specimens and the time invested in preservation are reasons enough for protecting them until they reach the safety of the museum or laboratory where they will be permanently stored. Dry skins and skulls and other bone material unfortunately are attractive to insects—particularly

flies, beetles, moths, bees, and ants—and fungi such as mildew and mold.

Dusting the inner surface of the skin with arsenic during specimen preparation is a simple expedient that mostly alleviates the insect problem. Use of no-pest strips in storage containers also repels and kills insects. Thorough drying and extremely dry storage partly alleviate the fungus problem. Liberal use of naphthalene flakes or crystals of paradichlorobenzene (PDB) in storage containers provides further protection against both insects and fungus. Naphthalene flakes are best. Naphthalene in the form of powder or "moth balls" is less effective. PDB stops insects and fungus perhaps better than naphthalene, but it has the disadvantages of drawing out grease from skin, and under warm conditions it will liquify and damage specimens, melt plastic, and cause fur to redden ("fox"). Furthermore, naphthalene and PDB are harmful for human beings to breathe. No-pest strips are supposed to be safer.

If insects are allowed to attack skulls and skeletal material in the field, there is danger of dislodged labels, damaged bones, disassociated parts, and mixup and confusion of bones among several specimens. Ants, bees, and fly larvae do not stop with devouring flesh; they damage cartilage and bone as well. Flies cause both skins and skeletal material to rot. Mold will attack the snout, ears, and feet of skins, and of course skulls and bones. Unfortunately, moldy skulls and bones must be cleaned by hand, because they are routinely shunned by the beetles used to clean them. Thoroughly dried skins should be stored in a cool, dry place with no-pest strips, naphthalene flakes, or PDB. Thoroughly dried skulls and bones should be stored without fumigant in plastic bags, tight boxes, or cans.

Specimens preserved in fluid are not immune to attack. If the fixative solution is too weak, specimens are liable to be attacked by fungus. This can be averted by the simple expedient of using a solution of adequate strength in the first place. After mold appears, transfer specimens to preservative and add a few crystals of thymol to the solution.

7. PACKING AND SHIPPING

Preserved specimens eventually must be transported to a museum or to a laboratory for permanent storage. Ideally, they should accompany the collector on the trip home. If this is not possible, they should be afforded the safest and most expeditious mode of transport. For international shipments this ordinarily will be by air.

Museum specimens should be packed to survive a worst case scenario—temperature and humidity extremes, insect attack, rough handling, theft, and long delay in transit. Strong containers, plastic bags, and generous quantities of resilient packing material are essential.

Shipping containers should match the specimens and the mode of transport. For ocean, rail, or truck freight, trunks and wooden boxes are safest. Boxes fastened together with long screws are remarkably resistant to theft. Strong, crush-proof corrugated cardboard containers are adequate for air shipments. Almost any lightweight cardboard box of appropriate dimensions will suffice for inclusion of a few specimens in personal luggage. Smaller boxes (2 to 3 cubic feet) often will receive more careful handling than large, awkward, heavy boxes, and are less likely to sustain damage when dropped. Thus, several small boxes may be a better choice than a single big one. If the number of specimens justifies it, a polypropylene lined fiber "Liquipak" drum is an excellent choice for wet specimens.

Specimen stuffing cotton, wadded newspaper, and plastic "waffles," "buttons," and "peanuts," if used in sufficient quantity, provide good cushioning within containers. These materials should be compressed enough to prevent shifting of specimens within the container.

Various kinds of specimens—fluid specimens, dry skins, and skulls and skeletons—should be packed in separate containers or in several containers within a larger one. The wet specimens must be completely fixed and the dry specimens absolutely dry before packing. Never pack wet and dry specimens together in the same container. Include no-pest strips or sprinkle a liberal quantity of naphthalene flakes into the container with dry skins (PDB is less desirable because high temperature will cause it to liquify and damage the specimens). Pack bone material without fumigant lest it later be distasteful to beetles in the cleaning process. Freezing for up to 48 h and redrying just before packing can eliminate the risk of including live insects in the bone container.

Line the container for dry specimens with a plastic bag—a garbage bag of appropriate size is fine. Lay down a layer of cushion material—cotton or plastic—on the bottom and sides. Stuffed skins, each with its label carefully tucked beneath it and wrapped in tissue or non-printed paper, can be laid in rows with a buffer of cotton separating the specimens wherever they overlap. Alternatively, the specimens should be separated by sheets of cotton or plastic waffle. Specimens wrapped in cotton come out with it stuck all over them. If the specimens do not completely fill the container, fill the empty space with cushion material. Seal the plastic liner. Place forwarding address and copies of any required shipping documents, such as permits, in a clear plastic bag and tape it to the liner. Close the container, and secure it with fiber or metal strapping tape, or if they are unavailable, use stout string. Fasten another set of shipping documents to the outside of the container. Follow the same packing procedure for skulls and skeletal material, but place the specimens in small groups in plastic bags within the larger liner. Force out excess air and seal each bag with a knot or a rubber band.

Remove fluid specimens from the fixative solution and wrap them in small groups in several layers of cheesecloth. Fixative from the specimens should saturate the cheesecloth. If it does not, submerge the packet in the fixative and then drain away the surplus solution. The cheesecloth keeps the specimens moist and immobilizes claws and teeth that might puncture plastic bags. Place each packet in a watertight plastic bag of appropriate size; force excess air from the bag, and seal it with a knot or a rubber band. Put that bag into a second bag, evacuate air, and seal it. Then put the second bag into a third and remove air and seal it. Altogether these precautions reduce the possibility of loss of fluid during transit. Many small bags in a shipping container are preferable to a few large bags. Use plastic packing material or wadded newspaper to cushion the bags of specimens and prevent their shifting around in the shipping container. Enclose shipping documents in the container and affix another set to the outside.

Obviously the procedures recommended here are most appropriate for long haul and international shipments. They may be modified and simplified for short hauls. In every case, however, dry specimens should be cushioned so that they cannot shift about in the container, and fixative or preservative fluid should always be drained from specimens preserved in fluid. Sloshing about in a solution during transit can ruin otherwise perfect specimens.

8.   SUMMARY

As more mammals become rare or endangered, it is important to salvage specimens for permanent collections. It is also advisable to preserve specimens as vouchers because it is so easy to confuse some species in the field. Many taxa can only be distinguished by studying a clean skull. In some parts of the world the chiropteran fauna is poorly known and poorly represented in museum collections. Consequently, many museums often will provide identifications and trade supplies and/or freight costs for well prepared and well documented specimens.

Preservation of bats is neither difficult nor time consuming, and techniques can be learned easily. Few supplies and little equipment are needed. The appearance and often the value of a specimen are directly correlated with its freshness at the time of preservation. Thus, it is advisable to prepare specimens

without delay. The value of a specimen is enhanced by the data that accompany it. Minimum data are locality, date, collector, sex, reproductive condition, external measurements, and a field number. Most specimens can be preserved in fluid, but some should be prepared as skins and skulls. With little extra effort the value of a skin and skull preparation can be greatly increased by extracting the skeleton from the wing and leg on one side.

Chiropteran preparation techniques are, in some ways, unique. Most mammal skins require wires for legs and tail, but bats are more valuable with the tail vertebrae and limb bones left intact. Pinning out the study skin of a bat is very different from pinning a mouse because the finger bones and wing membranes must be positioned properly. Specimens of bats preserved in fluid are more valuable, from a systematics standpoint, than those of most other mammals. Many of the diagnostic characters of bats are external. They are characters which become distorted when a study skin dries.

Planning is needed before the field work begins to make sure all supply needs are anticipated and that they arrive safely and in a timely manner. Thought must also be given to safe storage of specimens in the field and to a safe and expedient transport home.

9.   ACKNOWLEDGMENTS

The artwork, with the exception of Figure 1, is from the hand of Rosemary Calvert. Figure 1 in part was redrawn by Irene Jewett from Smithsonian Information Leaflet number 380. Comments of an anonymous reviewer, T. H. Kunz, D. Klingener, and R. L. Peterson, improved the manuscript. I am grateful to Jane Ailes Small for word processing, criticizing, and editing the manuscript.

10.   REFERENCES

Barbour, R. W., and W. H. Davis. 1969. Bats of America. University Press of Kentucky, Lexington, 286 pp.

DeBlase, A. F., and R. E. Martin. 1983. A manual of mammalogy, with keys to families of the world. Wm. C. Brown Co., Dubuque, Iowa, 436 pp.

Dowler, R. C., and H. H. Genoways. 1976. Supplies and suppliers for vertebrate collections. Museology, Texas Tech Univ., 4:1-83.

Hall, E. R. 1962. Collecting and preparing study specimens of vertebrates. Univ. Kans. Mus. Nat. Hist., Misc. Publ. 30:1-46.

Nagorsen, D. W., and R. L. Peterson. 1980. Mammal collectors' manual. Life Sciences Misc. Publ., Royal Ontario Museum, 79 pp.

Peterson, R. L. 1965. Collecting bat specimens for scientific purposes. Dept. Mammalogy Leaflet, Royal Ontario Mus., Toronto, 8 pp.

Setzer, H. W. 1968. Directions for preserving mammals for museum study. U.S. Natl. Mus., Nat. Hist. Information Leaflet, 380:1-19.

Chapter 27

Collecting and Preserving Ectoparasites for Ecological Study

John O. Whitaker, Jr.

Department of Life Sciences
Indiana State University
Terre Haute, Indiana 47809 USA

1. INTRODUCTION

Historically, two groups of biologists have contributed information on ectoparasites of bats. Mammalogists, if they collected ecto-parasites at all, have often done so by picking specimens directly from the pelage or by combing or brushing the pelage of the host. These methods usually oversample large parasites and overlook or undersample small ones, especially those which attach firmly to hairs or skin of the host. Parasitologists have generally worked exclusively with parasites as taxonomic units of special interest. They may have developed methods of collecting information and specimens of parasites in their special groups, but they have seldom published information on parasite ecology. The ecology of parasitism is best approached through concurrent studies of parasites and their hosts (Wenzel et al., 1966; Kunz, 1976). The purpose of this chapter is to summarize current methods and approaches used to study the ecology of bat ectoparasites. For a review of methods used to study ectoparasitic insects (including those on bats) see Marshall (1981, 1982).

2. PARASITES AND PARASITISM

A parasite is here defined as an organism that feeds at the expense of, but normally does not kill, its host. Most of the major kinds of organisms found in the pelage of bats fit this description, although there may be some question about the extent of injury caused by some species.

Fleas, flies, hemipterans, chiggers, and ticks that live on bats all appear to be true parasites—they are smaller than their hosts, attack relatively few host individuals, and do not kill their hosts. The same is true for the spinturnicids, nycteribiids, myobiids, macronyssids, and chirodiscids. All apparently suck blood or other body fluids (the chirodiscids apparently feed from hair follicles). Cheyletids and nycteriglyphids are sometimes found on bats, but apparently they are not parasitic. The cheyletids (uncommon on bats) may feed on other arthropods in the pelage, whereas the nycteriglyphids are essentially phoretic (i.e., they use bats as a means of transportation only). On other host groups (e.g., burrowing rodents and insectivores) there is often a greater diversity of forms—phoretics and perhaps even predators as well as parasites. Stragglers or "accidentals" are relatively common on bats as well as on other groups. It is generally unknown how these get onto a host, and one must consider the possibility that they are contaminants.

3.   BIOLOGY OF ECTOPARASITES

3.1.   Behavior and Life History

It is difficult to determine the biology of a parasite without some knowledge of the biology of its host. Considerable information can be gained about the ecology of ectoparasites by making observations at the time of host collection. Observations can be made as to the location of a parasite on its hosts, such as whether it is clinging to hairs, moving about on the wings, in the hair, or in the ears (e.g., Kunz, 1976; Marshall, 1980), whether the mouthparts are embedded in epidermal tissue or in hair follicles, and whether blood is present in the digestive tract of the parasite, as is commonly seen in spinturnicids (Rudnick, 1960).

Some parasites lay eggs, whereas others produce live young (Marshall, 1981, 1982). Eggs are often fastened to the hairs by secreted adhesive, as in myobiid mites. The eggs of batbugs are cemented to the substrate of bat roosting areas (Usinger, 1966). In those which produce live young (spinturnicid and chirodiscid mites; strebld, nycteribiid, and polyctenid flies), one can usually see the developing offspring in the abdomen of the female (see Rudnick, 1960). Information on number of offspring per female and the percentage of parous females can be noted. Frequently several life stages of an ectoparasite occur together on a bat, and sometimes one can preserve a parasite which retains the partly shed skin of the previous life stage. Observations of copulating pairs can help establish breeding periods.

Live parasites can be isolated in the laboratory and observed, taking note of different behaviors and transformation of nymphal stages (for examples for batbugs, see Usinger, 1966; and for macronyssid mites, see Radovsky, 1967). This approach should be valuable, but it may be difficult to provide appropriate environmental conditions for the parasites (see Usinger, 1966; Radovsky, 1967). Transfers of ectoparasites to alternate hosts, which are easier than bats to keep in captivity, have not been successful (Rudnick, 1960).

Parasites can also be observed with the aid of a dissecting microscope, either before or after death on captive individuals. Cooling the bats before observation may aid in this procedure. It is sometimes possible to make observations on portions of skin isolated from the host, although conditions may become unsuitable for parasites relatively soon after death of the host. With the increased success of keeping bats in captivity (Chapter 16), life history studies on bat ectoparasites seem more promising.

3.2.   Host Specificity

Host specificity is the tendency of parasites to occur on one or few host species versus a broader range of hosts. There are, of course, advantages to the parasite in being host specific but at times non-host specificity may be adaptive. Non-host specificity allows parasites the advantage of being able to expand their population beyond the taxonomic confines and geographic ranges of one or few hosts. Another advantage is that they can more easily find a host. The disadvantage is that they must remain rather generalized (i.e., they cannot become closely tied to the life history of a host). Host specific parasites, on the other hand, can evolve specifically to exploit the phenology and life history of its host. As long as the host maintains its abundance, the parasite will thrive since it has evolved in parallel with the host. Another advantage is that increased host specificity should tend to decrease competition (Wenzel and Tipton, 1966). Disadvantages of host specificity are that the parasite cannot expand its population beyond the confines of its host and also that if the host declines or becomes extinct, so will the parasite.

Besides ecological factors influencing host specificity, parasites can develop physiological associations with hosts such that they simply cannot exist on the chemical content of blood or other body fluids except on a normal host. This is undoubtedly much more common in internal than external parasites, but can surely be a factor in blood feeding ectoparasites.

Host specificity is well developed in bat parasites; many species are found only on a single host. Of 32 species of mites (excluding accidentals) known from North American bats through 1973, 20 of them or 62.5% were found on only one species of bat (Whitaker and Wilson, 1974). By contrast, two parasitic mites, *Spinturnix americanus* and *Macronyssus crosbyi,* were each known from 13 bat hosts. Similar results for spinturnicids, bat chiggers, and streblid flies from Panama are given in Wenzel and Tipton (1966). For 122 species, 52 (42.6%) were found on 1 host, 26 on 2, 16 on 3, 9 on 4, 5 on 5, 5 on 6, and only 9 (7.4%) were reported from more than 6 host species.

3.3. Effects on the Host

Generally, there has been an evolution in parasites towards a reduction of injury or harm to their hosts. Also, most host individuals harbor relatively small numbers of parasites. These two factors together tend to limit the detrimental effects of parasitism on the host. However, some parasites do pierce the skin, such as ticks, chiggers, and macronyssid mites. These forms leave temporary lesions, but most other forms cause less injury.

When collecting ectoparasites of bats, simultaneous detailed information on the bats also should be collected, such as sex and age information, reproductive status, habitat, and degree of association of the bats.

4. COLLECTING AND PRESERVING ECTOPARASITES

The method I have used for 25 years with good results is to examine the entire host using a 10-70 power zoom dissecting microscope. The hairs, base to tip, the skin, the ears, the ventral surface at the base of the wing, and the tail should all be carefully examined. Parasites may be found anywhere on the animal, but the nape, wings, head, and rump are often particularly productive. With small animals such as bats, this procedure may take only 15 minutes or so if few parasites are found, to an hour or more if numerous parasites are found. I count the parasites of each kind found, or when there are too many to count, I visually estimate numbers by scanning the various parts of the body, and record counts or estimates of each general kind of ectoparasite on each part of the body.

Samples of small mites can be mounted directly in Hoyer's solution (see Appendix 2), but most ectoparasites should be preserved in 75% ethanol with 5% glycerine added for later mounting in Hoyer's. Larger parasites should be cleared and stained in Nesbitt's solution (see Appendix 2) containing acid fuchsin stain for about 2-5 days before mounting in Hoyer's solution. Hoyer's solution is for delicate organisms; it does not completely dry but must be sealed around the edge with Euparal or fingernail polish.

A commonly used method for collecting ectoparasites is by washing as described by Henry and McKeever (1971). Items needed are a Buchner funnel, rubber stopper, filter paper, filtering flask, aspirator (or small vacuum pump), non-collapsible hose, Alconox (or other detergent), and a container with a lid. Insert a Buchner funnel and rubber stopper into a filtering flask (Fig. 1). Attach the aspirator to a faucet or a vacuum pump. Connect the flask and aspirator (or vacuum pump) with a tight-fitting non-collapsible hose, and place a piece of filter paper in the funnel. Place the animal in the container and fill 3/4 full with water (the container should be of appropriate size, i.e., one pint for most bats, a liter or more for very large bats). Add a small amount of detergent to the container. A pinch per ½ liter (about 0.1 g) is usually sufficient. Too much will clog the filter paper with suds. Attach the lid and shake vigorously for 30 sec to one min. Turn the faucet on full and pour some of the liquid into the funnel. The vacuum draws the water through, leaving parasites on the paper. Examine the filter paper under a dissecting microscope and collect the parasites with a dissecting needle, repeating the procedure until parasites no longer appear on the paper. Too much detergent may be remedied by diluting with more water. The washing technique gives good results for most species other than those which are firmly attached to the skin or hair of the host.

Hutson (1971) suggests putting the host into a polythene bag with a small piece of cotton wool containing chloroform. The cotton should be held by the knot in the bag or otherwise prevented from wetting the fur of the host. Host and bag are then examined and the host may be brushed or stroked. I have not used this method but suspect that smaller parasites that cling to hairs or skin would be greatly undersampled.

Some researchers have used a method of collecting ectoparasites where the skin or animal is dissolved away, leaving only the parasites. The entire skin or even the entire animal is placed into a potassium hydroxide solution (see Hilton, 1970). This method is particu-

larly good for getting accurate counts of parasites but it is very hard on the specimens, thus I do not use it.

5. RECORDING AND ANALYZING DATA

There is no specific sample size for research on ectoparasites of bats. Within reason I generally examine all bats obtained of each species. A good sample size to strive for is perhaps a hundred host individuals, when one is dealing with common species and numerous populations. This should provide reasonable data even on the less common parasites of a host. However, with less common species of bats much smaller samples must suffice, so as to avoid harming populations. With more common ectoparasites 20 or 30 host individuals often provide fairly good data on distribution and abundance. (Another point that may be made here is that if it is necessary to sacrifice bats, as much information should be collected on each individual as possible, for example, on endoparasites, food, and reproduction. Such information should be passed on to those who can use it.) Several types of data for each species of ectoparasite may be presented. Some of these are:

Incidence. This is the percentage of bats infested and is calculated:

$$\frac{\text{number of bats with parasites} \times 100}{\text{number of bats examined}}$$

Mean number of parasites per bat. This is calculated for each parasite species by:

$$\frac{\text{total number of parasites}}{\text{number of bats examined}}$$

It estimates the mean number of parasites for the entire host population. This value is directly comparable to averages for other species and thus is appropriate for parasite community estimates.

Mean number of parasites per infested host. Many individual hosts may not yield parasites of a particular species. Using the overall average as above causes numerous zeros to be included in the average. The average number of parasites per infested host estimates the population size a parasite is maintaining on the host. It is calculated for each parasite species as:

number of parasites per infested host
number of infested hosts examined

This value is especially useful to the biologist interested in the relationship of host and parasite. It is *not* comparable to values for other species since different numbers of infested hosts are involved. Hence this value cannot serve as an estimate for community assessment.

Tests for randomness using chi-square goodness of fit tests can often be used to compare distribution of ectoparasites on different species, sexes, or age groupings of hosts (e.g., Kunz, 1976).

Marshall (1981) gives additional information on field and laboratory methods (pp. 41-60) and population dynamics (pp. 278-347).

Bats may be collected in any of the normal ways (see Chapter 1), by hand from caves, buildings or other roosts, by shooting, or with traps or nets. Additional sources include donations from citizens and rabies examination laboratories. The major considerations are that bats be fresh, and it is most convenient if they are clean and dry. If not examined immediately, bats should be placed in individual plastic bags so parasites do not escape. Parasite examination is much easier when bats are examined when freshly killed, but they can be stored indefinitely in a freezer before examination. If freshly frozen, the major problems from freezing are that parasites are harder to find than when they are alive, and that some of the more mobile ones may have moved or dropped off into the bag. Even if bats have been dead for some hours before collection, they should still be examined. Fleas, flies and some of the larger mites, however, may leave the host relatively soon after death, or they may move about on the host. Many of the smaller forms, and those

that cling to individual hairs or use their mouthparts to penetrate the skin are unlikely to move about much and may remain longer on the host. Even those parasites which tend to leave a dead host may move to the tips of the fur until another warm body comes along. Thus, if one places a bat into a plastic bag immediately upon receipt it is possible to collect some of the parasites which otherwise might have left. Be sure to thoroughly examine the bag as well as the bat.

It is easiest and most accurate to make ectoparasite examinations on dead animals. However, there may be times (because a species is rare, or because of other studies) that one wishes to examine live bats for ectoparasites. Under certain conditions, especially with larger ectoparasites and where only one species is present, observations may be made directly on live bats in the field. For example, Kunz (1976) collected information on bats and their batflies during cave visitations. This is of course not possible where more than one species occur that may be confused. It is also possible to get some information by examining the live bat with a dissecting microscope. Cooling or etherizing the bat may help, but otherwise the bat should be examined the same as a dead bat.

6. IDENTIFICATION OF BAT ECTOPARASITES

The literature concerning the identification of bat ectoparasites is scattered since most parasitologists work on specific taxa. Therefore I have here attempted to list some of the major papers on the various groups of parasites (see Appendix 1). A worker can use these listings to gain access to the literature and to specialists in various groups. The non-parasitologist cannot expect to make definitive identifications of parasites. However, one can make valuable contributions by collecting parasites and sending them, along with biological information on bats and parasites, to a specialist. However, few specialists wish to receive large numbers of vials of mixed parasites. I suggest that bat ecologists collect and mount parasites, and tentatively identify them using available keys, and send a small sample to an appropriate specialist after receiving his approval. The specialist may confirm or reidentify the specimens, he may wish more slides, or he may wish unmounted material. A list of most of the groups of bat ectoparasites, information on life history (when available), and major taxonomic references are given in Appendix 1.

7. SUGGESTIONS FOR FUTURE STUDY

7.1. Host Taxonomy

Parasite-host relationships could be evaluated as taxonomic characters for bats as are morphological or behavioral characters. (One must be careful using this logic, however, since parasites sometimes successfully invade new hosts rather than remain with their primary hosts.)

In the family Spinturnicidae, for example, mites of the same genera are almost entirely restricted to families of bats, *Ancystrous* and *Meristapis* on Pteropidae, *Eyndhovenia* and *Paraperiglischrus* on Rhinolophidae, Vespertilionidae, and Natalidae (Rudnick, 1960). Wenzel et al. (1966) have shown how streblid fly relationships can be used to make inferences about host taxonomy.

7.2. Parasite Life History

For many of the known species of ectoparasites, there is little known on the various life stages, other than those on which taxonomy is based (often the adult female). Future research might concentrate more on collecting males and other life stages for those forms where only one stage has been described. A particularly interesting case of this type is with the large anal spinturnicid, *Spinturnix*

globosus, for which only females are presently known.

Additional information is needed on the presence and abundance of all life stages of parasites as they relate to season, age, sex, reproductive condition of the host, and habitat.

Many taxa are obviously parasitic, but for some, such as the cheyletid mites, this relationship is unclear. Cheyletids are thought by some to be predators living in the pelage of their host, because most species are free-living and feed on various tiny arthropods (Summers and Price, 1970). Interrelations between "parasites" and their hosts invite further study.

Ectoparasites form a community on the host, but interactions within ectoparasite communities have received little attention. The mechanism by which populations are regulated in ectoparasite communities should be of special interest. Does competition occur among parasites and is there evidence for resource partitioning? What long-term and seasonal changes occur in ectoparasite populations, such as during shifts in age structure of the bat colonies? What are effects of hibernation, migration, and reproduction of the bats on the parasite community? Can island biogeography theory be applied to parasite communities?

Lastly, parasites show many remarkable adaptations. Because life cycles of many species occur rapidly, and because the communities are often simple, i.e., contain few species, they might provide model systems for evaluating ecological, genetic, and evolutionary processes, both under natural and manipulated situations.

8. SUMMARY

Obviously, much is yet to be learned concerning ectoparasites of bats. New species are still being described at a rapid rate and relatively little is known of the biology of most of the known species. Thus, mammalogists and parasitologists may make many contributions to the study of bat ectoparasites. Many of the bat ectoparasites are rather highly host specific because of the rather isolated and specialized nature of the host. Collections of parasites are probably best made by direct search of the pelage and membranes using a microscope or by washing techniques. Data are needed on ectoparasite communities and on specific interrelationships of ectoparasites (and other associates) with each other and with the host. Major bat ectoparasites presently known consist of approximate numbers of species as follows: 256 nycteribiid and 224 streblid batflies, 70 species of fleas, 61 species of batbugs (Cimicidae), 32 species of polyctenid bugs, 5 species of earwigs (all on 1 host species), and numerous Acarina including ticks, chiggers, and other mites.

9. ACKNOWLEDGMENTS

Numerous parasitologists have helped me greatly over the years, but only a few are mentioned here, those with whom I have worked particularly closely—Alex Fain, Richard B. Loomis, Fritz Lukoschus, and Nixon Wilson. Thanks are also due to T. H. Kunz for his able editing of the manuscript.

10. REFERENCES

Amin, O. M. 1974. Comb variations in the rabbit flea *Cediopsylla simplex* (Baker). J. Med. Ent., 11:227-230.

Anciaux de Faveaux, M. 1971a. Catalogue des Acariens parasites et commensaux des Chiroptères. I. Ixodoidea and Mesostigmata. Pp. 1-91. Inst. Royal Sci. Nat. Belg. Brussels, Belgium.

Anciaux de Faveaux, M. 1971b. Catalogue des Acariens parasites et commensaux des Chiroptères. II. Trombidiformes and Sarcoptiformes. Pp. 92-200. Inst. Royal Sci. Nat. Belg. Brussels, Belgium.

Anciaux de Faveaux, M. 1971c. Catalogue des Acariens parasites et commensaux des Chiroptères. III. Tableaux des hôtes et de leurs parasites. Pp. 201-327. Inst. Royal Sci. Nat. Belg. Brussels, Belgium.

Anciaux de Faveaux, M. 1971d. Catalogue des Acariens parasites et commensaux des Chiroptères. IV-V. Bibliographie addenda et corrigenda. Pp. 328-451. Inst. Royal Sci. Nat. Belg. Brussels, Belgium.

Anciaux de Faveaux, M. 1976a. Catalogue des Acariens parasites et commensaux des Chiroptères. VI. Mise a jour des premiére et deuxiéme parties. Pp. 452-546. Inst. Royal Sci. Nat. Belg. Brussels, Belgium.

Anciaux de Faveaux, M. 1976b. Catalogue des Acariens parasites et commensaux des Chiroptères. VII. Mise a jour des troisiéme et quatriéme parties addendum. Pp. 547-637. Inst. Royal Sci. Nat. Belg. Brussels, Belgium.

Boyd, E. M., and M. H. Bernstein. 1950. A new species of sarcoptic mite from a bat (Acarina: Sarcoptidae). Proc. Ent. Soc. Wash., 52:95-99.

Brennan, J. M., and E. K. Jones. 1959. Keys to the chiggers of North America with synonymic notes and descriptions of two new genera (Acarina: Trombiculidae). Ann. Ent. Soc. Amer., 52:7-16.

Cooley, R. A., and G. M. Kohls. 1944. The Argasidae of North America, Central America and Cuba. Amer. Midl. Nat., Monogr. No. 1, 152 pp.

Desch, C. E., R. R. Lebel, W. B. Nutting, and F. Lukoschus. 1971. Parasitic mites of Surinam. I. *Demodex carolliae* sp. nov. (Acari: Demodicidae) from the bat *Carollia perspicillata*. Parasitology, 62:303-308.

Desch, C. E., W. B. Nutting, and F. Lukoschus. 1972. Parasitic mites of Surinam VII: *Demodex longissimus* n. sp. from *Carollia perspicillata* and *D. molossi* n. sp. from *Molossus molossus* (Demodicidae: Trombidiformes); Meibomian complex inhabitants of neotropical bats (Chiroptera). Acarologia, 14:35-53.

Dusbábek, F. 1967a. To the knowledge of mites of the subfamily Nycteriglyphinae (Acarina: Rosensteinidae) from Cuba. Folia Parasit., 14:239-246.

Dusbábek, F. 1967b. *Jamesonia,* a new genus (Acarina: Myobiidae) with seven new species from Cuban bats. Folia Parasit. 14:247-261.

Dusbábek, F. 1969. Generic revision of the myobiid mites (Acarina: Myobiidae) parasitic on bats. Folia Parasit., 16:1-17.

Dusbábek, F. 1973. A systematic review of the

genus *Pteracarus* (Acariformes: Myobiidae). Acarologia, 15:240-288.

Dusbábek, F., and J. de la Cruz. 1966. Nuevos géneros y especies de acaros (Acarina: Listrophoridae) parásitos de murciélagos Cubanos. Poeyana Inst. de Biol. La Habana, Cuba, Ser. A, 31:1-20.

Dusbábek, F., and F. Lukoschus. 1974. Parasitic mites of Surinam XXVI. Mites of the genus *Eudusbabekia* (Myobiidae: Trombidiformes) of the leaf-nosed bat subfamily Phyllostominae. Acarologia, 16:476-499.

Fain, A. 1958. Un nouveau Spéléognathe (Acarina—Ereynetidae) parasitant les fosses nasales du Murin [*Myotis myotis* (Borkh.)] en Belgique: *Speleognathopsis bastini* n. sp. Bull. Ann. Soc. R. Ent. Belg., 94:342-345.

Fain, A. 1959. Les acariens psoriques parasites des chauves-souris: IV. Le genre *Teinocoptes* Rodhain. Création d'une nouvelle famille: Teinocoptidae. Rev. Zool. Bot. Afr., 59:118-136.

Fain, A. 1960. Les acariens psoriques parasites des chauves-souris XIII. La famille Demodicidae Nicolet. Acarologia, 2:80-81.

Fain, A. 1965. Notes sur le genre *Notoedres* Railliet, 1893 (Sarcoptidae: Sarcoptiformes). Acarologia, 7:321-342.

Fain, A. 1967. Diagnoses d'acariens sarcoptiformes nouveaux. Rev. Zool. Bot. Afr., 75:378-382.

Fain, A. 1968a. Observations sur les Rodhainyssinae Acariens parasites des voies respiratoires des chauves-souris (Gastronyssidae: Sarcoptiforme). Acta Zool. Pathol. Antwerp., 44:3-35.

Fain, A. 1968b. Notes sur trois acariens remarquables (Sarcoptiformes). Acarologia, 10:276-291.

Fain, A. 1970. Diagnoses de nouveaux Lobalgides et Listrophorides (Acarina: Sarcoptiformes). Rev. Zool. Bot. Afr., 81:271-300.

Fain, A. 1971. Les listrophorides en Afrique au sud de Sahara (Acarina: Sarcoptiformes). II. Familles Listrophoridae et Chirodiscidae. Acta Zool. Pathol. Antwerp., 54:1-231.

Fain, A. 1973. Les listrophorides d'Amerique Neotropicale (Acarina: Sarcoptiformes) 1. Families Listrophoridae et Chirodiscidae. Bull. Inst. R. Sci. Nat. Belg., 49:1-149.

Fain, A., and F. S. Lukoschus. 1971a. Parasitic mites of Surinam. XV. Nasal ereynetid mites of bats with a key to the known species (Trombidiformes). Bull. Ann. Soc. R. Ent. Belg., 107:284-297.

Fain, A., and F. S. Lukoschus. 1971b. Parasitic

mites of Surinam. XVIII. Mites of the genera *Notoedres* and *Chirnyssoides* from bats (Sarcoptiformes: Sarcoptidae). Bull. Ann. Soc. R. Ent. Belg., 107:298-313.

Fain, A., and F. Lukoschus. 1975. Parasitic mites of Surinam. XXX. New observations on the genera *Chirnyssoides* and *Notoedres* from bats (Sarcoptiformes, Sarcoptidae). Acta Zool. Path. Antwerp., 61:92-118.

Fain, A., and J. O. Whitaker, Jr. 1976. Notes on the genus *Acanthophthirius* Perkins in North America (Acarina: Myobiidae). Bull. Ann. Soc. R. Belg. Ent., 112:127-143.

Fain, A., G. Anastos, J. Camin, and D. Johnston. 1967. Notes on the genus *Spelaeorhynchus.* Description of *S. praecursor* Neumann and of two new species. Acarologia, 9:535-556.

Fairchild, G. B., G. M. Kohls, and V. J. Tipton. 1966. The ticks of Panama (Acarina: Ixodoidae). Pp. 167-220, *in* Ectoparasites of Panama. (R. L. Wenzel and V. J. Tipton, eds.). Field Mus. Nat. Hist., Chicago 861 pp.

Ferris, G. F., and R. L. Usinger. 1939. The family Polyctenidae (Hemiptera: Heteroptera). Microentomology, 4:1-50.

Ferris, G. F., and R. L. Usinger. 1945. Notes and descriptions of American Polyctenidae (Hemiptera). Pan-Pacif. Ent., 21:121-124.

Goff, M. L. 1979. Host exploitation by chiggers (Acari: Trombiculidae) infesting Papua New Guinea land mammals. Pac. Insects, 20:321-353.

Goff, M. L., R. B. Loomis, W. C. Welbourn, and W. J. Wrenn. 1982. A glossary of chigger terminology (Acari: Trombiculidae). J. Med. Ent., 19:221-238.

Greenberg, B. 1952. A review of New World *Acomatacarus* (Acarina: Trombiculidae). Ann. Ent. Soc. Amer., 45:473-491.

Haas, G. E., A. J. Beck, and P. Q. Tomich. 1983. Bat fleas (Siphonaptera: Ischnopsyllidae) of California (USA). Bull. S. Calif. Acad. Sci., 82:103-104.

Hagan, H. R. 1951. Embryology of the viviparous insects. Ronald Press. New York, 472 pp.

Hedeen, R. A. 1953. A new species of *Sarcoptes* (Acarina: Sarcoptidae) from the Cave Bat. J. Parasit., 39:334-335.

Henry, L. G., and S. McKeever. 1971. A modification of the washing technique for quantitative evaluation of the ectoparasite load of small mammals. J. Med. Ent., 8:504-505.

Hilton, D. F. J. 1970. A technique for collecting ectoparasites from small birds and mammals. Can. J. Zool., 48:1445-1446.

Holloway, B. A. 1976. A new bat-fly family from New Zealand (Diptera: Mystacinobiidae). N.Z. J. Zool., 3:279-301.

Hutson, A. M. 1971. Ectoparasites of British bats. Mammal Review, 1:143-150.

Hyland, K. E., and H. G. Ford. 1961. The occurrence of the nasal mite *Speleognathopsis bastini* Fain (Speleognathidae) from the big brown bat, *Eptesicus fuscus* (Beauvois). Ent. News, 72:6.

Jones, E. K., and C. M. Clifford. 1972. The systematics of the subfamily Ornithodorinae (Acarina: Argasidae). V. A revised key to larval Argasidae of the Western Hemisphere and descriptions of seven new species of *Ornithodorus*. Ann. Ent. Soc. Amer., 65:730-740.

Kohls, G. M., D. E. Sonenshine, and C. M. Clifford. 1965. The systematics of the subfamily Ornithodorinae (Acarina: Argasidae). II. Identification of the larvae of the Western Hemisphere and descriptions of three new species. Ann. Ent. Soc. Amer., 58:331-364.

Kunz, T. H. 1976. Observations on the winter ecology of the batfly *Trichobius corynorhini* Cockerell (Diptera: Streblidae). J. Med. Ent., 12:631-636.

Lavoipierre, M. M. J., C. Rajamanickam, and P. Ward. 1967. Host parasite relationships of acarine parasites and their vertebrate hosts. I. The lesions produced by *Bakerocoptes cynopteris* in the skin of *Cynopterus brachyotis*. Acta Tropica, 24:1-18.

Lewis, R. E. 1978. A new species of *Myodopsylla* Jordan and Rothschild 1911, from northern United States with a key to the genus (Siphonaptera: Ischnopsyllidae). J. Parasit., 64:524-527.

Lewis, R. E., and N. Wilson. 1982. A new species of *Nycteridopsylla* (Siphonaptera: Ischnopsyllidae) from southwestern United States, with a key to the North American species. J. Med. Ent., 19:605-614.

Loomis, R. B. 1956. The chigger mites of Kansas (Acarina: Trombiculidae). Univ. Kansas Sci. Bull., 37:1195-1443.

Lukoschus, F., R. Jongman, and W. Nutting. 1972. Parasitic mites of Surinam. XII. *Demodex melanopteri* sp. n. (Demodicidae: Trombidiformes) from the Meibomian glands of the neotropical bat, *Eptesicus melanopterus*. Acarologia, 14:54-58.

Lukoschus, F. S., J. M. W. Louppen, and P. Fauran. 1979. Parasitic mites of Surinam, XIV. New observations on the genus *Psorergatoides* Fain, 1959 (Psorergatidae: Trombidiformes),

with a key to the known species. Int. J. Acarol., 5:311-324.

Maa, T. C. 1964. A review of the Old World Polyctenidae (Hemiptera: Cimicoidea). Pac. Insects, 6:494-516.

Maa, T. C. 1965a. An interim world list of batflies (Diptera: Nycteribiidae and Streblidae). J. Med. Ent., 1:377-386.

Maa, T. C. 1965b. Ascodipterinae of Africa (Diptera: Streblidae). J. Med. Ent. 4:311-326.

Maa, T. C. 1971a,b,c. Revision of the Australian batflies (Diptera: Streblidae and Nycteribiidae). An annotated bibliography of batflies (Diptera: Streblidae; Nycteribiidae). Review of the Streblidae parasitic on megachiropteran bats. Pac. Insects Monogr. 28:1-118, 119-122, 213-243.

Marshall, A. G. 1980. The function of combs in ectoparasitic insects. Pp. 79-87, *in* Fleas—Proc. Int. Conf. Fleas, June, 1977. (R. Traub and H. Starcke, eds.). Balkema, Rotterdam.

Marshall, A. G. 1981. The ecology of ectoparasitic insects. Academic Press, New York, 459 pp.

Marshall, A. G. 1982. Ecology of insects parasitic on bats. Pp. 369-401, *in* Ecology of bats. (T. H. Kunz, ed.). Plenum Press, New York, 425 pp.

McDaniel, B., and C. C. Coffman. 1970. The labidocarpid bat-mites of the United States. Proc. Helminth. Soc. Wash., 37:223-229.

Mitchell, C. J., and J. C. Hitchcock, Jr. 1965. Parasites from the Big Brown Bat, *Eptesicus fuscus* (Beauvois), in western Maryland (Acarina and Siphonaptera). J. Med. Ent., 1:334.

Nakata, S., and T. C. Maa. 1974. A review of the parasitic earwigs (Dermaptera: Arixeniina: Hemimerina). Pac. Insects, 16:307-374.

Peterson, B. V. 1960. New distribution and host records for bat flies, and a key to the North American species of *Basilia* Ribeiro (Diptera: Nycteribiidae). Proc. Ent. Soc. Ont., 90:30-37.

Phillips, C. J., J. K. Jones, Jr., and F. J. Radovsky. 1969. Macronyssid mites in oral mucosa of long-nosed bats: occurrence and associated pathology. Science, 165:1368-1369.

Pinichsponge, S. 1963. A review of the Chirodiscinae with descriptions of new taxa (Acarina: Listrophoridae). Acarologia, 5:81-91, 266-278, 397-404, 620-627.

Radovsky, F. J. 1967. The Macronyssidae and Laelapidae (Acarina: Mesostigmata) parasitic on bats. Univ. Calif. Publ. Ent., 46:1-288.

Radovsky, F. J., J. K. Jones, Jr., and C. J. Phillips. 1971. Three new species of *Radfordiella* (Acarina: Macronyssidae) parasitic in the mouth of phyllostomid bats. J. Med. Ent., 8:737-746.

Ross, A. 1961. Biological studies on bat ectoparasites of the genus *Trichobius* (Diptera: Streblidae) in North America, north of Mexico. Wasmann J. Biol., 19:229-246.

Rudnick, A. 1960. A revision of the mites of the family Spinturnicidae (Acarina). Univ. Calif. Publ. Ent., 17:157-283.

Ryberg, O. 1947. Studies on bats and bat parasites. Bokforlaget Svensk Natur., Stockholm, 330 pp.

Ryckman, R. E., D. G. Bentley, and E. F. Archbold. 1981. The Cimicidae of the Americas and oceanic islands: A checklist and bibliography. Bull. Soc. Vector Ecol., 6:93-142.

Ryckman, R. E., and M. A. Casdin. 1977. The Polyctenidae of the world, a checklist with bibliography. Calif. Vector Views, 24:25-31.

Strandtmann, R. W., and L. E. Garrett. 1967. *Neolaelaps palpispinosus,* a new species of laelapid mite from fruit bats in New Guinea (Acarina: Laelapidae). J. Med. Ent., 4:237-239.

Summers, F. M., and D. W. Price. 1970. Review of the mite family Cheyletidae. Univ. Calif. Publ. Ent., 61:1-153.

Theodor, O. 1967. An illustrated catalogue of the Rothschild collection of Nycteribiidae (Diptera) in the British Museum (Natural History). Brit. Mus. Nat. Hist. London.

Tipton, V. J., and E. Mendez. 1966. The fleas (Siphonaptera) of Panama. Pp. 289-386, *in* Ectoparasites of Panama. (R. L. Wenzel and V. J. Tipton, eds.). Field Mus. Nat. Hist., Chicago, 861 pp.

Traub, R. 1972. The relationship between spines, combs and other skeletal features of fleas (Siphonaptera) and the vestiture, affinities and habits of their hosts. J. Med. Ent., 9:601.

Ueshima, N. 1972. New World Polyctenidae (Hemiptera) with special reference to Venezuelan species. Brigham Young Univ. Sci. Bull., Biol. Ser., 17:13-21.

Usinger, R. L. 1966. Monograph of Cimicidae (Hemiptera-Heteroptera). The Thomas Say Foundation. Vol. VII. Ent. Soc. Amer., 585 pp.

Veal, R. A., K. M. T. Giesen, and J. O. Whitaker, Jr. 1984. A new species of the genus *Ophthalmodex* Lukoschus and Nutting 1979 (Prostigmata: Demodicidae) from *Myotis lucifugus* (Chiroptera: Vespertilionidae). Acarologia, 25:347-350.

Vercammen-Grandjean, P. H. 1965. Revision of the genera *Eltonella* Audy 1956 and *Microtrombicula* Ewing 1950, with description of fifty new species and transferral of subgenus *Chiroptella* to genus *Leptotrombidium* (Acarina: Trombiculidae). Acarologia, 7 (suppl.):34-257.

Vercammen-Grandjean, P. H. 1968. Revision of the genus *Myotrombicula* Womersley and Heaslip, 1943 (Trombiculidae: Acarina). Acarologia, 10:65-85.

Vercammen-Grandjean, P. H. 1971. Revision of the *Leptotrombidium* generic complex, based on palpal setation combined with other morphological characters. J. Med. Ent., 8:445-449.

Vercammen-Grandjean, P. H., S. G. Watkins, and A. J. Beck. 1965. Revision of *Whartonia glenni* Brennan, 1962, an American bat parasite (Acarina: Leeuwenhoekiidae). Acarologia, 7:492-509.

Webb, J. P., Jr., and R. B. Loomis. 1977. Ectoparasites. Pp. 57-119, *in* Biology of bats of the New World family Phyllostomatidae. Part II. (R. J. Baker, J. K. Jones, Jr., and D. C. Carter, eds.). Spec. Publ. Mus. Texas Tech Univ., Lubbock, 13:1-364.

Wenzel, R. L. and V. J. Tipton. (eds.). 1966. Ectoparasites of Panama. Field Mus. Nat. Hist., Chicago, 861 pp.

Wenzel, R. L., V. J. Tipton, and A. Kiewlicz. 1966. The streblid batflies of Panama (Diptera Calypterae: Streblidae). Pp. 405-675, *in* Ectoparasites of Panama (R. L. Wenzel and V. J. Tipton, eds.). Field Mus. Nat. Hist., Chicago, 861 pp.

Wharton, G. W., and H. S. Fuller. 1952. A manual of the chiggers. Mem. Ent. Soc. Wash., No. 4, 185 pp.

Whitaker, J. O., Jr., and N. Wilson. 1974. Host and distribution lists of mites (Acari), parasitic and phoretic, in the hair of wild mammals of North America, north of Mexico. Amer. Midl. Nat., 91:1-67.

Yunker, C. E. 1958. The parasitic mites of *Myotis lucifugus* (LeConte). Proc. Helminth. Soc. Wash., 25:31-34.

Yunker, C. E. 1961. A sampling technique for intranasal chiggers (Trombiculidae). J. Parasit., 47:720.

Yunker, C. E. 1970. A second species of the unique family Chirorhynchobiidae Fain, 1967 (Acarina: Sarcoptiformes). J. Parasit., 56:151-153.

Yunker, C. E., and E. K. Jones. 1961. Endoparasitic chiggers: I. Chiroptera, a new host order for intranasal chiggers, with descriptions of two new genera and species (Acarina: Trombiculidae). J. Parasit., 47:995-1000.

Appendix 1.   Major Groups of Bat Ectoparasites

INSECTS

Marshall (1982) reported that 687 species of four orders and six families of insects parasitize bats. Five of the six families are exclusively found on bats, whereas 68% of the cimicids are parasites of bats. Marshall (1981, 1982) summarized much of the information on the numbers and ecology of ectoparasitic insects of bats. Webb and Loomis (1977) summarized the literature on ectoparasites of phyllostomid bats.

Diptera

Nycteribiidae (Batflies)

All nycteribiids, including about 256 described species in 12 genera, are ectoparasites of bats. There are 3 subfamilies of nycteribiids. Two subfamilies, Archinycteribiinae with 1 genus and 3 species, and Cyclopodiinae with 4 genera and 62 species, are all Old World forms associated with Pteropidae. The remaining subfamily, Nycteribiinae, contains 191 species in 7 genera. All are found on Microchiroptera, mainly Vespertilionidae and Rhinolophidae. The biggest genus is *Basilia* with 103 species. It is found in both the Old and New World, mostly on Vespertilionidae, but also on Emballonuridae and Phyllostomidae.

Nycteribiids are highly specialized for a parasitic existence. They have completely lost their wings and are spiderlike in appearance. Their legs and small head all protrude from the dorsal surface, and the animals are somewhat dorsoventrally flattened. As in fleas, they have several combs. The combs are thought by some (for example Amin, 1974; Traub, 1972) to help keep the animal from being brushed backwards from the fur. However, Marshall (1980, 1981) believes the combs to be protective in nature, forming a dense shield over movable joints or organs which otherwise might be harmed by abrasive action of hair.

Nycteribiids are centered in the Old World, but are widespread particularly in the tropics. Some bats have more than one nycteribiid species. The females leave the hosts only to deposit young on the roost walls. They are obligate blood sucking, highly specialized, true flies which are usually highly host specific. Adults live their entire lives on the bats and hibernate there. One female produced 15 larvae in a three month period (Ryberg, 1947). Males attempt to copulate whenever they meet females, but particularly after hibernation, with the female normally trying to escape. Pregnancy may last up to 7-9 days. Fully developed larvae are produced (prepupae) which immediately pupate. This is the case in both nycteribiids and streblids.

References: Maa, 1965, 1971a,b,c
Peterson, 1960
Theodor, 1967

Streblidae (Batflies)

Streblids, like nycteribiids, are all ectoparasites of bats. A total of 224 species in 31 genera is currently known. One genus with eight species is associated with Megachiroptera; the rest are associated with Microchiroptera. Most are external parasites, except for the Old World genus *Ascodipteron,* the female of which embeds in the skin (Maa, 1965b). Most (79%) have wings, but they are weak flyers. Combs are sometimes present on the head. Streblids are found in the Old and the New World, but are far more numerous in the New World. Most inhabit the tropics and subtropics. As in nycteribiids, the females deposit the larvae on the roost walls. Host specificity is well developed. Streblids run backwards, forwards and sideways on the wing membranes, but rarely leave the host. They constantly feed as they "dive" in and out of the fur. One intrauterine larva develops at a time.

References: Maa, 1965a,b, 1971a,b,c
Kunz, 1976
Ross, 1961
Wenzel et al., 1966

Mystacinobiidae

This family includes only one species, *Mystacinobia zelandica.* It lives in close association with a bat from New Zealand (Holloway, 1976). There are two other species of flies which may be related to *Mystacinobia,* and both have been recorded from bat roosts. They are *Mormotomyobia hirsuta* (Mormotomyiidae) from Kenya, and *Chiropteromyza wegelii* (Chiropteromyzidae) from Finland. These three species may be parasitic but more likely they are commensals (Marshall, 1981, 1982).

Siphonaptera (Fleas)

Ischnopsyllidae

Currently over 2,000 species of fleas are known, about 5% of them from bats. All fleas of bats are in the family Ischnopsyllidae, and the only large family of fleas confined to one order of hosts is the Ischonopsyllidae, with about 70 species (Hutson, 1971).

Bat fleas are not very common; they were on only four of 95 species of Panama bats, and 5 of 86 bat species in Malaysia.

Ischnopsyllids are known from 9 families of bats, as follows: Desmodontidae, Emballonuridae, Megadermatidae, Molossidae, Noctilionidae, Pteropidae, Rhinolophidae, Rhinopomatidae, and Vespertilionidae.

Fleas are wingless, laterally compressed, jumping (usually) insects with combs on their bodies. Most fleas are parasitic on mammals, although some are found on birds. Only adults are parasitic, with few exceptions (the larvae are also apparently parasitic in at least 2 species), and all stages can often be found in large numbers in the roost. Flea larvae can be found in guano below the roosts but are difficult to identify. However, they will develop into adults if guano is kept moist in a plastic bag.

References: Haas et al., 1983
Lewis, 1978
Lewis and Wilson, 1982
Tipton and Mendez, 1966

Hemiptera (True Bugs)

Cimicidae (Batbugs)

Batbugs are wingless hemipterans. They live in roosts of bats and come to the host to feed on blood. They are temporary parasites, and consequently they are greatly influenced by the environmental conditions of the host's home. They do not have combs or clasping tarsi characteristic of many of the permanent parasites. They can exist for long periods without food. About 91 species have been described on bats, but some are on man, possibly flying lemurs, and a number are parasites of birds. Thirteen genera, including about 61 species, are associated with bats, and 10 entirely so. Mating is by forced (traumatic) insemination. The male pierces the abdomen of the female with the

hypertrophied left paramere, introducing large amounts of sperm into her abdominal cavity. Eggs are laid individually in the roost of the bat; they are coated with cement and adhere to the substrate. Description of hatching and the nymphal state is given by Usinger (1966). Usinger's work is an excellent treatise, including keys to the cimicids of the world.

References: Ryckman et al., 1981
Usinger, 1966

Polyctenidae

Polyctenids are rather rare bugs found in the tropics of the New and Old World. The name refers to the many combs on their body, which may help keep them in place in the fur, or which may serve as protection (see discussion under Nycteribiidae). Polyctenids are viviparous, not common among hemipterans. Development is rapid and Hagan (1951) reported that *H. fumarius* can mate before moulting to the adult stage. The last nymphal stage sometimes carries embryos. Eighteen species were recognized by Ferris and Usinger (1939), but presently 32 species in 5 genera are known. There is one genus, *Hesperoctenes,* in the New World, with 16 species; whereas 5 genera (including *Hesperoctenes*) and 16 species occur in the Old World. All polyctenids are parasitic only on microchiropteran bats, where they feed on blood. They are usually host specific and spend their entire lives on the host. They can exist for but a short period without food.

References: Ferris and Usinger, 1939, 1945
Maa, 1964
Ryckman and Casdin, 1977
Ueshima, 1972

Dermaptera (Earwigs)

There are two families of parasitic earwigs, the Hemimeridae with 11 species parasitic on African rodents, and the Arixeniidae with 5 species parasitic on bats.

There are two genera of Arixeniidae, *Arixenia* with 2 species and *Xeniaria* with 3 species. However, all 5 species are regularly associated only with the hairless molossid bat, *Cheiromeles torquatus* from a few caves and hollow trees from the Malaysian and Philippine subregions, although there are a few accidental records on *Tadarida,* which shares roosts with *Cheiromeles*. The parasites spend much or most of their time on walls or ceilings of the roost. The dermapterans have chewing mouthparts and feed on solid materials such as skin detritus and host feces, thus they may be commensals rather than true parasites. The greater amount of setae on *Xeniaria* than on *Arixenia* suggest that the former spends more time on guano and in the roosts while *Arixenia* spends more time on the body of the hosts (Nakata and Maa, 1974).

Reference: Nakata and Maa, 1974

ACARINA (Mites, Chiggers, and Ticks)

Most of the ectoparasites of bats, in abundance or in numbers of species, are Acarina, particularly of the families Macronyssidae, Myobiidae, and Spinturnicidae. Acarines vary greatly in form, behavior, and ecology.

Ticks and chiggers are both highly specialized groups of mites. Ticks are very large with a heavily armed piercing proboscis; chiggers are six-legged larvae of trombiculid mites.

Numerous species of Acarina have been described and the literature is scattered. However, Anciaux de Faveaux, in a seven-part series (1971a-d, 1976a,b) summarized much of the information given here on acarine parasites of bats, although many species have been described since then.

Argasidae and Ixodidae (Ticks)

Ticks are much enlarged, but otherwise are closely related to other mites. Most ticks regularly occurring on bats are in the family Argasidae (soft ticks), although Anciaux de Faveaux (1971a, 1976a) lists a number of Ixodidae (hard ticks) which have been recorded from bats of which at least *Ixodes simplex* and *I. vespertilionis* are regularly associated with bats. The same author (1971a, 1976a) lists about 50 records of Argasidae from bats, but many argasids are parasitic on birds, and some species occurring on bats may actually be bird ticks. Also, many argasids occur on a variety of hosts. Over 20 of the ticks appear to occur regularly on bats. Hard ticks feed once on a host before each molt for a long period of time (i.e., they remain attached and are carried about by the host usually for days). Soft ticks also feed once on a host before each molt but

they do so much more rapidly, generally in a matter of minutes. They do not attach, except for larvae which are carried about, as in the case of hard ticks. Argasids generally live in arid tropical or semi-tropical situations and are highly resistant to desiccation. Larvae of ticks have three pairs of legs, nymphs and adults have four. In argasid ticks, males and females are similar and have leathery, wrinkled integument. Eggs are laid in the roosting area, a few at a time, and all stages live in the roost.

References: Cooley and Kohls, 1944
Fairchild et al., 1966
Jones and Clifford, 1972
Kohls et al., 1965

Cheyletidae

Anciaux de Faveaux (1971b) lists only one cheyletid mite from bats, *Cheletonella vespertilionis*. It was originally described from an Australian bat, but there are now records of this species from a bat from Indiana and from soil from California. Cheyletid mites are predatory, although some are perhaps parasitic on mammals. Cheyletid mites often have well developed comblike setae on the palpal tarsus.

Reference: Summers and Price, 1969

Chirodiscidae

Chirodiscids are tiny cigar-shaped mites which crawl up and down individual hairs by means of the highly modified legs I and II. Feeding is probably on contents of the hair follicle. Anciaux de Faveaux (1971b) lists 67 species in 13 genera from bats.

References: Dusbábek and de la Cruz, 1966
Fain, 1970
Fain, 1971
Fain, 1973
McDaniel and Coffman, 1970
Pinichsponge, 1963

Chirorhynchobiidae

Only 2 species of Chirorhynchobiidae have been described: *Chirorhynchobia uroderma* from *Uroderma bilobatum* from Panama (Fain, 1967, 1968b) and *C. matsoni* from *Anoura geoffroyi* from Venezuela (Yunker, 1970). The individuals from

Anoura were all firmly attached by their highly modified mouthparts to the trailing edge of the bat wing membrane.

References: Fain, 1967
Fain, 1968b
Yunker, 1970

Laelapidae

This is a very large family including many parasitic species, but it contains only 2 genera and 4 species parasitic on bats, *Notolaelaps novaguinea* on *Syconycteris* from New Guinea; *Neolaelaps spinosa* and *N. vitzthumi* mostly from *Pteropus* from Asia, oceanic islands, and Australia; and *Neolaelaps palpispinosus* from New Guinea *Nyctimene* and *Syconycteris*. The deutonymph apparently feeds in these species. Radovsky (1967) gives information and keys to these mites except for *N. palpispinosus*.

References: Radovsky, 1967
Strandtmann and Garrett, 1967

Macronyssidae

Macronyssids are medium sized mites often parasitic on bats. They crawl about on the wings and body, feeding on blood or other body fluids of the host. Living young are produced by the female. *Radfordiella oricola* is known only from the protonymph which is parasitic in the tissue of the soft palate of *Leptonycteris nivalis*. Other life stages are unknown in this species.

Adults and protonymphs of most species are common on the pelage and membranes of bats. The following information is from *Chiroptonyssus robustipes* from *Tadarida brasiliensis*, as observed by Radovsky (1967) but may hold for other species. Protonymphs are often abundant on the bats, primarily on the wing membranes, but adults are few, probably because they remain on the host for only a short time. Eggs hatch in about 2 days. Larvae lasted slightly over a day, whereas protonymphs lasted from 3 to 6 days, deutonymphs 1 to 1.25 days, with time elapsed of about 10 to 12 days for a complete life cycle. Protonymphs in study tubes with adult females would often ride on the females, then would disembark when the female stopped moving. Adult males rode about on deutonymphs which subsequently moulted into females; they mated with females upon touching. The mites deposited their eggs on the cotton within the tubes; but females could produce 8-11 eggs within a three day period, although only one egg could be seen at a time in a female. Females were found to feed on eggs, this perhaps being a density regulating factor. Larvae and deutonymphs of macronyssids probably do not feed. Under natural conditions, eggs are laid in the nests. Radovsky (1967) published an excellent account on macronyssid (and laelapid) mites of bats, including keys to the genera and species. Anciaux de Faveaux (1971a, 1976a) lists 104 species in 15 genera from bats.

Reference: Radovsky, 1967

Myobiidae

Myobiids are rather small, elongate, light-colored mites with the first pair of legs modified for grasping hairs. They feed on blood and other body fluids of the host by means of the tiny stylet-like mouthparts. Myobiids spend their entire life cycle on the host, gluing their eggs to the host's hair. Anciaux de Faveaux (1971b, 1976a) lists 54 species in 9 genera for this family, but additional species have been described.

References: Dusbábek, 1967b, 1969, 1973
Dusbábek and Lukoschus, 1974
Fain and Whitaker, 1976

Rosensteiniidae

Rosensteiniids are cosmopolitan associates of bats. They are not parasitic and are uncommon on bats, but may be exceedingly abundant on guano and in roosts, where they probably feed on feces or on other organisms. Anciaux de Faveaux (1971b, 1976a) lists 20 species in 4 genera of rosensteiniids.

References: Dusbábek, 1967a

Spelaeorhynchidae

Three species are presently known from this family (Anciaux de Faveaux, 1971a, 1976a), all from Central and South America. Spelaeorhynchids are tick-like mites which were originally described as ticks. The head lacks the typical tick proboscis, and otherwise these parasites are much closer to the laelaptoid mites than to the ticks.

Reference: Fain et al., 1967

Spinturnicidae

Spinturnicid mites are all parasites of bats. They have a relatively small body and head but stout legs. Most species crawl about on the wings, membrane and body of the host, but *Spinturnix globosus* lives in the anus of certain species of *Myotis* in North America. The life cycle of spinturnicid mites consists of five stages, egg, larva, protonymph, deutonymph, and adult (Rudnick, 1960), but the first two stages occur within the body; the female gives birth directly to the protonymph, which molts once, developing into male or female deutonymphs, which in turn molt into adults. The time necessary for the life cycle to occur is unknown. An excellent publication including keys to the world species is available for this family (Rudnick, 1960). Anciaux de Faveaux (1971a, 1976a) lists at least 67 species in nine genera in this family.

Reference: Rudnick, 1960

Trombiculidae (Chiggers)

The term "chigger" refers to the larval stage of a mite of the family Trombiculidae. The larval stage in this family is parasitic on vertebrates, and subsequent, free-living stages (nymphs and adults) are predators of small arthropods and their eggs. At present the postlarval stages of trombiculid mites are poorly known and the classification is based almost entirely on the larval stage, or chigger. Of the approximately 3,000 species currently described, less than 10% are known from postlarval stages (Goff et al., 1982). Chiggers are generally habitat-specific rather than host-specific ectoparasites and any vertebrate entering a chigger-infested habitat stands an almost equal chance of being infested by chiggers. As noted by Goff (1979), distribution of chigger species is not determined by the requirements of the larval stage, but rather by the requirements of the postlarval stages. The parasitic larva serves as a mechanism for dispersal, while the ability of the postlarval stages to survive is the "anchor," restricting a given species to a given habitat. In some instances, the specialized nature of the habitat exploited by the postlarval stages has severely restricted the hosts available to the parasitic larvae, as in the case of many of the bat-infesting species treated here. While many of these species are normally recovered only from bats, they appear to be capable of completing their development on other hosts which may invade the habitat. One such instance was noted by Loomis (1956) where *Albeckia senase* (Greenberg, 1952), normally recovered from cave bats, *Myotis velifer,* in Kansas, was also recovered from a wood rat, *Neotoma micropus,* which invaded the cave occupied by the bats. Thus, chiggers found infesting bats are actually habitat-specific ectoparasites although appearing to be host-specific. Anciaux de Faveaux (1971b, 1976a) includes about 235 species of chiggers in 38 genera which have been taken from bats.

References: Brennan and Jones, 1959
Goff et al., 1982
Vercammen-Grandjean, 1965
Vercammen-Grandjean, 1968
Vercammen-Grandjean, 1971
Vercammen-Grandjean et al., 1965
Wharton and Fuller, 1952

Parasites of hidden biotopes

The purpose of this chapter is to present information on collecting and preserving ectoparasites of bats. However, there are some interesting endoparasitic arthropod species not generally studied by workers on endoparasites. I refer here to some of the groups of smaller mites inhabiting "hidden biotopes," such as nasal, ear, and mouth cavities, meibomian glands, and the space under the skin. The various cavities can be cut open and the inside examined for mites; also the nasal cavities can be flushed out via a hypodermic needle (see Yunker, 1961). Material from Meibomian glands or hair follicles can be forced out with watchmakers' forceps. The skin can be peeled back and both the outside and the underside can be examined for small protrusions, which in turn can be examined for mites. The various mites discussed here are exceedingly difficult to find, however. Mites found in hidden biotopes can be mounted immediately in Hoyer's solution on a slide and covered with a cover slip.

Several families of mites of hidden biotopes are discussed below. In addition, members of some of the families already discussed have endoparasitic members. For example, some of the chiggers and other mites are found in the nasal cavities (see Yunker and Jones, 1966; Fain and Lukoschus, 1971a); some of the macronyssids live in the mouths of bats (see Phillips et al., 1969; Radovsky et al., 1971), and females of the streblid fly

Ascodipteron embed in the skin. *Ancystropus zeleborii* and *Spinturnix globosus* occur in the eyes and anus of bats, respectively.

Bakerocoptidae

One species, *Bakerocoptes cynopteri,* is known. All developmental stages are found in cysts entirely within the tissues of the wing membrane. The tissues of the wing membrane are thickened and there is a small opening to the outside.

Reference: Lavoipierre et al., 1967

Demodicidae

Anciaux de Faveaux (1971b, 1976a) lists 9 species in 2 genera in this family from bats, but at least 2 additional genera and 6 species have been described since. Species are found in places such as hair follicles and Meibomian glands of the eyelids, under the skin, in the patagium, in the buccal mucosa, and in the eye sockets.

References: Desch et al., 1971
Desch et al, 1972
Fain, 1960
Lukoschus et al., 1972
Veal et al., 1984

Gastronyssidae

Five genera including 20 species of gastronyssid mites occur in bats. One genus with one species, *Gastronyssus bakeri,* lives attached to the intestinal mucosa of the stomach and intestines, but most live in the nasal fossae.

Reference: Fain, 1968a

Notoedridae

Species of the genus *Notoedres* have been described from a diverse group of mammals—carnivores, lagomorphs, rodents, and primates, as well as bats. Mites of this genus occur in the skin, and usually are found because of the lesions or mange conditions which they cause. There are 39 species in 5 genera from bats in this family (Anciaux de Faveaux, 1971b, 1976a).

References: Boyd and Bernstein, 1950
Fain, 1965

Fain and Lukoschus, 1971b
Fain and Lukoschus, 1975
Hedeen, 1953
Yunker, 1958

Psorergatidae

Mites of the genus *Psorergatoides* are itch mites of bats. They are exceedingly small and live in the epidermis between the stratum corneum and stratum granulosum of the wing. The parasitized areas lack pigment. Fourteen species of itch mites are known from bats (Lukoschus et al., 1979).

Reference: Lukoschus et al., 1979

Speleognathidae (= Erynetidae)

Mites of this family occur in the nasal cavity of bats; three genera and eleven species were listed by Anciaux de Faveaux (1971b, 1976a).

References: Fain, 1958
Fain and Lukoschus, 1971a
Hyland and Ford, 1961
Mitchell and Hitchcock, 1965

Teinocoptidae

This family includes 19 species in 2 genera (Anciaux de Faveaux, 1971b, 1976a). Teinocoptids occur in the skin of the host.

Reference: Fain, 1959

Appendix 2. Solutions Useful in Preserving Ectoparasites
Hoyer's Solution

50 ml	distilled water
30 g	gum arabic
200 g	chloral hydrate
20 g	glycerine

The items must be mixed and dissolved in the above sequence. These chemicals are often difficult to dissolve, and will not dissolve if used in the wrong sequence.

Nesbitt's Solution

80 g	chloral hydrate
50 ml	distilled water
5 ml	HCl

Dissolve the materials and add a tiny amount of acid fuchsin to color solution reddish.

Chapter 28

Methods for the Ecological Study of Bat Endoparasites

James R. Coggins

Department of Biological Sciences
University of Wisconsin-Milwaukee
Milwaukee, Wisconsin 53201 USA

1. INTRODUCTION

Endoparasites of bats have been extensively studied taxonomically but few investigators have conducted ecological investigations. The association of bats with medical and veterinary disease transmission should, however, be cause for extensive ecological and behavioral research on both bats and their associated endoparasites. Of course, medical and veterinary consideration should not be the only reasons for studying the ecology of bat endoparasites. Bats in general have been neglected as topics for study in parasite ecology just as parasites have been ignored in previous investigations of ecosystems. Bats, with their wide geographic distribution, secretive habits, and diverse lifestyles may serve as important models for investigations in parasite ecology. The parasite-host relationship between these animals may be valuable in studies of niche ecology and questions of competitive exclusion, evolutionary and taxonomic principles, population dynamics, and in the study of both biotic and abiotic ecological factors. The purpose of this chapter is to review the literature on bat endoparasites with an emphasis on ecological studies and to discuss methodology of conducting research on bat parasites.

Numerous reviews, checklists, keys, and other sources exist that may guide the interested reader to pertinent publications in taxonomy and morphology of bat endoparasites. Noteworthy summaries and reviews include those of Stiles and Nolan (1931) on all bat parasites known at that time. Ubelaker (1970) and Guilford (1952) have provided reviews of both ecto- and endoparasites of bats. More recently, Ubelaker et al. (1977) provided a comprehensive review of the parasitic helminths of bats in the family Phyllostomidae. Barus and Rysavy (1971) and Durette-Desset and Chabaud (1975) published checklists of nematodes for the family Trichostrongylidae from bats. Coggins et al. (1981, 1982) studied endoparasites of *Myotis* sp. and reviewed the literature on these groups. Lotz and Font (1983) published a taxonomic review of the family Lecithodendriidae from *Eptesicus fuscus.* Hoare (1965) and Marinkelle (1976) provided information on the trypanosomes of bats and vampire bats as vectors and hosts for trypanosomiasis. Other reviews, checklists and keys have dealt with specific geographic locations but may be valuable to workers in other regions. These may be indexed through the references listed above. The publications of Caballero (1942-1960), Macy (1931-1960), and Dubois (1955-1963) have contributed much to this field.

2. METHODS OF CAPTURING BATS AND HOST EXAMINATIONS

Methods for the capture of bats are reviewed in Chapter 1 and will not be discussed in detail here. In general those methods employed in the collection of bats for other types of studies are adequate for parasitological research as long as the animal is captured alive or examined soon after capture. For many parasitological studies investigators have used bats discarded by health laboratories. This is an erratic and unreliable source of material for any type of ecological study. Specimens submitted to state or university health laboratories have probably been dead for an extended period of time and probably were not killed or fixed in an acceptable manner. Death without proper fixation can cause rapid decomposition of associated endoparasites, rendering them unsuitable for later identification and study. If host animals are obtained while still alive, little is usually known of the condition or length of captivity. The animals may have been under consider-

able stress, a condition that can cause endoparasites to be voided from the host. Additionally, data on host collection may be minimal or absent altogether. It may be impossible to collect additional host specimens from the same locality to verify identifications or collect fresh parasite material. In general, this type of collection method should be avoided for ecological or behavioral studies.

2.1. Methods of Host Preservation

Endoparasites are not static but rather migrate within a host due to changes in host physiology (Read, 1970) or the presence of other parasites (Read and Simmons, 1963). When hosts are allowed to die or remain in captivity for prolonged periods, parasites may change their location within the host or be voided altogether. When it is not possible to examine freshly captured bats, there are several methods that aid in preserving the integrity of parasites to be collected. Cooling of hosts should only be used for periods of less than 24 hours. Although freezing is not generally recommended, it may be necessary under some circumstances. If so, a faster freezing rate gives better results (Pritchard and Kruse, 1982). Heat treatment, a third method, involves killing the host by conventional means, placing the freshly removed organs of the animal (not the entire animal) into isolated containers, and adding boiling water. Only minimal time is needed for heat to penetrate organs and give satisfactory results for enclosed helminths. After thoroughly heated, organs may then be transferred to containers of fixative. The use of "whirl-pak" plastic bags for storage of fixed specimens to alleviate the need of carrying large numbers of glass containers into the field is also recommended (Sinclair and John, 1973). Heat treatment has the advantage of relaxing helminths before fixation and yields more useful specimens. Organs may also be placed directly in fixative, but endoparasite specimens preserved in this manner are usually contracted and are less useful for subsequent processing.

2.2. Methods of Host Examination

Several types of endoparasites have been reported from bats, including protozoa, digenea, cestodes, nematodes, acanthocephala, and pentastomes. The typical endoparasites encountered include the following:

1) Protozoa—Found in bloodstream and digestive tract.
2) Digenea (trematodes)—Adults in any body cavity, most commonly in digestive tract where eggs are voided by the host. Larvae (metacercariae) may occur in any location.
3) Cestodes—Adult tapeworms normally live only in the intestine. Since these parasites are large they are easily seen upon opening the intestine. I am unaware of any cestode larvae reported from bats.
4) Nematodes—Adults and larvae can occur in any location of the body. Nematodes are common in intestine and stomach.
5) Acanthocephala—Adults live only within the intestine. Juvenile acanthocephala may be encysted in organs. Acanthocephalans have rarely been reported from bats (Rutkowska, 1980).

Each type of parasite may require different methods of processing for optimum results. Several excellent references exist with detailed methods for host autopsy and parasite preservation (Cable, 1977; Meyer and Olsen, 1980; Pritchard and Kruse, 1982). These authors all stress two points. First, the handling of specimens before fixation can have important consequences; and, secondly, precise data collection is essential.

2.2.1. Collection of Protozoans

Since endoparasites may occur in any organ of the body a careful and thorough examination of the host is essential. Bats harbor several species of blood protozoans (Marinkelle, 1976). Generally, both thick and thin blood smears should be made. Routine microscopic examination of fresh blood may be useful for detecting trypanosomes. Trypanosomes may be easily recognized by their characteristic motility (rapid undulation and twisting motion) in a thick blood film. However, one should not assume an animal negative on examination of fresh blood alone. A properly stained thin blood film is necessary. Several methods have been described for preparation and staining of blood films and concentrating parasites from blood. Woo (1969) has described a hematocrit centrifuge technique for the recovery of trypanosomes in blood. Detailed instructions for preparation of blood films may be found in Markel and Voge (1981) and Garcia and Ash (1979). Stains employed for blood films fall into two basic types. In the first, fixative is a basic component of the staining solution. For example, Wright's stain incorporates methyl alcohol as the fixative. Using this stain, fixation and staining are accomplished simultaneously. Generally, less processing time is required with this type of stain. In the second category are stains that do not incorporate a fixation into the formulation. Giemsa's stain is but one example. Using these stains, blood films must first be fixed, usually in methyl alcohol, and air-dried before staining. This category of stain usually yields better resolution of detail but is more time consuming. A Giemsa stain should be used for any type of specimen. Tissue parasites, including cysts, may be detected by a tissue smear (Pritchard and Kruse, 1982), pressing pieces of tissue between glass plates and examining them under low power microscopy, or by enzymatic digestion of tissue (Coulombe, 1970). The staining of tissue impressions was discussed by Markell and Voge (1981).

2.2.2. Collection of Helminths

Prior to opening the host specimen for examination of internal organs, it is helpful to wet the ventral surface of the body with alcohol or water to prevent excessive contamination of the area with hair. After opening the body cavity but before organ removal, the body cavity, mesenteries, and organ surfaces should be carefully perused. Parasitic cysts can usually be recognized. Those of digeneans are usually thin with a hyaline membrane. Size varies but is usually less than 5 mm. Encysted larval cestodes and nematodes are thicker and more opaque.

In the search for endoparasitic helminths, it is preferable to place individual organs or sections of digestive tract into separate containers for examination to prevent mixing of parasites from different locations. As noted earlier, each parasite species may have its own optimum microhabitat. Upon death of the host, decay begins immediately and parasites may migrate, be voided, or actually digested. In separating organs, the exact location of parasites collected can easily be noted and much time can be saved in later identifications. It is also important to establish a standard routine of examination so that methods will not affect results obtained later.

The intestinal tract should be opened along its entire length with scissors and examined in a dish of physiological saline under a microscope. Since the digestive tract of many bats is extremely small, a pair of sharp, fine dissecting scissors is essential. The gut may also be gently torn along its length by use of dissecting needles. It is helpful to bend needles at a 45-degree angle approximately 20 mm from the tip to facilitate use. The intestine should be washed vigorously in saline and any detached worms transferred to a dish of fresh saline. The inside of the intestine should then be scraped using a pair of forceps to pull the digestive tract up over the edge of the container. Scrapings should be thoroughly mixed with saline in the dish and allowed to settle. Small aliquots of this liquid can then be examined under a microscope. Many smaller digeneans will be completely hidden in the gut mucosa and scraping with subsequent examination is necessary for detection.

The handling of small delicate helminths presents special problems. Cestodes can usually be cleaned of intestinal debris and trans-

ferred to fresh saline or fixative by picking up the worm with one or more dissecting needles. Small digeneans and nematodes should be transferred by use of a fine-tipped camel-hair brush or by use of a Pasteur pipette. The sharp edges on the pipette tip should be removed by flaming in a bunsen burner. Without this precaution small digeneans can be torn. For larger digeneans and nematodes the bore of the pipette may be enlarged by breaking at various lengths from the tip. An even break is necessary and the edges must be flamed. A small, stiff bird feather trimmed to make a straining scoop (Berland, 1982) can also be used for transferring delicate specimens. To facilitate collection and handling of small helminths, collecting and processing sieves may be fashioned from polyethylene tubing of suitable diameter. This is cut to a desired depth and nylon mesh is adhered to one end by gentle heating on a hotplate (Berland, 1982). Other workers have utilized plastic BEEM capsules available in electron microscopy laboratories for embedding samples for transmission electron microscopy. The conical end is removed and the open ends are capped with anything from wire mesh screening to membrane or paper filters. Carriers can also be made by simply puncturing the plastic BEEM capsule several times with a hot needle (Postek et al., 1980).

2.3. General Fixation Techniques

Fixation may denote killing and fixing in one operation, or these two processes may occur separately. The importance of using heat to relax and kill helminth specimens before fixation has been accepted for many years. Hot fixation or relaxation by immersion in hot (near-boiling) water with subsequent fixation should yield excellently prepared specimens. With the commonly used fixatives discussed below, I would recommend that cestodes and digeneans be relaxed in hot water prior to fixation. This is easily accomplished by gently heating the container on a hotplate until worms relax and cease movement. Cestodes may also be placed in hot water and gently agitated in a circular motion using a dissecting needle until relaxed.

Several fixatives are available for helminth parasites other than nematodes. Ten percent buffered formalin and a mixture of alcohol:formalin:acetic acid (A.F.A.) have been considered "standard" fixatives; although, as pointed out by Berland (1982), "standard methods" for the processing of biological materials simply do not exist. Methods depend traditionally on schools of training and not on the requirements of the tissue. Glacial acetic acid alone or mixed with formalin (Gibson, 1979) has been advocated as a good general purpose fixative for many helminths (Berland, 1961, 1982). These fixatives have also been employed for nematodes with good results. It should be noted that glacial acetic acid may cause cells to swell. Helminths placed in this fixative will usually straighten and die in an extended position within seconds. Neutral buffered formalin (10 parts formalin in 90 parts buffer) has also been recommended (Pritchard and Kruse, 1982).

2.4. Fixation of Nematodes

Nematodes require special fixation techniques. Glacial acetic acid probably is the best fixative (Berland, 1961). Nematodes also can be fixed by immersing them in hot (nearly boiling) 70% ethanol or in a mixture of 70% ethanol-glycerol (9:1) (Cable, 1977). Other fixatives used for nematodes include hot 10% formalin or hot Bouin's fixative.

Fixed specimens may be stored indefinitely in 70% ethyl alcohol with 5% glycerol added to prevent dehydration of the specimen if the alcohol evaporates. Specimens should be stored in glass vials with plastic (not cork) caps. Use of parafilm beneath and wrapped around the outside of the cap will also help retard evaporation.

2.5. Fixation of Protozoa

Lumen dwelling protozoa may be examined as direct wet smears either unstained or as iodine stained mounts. For the latter, a drop of fecal material is mixed with a drop of iodine-eosin (Pritchard and Kruze, 1982). A systematic scan of the stained smear will reveal protozoan trophozoites or cysts, if present. Fluid samples containing protozoa may be fixed using polyvinyl alcohol (PVA) (Pritchard and Kruze, 1982) or merthiolate-iodine-formalin (MIF) (Markell and Voge, 1981). Both of these methods yield good results if specimens are to be stored for later use. Although there are few records of coccidians from bats, Ubelaker et al. (1977) estimated that there may be about 900 species of *Eimeria* in bats. Endogenous stages of coccidians may occur in the intestinal epithelium while oocysts may be recovered from feces. Several techniques for the recovery of oocysts from feces have been published (Dubey et al., 1972; Davis, 1973). Additionally, Davis (1973) lists several techniques valuable in research on both oocysts and endogenous stages of coccidia.

3. SLIDE PREPARATION

Preparation of slides is always necessary for positive identification of endoparasites of bats. Additionally, as discussed below, permanent slides are necessary for the preparation of voucher specimens. Many stains and staining methods are available. Generally, hematoxylin and carmine stains are employed. A different counterstain is often used for enhanced contrast of tegumental or cuticular structure of helminths. Fast green is probably the most commonly used counterstain, although eosin or indulin may also be used (Cable, 1977). Both hematoxylin and carmine are regressive nuclear stains, while counterstains employed are progressive cytoplasmic stains. Although counterstains are useful in bringing out surface detail, they may obscure internal structures if overdone. Formulation and use of these stains for parasitology are described in greater detail in several publications (Cable, 1977; Meyer and Olsen, 1980; Pritchard and Kruse, 1982).

Specimens may be dehydrated using any number of dehydrating agents. Ethyl alcohol is most commonly used, although methyl alcohol, tetrabutyl alcohol, or acetone may also be used. Whichever dehydrating agent is used, an ascending series is utilized beginning with either water or 70% dehydrating agent and continuing to 100%. The beginning concentration is determined by the concentration of the solution in which the stain is dissolved. After complete dehydration, the specimen is cleared with a clearing agent such as xylene, toluene, terpineol, or cedarwood oil. The clearing agent renders the specimen transparent and is miscible with both the dehydrating fluid and the mounting medium. After staining, dehydration and clearing, individual parasites are mounted on slides by use of a mounting medium such as Canada balsam. This medium works well with thick parasite specimens and it withstands long periods of storage. Synthetic mounting media are not recommended for thick worms. The synthetic media were designed for sectioned tissue and their use with larger parasites, perhaps because of the large amounts needed for intact helminths, tends to produce air bubbles, cracks and discoloration with time. The careful preparation of permanent slides is especially important for bat helminths since they tend to be minute and require extensive examination for proper identification.

3.1. Staining Permanent Slides

Permanent slides of parasites should be stained using any of a number of stains (e.g., iron alum hematoxylin). Procedures exist in several references (Pritchard and Kruse, 1982; Markell and Voge, 1981; Meyer and Olsen, 1980). Since methods for protozoa differ from techniques used for adult helminths, special care should be taken if one suspects a protozoan component to the intestinal contents.

3.2. Restoration Procedures

Under certain circumstances endoparasitic helminths may be collected when it is imprac-

tical or impossible to follow proper procedures for collection and preservation. Parasites that have been fixed *in situ* or are distorted due to improper fixation can be salvaged by the proper technique (Pritchard and Kruse, 1982). The parasite should first be transferred to a solution containing equal parts of 70% ethanol and glycerine and left for approximately one week. Glycerine is then removed by subsequent washing in 70% ethanol. After staining, the distorted specimen is again placed in 70% ethanol. The specimen is then placed on a microscope slide and a capillary tube placed onto the specimen where it is in contact with the slide. Additional tubes are added until the specimen is straightened. Then a second glass slide is placed on top of the tubes, clamped if needed, and the specimen is dehydrated to 95% ethanol. After several days in ethanol, the specimen should have flattened. Dehydration and mounting can then continue. Smaller specimens can be salvaged by using two glass slides to flatten the worm. However, these procedures can produce artifacts and are not a substitute for freshly prepared specimens.

The restoration of dried out specimens can also be accomplished using the above technique preceded by soaking the specimen in 0.25% sodium tri-phosphate in distilled water (Van Cleave and Ross, 1947) or by use of a glacial acetic acid soak followed by lactic acid (Berland, 1982). Other techniques for this procedure have been suggested (Hetherington, 1922; Burck, 1973).

3.3. Deposition of Voucher Specimens

In any study of bat endoparasites, voucher specimens should be deposited in a recognized museum or parasite collection. The depository used should be a public museum or collection that is supported by regular budgets and curated by permanent staff. Specimens should be freely and promptly loaned to qualified researchers. A guide to 74 major parasite collections in the world is available (Lichtenfels and Pritchard, 1982). If there is any question whether a specific depository is appropriate for a particular type of specimen, do not hesitate to inquire.

In the United States, there are three National Resource Centers for Parasitology. The U.S. National Parasite Collection, Beltsville, Maryland, is maintained by the U.S. Department of Agriculture. This collection is recommended for all holotypes. The Harold W. Manter Laboratory within the University of Nebraska State Museum may be used for paratypes and voucher specimens. The American Type Culture Collection, Rockville, Maryland, maintains specialized collections of protozoans.

When depositing specimens in any museum, all pertinent data should be supplied along with the specimens. Acquisition numbers should be cited in any publication concerning these specimens and these numbers should also be retained in the author's files. It is considered proper to send a reprint of any articles concerning the specimens to the depository.

4. ECOLOGICAL FACTORS

The field of parasitology was long dominated by morphological and systematic studies. Through the pioneering efforts of Dogiel and many others, ecological parasitology has made slow but steady growth and is now universally accepted as a valid subdiscipline (Kennedy, 1975). Most work in this field has been confined to aquatic ecosystems or economically and medically important parasites (Fallis, 1971; Kennedy, 1976; Anderson, 1982a). There are few studies of bat-parasite systems. The field of host-parasite ecology has recently been reviewed with respect to abiotic factors (Esch, 1982), biotic factors (Kennedy, 1982), and host-parasite population biology (Anderson, 1982a, 1982b). It is important that ecological investigations be extended into other areas, including that of bat-parasite ecology. The present studies in this field do little more than provide a crude basis upon which to build. Additional long-term and quantitive work is badly needed.

4.1. Terminology

Because of the relative newness of this field, there is no standardized vocabulary. Several recent attempts have been made to establish working definitions of terms used and misused by parasite ecologists (Margolis et al., 1982a, 1982b). More specialized treatments of ecological terms useful for parasitological investigations are those of Whitaker et al. (1973), Esch et al. (1975), and Durfee (1978).

Infrapopulations of endoparasites are not normally distributed in host populations. These endoparasites display either an overdispersed or random distribution. Although several models have been constructed in order to describe parasite populations in mathematical terms (Hirsch, 1977), these models are hypothetical in nature and are useful only for their heuristic value (Esch, per. comm.).

4.2. Statistical Considerations

As pointed out by Kennedy (1977), Chubb (1979) and Aho et al. (1982), a serious shortcoming in ecological parasitology is the lack of long-term investigations. With few exceptions studies of host-parasite ecology have relied on data collected over a short period of time. One consequence of the general lack of a sufficient data base has been a reliance on non-parametric statistics to analyze parasite populations. Data should be treated with parametric rather than non-parametric statistics. In designing ecological studies in parasitology, one should strive to obtain a sufficiently large data base so that heteroscedasticity does not threaten the validity of the statistical methods used (see Aho et al., 1982). The lack of a sufficient data base should not force researchers to use invalid or inappropriate statistics. For further information the reader should consult a textbook of biometry such as Sokal and Rohlf (1969).

4.3. Seasonal Ecology

References in the literature to the ecology of bat parasites are rare. Ubelaker (1970) categorized bat parasites and discussed several ecological and nutritional problems encountered by these organisms. Holmes (1968) has studied zoogeography and host specificity of bat helminths. The seasonal prevalence of parasites in bats of eight species in Kansas, Nebraska, and Oklahoma was investigated by Nickel and Hansen (1967) and in Iowa by Blankespoor and Ulmer (1970). These workers reported that parasite intensities were low in spring, increased during summer, and peaked in autumn. Both prevalence and intensity were higher in males than females. Blankespoor and Ulmer (1972) reported *Prosthodendrium volaticum* to be more prevalent in summer and autumn. Thus, it has generally been accepted that parasite prevalence and intensity in insectivorous bats are low in spring and increase during summer as insects, the intermediate host for the majority of bat parasites, become available as a food source. However, Coggins et al. (1982) observed an altered seasonal pattern for the digenean parasites of *Myotis lucifugus* in southeastern Wisconsin. Parasite intensity and prevalence were high during autumn and spring but low in summer. Earlier workers had cited loss of parasites during hibernation as a possible source of low spring values. However, hibernating bats in the Wisconsin study possessed an abundant parasite fauna. The high spring intensity and prevalence was postulated to result from an altered hibernation pattern for *M. lucifugus* in Wisconsin. Bats in Iowa hibernated from January to May (Blankespoor and Ulmer, 1972) and a similar pattern probably occurs in Kansas. Since presumably no parasite recruitment occurs during hibernation, low spring intensities suggest that parasites are lost during hibernation. In contrast, bats in Wisconsin hibernated for a much longer period, from October through late May. Since there is a shorter period for parasite recruitment (spring-fall), parasites must overwinter as adults in the definitive host, the bat, instead of a juvenile stage in an insect larva or as a quiescent egg. In this manner adult parasite growth and development can occur quickly when bats become active in spring. Coggins et al. (1982) suggested

the life cycles for most parasites of *M. lucifugus* would be shifted toward autumn and would require less than 12 months to complete since the greatest recruitment of larval stages appeared to occur in late summer and fall and most adults were lost from bats during summer.

Interpretation of conflicting results on seasonal occurrence of bat helminths is complicated by lack of knowledge of host ecology. Autumn swarming, winter hibernation, and spring emergence may involve bats from widely differing localities. Bats are known to migrate great distances from summer roosts to aggregate at hibernacula (Davis and Hitchcock, 1965; Fenton, 1969; Humphrey and Cope, 1976). Thus, spring and autumn collections taken at a hibernaculum may involve a heterogeneous assemblage consisting of several discrete host populations. Collections made at maternity roosts may represent less host diversity and greater intercolony variance. This may lead to fewer infected hosts (prevalence) and fewer parasites per host (intensity) and possibly hosts sexual differences in these two parameters. The discrepancies observed among published studies probably reflect upon host ecology, an allied subject that must be taken into account during studies on parasite ecology or behavior. To date, there have been too few studies to develop firm conclusions.

To my knowledge there have been no reports concerning ecology of endoparasites of non-hibernating bats. Martin (1969) examined lecithodendriid trematodes of *Peropteryx kappleri* in Colombia in a study of allometric growth. This author found evidence of interspecific ecological isolation within the host intestinal tract. He suggested that certain morphological differences observed in trematodes might be accounted for by an endoparasite species living near the limit of its geographic range.

4.4. Effects of Migration

Among those factors influencing the endoparasitic fauna are migrations of the host. To my knowledge there have been no ecological studies investigating the effect of bat migration on endoparasitic fauna. However, extensive work has been done on fish, particularly salmon, that migrate great distances and on migratory birds. The literature on parasites of migratory birds and fish has been reviewed by Dogiel (1966). Coggins et al. (1982) speculated on the effect of bat migration on parasite diversity. However, little data was available to support valid conclusions. Additional work is needed in this area.

4.5. Effects of Host Hibernation

Little is known of the ability of endoparasitic organisms to overwinter in hibernating animals (Chute, 1960, 1964; Schmidt, 1967). Several workers have shown that some species of parasitic helminths are eliminated from their hosts during hibernation (Simitch and Petrovitch, 1953, 1954). Blanchard and Blatin (1907) found that the parasites of *Marmota marmox* were voided during hibernation. Adult *Fasciola hepatica* could not be maintained in hibernating *Citellus tridecemlineatus* over a two-month period (Ford and Lang, 1967). Development and maturation of *F. hepatica* were also greatly retarded during hibernation. Hibernation may either prevent or retard development of *Trichinella spiralis* in golden hamsters (Chute, 1961). Only 48 to 72 hours of hibernation were required for complete protection of the host if the temperature drop occurred within 36 hours after infection. Longer periods of hibernation were required for protection later in the infection. *Trichinella spiralis* developed to the adult stage in bats held at 30-34°C while development was inhibited in bats held at 5, 23 or 26°C (Chute and Covalt, 1960). These workers concluded that lowered body temperature may inhibit development without resulting in total elimination from the host. Cahill et al. (1967) found that the nematode *Nippostrongylus brasiliensis* was lost from hibernating *Citellus tridecemlineatus.*

Although most work concerning parasites in hibernating bats has been conducted under laboratory conditions, the assumption usually has been made that endoparasites are voided from naturally infected hibernating bats (Ubelaker, 1970). However, as early as 1873 Van Beneden noticed an abundant parasite fauna in hibernating bats of Belgium. During a seasonal study of the parasite fauna of two bat species in Russia, Markova (1938) reported that bats emerging from prolonged hibernation had an abundant trematode fauna identical to those parasites occurring in adult bats throughout summer. These trematodes were in different stages of growth and development, some being very young. A possible explanation is that metaceraciae may have been ingested before the host entered hibernation, overwintered as immature stages, and were recovered in spring before significant growth and development could occur. Several other investigators have reported a helminth fauna in hibernating or newly emerged bats (Macy, 1936; Byrd and Macy, 1942; Manter and Debus, 1945).

Coggins et al. (1982) collected bats at varying intervals before, during, and after an extended hibernation. Bats retained a rich and varied helminth fauna after more than seven months. All bats collected contained four to seven parasite species with mean densities similar to spring values. Of those helminths normally encountered during summer, all but one were present during hibernation. Interestingly, this parasite, *Prosthodendrium volaticum,* was reported absent from hibernating bats by Blankespoor and Ulmer (1972). Hibernating *M. lucifugus* in Wisconsin maintain a body temperature of 5°C (Rupprecht, 1980). This temperature is well below those reported to prevent development of *T. spiralis* (Chute and Covalt, 1960) and cause elimination of *F. hepatica* (Ford and Lang, 1967).

Thus, there appears to be at least two distinct survival strategies adopted by helminth parasites for overwintering. Certain species are eliminated from bats during hibernation. In mild climates where hibernation is short, this strategy would be advantageous. These parasites overwinter either as eggs or an immature stage in an intermediate host, usually an insect. However, other helminth species are retained throughout hibernation. In areas with severe climates, hibernation may extend for 7-8 months, a period greatly exceeding the activity period of the host. A shorter period of activity leaves less time for parasite recruitment, growth, and sexual development. Furthermore, the insects upon which bats feed emerge later and are present for a shorter time in these locations. Clearly, further research is needed to fully explore the role of overwintering in parasite ecology.

4.6. Life Cycles

The earliest studies in parasite ecology were investigations into the life history patterns of animal parasites and their general ecological requirements in the physical and biological environment (Olsen, 1974). While the general patterns for the life cycles of major groups of endoparasites are known, we still lack information on the life cycles for specific bat endohelminths. Digeneans appear to constitute the bulk of bat endoparasites and the digenea is certainly the most diverse group inhabiting bats. Ubelaker (1970) listed four genera and eight species of bat trematodes for which complete life histories were known. Nematodes of bats are restricted to capillarids and a number of highly specialized trichostrongyles (Cameron, 1964) although Lichtenfels et al. (1981) reported filarioid nematodes from bat tissue. Thus, although nematode infections in individual hosts may be massive, the nematodes infecting bats are restricted to only a few of the myriad of nematode species. The only cestodes reported from bats have been representatives of the families Hymenolepididae and Anoplocephalidae, the former being more prevalent in bats. The vast majority of cestodes occur in insectivorous bats, although a few have been reported from pollen feeders and fruit eaters (Ubelaker, 1970).

Bats generally become infected with digeneans (trematodes) by ingesting an intermediate host containing the encysted juvenile (metacercaria). Few life cycle studies have been conducted. Knight and Pratt (1955) reported that *Allassogonoporus marginalis* develops in snails, either *Oxytrema silicula* or *Flumenicola virens,* which produce virgulate xiphidiocercariae. Caddisfly larvae, *Limnephilus* sp., function as the second intermediate host. Other bat digeneans have been reported from caddisfly larvae (Knight and Pratt, 1955), mayflies (Etges, 1959), chironomids, mosquitoes, and dragonfly naiads (McMullen, 1937; Macy, 1960). Williams (1967) experimental completed the life cycle of *Prosthodendrium naviculum,* in which the metacercariae were found in crayfish. Since this parasite also occurs in raccoons, crayfish (instead of bats) probably represent the source of infection for this animal. The digenean *Urotrema shillingeri* was described by Price (1932) from a muskrat *Ondatra zibethica,* although *Urotrema* sp. is primarily a parasite of bats. Although the mode of infection was not determined for this parasite, Price speculated that the occurrence of this worm in a muskrat was accidental. The lack of life cycle studies is not surprising considering the difficulty of experimentally completing these cycles. An excellent treatment of this area may be found in Olsen (1974). Interested readers are also referred to the books by Schell (1970) and Schmidt (1970).

4.7. Host Feeding and Foraging Strategy

The feeding habits and foraging strategies of insectivorous bats (Chapter 11) may be important factors in determining the types of endoparasites found. Most endoparasites are ingested when the insects serving as intermediate hosts are eaten as prey. There are many studies of bat feeding behavior and widespread disagreement as to the amount of diet specialization among insectivorous species. For example, *Myotis lucifugus* has been described as highly selective (Buchler, 1976) and selectively opportunistic (Anthony and Kunz, 1977). However, Fenton et al. (1977) and Fenton and Thomas (1980) presented evidence that certain African insectivorous bats act as partitioners (specialists) during the wet season but become opportunistic during the dry season when food becomes scarce. This view is supported by a number of other studies (Anthony and Kunz, 1977; Fenton and Morris, 1976).

Foraging strategies of insectivorous bats may be important in determining density of endoparasites. Several foraging strategies have been reported; e.g., short and long distance foragers, reaction distances, capture attempts, etc. However, caution must be exercised in categorizing bats by foraging strategy (Fenton, 1982). Endoparasites have been used as biological tags for zoogeographic studies among fish (see Dogiel, 1966). Perhaps they could also help resolve some of the unanswered questions in bat feeding behavior, especially in light of their unique association with insect prey.

5. SUMMARY

Extensive taxonomic and morphological records exist on endoparasites of bats. However, bat endoparasites have been neglected as subjects for ecological studies. Bats potentially serve as excellent models for studies on parasite ecology because of their abundance, diverse lifestyles, wide geographic range, and the migratory behavior of certain groups.

Studies of bat endoparasites require an ample and steady supply of hosts. Examination for parasites should occur as quickly after host collection as possible. It is important to make a thorough examination of the animal since endoparasites may occur in any organ of the body. Major groups of endoparasites commonly found within bats include protozoans, digeneans, cestodes, and nematodes. Other groups, acanthocephalans, pentastomes, and mites, have occasionally been reported from bats. Parasites should be recovered alive and processed immediately. Although several adequate fixation techniques are available, the fixation fluid used varies according to the needs of the investigators.

The preparation of permanent slides is usually necessary for accurate identification of endoparasites. The preparation requires that material be stained to facilitate examination. Unstained temporary mounts can also be prepared but do not replace permanently mounted slides. Several special techniques are available for salvaging distorted specimens due to improper fixation or dried-out specimens. Representative voucher or type specimens should always be deposited in a recognized parasite collection so that specimens can be made available to other researchers.

Most studies in the relatively new field of parasite ecology have dealt with parasites of medical or veterinary importance or parasites in closed aquatic ecosystems. The few studies on the ecology of bat endoparasites have produced interesting, but conflicting, results. In this work standardized terminology and methodology is essential, and there have been several recent attempts to standardize commonly used terms in parasite ecology. Information is available on the life histories of bat endoparasites, primarily digeneans. Since most digeneans occur in insectivorous bats, the feeding habits and foraging strategies of these animals may be important factors in determining the types of endoparasites found.

6. REFERENCES

Aho, J. M., J. W. Camp, and G. W. Esch. 1982. Long-term studies on the population biology of *Diplostomulum scheuringi* in a thermally altered reservoir. J. Parasitol., 68:695-708.

Anderson, R. M. 1982a Epidemiology. Pp. 204-251, *in* Modern Parasitology. (F. E. G. Cox, ed.). Blackwell Sci. Publ., London, 346 pp.

Anderson, R. M. 1982b. Host-parasite population biology. Pp. 303-312, *in* Parasites—Their World and Ours. Proc. 5th Int. Cong. Parasitol. (D. F. Mettrick and S. S. Desser, eds.). Elsevier Biomedical Press, Amsterdam. 465 pp.

Anthony, E. L. P., and T. H. Kunz. 1977. Feeding strategies of the little brown bat, *Myotis lucifugus,* in southern New Hampshire. Ecology, 58:775-786.

Barus, V., and B. Rysavy. 1971. An analysis of the biogeography of nematodes of the family Trichostronylidae parasitizing bats of the suborder Microchiroptera. Folia Parasitol., 18:1-14.

Berland, B. 1961. Use of glacial acetic acid for killing parasitic nematodes for collection purposes. Nature, 191:1320-1321.

Berland, B. 1982. Basic techniques involved in helminth preservation. P. 757, *in* Workshop: Technology as applied to museum parasite collections. 5th Int. Cong. Parasit., Toronto, Canada.

Blanchard, R., and M. Blatin. 1907. Immunite de la marmotte en hibernation a l'egard des maladies parasitaires. Arch. Parasitol., 11:361-378.

Blankespoor, H. D., and M. J. Ulmer. 1970. Helminths from six species of Iowa bats. Proc. Iowa Acad. Sci., 77:200-206.

Blankespoor, H. D., and M. J. Ulmer. 1972. *Prosthodendrium volaticum* sp. n. (Trematoda: Lecithodendriidae) from two species of Iowa bats. Proc. Helminthol. Soc. Wash., 39:224-226.

Buchler, E. R. 1976. Prey selection by *Myotis lucifugus* (Chiroptera: Vespertilionidae). Amer. Nat., 110:619-628.

Burck, H. P. 1973. Histologische technik (3rd ed.). G. Thieme, Stuttgart.

Byrd, E. E., and R. W. Macy. 1942. Mammalian trematodes. III. Certain species from bats. J. Tenn. Acad. Sci., 17:149-156.

Caballero y Caballero, E. 1942. Tremátodes de los murciélagos de México. III. Descriptión de *Urotrema scabridum* Braun, 1900 y posición sistematica de las especies norte-americanas de este género. Ann. Inst. Biol., Univ. Autonoma Mexico, 13:641-648.

Caballero y Caballero, E. 1944. Una nueva especie del género *Litomosoides* y consideraciones a cerca de los caracteres sistematicos de este género. Ann. Inst. Biol. Univ. Nac. Autonoma Mexico, 15:383-388.

Caballero y Caballero, E. 1960. Trematodos de los murciélagos de México (Mammalia, Chiroptera Blumenbach, 1774). Ann. Inst. Biol., Univ. Nac. Autonoma Mexico, 31:215-287.

Cable, R. M. 1977. An illustrated laboratory manual of parasitology. (5th ed.). Burgess Publ. Co., Minneapolis, Minnesota, 275 pp.

Cahill, J. E., R. M. Lewert, and B. N. Jaroslow. 1967. Effect of hibernation on course of infec-

tion and immune response in *Citellus tridecemineatus* infected with *Nippostrongylus brasiliensis.* J. Parasitol., 53:110-115.

Cameron, T. W. M. 1964. Host specificity and the evolution of helminthic parasites. Pp. 1-34, *in* Advances in Parasitology. Vol. 2. (Dawes, B., ed.). Academic Press, New York, 332 pp.

Chubb, J. C. 1979. Seasonal occurrence of helminths in freshwater fishes. Part II. Trematoda. Pp. 141-313, *in* Advances in Parasitology, Vol. 17. (Lumsden, W. H. R., R. Muller, and J. R. Baker, eds.). Academic Press, New York.

Chute, R. M. 1960. Overwintering of helminths in hibernating animals. J. Parasitol., 46:539.

Chute, R. M. 1961. Infections of *Trichinella spiralis* in hibernating hamsters. J. Parasitol., 47:25-29.

Chute, R. M. 1964. Hibernation and parasitism: Recent developments and some theoretical considerations. Ann. Acad. Sci. Fenn., A:IV:71:115-122.

Chute, R. M., and D. B. Covalt. 1960. The effect of body temperature on the development of *Trichinella spiralis* in bats. J. Parasitol., 46:855-858.

Coggins, J. R., J. L. Tedesco, and C. E. Rupprecht. 1981. Intestinal helminths of the bat, *Myotis keenii* (Merriam), from southeastern Wisconsin. Proc. Helminthol. Soc. Wash., 48:93-96.

Coggins, J. R., J. L. Tedesco, and C. E. Rupprecht. 1982. Seasonal changes and overwintering of parasites in the bat, *Myotis lucifugus* (Le Conte), in a Wisconsin hibernaculum. Amer. Midl. Nat., 107:305-315.

Coulombe, L. S. 1970. Maintenance of *Trichinella spiralis.* Pp. 144-145, *in* Experiments and Techniques in Parasitology. (Macinnis, A. J., and M. Voge, eds.). W. H. Freeman Co., San Francisco, California, 232 pp.

Davis, L. R. 1973. Techniques. Pp. 411-458, *in* The Coccidia. (D. M. Hammond and P. L. Long, eds.). University Park Press, Baltimore, 482 pp.

Davis, W. H., and H. B. Hitchcock. 1965. Biology and migration of the bat, *Myotis lucifugus,* in New England. J. Mammal., 46:296-313.

Dogiel, V. A. 1966. General Parasitology. Academic Press, New York, 516 pp.

Dubey, J. P., G. V. Swan, and J. K. Frenkel. 1972. A simplified method for isolation of *Toxoplasma gondii* from the feces of cats. J. Parasitol., 58:1005-1006.

Dubois, G. 1955. Les trématodes de chiroptères de la collection Villy Aellen. Étude suivie d'une revision du sous-genre *Prosthodendrium*

Dollfus 1937 (Lecithodendriinae Lühe). Rev. Suisse Zool., 62:469-506.

Dubois, G. 1960. Contribution à l'étude des trématodes de chiroptères. Revision du sous-genre *Prosthodendrium* dollus 1931 et des genres *Lecithodendrium* Looss 1896 et *Pycnoporus* Looss 1899. Rev. Suisse Zool., 67:1-80.

Dubois, G. 1961. Contribution à l'étude des trématodes de chiroptères. Le genre *Acanthatrium* Faust 1919. Rev. Suisse Zool., 68:273-302.

Dubois, G. 1962. Contribution à l'étude des trématodes de chiroptères. Revision du sous-genre Paralecithodendrium Odhner 1911. Rev. Suisse Zool., 69:385-407.

Dubois, G. 1963. Contribution à l'étude trématodes de chiroptères. Revision du genre *Allassogonoporus* Olivier 1938 et note additionnelle sur le sous-genre *Prosthodendrium* Dollus 1931. Rev. Suisse Zool., 70:103-125..

Durette-Desset, M. C., and A. G. Chabaud. 1975. Nématodes Trichostrongyloidea Parasites de Microchiroptères. Ann. Parasitol. (Paris), 50:303-337.

Durfee, P. T. 1978. Incidence and prevalence defined. Aust. Vet. J., 54:405-406.

Esch, G. W. 1982. Abiotic factors: An overview. Pp. 279-292, *in* Parasites—Their world and ours. Proc. 5th Int. Cong. Parasitol. (Mettrick, D. F., and S. S. Desser, eds.). Elsevier Biomedical Press, Amsterdam. 465 pp.

Esch, G. W., J. W. Gibbons, and J. E. Bourque. 1975. An analysis of the relationship between stress and parasitism. Amer. Midl. Nat., 93:339-353.

Etges, F. I. 1959. Studies on the life history of a species of *Acanthatrium* (Trematoda: Lecithodendriidae). J. Parasitol., 45(Suppl.):18.

Fallis, A. M. (ed.). 1971. Ecology and physiology of parasites. Univ. Toronto Press, Toronto, 258 pp.

Fenton, M. B. 1969. Summer activity of *Myotis lucifugus* (Chiroptera: Vesperilionidea) at hibernacula in Ontario and Quebec. Can. J. Zool., 47:597-602.

Fenton, M. B. 1982. Echolocation, insect hearing, and feeding ecology of insectivorous bats. Pp. 261-285, *in* Ecology of bats. (T. H. Kunz, ed.). Plenum Press, New York, 425 pp.

Fenton, M. B., N. G. H. Boyle, T. M. Harrison, and D. J. Oxley. 1977. Activity patterns, habitat use, and prey selection by some African insectivorous bats. Biotropica, 9:73-85.

Fenton, M. B., and G. K. Morris. 1976. Opportun-

istic feeding by desert bats (*Myotis* spp.). Can. J. Zool., 54:526-530.

Fenton, M. B., and D. W. Thomas. 1980. Dry season overlap in activity patterns, habitat use, and prey selection by sympatric African insectivorous bats. Biotropica, 12:81-90.

Ford, B. R., and B. Z. Lang. 1967. *Fasciola hepatica* in hibernating *Citellus tridecemlineatus* (Mitchell). J. Parasitol., 53:1073.

Garcia, L. S., and L. R. Ash. 1979. Diagnostic parasitology. (2nd ed.). C. V. Mosby Co., St. Louis, 174 pp.

Gibson, D. I. 1979. Materials and methods in helminth alpha-taxonomy. Parasitology, 79:xxxvi.

Guilford, J. H. 1952. Studies of the trematodes of certain midwestern bats. Unpubl. M. S. thesis, Univ. Illinois, Urbana.

Hetherington, D. C. 1922. Some new methods in nematode technique. J. Parasitol., 9:102-104.

Hirsch, R. P. 1977. Use of mathematical models in parasitology. Pp. 169-207, *in* Regulation of parasite populations. (G. W. Esch, ed.). Academic Press, New York, 253 pp.

Hoare, C. A. 1965. Vampire bats as vectors and hosts of equine and bovine trypanosomes. Acta Trop., 22:204-216.

Holmes, J. C. 1968. Factors influencing the trematode fauna of bats. 1st Int. Cong. Parasitol. (C) 2:490-492.

Humphrey, S. R., and J. B. Cope. 1976. Population ecology of the little brown bat, *Myotis lucifugus,* in Indiana and north-central Kentucky. Spec. Publ. 4, Amer. Soc. Mammal., 81 pp.

Kennedy, C. R. 1975. Ecological animal parasitology. John Wiley Co., New York, 163 pp.

Kennedy, C. R. (ed.). 1976. Ecological aspects of parasitology. North Holland Publ. 6, Amsterdam, 474 pp.

Kennedy, C. R. 1977. The regulation of fish parasite populations. Pp. 63-109, *in* Regulation of parasite populations. (Esch, G. W., ed.). Academic Press, New York, 253 pp.

Kennedy, C. R. 1982. Biotic factors. Pp. 293-302, *in* Parasites—Their world and ours. Proc. 5th Int. Cong. Parasitol. (Mettrick, D. F., and S. S. Desser, eds.). Elsevier Biomedical Press, Amsterdam, 465 pp.

Knight, R. A., and I. Pratt. 1955. The life histories of *Allassogonoporous vespertilionis* Macy and *Acanthatrium oregonense* Macy (Trematoda: Lecithodendriidae). J. Parasitol., 41:248-255.

Lichtenfels, J. R., K. P. Bhatnagar, F. A. Whittaker, and H. D. Frahm. 1981. Filarioid nematodes in olfactory mucosa, olfactory bulb, and brain ventricular system of bats. Trans. Amer. Microsc. Soc., 100:216-219.

Lichtenfels, J. R., and M. H. Pritchard. 1982. A guide to the parasite collections of the world. American Society of Parasitologists. Cited in Proc. Helminthol. Soc. Wash., 50:82.

Lotz, J. M. and W. F. Font. 1983. Review of the Lecithodendriidae (Trematoda) from *Eptesicus fuscus* in Wisconsin and Minnesota. Proc. Helminthol. Soc. Wash., 50:83-102.

Macy, R. W. 1931. A key to the species of *Hymenolepis* found in bats and the description of a new species, *H. christensoni,* from *Myotis lucifugus.* Trans. Amer. Microsc. Soc., 50:344-347.

Macy, R. W. 1935a. *Gyrabascus brevigastrus,* new genus, new species, a bat trematode, with a note on *Distomum mehelyi* Mödlinger. J. Parasitol., 21:413-415.

Macy, R. W. 1935b. A new trematode, *Limatulum gastroides* (Lecithodendriidae), from the little brown bat, *Myotis lucifugus.* Proc. Helminthol. Soc. Wash., 2:74-75.

Macy, R. W. 1936. Three new trematodes of Minnesota bats with a key to the genus *Prosthodendrium.* Trans. Amer. Microsc. Soc., 55:352-359.

Macy, R. W. 1947. Parasites found in certain Oregon bats with the description of a new cestode, *Hymenolepis gertschi.* Amer. Midl. Nat., 37:375-378.

Macy, R. W. 1960. The life cycle of *Plagiorchis vespertilionis parorchis,* n. ssp. (Trematoda: Plagiorchiidae), and observations on the effects of light on the emergence of the cercaria. J. Parasitol., 46:337-345.

Manter, H. W., and J. S. Debus. 1945. Two trematodes from a hibernating bat, *Myotis californicus.* Trans. Amer. Microsc. Soc., 64:297-299.

Margolis, L., R. C. Anderson, and J. C. Holmes. 1982. Recommended usage of selected terms in ecological and epidemiological parasitology. Bull. Can. Soc. Zool., 13:14.

Margolis, L., G. W. Esch, J. C. Holmes, A. M. Kuris, and G. A. Schad. 1982. The use of ecological terms in parasitology (report of an ad hoc committee of the American Society of Parasitologists). J. Parasitol., 68:131-133.

Marinkelle, C. J. 1976. Biology of the trypanosomes of bats. Pp. 175-216, *in* Biology of the Kinetoplastida. (Lumsden, W. H. B., and D. A. Evans, eds.). Academic Press, New York.

Markell, E. K., and M. Voge. 1981. Medical parasitology. W. B. Saunders Co., Philadelphia, 374 pp.

Markova, L. I. 1938. The effect of hibernation on the condition of the parasite fauna of bats. Zool. Zh., 17:133-144.

Martin, D. R. 1969. Lecithodendriid trematodes from the bat, *Peropteryx kappeleri,* In Colombia, including discussions of allometric growth and significance of ecological isolation. Proc. Helminthol. Soc. Wash., 36:250-260.

McMullen, D. B. 1937. The life histories of three trematodes, parasites in birds and mammals, belonging to the genus *Plagiorchis.* J. Parasitol., 23:235-243.

Meyer, M. C., and O. W. Olsen. 1980. Essentials of parasitology. (3rd ed.). W. C. Brown Co., Dubuque, Iowa, 266 pp.

Nickel, P. A., and M. F. Hansen. 1967. Helminths of bats collected in Kansas, Nebraska and Oklahoma. Amer. Midl. Nat., 78:481-486.

Olsen, O. W. 1974. Animal parasites, their life cycles and ecology. (3rd ed.). University Park Press, Baltimore, 562 pp.

Postek, M. T., K. S. Howard, A. H. Johnson, and K. L. McMichael. 1980. Scanning electron microscopy, A Student's Handbook. Ladd Research Industries, Inc., Burlington, Vermont, 305 pp.

Price, E. W. 1932. Four new species of trematode worms from the muskrat, *Ondatra zibethica,* with a key to the trematode parasites of the muskrat. Proc. U.S. Natl. Mus., 79:1-13.

Pritchard, M. H., and G. O. Kruse. 1982. The collection and preservation of animal parasites. Univ. Nebraska Press, Lincoln, 141 pp.

Read, C. P. 1970. Some physiological and biochemical aspects of host-parasite relations. J. Parasitol., 56:643-652.

Read, C. P., and J. E. Simmons, Jr. 1963. The physiology and biochemistry of tapeworms. Physiol. Rev., 43:263-305.

Rupprecht, C. E. 1980. Annual activity cycles and hibernation strategies in a north temperate bat community. M. S. thesis, Univ. Wisconsin-Milwaukee. 84 pp.

Rutkowska, M. A. 1980. The helminthofauna of bats (Chiroptera) from Cuba. I. A review of nematodes and acanthocephalans. Acta Parasit. Pol., 26:153-186.

Schell, S. C. 1970. How to know the trematodes. W. C. Brown Co., Dubuque, Iowa, 355 pp.

Schmidt, G. D. 1970. How to know the tapeworms. W. C. Brown Co., Dubuque, Iowa, 266 pp.

Schmidt, J. P. 1967. Response of hibernating mammals to physical, parasitic and infectious agents. Pp. 421-438, *in* Mammalian hibernation III. (K C. Fisher, A. R. Dawe, C. P. Lyman, E. Schöhbaum, and F. E. South, Jr., eds.). American Elsevier Publ. Co., New York, 535 pp.

Simitch, T., and Z. Petrovitch. 1953. La reinfestation de *Citellus citellus* par *Hymenolepis nana* apres le sommeil hibernal, est-elle possible? Arach. Inst. past. Alg., 31:397-399.

Simitch, T., and Z. Petrovitch. 1954. Ce qu'il advient avec les helminths du *Citellus citellus* au cours du sommeil hibernal de ce rongeur. Riv. Parassit., 15:655-662.

Sinclair, N. R., and D. I. John. 1973. Hot water as a tool in mass field preparation of platyhelminth parasites. J. Parasitol., 59:935-936.

Sokal, R. R., and F. J. Rohlf. 1969. Biometry. (2nd ed.). W. H. Freeman Co., San Francisco, 359 pp.

Stiles, C. W., and M. O. Nolan, 1931. Key-catalogue of parasites reported for Chiroptera (bats) with their possible public health importance. Natl. Inst. Health Bull., 155:603-742, 768-789.

Ubelaker, J. E. 1970. Some observations on ecto- and endoparasites of Chiroptera. Pp. 247-261, *in* About Bats. (B. H. Slaughter and D. W. Walton, eds.). Southern Methodist Univ. Press, Dallas, Texas, 339 pp.

Ubelaker, J. E., R. D. Specian, and D. W. Duszynski. 1977. Endoparasites. Pp. 7-56, *in* Biology of bats of the new world family Phyllostomatidae. Part. II. (R. J. Baker, J. K. Jones, Jr., and D. C. Carter, eds.). Spec. Publ. Mus. Texas Tech. Univ., 13:1-364.

Van Beneden, P. J. 1873. Les parasites des chauves-sourisde Belgique. Mem. Acad. R. Belg., Cl. Sci., 40:1-42.

Van Cleave, H. J., and J. A. Ross. 1947. Use of trisodium phosphate in microscopical technic. Science, 106:194.

Whitaker, R. H., S. A. Levin, and R. B. Root. 1973. Niche, habitat, and ecotope. Amer. Nat., 107:321-338.

Williams, R. R. 1967. Metacercariae of *Prosthodendrium naviculum* Macy, 1936, (Trematoda: Lecithodendriidae) from the crayfish, *Orconectes rusticus* (Girard). Proc. Penn. Acad. Sci., 41:38-41.

Woo, P. T. K. 1969. The haematocrit centrifuge for the detection of trypanosomes in blood. Can. J. Zool., 47:921-923.

Chapter 29

Health Precautions for Bat Researchers

Denny G. Constantine

California Department of Health Services
Berkeley, California 94704 U S A

1. INTRODUCTION

Investigators often become preoccupied with reaching an objective and fail to recognize health hazards they inflict on themselves or on wildlife in the course of their studies. There seems to be an endless list of potential health problems of concern to the bat researcher. During the past 30 years, bats have been extensively studied for evidence of infection by various pathogens, and it is not surprising that evidence of infection by numerous agents of disease has been found. In the great majority of cases, bats merely join man and other animal species as incidental, dead-end victims rather than sources of the infections. Known and potential public health problems associated with bats have been reviewed (Constantine, 1970). This chapter updates pressing problem areas and addresses others that have received little or no previous attention.

Gases, such as ammonia, carbon dioxide, and methane, can accumulate in bat caves and mine tunnels and may threaten the safety of investigators. Acute exposure to bat ectoparasites and bat urine, sometimes experienced by researchers in exceedingly populous bat caves, could be hazardous. Knowledge of bat rabies continues to grow and the subject is updated in this chapter, as well as new information on rabies prevention. Investigators should also be aware of the recently-recognized rabies-related viruses in Africa and Europe for which there is no specific protection. These and other pathogenic viruses found in saliva of certain bats suggest caution to avoid bat bites even if one is adequately vaccinated against rabies infection. Bat-associated histoplasmosis is another important problem updated here. Researchers may inadvertently transfer pathogens between bat roosts or between bat species, and they might introduce disease agents of human origin into bat populations.

2. HAZARDOUS ATMOSPHERIC GASES IN CAVES AND MINE TUNNELS

Caves, mine tunnels, wells, and similar underground spaces sometimes contain deadly atmospheres due to the presence of noxious gases and/or the absence of oxygen (O_2). Noxious gases are encountered most frequently in mine tunnels although published information is scarce. Most of these gases are odorless and, if present in high concentrations, they may overcome the victim without warning. Mixtures of the gases are often present, complicating detection and safety methods.

Although many atmospheric gas problems are known in caves, reports of fatalities are not common. Speleologists tend to exchange warnings of problem caves, avoid those emitting the odoriferous noxious gases, and are not eager to advertise problems that would elicit the destructive solutions humankind may devise. Thus, published data are too few to be meaningful except on a local basis in rare instances.

Most of the available information on the responses of humans to atmospheric gas is based on studies of young, healthy subjects at rest, at room temperature, and experimentally subjected to low concentrations of a single gas. Industrial accidents provide opportunities to record the results of exposures to higher, often unmeasured concentrations. However, such data can be misleading when applied to conditions prevailing in bat roosts located in caves and mines. Mixtures of noxious gases are usually present, and O_2 may be deficient for various reasons. Moreover, the strenuous exercise characteristic of activity in these places and the excessive heat and humidity that often prevail not only directly affect humans adversely but they also increase the depth and frequency of respira-

tions, consequently increasing exposure to the gases. Brief encounters with relatively low concentrations of the gases may not seriously affect young or healthy adults, but far more serious effects may result in older persons or those of any age with impaired cardiovascular, pulmonary-respiratory or neurological functions.

Gases discussed herein are included in Table 1. They are categorized as: 1) irritants, including ammonia (NH_3) and sulfur dioxide (SO_2) or 2) simple asphyxiants that block access to atmospheric O_2 by displacement or dilution. These include carbon dioxide (CO_2), methane (CH_4), and nitrogen (N_2). Toxic asphyxiants include hydrogen sulfide (H_2S) and carbon monoxide (CO). The foregoing categories are not necessarily absolute (i.e., some gases have more than one inimical property). Oxygen may be deficient due to the presence and concentrations of other gases or due to chemical reactions. Nitrogen and its compounds may contribute additional atmospheric problems in some wet bat roosts, where anaerobic bacteria use nitrate to evolve nitrogen (James, 1977).

These gases may be present only seasonally and locally within an underground system. Some gases (CO_2, H_2S, and SO_2) are heavier than air and are usually found at floor level or in lower strata unless they are blocked while sinking or they are produced locally as CO_2 is produced by bat colonies. Other gases (NH_3, CH_4) are lighter than air and rise to leave by openings or to be trapped in uppermost dead-end chambers.

2.1. Detecting and Measuring Atmospheric Gases

It is in the researcher's best interest to obtain local expert (i.e., mine safety authorities and speleologists) knowledge of underground atmospheres where that information is available. For sites within the United States, the U.S. Department of Labor, Mine Safety Health Administration and the National Speleological Society should be able to identify state or local offices or societies that can help.

Table 1. Some characteristics and exposure limits of certain gases.

	Density	Odor	Explosive Concentrations	NIOSH*-recommended Exposure Limit
Methane (CH_4)	0.7168	None	50,000-150,000 ppm (5-15 vol %)	None. Leave at once.
Ammonia (NH_3)	0.7708	Sharp	160,000-250,000 ppm (16-25 vol %)	Under 50 ppm (with a ceiling of 50 ppm for 5 min) per 10-hr work shift, 40-h work week
Carbon monoxide (CO)	1.2504	None	125,000-742,000 ppm (12.5-74.2 vol %)	35 ppm (with a ceiling of 200 ppm) average per 10-h work shift, 40-h work week
Nitrogen (N_2)	1.2506	None	NA	NA
Air	1.2930	None	NA	NA
Oxygen (O_2)	1.4290	None	NA	NA
Hydrogen sulfide (H_2S)	1.5392	Rotten eggs	43,000-460,000 ppm (4.3-46 vol %)	Under 10 ppm (with a ceiling of 10 ppm for 10 min) per 10-h work shift, 40-h work week
Carbon dioxide (CO_2)	1.9768	None	NA	10,000 ppm average (with a ceiling of 30,000 ppm for 10 min) per 10-h work shift, 40-h work week
Sulfur dioxide (SO_2)	2.9266	Burning matches	NA	0.5 ppm per 10-h work shift, 40-h work week

* National Institute for Occupational Safety and Health, U.S. Public Health Serivce.
NA = Not applicable.

Researchers should present evidence of qualifications and responsibility concerning personal safety and faunal conservation to justify the kind of response being sought.

Methods for detecting and measuring the atmospheric gases of major health interest during explorations of mine tunnels and caves are summarized in Table 2. Approved and certified detectors are listed in Appendix 1. One should proceed into the underground passage with the detector instruments attached to a belt or elsewhere. Audible alarms on these devices signal the presence of noxious gas, or O_2 deficit. Tube gas samplers can be used to identify and measure certain gases. Automatic detectors are pocket-size, battery-operated, continuous-sampling instruments with digital liquid crystal panels that display atmospheric gas concentrations. They are expensive and require maintenance and calibration equipment and supplies. Unfortunately, the CO detector is plagued by interference from various other gases, some of which may be present.

The combined O_2-CH_4 detector, which has Mine Safety and Health Administration (MSHA) approval, can be less satisfactorily replaced with an inexpensive mine safety lamp. The lamp is constructed so explosions will not occur in the presence of flammable gases; detecting CH_4 concentrations as low as 1.5%, the flame lengthens, eventually extinguishing with popping sounds in an explosive atmosphere, and it shortens if O_2 is deficient, usually reflecting the CO_2 excess expected to accompany an O_2 deficit.

The CO automatic detector will also indicate dangerous or lethal levels of CH_4, H_2S, NH_3, and SO_2, but the instrument will not specify which gas or combination of gases

Table 2. Field methods for detecting and measuring atmospheric gases.

Gas	Levels that might occur in mines or caves	Minimal dangerous levels*	Odor	Initial Detection			Tube gas samplers to differentiate gases that interfere with automatic samplers and/or to determine gas concentrations+				
				O_2 deficit automatic detector with readout of concentration, audible alarm**	CH_4 automatic detector with readout of concentration & audible alarm**	CO automatic detector with readout of concentration & audible alarm***	CO	H_2S	NH_3	CO_2	SO_2
O_2 (deficit)	0-21 Vol%	<16 Vol%	None	0-100 Vol %							
CH_4	0-100 Vol%	Any level	None		0-3 Vol%	By interference 10,000 ppm (1 Vol%) CH_4 registers as 1ppm CO					
CO	0-5,000 ppm	> 50 ppm	None			0-500 ppm	5-700 ppm + 10-3,000 ppm				
H_2S	0-1,000 ppm	> 10 ppm	Noticeable at < 1 ppm but transient due to olfactory paralysis			By interference 0.1 ppm H_2S registers as 1 ppm CO		1-200 ppm + 5-600 ppm			
NH_3	0-5,000 ppm	> 50 ppm	First noticeable at 1-30 ppm			By interference, 55 ppm NH_3 registers as 1 ppm CO			5-700 ppm		
CO_2	0-15 Vol%	> 1 Vol% (10,000 ppm)	None	The presence of CO_2 is usually inferred in an O_2 deficit						0.1-6 Vol%	
SO_2	Few data	10 ppm	First noticeable at 0.3-1 ppm			By interference, 2 ppm SO_2 registers as 1 ppm CO					0.5-22 ppm + 1-400 ppm

* From NIOSH, 1983. Levels are based on short exposures in the unlikely absence of other adverse factors such as other debilitating gases, smoking, work, excessive heat or humidity, advanced age, abnormal cardiovascular, pulmonary-respiratory, or neurological functions.
** Available as a combination, pocket-size unit (Nat. Mine Safety Service Co. Model Mx240 oxygen and methane gas monitor). A mine safety lamp provides qualitative evidence of O_2 deficit (thus inferred CO_2 excess) and the presence of explosive gases.
*** Available as a pocket-size unit (Mine Safety Appliances Co. Model IV MiniCO carbon monoxide indicator and alarm). Other interfering gases, present in select circumstances, would include H_2, NO_2, NO, and C_2H_5OH.
+ NIOSH-certified tubes produced by Draegar for use with the Draegar Multi-Gas Detector are cited herein. Many other firms' tubes are not constructed to eliminate interference from other gases.

are present. However, the first of these interfering gases would be recorded on the O_2-CH_4 detecting instrument, and the second, third, and fourth gases should be evident by odor, although one soon loses the ability to smell H_2S.

The tube gas sampling method is based on drawing a measured volume of air through a small tube that contains crystals or particles which upon contact with a particular gas will change color. The length of discoloration of the column is proportional to the concentration of the gas in the atmosphere. With this system, presence or absence of CO, H_2S, NH_3, SO_2, or CO_2 is substantiated. Sampling by this method is relatively inexpensive though somewhat lacking in precision. Tubes produced by some manufacturers are plagued by interfering gases. Greater precision can be obtained by performing tests on field samples upon returning to the laboratory. Instruction sheets provided by the manufacturer should be read carefully; especially critical are storage conditions, shelf life, and interfering gases and vapors.

2.2. Protection, First Aid, and Rescue

Certain bats live in concentrations of NH_3 that would soon kill persons, and other bats live in CO_2 concentrations similarly lethal for people. Therefore it cannot be assumed that presence of bats signifies a safe atmosphere. Unexplained mortality of hundreds or thousands of bats, sometimes evident from remains observed in caves, may be due to exposure to lethal concentrations of gases.

U. S. Government agencies have recommended limits for human exposure to various harmful gases (Table 1). Bat researchers are advised to heed these standards or risk lifelong debilitation, such as brain damage or permanent pulmonary impairment, if not death. In fact, government standards are not restrictive enough for researchers who work in caves and mines when one considers the additive effects of multiple gas insults, excessive heat, humidity, and strenuous exercise.

Before working in a cave or mine, one should be equipped with appropriate respiratory apparatus for the kind and concentration of contaminant gas for the projected work period, and know that there is at last 19.5% O_2 in the atmosphere. Various kinds of respiratory protection systems for use in particular concentrations of gas are given in Mackison et al. (1981). Respirator masks or facepieces are usually available in different sizes and must be individually fitted to ensure effectiveness. If cartridge filters are used, one should take care to not exhaust their useful lives. For example, as filters fail, one can imperceptibly inhale ever-increasing ammonia quantities, because one tends to lose the ability to perceive the odor after continuous exposure.

Gas detector failure, carelessness, or other factors may result in persons becoming incapacitated by dangerous gases while deep underground. Ideally, the aid of expert rescue teams would be sought, but time and distance might preclude that option. Self-rescue or the rescue of others may be indicated. A self-contained source of O_2 should suffice to resolve most atmospheric gas problems, assuming the problem duration does not exceed the O_2 supply. A relatively small (3.8 kg), rugged, self-contained O_2 rebreathing apparatus (Draeger Model OXY-SR 60B), designed for self-rescue, sustains the wearer for one hour of extreme physical exertion or for five hours of rest. A larger (13.5 kg), rugged, back-mounted, self-contained O_2 rebreathing apparatus (Draeger Model BG-174A) is good for four hours of work. They are proportionately expensive, and the larger unit requires expensive support equipment.

Knowledge of first-aid as practiced by cavers, and familiarization with speleological rescue techniques (Halliday, 1982) is recommended. Mine safety engineers with state and federal mine health agencies may provide consultation and sometimes training to those seeking information on mine safety matters; they may also be available for rescue teams. If one is fortunate enough to be able to summon help for a rescue attempt, mine safety agencies recommend calling the county sheriff, who should activate a previously established rescue network. For cave search and rescue, the National Speleological Society recommends that one contact the National Cave Rescue Commission (via the U. S. Air Force Rescue Coordination Center). See Appendix 1 for advice plus reasonably quick assistance throughout the continental United States.

2.3. Ammonia

Atmospheric ammonia accumulates in many populous bat roosts in caves and mine tunnels, especially in tropical and subtropical areas. Concentrations are sometimes high enough to bleach hair of bats (Constantine, 1958). Ammonia is released from voided urine and from the decomposition of bat carcasses and guano. Concentrations harmful to or lethal for man develop in some caves.

The National Institute of Occupational Safety and Health (NIOSH) established a maximum NH_3 exposure limit of less than 50 parts per million (ppm) (with a ceiling of 50 ppm for 5 minutes) per 10-hour work period, for a 40-hour work week (NIOSH, 1983). *Tadarida brasiliensis* can live in 100 times that concentration (5,000 ppm) according to Studier et al. (1967). Atmospheric NH_3 levels of 10 to 195 ppm were present in five Texas caves occupied by *T. brasiliensis* (Constantine, 1967a). After 30 min in an NH_3 concentration of 195 ppm, a companion and I experienced laryngospasms in reaction to the gas. The NH_3 concentration was as high as 1,850 ppm in another *T. brasiliensis* cave roost in Mexico (Mitchell, 1964) where I had a similar reaction after a few minutes exposure on an earlier date.

Ammonia is absorbed by respiratory mucus, which coats the entire respiratory tract except for the respiratory bronchioles and alveoli. The resulting caustic fluid quickly destroys epithelial cilia and can cause extensive tissue erosion and ultimately death. Short-term exposure to the gas may cause burning of the eyes, runny nose, coughing, chest pain, cessation of respiration, and death. It can cause severe breathing difficulties which may be delayed in onset. Repeated, long-term exposure may cause chronic irritation of the eyes and of the upper respiratory tract.

Pulmonary edema has preceded death following accidental industrial exposures to NH_3 concentrations that presumably resemble the higher levels reported in bat caves. However, persons involved in industrial accidents are usually quickly removed from the site of exposure. As one of two persons who experienced larynogospasm after 30 min of exposure to 195 ppm of the gas, I doubt that similarly afflicted persons deep in a cave could leave without help. We were approaching the cave exit at the time of the reaction and escaped in about one min, having to force breathing, which was inefficient, contributing to exhaustion and an impending feeling of panic. Excessive heat, high humidity, and the effects of difficult work were contributing factors. Other gases could have had compounding effects. Sulfur dioxide, not checked on this occasion, had been present in 2.5 ppm concentration two months earlier.

As treatment, Gadaskina (1983) recommends fresh air and inhalation of warm water vapor (if possible with the addition of vinegar or citric acid) and a 10% solution of menthol in chloroform. Warm milk should be imbibed. In the event of asphyxia, oxygen should be inhaled, preferably under low pressure, until dyspnea or cyanosis lessens, followed by a subcutaneous inoculation of 1 ml of a 1% solution of atropine. If breathing is interrupted or stops, resuscitation must be applied.

The odor of ammonia is distinctive and should suffice as warning. NIOSH-certified detector tube samplers can be used to measure atmospheric ammonia concentrations. Mackison et al. (1981) lists apparatus for respiratory protection against ammonia.

2.4. Carbon Dioxide

James (1977) summarized recognized sources of CO_2 in caves: 1) diffusion of gaseous CO_2 through soil and rock into the cave, 2) release of CO_2 from mineralized waters that enter the cave, 3) production of CO_2 by microorganisms in organic deposits such as vegetation or guano, 4) respiration of plants and animals, 5) burning of hydrocarbons, and 6) volcanic gases. Of these, mineralized water, microorganisms active in organic deposits, and the metabolic activities of bats are usually the major contributors of CO_2. Exceptionally, volcanic gases, which are rarely and only locally encountered, are known to produce atmospheric CO_2 concentrations as high as 36%. Carbon dioxide forms carbonic acid in water, dissolving limestone and enlarging cave rooms. Thus, exhaled CO_2 from bats is among CO_2 sources that enlarge bat living quarters.

The normal air we inhale usually contains about 0.03% CO_2, and the air we exhale contains about 4.38%. NIOSH (1983) has established a permissible exposure limit of 10,000 ppm (1%) averaged over a 10-h work shift, 40-h work week, with a ceiling of 30,000 ppm (3%) averaged over a 10-min period. The highest published CO_2 level reported in a cave in the United States was 8% in a Missouri cave for which the gas source was not reported (Halliday, 1982). The greatest concentration found in a series of five Texas bat caves was 2.1%, the others being between 0.08 and 0.46% (Constantine, 1967a).

Considerable research has been done on "foul air" (elevated CO_2, lowered O_2, increased N_2) in Australian bat caves (James et al., 1975; James, 1977; Osborne, 1981; Halbert, 1982) where CO_2 concentrations exceeding 12% have been detected. As anticipated, studies demonstrated that CO_2 almost exactly replaces O_2, volume for volume, except where N_2 production by microorganisms lowers the O_2 level still further. Table 3 illustrates these phenomena. Concentrations of CO_2 vary from place-to-place within a

Table 3. Major gas analyses in normal air and in two Australian caves. (See text for reference sources.)

	CO_2%	O_2%	N_2%*
Outside air	0.033	20.95	79.03
Cave 1	3.0	18.0	79.0
Cave 2	4.6	11.0	84.0

*Also includes argon, rare gases, and water vapor.

cave, and they can vary tremendously in time within a cave room. Carbon dioxide tends to settle to lower cave levels, but it can occur in high concentration at any level where it is being produced, such as in the vicinity of bat aggregations. The gas tends to concentrate on the floor of undisturbed horizontal passages but rises dangerously in response to persons walking through it.

Because increased atmospheric CO_2 is generally accompanied by an equal decrease in O_2, reactions of exposed persons are usually referable to both changes (Note, however, that O_2 can be totally absent from some atmospheres in caves or mines for reasons discussed elsewhere in this chapter). Resting humans at room temperature double their respiratory volumes following an increase of atmospheric CO_2 from the normal 0.04% to 4%, redoubling it at 5%. At 7.6% the heart rate and blood pressure increase, accompanied by headache, dizziness, and sweating. In a 10% CO_2 atmosphere, unconsciousness supervenes, occurring in a minute or less at 11% (Mackison et al., 1981). Some persons do not experience the increased respiration and other warning symptoms, and thus are in extreme danger of sudden unconsciousness except for signs of cyanosis (blue lips, mucous membranes, conjunctivae, ear lobes, and nail beds) which might not be noticed in the darkness of a cave. Resting persons may be overcome imperceptibly and are unable to lift their feet upon trying to leave (James et al., 1975).

Reactions of persons in bat caves can be exacerbated by excessive heat, humidity, the presence of other gases, and the necessity to expend energy. A CO_2 concentration of 2.10% in a *Myotis velifer* cave roost elicited apprehension and gasping in persons who could tolerate the hot, humid atmosphere a maximum of about 15 min (Constantine, 1970). Serious distress can occur in concentrations as low as 1%; victims become drowsy (James et al., 1975).

In studying atmospheres in Australian caves, James and others mentioned above were unprotected in CO_2 concentrations as great as 4%, an exposure now known to have permanent deleterious effects (Matheson, 1983). They concluded that persons who have spent some time in a high CO_2 atmosphere should depart slowly, taking several minutes to ensure a gradual transition to a normal atmosphere in order to avoid "off effects," which include extreme hyperventilation, vomiting, shouting, and uncontrollable laughter or crying. They advised administering O_2 or compressed air to seriously distressed persons prior to moving them. However, "off effects" could be elicited by quickly switching from high CO_2 concentrations to the fresh air in an accessory breathing apparatus, producing potentially disastrous results, so the change has to be made slowly. The person who has inhaled excessive amounts of CO_2 should be moved to fresh air by persons wearing auxiliary breathing apparatus. If breathing has stopped, artificial respiration should be performed. Medical attention should be obtained as soon as possible (Mackison et al., 1981).

Carbon dioxide is an odorless gas that is not detectable by the senses, nor is the usual corresponding O_2 deficit readily noticeable. Australian cavers estimate CO_2 concentration by use of flame extinction tests, which proved satisfactory in their circumstances, but explosive CH_4, present in some caves and mines, argues against the use of open flames. The flame safety lamp, described in Section 2.1, obviates explosions. Detector tubes, certified by NIOSH, may be used to identify and measure atmospheric CO_2. Mackison et al. (1981) designate approved respiratory protection for CO_2.

2.5. Methane

Pre-formed methane occurs in some mines, also as "marsh gas" produced by decay of vegetable matter under water. It and other gases can collect in caves and mines through decomposition of organic materials such as washed-in vegetation, garbage, or sewage, sometimes deposited through human agency.

Formed during the carboniferous period, CH_4 is very common in coal and lignite strata, hence it is common in these mines. It is also known in potassium mines, in bituminous shale, and in certain other mines. Some layers of coal suddenly give off large quantities of the gas with an explosion-like force, projecting fine coal before it. It is explosive at concentrations in air between five and 15%. Persons not killed by the explosions may be asphyxiated by the resulting CO_2. The deadly atmosphere may linger to affect later visitors.

Methane explosions have occurred in various abandoned mine tunnels. Halliday (1982) describes explosions of gas ignited by carbide lights after pockets of gas were released from stream-bottom mud in caves by wading speleologists. Pounder (1982) quotes observations of gigantic spontaneous explosions within a cave system in England with issuing of flames to the exterior.

Methane is said to have practically no physiological effect when present under the lower flammable limit (5%), although it can act as a simple asphyxiant at concentrations of 87% or greater. The explosive properties of the gas and consequent noxious gas-laden O_2-deficient atmosphere are practical problems of concern here.

Methane is odorless. The gas safety lamp (Appendix 1) has been used by miners for many years to detect the presence of CH_4 or other flammable gases and also to indicate an O_2 deficit. Alternatively, a pocket-size, battery-operated methanometer with digital liquid crystal readout and audible alarm may be worn on one's belt to provide warning and to indicate atmospheric concentration. A similar device, available alone or in combination with the methanometer, provides audible warning of low O_2 levels and also provides a digital liquid crystal readout of the atmospheric O_2 concentration. Sampler tube detectors indicate the qualitative (but not quantitative) presence of CH_4.

Methane must be avoided because of the extreme hazard of explosion. Thus, no specific respiratory protection is approved for use in atmospheric CH_4. The only protection is the warning afforded by one of the devices cited above, whereupon one should depart, taking care not to create sparks or flames. Obviously, one should not smoke underground.

2.6. Carbon Monoxide

Usually produced by incomplete combustion, CO emanates from explosions, internal combustion engines, coal, liquid manure, burning tobacco, or any fire. The ignition of coal dust produces CO and CO_2. More persons have died in caves from the CO produced by campfires foolishly made within caves than from all other forms of cave "bad air" (Halliday, 1982). Many persons have died in mines for the same reason. Persons in the United States occasionally try to drive bats out of mines or caves by fire, only to perish of CO poisoning upon entering to evaluate the results. Massive fires are sometimes created in Latin American caves in desperate efforts to control vampire bat-borne rabies; a regional campaign may involve many caves. Bat guano may ignite spontaneously or from lightning strikes that follow cave channels. These events produce CO, which may remain to afflict unwary visitors.

Carbon monoxide has an affinity for hemoglobin 240 times that of O_2. Its primary toxic action is a direct result of the hypoxia produced. NIOSH (1983) permits an atmospheric CO concentration of 35 ppm (no peaks over 200 ppm) during a 10-h work period, 40-h work week. A concentration of 50 ppm for 8 h greatly increases the risk of angina pectoris and coronary infarctions by decreasing the oxygen supply in the blood and in myoglobin of heart muscle. The effects are aggravated by heavy work, high ambient temperatures, high altitudes, and especially by smoking (cigarette smoke contains 40,000 ppm CO). From 500 to 1,000 ppm atmospheric CO causes headache, rapid breathing, nausea, weakness, dizziness, mental confusion, sometimes hallucinations, and may result in brain damage. Exposure to concentrations of 4,000 ppm (0.4%) and above may produce death within a few minutes, only transient weakness and dizziness being experienced before coma supervenes. At much greater concentrations (12.5 to 74.2%) the gas may be explosive (Mackison et al., 1981). Skin, nailbeds, and mucous membranes may appear pale during early stages of poisoning; later they become cherry red.

After immediate removal to fresh air by persons supplied with self-contained breathing apparatus or gas masks, mouth-to-mouth resuscitation should be started without delay, and, if necessary, external cardiac massage should be administered. Oxygen should be given, preferably under medical supervision which should be obtained as soon as possible (Kurppa and Rantanen, 1983).

A caged canary, which will fall from its perch before people begin to be affected, has been the traditional CO monitoring method. A pocket-sized CO indicator with alarm and digital liquid crystal readout is now available (Appendix 1). Interfering gases apt to occur in bat roosts that may register on the instrument as CO include CH_4, H_2S, SO_2, and NH_3, but these can be readily confirmed or eliminated by odor, the methanometer reading, or by tube gas sampling as explained above (Section 2.1 and Table 2). Respiratory protection for CO_2 is described in Mackison et al. (1981).

2.7. Hydrogen Sulfide

Heavier than air, H_2S accumulates at lower levels in mines, especially those that yield lead sulfide, zinc, gypsum, and sulfur. Referred to as "stink damp," it can be produced from the decomposition of iron pyrites by water in coal mines. It is produced in pools of sewage sludge and liquid manure, from which it is released by stirring. Hydrogen sulfide may be released from some soil deposits during excavation and from pools of stagnant water. It enters caves in thermal waters and vents.

This gas interferes with the function of oxidative enzymes, resulting in tissue hypoxia, including the respiratory center of the brain, often resulting in simultaneous respiratory arrest and anoxic seizure. NOISH (1983) has recommended a permissible exposure limit of less than 10 ppm (with a ceiling of 10 ppm averaged over a 10-min period) per 10-h work period, 40-h work week.

The rotten egg odor of H_2S is lost in 2 to 15 min at 100 ppm due to olfactory fatigue. At 20 ppm conjunctivitis is experienced, sometimes progressing to keratitis. Headache and leg pain develop at 10-100 ppm. Respiratory irritation occurs at 50-500 ppm. Prolonged exposure to 200 to 250 ppm produces pulmonary edema and bronchial pneumonia; coma develops after 20 min in 300 ppm. Unconsciousness and death through respiratory paralysis develop in atmospheres of 500 ppm and above, instantaneously at 1,000 ppm. Corneal injury develops after a few hours at low concentrations in addition to the eventual development of symptoms suggestive of brain damage: headache, sleep disturbances, nausea, weight loss, and other signs (ACGIH, 1982; Caccuri, 1983; Kurt, 1983; Mackison et al., 1981). Hydrogen sulfide is flammable at 4.3% (43,000 ppm) to 46% and may explode violently. Being heavier than air, the gas may spread over the ground to a source of ignition and then flash back.

Ideally, an acutely poisoned victim would be taken immediately to a resuscitation center for hyperbaric O_2 treatment, but in the absence of such facilities one should carry out artificial respiration in fresh air, preferably with inhalation of O_2. Medical assistance should be sought at once (The respiratory center may be stimulated by 1 ml of lobelin and 5 ml of nikethamine).

Eye exposure should be treated with boric acid solution or isotonic physiological solutions; instillation of a drop of olive oil has also been recommended as an immediate measure. One percent adrenalin drops and the application of hot and cold compresses are recommended for more serious cases (Caccuri, 1983).

The sensible reaction to olfactory detection of H_2S is to leave at once. A battery-operated, pocket-sized H_2S indicator with audible alarm and liquid crystal display (Appendix 1) provides both warning and measurement of atmosphere H_2S concentrations up to 200 ppm. Unfortunately, like the comparable CO detector, certain other gases are mistakenly recorded as H_2S by this instrument. These include NH_3 (detectable by odor), sulfur dioxide (SO_2, which has a characteristic odor), CH_4 also detected by the methanometer), and other gases. However, the comparable CO detector would seem to suffice, because it mistakenly records 0.1 ppm H_2S as 1 ppm CO, and it too mistakenly records NH_3, CH_4, SO_2, and other gases (Table 2). Tube sampling reveals the atmospheric H_2S concentration. Respiratory protective apparatus for H_2S is listed in Mackison et al. (1981).

2.8. Sulfur Dioxide

Sources of SO_2 in caves usually are referable to volcanic gases or warm spring water. The gas was reported from atmospheres of two of four natural caves sampled in Texas that contain massive *Tadarida brasiliensis* aggregations (Constantine, 1967a). Concentrations were 2.5 ppm in Bracken Cave and 6 ppm in Davis Cave, where air temperatures were 33.6°C and 35.5°C, respectively. The gas was not detected in Goodrich Cave or Frio Cave, where temperatures were 28.3°C and 32.2°C. Sources of SO_2 in mines can include volcanic emanations and breakdown of pyrite (Bell, 1980). Heat is usually responsible for its production. Its water solubility may markedly reduce atmospheric concentrations of the gas in the presence of water.

This irritant gas dissolves in the fluids on mucosal surfaces, wet skin, and in saliva, whereupon it becomes sulfurous acid and sulfuric acid. Thus, it creates pain and/or tissue destruction in the skin, eyes, respiratory system, mouth, teeth, pharynx, esophagus, and stomach. It disrupts carbohydrate and protein metabolism and causes Vitamin B and C deficiencies. It also effects oxidase inhibition, hemopoetic system disorders and production of methemoglobin. Acute reactions from inhaling high concentrations include intense irritation of the eyes and upper respiratory tract. Death can result from respiratory paralysis and pulmonary edema, from spasm of the larynx, circulatory arrest in the lungs, or shock. Chronic exposure to relatively low doses leaves affected tissues hyperemic, atrophic, and ulcerated. Chronic bronchitis, bronchiectasis, emphysema, right heart deficiency, nervous disorders, and tooth and gum destruction can eventually result (Aleksieva, 1983; Mackison et al., 1981).

NIOSH recommends an exposure limit average of 0.5 ppm over a 10-h work period, 40-h work week. The gas is first noticed, probably by taste, at 0.3 to 1 ppm. Slight bronchoconstriction produces some air flow resistance between 1 and 3 ppm, when the gas odor is easily detected. Five ppm irritates the upper respiratory tract, where 90% of inhaled gas is absorbed, and there is a 40% increase in air flow resistance. At 10 ppm, symptoms worsen, with eye irritation, some nosebleeds, increased coughing, choking, and bronchoconstriction. Brief exposure to 13% SO_2 elicits a 73% increase in pulmonary flow resistance (Mackison et al., 1981).

Persons who regularly work in contaminated atmospheres have been advised to rinse out their mouths with 10% sodium bicarbonate solution during working hours, and after work they should bathe, clean their teeth, and inhale alkaline substances. They should eat a protein- and vitamin-rich diet and exercise to maintain respiratory function (Aleksieva, 1983).

After removal from a heavily contaminated atmosphere, O_2 therapy is advisable. If breathing has stopped, perform artificial respiration. Affected eyes and nose should be bathed with a 2% sodium bicarbonate solution, and drops of 2-3% ephedrine instilled into the nose (Mackison et al., 1981; Aleksieva, 1983).

The burning match-like odor of SO_2 is characteristic and ordinarily should suffice as a warning. However, perception of the odor might be confused by the presence of other odors. Ammonia masked its presence in Bracken and Davis Caves, as noted above. The automatic CO detector mistakenly registers 2 ppm SO_2 as 1 ppm CO. SO_2 can be detected and its atmospheric concentration measured on a SO_2 tube sampler (Table 2). Mackison et al. (1981) list respiratory protective apparatus for SO_2.

2.9. Oxygen Deficit

Hypoxia or anoxia may develop in mines or caves in various ways. Absolute O_2 concentration is decreased at high elevations. Simple asphyxiants such as CO_2 or N_2 may be so abundant that O_2 becomes diluted or displaced. Toxic asphyxiants like CO or H_2S can have similar effects, but they act primarily by interference with cellular respiration, in effect making O_2 unavailable even though present. Free O_2 can be decreased or eliminated from underground atmospheres by chemical reactions in which the gas is incorporated into other chemicals. Such reactions include combustion (fires, explosions), respiration (plant and animal), and the decay or microbial breakdown of plant or animal tissues or other organic wastes.

One may appear normal in an atmospheric O_2 deficit until the concentration is lowered to 12-16%, resulting in increased rate and depth of breathing, increased heartbeat, and slight incoordination or dizziness. At 10-14% one may become emotionally unstable and feel exhausted with minimal effort. Further O_2 decrease to between 6-10% can precipitate nausea, vomiting, lethargic movements and, perhaps, unconsciousness. Concentrations below 6% produce convulsions and death. Hypoxic tissue damage, including brain damage, may not be reversible (Osbern, 1983). Bats of the genus *Myotis* show extraordinary resistance to anoxia (Britton and Kline, 1945).

Victims should be treated with cardio-pulmonary resuscitation, O_2, mechanical ventilation, and positive end-expiratory pressure, as needed. Asphyxiant gases are usually involved, and these should be identified rapidly so that definitive therapy can be instituted (Osbern, 1983).

A mine safety lamp flame burns in a characteristic manner in an acceptable O_2 concentration. The flame shortens and changes color in an O_2-deficient atmosphere. A pocket-size, battery-operated O_2 detector reveals ambient O_2 atmospheric concentration and signals by audible alarm if the level of the gas is low.

A supplied-air respirator or a self-contained breathing apparatus suffices for protection in most O_2-deficient atmospheres. Only NIOSH-approved or MSHA-approved equipment should be used.

2.10. Other Problematic Atmospheric Factors in Mines and Caves

Some metallic ore mines have long been known as sources of bronchopulmonary cancer due to radiation. Whereas bat researchers are not likely to enter radium or uranium mines, excessive cancer mortality is attributed to radioactivity in iron mines. On the other hand, an appreciable increase in bronchopulmonary cancer has recently been associated with these mines in sedimentary basins without excessive radiation. Poisonous dusts and fumes from arsenic, manganese, mercury, and sulphur may be inhaled in some mines. Some dangerous dusts include iron, asbestos, talc, and tin (Amoudru, 1983).

Cave-dust pneumonitis or "dust pneumonia," a common chest problem in dry cave areas, may be an allergic or chemical response to organic substances in the dust such as guano particles. Discomfort upon inhalation begins within a few minutes or hours and develops into a dry cough. This condition lasts a few hours or a few days (Halliday, 1982).

2.11. Deliberate Contamination of Bats and Bat Roosts with Anticoagulants and Poisonous Gases

Intentional and unintentional pesticide contamination of bats has been reviewed by Clark (1981) and Clark et al. (1982). Many toxicant-treated bat roosts in buildings contain residual organochlorines that continue to sicken bats and may contaminate persons who enter these places. Poisonous gassing of bats in caves with an organophosphorus compound is among numerous methods used to combat vampire bat-borne rabies in Latin America. Cyanide gas has been used in vampire roosts, including wells (Fornes et al., 1974). In the latter study, the senior author perished when his mask failed while inspecting a gassed well.

Anticoagulants in petroleum jelly are sometimes smeared on captured vampires which are then released to contaminate colony members who consume it during mutual grooming (Linhart et al., 1972). This technique appears to be nearly if not completely species-specific as well as highly effective. Thus, it is preferred over indiscriminately destructive methods. In a few instances, however, vampire niches within underground roosts have been smeared with the anticoagulant preparation by overzealous workers, creating a hazard for people as well as nontarget bats (Flores Crespo and Morales Ruiz, 1975). Persons should avoid contaminating themselves by contact with smeared cave surfaces or by handling contaminated bats, because the anticoagulant passes through skin. Inquiry to national and local livestock disease control authorities in Latin America is advisable to learn where specific methods have been applied and consequent danger may exist.

A far greater hazard to the general public and especially to homeowners and persons who enter attics are rodenticide "tracking powders," used in attempts to control bat colonies in buildings. These poisons, developed to kill rodents, are intended for use in tamper-resistant bait boxes, rodent runways, or other locations inaccessible to children and animals. Rodents typically ingest the poison while grooming with the tongue. Powder placements are supposed to be removed after 20 days. There are several kinds of these powders, containing different poisons. The U. S. Environmental Protection Agency (EPA) became concerned when the producer of an anticoagulant tracking powder (Rozol), considered a public health hazard when used against bats, set out to circumvent EPA's objections by seeking approval on a state-by-state basis under the provisions of the Federal Insecticide, Fungicide, and Rodenticide Act, Section 24(c) (Greenhall, 1982). The agency cautioned each state. Although one state revoked permission, some 20 other states have permitted its use, and it has been used illegally elsewhere.

As much as 12.3 kg of anticoagulant tracking powder have been blown into attics through louvres or attic access openings. Anticoagulant tracking powders can be absorbed across skin, inhaled, or ingested with contaminated food. They cause neurologic and cardiopulmonary injury in laboratory animals, often leading to death before hemorrhage occurs. In some cases, homeowners have not been informed that the product is an anticoagulant, which has led to years of delay in identifying the poison source and obtaining a proper diagnosis and treatment.

A slow-acting anticoagulant tracking powder guarantees that poisoned bats will be scattered widely. Grounded, sick bats are readily handled by children and animals. Consequently, there results not only contaminated or poisoned people and pets but also a proportionate increase in bitten persons and pets, antirabies treatments and quarantined or sacrificed pets. Treated bat roosts are only uncommonly sealed and made batproof by professional exterminators. Unsealed roosts can be a continuing source of sick bats as repopulation occurs, further frightening the public and stimulating more poisoning. The data I have examined indicate that this material, like DDT, is relatively ineffective in its "announced" purpose of eliminating bat colonies. The evidence indicates that the majority of bats may be temporarily repelled if the powder is blown into their faces, although some adequately-exposed bats will die after the anticoagulant takes effect.

Accordingly, bat researchers should beware of powders in bat roosts or on bats. Poisoned bats are finding their way into laboratories for rabies testing after prior handling by children, pets, animal control personnel, and others, and they will doubtless be donated to museums as well.

3. ECTOPARASITES AND URINE

No diseases in man are known from ectoparasites of bats or the urine of bats. Certain bat ectoparasites have been implicated in the transmission of various infections among bats, and although humans may not ordinarily suffer illness from these specialized disease agents, some researchers may find them repugnant. Exposure to urine would be expected to enhance opportunities for infection by agents that may be contained therein. For example, leptospirosis, acquired by contamination of mucous membranes or skin breaks by infective urine, is known from some of the Old World bats that have been sampled. Insect repellents applied to clothing prior to entering a populous bat cave can be effective. To reduce exposure one should avoid walking under the bat clusters, where ectoparasites abound and urine is falling. A respirator will decrease exposure to bat urine. Bathing with a portable shower has been found useful following exposure.

4. RABIES

Rabies and rabies-like viruses are classified in the genus *Lyssavirus* within the Rhabdoviridae (rhabdoviruses), a family of viruses isolated from vertebrate, invertebrate, and plant hosts.

4.1. Transmission Cycle

Rabies virus typically enters the host's body in the saliva that contaminates a bite wound. It can also enter via the digestive tract, the respiratory system, and through intact mucous membranes. The virus progresses along nerves to the spinal cord and brain, whereupon it reverses direction and proceeds centrifugally along nerves, eventually invading the nerves in all organs including skin. It especially multiplies in nervous tissues and salivary glands. Provided with infectious saliva, many animals often experience central nervous system stimulation to engage in savage attacks, thereupon effecting viral transmission and continuation of the cycle. Infected bats are only rarely involved in unprovoked attacks and may not appear abnormal except for gradual weakness due to developing paralysis, followed by death. Apparently, there is no need for savage attacks to maintain transmission among gregarious bats, inasmuch as normal biting is common. Moreover, "outbreaks" of rabies among bats have not been observed; only the occasional, perhaps immunodeficient bat becomes patently infected within colonies of hundreds or thousands. The lack of furious behavior and the low incidence of infection among gregarious bats evidently accounts for the failure to detect rabies in North American bats until 1953, after which awareness increased in response to increased interest and effort (Constantine, 1967b).

4.2. Viral Strain Compartmentalization

"Compartmentalization" of rabies refers to serial transmission of the virus within a given species of host, and an absence of transmis-

sion to or from other species except for possible rare, dead-end infections (Winkler, 1975). Under these circumstances, a skunk rabies outbreak may proceed in the presence of an uninfected fox population and vice versa. At least two kinds of transmission seem necessary to break down compartmentalization: interspecies transmission and serial intraspecies transmission thereafter. Various explanations have been proposed to explain compartmentalization: a lack of interspecies contact because of behavioral or ecological isolation, a lack of opportunity for intraspecies contact in the uninfected species due to low population density of the latter, failure of small animals to survive the transmission bite injury of larger animal species, and viral dose barriers. As examples of the latter, foxes may transmit too little virus to infect skunks, and skunks may transmit so much virus that bitten foxes die before the virus reaches their salivary glands (Sikes, 1962). Finally, the existence of various host species-specific strains of rabies virus have been suggested as an explanation for compartmentalization, finding support in viral strain characterization, first by demonstrating differing susceptibilities and reactions of various Carnivora and Rodentia species to various viral strains (Constantine, 1966a, 1966b, 1967b; Constantine and Woodall, 1966; Constantine et al., 1968a, 1968b) and recently by monoclonal antibody studies of viral strains (Schneider and Meyer, 1981; Sureau et al., 1983; Smith et al., 1984).

Some or all of the foregoing explanations might play contributing roles in compartmentalization. The isolation of virus afforded by compartmentalization, whatever the causes, would favor differentiation of the virus if not the host. Compartmentalization is recognized universally by rabies specialists, not only in reference to viral strain distinctiveness within a given host species, but regional and intercontinental differences in viral characteristics are recognized as well.

This information should find practical application in determining rabies vaccine efficacy, the spectrum of hosts susceptible to each strain, and to retrospectively determine host species origin of infection for a given victim. The World Health Organization (WHO) Expert Committee on Rabies (1984) has called for the selection of vaccine viral strains to match best with locally-occurring viral strains. Strains isolated from bats in the United States may fall into a distinct group compared to strains from Carnivora. As known to date, viral isolates may show minor variations when recovered from a given species of bat, and they may differ from strains isolated from other species of bats. Experiments in laboratory animals suggest that older rabies vaccines may have failed to protect some persons against some bat rabies virus strains, but WHO is confident that recent potent vaccines, such as the one now used in the United States, are sufficiently protective.

The dependable application of the monoclonal antibody technique to retrospectively infer the identity of the species of host that infected a given victim must await the utilization of a sufficiently large and representative panel of monoclonal antibodies and extensive viral strain surveys to establish acceptable baseline data. This exciting but yet undeveloped field has stimulated premature interpretations that have required serial revisions. Only partial, supportive data have been reported in some cases and little or none in others. Whetstone et al. (1984) concluded that a dog had been infected by a bat, because the rabies isolate from the dog, like 5 of 6 bat rabies isolates studied, failed to react with any member of an abbreviated panel of monoclonal antibodies; thus, interpretation was based wholly on data voids.

4.3. Prevalence and Sampling Techniques

Bats have been reported as rabies hosts principally in the Americas, in a few instances in Europe, and once in Asia (Tables 4 and 5). Infected bats representing six of the nine American families have been reported, distributed from Canada to Argentina.

Numbers of infected bats detected in the

Table 4. Reports of rabies (+) and rabies-like viruses (++) in bats.

Family	Americas	Europe	Asia	Africa
Pteropidae			+	++
Emballonuridae	+			
Rhinolophidae		+		
Noctilionidae	+			
Mormoopidae	+			
Phyllostomidae	+			
Vespertilionidae	+	+,++		++
Molossidae	+			

Americas are usually proportional to effort and are greatly influenced by method of collection. There were no reports of rabies-infected bats in the United States prior to 1953, when it appears the first bat was tested due to the insistence of a bitten child's parents, who had knowledge of rabies in vampire bats. Increasing numbers of bats were tested after 1953 as a consequence of increasing awareness of the problem, and numbers of rabid bat reports increased annually; in 1982, 975 rabies-infected bats were detected in the United States. The infected bats were among many thousands of bats submitted for testing, usually because the bats, either disabled or dead, had been captured by pets or children, and bites were known or suspected to have occurred. About ten percent of the bats submitted in this manner for testing in the United States prove to be infected, a proportion that has not changed over the years. It should be emphasized that these bats represent a highly biased sample, because nearly all of them were ill or dead at the time of collection.

Surveys of bats to determine rabies prevalence can be misleading, depending on collection techniques and collection sites. Ill bats are easily collected from their roosts in contrast to healthy bats, which escape more readily. A day roost that also serves as a popular night roost may accumulate sick bats during nightly visits of hundreds or thousands of bats. Thus, a popular night roost may contain only incapacitated bats by day, i.e., bats that

Table 5. Reported rabies viral infections in bats.*

Family and species**	Country***
Pteropidae	
Pteropus poliocephalus (sic)	India
Emballonuridae	
Diclidurus albus	Trinidad
Rhinolophidae	
Rhinolophus ferrumequinum	Turkey
Noctilionidae	
Noctilio leporinus	Mexico
Noctilio sp.	Panama
Mormoopidae	
Mormoops megalophylla	USA, Mexico
Pteronotus davyi	Mexico, Trinidad
Pteronotus parnellii	Mexico, Trinidad
Pteronotus personatus	Mexico
Phyllostomidae	
Artibeus jamaicensis	Mexico, Panama, Trinidad, Grenada
Artibeus lituratus	Mexico, Guatemala, Belize, Trinidad, Brazil
Artibeus planirostris	Bolivia
Artibeus sp.	Mexico, Peru
Carollia perspicillata	Trinidad, Colombia, Peru
Chrotopterus auritus	Brazil
Desmodus rotundus	Mexico, Guatemala, Belize, Trinidad, Bolivia, Brazil, Argentina
Desmodus youngi	Trinidad
Diphylla ecaudata	Brazil
Glossophaga soricina	Mexico
Leptonycteris nivalis	Mexico
Macrotus californicus	USA
Macrotus waterhousii	Mexico
Micronycteris megalotis	Panama, Peru
Phyllostomus discolor	Mexico, Guatemala, Belize
Phyllostomus hastatus	Peru, Brazil
Uroderma bilobatum	Panama
Vespertilionidae	
Antrozous pallidus	USA
Eptesicus fuscus	Canada, USA, Cuba
Eptesicus serotinus	Germany (E)
Euderma maculatum	USA
Histiotus velatus	Brazil
Lasionycteris noctivagans	Canada, USA
Lasiurus borealis	Canada, USA
Lasiurus cinereus	Canada, USA, Argentina
Lasiurus ega	USA
Lasiurus intermedius	USA
Lasiurus seminolus	USA
Myotis austroriparius	USA
Myotis californicus	USA
Myotis evotis	USA
Myotis fortidens	Guatemala, Belize
Myotis grisecens	USA
Myotis keenii	Canada, USA
Myotis leibii	USA
Myotis lucifugus	Canada, USA
Myotis myotis	Germany (Berlin)

Table 5. Continued

Family and species**	Country***
Myotis nigricans	Panama, Peru
Myotis thysanodes	USA
Myotis velifer	USA, Mexico
Myotis volans	USA
Myotis yumanensis	USA
Nyctalus noctula	Germany (W), Yugoslavia
Nycticeius humeralis	USA
Pipistrellus hesperus	USA
Pipistrellus subflavus	Canada, USA
Plecotus townsendii	USA
Rhogeessa tumida	Mexico
Molossidae	
Eumops perotis	USA
Eumops auripendulus	Brazil
Molossops planirostris	Panama
Molossus ater	Venezuela
Molossus bondae	Panama
Molossus major	Trinidad, Peru
Molossus molossus	Brazil
Molossus sinaloae	Guatemala, Belize, Honduras
Nyctinomops macrotis	USA
Tadarida brasiliensis	USA, Argentina

*Many reports were not included, because viruses other than rabies may have been represented. The report of rabies in *Cynopterus brachyotis* in Thailand (Smith et al., 1967) evidently was mistaken; so it is not included. Even so, single, isolated reports preferably should be supported by additional isolations. However, the single rabies case in an Indian *Pteropus* could readily occur as a dead-end infection resulting from the bite of a rabid monkey, for example, because *Pteropus* is large enough to survive the bite and live to develop the disease.

**Pteropus poliocephalus* (Pal et al., 1980) does not occur in India; apparently the correct name should be *P. giganteus.* The taxonomy used herein follows Honacki et al. (1982) and Freeman (1981). Thus, *Pteronotus psilotis* again becomes *P. personatus; Diaemus youngi* becomes *Desmodus youngi; Tadarida macrotis* becomes *Nyctinomops macrotis; Molossus coibensis* becomes *M. bondae; Molossus obscurus* and *M. currentium* become *M. molossus;* and *Eumops abrasus* becomes *E. auripendulus.* The name of the German (W) bat, given as *Nyctalus noctula,* was admittedly surmised by that author (Mohr, 1957).

***References include those cited in Table III of Constantine (1970) and the following: Aucar and Mayer, 1975; DeAmorin et al., 1970; Beauregard, 1969; Center for Disease Control, 1971; Constantine et al., 1979; Delpietra et al., 1969, 1972; Goodwin and Greenhall, 1961; Hentschke and Hellman, 1975; Main, 1979; Matheney and Gale, 1962; Medeiros and Heckmann, 1971; Pal et al., 1980; Price and Everard, 1977; Retamoso Yepez et al., 1972; Sileoni et al., 1971; DaSilva and Alencar, 1968; Silva Taboada and Herrada Llibre, 1974; Stouraitis and Salvatierra, 1978; Villa R., 1966; DeYosti et al., 1971; Rodrigues et al., 1975.

fell ill during a nighttime visit and could not leave, conveying the impression that a rabies "outbreak" is in progress. Multiple births by an infected female can result in all litter members becoming infected, skewing survey samples and creating the impression that a small "outbreak" is in progress. But nothing resembling an "outbreak" or large-scale rabies destruction of a bat colony has been detected, despite careful seeking.

The most reliable and useful survey samples are of bats capable of flight, such as bats issuing from cave entrances. From such sampling, it has been learned that only a small proportion (from < 0.1 to 0.5 percent) may be infected, i.e., in incubational stages, recognizable only by laboratory tests on brain tissue; such animals would be destined to die of the disease. Thus, only about one in 1,000 clinically-normal bats is infected in most of North America, and a somewhat higher proportion, one in 200, has been observed in free-tailed bats that occupy the populous bat caves of Texas and New Mexico.

4.4. Disease Development

Presumably, bats infect each other via infectious saliva, usually by bites, and possibly by inhaling aerosolized infectious saliva in dense populous aggregations. My tests on many fetal bats extracted from within infected mothers indicate they do not acquire infection before birth, although they may become infected during and after birth via bites or licking. Prenatal rabies antibodies of maternal origin have been demonstrated in bats (Constantine et al., 1968b), and rabies antibodies have been detected in bat milk (R. McLean, pers. comm.). Passively-immune suckling bats would be expected to become actively immune in response to exposure to the virus. That sequence of events may account for the high incidence of rabies antibodies observed in some samples of gregarious bats, although a relatively high innate resistance could play an important role. My studies show that up to 80 percent of rabies virus-free *Tadarida* from Texas caves possess serum rabies neutralizing antibodies, indicating previous nonfatal experience with the virus. The lack of rabies outbreak activity among such dense aggregations is truly astonishing and suggestive of a long-established, balanced relationship between an ordinarily deadly virus and this host. Perhaps only immunodeficient or otherwise compromised bats fall victim to the virus.

The incubation period in rabies usually is several weeks in duration, but it may be over a year. Bats probably are not exceptional. The reduced metabolic rate characteristic of hypothermia in hibernating or resting heterothermic bats can lengthen rabies incubation periods (Sadler and Enright, 1959) and lengthen or influence other phases of the infection, including the symptomatic period. Data from bats are not plentiful for several reasons, including the difficulty of distinguishing signs of disease from normal behavior under the conditions of usual observation.

The longest incubation period segment reported in a bat was an *Eptesicus fuscus* which developed noticeable signs of the disease 209 days after capture, and it died four days after the signs were noted (Moore and Raymond, 1970).

Rabies virus often is present in the host's saliva for one to several days before signs of disease appear, with known extremes of five days in a dog and eight days in a skunk. Little information is available for bats. Experimentally-infected *T. brasiliensis* usually had infectious saliva for up to five days prior to symptoms, but one bat had the virus in its saliva 12 days before recognition of signs (Baer and Bales, 1967). A naturally-infected *E. fuscus* died of rabies 24 days after its saliva was retrospectively determined to be infectious, but the bat may have had cryptic signs of disease for a substantial portion of that period because it was not closely observed (Bell et al., 1969). Apparently, bats are not the long-term or lifelong asymptomatic disseminators of rabies virus described in early South American studies on vampires or in later reports on North American insectivorous bats. Evidently other viruses, now known to be resident in salivary glands of asymptomatic bats, were mistakenly identified as rabies.

Rabies signs are initiated in most mammals by a prodromal phase several days in duration whereupon the animal may exhibit a change in behavior, being unusually friendly and fearless or becoming unusually shy or irritable. Anxiety and an increased sensitivity to light and sound are other early signs of the disease, and the site of viral entry may appear to be paresthetic. The disease progresses to either or both of two additional phases: the excitable (aggressive or "furious") phase and the paralytic phase. During the excitable phase, which may be absent or last a week, the host becomes vicious, attacking animate or inanimate objects as it wanders aimlessly. If the animal does not die in a convulsive seizure, the disease may progress to the final or paralytic phase of some four days duration. Not all strains of rabies virus produce the disease as described above. For example, rabies virus from *T. brasiliensis* kills Carnivora within 24 h of the first symptom and sometimes within three hours.

Appetite loss is often the first sign observed in captive bats, in which the disease progresses to paralysis and death without excitement except for occasional signs of annoyance, associated with frustrated efforts to use paralyzed limbs. Paralytic rabies, lacking the excitable phase, is the only form of rabies observed by the author in nearly all species of North American bats. Rarely, however, certain species of tiny, solitarily-roosting bats (*Pipistrellus hesperus*, *Myotis californicus*, and *M. leibii*), which do not normally inhabit buildings, will develop the excitable phase and attempt to bite persons by flying to them or even shuffling to them on the ground (Constantine, 1967b).

The report by Bell (1980) of a foraging *Lasiurus cinereus* attacking and biting three other foraging bats (*Lasionycteris noctivagans*, *E. fuscus*, and *T. brasiliensis*), though suggestive of rabies infection, was not confirmed by reliable rabies diagnostic tests. The bat that was tested was probably the same animal that bit the other bats. Although the aggressive behavior was abnormal when compared to Bell's other observations, similar behavior of hoary bats has been observed (Bishop, 1949; Orr, 1950). Other explanations, such as territoriality, predation, or pathology due to other agents, are possible. Nevertheless, this important observation augments the earlier accounts of interspecific biting, providing opportunities for viral transmission, whether or not infections that might result would be dead-end or serial in effect.

Knowledge of disease signs in bats is derived from observation of natural infections and from experimental infections. The latter can be misleading. Paralytic rabies generally results when bats are given virus by intramuscular route, simulating bite transmission, but furious rabies can result after the virus is inoculated directly into the bat's brain.

Paralysis or atypical behavior referable to paralysis are among the early pathological signs observed in bats whereupon the animals may remain in open night roosts by day, rest by day in other atypical places, fly during daytime, or blunder into inanimate or animate objects during flight. Paralysis and weakness may lead directly to death or be accompanied by tremors and sometimes by squeaking as the bat experiences frustration or irritability in its failing attempts to escape the hindering effects of paralysis.

Sound is known to elicit squeaking in infected bats, as if sound is annoying. Infected persons experience increased sensitivity to sound, and infected bats may be especially sensitive in view of their exceptional abilities in sound production and perception. Certain bat sounds can produce ear pain in man (Cockrum and Gardner, 1960; Constantine, 1961). It is conceivable that infected bats experience sound-elicited pain. Sound might stimulate attacks by the small, solitarily-roosting species of bat cited above, thereby being an important factor in assuring intraspecies transmission.

The symptomatic infected bat occasionally found in a colonial bat roost is often thin, dehydrated, weak, and partially paralyzed. Frequently, it hangs alone, and it may be in a state of hypothermia. The wings may droop slightly. It may die in this position or after falling. Fat sucklings or fat adults that develop the disease may die before they become emaciated.

The infected bat with failing flight capability may attempt to initiate its foraging flight but fall instead, either at once or later during the flight. It may alight on any elevated site within reach to avoid landing on the ground, from which launching would be especially difficult. Infected bats have landed on buildings, trees, poles, and even on standing persons. After daybreak, disabled bats exposed in this manner have been attacked by birds and other animals, sometimes stimulating the animal into faltering flight whereupon it may blunder into obstacles (Constantine, 1967b).

4.5. Rabies Exposures

Rabies is nearly always fatal in man and most mammals after symptoms appear, so the possibility of exposure should be investigated without delay. Treatment, if indicated, should be initiated as soon as possible. Occasionally the victim develops the disease despite immediate initiation of treatment, so questions of exposure and treatment should receive prompt attention and top priority. National and international health authorities recommend immediate initiation of the rabies prophylactic treatment following bites or other potential exposures from bats and wild Carnivora. Treatment can be terminated if test results show the animal to be uninfected. Some health departments defer treatment for 24 h if the test can be performed in that interval. The decision to treat may be influenced by knowledge of the presence or absence of the disease in the exposing species in the geographic area and the circumstances of the bite. However, rabies is present in bats throughout the Americas, and the disabled bats that humans contact have generally been shown to be a high-risk group.

Exposures to rabies-infected bats are most often defensive bites experienced when the recipient restrains the incapacitated bat. Pets, especially cats, magnify the exposure problem by bringing home bats, some of which subsequently expose children who handle them. Sometimes a bat, released by a cat, will wander aimlessly, occasionally biting persons who roll on it in bed. Four or five persons infected with rabies through bat bites were bitten during sleep (Table 6). Similarly, many persons have been bitten by uninfected bats brought home by cats. Scratches from claws of some infected bats may be hazardous if the claws have been contaminated with saliva, as occurs in grooming. The claws of hoary bats (*Lasiurus cinereus*) easily inflict small penetrating wounds.

Bites from untested nonrabid bats appear to be a far greater problem than exposures to proved rabid bats, due to necessary antirabies precautions. Many bats fly away after the hand that restrains them opens in response to a bite. Others are deliberately discarded or destroyed before the victim thinks of rabies. Still others become so mutilated while being killed that reliable rabies tests cannot be done on them. Statistics are difficult to assemble because of inadequate reporting.

Twelve Colorado residents were given antirabies treatment following exposures to symptomatic bats in 1978; only two of the twelve had been exposed to proven infected bats. Probably, only one or two of the ten untested bats were infected, because 37 of 257 (14.4%) symptomatic contact bats tested that year had rabies. In this limited sample, the number of treatments given after exposures to nonrabid bats was nearly three-fold greater than those given after exposures to infected bats. This small sample may provide a deceptively conservative estimate, because laboratory tests show that the total number of rabies-negative bats tested after contact (usually with pets) was six-fold (rather than three-fold) greater than the number of positives.

The foregoing data are disturbing, but a far worse scenario awaits those states that permit use of toxicants or other methods to disable bats in misguided efforts to eliminate bat colonies from buildings by methods other than exclusion. Exposures to bats and consequent rabies precautions (human antirabies treatments, quarantine or destruction of pets) can increase ten-fold on a statewide basis, according to reduced proportions of positives to negatives among bats submitted for laboratory testing. Thus, a bat exposure problem that costs a state one-half million dollars annually can escalate to a cost of five million dollars as a consequence of widespread poisoning of bats.

Exposure to disabled bats may occur when the animal blunders into or lands on a person, and the person may be bitten as he brushes the bat off. The rare unprovoked attacks undertaken by the tiny bats cited earlier should be relatively ineffectual in viral transmission due to the difficulty most small

Table 6. Summary of 10 human cases of rabies attributed to exposure to insectivorous bats, United States and Canada, 1950-1984.*

Year of Exposure	Locality	Bat Species	Circumstances of Exposure
1951	Big Spring, Texas	Unknown	Bitten while handling moribund bat. Bat not tested.
1955	Frio Cave, Texas	Free-tailed bats (*Tadarida brasiliensis*)	Airborne infection probable; 0.5% infected among millions of bats present.
1958	Magalia, California	Silver-haired bat (*Lasionycteris noctivagans*)	Bitten while handling moribund bat. Bat rabies positive.
1959	Frio Cave, Texas	Free-tailed bats (*Tadarida brasiliensis*)	Airborne infection probable; 0.5% infected among millions of bats present.
1959	Blue River, Wisconsin	Unknown	Sleeping person bitten on ear. Bat not tested.
1970	Willshire, Ohio	Big brown bat (*Eptesicus fuscus*)	Bitten on the thumb while asleep. Bat rabies positive. Patient survived.
1970	Saskatchewan, Canada	Unknown	Bitten on the face while in bed. Bat not tested.
1971	Sussex County, New Jersey	Unknown	Person bitten on lower lip. Bat not captured.
1973	Lexington, Kentucky	Unknown	Bitten on ear while asleep. Bat escaped.
1976	Cecil County, Maryland	Big brown bat (*Eptesicus Fuscus*)	Bitten while brushing bat off shoulder. Bat rabies positive.

*Another case, possibly bat transmitted, occurred in Michigan in 1983 about seven (7) months after a 5-year-old child, who died of rabies, may have been bitten as an older child teased her with an untested, disabled bat.

bats have inflicting penetrating bites into human skin, but any wound would justify antirabies treatment.

Limited knowledge of the susceptibility of various Carnivora to insectivorous bat rabies virus strains was obtained in laboratory and field studies (Constantine, 1967b). Transmission by bite was rare and unrealistically difficult. Additional transmission studies should be done. Experience shows that persons are only rarely infected by rabid insectivorous bats, so transmission to Carnivora might also occur rarely. Significantly, however, one would expect such transmission to result in a dead-end infection, according to

available survey, experimental, and epizootiological information, which indicates that bats are not responsible for outbreaks of rabies in Carnivora.

4.5.1. Transmission by Aerosolized Rabies Virus

Two persons who entered Frio Cave, Uvalde County, Texas, at different times later died of rabies. Sentinel animals subsequently held in Frio Cave and others held in Lava Cave, Socorro County, New Mexico, also died of rabies (Constantine, 1967a). Neither the human nor animal victims experienced bat bites, but they were in the presence of a million or more *T. brasiliensis*. Rabies virus was recovered when the air of Frio Cave was mechanically sampled (Winkler, 1968). It seems possible that the danger exists in comparable aggregations of bats of various species throughout tropical and subtropical America. Numerous persons, vaccinated and successfully immunized against rabies infection, have subsequently worked in Frio Cave without developing the disease.

4.5.2.   Transmission by Ingestion

There is a possibility that an animal which eats an infected bat may become infected and develop the disease after an appropriate incubation period. Six of 18 striped skunks fed one rabid mouse each developed rabies; the virus strain originated in a naturally-infected *L. noctivagans* (Bell and Moore, 1971). However, none of 53 cats that ate one infected mouse each, and none of 12 cats that ate 25 infected mice each developed rabies. None of nine ferrets fed single rabid mice developed rabies. Other viral strains used in these studies originated from *Lasiurus cinereus* (5 cats exposed), *Myotis* sp. (8 cats and 5 ferrets exposed), and *Mephitis mephitis* (5 cats exposed).

4.5.3.   Potential Mechanical Transmission Via Bat-Eating Pets

A cat or other animal that chews an infected bat can get rabies virus in its mouth, and thus must be regarded an an immediate, if only temporary, source of the virus by way of bites or claw scratches or by contamination of other open wounds or intact mucosal surfaces with its contaminated oral fluids. Persons licked on open wounds or on the mouth, nares, eyes, or any mucosal surface may become infected with the virus. The duration of viral survival in the animal's mouth is unknown. However, live rabies virus was not demonstrated in oral fluids sampled by cotton swab technique one hour after 42 cats had

been fed one rabid mouse each (Bell and Moore, 1971). Many bats must be eaten by foraging cats without the owner's knowledge.

4.5.4.   Transmission When Dissecting Bats

Live or dead bats donated by the public to museums and universities represent a relatively high-risk group. Freezing preserves the virus, which has been recovered from the carcass of an animal that was frozen 12 years earlier (Bell and Moore, 1971).

A bat selected for dissection, for example, to prepare a study skin (Chapter 26), could be incubating rabies though normal in appearance. A person apparently died of rabies as a consequence of dissecting a rabid vampire bat (Pawan, 1936). Rubber gloves or plastic gloves should be worn while dissecting bats to avoid contamination of known or undetected wounds by the animal's tissues or tissue fluids, any of which could contain rabies virus. Brown fat, which can be plentiful subcutaneously in autumn through midwinter, can be a potent source of virus. Care should be taken to avoid rubbing potential sources of virus onto one's mucosal surfaces, such as into the eyes, nostrils, or mouth. A plastic face shield is preferably worn. One should work on a surface that can later be sterilized. Aluminum foil overlaid with paper for absorbing fluids is a convenient surface that can subsequently be autoclaved or incinerated along with gloves and discarded tissues. Instruments can be autoclaved or boiled. Should there be a desire to test the bat for rabies, brain tissue should be saved for testing. Ordinarily public health laboratories remove the brain (after removing the top of the cranium) prior to preparation of a brain smear for testing by the fluorescent rabies antibody test. However, biologists may prefer to preserve an undamaged skull, in which case the brain tissue can be drawn through a hypodermic needle into a syringe via the foramen magnum (Greenhall, 1965), deposited in a clean, preferably sterile, vial, and delivered on ice or frozen to the laboratory that has agreed to test it. The brain tissue should not be allowed to dry out.

What happens to rabies virus in the skin and other tissues of the dissected bat? Pasteur found that rabies virus in spinal cords of rabbits was usually inactivated after being permitted to dry 15 days. Based upon studies indicating that the virus in saliva was inactivated upon drying of the saliva, Tierkel (1963) thought it was unnecessary to carry out extensive disinfection of objects or places contaminated with saliva. Thus, study skins would presumably be free of viable virus when thoroughly dried. Prior fleshing of carcasses that are to be skeletonized should hasten drying. Freeze-drying is used to preserve the modified live virus used in some animal rabies vaccines, thus freeze-drying of entire carcasses may preserve the virus as well. One minute in 45-70% ethyl alcohol kills the virus (Kaplan, 1973), so small carcasses, preferably fleshed, might be rendered free of live virus after a period of immersion long enough for the fluid to penetrate all tissues, including brain and spinal cord. Also lethal to the virus are a 1:500 dilution of quaternary ammonia disinfectants, a 1% soap solution, and 5-7% iodine solutions, which, however, may be hard on dermestid colonies used to clean skeletons. An excess of any of these disinfectants, including absolute alcohol, would be required to make up for the loss of effectiveness due to reaction with carcass tissues. Probably a combination of alcohol plus thorough drying would free fleshed carcasses of the virus. Heating virus-bearing tissues to the boiling point of water for one hour should destroy the virus.

4.5.5. Rabies-Contaminated Dermestids

Are dermestid beetles and larvae in a museum colony dangerous after feeding on live rabies-bearing tissues? The virus should be inactivated before offering such tissues to dermestids, rendering the question unnecessary. Realistically, however, the question

probably applies to every museum colony of dermestids, any of which could have consumed infective tissues. Of course, beetles and their larvae invade the cranial cavity, and their exteriors become contaminated with infective brain tissue. It seems logical that beetles and larvae with contaminated mouthparts could mechanically transmit the virus by biting a susceptible host. Fortunately, dermestids usually prefer to eat dead animals. However, in the populous Texas bat caves, dermestids eat both dead bats and sick bats, and they often attack normal bats, especially young sucklings. I have captured flying mature bats with individual beetles clinging to them. At times, the flying beetles will attack people, sometimes in small swarms, although I have experienced no more than a sharp pinch from beetles that have gotten under clothing with no evidence of actual skin penetration. In several trials, I failed to achieve transmission by permitting beetles and larvae of Texas bat cave origin to bite suckling laboratory white mice after they had consumed infective brain. Perhaps with repetition, success would be achieved. No virus could be isolated from the dermestids several weeks later. However, when ground up prior to testing, the released fluids proved lethal to live virus, so the question remains unanswered.

4.5.6. Rabies in Captive Bats

Not unlike wild Carnivora, any normal-appearing bat might be incubating rabies and develop the disease many months later, perhaps a year or more. Therefore, bats that have just been captured are preferably quarantined, perhaps for a compromise period of 6 months, providing opportunity for them to succumb to rabies prior to introducing them to a captive colony. Uninfected bats should not use unsterilized food or water vessels previously used by potentially infected bats due to the possibility, if remote, of acquiring rabies infection through ingestion of infectious saliva, as reported in kudu-antelopes in

South West Africa/Namibia (Barnard et al., 1982).

4.6. Rabies Prevention

4.6.1. Immunization

Rabies immunization recommendations of the U. S. Public Health Service, Advisory Committee on Immunization Practices (ACIP)(1984) should be carefully studied by anyone whose activities may result in exposure to rabies. Pre-exposure immunization, resulting in a serum rabies neutralizing antibody titer of at least 1:5, is considered by the ACIP to be an appropriate precaution for most bat researchers in the Americas and other areas where bat rabies may exist. Numerous persons so protected survived prolonged exposures to airborne rabies virus in bat caves where unimmunized sentinel animals became infected. Instead of taking a booster dose of vaccine every two years, I prefer to have a serum antibody test performed on a sample of my serum, thereby avoiding contributing to chances of a systemic allergic reaction. However, boosters are indicated after an exposure. Pre-exposure immunization, conferred by the three 1-ml doses of vaccine given intramuscularly, yields higher titers of longer duration than those conferred by three 0.1-ml doses given intradermally. As the ACIP (1984) explains, the latter method has been satisfactory in the United States but unsatisfactory in some groups of persons vaccinated overseas for several possible reasons. One study indicated that concurrent malaria prophylaxis using chloroquine and/or pyrimethamine-sulphadoxamine may have interferred with antibody response (Taylor et al., 1984), although other factors may be responsible as well.

4.6.2. Avoiding Exposures

Bites from most bats can be avoided by wearing pliable leather work gloves to handle them. To avoid being bitten while extracting bats from mist nets, a bat should be restrained with a gloved hand and the net manipulated with an ungloved hand (See Chapter 1). Any bat bite should be scrubbed with soap and water or detergent and water without delay. In the Americas or any area where bat rabies is known or suspected to occur, a bat bite should be considered a rabies exposure until proved otherwise. As noted above, the bite of a rabid bat can be infectious as early as 24 days prior to the bat's death, by which time the bitten person could have already died of the disease. Bat workers who fail to take proper precautions can receive numerous bites and be at exceptional risk. Direct or indirect contamination of open wounds or intact mucosal surfaces with infective bat saliva, tissues, or tissue fluids could represent a rabies exposure. Inhalation of aerolized rabies virus has long been known as a source of rabies infection in experimental animals. There appear to be four cases on record of such infections in man, the first two occurring in a bat cave and the other two resulting from inhaling aerosolized rabies virus emanating from faulty laboratory apparatus (Winkler, 1973; Tillotson et al., 1977a, 1977b).

5. RABIES-RELATED VIRUSES AND OTHER VIRAL INFECTIONS IN BATS

Rabies-related viruses have been found throughout Africa. Infections, first found in wildlife, have since been observed in man, dogs, and cats. Diseases produced by these viruses resemble paralytic rabies. However, fluorescent rabies antibody (FRA) testing of brain tissues may show dull fluorescence or none at all. Rabies vaccines offer questionable protection against these viruses. These limitations in diagnostic, preventive, and treatment capabilities make exposures to these viruses or their accidental introduction into other geographic areas especially undesirable.

Rabies virus and at least three other viruses (Mokola, Duvenhage, and Lagos bat) belong to the genus *Lyssavirus*. Some taxonomists also include Kotonkan virus and Obodhiang virus, isolated from hematophagous Diptera. All of the lyssaviruses, except rabies and Duvenhage, appear to be restricted to Africa, and all are known to produce encephalitis in laboratory animals (Shope, 1982). Lagos bat, Duvenhage, and Mokola viruses have been reported in bats.

Lagos bat virus has been reported from the brains of fruit bats, *Eidolon helvum, Micropteropus pusillus,* and *Epomophorus wahlbergi,* in Nigeria, the Central African Republic, and South Africa, respectively (Boulger and Porterfield, 1958; Sureau et al., 1977; Meredith and Standing, 1981). However, South African isolates were subsequently identified as Mokola virus (Schneider et al., 1985). In experiments, Lagos bat virus was pathogenic for dogs and rhesus monkeys, and it should be considered potentially pathogenic for man (Tignor et al., 1973).

Duvenhage virus was first reported from the brain of a man in South Africa who died with rabies-like symptoms about a month after being bitten by a bat while sleeping (Meredith et al., 1971). The bat was not tested, but the virus has since been isolated from another South African bat (Meredith, 1983). The bats, both unidentified, were said to resemble *Miniopterus schreibersii.* A nearly identical virus was subsequently isolated from two unidentified bats in Germany (Schneider and Meyer, 1981), followed by isolations from *Eptesicus serotinus* in Poland, Denmark, and Germany, *Myotis daubontoni* in Denmark and Germany, *Myotis dasycneme* in Denmark, and *Pipistrellus nathusii* in Germany (Schneider et al., 1986). A different strain of virus was found in the brain of a person in Finland who died after being bitten by bats he was handling (Lumio et al., 1986; Bitsch et al., 1986). Either atypical rabies or rabies-like viral isolates, still under study, were recovered from *E. serotinus* and from two persons who died with rabies symptoms that developed 21 and 35 days after being bitten by untested bats in Russia (Selimov et al., 1986). Studies in mice indicate certain human and animal rabies vaccines may offer protection from Danish isolates (Bitsch et al., 1986), but other rabies vaccines gave poor protection (Lumio et al., 1986).

Mokola virus has been reported in Nigeria, in Cameroon, and in Zimbabwe. First detected in shrews (*Crocidura* sp.), two human cases including one fatality were observed later; recently, the rabies-like disease was reported in an outbreak involving at least six cats and one dog. The dog had been vaccinated six months earlier with a potent, inactivated rabies vaccine (Foggin, 1983). As noted above, this virus was reported from *Epomophorus wahlbergi* in South Africa. Like typical rabies, it has a demonstrated potential to spread from a native host to man and domestic animals, and it probably can infect other native as well as foreign wildlife.

Specific fluorescent antibody tests for various lyssaviruses are under development for use in Africa. However, rabies vaccines and globulins might provide inadequate protection against the rabies-like viruses, and no specific biologicals are available for immunization against them.

6. HISTOPLASMOSIS

Histoplasmosis is a disease of man and other mammals caused by the dimorphic fungus *Histoplasma capsulatum* Darling var. *capsulatum* on all continents and also by var. *duboisii* (Vanbreuseghem) Ciferri in Africa. Occurring naturally as a soil saprophyte in relatively warm, humid areas, its development is enhanced by suitable organic materials such as the feces of birds or bats. Infection occurs upon inhalation of the fungal spores, which are readily made airborne by disturbing dry fecal deposits.

6.1. Host Species and Geographic Distribution

The histoplasmin skin test has been used to indicate presence of histoplasmosis in many populations of the world (Edwards and Bill-

Figure 1. Isolations of *Histoplasma capsulatum* from natural sources in the contiguous United States.

ings, 1971). Geographic areas where *H. capsulatum* is present can be identified, but false positives may result due to cross-reaction with other mycotic agents. For example, positive histoplasmin skin tests in persons living in the southwestern United States are usually cross reactions with *Coccidiodes immitis*. Isolations of *H. capsulatum* from soil or lifelong residents are required to establish beyond doubt the presence of the agent in a particular geographic area.

In the United States, histoplasmosis is known primarily in the Mississippi and Ohio River valleys and adjacent areas where soil and warm, humid climatic conditions favor growth of the fungus, especially in deposits of avian droppings. Bat shelters, especially warm, humid caves, evidently encourage fungal growth in bat guano and cave soil, providing point sources within, and extending south and west of the endemic areas cited above

(Fig. 1). Bat caves where the fungus has been found in Oklahoma, Texas, New Mexico, and Arizona accommodate bats that migrate into Mexico where the bats live in similar Histoplasma-laden caves. Colonial bats, associated with deposits of guano, are the species that are typically infected (Table 7). Although California has been extensively surveyed, *H. capsulatum* has not been recovered there from bats, bat guano, or any native source; occasional human cases have originated from other geographic areas.

The fungus is endemic throughout Central and South America and the Caribbean (MacKinnon, 1971). Numerous cases are reported each year among guano miners and others who enter bat roosts in Mexican caves and mine tunnels and there are similar reports from the rest of Latin America. As in the United States, many isolations have been made from colonial bats and soil or guano in colonial bat roosts.

Table 7. Reported isolations of *Histoplasma capsulatum* from bats.

Family and Species*	Country**
Noctilionidae	
Noctilio labialis	Panama
Mormoopidae	
Mormoops blainvillii	Cuba
Pteronotus parnellii	Panama, Belize
Pteronotus suapurensis	Panama
Phyllostomidae	
Artibeus jamaicensis	El Salvador, Cuba
Brachyphylla cavernarum	Puerto Rico
Brachyphylla nana	Cuba
Carollia perspicillata	Panama, Colombia, Ecuador
Desmodus rotundus	Panama, Colombia
Glossopha soricina	Panama, Colombia
Leptonycteris sanborni	USA
Lonchophylla robusta	Panama
Lonchorhina aurita	Panama
Micronycteris megalotis	Panama
Phyllostomus discolor	Panama, El Salvador
Phyllostomus hastatus	Panama
Tonatia bidens	Panama
Vespertilionidae	
Eptesicus brasiliensis	Colombia
Eptesicus fuscus	USA, Cuba
Myotis austroriparius	USA
Myotis grisescens	USA
Myotis lucifugus	USA
Myotis myotis	Israel
Myotis sodalis	USA
Nycticeius humeralis	USA
Pipistrellus subflavus	USA
Molossidae	
Molossus molossus	Panama, Ecuador
Molossus sp.	Panama
Nyctinomops laticaudatus	Panama
Tadarida brasiliensis	USA

*The taxonomic nomenclature used herein follows Honacki et al., (1982) and Freeman (1981). Thus, *Tadarida yucatanica* becomes *Nyctinomops laticaudatus,* and *Molossus major* and *M. daulensis* become *Molossus molossus.*

**References include those cited in Constantine (1970) and the following: Ajello et al., 1977; Carvajal-Zamora, 1977; D'Escoubet and Macola Olano, 1976; Hasenclever, 1972; Hasenclever et al., 1969; Hoff and Bigler, 1981; Johnson et al., 1970; Lottenberg et al., 1979; Quinones et al., 1978; Rodríguez, 1969.

Less is know of histoplasmosis elsewhere. With few exceptions, it appears to be uncommon in lifelong residents of Europe (Sotgiu et al., 1970). The fungus was isolated from guano in a Romanian bat cave (Alteras, 1966). Two cases were reported in persons who visited a bat cave on Cyprus (Stoker, 1964). The only isolations made in a survey of the Middle East were from a bat cave in Israel, where soil and a bat (*Myotis myotis*) yielded the fungus (Ajello et al., 1977).

In Africa, persons developed the disease after visiting bat caves in South Africa, Zambia, Rhodesia, and Tanzania; *H. capsulatum* was recovered from air in one of the South African bat caves and from guano in a Tanzanian cave (see review in Constantine, 1970). Speleologists and sentinel mice were reportedly infected in a bat cave in southern Zaire (Anciaux de Faveaux, 1964; Pottyn and Delville, 1960).

In Asia, skin tests suggest specific sensitivity in sizeable proportions of populations from India to Japan and the Philippines, and human cases, confirmed by culture, are known from India, Malaysia, Indonesia, Singapore, Thailand, Vietnam, and Japan, although it is not certain that the cases were contracted locally (Randhawa, 1970). The only field *H. capsulatum* isolation reported from southeast Asia was from guano in a cave near Kuala Lumpur, Malaysia (Ponnampalam, 1963).

Prior to 1972, Australia had reported seven human cases of histoplasmosis, four of which were in persons who had never been out of the country. The only soil isolations were from a fowl yard and garden adjacent to one victim's home. That victim was an active speleologist (Fewings et al., 1970). Another victim was a geologist and speleologist visitor from the United States. In 1972, 16 cases were reported in persons who visited Church Cave, near Wee Jasper, New South Wales (Isbister et al., 1976). Four of eight subsequent visitors to the cave became ill two to four weeks later (Hunt et al., 1974). The eight visitors wore "agricultural masks" that contained filters, but three persons who developed severe disease had ill-fitting masks. *H. capsulatum* was isolated from soil-guano, respiratory filters, sputum of a patient, and from sentinel mice caged in the cave. Church Cave is one of eleven reported maternity roosts of *Miniopterus schreibersii* in eastern Australia.

6.2. The Disease in Man

Disease manifestation depends largely on the dose inhaled. Surveys in endemic areas indicate that about 80% of some populations have experienced a benign, asymptomatic, primary pulmonary form of the disease, and these persons generally are considered resistant to reinfection, although reinfection is known to occur. Even in the benign disease,

germination in lungs leads to necrotic foci to which the host successfully responds by encapsulation and eventual calcification of the sites. In some individuals there is early dissemination to, and similar resolution within, tissues such as the spleen, liver, adrenal glands, lymph nodes, gastrointestinal system, skin, mucous membranes, bone marrow, and infrequently the central nervous system and heart.

About 10% of infected persons experience one or more of the symptomatic forms of the disease. Symptoms usually appear after an incubation period of one or two weeks. Disease manifestation follows an inadequate host response due to any of a variety of reasons: an overwhelming dose, unresponsive age (very young or very old), preexisting debilatory disease, emphysema, or immunosuppressive treatment such as corticosteroids. Symptomatic forms of the disease are usually described as: 1) acute, pulmonary histoplasmosis, 2) progressive disseminated histoplasmosis, and 3) chronic, cavitary histoplasmosis.

Acute, pulmonary histoplasmosis produces signs that vary from flu-like symptoms (labored breathing, unproductive cough, chest pain) to an exaggeration of these signs with fever, nightsweats, loss of body mass, and blood-stained sputum. Usually less severe than the following two manifestations, the severity of this form of the disease is proportional to the dose received and can be serious, even fatal.

Progressive disseminated histoplasmosis, seen in infants or aged persons, is generally regarded as an extension of acute pulmonary histoplasmosis. It is characterized by enlargement of the liver and spleen, anemia, leukopenia, and mass loss. It is fatal in 90% of cases unless diagnosed and treated promptly.

Cavitary histoplasmosis is rare, and it is thought to result from a combination of histoplasmosis with co-existing chronic obstructive pulmonary disease (e.g., emphysema), and perhaps with host hypersensitivity to the persistently present fungus. This chronic disease is characterized by a productive cough, low fever, and intermittent blood-stained sputum. Fifty percent of victims die within five years, although chemotherapy reduces mortality to 28%.

It has been suggested that *H. capsulatum* may be involved in the etiology of granulomatous uveitis, which consequently was called the presumed ocular histoplasmosis syndrome (POHS). However, the syndrome also occurs in areas of the world that are not endemic for the fungus, suggesting that POHS may either have multiple etiologies or the cases wherein the fungus was detected in the lesions represented coincidental disseminated histoplasmosis and POHS.

Histoplasma capsulatum var. *duboisii* uncommonly produces pulmonary disease. Instead, it usually produces cutaneous lesions (nodules, papules, or ulcers), and lymphadenopathy, sometimes involving bone (such as the skull or long bones) underlying cutaneous lesions or viscera.

Acute pulmonary histoplasmosis is the form of the disease that has been classically associated with exposure to infective bat guano. Whereas some persons have asymptomatic infections, others suffer severely. Mortality is frequent among Mexican guano miners, as high as 40% (6/15) in one outbreak (Velasco-Castrejón and González-Ochoa, 1977).

Histoplasmosis is not contagious between persons. It is necessary for the fungus to change from the yeast form present in tissues to the spore-bearing form it assumes in enriched soil.

Histoplasmosis is reliably diagnosed by isolation of the fungus from sputum, blood, urine, or lesions. A positive histoplasmin skin test can indicate exposure at some time in the past, but the test may not yet be positive in acute illness. The skin test, which frequently cross-reacts with blastomycin, may induce or increase complement-fixing antibodies in previously-infected persons. Thus, definitive fungal isolation is most desirable.

Pulmonary histoplasmosis may simulate, and must be differentiated from, tuberculosis. Therapy includes supportive care, often surgery, and chemotherapy with amphotericin B.

6.3. The Disease in Bats

When bats are experimentally infected by the natural route (inhalation), no disease signs are observed, but some bats develop small lesions in the intestinal mucosa from which the yeasts are shed into the feces (Klite and Dierks, 1965). Bats infected by inhaling the spores in guano dust may in turn contribute to guano contamination.

6.4. Prevention

Persons entering known or potentially contaminated bat roosts should breathe filtered air or have a self-contained air supply. Respirators should be worn with filter cartridges capable of filtering out particles as small as two microns in diameter. Some persons have become infected while wearing appropriate respirators, emphasizing the importance of wearing a properly fitted respirator.

There is no vaccine to prevent histoplasmosis. However, most people from endemic areas or who have visited contaminated bird or bat roosts may have positive histoplasmin skin tests, probably reflecting prior infection and resistance to subsequent infection. However, reinfection can occur, especially in response to a large dose. Persons with negative skin tests should be especially careful to avoid massive exposures. Individuals should wear protective clothing which should be removed at the site for decontamination or disposal. Care should be taken to avoid creating airborne dust from guano or soil. Wetting of small guano deposits may be a practical preventive measure in some circumstances.

A chemical preparation that has proved effective for decontamination of soil, guano, clothing, etc., is 3% formalin, prepared by mixing three parts formaldehyde (37% by mass formaldehyde gas in water, stabilized with 10-15% methanol) with 97 parts of water. This mixture has eliminated the fungus from soil under bird roosts. For each square foot (0.093 m²) of contaminated area, one should use one gal (4.5 l), a third of which should be applied on each of three successive days. The mixture was used to decontaminate protective clothing, which was removed at the site, drenched with the fungicide, and placed in a plastic bag until it could be washed in hot water and detergent (Tosh and Weeks, n.d.). However, since the foregoing studies were done, carcinogenic properties of formaldehyde have been recognized, indicating more restricted use of this chemical.

Contaminated clothing, boots, or equipment can be sources of infection for persons or sources of contamination for other soils or bat roosts. In recent years I have worn disposable paper-like coveralls and plastic gloves into contaminated bat caves, burning them after use. I prefer to bathe after departing a contaminated cave, if only in a portable shower spray.

7. BAT HEALTH AND HUMAN HEALTH PROBLEMS CAUSED BY BAT BIOLOGISTS

Bat researchers sometimes join specimen collectors, speleologists, and others in activities detrimental to bat populations such as overcollecting, awakening hibernating aggregations, and disturbing maternity groups, thus causing miscarriages and separations of sucklings. But unrecognized, more profound damage may result.

Diseases have not been considered among the negative forces bat biologists inflict on bats. Bat roosts are probably sometimes cross-contaminated with disease agents such as *Histoplasma capsulatum* by persons who transport the hardy spores in guano particles on their boots, clothing, or equipment. Intercontinental cross-contamination could occur with serious consequences for humans, bats, and other species.

Animals typically are hosts to microorganisms to which they have adapted, rarely experiencing disease, whereas unadapted hosts may suffer illness after exposure to the same microorganisms. Direct or indirect contact between bat species that are normally separated either geographically or ecologically might result in transmission of microorganisms and consequent illness. Keeping such bats together in cages may bring about transmission by various routes such as by mere contact, by bite, by ingestion, or by inhalation. Similarly, microorganisms resident in the researcher might be transmitted to bats. Bats might be infected via ectoparasites or excreta left in a cage that previously housed another bat. Should the newly-infected bat be released, it might spread the organisms to other bats.

What precautions should be taken to avoid the introduction of disease-producing microorganisms into bat roosts or bat populations? A commonsense approach is indicated, because no standards have been established. To avoid cross-contamination of bat roosts with infective guano, the recommendations for decontaminating or changing clothing and equipment exposed to the spores of *H. capsulatum* should solve many problems. Disposable, paper ice-cream carton cages with mesh lids may be used to house bats in the field or laboratory (Constantine, 1978). Contaminated larger cages can be autoclaved or fumigated. Cross-infection and cross-infestation between species can be curtailed by not keeping different species of bats in the same or adjacent cages, by scrupulously cleaning used cages, the cage environment and food and water vessels, and by not using the same gloves or instruments for manipulating more than one species. Ordinary methods used to minimize human-to-human transmission should minimize exposures of bats to microbial pathogens from humans. Pools of water in caves, sometimes sources of drinking water for bats, are especially vulnerable to contamination by human visitors.

8. SUMMARY

Health hazards that investigators may encounter or generate in the course of their work with bats are described or updated as are methods of dealing with them. Gases (ammonia, carbon dioxide, carbon monoxide, hydrogen sulfide, methane, sulfur dioxide, or a deficit of oxygen) in caves or old mines can kill with little or no warning. Safety measures include devices that signal the presence of and measure the gases, protective masks and other apparatus to prevent exposures, and first-aid for exposed persons. Thorough inquiry is indicated to avoid exposures to these and other lethal gases in addition to those poisons used to control vampire bats in Latin American caves. Powdered anticoagulants are used legally or illegally in some countries in a futile effort to eliminate bats from buildings rather than seal-out the bats. Persons who live in treated buildings and especially persons who enter the attics into which the anticoagulant powder has been blown risk exposure. People or pets who contact the extensive scattering of stricken bats may become contaminated; if bitten, they should be treated as possible rabies exposures. Diagnosis and appropriate treatment are problematic because exposed persons may be unaware of exposure to an anticoagulant.

Bat ectoparasites and bat urine are not demonstrated sources of disease for man. Ordinary repugnance tends to preclude massive exposure to them in crowded bat caves.

Bat rabies information, essential to workers and to public safety, is reviewed, including the transmission by aerosolized virus or by ingestion, potential mechanical transmission by bat-eating pets or when dissecting bats, potential insect vectors, and quarantine of captive bats. Current information on rabies prevention by immunization and methods of avoiding rabies exposures are detailed.

Rabies-related viruses, known in bats, people, dogs, cats, arthropods and wildlife throughout Africa and recently Europe may be mistaken for rabies if not overlooked altogether during rabies tests. Unfortunately, rabies vaccines and globulins apparently provide little or no protection against these viruses, some of which are lethal. These and numerous other viruses of known or unknown disease potential have been found in bat salivary glands and provide additional reasons to avoid bat bites.

Histoplasmosis is reviewed with emphasis on bat involvement, including worldwide distribution, bat species reported infected, disease manifestations in man and in bats, and methods of avoiding infection and further spread of the fungus.

Bat researchers may inadvertently cross-contaminate bat roosts with disease agents such as *Histoplasma* spores, or they may introduce diseases into previously uninfected bat populations by temporarily housing together animals that are normally geographically or ecologically separated, thereby facilitating transmission from infected individuals. Bats are susceptible to infection by at least some diseases of man, and it is reasonable to expect that some human diseases could be introduced into bat populations by ill or careless workers. Procedures to avoid these problems are suggested.

9. ACKNOWLEDGMENTS

I am grateful to numerous persons who helped in various ways to prepare this chapter. Dr. Libero Ajello, United States Department of Human and Health Services, Centers for Disease Control, and Dr. Warren C. Lewis, National Speleological Society, helped assemble recent histoplasmosis reports. Representing the California Department of Industrial Relations, Division of Occupational Safety and Health, George Denton and Donn Stevens provided extensive information on mine atmospheric gas problems, their detection, and relevant safety precautions, and John Nagel demonstrated mask fitting procedures. Representing the California Department of Health Services, Dr. Linda A. Rudolph provided some literature on atmospheric gases, Robert Graul gave consultation on gas detection techniques, Hazel Anderholm prepared the histoplasmosis distribution map, and Pearl Wong typed the manuscript. As representatives of the United States Department of Labor, Mine Safety and Health Administration, Leo Hayden, John Widows, and Ralph Foster offered general information on mine safety matters and specific information on gas concentrations found in mine tunnels.

10. REFERENCES

Ajello, L., E. S. Kutlin, A. M. Beemer, W. Kaplan, and A. Padhye. 1977. Occurrence of *Histoplasma capsulatum* Darling, 1906 in Israel, with a review of the current status of histoplasmosis in the Middle East. Amer. J. Trop. Med. Hyg., 26:140-147.

Aleksieva, Z. 1983. Sulphur compounds. Pp. 2122-2124, *in* Encyclopaedia of occupational health and safety. (L. Parmeggiani, ed.). Int. Labour Office, Geneva, 2:1-2538.

Alteras, I. 1966. First Romanian isolation of *Histoplasma capsulatum* from the soil. Dermatol. Int., 5:60-71.

American Conference of Governmental Industrial Hygienists (ACGIH). 1982. Documentation of the threshold limit values. 4th Amer. Conf. Gov. Indust. Hyg., Cincinnati, 486 pp.

Amoudru, C. 1983. Mines, occupational health in. Pp. 1379-1381, *in* Encyclopaedia of occupational health and safety. (L. Parmeggiani, ed.). Int. Labour Office, Geneva, 2:1-2538.

Anciaux de Faveaux, F. 1964. L'histoplasmose dans les grottes du Haut-Katanga. 3rd Int. Congr. Speleol. Vienna, 1961. 3:7-10.

Aucar, V. G., and H. F. Mayer. 1975. Aislamientos de virus rabico en quiropteros de la Provincia de Corrientes. Gac. Vet. (Buenos Aires), 37:141-146.

Baer, G. M., and G. L. Bales. 1967. Experimental rabies infection in the Mexican freetail bat. J. Infec. Dis., 117:82-90.

Barnard, B. J. H., R. H. Hassel, H. J. Geyer, and W. C. De Koker. 1982. Non-bite transmission of rabies in kudu (*Tragelaphus strepsiceros*). Onderstepoort Jour. Vet. Res., 48:191-192.

Beauregard, M. 1969. Bat rabies in Canada 1963-1967. Can J. Comp. Med., 33:220-226.

Bell, F. G. 1980. Engineering geology and geotechnics. Newnes-Butterworths., London, 497 pp.

Bell, J. F., and G. J. Moore. 1971. Susceptibility of Carnivora to rabies virus administered orally. Amer. J. Epidemiol., 93:176-182.

Bell, J. F., G. J. Moore, and G. H. Raymond. 1969. Protracted survival of a rabies-infected insectivorous bat after infective bite. Amer. J. Trop. Med. Hyg., 18:61-66.

Bell, G. P. 1980. A possible case of interspecific transmission of rabies in insectivorous bats. J. Mammal., 61:528-530.

Bishop, S. C. 1947. Curious behavior of a hoary bat. J. Mammal., 28:293-294.

Bitsch, V. J. Westergaard, and M. Valle. 1986. Bat rabies—Europe. Morbid. Mortal. Week. Rep., 35:430-432.

Boulger, L. R. and J. S. Porterfield. 1958. Isolation of a virus from Nigerian fruit bats. Trans. R. Soc.

Britton, S. W., and R. F. Kline. 1945. Age, sex, carbohydrate, adrenal cortex and other factors in anoxia. Amer. J. Physiol., 145:190-202.

Caccuri, S. 1983. Hydrogen sulphide. Pp. 1090-1091, *in* Encyclopaedia of occupational health and safety (L. Parmeggiani, ed.). Int. Labour Office, Geneva, 1:1-1176.

Carvajal-Zamora, J. R. 1977. Isolation of Histoplasma capsulatum from tissues of bats captured in the Aguas Buenas Caves, Aguas Buenos, Puerto Rico. Mycopathologia, 60:167-169.

Center for Disease Control. 1971. Monthly rabies summary July 1971. Zoonoses Surveillance. Atlanta, Georgia, 10 pp.

Clark, D. R., Jr. 1981. Bats and environmental contaminents: A review. U. S. Fish and Wildl. Serv., Spec. Sci. Rep.—Wildlife, 235:1-27.

Clark, D. R., R. K. LaVal, and M. D. Tuttle. 1982. Estimating pesticide burdens of bats from guano analyses. Bull. Environ. Contam. Toxicol., 29:214-220.

Cockrum, E. L., and A. L. Gardner. 1960. Underwood's mastiff bat in Arizona. J. Mammal., 41:510-511.

Constantine, D. G. 1958. Bleaching of hair pigment in bats by the atmosphere in caves. J. Mammal., 39:513-520.

Constantine, D. G. 1961. Locality records and notes on western bats. J. Mammal., 42:404-405.

Constantine, D. G. 1966a. Transmission experiments with bat rabies isolates: Reactions of certain Carnivora, opossum, and bats to intramuscular inoculations of rabies virus isolated from free-tailed bats. Amer. J. Vet. Res., 27:16-19.

Constantine, D. G. 1966b. Transmission experiments with bat rabies isolates: Bite transmission of rabies to foxes and coyote by free-tailed bats. Amer. J. Vet. Res., 27:20-23.

Constantine, D. G. 1967a. Rabies transmission by air in bat caves. U. S. Pub. Health Serv., Publ. 1617., U. S. Gov. Printing Office, Washington, D. C., 51 pp.

Constantine, D. G. 1967b. Bat rabies in the southwestern United States. Pub. Health Rep., 82:867-888.

Constantine, D. G. 1970. Bats in relation to the health, welfare, and economy of man. Pp. 319-449, *in* Biology of bats. Vol II. (W. A. Wimsatt, ed.). Academic Press. New York, 477 pp.

Constantine, D. G. 1978. Insectivorous bats. Pp. 513-521, *in* Zoo and wild animal medicine. (M. E. Fowler, ed.). W. G. Saunders, Philadelphia, 951 pp.

Constantine, D. G., and D. F. Woodall. 1966. Transmission experiments with bat rabies isolates: Reactions of certain Carnivora, opossum, rodents, and bats to rabies of red bat origin when exposed by bat bite or by intramuscular inoculation. Amer. J. Vet. Res., 27:24-32.

Constantine, D. G., G. C. Solomon, and D. F. Woodall. 1968a. Transmission experiments with bat rabies isolates: Responses of certain carnivores and rodents to rabies viruses from four species of bats. Amer. J. Vet. Res., 29:181-190.

Constantine, D. G., E. S. Tierkel, M. D. Kleckner, and D. M. Hawkins. 1968b. Rabies in New Mexico cavern bats. Pub. Health Rep., 83:303-316.

Constantine, D. G., G. L. Humphrey, and T. B. Herbenick. 1979. Rabies in *Myotis thysanodes, Lasiurus ega, Euderma maculatum,* and *Eumops perotis* in California. J. Wildl. Dis., 15:343-345.

Da Silva, R. A., and O. A. Alencar. 1968. Isolamento de virus rabico das glandulas salivares de morcegos carnivoros da especie *Chrotopterus auritus auritus* Peters. Separ. Vet., 21:7-10.

DeAmorim, A. F., R. A. Da Silva, and N. M. Da Silva. 1970. Isolamento do virus rabico de morcego insetivoro, *Histiotus velatus,* capturado no Estado de Santa Catarina. Pesq. Agropec. Bras., 5:433-435.

Delpietro, H. A., E. C. Boehringer, and A. Fornes. 1969. Rabia en murciélagos insectivoros (Primer caso en el género *Eumops*). Rev. Med. Vet. (Buenos Aires), 50:57-61.

Delpietro, H., A. M. C. de Diaz, E. Fuenzalida, and J. F. Bell. 1972. Determinación de la tasa de ataque de rabia en murciélagos. Bol. Of. Sanit. Panamer., 73:222-230.

De Yosti, N. I., C. Lora, B. Morán, and R. Urbina. 1971. Primer informe en el Peru de rabia paralitica bovina transmitida por quiropteros. Bol. Of. Sanit. Panamer., 71:378-386.

Edwards, P. Q., and E. L. Billings. 1971. Worldwide pattern of skin sensitivity to histoplasmin. Amer. J. Trop. Med. Hyg., 20:288-319.

Fewings, J. D., H. Lander, K. F. Anderson, F. R. Henning, B. G. Radden, and B. J. Jeanes. 1970. Case report. Disseminated histoplasmosis. Aust. Ann. Med., 19:151-158.

Flores Crespo, R., and J. Morales Ruiz, 1975. Metodos para combatir los vampiros. Tec. Pec. Mexico, 29:73-80.

Foggin, C. M. 1983. Mokola virus infection in cats and a dog in Zimbabwe. Vet. Rec., 113:115.

Font D'Escoubet, E., and S. Macola Olano. 1976. *Histoplasma capsulatum:* Aislamiento de murciélagos en Cuba. Rev. Cuban Med. Trop., 28:119-125.

Fornes, A., R. D. Lord, M. L. Kuns, O. P. Larghi, E. Fuenzalida, and L. Lazara. 1974. Control of bovine rabies through vampire bat control. J. Wildl. Dis., 10:310-316.

Freeman, P. W. 1981. A multivariate study of the family Molossidae (Mammalia, Chiroptera): Morphology, ecology, evolution. Fieldiana Zool., n.s. 7, 1316:1-173.

Gadskina, I. D. 1983. Ammonia. Pp. 148-150, *in* Encyclopaedia of occupational health and safety. (L. Parmeggiani, ed.). Int. Labour Office, Geneva, 1:1-1176.

Goodwin, G. G., and A. M. Greenhall. 1961. A review of the bats of Trinidad and Tobago. Bull. Amer. Mus. Nat. Hist., 122:187-301.

Greenhall, A. M. 1965. Technique for the removal of brain in bats. Nature, 208:1014-1015.

Greenhall, A. M. 1982. House bat management. U. S. Fish and Wildl. Serv., Res. Publ. 143:1-33 + iv.

Halbert, E. J. M. 1982. Evaluation of carbon dioxide and oxygen data in cave atmospheres using the Gibbs triangle and the cave air index. Helictite, 20:60-68.

Halliday, W. R. 1982. American caves and caving. Revised ed. Barnes and Noble Books, New York, 348 pp.

Hasenclever, H. F. 1972. Histoplasmosis in bats. Health Lab. Sci., 9:125-132.

Hasenclever, H. F., A. W. Hunter, E. George, and J. Schwarz. 1969. The use of cultural and histological methods for the detection of *Histoplasma capsulatum* in bats: Absence of a cellular response. Amer. J. Epidemiol., 90:77-83.

Hentschke, J., and E. Hellman. 1975. Nachweis der Tollwut bei einer Fledermaus in Berlin. Berl. Munch. Tieraerz H. Wochenschr., 88:92-94.

Hoff, G. L., and W. J. Bigler, 1981. The role of bats in the propagation and spread of histoplasmosis: A review. J. Wildl. Dis., 17:191-196.

Honacki, J. H., K. E. Kinman, and J. W. Koeppl. 1982. Mammal species of the world. Assoc. Syst. Collect., Lawrence, Kansas, 694 pp.

Hunt, P. J., T. J. Harden, M. Hibbins, R. C. Pritchard, D. B. Muir, and F. J. Gardner. 1984. *Histoplasma capsulatum*. Isolation from an Australian cave environment and from a patient. Med. J. Aust., 141:280-283.

Isbister, J., M. Elliott, and S. Nogrady. 1976. Histoplasmosis: An outbreak occurring among young men who visited one cave. Med. J. Aust., 2:243-248.

James, J. M. 1977. Carbon dioxide in the cave atmosphere. Trans. British Cave Res. Assoc., 4:417-429.

James, J. M., A. J. Pavey, and A. F. Rogers. 1975. Foul air and the resulting hazards to cavers. Trans. British Cave Res. Assoc., 2:79-88.

Johnson, J. E., G. Radimer, A. F. Di Salvo, L. Ajello, and W. Bigler. 1970. Histoplasmosis in Florida: I. Report of a case and epidemiologic studies. Amer. Rev. Resp. Dis., 101:299-305.

Kaplan, M. M. 1973. Safety precautions in handling rabies virus. Pp. 13-18, *in* Laboratory techniques in rabies. 3rd ed. (M. M. Kaplan and H. Koprowski, eds.). World Health Organization, Geneva, Monogr. Ser., 23:5-367.

Klite, P. D., and F. H. Diercks, 1965. *Histoplasma capsulatum* in fecal contents and organs of bats in the Canal Zone. Amer. J. Trop. Med. Hyg., 14:433-439.

Kurppa, O., and J. Rantanen. 1983. Carbon monoxide. Pp. 395-399, *in* Encyclopaedia of occupational health and safety. (L. Parmeggiani, ed.). Internat. Labour Office, Geneva, 1:1-1176.

Kurt, T. L. 1983. Chemical asphyxiants. Pp. 289-300, *in* Environmental and occupational medicine. (W. N. Rom, ed.). Little, Brown and Co., Boston. 1015 pp.

Linhart, S. B., R. Flores Crespo, and G. C. Mitchell. 1972. Control of vampire bats by topical application of an anticoagulant, chlorophacinone. Bol. Of. Sanit. Panamer., English edition, 6:31-38.

Lottenberg, R., R. H. Waldman, L. Ajello, G. L. Hoff, W. Bigler, and S. R. Zellner. 1979. Pulmonary histoplasmosis associated with exploration of a bat cave. Amer. J. Epidemiol., 110:156-161.

Lumio, J., M. Hillborn, R. Roine, L. Ketonen, M. Haltia, M. Valle, E. Neuvonen, and J. Lahdevirta. 1986. Human rabies of bat origin in Europe. Lancet, i (8477):378.

Mackinnon, J. E. 1971. Histoplasmosis in Latin America. Pp. 129-139, *in* Histoplasmosis. (L. Ajello, E. W. Chick, and M. L. Furcolow, eds.). Charles C. Thomas, Springfield, Illinois, 516 pp.

Mackison, F. W., R. S. Stricoff, and L. J. Partridge, Jr. (eds.). 1981. NIOSH/OSHA occupational health guidelines for chemical hazards. U. S. Dep. Health and Human Services (NIOSH) Publ. 81-123., U. S. Gov. Printing Office, Washington, D. C. Looseleaf, not consecutively numbered. 3 vols.

Main, A. J. 1979. Virologic and serologic survey for eastern equine encephalomyelitis and certain other viruses in colonial bats of New England. J. Wildl. Dis., 15:455-466.

Matheney, R. G., and N. B. Gale. 1962. Rabies: Its history in Panama. Bien. Vet. Conf., Communicable Disease Center, U.S.P.H.S., Atlanta, Georgia, Aug. 6-10.

Matheson, D. 1983. Carbon dioxide. Pp. 392-393, *in* Encyclopaedia of occupational health and safety. (L. Parmeggiani, ed.). Internat. Labour Office, Geneva, 1:1-1176.

Medeiros, J. L., and R. A. Heckmann. 1971. *Euderma maculatum* from California infected with rabies virus. J. Mammal., 52:858.

Meredith, C. D. 1983. Isolation of Duvenhage virus from a microchiropteran bat. Rabies Information Exchange (C.D.C., Atlanta, Georgia), 7:53.

Meredith, C. D., and E. Standing. 1981. Lagos bat virus in South Africa. Lancet, i (8224):832-833.

Meredith, C. D., A. P. Rossouw, and H. van Praag Koch. 1971. An unusual case of human rabies thought to be of Chiropteran origin. S. Afr. Med. J., 45:767-769.

Mitchell, H. A. 1964. Investigations of the cave atmosphere of a Mexican bat colony. J. Mammal., 45:568-577.

Mohr, W. 1957. Die Tollwut. Med. Klin. (Munich), 52:1057-1060.

Moore, G. J., and G. H. Raymond. 1970. Prolonged incubation period of rabies in a naturally infected insectivorous bat, *Eptesicus fuscus* (Beauvois). J. Wildl. Dis., 6:167-168.

National Institute for Occupational Safety and Health. 1983. NIOSH Recommendations for Occupational Health Standards. Morbid. Mortal. Week. Rep. 32, No. 1S:1S-22S.

Orr, R. T. 1950. Unusual behavior and occurrence of a hoary bat. J. Mammal., 31:456-457.

Osbern, L. N. 1983. Simple asphyxiants. Pp. 285-288, *in* Environmental and occupational medicine. (W. N. Rom, ed.). Little, Brown and Co., Boston, 1015 pp.

Osborne, R. A. L. 1981. Towards an air quality standard for tourist caves: Studies of carbon dioxide enriched atmospheres in Gaden-Coral Cave, Wellington Caves, N. S. W. Helictite, 19:48-56.

Pal, S. R., A. Bimla, P. N. Chhuttani, S. Broor, S. Choudhury, R. M. Joshi, and S. D. Ray. 1980. Rabies virus infection in a flying fox bat, *Pteropus poliocephalus*, in Chandigarh, Northern India. Trop. Geogr. Med., 32:265-267.

Pawan, J. L. 1936. The transmission of paralytic rabies in Trinidad by the vampire bat (*Desmodus rotundus murinus* Wagner, 1840). Ann. Trop. Med. Parasitol., 30:101-130.

Ponnampalam, J. 1963. Isolation of *Histoplasma capsulatum* from the soil of a cave in central Malaya. Amer. J. Trop. Med. Hyg., 12:775-776.

Pottyn, S. R., and J. P. Delville. 1960. Etude mycologique. Mise en evidence d'histoplasmes dans une grotte du Katanga. Ann. Soc. Belge Méd. Trop., XL(2):303-305.

Pounder, C. 1982. Speculations on natural explosions at Old Hannah's Cave, Staffordshire, England. Nat. Speleol. Soc. Bull., 44:11-14.

Price, J. L., and C. O. R. Everard. 1977. Rabies virus and antibody in bats in Grenada and Trinidad. J. Wildl. Dis., 13:131-134.

Public Health Service Advisory Committee on Immunization Practices (ACIP). 1984. Rabies prevention—United States, 1984. Morbid. Mortal. Week. Rep., 33:393-402, 407.

Quinones, F., J. P. Koplan, L. Pike, F. Staine, and L. Ajello. 1978. Histoplasmosis in Belize, Central America. Amer. J. Trop. Med. Hyg., 27:558-561.

Randhawa, H. S. 1970. Occurrence of histoplasmosis in Asia. Mycopathol. Mycol. Appl., 41:75-89.

Retamoso Yepez, A., M. La Mata, and A. Fornes. 1972. Aislamiento de virus rábico en cerebro y glándulas de un murciélago insectívoro *Lasiurus cinereus villosissimus*. Rev. Med. Vet., Buenos Aires, 53:281-285.

Rodrígues, F. M., C. A. Nagata, Z. M. P. Peixoto, and M. R. Nilson. 1975. Isolamento do vírus da raiva de morcego insetívoro *Molossus obscurus* (Geoffroy, 1805), no Estado de São Paulo. Arq. Inst. Biol., São Paulo, 42:193-196.

Rodríguez M., J. D. 1969. Histoplasma capsulatum en murciélagos de la Prov. del Guayas. Rev. Ecuat. Hig. Med. Trop., 26:95-101.

Sadler, W. W., and J. B. Enright. 1959. Effect of metabolic level of the host upon the pathogenesis of rabies in the bat. J. Infec. Dis., 105:267-273.

Schneider, L. G., and S. Meyer. 1981. Antigenic determinants of rabies virus as demonstrated by monoclonal antibody. Dev. Cell. Biol., 7:947-953.

Schneider, L. G., B. J. H. Barnard, H. P. Schneider, O. A. Odeguard, J. Mueller, M. Selimov, J. H. Cox, A. I. Wandeler, J. Blancou, and S. Meyer. 1985. Application of monoclonal antibodies for epidemiological investigations and oral vaccination studies. Pp. 47-59, *in* Rabies in the Tropics. (E. Kuwert, C. Merieux, H. Koprowski, and K. Bogel, eds.). Springer-Verlag, Berlin, New York, 786 pp.

Schneider, L. G., W. W. Mueller, and K. P. Hohnsbeen (eds). 1986. Rabies surveillance report. Rabies Bull. Europe, 10:1-3.

Selimov, M. A., A. G. Tatarov, L. A. Antonova, Yu. N. Shcherbak, E. A. Shablovskaya, A. M. Smekhov, and B. Yu. Mogilevsky. 1986. To the issue of chiropteric rabic infection. Rabies Information Exchange. (C.D.C., Atlanta, Georgia), 14:9-12.

Shope, R. E. 1982. Rabies-related viruses. Yale J. Biol. Med., 55:271-275.

Sikes, R. K. 1962. Pathogenesis of rabies in wildlife. 1. Comparative effect of varying doses of rabies virus inoculated into foxes and skunks. Amer. J. Vet. Res., 23:1041-1047.

Sileoni, S., O. Rossetti, A. Márquez, A. C. Menoyo, and R. A. de Torres. 1971. Aislamiento de virus rabico de murcielagos insectivoros en Cordoba, Argentina. Bol. Of. Sanit. Panamer., 70:456-462.

Silva Taboada, G., and M. Herrada Llibre, 1974. Primer caso comprobada de rabia en un murcielago Cubano. Poeyana, 126:1-5.

Smith, J. S., J. W. Summer, L. F. Roumillat, G. M. Baer, and W. G. Winkler. 1984. Antigenic characteristics of isolates associated with a new epizootic of raccoon rabies in the United States. J. Infec. Dis., 149:769-774.

Smith, P. C., K. Lawhaswasdi, W. E. Vick, and J. S. Stanton. 1967. Isolation of rabies virus from fruit bats in Thailand. Nature, 216:384.

Sotgiu, G., A. Mantovani, and A. Mazzoni. 1970. Histoplasmosis in Europe. Mycopathol. Mycol. Appl., 40:53-74.

Stoker, D. J. 1964. Histoplasmosis in Cyprus: Report of two cases. British Med. J., 2:793-795.

Stouraitis, P., and J. Salvatierra. 1978. Isolation of rabies virus from bats in Bolivia. Trop. Anim. Health Prod., 10:101-102.

Studier, E. H., L. R. Beck, and R. G. Lindeborg. 1967. Tolerance and initial metabolic response to ammonia intoxication in selected bats and rodents. J. Mammal., 48:564-572.

Sureau, P., P. Rollin, and T. J. Wiktor. 1983. Epidemiologic analysis of antigenic variations of street rabies virus: Detection by monoclonal antibodies. Amer. J. Epidemiol., 117:605-609.

Sureau, P., M. Germain, J. P. Herve, B. Geoffroy, J. P. Cornet, G. Heme, and Y. Robin. 1977. Isolement du virus Lagos bat en Empire Centrafricain. Bull. Soc. Path. Exot., 70:467-470.

Taylor, D. N., C. Wasi, and K. Bernard. 1984. Chloroquine prophylaxis associated with a poor antibody response to human diploid cell rabies vaccine. Lancet, i:1405.

Tierkel, E. S. 1963. Rabies. Pp. 293-349, in Diseases transmitted from animals to man. (T. G. Hull, ed.). Thomas, Springfield, Illinois, 967 pp.

Tignor, G. H., R. E. Shope, P. N. Bhatt, and D. H. Percy. 1973. Experimental infection of dogs and monkeys with two rabies sero-group viruses, Lagos Bat and Mokola (IbAn 27377): Clinical, serologic, virologic, and fluorescent-antibody studies. J. Infec. Dis., 128:471-478.

Tillotson, J. R., D. Axelrod, and D. O. Lyman, 1977a. Rabies in a laboratory worker—New York. Morbid. Mortal. Week. Rep., 26:183-184.

Tillotson, J. R., D. Axelrod, and D. O. Lyman, 1977b. Follow-up on rabies—New York. Morbid. Mortal. Week. Rep., 26:249-250.

Tosh, F. E., and R. J. Weeks. (no date). Histoplasmosis control: Decontamination of bird roosts, chicken houses and other point sources. U. S. Pub. Health Serv., CDC Publ. 00-3021.

Velasco-Castrejón, O., and A. González-Ochoa. 1977. Primary pulmonary epidemic histoplasmosis in an abandoned mine. Mykosen, 20:393-399.

Villa R., B. 1966. Los Murciélagos de México. Inst. Biol., Univ. Nac. Auton. Méx., México, 491 pp.

Whetstone, C. A., T. O. Bunn, R. W. Emmons, and T. J. Wiktor. 1984. Use of monoclonal antibodies to confirm vaccine-induced rabies in ten dogs, two cats, and one fox. J. Amer. Vet. Med. Assoc., 185:285-288.

Winkler, W. G. 1968. Airborne rabies virus isolation. Bull. Wildl. Dis. Assoc., 4:37-40.

Winkler, W. G. 1975. Fox rabies. Pp. 3-22, in The natural history of rabies. Vol. II. (G. M. Baer, ed.). Academic Press. New York, 387 pp.

Winkler, W. G., T. R. Fashinell, L. Leffingwell, P. Howard, and J. Conomy. 1973. Airborne rabies transmission in a laboratory worker. J. Amer. Med. Assoc., 226:1219-1221.

World Health Organization Expert Committee on Rabies. 1984. Seventh report. World Health Organ., Tech. Rep. Ser. 709, 104 pp.

Appendix 1. Products, Services, and Sources for Health Protection and Personal Safety

PRODUCT OR SERVICE

Respirators
  Comfo II[a] (rubber, half-mask facepiece, with 2 receptacles for filter/cartridges)

  Mine Safety Appliances (MSA)
  600 Penn Center Boulevard
  Pittsburgh, Pennsylvania 15235 USA

  Ultra-Twin[a] (rubber, full facepiece, with single lens and 2 receptacles)

  MSA

Combination filter/cartridges for use with Comfo II or Ultra twin to remove either NH₃ or SO₂ and histoplasmal spore-size particles.

GMD-H.[a] For use in not over 300 ppm NH₃, 2 cartridges providing over 16 hrs service at that concentration according to manufacturer.

MSA

GMB-H.[a] For use in not over 50 ppm SO₂. Manufacturer claims 2 cartridges give 3 hrs of service at 500 ppm.

MSA

4-hour Oxygen Breathing Apparatus[b] Draeger Model BG-174A Full facepiece

National Mine Service Co. (NMSC)
4900/600 Grant Street
Pittsburgh, Pennsylvania 15216 USA

1-hour O₂ breathing apparatus[b] Self-contained oxygen self-rescuer Draeger Model OXY-SR 60B No facepiece

NMSC

Koehler Flame Safety Lamp[c] Model 257-E

NMSC

Dual-Sensor Oxygen & Methane Gas Monitor[c] Model MX240

NMSC

MiniCO Carbon monoxide indicator with alarm. Model IV

MSA

Pump to draw measured quantities of air through Draeger gas detector tubes
  Draeger Bellows Pump Gas Detector (also available in a kit that includes carrying case, tools, and spare parts)

NMSC

Draeger gas testing tubes for use with above
  Ammonia 5/a[a] (5-700 ppm)
  No. CH 20501

NMSC

Carbon dioxide 0.1%/a[a] (0.1-6 vol%)
No. CH 23501

NMSC

Carbon monoxide 5/c [a] (5-700 ppm)
No. CH 25501

NMSC

Carbon monoxide 10/b [a] (10-3,000 ppm)
No. CH 20601

NMSC

Hydrogen sulphide 1/c [a] (1-200 ppm)
No. CH 19001

NMSC

Hydrogen sulphide 5/b [a] (5-600 ppm)
No. CH 29801

NMSC

Sulfur dioxide 0.5/a[a] (0.5-22 ppm
No. 67 28491

NMSC

Pump to draw measured quantities of air through MSA gas detector tubes
  Samplair Pump, Model A[d]
  Manual-operated, piston-type
  Includes carrying case, spare parts

MSA

MSA gas detector tubes for use with the above pump
  Ammonia No. 460103[d] (5-1600 ppm)
  Carbon dioxide No. 85976[d] (200-120,000 ppm)
  Carbon monoxide No. 465519 [d] (0-3000 ppm)
  Hydrogen sulfide No. 463875[d] (10-2000 ppm)
  Sulfur dioxide No. 92623[d] (1-400 ppm)

MSA

TYVEK coveralls. Disposable. Spun-bonded polyethylene fiber material. Standard material. Varieties of TYVEK materials, hoods, boots, available.

Lab. Safety Supply
3430 Palmer Drive
Janesville, Wisconsin 53547-1368 USA

Histoplasmosis skin test antigen:
Histoplasmin[e]

Parke-Davis
Joseph Campau at the River
Detroit, MI 48232 USA

Rabies vaccines for use in USA:
(Human diploid cell vaccine or HDCV)
RABIES VACCINE[e]

Merieux Institute, Inc.
1200 N. W. 78th Ave., Suite 109
Miami, FL 33126 USA

Globulins for use in USA:
Rabies immune globulin, human (RIG)
HYPERAB[e]

Cutter Laboratories
2480 Baumann Avenue
San Lorenzo, California 94580 USA
or
4542 McEwan Road
Dallas, Texas 95240 USA

IMOGAM[e]

Merieux Institute, Inc.
1200 N. W. 78th Ave., Suite 109
Miami, Florida 33126 USA

Antirabies Serum, Equine (ARS)
ANTIRABIES SERUM[e]

Lederle Laboratories
Pearl River, New York 10965 USA
or
Sclavo, Inc., 5 Monsard Ct.
Wayne, New Jersey 07470 USA

Test for rabies-neutralizing antibodies as evidence of immunization against rabies

Physician should contact local or state health department concerning availability of service from state or commercial laboratories.

Information on unsafe underground atmospheres

U. S. Department of Labor
Mine Safety Health Administration
4015 Wilson Boulevard
Arlington, Virginia 22203 USA
or
National Speleological Society
Cave Avenue
Huntsville, Alabama 35810 USA

Mine or cave rescues

Regional rescue network
County Sheriff (United States)

Cave rescues

Air Force Rescue Coordination Center
(continental United States)
(800) 851-3051

[a]NIOSH-approved
[b]MSHA/NIOSH-certified
[c]MSHA-approved
[d]NIOSH-certified (the pump when used with certified tubes)
[e]Immunobiologic products are available only through producers or pharmacies. Health departments or hospitals may have emergency supplies of rabies products.

Subject Index

allozyme techniques
    collection of blood, and other tissues, 142–143
    electrophoresis, 143–145, 154–156
    interpreting gels, 145–148
ageing methods
    body mass, 55
    epiphyeseal growth plates, 53–54
    forearm length, 52
    incremental tooth lines, 51–52
    pelage coloration, 55–56
    tooth wear, 48–51
anemometers
    hot wire, 314
    thermister, 314–315
anesthesia, 260
ash content, 394–396
ash-free dry mass, 391, 393–394
average daily metabolic rate, 355

bands (tags, rings)
    metallic, 60–61
    plastic, 61
    reflective, 61–62
basal metabolic rate, 354
bat detectors, 68, 80, 84, 92, 94–96, 102
bat-fruit syndrome, 223–224
bat passes, 68, 79
batteries
    head lamps, 2, 29
    instruments, 102
    radiotransmitters, 110–111, 124
beam splitter, 79
behavior shaping, 267–269
behavioral training techniques
    forced choice (Y-maze) format, 266–267
    go no-go format, 266
    motivation, 270
    obstacle avoidance, 266
    protocols, 266–269
    reinforcement, 270
    retrieval format, 267
    species variation, 271–272
betalights, 62
blood

sample treatment, 142, 285
    sampling protocols, 142, 281, 283–284, 381
body composition analysis (*see also* carcass analysis)
    ash content, 391, 394–397
    energy content, 391, 397
    fat content, 391–393
    lean dry mass, 391, 393–394
    total body water, 389–392
body temperature measurement
    continuous, 338
    core temperature, 337
    non-continuous, 339
    nutritional effects, 339–340
    rectal temperature, 336–339

calorimetry
    bomb, 241, 395, 397
    direct, 354
    indirect, 354–364
    microbomb, 241, 397
captive bats
    acclimation, 341–343
    dietary deficiencies, 255
    diets, 248–259
    feeding schedules, 255
    health precautions, 260–261
    housing requirements, 256–258
    management, 258–259
    nutritional requirements, 254–255
    rabies, 513–514
    training, 249, 265–273
capture methods
    bag traps, 5–6
    bucket traps, 5
    funnel traps, 5–6
    hand capture, 3–4
    harp traps, 17–21
    hoop nets, 4–5, 29
    miscellaneous, 21
    mist nets, 6–17
carcass analysis (*see also* body composition analysis)
    data recording, 388
    statistical analysis, 388–389
cave and mine gases
    detection and measurement, 492–503
    exposure limits, 493
    protection, first-aid, and rescue, 495–496
census methods

capture-mark-recapture, 82, 85–87
captures, 80, 82
electronic, 79–80
emergence counts, 78–79
photographic, 80
at roosts, 77–83
climbing equipment, 29
clustering, 292, 343–344
collecting laws, 28
conduction, 315–316
copulation, 40
cyalume (light tag), 2, 62

dentition
incremental lines, 51–52
pulp cavity, 52
tooth wear, 48–52
diet (see food habits)
diets, in captivity
carnivorous, 252
frugivorous, 253–254
insectivorous, 248–249
nectarivorous, 253–254
piscivorous, 252
sanguivorous, 242–253
diets, plant-visiting bats, 209–219
digestibility, 234–236
doubly labeled water method
assumptions and errors, 278–280
costs, 285–286
field protocol, 280–285
injection procedures, 281–282
isotope analysis, 286–287
isotope equilibration, 282–283
practical considerations, 280–282
rationale, 278
sample preparation, 285
selection of subjects, 280
validation, 286

ectoparasites
behavior, 460
captive, 260
collecting and preserving, 461–462
data analysis, 462–463
host specificity, 460–461
host taxonomy, 464
identification, 463–464, 469–474
life history, 460, 464
endoparasites
collection, 474–478
ecology, 481
fixation techniques, 478–479
host examination, 476
host food habits, 484–485
host hibernation, 483–484
host migration, 482–483

life history, 484
preparation of slide mounts, 479
electron microscopy, 417–419
electrophoresis, 143–145, 154–156
energetics
fat deposition, 296
foraging, 293–294
lactation, 295
pregnancy, 294
protein deposition, 296
reproduction, 291–292, 294–297
energy budget analysis, 278–297
energy equivalents
bat carcass, 389
insects, 204
energy transfer
feeding rates, 294
foraging efficiencies, 294
growth, 295–296
estrus, 39–40
evaporative water loss, 316–317, 364, 377–378
export regulations, 28

fat content
energy equivalent, 389
extraction methods, 392–393
fecal analysis (see stomach content analysis)
feeding buzz, 68, 91
feeding rates, 294
field metabolic rate, 278–279, 293
fixatives
commercial products, 423–424
light microscopy, 411–415
selected recipes, 408–410
voucher specimen preparation, 443–444
food habits analysis (see also diet)
frugivorous, 212–217
nectarivorous, 217–219
food habits analysis (insectivorous), 171–189
culled parts, 173
direct observation, 173
feces, 172–173
stomach contents, 172–173
food intake, 287–289
food transit time, 216, 236
foraging costs, 293
fruit availability
fruit production, 222–225
fruiting phenology, 225
mapping studies, 226–227
production transects, 227
seed traps, 225
fruit production
spatial variation, 227–228
temporal variation, 227–228

growth efficiency, 295

harp trap
  Constantine, 17
  effectiveness, 20
  placement, 18–20
  portability, 17
  potential bias, 20
  Tuttle, 17–20
health precautions
  cave gases, 492–503
  ectoparasites, 503
  histoplasmosis, 515–520
  rabies, 504–515
health protection, 526–528
heat transfer analysis, 304–307
histochemical methods, 412–417
histoplasmosis
  geographic distribution, 515–518
  host species, 515
  preventive measures, 519–520
holding devices
  bags, 21–24
  cages, 21–24, 341
  metabolic chamber, 358
home range
  models, 113
  non-parametric, 114–115
  parametric, 113
  sample considerations, 116–118
  three-dimensional, 114
housing for captives, 256–258

immunohistochemistry, 415–417
import regulations, 28
insect sampling
  biomass, 203
  energy content, 203–204
  enumeration, 202
  remote sensing, 201–202
  sample units, 192
  trapping devices, 192–201
insect traps
  emergence, 199
  impaction, 196–197
  light, 200–201
  Malaise, 195, 209
  pitfall, 199–200, 209
  rotary, 193–194
  sticky, 197–198, 208–210
  suction, 193–194, 209
  tow, 195, 209
isotopes and isotope analysis, 286–287

karyotyping
  C-banding, 429–430
  cell cultures, 430–433
  G-banding, 428–429
  recipes and supplies, 434–435

kinship assessment, 145, 148–151

lactation, 41–42, 295
light-emitting diode, 62
light sources, 2–3, 29
light tags, 62

male reproduction
  puberty, 37–38
  spermatogenesis, 37–39
  testicular development, 36–37
mammary glands, 41
mark-recapture analysis (of survival)
  assumptions, 160–163
  Cormack method, 159–160
  life expectancy, 167–168
  life-table analysis, 166–167
  regression techniques, 164–166
  survival rates, 167–168
marking techniques
  betalights, 64
  fluorescent paint, 65
  light-emitting diodes (LEDs), 62
  light tags (Cyalume), 62–64
  necklaces, 62
  punch-marking, 65
  radioactive wire, 65
  radiotransmitters, 64
  reflective tape, 61–62
  toe-clipping, 65
  wing bands, 60–61
maternal investment (*see also* milk)
  fetal production, 294
  lactation costs, 295
  milk production efficiency, 295
  milk yield, 290, 380
maternity assessment, 149–150
metabolic chambers, 358
metabolic water
  equivalents, 375
  production, 374–375
metabolism
  field measurements, 278–279, 293, 354
  laboratory measurements, 354–367
meteorological services, 318–319
microclimate analysis, 303–319
milk
  allometry, 292
  energy, 279
  intake, 290–291
  sampling, 259, 380
  yield, 290, 380
mist net
  biases, 16
  canopy, 12–16
  deployment, 8–11
  dismantling, 16–17

maintenance, 16–17
poles, 7–8, 10–14
preparation for field use, 7
removal of bats, 10–12
shyness, 16
suppliers, 29
types, 6–7
mitotic index, 427

night vision devices, 66–67
nutritional analysis (fruits)
  ash content, 237
  available carbohydrates, 238–239
  dietary fiber, 237–238
  energy content, 241–242
  lipids, 239–240
  mineral content, 237
  nitrogen and protein, 240–244
  sample preparation, 236–237

observational techniques
  acoustic monitoring, 68–69
  data recording, 69–70
  focal sampling, 70
  magnetic detectors, 69
  radar, 69
  scan sampling, 70
operative temperature, 292, 307–308
oxygen consumption
  apparatus for measurement, 356–361, 370–371
  equations for analysis, 361–364

parturition, 41–42
paternity assessment, 148–149
pelage, 32, 38–39
photography
  automatic triggering, 131–132
  cinematography, 134–138
  electronic flash, 127–129, 135–139
  illumination, 126–130
  multi-flash illumination, 130
  portrait, 129–130
  slave units, 128, 139
  still, 126–132
  time-lapse, 133–134
population estimates
  mist netting, 85
  roost counts, 83–84
  trapping, 85
  ultrasonic (bat) detector, 84
  vampire bites, 84
  visual counts, 84
pregnancy, 40–41
preserved specimens
  packing and shipping, 455

permits, 28
protection, 454
prey (insect)
  availability, 176–177, 191–204
  selection, 176–177, 202–203
protein deposition, 296
puberty, 37–38

rabies
  disease development, 508–509
  exposure, 510–511
  human cases, 511
  immunization, 514
  prevalence, 505–508
  prevention, 514
  related viruses, 514–515
  transmission, 504, 511
  treatment, 510
radiation
  animal properties, 310–313
  thermal, 310
radiotelemetry
  antennae, 108, 112, 123
  data recording, 112
  errors, 112
  home range analysis, 113–118
  receivers, 111, 123
  recording data, 112
radiotransmitters
  assembly, 106–111, 120–122
  attachment, 111
  components, 123–124
  potting, 111
  power sources, 110–111
  temperature sensitive, 335–336
reproduction
  assessment, 31–43
  copulation, 40
  estrus, 39–40
  lactation, 41–42
  parturition, 41–42
  pregnancy, 40–41
respiratory quotient, 355
respirometry (*see also* metabolism)
  closed system, 356
  open system, 356–366
  system configuration, 357
resting metabolic rate, 355

sex identification, 31–36
sexual dimorphism, 32–33
social facilitation, 344–345
sonographs, 101, 104
specimen preparation
  dry preservation, 445–454
  euthanasia, 439

external measurements, 441–443
labeling, 440
supplies, 438
wet preservation, 443–444
spectral absorptance, 310–311
spectral irradiance, 311
spermatogenesis, 37–39
stable isotopes, 387
standard metabolic rate, 354
standard operative temperature, 303
stomach content analysis (insectivorous)
collection of bats, 174
identification of foot items, 174–175
prey size, 175
sample analysis, 175–176
sample preparation, 174
survey methods (at roosts)
captures, 80
electronic counters, 79–80
emergence counts, 78–80
photography, 80, 82–83

taxidermic mounts, 292
teeth (*see also* dentition)
incremental wear, 48–51
temperature measurements
infrared thermister, 310, 312
radiotransmitters, 335–336
thermisters, 309, 335
thermocouples, 334–336
thermometers, 336
thermoregulation
captivity effects, 341–343
clustering effects, 343–344
sex differences, 343
social facilitation, 344–345
time-budgets, 292–293
tissue preparation and fixation
electron microscopy, 417–419
immunohistochemistry, 415–417
histochemistry, 412–415
light microscopy, 407–419
tooth wear, 48–51
tunica vaginalis, 39
Tuttle trap (*see* capture methods)

urine
analysis, 381
sample methods, 260, 381

vaginal smears, 39–40
vocalizations
analysis, 99–101
detection, 92–96
recording/displaying, 97–98, 104

water balance
input, 379
output, 376–380
water recycling, 291
water vapor density, 317–318
wind measurement
convection, 313
convective conductance, 313–314
flow tracers, 315
instrumentation, 328–332